Harper's Review of Biochemistry

A Concise Medical Library for Practitioner and Student

Harper's Review of Biochemistry

David W. Martin, Jr., MD
Vice-President–Research
Genentech, Inc.
Adjunct Professor of Medicine and Biochemistry
University of California School of Medicine
San Francisco

Peter A. Mayes, PhD, DSc
Reader in Biochemistry
Royal Veterinary College
University of London

Victor W. Rodwell, PhD
Professor of Biochemistry
Purdue University
Lafayette, Indiana

Daryl K. Granner, MD
Professor and Chairman,
Department of Molecular Physiology and Biophysics
Professor of Medicine
Vanderbilt University
Nashville, Tennessee

Twentieth Edition

LANGE MEDICAL PUBLICATIONS
LOS ALTOS, CALIFORNIA 94023

Table of Contents

Preface

Harper's Review of Biochemistry is intended to provide the student with a broad general knowledge of the principles of biochemistry and molecular biology. At the same time, it offers insights into the physiologic and pathologic applications of biochemistry for the student with an interest in clinical disorders resulting from or associated with biochemical derangements.

For the twentieth edition, the eight chapters on the hormones have been completely rewritten by a new author. Other notable changes include new data and concepts pertaining to developments in the regulation of gene expression; RNA processing to form mature mRNA; the molecular basis of oncogenesis; the processes of protein secretion; the role of fatty acid derivatives in the inflammatory response; and the biochemical basis of blood clotting.

The authors wish to extend their gratitude to professional colleagues and friends throughout the world who have conveyed to us their suggestions, corrections, and additions. We wish to encourage their continued effort and interest.

The authors are most gratified by the broad base of acceptance and support this book has received all over the world. Several editions of the English language version have been reprinted in Japan, Lebanon, Taiwan, the Philippines, and Korea. In addition, there are now translations in Italian, Spanish, French, Portuguese, Japanese, Polish, German, Indonesian, Serbo-Croatian, and Greek.

David W. Martin, Jr.
Peter A. Mayes
Victor W. Rodwell
Daryl K. Granner

San Francisco
July, 1985

The Authors

Daryl K. Granner, MD
   Professor and Chairman, Department of Molecular Physiology and Biophysics, and Professor of Medicine, Vanderbilt University, Nashville, Tennessee.

David W. Martin, Jr., MD
   Vice-President–Research, Genentech, Inc., South San Francisco; Adjunct Professor of Medicine and Biochemistry, University of California School of Medicine, San Francisco.

Peter A. Mayes, PhD, DSc
   Reader in Biochemistry, Royal Veterinary College, University of London.

Marion Nestle, PhD
   Associate Dean and Lecturer in Medicine and Biochemistry, University of California School of Medicine, San Francisco.

Victor W. Rodwell, PhD
   Professor of Biochemistry, Purdue University, Lafayette, Indiana.

Victor W. Rodwell, PhD

This chapter reviews certain aspects of organic chemistry relevant to biochemistry and provides guidelines to assist in learning and integrating the information. The early chapters of this book present basic data on the structures and chemical properties of important biochemical compounds. While some of these will be familiar, others are complex structures (eg, heterocyclic structures*) perhaps not previously encountered by the student. The biochemistry of unfamiliar molecules is largely predictable from that of structurally similar molecules (eg, molecules that possess the same functional groups†). **Each functional group in a molecule generally behaves in a predictable way with respect to its biochemical reactions.** This guideline simplifies the understanding of enzyme-catalyzed transformations in living cells. Although most biochemically important molecules contain multiple functional groups, as a rule, **only a single functional group undergoes change in a given enzyme-catalyzed reaction.** Learning is therefore enhanced by focusing attention **exclusively on that change** to the virtual exclusion of all other aspects of the molecule. The complexities of intermediary metabolism can generally be made manageable in this way.

STEREOISOMERS

Stereoisomers differ only in the way in which the constituent atoms are oriented in space. In methane (CH₄), the hydrogen atoms are at the vertices of an equilateral tetrahedron (4-sided pyramid) with the carbon atom at the center.

*****Hetero atoms** (Greek *heteros* ''other'') such as O, N, and S also form covalent bonds with carbon, eg, in ethylamine, $C_2H_5NH_2$; ethyl alcohol, C_2H_5OH; and ethyl mercaptan, C_2H_5SH. Hetero atoms have one or more pairs of electrons not involved in covalent bonding. Since these unshared electrons have a negative field, **compounds with hetero atoms** attract protons; ie, they **act as bases** (see Chapter 2). Heterocyclic structures are cyclic structures that contain hetero atoms.

†**A functional group** (eg, –NH₂, –COOH, –OH) is a specific arrangement of linked chemical elements that has well-defined chemical and physical properties.

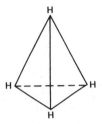

A carbon atom to which 4 different atoms or groups of atoms are attached is known as an asymmetric carbon atom. For example, in the formula for alanine, the asymmetric (alpha) carbon atom is starred (*).

$$CH_3 - \overset{\overset{\displaystyle H}{|}}{\underset{\underset{\displaystyle NH_2}{|}}{C^*}} - COOH$$

Alanine

Since many biochemicals contain 2 or more asymmetric C atoms, a thorough understanding of the stereochemistry of systems with more than one asymmetric center is essential.

Representation of Spatial Relationships Between Atoms

Certain spatial relationships are readily visualized using ball-and-stick atomic models. A compound having asymmetric carbon atoms exhibits **optical isomerism.** Thus, lactic acid has 2 nonequivalent optical isomers, one being the mirror image or **enantiomer** of the other (Fig 1–1).

The reader may show that these structures are indeed different by rotating either enantiomer about any axis and attempting to superimpose one structure on the other.

Although enantiomers of a given compound have the same chemical properties, certain of their physical properties and essentially all of their physiologic properties are different. Enantiomers rotate the plane of plane-polarized light to an equal extent but in opposite directions. Since almost all enzymes act on only one of a pair of enantiomers, only half of a **racemic mixture**

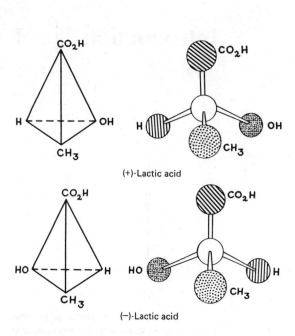

Figure 1–1. Tetrahedral and ball-and-stick model representation of lactic acid enantiomers.

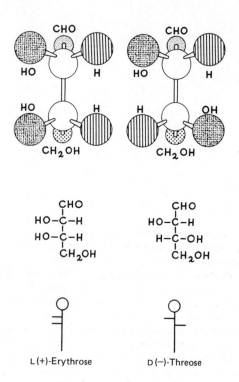

Figure 1–3. Two aldotetroses. *Top:* Ball-and-stick models. *Middle:* Fischer projection formulas. *Bottom:* Abbreviated projection formulas.

(a mixture of equal quantities of both enantiomers) generally is physiologically active.

The number of possible different isomers is 2^n, where n = the number of different asymmetric carbon atoms. An aldotetrose, for example, contains 2 asymmetric carbon atoms; hence, there are $2^2 = 4$ optical isomers.

To represent 3-dimensional molecules in 2 dimensions, **projection formulas,** introduced by Emil Fischer, are used. The molecule is placed with the asymmetric carbon in the plane of the projection. The groups at the top and bottom project **behind** the plane of projection. Those to the right and left project equally **above** the plane of projection. The molecule is then projected in the form of a cross (Fig 1–2).

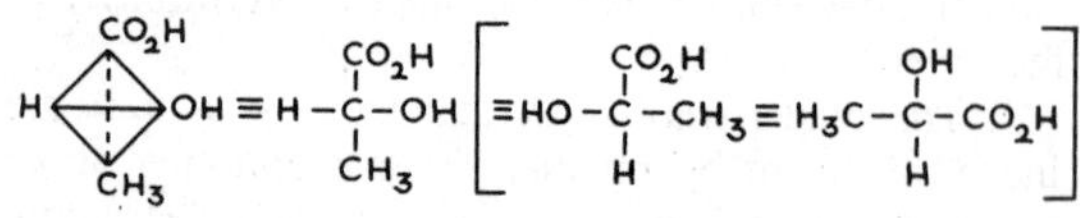

Figure 1–2. Fischer projection formula of (−)-lactic acid.

Unfortunately, the orientation of the tetrahedron differs from that of Fig 1–1. **Fischer projection formulas may never be mentally lifted from the plane of the paper and turned over.** Since the vertical bonds are really **below** the projection plane while the

horizontal bonds are **above it, it also is not permissible to rotate the Fischer projection formula within the plane of the paper by either a 90-degree or a 270-degree angle, although it is permissible to rotate it 180 degrees.**

The nomenclature for molecules with 2 asymmetric carbon atoms derives from the names of the 4-carbon sugars erythrose and threose. If 2 like groups (eg, two OH groups) are on the same side, the isomer is called the **"erythro"** form; if on the opposite side, the **"threo"** isomer. Fischer projection formulas inadequately represent one feature of these molecules. Look at the models from which these formulas are

Erythro   Threo

Figure 1–4. Sawhorse representations of the erythro and threo enantiomers of 3-amino-2-butanol. The **erythro** and **threo** refer to the relative positions of −OH and −NH₂ groups. Note that there are 3 ways to stagger C_2 with respect to C_3. That shown represents a structure with the bulky CH_3 groups oriented as far away from each other as possible.

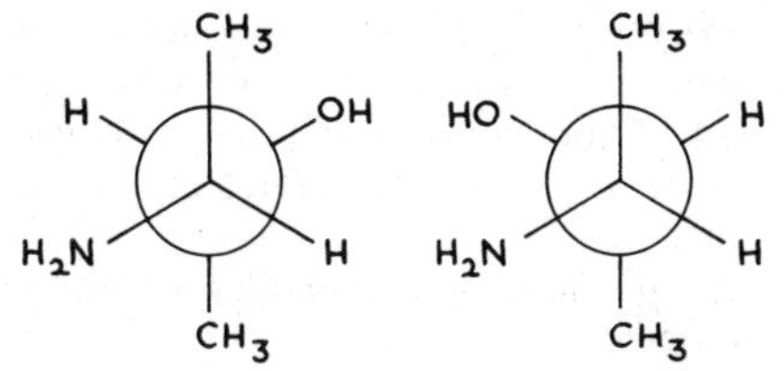

CH_3

H—————OH   HO—————H

H_2N—————H H_2N—————H

CH_3 CH_3

Erythro   Threo

Figure 1–5. Staggered Newman projection formulas for the erythro and threo enantiomers of 3-amino-2-butanol.

derived. The upper part of Fig 1–3 represents molecules in the **"eclipsed"** form in which the groups attached to C_2 and C_3 approach each other as closely as possible. The real shape of the molecule more closely approximates an arrangement with C_2 and C_3 rotated with respect to each other by an angle of 60 degrees, so that their substituents are **staggered** with respect to each other and are as far apart as possible. One way to represent "staggered" formulas is to use **"sawhorse"** representations (Fig 1–4). **Newman projection formulas** (Fig 1–5) view the molecule front-to-back along the bond joining the asymmetric carbon atoms. These C atoms, which eclipse each other, are represented as 2 superimposed circles (only one is shown). The bonds and groups attached to the asymmetric C atoms are projected in a vertical plane and appear as "spokes" at angles of 120 degrees for each C atom. The spokes on the rear atom are offset 60 degrees with respect to those on the front C atom. Bonds to the front carbon are drawn to the center of the circle and those for the rear carbon only to its periphery (Fig 1–5).

It is desirable to be able to convert Fischer projection formulas to sawhorse or Newman projection formulas. These most accurately illustrate the true shape of the molecule and hence are most useful in understanding its chemical and biologic properties. One way

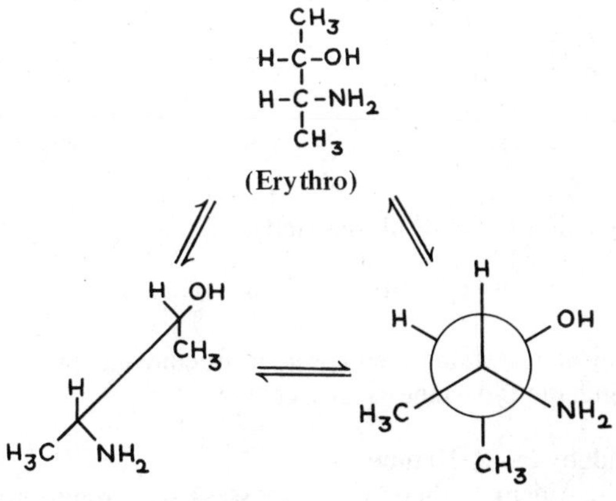

CH_3
H–C–OH
H–C–NH_2
CH_3

(Erythro)

H OH

CH_3

H

H_3C NH_2

⇌

H

H   OH

H_3C NH_2

CH_3

Figure 1–6. Transformation from Fischer to sawhorse or Newman formula.

is to build a model* corresponding to the Fischer projection formula, stagger the atoms, and draw the sawhorse or Newman formulas. Fig 1–6 shows how to interconvert these formulas without models. The Fischer projection formula is converted to an "eclipsed sawhorse" or Newman projection which then is rotated 180 degrees about the C_2–C_3 bond, producing a staggered sawhorse or Newman projection.

Cis-Trans Isomerism

Cis-trans isomerism (Latin *cis* "this side," *trans* "across") occurs in compounds with double bonds. Since the double bond is rigid, the atoms attached to it are not free to rotate as are those attached to a single bond. Thus the structures

H–C–COOH   H–C–COOH
‖   ‖
H–C–COOH   HOOC–C–H

Maleic acid *(cis)***   Fumaric acid *(trans)***

are not equivalent and have **different chemical and physiologic properties.** Fumaric acid, but not maleic acid, is physiologically active. The *cis* isomer has the 2 more "bulky" groups on the same side of the double

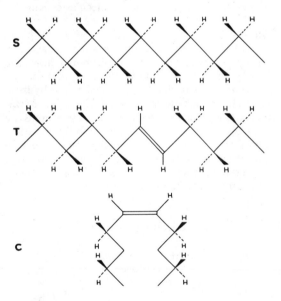

Figure 1–7. Representation of portions of the hydrocarbon backbones of a saturated fatty acid (**S**), an unsaturated fatty acid with a single *trans* double bond (**T**), and one with a single *cis* double bond (**C**). Bonds drawn as solid lines are in the plane of the paper. Bonds drawn as dotted lines project behind, and those drawn ◢ project in front of the plane of the paper.

*The student is urged to purchase an inexpensive set of models. These will prove invaluable in studying the chemistry of sugars, amino acids, and steroids in particular.

bond. If they are on opposite sides of the double bond, the *trans* isomer is produced.

Introduction of *trans* double bonds in an otherwise saturated hydrocarbon chain deforms the shape of the molecule relatively little. A *cis* double bond, by contrast, entirely changes its shape. It can thus be appreciated why *cis* and *trans* isomers of a compound are not interchangeable in cells. Membranes composed of *trans* and *cis* unsaturated fatty acid isomers would have entirely different shapes. Enzymes acting on one isomer might be expected to be inert with the other.

Again, the usual formulas fail to represent the actual shape of the molecules. Portions of the hydrocarbon backbone of a saturated fatty acid and of the *cis* and *trans* isomers of an 18-carbon unsaturated fatty acid are represented in Fig 1–7.

FUNCTIONAL GROUPS IMPORTANT IN BIOCHEMISTRY

A **functional group** is a specific arrangement of elements (generally C, H, O, N, P, and S) that has well-defined chemical and physical properties. The properties of biochemical molecules are best understood in terms of the chemical and physical properties of the functional groups these molecules contain.

Alcohols

Many biochemical compounds (eg, sugars, certain lipids, and amino acids) are **alcohols.** These have both **polar** (hydroxy, OH) and **nonpolar** (alkyl) character. They are thus best regarded both as **hydroxylated hydrocarbons** and as **alkyl derivatives of water.** Although alcohols with up to 3 carbon atoms are infinitely soluble in water, water solubility decreases with increasing length of the carbon chain, ie, with increasing nonpolar character. Primary, secondary, and tertiary alcohols have respectively one, 2, and 3 alkyl groups attached to the carbon atom bearing the –OH group.

$$CH_3CH_2CH_2CH_2-OH$$

Primary butyl alcohol
(1-butanol)

$$CH_3-CH_2-\overset{\overset{\displaystyle H}{|}}{\underset{\underset{\displaystyle CH_3}{|}}{C}}-OH \qquad\qquad CH_3-\overset{\overset{\displaystyle CH_3}{|}}{\underset{\underset{\displaystyle CH_3}{|}}{C}}-OH$$

Secondary butyl alcohol   **Tertiary butyl alcohol**
(1-methylpropanol)   **(1,1-dimethylethanol)**

Both monohydric (one –OH group) and polyhydric (more than one –OH group) alcohols are of physiologic significance. Sugars are derivatives of polyhydric alcohols, as are cyclic or ring-containing alcohols such as **inositol.** Their highly polar character

makes polyhydric alcohols far more water-soluble than corresponding monohydric alcohols with equivalent numbers of carbon atoms. Thus, even polyhydric alcohols with 6 or more carbon atoms (eg, sugars) are highly water-soluble.

Chemical reactions of alcohols with biochemical analogies include:

A. Oxidation: Primary alcohols are oxidized by strong oxidizing agents to aldehydes and acids, whereas secondary alcohols are oxidized to ketones.

Primary:

$$R-CH_2OH \xrightarrow{[O]} RCHO + RCOOH$$

Secondary:

$$\begin{matrix} R_1 \\ \quad \\ R_2 \end{matrix}\!\!\!\!>\!CHOH \xrightarrow{[O]} \begin{matrix} R_1 \\ \quad \\ R_2 \end{matrix}\!\!\!\!>\!C\!=\!O$$

Tertiary alcohols cannot be oxidized (dehydrogenated) without rupture of a C–C bond.

B. Esterification: An ester is formed when water is split out between an alcohol and an acid.

$$\overset{\overset{\displaystyle O}{\parallel}}{R-C}-OH + HO-R' \longrightarrow \overset{\overset{\displaystyle O}{\parallel}}{R-C}-O-R' + H_2O$$

The acid may be organic or inorganic. Esters of H_3PO_4 (eg, phosphorylated sugars and phospholipids) and H_2SO_4 are of great significance in biochemistry. Many lipids contain carboxylic ester linkages.

C. Ether Formation: Ethers are derivatives of alcohols in which the hydrogen of the –OH group is replaced by an alkyl group (R–O–R'). The ether linkage is comparatively uncommon in living tissues.

Sulfur, which is in the same group of the periodic table as oxygen, forms similar compounds. Thioalcohols (thiols, mercaptans), thioesters, and thioethers all occur in nature.

$$R-CH_2-SH \qquad\qquad \overset{\overset{\displaystyle O}{\parallel}}{R-C}-S-R' \qquad\qquad R-S-R'$$

Thioalcohol   **Thioester**   **Thioether**

In addition, the disulfides (left) and peroxides (right)

$$R-S-S-R' \qquad\qquad R-O-O-R'$$

play an important role in protein structure and in prostaglandin biosynthesis, respectively.

Aldehydes & Ketones

Aldehydes and ketones possess the strongly reducing carbonyl group $>C\!=\!O$. Aldehydes have one and ketones 2 alkyl groups attached to the carbon bearing the carbonyl group:

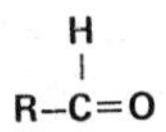

$$\underset{\text{Aldehyde}}{\overset{\overset{\displaystyle H}{|}}{R-C=O}} \qquad \underset{\text{Ketone}}{\overset{R}{\underset{R'}{\diagdown}}C=O}$$

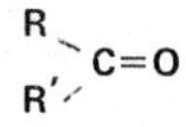

The sugars, in addition to being polyhydric alcohols, are also either aldehydes or ketones.

Reactions of aldehydes and ketones of biochemical interest include the following:

A. Oxidation: Oxidation of an aldehyde yields the corresponding carboxylic acid. Ketones are not readily oxidized, since, like tertiary alcohols, they cannot lose hydrogen without rupture of a C–C bond.

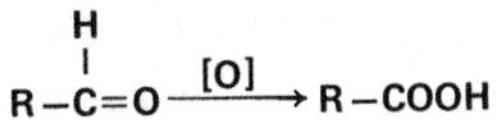

$$\overset{\overset{\displaystyle H}{|}}{R-C=O} \xrightarrow{\text{[O]}} R-COOH$$

B. Reduction: Reduction of an aldehyde yields the corresponding primary alcohol, and reduction of a ketone yields the corresponding secondary alcohol.

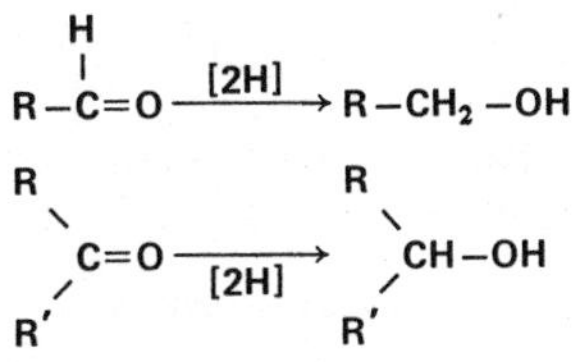

$$\overset{\overset{\displaystyle H}{|}}{R-C=O} \xrightarrow{\text{[2H]}} R-CH_2-OH$$

$$\overset{R}{\underset{R'}{\diagdown}}C=O \xrightarrow{\text{[2H]}} \overset{R}{\underset{R'}{\diagdown}}CH-OH$$

C. Hemiacetal and Acetal Formation: Under acidic conditions, aldehydes can combine with one or 2 of the hydroxyl groups of an alcohol, forming, respectively, a hemiacetal or an acetal:

$$\overset{\overset{\displaystyle H}{|}}{R-C=O} + R'OH \qquad \overset{\overset{\displaystyle H}{|}}{\underset{\underset{\displaystyle O-R'}{|}}{R-C-OH}}$$

A hemiacetal

$$\overset{\overset{\displaystyle H}{|}}{R-C=O} + 2\,R'OH \xrightarrow{\overset{H_2O}{\nearrow}} \overset{\overset{\displaystyle H}{|}}{\underset{\underset{\displaystyle OR'}{|}}{R-C-OR'}}$$

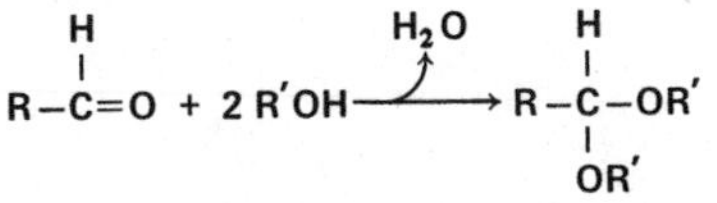

An acetal

The carbonyl and alcohol functions may be part of the same molecule. For example, the aldose (aldehyde) sugars exist in solution primarily as internal hemiacetals. Analogous structures (hemiketals and ketals) are formed from alcohols and ketones.

Aldehydes may also form **thiohemiacetals** and **thioacetals** with thioalcohols. Thiohemiacetals function as enzyme-bound intermediates in the enzymic oxidation of aldehydes to acids.

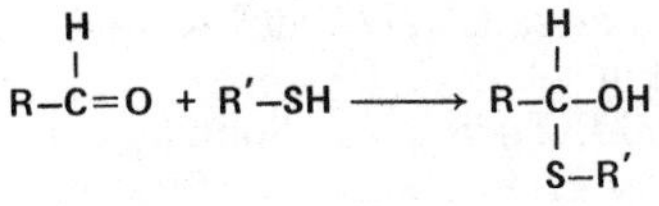

$$\overset{\overset{\displaystyle H}{|}}{R-C=O} + R'-SH \longrightarrow \overset{\overset{\displaystyle H}{|}}{\underset{\underset{\displaystyle S-R'}{|}}{R-C-OH}}$$

A thiohemiacetal

D. Aldol Condensation: In alkali, aldehydes and, to a lesser extent, ketones undergo condensation between their carbonyl and their α-carbon atoms to form aldols or β-hydroxy aldehydes or ketones. The β-hydroxy acids derived from these are important in fatty acid metabolism.

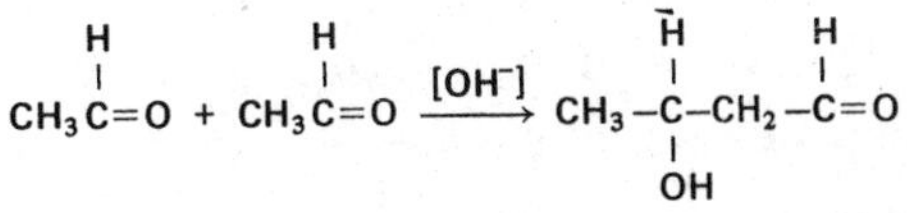

$$\overset{\overset{\displaystyle H}{|}}{CH_3C=O} + \overset{\overset{\displaystyle H}{|}}{CH_3C=O} \xrightarrow{\text{[OH}^-\text{]}} \overset{\overset{\displaystyle \bar{H}}{|}}{\underset{\underset{\displaystyle OH}{|}}{CH_3-C-CH_2}}-\overset{\overset{\displaystyle H}{|}}{C=O}$$

Carboxylic Acids

Carboxylic acids have both a carbonyl ($> C=O$) and a hydroxyl group on the same carbon atom. They are typical **weak acids** and only partially dissociate in water to form a hydrogen ion (H^+) and a **carboxylate anion** ($R-COO^-$) with the negative charge shared equally by the 2 oxygen atoms. Some reactions of carboxylic acids of biochemical interest include the following:

A. Reduction: Complete **reduction** yields the corresponding **primary alcohol.**

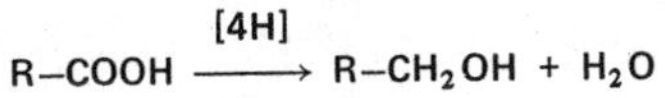

$$R-COOH \xrightarrow{\text{[4H]}} R-CH_2OH + H_2O$$

B. Ester and Thioester Formation: See Alcohols, above.

C. Acid Anhydride Formation: A molecule of water is split out between the carboxyl groups of 2 acid molecules.

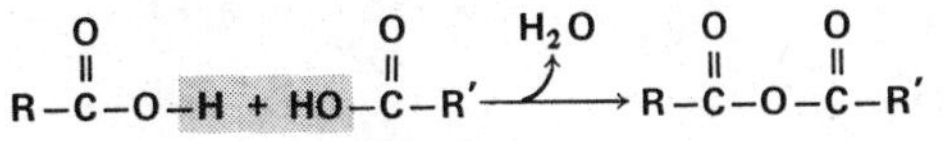

$$\overset{\overset{\displaystyle O}{\|}}{R-C-O-H} + HO-\overset{\overset{\displaystyle O}{\|}}{C-R'} \xrightarrow{\overset{H_2O}{\nearrow}} \overset{\overset{\displaystyle O}{\|}}{R-C-O}-\overset{\overset{\displaystyle O}{\|}}{C-R'}$$

When both acid molecules are the same, a **symmetric anhydride** is produced. Molecules of different acids yield **mixed anhydrides.** Anhydrides found in nature include those of phosphoric acid (in ATP) and the **mixed anhydrides** formed from phosphoric acid and a carboxylic acid, eg:

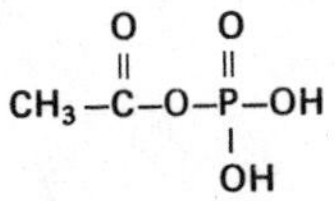

$$\overset{\overset{\displaystyle O}{\|}}{CH_3-C-O}-\overset{\overset{\displaystyle O}{\|}}{\underset{\underset{\displaystyle OH}{|}}{P-OH}}$$

Acetyl phosphate

D. Salt Formation: Carboxylic acids react stoichiometrically (equivalent for equivalent) with bases to form salts. Na^+ and K^+ salts are 100% dissociated in solution.

E. Amide Formation: Splitting out a molecule of water between a carboxylic acid and ammonia or an amine forms an amide. Particularly important amides are **peptides,** formed from the amino group of one amino acid and the carboxyl group of another.

$$CH_3-\underset{\underset{O}{\|}}{C}-OH + H-NH_2 \xrightarrow{H_2O} CH_3-\underset{\underset{O}{\|}}{C}-NH_2$$

Acetic acid   Acetamide

$$R-\underset{\underset{H}{|}}{\overset{\overset{COOH}{|}}{C}}-\underset{\underset{H}{|}}{N}-H + HO-\underset{\underset{NH_2}{|}}{\overset{\overset{O}{\|}}{C}}-C-R' \xrightarrow{H_2O} R-\underset{\underset{H}{|}}{\overset{\overset{COOH}{|}}{C}}-\underset{\underset{H}{|}}{N}-\underset{\underset{NH_2}{|}}{\overset{\overset{O}{\|}}{C}}-C-R'$$

Peptide bond

Amines

Amines, alkyl derivatives of ammonia, are usually gases or volatile liquids with odors resembling ammonia but more "fishlike." Primary, secondary, and tertiary amines are formed by replacement of one, 2, or 3 of the hydrogens of ammonia, respectively.

$\overset{H}{\underset{H}{\diagdown N-H}}$	$R-NH_2$	$\overset{R}{\underset{R'}{\diagup NH}}$	$\overset{R}{\underset{R''}{R'-N}}$
Ammonia	Primary amine	Secondary amine	Tertiary amine

Ammonia in solution exists in both charged and uncharged forms:

$$NH_3 + H^+ \rightleftharpoons NH_4^+$$

Ammonia   Ammonium ion

Amines behave in an entirely analogous way:

$$\overset{R}{\underset{R'}{\diagdown}}NH + H^+ \rightleftharpoons \overset{R}{\underset{R'}{\diagdown}}\overset{H}{\underset{H}{\diagup}}N$$

An amine   An alkylammonium ion

Water | 2

Victor W. Rodwell, PhD

INTRODUCTION

Biochemistry is concerned, for the most part, with the properties and reactions of organic compounds. However, it must not be forgotten that **in living cells most biochemicals exist and most reactions occur in an aqueous environment. Water is an active participant in many biochemical reactions and is an important determinant of the properties of macromolecules such as proteins.** It is therefore appropriate to consider those properties of water that enable it to play such a key role in biochemistry.

MOLECULAR STRUCTURE OF WATER

The water molecule is an irregular tetrahedron with oxygen at its center (Fig 2–1). The 2 bonds with hydrogen are directed toward 2 corners of the tetrahedron, while the unshared electrons on the 2 sp^3-hybridized orbitals occupy the 2 remaining corners. The angle between the 2 hydrogen atoms (105 degrees) is slightly less than the tetrahedral angle (109.5 degrees), forming a slightly skewed tetrahedron. In contrast to methane, electrical charge is not uniformly distributed about the water molecule. The side of the oxygen opposite to the 2 hydrogens is relatively rich in electrons, while on the other side the relatively unshielded hydrogen nuclei form a region of local positive charge. The term **dipole** refers to molecules such as water that have electrical charge (electrons) unequally distributed about their structure. Ammonia is a dipole and, like water, has a tetrahedral structure (Fig 2–2). In ammonia, the bond angles between the hydrogens (107 degrees) approach the tetrahedral angle even more closely than in water. Many biochemicals are dipoles. Examples include alcohols, phospholipids, amino acids, and nucleic acids.

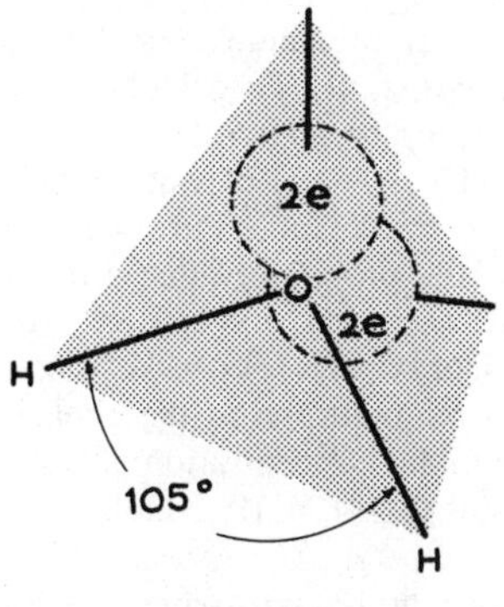

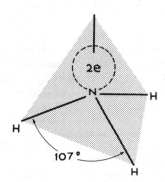

Figure 2–2. Tetrahedral structure of ammonia.

MACROMOLECULAR STRUCTURE OF WATER

Water molecules can assume ordered arrangements (recall a snowflake). Molecular ordering of water molecules is not, however, restricted to ice. Liquid water exhibits macromolecular structure that parallels the geometric disposition of water molecules in ice. The ability of water molecules to associate with one another in both solid and liquid states arises from the dipolar character of water. It remains a liquid rather than a solid because of the transient nature of these macromolecular complexes (the half-life for association-dissociation of water molecules is about 1 microsecond). In the solid state, each water molecule is associated with 4 other water molecules. In the liquid state, the number is somewhat less (about 3.5). With the exception of the transient nature of intermolecular interactions in liquid water, it thus resembles ice in its macromolecular structure more closely than might at first be imagined.

Figure 2–1. Tetrahedral structure of water.

HYDROGEN BONDS

The dipolar character of water molecules favors their mutual association in ordered arrays with a precise geometry dictated by the internal geometry of the water molecule (Fig 2–3).

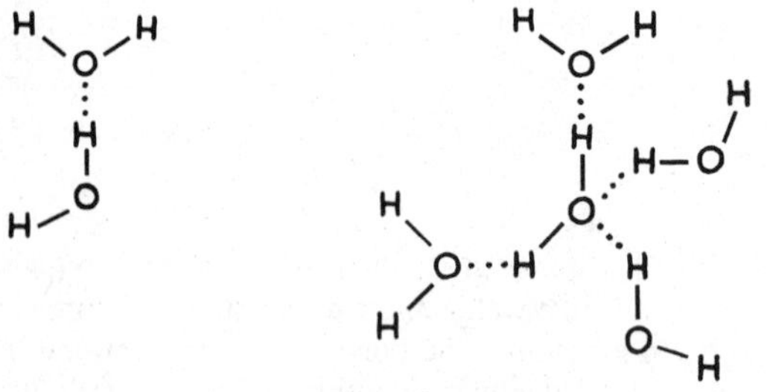

Figure 2–3. *Left:* Association of 2 dipolar water molecules. The dotted line represents a hydrogen bond. *Right:* Association of a central water molecule with 4 other water molecules by hydrogen bonding. This structure is typical of ice and, to a lesser extent, of liquid water.

The electrostatic interaction between the hydrogen nucleus of one water molecule and the unshared electron pair of another is termed a hydrogen bond. Compared to covalent bonds, hydrogen bonds are quite weak. To break a hydrogen bond in liquid water requires about 4.5 kcal of energy per mole—about 4% of the energy required to rupture the O–H bond in water (110 kcal/mol). While individually weak, hydrogen bonds play significant roles in biochemistry because they can be formed in large numbers. Multiple hydrogen bonds confer significant structure not only upon water but also upon other dipolar molecules as diverse as alcohols, DNA, and proteins. Fig 2–4 illustrates hydrogen bonds formed between representative biochemicals.

Note that hydrogen bonds are not restricted to

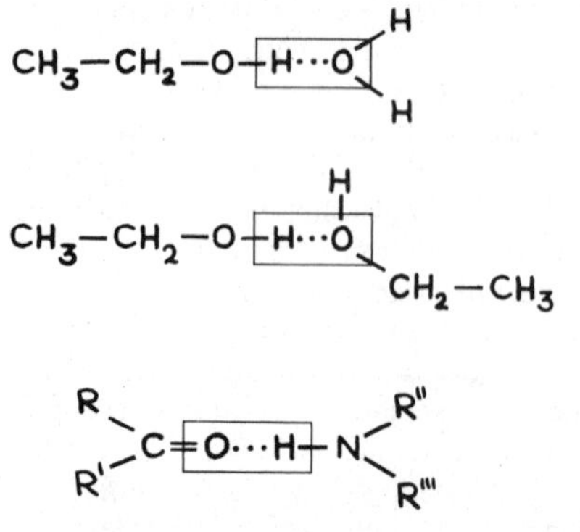

Figure 2–4. Formation of hydrogen bonds between an alcohol and water, between 2 molecules of ethanol, and between the peptide carbonyl oxygen and the hydrogen on the peptide nitrogen of an adjacent peptide.

water molecules, and in particular that the hydrogens of nitrogen atoms can also participate in hydrogen bonding. This topic will again be considered in connection with the 3-dimensional structure of proteins and with base pairing in DNA.

DISSOCIATION OF WATER

Water molecules have a limited tendency to dissociate (ionize) into H^+ and OH^- ions:

$$H_2O \rightleftharpoons H^+ + OH^-$$

Since ions are continuously recombining to form water molecules and vice versa, it cannot be stated whether an individual hydrogen or oxygen is present as an ion or as part of a water molecule. At one instant it is an ion; an instant later, part of a molecule. Fortunately, individual ions or molecules need not be considered. Since 1 gram of water contains 3.46×10^{22} molecules, the ionization of water can be described statistically. It is sufficient to know the **probability** that a hydrogen will be present as an ion or as part of a water molecule.

To state that the probability that a hydrogen exists as an ion is 0.01, means that a hydrogen atom has one chance in 100 of being an ion and 99 chances out of 100 of being in a water molecule. The actual probability of a hydrogen atom in pure water existing as a hydrogen ion is approximately 0.0000000018, or 1.8×10^{-9}. Consequently, the probability of its being part of a molecule is almost unity. Stated another way, for every hydrogen ion and hydroxyl ion in pure water, there are 1.8 billion or 1.8×10^9 water molecules. Hydrogen and hydroxyl ions nevertheless contribute significantly to the properties of water.

The tendency of water to dissociate is expressed as follows:

$$K = \frac{[H^+] [OH^-]}{[H_2O]}$$

where the bracketed terms represent the molar concentrations of hydrogen ions, hydroxyl ions, and undissociated water molecules,* and K is termed the **dissociation constant.** To calculate the dissociation constant for water, recall that 1 mol of water weighs 18 g. One liter (L) (1000 g) of water therefore contains $1000 \div 18 = 55.56$ mol. Pure water is thus 55.56 molar. Since the probability that a hydrogen in pure water will exist as an H^+ ion is 1.8×10^{-9}, the molar concentration of H^+ ions (or of OH^- ions) in pure water is calculated by multiplying the probability, 1.8×10^{-9}, by the molar concentration of water, 55.56 molar. This result is 1.0×10^{-7} molar.

*Strictly speaking, the bracketed terms represent molar activity rather than molar concentration.

We can now calculate K for water:

$$K = \frac{[H^+]\ [OH^-]}{[H_2O]} = \frac{[10^{-7}]\ [10^{-7}]}{[55.56]}$$

$$= 0.018 \times 10^{-14} = 1.8 \times 10^{-16}\ molar$$

The high concentration of molecular water (55.56 molar) is not significantly affected by dissociation. It is therefore convenient to consider it as essentially constant. This constant may then be incorporated into the dissociation constant, K, to provide a new constant, K_w, termed the **ion product** for water. The relationship between K_w and K is shown below:

$$K = \frac{[H^+]\ [OH^-]}{[H_2O]} = 1.8 \times 10^{-16}\ molar$$

$$K_w = (K)\ [H_2O] = [H^+]\ [OH^-]$$

$$= (1.8 \times 10^{-16}\ molar)\ (55.56\ molar)$$

$$= 1.00 \times 10^{-14}\ molar^2$$

Note that the dimensions of K are moles per liter and of K_w moles^2 per liter^2. As its name suggests, the ion product, K_w, is numerically equal to the product of the molar concentrations of H^+ and OH^-:

$$K_w = [H^+]\ [OH^-]$$

At 25 °C, $K_w = (10^{-7})^2 = 10^{-14}$ molar^2. At temperatures below 25 °C, K_w is less than 10^{-14}, and, at the temperatures above 25 °C, greater than 10^{-14}. For example, at the temperature of the human body (37 °C), the concentration of H^+ in pure water is slightly more than 10^{-7} molar. Within the stated limitations of the effect of temperature, $K_w = 10^{-14}\ molar^2$ **for all aqueous solutions**—even those that contain acids or bases. We shall use this constant in the calculation of pH values for acidic and basic solutions.

THE CONCEPT OF pH

The term **pH** was introduced in 1909 by Sorensen, who defined pH as **the negative log of the hydrogen ion concentration:**

$$pH = -\log\ [H^+]$$

This definition—while not rigorous*—is adequate for most biochemical purposes. To calculate the pH of a solution:

(1) Calculate hydrogen ion concentration, $[H^+]$.
(2) Calculate the base 10 logarithm of $[H^+]$.
(3) pH is the negative of the value found in step 2.

*pH = $-\log$ (H^+ activity).

For example, for pure water at 25 °C:

$$pH = -\log\ [H^+] = -\log 10^{-7} = -(-7) = 7.0$$

Low pH values correspond to high concentrations of H^+, and high pH values to low concentrations of H^+.

Acids are **proton donors,** and bases are **proton acceptors.** A distinction is made, however, between strong acids (eg, HCl, H_2SO_4), which completely dissociate even in strongly acidic solutions (low pH); and **weak acids,** which dissociate only partially in acidic solutions. A similar distinction is made between **strong bases** (eg, KOH, NaOH) and **weak bases** (eg, Ca[OH]$_2$). Only strong bases are dissociated at high pH. Many biochemicals are **weak acids.** Exceptions include phosphorylated intermediates, which also possess the strongly acidic primary phosphoric acid group.

The following examples illustrate how to calculate the pH of acidic and basic solutions.

Example: What is the pH of a solution whose hydrogen ion concentration is 3.2×10^{-4} molar?

$$pH = -\log\ [H^+]$$
$$= -\log\ (3.2 \times 10^{-4})$$
$$= -\log\ (3.2) - \log\ (10^{-4})$$
$$= -0.5 + 4.0$$
$$= 3.5$$

Example: What is the pH of a solution whose hydroxide ion concentration is 4.0×10^{-4} molar?

To approach this problem, we define a quantity **pOH** that is equal to $-\log\ [OH^-]$ and that may be derived from the definition of K_w:

$$K_w = [H^+]\ [OH^-] = 10^{-14}$$
therefore:
$$\log\ [H^+] + \log\ [OH^-] = \log 10^{-14}$$
or:
$$pH + pOH = 14$$

To solve the problem by this approach:

$$[OH^-] = 4.0 \times 10^{-4}$$
$$pOH = -\log\ [OH^-]$$
$$= -\log\ (4.0 \times 10^{-4})$$
$$= -\log\ (4.0) - \log\ (10^{-4})$$
$$= -0.60 + 4.0$$
$$= 3.4$$

Now:
$$pH = 14 - pOH = 14 - 3.40$$
$$= 10.6$$

Example: What is the pH of (a) 2.0×10^{-2} molar KOH, (b) 2.0×10^{-6} molar KOH? The OH^- arises from 2 sources: KOH and water. Since pH is determined by the **total** $[H^+]$ (and pOH by the **total** $[OH^-]$), both sources must be considered. In the first case, the contribution of water to the total $[OH^-]$ is negligible. The same cannot be said for the second case:

	Concentration (mol/L)	
	(a)	(b)
Molarity of KOH	2.0×10^{-2}	2.0×10^{-6}
$[OH^-]$ from KOH	2.0×10^{-2}	2.0×10^{-6}
$[OH^-]$ from water	1.0×10^{-7}	1.0×10^{-7}
Total $[OH^-]$	2.00001×10^{-2}	2.1×10^{-6}

Once a decision has been reached about the significance of the contribution by water, pH may be calculated as above.

In the above examples, it was assumed that the strong base KOH was completely dissociated in solution and that the molar concentration of OH^- ions was thus equal to the molar concentration of KOH. This assumption is valid for relatively dilute solutions of **strong** bases or acids but **not for solutions of weak bases or acids.** Since these weak electrolytes dissociate only slightly in solution, we must calculate the concentration of H^+ (or $[OH^-]$) produced by a given molarity of the acid (or base) using the **dissociation constant** before calculating total $[H^+]$ (or total $[OH^-]$), and subsequently calculating the pH.

PROTONIC EQUILIBRIA OF FUNCTIONAL GROUPS THAT ARE WEAK ACIDS OR BASES

Dissociation Behavior & Acid Strength

Many biochemicals possess functional groups that are weak acids or bases. One or more of these functional groups—frequently carboxyl groups, amino groups, or the secondary phosphate dissociation of phosphate esters—are present in all proteins and nucleic acids, most coenzymes, and most intermediary metabolites. The dissociation behavior (protonic equilibria) of weakly acidic and weakly basic functional groups is therefore fundamental to an understanding of the influence of intracellular pH on the structure and biochemical activity of these compounds. Their separation and identification in research and clinical laboratories is also facilitated by knowledge of the dissociation behavior of their functional groups.

We term the protonated form of an acid (eg, HA or RNH_3^+) the **acid** and the unprotonated form (eg, A^- or RNH_2) its **conjugate base** (Table 2–1). Similarly, we may refer to a **base** (eg, A^- or RNH_2) and its **conjugate acid** (eg, HA or RNH_3^+) (Latin *coniungere* "to join together").

The relative strengths of weak acids and of weak bases are expressed quantitatively as their **dissociation constants,** which express their tendency to ionize. Shown below are the expressions for the dissociation

Table 2–1. Selected examples of weak acids and their conjugate bases.

Acid	Conjugate Base
CH_3COOH	CH_3COO^-
$CH_3NH_3^+$	CH_3NH_2

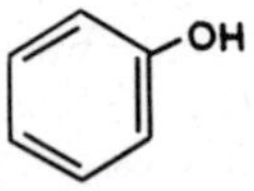

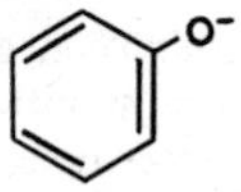

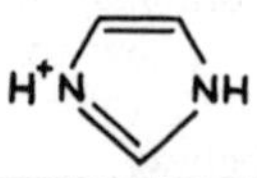

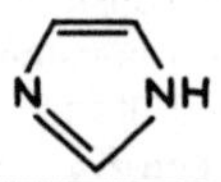

constant (K) for 2 representative weak acids, $R-COOH$ and $R-NH_3^+$.

$$R-COOH \rightleftharpoons R-COO^- + H^+$$

$$K = \frac{[R-COO^-][H^+]}{[R-COOH]}$$

$$R-NH_3^+ \rightleftharpoons R-NH_2 + H^+$$

$$K = \frac{[R-NH_2][H^+]}{[R-NH_3^+]}$$

Since the numerical values of K for weak acids are negative exponential numbers, it is convenient to express K as pK, where

$$pK = -\log K$$

Note that pK is related to K as pH is to H^+ concentration. Table 2–2 lists illustrative K and pK values for a monocarboxylic, a dicarboxylic, and a tricarboxylic acid. Observe that the **stronger acid groups have lower pK values.**

Table 2–2. Dissociation constants and pK values for representative carboxylic acids.

Acid		K	pK
Acetic		1.76×10^{-5}	4.75
Glutaric	(1st)	4.58×10^{-5}	4.34
	(2nd)	3.89×10^{-6}	5.41
Citric	(1st)	8.40×10^{-4}	3.08
	(2nd)	1.80×10^{-5}	4.74
	(3rd)	4.00×10^{-6}	5.40

From the above equations that relate K to $[H^+]$ and to the concentrations of undissociated acid and its conjugate base, note that when

$$[R-COO^-] = [R-COOH]$$

or when

$$[R-NH_2] = [R-NH_3^+]$$

then

$$K = [H^+]$$

In words, **when the associated (protonated) and dissociated (conjugate base) species are present in equal concentration, the prevailing hydrogen ion concentration $[H^+]$ is numerically equal to the dissociation constant, K.** If the logarithms of both sides of the above equation are taken and both sides are multiplied by -1, the expressions would be as follows:

$$K = [H^+]$$

$$-\log K = -\log [H^+]$$

$-\log K$ is defined as pK, and $-\log [H^+]$ is the definition of pH. Consequently, the equation may be rewritten as

$$pK = pH$$

ie, **the pK of an acid group is that pH at which the protonated and unprotonated species are present at equal concentrations.** The pK for an acid may be determined experimentally by adding 0.5 equivalent of alkali per equivalent of acid. The resulting pH will be equal to the pK of the acid.

Inductive Effects of Neighboring Groups on Acid Strength

The electrons of covalent bonds between dissimilar atoms tend to associate with the more electronegative (electron-attracting) atom, forming a **dipole:**

$$\boxed{Cl \longleftarrow CH_2-CH_3}$$
$$\underset{-}{} \qquad \underset{+}{}$$

The arrow $\longleftarrow$ represents the direction of electron "drift." Factors that increase the electron density on the carboxyl group from which the positively charged proton must dissociate hinder its leaving and have an **acid-weakening effect.** Conversely, anything that decreases the electron density on the carbonyl group will assist dissociation of the proton and have an **acid-strengthening effect.** The closer an electronegative atom is to the carboxyl group, the more pronounced the acid-strengthening effect. These effects are readily seen with the strongly electronegative atom chlorine:

	pK
CH_3CH_2COOH	4.9
$\underset{\underset{Cl}{\vert}}{CH_2}-CH_2-COOH$	4.1
$CH_3\underset{\underset{Cl}{\vert}}{CH}-COOH$	2.8

Alkyl groups supply electrons, but in a less dramatic manner:

	pK
CH_3COOH	4.7
CH_3-CH_2COOH	4.9
$(CH_3)_3C-COOH$	5.0

Charged groups may either supply or withdraw electrons:

		pK For carboxyl
Acetic acid	CH_3-COOH	4.7
Glycine	$\underset{\underset{NH_3^+}{\vert}}{CH_2}-COOH$	2.3
Glutamic acid ($a-COOH$)	$HOOC-{}^aCH_2-\underset{\underset{NH_3^+}{\vert}}{CH_2}-\underset{\underset{COOH}{\vert}}{CH_2}$	2.2

The second (γ) carboxyl dissociation of glutamic acid (pK = 4.2) is intermediate in acid strength between that of glycine and acetic acid, since the molecule has both $+$ and $-$ charged groups.

Oxo and hydroxyl groups also exert inductive effects and are acid strengthening:

		pK
Propionic acid	CH_3CH_2COOH	4.9
Lactic acid	$CH_3-\underset{\underset{OH}{\vert}}{CH}-COOH$	2.9
Pyruvic acid	$CH_3\underset{\underset{O}{\vert\vert}}{C}-COOH$	2.7

The aromatic amines such as aniline and the nitrogen atoms of cyclic amines such as pyridine or purines and pyrimidines are, by contrast, moderately strong acids. **Aromatic amines, therefore, exist for the most part in the dissociated or uncharged form at pH 7.4.** Their acidity is attributable to their aromatic "electron sink," which reduces the negative charge on

Table 2–3. Acid dissociation constants of the conjugate acids of selected amines.[*]

	Acid Form	pK
Ammonia	NH_4^+	9.26
Methylamine	$CH_3NH_3^+$	10.64
Dimethylamine	$(CH_3)_2NH_2^+$	10.72
Trimethylamine	$(CH_3)_3NH^+$	9.74
Aniline	$C_6H_5NH_3^+$	4.58
Pyridine	$C_5H_5NH^+$	5.23

[*]From Weast RC (editor): *Handbook of Chemistry & Physics,* 46th ed. Chemical Rubber Publishing Co., 1965–1966.

the nitrogen and facilitates dissociation of a proton.

Many drugs and other pharmacologically active compounds are amines. The uncharged forms are bases, ie, proton acceptors, whereas the charged forms are acids, ie, proton donors. The relative strengths of various amines may be expressed by the pK_a values for the dissociation:

$$\underset{R^1}{\overset{R}{\underset{H}{\diagup}}}\overset{+}{N}\overset{H}{\diagdown} \rightleftharpoons H^+ + \underset{R^1}{\overset{R}{\diagdown}}N{-}H$$

Some prefer to use pK_b values for amines. Conversion of pK_b to pK_a is accomplished thus:

$$pK_a = 14 - pK_b$$

The pK_a values show that the aliphatic amines are weaker acids (stronger bases) than ammonia and that **at pH 7.4 essentially all of an aliphatic amine is in the protonated (or charged) form.** In body fluids, therefore, these amines are associated with an anion such as Cl^-.

HENDERSON-HASSELBALCH EQUATION

The pH of a solution containing a weak acid is related to its acid dissociation constant, as shown above for the weak acid water. The relationship can be stated in the convenient form of the **Henderson-Hasselbalch** equation, derived below.

A weak acid, HA, ionizes as follows:

$$HA \rightleftharpoons H^+ + A^-$$

The equilibrium constant for this dissociation is written:

$$K = \frac{[H^+][A^-]}{[HA]}$$

cross-multiply,

$$[H^+][A^-] = K[HA]$$

divide both sides by $[A^-]$,

$$[H^+] = K\frac{[HA]}{[A^-]}$$

take the log of both sides,

$$\log[H^+] = \log\left(K\frac{[HA]}{[A^-]}\right) = \log K + \log\frac{[HA]}{[A^-]}$$

multiply through by -1,

$$-\log[H^+] = -\log K - \log\frac{[HA]}{[A^-]}$$

substitute pH and pK for $-\log[H^+]$ and $-\log K$, respectively; then

$$pH = pK - \log\frac{[HA]}{[A^-]}$$

Then, to remove the minus sign, invert the last term.

$$\boxed{pH = pK + \log\frac{[A^-]}{[HA]}}$$

The Henderson-Hasselbalch equation has proved to be an expression of great predictive value in protonic equilibria. For example,

(1) When an acid is exactly half neutralized, $[A^-] = [HA]$. Under these conditions,

$$pH = pK + \log\frac{[A^-]}{[HA]} = pK + \log\frac{1}{1} = pK + 0$$

Therefore, at half neutralization, pH = pK.

(2) When the ratio $[A^-]/[HA] = 100$ to 1,

$$pH = pK + \log\frac{[A^-]}{[HA]}$$

$$pH = pK + \log 100/1 = pK + 2$$

(3) When the ratio $[A^-]/[HA] = 1$ to 10,

$$pH = pK + \log 1/10 = pK + (-1)$$

If the equation is evaluated at several ratios of $[A^-]/[HA]$ between the limits 10^3 and 10^{-3}, and the calculated pH values plotted, the result obtained describes the titration curve for a weak acid (Fig 2–5).

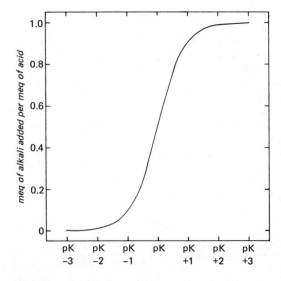

Figure 2–5. General form of a titration curve calculated from the Henderson-Hasselbalch equation.

BUFFERS & BUFFERING

Solutions of weak acids and their conjugate bases (or of weak bases and their conjugate acids) exhibit the phenomenon of **buffering—the tendency of a solution to resist more effectively a change in pH following addition of a strong acid or base than does an equal volume of water.** The phenomenon of buffering is best illustrated by titrating a weak acid or base using a pH meter. Alternatively, we may calculate the pH shift that accompanies addition of acid or base to a buffered solution. In the example, the buffered solution (a mixture of a weak acid, $pK = 5.0$, and its conjugate base) is present initially at one of 4 pH values. We will calculate the pH shift that results when 0.1 meq of KOH is added to 1 meq of each of these solutions:

Initial pH	5.00	5.37	5.60	5.86
$[A^-]_{initial}$	0.50	0.70	0.80	0.88
$[HA]_{initial}$	0.50	0.30	0.20	0.12
$([A^-]/[HA])_{initial}$	1.00	2.33	4.00	7.33

Addition of 0.1 meq of KOH produces

$[A^-]_{final}$	0.60	0.80	0.90	0.98
$[HA]_{final}$	0.40	0.20	0.10	0.02
$([A^-]/[HA])_{final}$	1.50	4.00	9.00	49.0
$\log([A^-]/[HA])_{final}$	0.176	0.602	0.95	1.69
Final pH	5.18	5.60	5.95	6.69
Δ pH	0.18	0.60	0.95	1.69

Observe that the pH change per milliequivalent of OH^- added varies greatly depending on the pH. At pH values close to pK, the solution resists changes in pH most effectively, and it is said to exert a **buffering effect. Solutions of weak acids and their conjugate bases buffer most effectively in the pH range pK ±**

2.0 pH units. This means that if it is desired to buffer a solution at pH X, a weak acid or base whose pK is no more than 2.0 pH units removed from pH X should be used.

Shown in Fig 2–6 is the net charge on one molecule of the acid as a function of pH. A fractional charge of -0.5 does not mean that an individual molecule bears a fractional charge but that the statistical probability that a given molecule has a unit negative charge is 0.5. Consideration of the net charge on macromolecules as a function of pH provides the basis for many separatory techniques, including the electrophoretic separation of amino acids, plasma proteins, and abnormal hemoglobins (see Chapters 3 and 4).

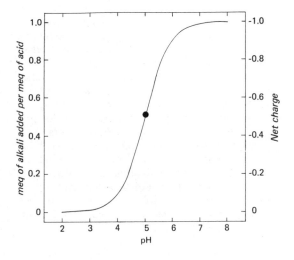

Figure 2–6. Titration curve for an acid of the type HA having pK = 5.0 (•).

• • •

Reference

Segel IM: *Biochemical Calculations*. Wiley, 1968.

3 | Amino Acids & Peptides

Victor W. Rodwell, PhD

INTRODUCTION

Living cells produce an impressive variety of **macromolecules (proteins, nucleic acids, polysaccharides)** that serve as structural components, biocatalysts, hormones, receptors, or repositories of genetic information. These macromolecules are **biopolymers** constructed of **monomer units** or **building blocks.** For nucleic acids, the monomer units are **nucleotides;** for complex polysaccharides, the monomer units are **sugar derivatives;** and for proteins, the monomer units are L-α-**amino acids.**

While proteins may also contain substances other than amino acids, the 3-dimensional structure and thus the biologic properties of proteins are determined largely by the **kinds of amino acids present,** the **order in which they are linked together** in a polypeptide chain, and thereby the **spatial relationship of one amino acid to another.**

AMINO ACIDS

Amino acids contain both amino and carboxylic acid functional groups. In an α-amino acid, both are attached to the same (α) carbon atom (Fig 3–1).

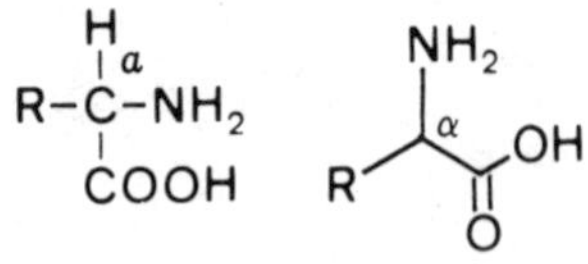

Figure 3–1. Two representations of an α-amino acid.

Although about 300 amino acids occur in nature, only 20 of these occur in proteins. Complete hydrolysis* of proteins produces the 20 L-α-amino acids listed in Table 3–2. The same 20 amino acids are present in

*Hydrolysis = rupture of a covalent bond with addition of the elements of water.

proteins from all forms of life—plant, animal, or microbial. The reason for this becomes apparent when the universality of the genetic code is discussed (see Chapter 30). However, some proteins contain amino acid derivatives that are generated after incorporation of the amino acid into the protein molecule (see Tables 4–2 and 4–3).

With the exception of glycine, for which R = a hydrogen atom (see Fig 3–1), all 4 groups linked to the α-carbon atom of amino acids are different. This tetrahedral orientation of 4 different groups about the α-carbon atom confers optical activity (the ability to rotate the plane of plane-polarized light) on amino acids. Although some amino acids found in proteins are dextrorotatory and some levorotatory at pH 7.0, all have the **absolute configurations** of L-glyceraldehyde and hence are L-α-**amino acids.** Threonine, isoleucine, 4-hydroxyproline, and hydroxylysine each have 2 asymmetric centers and hence 4 isomers (see Chapter 1). Of these, only one isomer is found in proteins.

IONIC FORMS OF AMINO ACIDS

Amino acids bear at least 2 ionizable weak acid groups, a –COOH and an –NH$_3^+$. In solution, 2 forms of these groups, one charged and one uncharged, exist in protonic equilibrium:

$$R-COOH \rightleftharpoons R-COO^- + H^+$$

$$R-NH_3^+ \rightleftharpoons R-NH_2 + H^+$$

R–COOH and R–NH$_3^+$ represent the **protonated** or **acidic** partners in these equilibria. R–COO$^-$ and R–NH$_2$ are the **conjugate bases** (ie, proton acceptors) of the corresponding acids. Although both R–COOH and R–NH$_3^+$ are weak acids, R–COOH is a several thousand times stronger acid than is R–NH$_3^+$. At the pH of blood plasma or the intracellular space (7.4 and 7.1, respectively), carboxyl groups exist almost entirely as **carboxylate ions, R–COO$^-$.** At these pH values, most amino groups are predominantly in the associated (protonated) form, R–NH$_3^+$. The prevalent ionic species of amino acids present in blood and most tissues should be represented as shown in Fig 3–2(A).

Table 3–1. Weak acid groups of the amino acids present in proteins.

	Conjugate Acid	Conjugate Base	Approximate pK_a
a-Carboxyl	R–COOH	R–COO$^-$	2.1 ± 0.5
Non-a-carboxyl (aspartate, glutamate)	R–COOH	R–COO$^-$	4.0 ± 0.3
Imidazolium (histidine)	 HN$\overset{+}{\cdots}$NH (R)	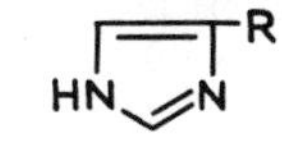 HN=N (R)	6.0
a-Amino	R–NH$_3^+$	R–NH$_2$	9.8 ± 1.0
ϵ-Amino (lysine)	R–NH$_3^+$	R–NH$_2$	10.5
Phenolic OH (tyrosine)	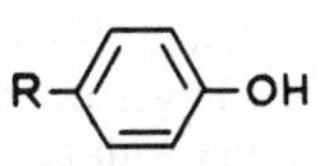 R–⟨⟩–OH	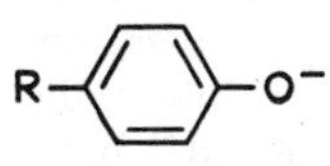 R–⟨⟩–O$^-$	10.1
Guanidinium (arginine)	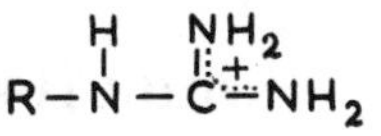 R–N(H)–$\overset{+}{C}$=NH$_2$ (NH$_2$)	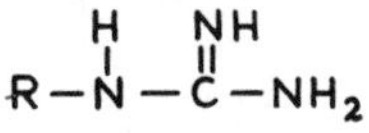 R–N(H)–C(=NH)–NH$_2$	12.5
Sulfhydryl (cysteine)	R–SH	R–S$^-$	8.3

Structure B (Fig 3–2) cannot exist at *any* pH. At a pH sufficiently low to protonate the carboxyl group, the more weakly acidic amino group would also be protonated. The approximate pK_a values for α-carboxyl and α-amino groups of an α-amino acid are 2 and 10, respectively (Table 3–1). At a pH below its pK_a, an acid will be predominantly protonated, and at a pH 2 units below its pK_a, it will be approximately 99% protonated. If the pH is gradually raised, the proton from the carboxylic acid will be lost long before that from the R–NH$_3^+$. At any pH sufficiently high for the uncharged conjugate base of the amino group to predominate, a carboxyl group is present as the carboxylate ion (R–COO$^-$). However, for convenience the B representation is used for many equations not involving protonic equilibria.

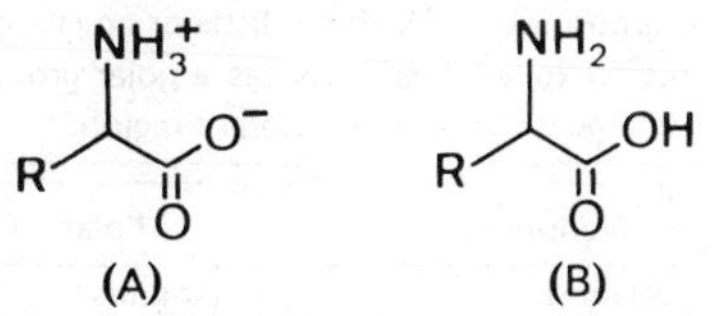

(A)   (B)

Figure 3–2. Ionically correct structure for an amino acid at or near physiologic pH *(A)*. The uncharged structure shown as *(B)* cannot exist at any pH but may be used as a convenience when discussing the chemistry of amino acids.

As discussed in Chapter 2, the relative acid strengths of weak acids may be expressed in terms of their acid dissociation constant, K_a, or of their pK_a, the negative log of the dissociation constant, ie,

$$pK_a = -\log K_a*$$

Table 3–1 lists the acidic groups and their pK values for the functional groups present on the 20 amino acids of proteins.

The **net charge** (the algebraic sum of all the positively and negatively charged groups present) of an amino acid **depends upon the pH, or proton concentration, of the surrounding solution.** The ability to alter the charge on amino acids or their derivatives by manipulating the pH facilitates the physical separation of amino acids, peptides, and proteins.

The pH at which an amino acid **bears no net charge** and hence does not move in a direct current electrical field is termed its **isoelectric pH (pI).** For an aliphatic amino acid such as alanine, the isoelectric species is the form shown in Fig 3–3.

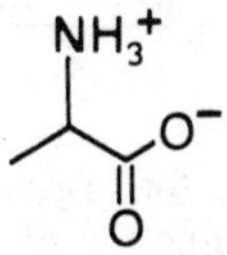

Figure 3–3. Isoelectric or "zwitterionic" structure of alanine. Although charged, the zwitterion bears no *net* charge and hence does not migrate in a direct current electrical field.

*For convenience, the a subscript in K_a and pK_a will be implied but dropped hereafter from the notation.

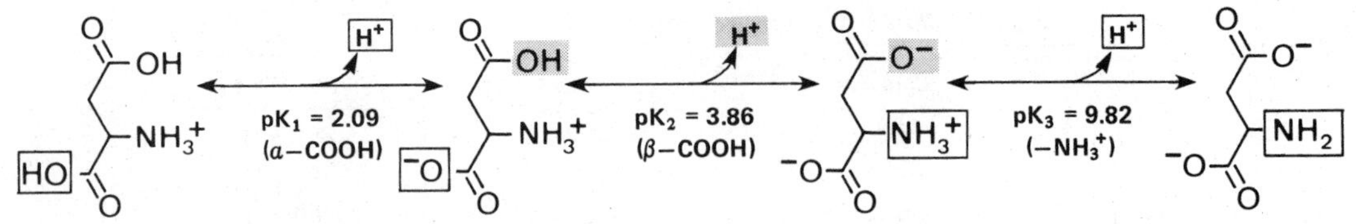

Figure 3–4. Protonic equilibria of aspartic acid.

The isoelectric pH is the pH midway between pK values on either side of the isoelectric species. For an amino acid with only 2 dissociating groups, there can be no possible ambiguity, as is shown below in the calculation of the pI for alanine. Since pK_1 (RCOOH) = 2.35 and pK_2 (RNH_3^+) = 9.69, the isoelectric pH (pI) of alanine is:

$$pI = \frac{pK_1 + pK_2}{2} = \frac{2.35 + 9.69}{2} = 6.02$$

Calculation of pI for a compound with more than 2 dissociable groups carries more possibility for error. For example, from consideration of Fig 3–4, what would be the isoelectric pH (pI) for aspartic acid? To answer such a query unambiguously, write out all possible ionic structures for a compound in the order in which they occur as one proceeds from strongly acidic to basic solution (eg, as for aspartic acid in Fig 3–4). Next, identify the isoionic, zwitterionic, or neutral representation (as in Fig 3–4, structure [B]). pI is the pH at the midpoint between the pK values on either side of the isoionic species. In this example,

$$pI = \frac{2.09 + 3.86}{2} = 2.98$$

This approach works equally well for amino acids with additional dissociating groups, eg, lysine or histidine. After writing the formulas for all possible charged species of the basic amino acids lysine and arginine, observe that

$$pI = \frac{pK_2 + pK_3}{2}$$

For lysine, pI is 9.7; for arginine, pI is 10.8. The student should determine the pI for histidine.

The above approach, that of determining by inspection of charged structures the two pK values on either side of the zwitterion, is by no means limited in applicability to amino acids. It may be applied to calculation of the charge on a molecule with any number of dissociating groups. The ability to perform calculations of this type is of value in the clinical laboratory to predict the mobility of compounds in electrical fields and to select appropriate buffers for separations. For example, a buffer at pH 7.0 would suffice to separate 2 molecules with a pI of 6 and 8, respectively, because the molecule with pI = 6 will have a larger net negative charge at pH 7.0 than the molecule with pI = 8.

STRUCTURES OF AMINO ACIDS

The amino acids present in proteins may be divided into 2 broad groups on the basis of whether the R groups attached to the α-carbon atoms are polar or nonpolar (Table 3–2).

Table 3–3 gives, in addition, the 3-letter and single-letter abbreviations in common use among protein chemists. In this book, the 3-letter abbreviations will frequently be used. The single-letter abbreviations are used to represent extremely long sequences of amino acids such as is necessary for listing the complete sequence of amino acids in a protein. Tables 3–4 and 3–5 list selected examples of important amino acids that occur in various natural products but not in proteins.

Various other amino acids (Tables 3–4 and 3–5) that occur in free or combined states (but not in proteins) fulfill important roles in metabolic processes.

Table 3–2. Classification of the L-α-amino acids present in proteins on the basis of the relative polarities of their R groups. A nonpolar group is one which has little or no charge difference from one region to another, whereas a polar group has a relatively large charge difference in different regions.

Nonpolar	Polar
Alanine	Arginine
Isoleucine	Asparagine
Leucine	Aspartic acid
Methionine	Cysteine
Phenylalanine	Glutamic acid
Proline	Glutamine
Tryptophan	Glycine
Valine	Histidine
	Lysine
	Serine
	Threonine
	Tyrosine

Table 3–3. L-α-Amino acids present in proteins.*

Name	Symbol	Structural Formula
With Aliphatic Side Chains		
Glycine	Gly [G]	$H-\underset{\underset{+NH_3}{\mid}}{CH}-COO^-$
Alanine	Ala [A]	$CH_3-\underset{\underset{+NH_3}{\mid}}{CH}-COO^-$
Valine	Val [V]	$\underset{H_3C}{\overset{H_3C}{>}}CH-\underset{\underset{+NH_3}{\mid}}{CH}-COO^-$
Leucine	Leu [L]	$\underset{H_3C}{\overset{H_3C}{>}}CH-CH_2-\underset{\underset{+NH_3}{\mid}}{CH}-COO^-$
Isoleucine	Ile [I]	$\underset{CH_3}{\overset{CH_3}{\underset{\mid}{\overset{\mid}{CH_2}}}}CH-\underset{\underset{+NH_3}{\mid}}{CH}-COO^-$
With Side Chains Containing Hydroxylic (OH) Groups		
Serine	Ser [S]	$\underset{OH}{\overset{\mid}{CH_2}}-\underset{\underset{+NH_3}{\mid}}{CH}-COO^-$
Threonine	Thr [T]	$CH_3-\underset{OH}{\overset{\mid}{CH}}-\underset{\underset{+NH_3}{\mid}}{CH}-COO^-$
Tyrosine	Tyr [Y]	See below.
With Side Chains Containing Sulfur Atoms		
Cysteine†	Cys [C]	$\underset{SH}{\overset{\mid}{CH_2}}-\underset{\underset{+NH_3}{\mid}}{CH}-COO^-$
Methionine	Met [M]	$\underset{S-CH_3}{\overset{\mid}{CH_2}}-CH_2-\underset{\underset{+NH_3}{\mid}}{CH}-COO^-$
With Side Chains Containing Acidic Groups or Their Amides		
Aspartic acid	Asp [D]	$^-OOC-CH_2-\underset{\underset{+NH_3}{\mid}}{CH}-COO^-$
Asparagine	Asn [N]	$H_2N-\underset{\underset{O}{\mid\mid}}{C}-CH_2-\underset{\underset{+NH_3}{\mid}}{CH}-COO^-$

*Except for hydroxylysine (Hyl) and hydroxyproline (Hyp), which are incorporated into polypeptide linkages as lysine and proline and subsequently hydroxylated (see Chapters 20 and 33), specific transfer RNA molecules exist for all the amino acids listed in Table 3–3. Their incorporation into proteins is thus under direct genetic control.

†Cystine consists of 2 cysteine residues linked by a disulfide bond:

$$HOOC-\underset{\underset{NH_2}{\mid}}{CH}-CH_2-S-S-CH_2-\underset{\underset{NH_2}{\mid}}{CH}-COOH$$

Table 3–3 (cont'd). L-α-Amino acids present in proteins.*

Name	Symbol	Structural Formula
Glutamic acid	Glu [E]	$^-OOC-CH_2-CH_2-\underset{\underset{+NH_3}{\mid}}{CH}-COO^-$
Glutamine	Gln [Q]	$H_2N-\underset{\underset{O}{\parallel}}{C}-CH_2-CH_2-\underset{\underset{+NH_3}{\mid}}{CH}-COO^-$

With Side Chains Containing Basic Groups

Name	Symbol	Structural Formula
Arginine	Arg [R]	$H-\underset{\underset{NH_2}{\mid}}{\underset{C=\overset{+}{N}H_2}{\mid}}{N}-CH_2-CH_2-CH_2-\underset{\underset{+NH_3}{\mid}}{CH}-COO^-$
Lysine	Lys [K]	$\underset{\underset{+NH_3}{\mid}}{CH_2}-CH_2-CH_2-CH_2-\underset{\underset{+NH_3}{\mid}}{CH}-COO^-$
Histidine	His [H]	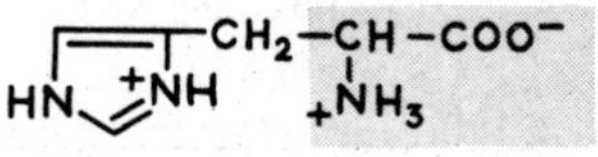 (imidazole ring) $-CH_2-\underset{\underset{+NH_3}{\mid}}{CH}-COO^-$

Containing Aromatic Rings

Name	Symbol	Structural Formula
Histidine	His [H]	See above.
Phenylalanine	Phe [F]	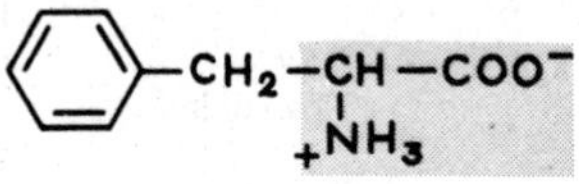 (benzene ring) $-CH_2-\underset{\underset{+NH_3}{\mid}}{CH}-COO^-$
Tyrosine	Tyr [Y]	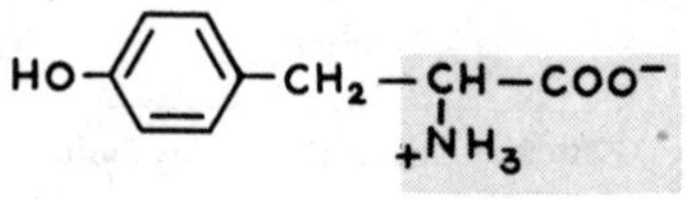 $HO-$ (benzene ring) $-CH_2-\underset{\underset{+NH_3}{\mid}}{CH}-COO^-$
Tryptophan	Trp [W]	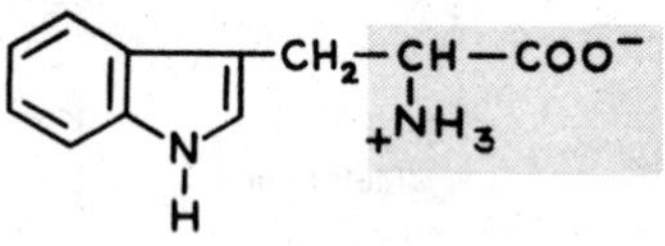 (indole ring) $-CH_2-\underset{\underset{+NH_3}{\mid}}{CH}-COO^-$

Imino Acids

Name	Symbol	Structural Formula
Proline	Pro [P]	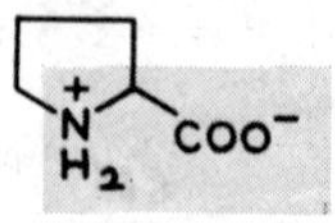 (pyrrolidine ring) $\underset{\underset{H_2}{\mid}}{\overset{+}{N}}-COO^-$

Table 3–4. Selected examples of α-amino acids that do not occur in proteins
but perform essential functions in mammalian metabolism.

Common and Systematic Names	Formula at Neutral pH	Significance
Homocysteine (2-amino-4-mercapto-butanoic acid)	$CH_2-CH_2-CH-COO^-$ $\quad SH \qquad\quad {}_+NH_3$	Intermediate in methionine biosynthesis (see Chapter 20).
Cysteine sulfinic acid (2-amino-3-sulfinopro-panoic acid)	$CH_2-CH-COO^-$ $\quad SO_2^- \;\; {}_+NH_3$	Intermediate in cysteine catabolism (see Chapter 22).
Homoserine (2-amino-4-hydroxy-butanoic acid)	$CH_2-CH_2-CH-COO^-$ $\quad OH \qquad\quad {}_+NH_3$	An intermediate in threonine, aspartate, and methionine metabolism (see Chapter 22).
Ornithine (2,5-bisaminopentanoic acid)	$CH_2-CH_2-CH_2-CH-COO^-$ $\;\; {}_+NH_3 \qquad\qquad {}_+NH_3$	Intermediate in threonine, aspartate, and methionine metabolism (see Chapter 22).
Citrulline (2-amino-5-ureidopenta-noic acid)	$CH_2-CH_2-CH_2-CH-COO^-$ $\;\; NH \qquad\qquad {}_+NH_3$ $\;\; C=O$ $\;\; NH_2$	Intermediate in the biosynthesis of urea (see Chapter 21).
Argininosuccinic acid	${}_+NH \; CH_2-CH_2-CH_2-CH-COO^-$ $\; \| \qquad\qquad\qquad\qquad {}_+NH_3$ $HN-C-NH$ $^-OOC-CH_2-C-COO^-$	Intermediate in the biosynthesis of urea (see Chapter 21).
Dopa (3,4-dihydroxyphenyl-alanine)	$HO-\langle\;\rangle-CH_2-CH-COO^-$ $HO \qquad\qquad\qquad {}_+NH_3$	Precursor of melanin (see Chapter 23).
3-Monoiodotyrosine	I $HO-\langle\;\rangle-CH_2-CH-COO^-$ $\qquad\qquad\qquad NH_3{}_+$	Precursor of thyroid hormones.
3,5-Diiodotyrosine	I $HO-\langle\;\rangle-CH_2-CH-COO^-$ $I \qquad\qquad\qquad {}_+NH_3$	Precursor of thyroid hormones.
3,5,3'-Triiodothyronine (T_3)	$I \qquad\quad I$ $HO-\langle\;\rangle-O-\langle\;\rangle-CH_2-CH-COO^-$ $\qquad\qquad I \qquad\qquad\quad {}_+NH_3$	Precursor of thyroid hormones.
Thyroxine (3,5,3',5'-tetraiodo-thyronine) (T_4)	$I \qquad\quad I$ $HO-\langle\;\rangle-O-\langle\;\rangle-CH_2-CH-COO^-$ $I \qquad\quad I \qquad\qquad {}_+NH_3$	Precursor of thyroid hormones.

Table 3–5. Selected examples of amino acids with non-α-amino groups that perform important functions in mammalian metabolism.

Common and Systematic Names	Formula at Neutral pH	Significance
β-Alanine (3-aminopropanoic acid)	$\underset{\underset{+NH_3}{\mid}}{CH_2}-CH_2-COO^-$	Part of coenzyme A and of the vitamin pantetheine (see Chapter 10).
Taurine (2-aminoethylsulfonic acid)	$\underset{\underset{+NH_3}{\mid}}{CH_2}-CH_2-SO_3^-$	Occurs in bile combined with bile acids (see Chapter 44).
γ-Aminobutyric acid (GABA) (4-aminobutanoic acid)	$\underset{\underset{+NH_3}{\mid}}{CH_2}-CH_2-CH_2-COO^-$	Neurotransmitter formed from glutamate in brain tissue (see Chapter 23).
β-Aminoisobutyric acid (2-methyl-3-aminopropanoic acid)	$H_3N^+-CH_2-\underset{\underset{CH_3}{\mid}}{CH}-COO^-$	End product of pyrimidine catabolism in urine of some persons (see Chapter 26).

For example, the amino acids ornithine, citrulline, and argininosuccinic acid (see Table 3–4) participate in the metabolism of urea. Over 20 D-amino acids occur naturally. These include the D-alanine and D-glutamic acid of certain bacterial cell walls and a variety of D-amino acids in antibiotics.

SOLUBILITY OF AMINO ACIDS

The presence of multiple charged groups on amino acids dictates that they are readily solvated by and hence soluble in polar solvents such as water and ethanol but insoluble in nonpolar solvents such as benzene, hexane, and ether. Their high melting points (above 200 °C) reflect the presence of charged groups—ie, the high energy needed to disrupt the ionic forces maintaining the crystal lattice.

GENERAL CHEMICAL REACTIONS

The carboxyl and amino groups of amino acids exhibit all the expected reactions of these functions, eg, salt formation, esterification, and acylation (see Chapter 1).

Color Reactions

Ninhydrin (Fig 3–5) oxidatively decarboxylates α-amino acids to CO_2, NH_3, and an aldehyde with one less carbon atom than the parent amino acid. The reduced ninhydrin then reacts with the liberated ammonia, forming a blue complex that maximally absorbs light of wavelength 570 nm. This blue color forms the basis of a **quantitative test for α-amino acids** that can detect as little as 1 μg of amino acid. Amines other than α-amino acids also react with ninhydrin, forming a blue color but without evolving CO_2. The evolution of CO_2 is thus indicative of an α-amino acid. NH_3 and peptides also react but more slowly than α-amino acids. Proline and 4-hydroxyproline produce a yellow color with ninhydrin.

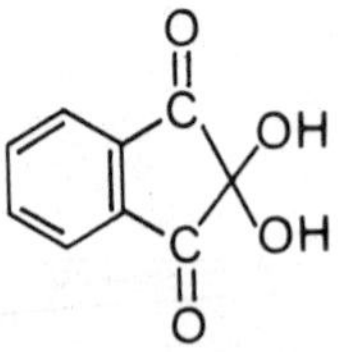

Fluorescamine, an even more sensitive reagent, can detect nanogram quantities of an amino acid (Fig 3–6). Like ninhydrin, fluorescamine forms a complex with amines other than amino acids.

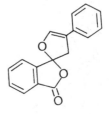

Figure 3–6. Fluorescamine.

Formation of Peptide Bonds

The most important reaction of amino acids is the formation of the **peptide bond.** In principle, peptide bond formation involves removal of 1 mol of water between the α-amino group of one amino acid and the α-carboxyl group of a second amino acid (Fig 3–7).

This reaction does not, however, proceed as written, since the equilibrium constant strongly favors peptide bond hydrolysis. To synthesize peptide bonds between 2 amino acids, the carboxyl group must first be **activated.** Chemically, this may involve prior conversion to an acid chloride. **Biologically, activation involves initial condensation with ATP** (see Chapter 30).

Figure 3–5. Ninhydrin.

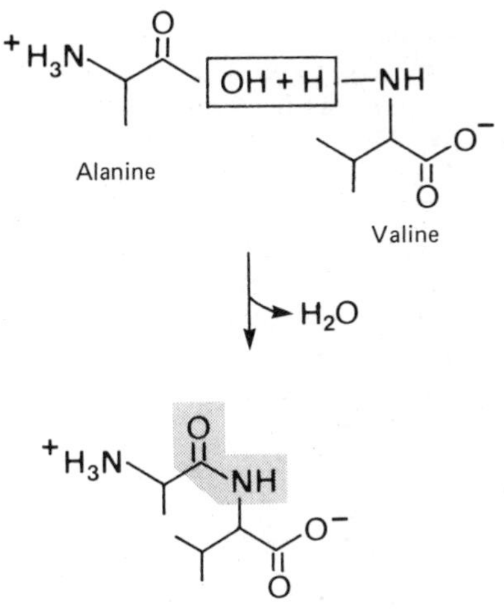

Alanine

Valine

Alanyl-valine (Ala-Val), a dipeptide

Figure 3–7. Amino acids united by a peptide bond (shaded portion).

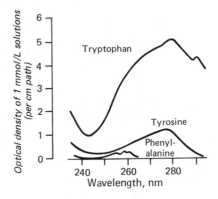

Figure 3–8. The ultraviolet absorption spectra of tryptophan, tyrosine, and phenylalanine.

PROPERTIES OF INDIVIDUAL AMINO ACIDS

Glycine, the smallest of the amino acids, can fit into regions of the 3-dimensional structure of proteins inaccessible to other amino acids.

The aliphatic R groups of alanine, valine, leucine, and isoleucine and the aromatic R groups of phenylalanine, tyrosine, and tryptophan are hydrophobic, a property that has important consequences for the ordering of water molecules in proteins in their immediate neighborhood.

The charged R groups of both the basic and acidic amino acids perform key roles in stabilization of specific protein conformations via formation of salt bonds. In addition, and together with histidine, amino acids with positively or negatively charged R groups function in the "charge relay" systems that transmit charges across considerable distances during enzymatic catalysis. Finally, histidine occupies a unique and important place in enzymatic catalysis, since the pK of its imidazole proton permits it, at pH 7.0, to function alternatively as either a base or an acid during catalysis.

The primary alcohol group of serine and the primary thioalcohol (–SH) group of cysteine are excellent nucleophiles and function as such during many instances of enzymatic catalysis. While the secondary alcohol group of threonine also is a good nucleophile, it is not known to perform this role in catalysis. In addition to its catalytic role, the –OH of serine functions in regulation of the activity of certain key metabolic enzymes whose catalytic activity depends upon the phosphorylation state of specific seryl residues.

Amino acids do not absorb visible light (ie, they are colorless) and, with the exceptions of the aromatic amino acids tryptophan, tyrosine, phenylalanine, and histidine, do not absorb ultraviolet light of a wavelength above 240 nm. As shown in Fig 3–8, above 240 nm, **most of the ultraviolet absorption of proteins is due to their tryptophan content.**

PEPTIDES

Definitions

When the amino and carboxyl groups of amino acids combine to form peptide bonds, the constituent amino acids are termed amino acid residues. **A peptide consists of 2 or more amino acid residues linked by peptide bonds.** Peptides of more than 10 amino acid residues are termed **polypeptides.**

Representation of Peptide Structures

Fig 3–9 shows a tripeptide made up of the amino acid residues alanine, cysteine, and valine. Note that **a tripeptide is one with 3 residues, not 3 peptide bonds.** By convention, peptide structures are written with the **N-terminal residue** (the residue with a free α-amino group) **at the left** and with the **C-terminal residue** (the residue with a free α-carboxyl group) **at the right.** This peptide has a **single** free α-amino group and a **single** free α-carboxyl group (circled). This is true for all polypeptides comprised solely of amino

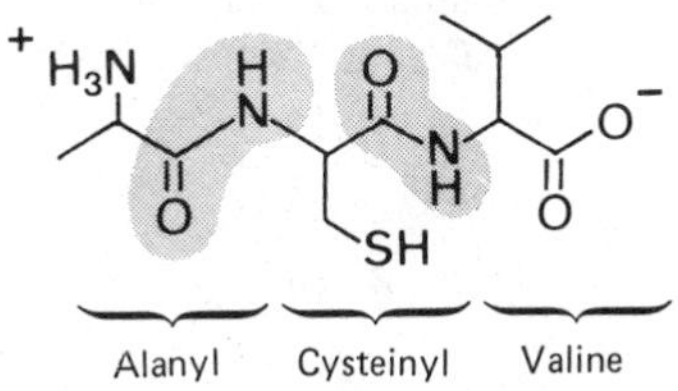

Alanyl   Cysteinyl   Valine

Figure 3–9. Structural formula for a tripeptide. Peptide bonds shaded for emphasis.

acid residues linked by peptide bonds formed between α-amino and α-carboxyl groups. In some peptides, the terminal amino or carboxyl groups may be derivatized (eg, an N-formyl amine or an amide of the carboxyl group) and thus not free.

Writing Structural Formulas of Peptides

What follows is a simple way to write peptide structures. First, draw its "backbone" of linked α-NH₂, α-COOH, and α-carbon atoms. These alternate along the backbone. Next, insert the appropriate side chains on the α-carbon atoms. This is illustrated below.

(1) Write a zig-zag of arbitrary length, and insert the N-terminal amino group:

(2) Insert the α-carbon, α-carboxyl, and α-amino groups:

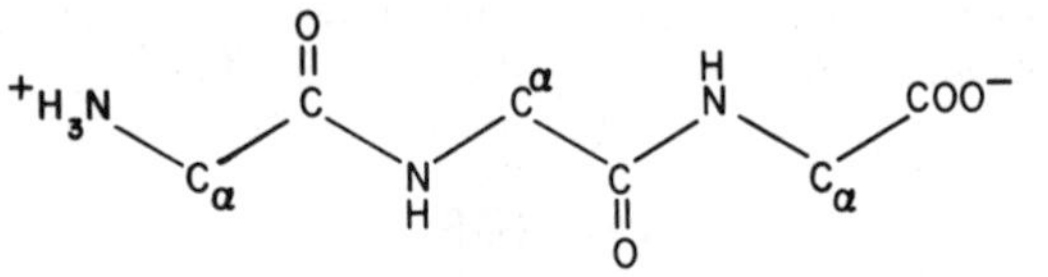

(3) Add the appropriate R groups (shaded) and α-hydrogens to the α-carbon atoms:

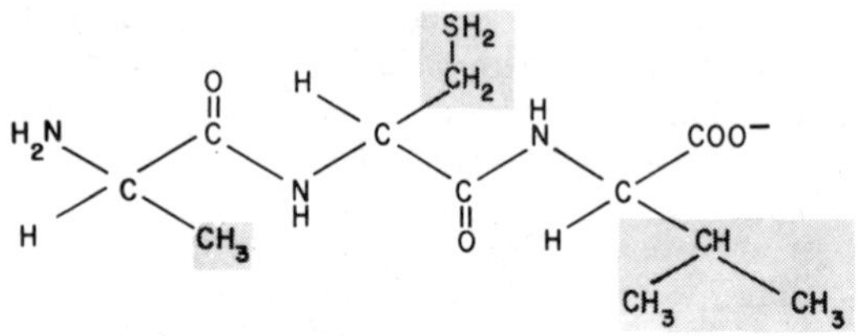

Primary Structure of Peptides

The linear sequence of amino acid residues in a polypeptide constitutes its **primary structure.** When the **number, chemical structure,** and **order** of all of the amino acid residues in a polypeptide are known, its primary structure has been determined.

Since polypeptides (proteins) may contain 100 or more residues, it is often inconvenient to use conventional structural formulas to represent primary structure. The "chemical shorthand" used is either the

Glu-Ala-Lys-Gly-Tyr-Ala

E   A   K   G   Y   A

Figure 3–10. Use of 3-letter and one-letter abbreviations for amino acid residues to represent the primary structure of a hexapeptide with glutamate (Glu, E) at the N terminus and alanine (Ala, A) at the C terminus.

3-letter or one-letter abbreviation for the amino acids shown in column 2 of Table 3–3 (Fig 3–10). Note that **peptides are named as derivatives of the C-terminal amino acid residue.**

Three-letter abbreviations for amino acid residues linked by straight lines represent the primary structure that is known and unambiguous. These lines are omitted for single-letter abbreviations. Where there is uncertainty about the precise **order** of the amino acid residues of a portion of a polypeptide, the questionable residues are enclosed in brackets and separated by commas (Fig 3–11).

Glu-Lys-(Ala,Gly,Tyr)-His-Ala

Figure 3–11. A heptapeptide containing a region of uncertain primary structure.

Physiologic Consequences of Changes in Primary Structure

Substitution of a single amino acid for another in a linear sequence of possibly 100 or more amino acids may reduce or abolish biologic activity, with potentially serious consequences (eg, sickle cell disease; see Chapter 5). Indeed, many inherited metabolic errors may involve no more than a single change of this type. The introduction of powerful new methods to determine protein and DNA structure has greatly increased our understanding of the biochemical basis for many inherited metabolic diseases.

Ionic Forms of Peptides

The peptide (amide) bond is uncharged at any pH of physiologic interest. Formation of peptides from amino acids at pH 7.4 is therefore accompanied by a net loss of one positive and one negative charge per peptide bond formed. Peptides are, however, charged molecules at physiologic pH owing to the charges on the C- and N-terminal groups and on functional groups present in polar amino acid residues attached to the α-carbon atoms (see Table 3–1).

Polypeptides, like amino acids and other charged molecules, may be isolated by techniques (eg, electrophoresis, ion exchange chromatography) that separate on the basis of charge. The pK value for the C-terminal carboxyl group of a polypeptide is higher than that of the α-carboxyl group in the corresponding amino acid (ie, the peptide COOH is a weaker acid). Conversely, the N-terminal amino group is a stronger acid (has a lower pK) than the amino acid from which it was derived (Table 3–6).

Table 3–6. pK values for glycine and glycine peptides.

	pK (COOH)	pK (NH₃⁺)
Gly	2.34	9.60
Gly-Gly	3.12	8.17
Gly-Gly-Gly	3.26	7.91

Conformation of Peptides in Solution

A large number of conformations (spatial arrangements) are possible for a polypeptide. The available evidence suggests, however, that in solution a narrow range of conformations tends to predominate. These favored conformations result from factors such as steric hindrance, coulombic interactions, H bonding, and hydrophobic interactions (see Chapter 4). As is the case for proteins, specific conformations are required for physiologic activity of polypeptides such as angiotensin and vasopressin (see Chapters 37 and 40).

PHYSIOLOGICALLY ACTIVE PEPTIDES

Animal, plant, and bacterial cells contain a wide variety of low-molecular-weight polypeptides (3–100 amino acid residues) having profound physiologic activity. Some, including most mammalian polypeptide hormones, contain only peptide bonds formed between α-amino and α-carboxyl groups of the 20 L-α-amino acids present in proteins. However, additional amino acids or derivatives of the protein amino acids may also be present in polypeptides (though not in proteins). Shown below are a few selected examples.

The short polypeptides bradykinin and kallidin are smooth muscle hypotensive agents liberated from specific plasma proteins by proteolysis. Since they are derived from proteins, these peptides contain only the amino acids of proteins.

Arg-Pro-Pro-Gly-Phe-Ser-Pro-Phe-Arg

Bradykinin

Lys-Arg-Pro-Pro-Gly-Phe-Ser-Pro-Phe-Arg

Kallidin

Glutathione (Fig 3–12), an atypical tripeptide in which the N-terminal glutamate is linked to cysteine via a non-α-peptidyl bond, is present in all forms of life. In humans and other animals, glutathione is required for the action of several enzymes. It is believed that glutathione and the enzyme glutathione reductase participate in the formation of the correct disulfide

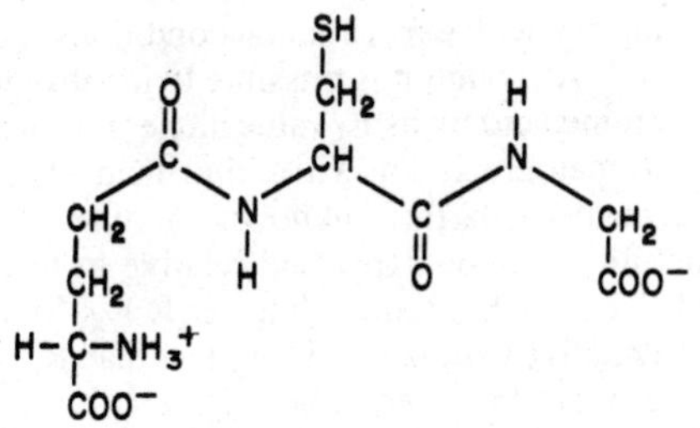

Figure 3–12. Glutathione (γ-glutamyl-cysteinyl-glycine).

bonds of many proteins and polypeptide hormones (see Chapter 4).

Polypeptide antibiotics elaborated by fungi frequently contain both D- and L-amino acids and amino acids not present in proteins. Examples include tyrocidine and gramicidin S, cyclic polypeptides that contain D-phenylalanine, and the nonprotein amino acid ornithine. These polypeptides are not synthesized on ribosomes.

Thyrotropin-releasing hormone (TRH) (Fig 3–13) illustrates yet another variant. The N-terminal glutamate is cyclized to pyroglutamic acid, and the C-terminal prolyl carboxyl is amidated.

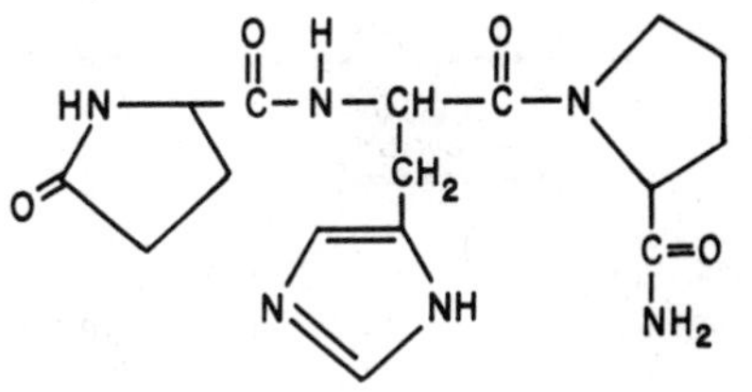

Figure 3–13. TRH (pyroglutamylhistidylprolinamide).

A mammalian polypeptide may contain more than one physiologically potent polypeptide. Within the primary structure of β-lipotropin—a hypophyseal hormone that stimulates the release of fatty acids from adipose tissue—are sequences of amino acids that are common to several other polypeptide hormones with diverse physiologic activities (Fig 3–14). The large polypeptide is a precursor of the smaller polypeptides.

SEPARATORY TECHNIQUES FOR AMINO ACIDS & PEPTIDES

Chromatography

In all chromatographic separations, molecules are **partitioned between a stationary and a mobile phase** (Table 3–7). **Separation depends on the rela-**

Table 3–7. Phase relationships for chromatographic systems important in biochemistry.

Form of Chromatography	Stationary Phase	Mobile Phase
Partition chromatography on paper sheets, thin layers of cellulose powder, or columns of inert supports coated with thin layers of liquid; gel filtration.	Liquid	Liquid
Ion exchange; adsorption on thin layers or particles in columns.	Solid	Liquid
Partition chromatography between thin layer of liquid on support and mobile gas.	Liquid	Gas

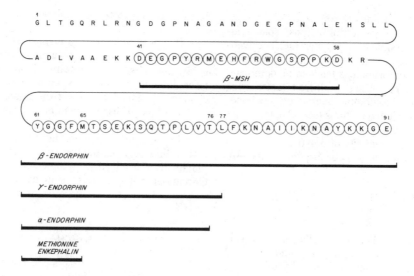

Figure 3–14. Primary structure of β-lipotropin. Residues 41–58 are melanocyte-stimulating hormone (β-MSH). Residues 61–91 contain the primary structures of the indicated endorphins.

tive tendencies of molecules in a mixture to associate more strongly with one or the other phase.

While these separatory techniques are discussed principally with respect to amino acids and peptides, their use is by no means restricted to these molecules.

Paper Chromatography

While to a large extent supplanted by more sophisticated techniques, paper chromatography still finds application in amino acid separations. Samples are applied at a marked point about 5 cm from the end of a filter paper strip and suspended in a sealed vessel that contains the chromatographic solvent (Fig 3–15).

For amino acid separations, solvents are polar binary, ternary, or more complex mixtures of water, alcohols, and acids or bases. The more polar components of the solvent associate with the cellulose and form the stationary phase. The less polar components constitute the mobile phase. This is **normal partition chromatography.** For **reversed phase partition chromatography,** the polarities of the mobile and stationary phases are reversed (eg, by first dipping the paper in a solution of a silicone). Reversed phase partition chromatography is used to separate nonpolar peptides or lipids, not polar compounds such as amino acids. The solvent may migrate up or down the paper (ascending or descending chromatography). When it has migrated almost to the end, the strip is dried and treated to allow visualization of the molecules of interest (eg, for amino acids, with 0.5% ninhydrin in acetone followed by heating at 90–110 °C for a few minutes). Amino acids with large nonpolar side chains (Leu, Ile, Phe, Trp, Val, Met, Tyr) migrate farther than those with shorter nonpolar side chains (Pro, Ala, Gly) or with polar side chains (Thr, Glu, Ser, Arg, Asp, His, Lys, Cys). (See Fig 3–16.) This reflects the greater relative solubility of polar molecules in the hydrophilic stationary phase and of nonpolar molecules in organic solvents. Note that, for a nonpolar series (Gly, Ala, Val, Leu), increasing length of the nonpolar side chain, which increases nonpolar character, results in increased mobility.

The ratio of the distance traveled by an amino acid to that traveled by the solvent front, both measured from the marked point of application of the amino acid mixture, is called the **R_f value** (mobility relative to the solvent front) for that amino acid. R_f values for a given amino acid vary with experimental conditions, eg, the solvent used. Although it is possible to identify tentatively an amino acid by its R_f value alone, it is preferable to chromatograph known amino acid standards simultaneously with the unknown mixture. In this case, mobility may be expressed relative to that of a standard (eg, as R_{ala} rather than as R_f). Mobilities expressed relative to a standard vary less than R_f values from experiment to experiment.

Quantitation of amino acids may be accomplished by cutting out each spot, eluting with a suitable

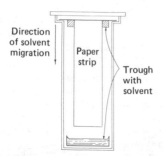

Figure 3–15. Apparatus for descending paper chromatography.

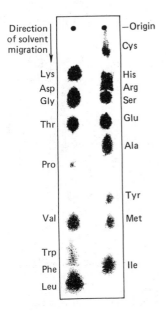

Figure 3–16. Identification of amino acids present in proteins. After descending paper chromatography in butanol-acetic acid, spots were visualized with ninhydrin.

solvent, and performing a quantitative colorimetric (ninhydrin) analysis. Alternatively, the paper may be sprayed with ninhydrin and the color densities of the spots measured with a recording transmittance or reflectance photometer.

For **2-dimensional paper chromatography,** sample is applied to one corner of a square sheet of paper or other suitable medium and chromatographed in one solvent mixture. The sheet is then removed, dried, turned through 90 degrees, and chromatographed in a second solvent (Fig 3–17).

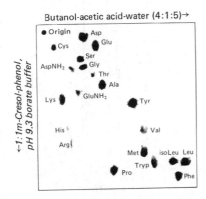

Figure 3–17. Two-dimensional chromatogram of protein amino acids. (Redrawn, slightly modified, from Levy AL, Chung D: Two-dimensional chromatography of amino acids on buffered papers. *Anal Chem* 1953;25:396. Copyright © 1953 by American Chemical Society; reproduced with permission.)

Thin Layer Chromatography

There are 2 distinct classes of thin layer chromatography (TLC). Partition TLC (PTLC) closely resembles partition chromatography on paper. Adsorption TLC (ATLC) bears no similarity to paper chromatography and is based on entirely different principles.

For PTLC on powdered cellulose or other relatively inert supports, the solvent systems and detection reagents used for paper chromatography are fully applicable. Reversed phase PTLC also is possible.

For ATLC, chromatography depends on the ability of the solvent (which need not be binary or more complex) to elute sample components from adsorption sites on an activated sorbent such as heated silica gel. ATLC is applicable to nonpolar materials such as lipids and hence not to amino acids or most peptides.

Automated Ion Exchange Chromatography

While amino acids may be separated by various techniques, analysis of amino acid residues after hydrolysis of a polypeptide generally involves **automated ion exchange chromatography.** Complete separation, identification, and quantitation require less than 3 hours. The procedure of Moore and Stein uses a short and long column containing the Na^+ form of a sulfonated polystyrene resin. When acid hydrolysate at pH 2 is applied to the columns, the amino acids bind via cation exchange with Na^+. The columns are then eluted with sodium citrate under preprogrammed conditions of pH and temperature. The short column requires a single elution buffer; the long column, two. Eluted material is reacted with ninhydrin reagent, and color densities are monitored in a flow-through colorimeter. Data are displayed on a strip chart recorder that may incorporate computer-linked integration of peak areas (Fig 3–18).

Gel Filtration

Automated sequencing utilizes small numbers of large (30- to 100-residue) peptides. However, many denatured, high-molecular-weight polypeptides may be insoluble owing to exposure during denaturation of previously buried hydrophobic residues. While insolubility can be overcome by urea, alcohols, organic acids, or bases, these restrict the subsequent use of ion exchange techniques for peptide purification. Gel filtration of large hydrophobic peptides may, however, be performed in 1–4 molar formic or acetic acid (Fig 3–19).

Reversed Phase High-Pressure Liquid Chromatography (RPHPLC)

A powerful technique for purification of high-molecular-weight nonpolar peptides is high-pressure liquid chromatography on nonpolar materials with elution by polar solvents (RPHPLC). Fig 3–20 illustrates resolution of the same cyanogen bromide fragments of human fetal globin as shown in Fig 3–19 by this technique. Gel filtration and RPHPLC are used in conjunction to purify complex mixtures of peptides that result from partial digestion of proteins (Mahoney

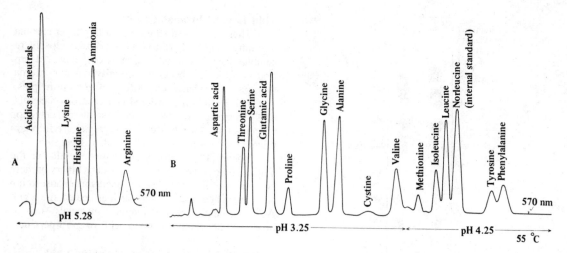

Figure 3–18. Automated analysis of an acid hydrolysate of corn endosperm on Moore-Stein Dowex 50 columns (at 55 °C). *A:* A short (5.0 × 0.9 cm) column used to resolve basic amino acids by elution at pH 5.28. Time required = 60 minutes. *B:* A longer (55 × 0.9 cm) column used to resolve neutral and acidic amino acids by elution first with pH 3.25 and then with pH 4.25 buffer. An internal standard of norleucine is included for reference. Basic amino acids remain bound to the column. Time required = 180 minutes. Emerging samples are automatically reacted with ninhydrin and the optical density of samples recorded at 570 nm and 440 nm. The latter wavelength is used solely to detect proline and hydroxyproline (absent from corn endosperm). Ordinate = optical density plotted on a log scale. Abscissa = time in minutes. (Courtesy of Professor ET Mertz, Purdue University.)

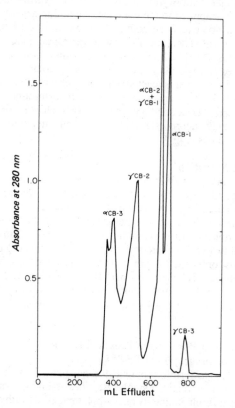

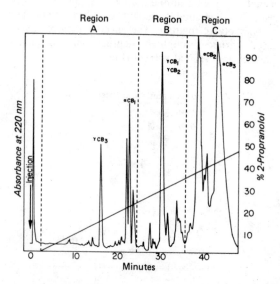

Figure 3–19. Gel filtration chromatography of cyanogen bromide (CB) fragments of human fetal globin. Chromatography was on G-50 Sephadex equilibrated and eluted with 1% HCOOH. Designations refer to arbitrarily numbered fragments from the α or γ chains. (Courtesy of JD Pearson et al, Department of Biochemistry, Purdue University.)

Figure 3–20. RPHPLC elution profile for cyanogen bromide (CB) fragments of human fetal globin. Designations are for arbitrarily numbered fragments from the α and γ chains. (Courtesy of JD Pearson et al, Department of Biochemistry, Purdue University.)

and Hermodson, 1979). New stationary phases have been developed for resolution of large peptides (Pearson et al, 1981).

Electrophoresis

Separations of amino acids, polypeptides, and other ampholytes (molecules whose net charge depends on the pH of the surrounding medium) in an imposed direct current field have extensive applications in biochemistry.

A. High-Voltage Electrophoresis (HVE) on Inert Supports: Paper sheets or thin layers of powdered cellulose are most frequently used as inert supports. Separations in a 2000- to 5000-volt direct current field for 0.5–2 hours depend upon the net charge on the ampholyte and its molecular weight. For molecules with identical charge, those of lower molecular weight migrate farther. Net charge is, however, the more important factor in determining separation. Applications include amino acids, low-molecular-weight polypeptides, certain proteins, nucleotides, and phosphosugars. Samples are applied to the support, which is then moistened with buffer of an appropriate pH and connected to buffer reservoirs by paper wicks. The paper may be covered by a glass plate or immersed in a hydrocarbon coolant. When current is applied, molecules with a net negative charge at the selected pH migrate toward the anode and those with a net positive charge toward the cathode. For visualization, the dried **electropherogram** is treated with ninhydrin (amino acids, peptides) or exposed to ultraviolet light (nucleotides), etc.

The choice of pH is dictated by the pK values of the dissociating groups on the molecules in the mixture. At pH 6.4, glutamate and aspartate bear a net charge of about -1, move toward the anode, and are readily separated on the basis of their difference in molecular weight. Lysine, arginine, and histidine move in the opposite direction, whereas all of the other protein amino acids remain at or near the point of application. For separation of the peptides resulting from enzymic digestion of a protein, a pH of 3.5 will induce a greater cationic charge on the molecules and thus provide better resolution.

B. HVE on Molecular Sieves: Molecular sieving may be superimposed on charge separation to facilitate separation. While starch and agarose are used, most commonly the support is a cross-linked polymer of acrylamide ($CH_2 = CH \cdot CONH_2$). For **polyacrylamide gel electrophoresis (PAGE),** protein solutions are applied to buffered tubes or slabs of polyacrylamide cross-linked 2–10% by inclusion of methylene bisacrylamide ("bis") or similar cross-linking reagents. Direct current is then applied. Visualization is by staining with Coomassie blue or Ag^+ (polypeptides), ethidium bromide (polynucleotides), etc. A popular variant is PAGE under denaturing conditions. Proteins are boiled and subsequently electrophoresed in the presence of the denaturing agents, urea or sodium dodecyl sulfate (SDS), to produce conditions that favor separation based strictly on molecular size. SDS-PAGE is widely used to establish subunit molecular weights of proteins by comparison of mobilities with those of standards of known molecular weight.

DETERMINATION OF THE AMINO ACID COMPOSITION OF PEPTIDES

The peptide bonds linking the amino acids are first broken by hydrolysis. Since peptide bonds are stable at neutral pH, catalysis by acid or base is employed. Enzymic catalysis is relatively unsuitable for complete hydrolysis. No procedure completely hydrolyzes proteins to constituent amino acids without partial loss of certain amino acid residues. The method of choice generally is hydrolysis in 6 N HCl at 110 °C in a sealed evacuated tube. Under these conditions, all of the tryptophan and cysteine and most of the cystine are destroyed. If metals are present, methionine and tyrosine are partially lost. Glutamine and asparagine are quantitatively deamidated to glutamate and aspartate. Recovery of serine and threonine is incomplete and decreases with increasing time of hydrolysis. Finally, certain bonds between neutral residues (Val-Val, Ile-Ile, Val-Ile, Ile-Val) are only 50% hydrolyzed after 20 hours. Typically, replicate samples are hydrolyzed for 24, 48, 72, and 96 hours. Serine and threonine data are then plotted on semilog paper and extrapolated back to zero time of hydrolysis. Valine and isoleucine are taken from 96-hour data. Dicarboxylic acids and their amides are determined together and are reported collectively as "Glx" or "Asx." Cysteine and cystine are converted to an acid-stable derivative (eg, cysteic acid) prior to hydrolysis. Base-catalyzed hydrolysis, which destroys serine, threonine, arginine, and cyteine and racemizes all amino acids, is employed to analyze for tryptophan. Following hydrolysis, amino acid composition is determined by **automated ion exchange chromatography.**

DETERMINATION OF THE PRIMARY STRUCTURE OF POLYPEPTIDES

General Approach

Almost 3 decades have elapsed since Sanger amazed the biochemical world by applying chemical and enzymatic techniques to determine the complete primary structure of the polypeptide hormone insulin. Sanger's approach was first to separate the 2 polypeptide chains, A and B, of insulin and then to convert them by specific enzymic cleavage into smaller peptides that contained regions of overlapping sequence. Using the reagent 1-fluoro-2,4-dinitrobenzene (Fig 3–21), he then removed and identified, one at a time, the N-terminal amino acid residues of these peptides. By comparison of the sequences of overlapping pep-

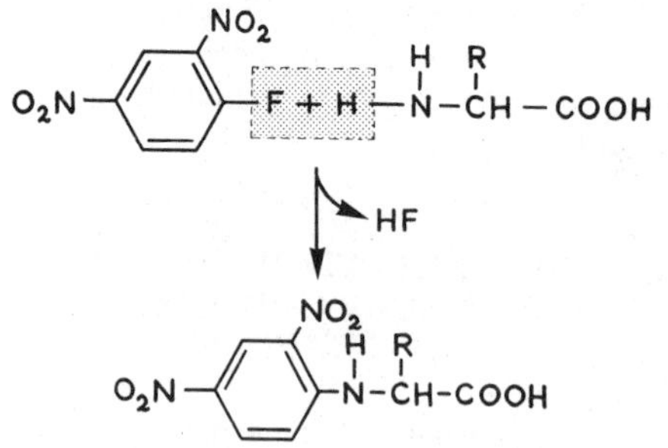

Figure 3–21. Reaction of an amino acid with 1-fluoro-2,4-dinitrobenzene (Sanger's reagent). The reagent is named for the Nobel laureate (1958) biochemist Frederick Sanger, who used it to determine the primary structure of insulin. This quantitatively arylates all free amino groups, producing intensely yellow 2,4-dinitrophenyl amino acids. These derivatives are readily quantitated by spectrophotometry. In addition to the N-terminal residue, the ϵ-amino groups of lysine, the imidazole of histidine, the OH of tyrosine, and the SH of cysteine also react with fluorodinitrobenzene. Since the dinitrophenyl group is resistant to removal by acid hydrolysis, it was used to determine the N-terminal amino acid of polypeptides.

tides, he was able to deduce an unambiguous primary structure for both the A and the B chains.

While the overall strategy of Sanger's approach remains valid to the present day, the ensuing decades have witnessed the introduction of 2 techniques that have revolutionized determination of the primary structures of polypeptides (proteins). The first of these was the introduction, in 1967, of an automated procedure for the sequential removal and identification of N-terminal amino acid residues as their phenylthiohydantoin derivatives. The second was the independent introduction by Sanger and by Maxam and Gilbert of techniques for the rapid and unambiguous sequencing of the DNA of the gene that codes for the protein in question. At present, optimal strategy is to utilize both approaches simultaneously. The automated Edman technique, while rapid compared to the manual methods used by Sanger, is slow relative to DNA sequencing methods, and difficulties may be encountered. On the other hand, DNA sequencing techniques do not infallibly yield unambiguous primary structures for the protein of interest. A major complication in sequencing eukaryotic genes is the presence of **introns** (see Chapter 28) within the gene that are not expressed in the mature protein. A major advantage of DNA sequencing is, however, the relative ease of detection and sequencing of regions of precursor molecules that may have eluded detection by the automated Edman technique owing to maturation of the protein prior to its isolation. DNA sequencing and the automated Edman technique thus are complementary techniques that have revolutionized and vastly expanded our knowledge of the primary structures of proteins. The former is discussed in Chapter 28; the latter is described below.

AUTOMATED EDMAN TECHNIQUE FOR DETERMINATION OF POLYPEPTIDE STRUCTURES

Resolution Into Linear Polypeptides

Since many proteins consist of more than one polypeptide chain associated by noncovalent forces or disulfide bridges, the first step may be to dissociate and resolve individual polypeptide chains. Denaturing agents (urea, guanidine hydrochloride) that disrupt hydrogen bonds dissociate noncovalently associated polypeptides. Oxidizing and reducing agents disrupt disulfide bridges (Fig 3–22). Polypeptides are then separated by chromatographic techniques.

Cleavage of Polypeptides Into Fragments Suitable for Automated Sequencing

Automated sequencing instruments (sequenators) operate most efficiently on polypeptides 20–60 residues long. Automated techniques have therefore greatly influenced selection of the techniques for initial cleavage of polypeptides and for purification of the resulting fragments. Emphasis has shifted from production of large numbers of small fragments suitable for manual sequencing to small numbers of large (30- to 100-residue) fragments. Highly specific and complete cleavage at a restricted number of sites is therefore desired. Cleavage with cyanogen bromide (CNBr), trypsin, or o-iodosobenzene meets these requirements.

A. CNBr: Cysteine residues are first modified with iodoacetic acid. CNBr then cleaves Met-peptide bonds specifically and, in most instances, quantitatively, on the COOH side of Met. Since Met is comparatively rare in polypeptides, this usually generates

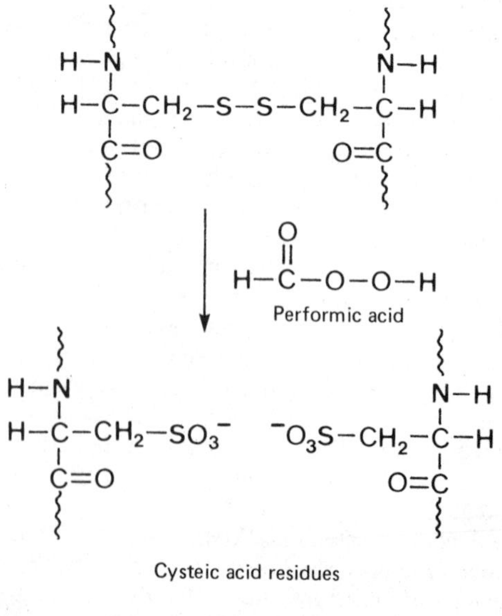

Figure 3–22. Cleavage of the disulfide bonds of proteins by treatment with performic acid.

peptide fragments of the desired size range (Mahoney et al, 1979, 1981).

B. Trypsin: Trypsin cleaves on the COOH side of Lys and Arg residues. To restrict the number of cleavage sites, Lys residues are first derivatized with citraconic anhydride (a reversible reaction) to change the charge on Lys residues from positive to negative (Patthy and Smith, 1975). Derivatization of Arg residues is less useful because of the relative abundance of Lys residues. It is, however, useful for subsequent cleavage of CNBr fragments.

C. *o*-Iodosobenzene: *o*-Iodosobenzene cleaves specifically and quantitatively at the comparatively rare Trp-X residues. It requires no prior protection of other residues.

D. Hydroxylamine: Hydroxylamine cleaves comparatively rare Asn-Gly bonds, although generally not in quantitative yield (Bornstein and Balian, 1970).

E. Protease: *Staphylococcus aureus* protease V8 cleaves Glu-X-peptide residues with a preference for situations where X is hydrophobic. Glu-Lys resists cleavage. This reaction is useful for subsequent degradation of CNBr fragments (Houmard and Drapeau, 1972).

F. Mild Acid Hydrolysis: This cleaves the rare Asp-Pro bond (Jauregui-Adell and Marti, 1975).

Two or 3 digests of the original polypeptide, normally at Met, Trp, Arg, and Asn-Gly, combined with appropriate subdigests of the resulting fragments, usually will permit determination of the entire primary structure of the polypeptide. Barring unusual difficulties in purification of fragments, this can—with care—be accomplished with a few micromoles of polypeptide (Hermodson, Schmer, and Kurachi, 1977).

Fragment purification is achieved chiefly by gel filtration in acetic or formic acid (Fig 3–19), by RPHLC (Fig 3–20), or by ion exchange chromatography on phosphocellulose or sulfophenyl Sephadex in solutions of phosphoric acid (Chin and Wold, 1977).

The Edman Reagent & Edman Reaction

The role performed initially by Sanger's reagent is replaced in automated sequencing by phenylisothiocyanate (Edman reagent) and a sequence of reactions that result in the removal of the N-terminal residue as its phenylthiohydantoin derivative (the Edman reaction, Fig 3–23).

The heart of the instrument is a spinning cup reaction chamber in which reactions occur in a thin film of solution on the cup wall. This facilitates extractions and subsequent removal of solvents. Several companies now market fully automated apparatus for the determination of polypeptide sequences of up to 30–40 residues (or, in exceptional cases, up to 60 or even 80 residues) in one continuous operation. The apparatus is programmed to perform sequential Edman degradations on the N-terminal residue of a polypeptide. After the initial N-terminal amino acid has been removed, separated, and identified, an Edman derivative (Fig 3–23) of the next one in the sequence is

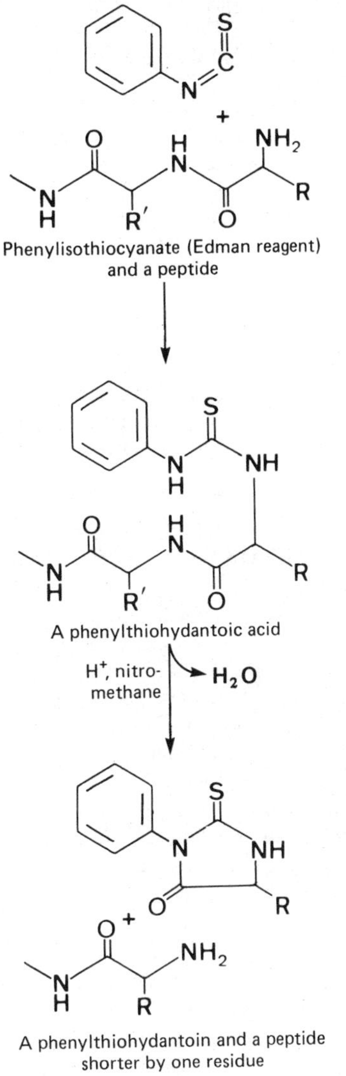

Figure 3–23. Conversion of an amino acid (or of the N-terminal residue of a polypeptide) to a phenylthiohydantoin. Phenylisothiocyanate reacts with the amino groups of amino acids and peptides, yielding phenylthiohydantoic acids. On treatment with acid in nonhydroxylic solvents, these cyclize to phenylthiohydantoins. The principal use of this reaction, which identifies the N-terminal residues of a peptide, is in automated sequencing of polypeptides.

formed, etc. Separation of the phenylthiohydantoin derivatives is accomplished by high-pressure liquid chromatography. The apparatus materially extends the sequence that can be determined by manual techniques and is incomparably faster.

Deduction of the Complete Primary Structure by Comparison of the Residue Sequences of Overlapping Peptides

The final step is to deduce the order of the constituent peptides derived from the unmodified protein. For this purpose, it is essential to have sequenced

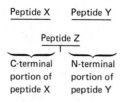

Figure 3–24. Use of the overlapping peptide Z to deduce that peptides X and Y are present in the original protein in the order X → Y, not Y → X.

peptides produced by techniques (eg, digestion with trypsin and chymotrypsin) that cleave the protein at different locations. These are then compared to establish an unequivocal primary structure (Fig 3–24).

SYNTHESIS BY AUTOMATED TECHNIQUES

While classic chemical techniques were adequate for synthesis of the octapeptides vasopressin and oxytocin, and later of bradykinin (see below), the yields of final product are too low to permit synthesis of long polypeptides or proteins. This has been achieved by the automated, solid-phase synthesis technique developed by Merrifield. In this process, an automated synthesis is carried out in a single vessel by a machine programmed to add reagents, remove products, etc, at timed intervals. The steps involved are as follows:

(1) The amino acid that ultimately will form the C-terminal end of the polypeptide is attached to an insoluble resin particle.

(2) The second amino acid bearing an appropriately blocked amino group is introduced and the peptide bond is formed in the presence of the dehydrating agent dicyclohexylcarbodiimide.

(3) The blocking group is removed with acid, forming gaseous products, which are removed.

(4) Steps 2 and 3 are repeated with the next amino acid in sequence, then the next, until the entire polypeptide attached to the resin particle has been synthesized.

(5) The polypeptide is cleaved from the resin particle.

The process proceeds rapidly and with excellent yields. About 3 hours are required per peptide bond synthesized. By this technique, the A chain of insulin (21 residues) was synthesized in 8 days and the B chain (30 residues) in 11 days. The crowning achievement to date has been the total synthesis of pancreatic ribonuclease (124 residues; see Fig 4–13) in 18% overall yield, the first total synthesis of an enzyme. It foreshadows a new era not only in confirmation of protein structures but in related areas such as immunology and vaccine production and perhaps in the treatment of inborn errors of metabolism. A variety of physiologically important peptides, prepared synthetically from L-amino acids by routes that involve no racemization, have full physiologic activity. These include the octapeptides oxytocin and vasopressin, ACTH, and melanocyte-stimulating hormone (see Chapter 37).

•   •   •

References

Bornstein P, Balian G: The specific nonenzymatic cleavage of bovine ribonuclease with hydroxylamine. *J Biol Chem* 1970;**245**:4854.

Cantor CR, Schimmel PR: *Biophysical Chemistry, Part I: The Conformation of Macromolecules.* Freeman, 1980.

Chin CCQ, Wold F: Separation of peptides on phosphocellulose and other cellulose ion exchangers. *Methods Enzymol* 1977;**47**:204.

Cooper TG: *The Tools of Biochemistry.* Wiley, 1977.

Craig LC, Cowburn D, Bleich H: Methods for the study of small polypeptide hormones and antibiotics in solution. *Annu Rev Biochem* 1975;**44**:509.

Dayhoff M (editor): *Atlas of Protein Sequence and Structure.* Vol 5. National Biomedical Research Foundation, Washington, DC, 1972.

Greenstein JP, Winitz M: *Chemistry of the Amino Acids.* 3 vols. Wiley, 1961.

Hash JH (editor): Antibiotics. In: *Methods in Enzymology.* Vol 43. Academic Press, 1975.

Heftman E: *Chromatography: A Laboratory Handbook of Chromatographic and Electrophoretic Methods,* 3rd ed. Van Nostrand, 1975.

Hermodson MA, Schmer G, Kurachi K: Isolation, crystallization and primary amino acid sequence of human platelet factor 4. *J Biol Chem* 1977;**252**:6276.

Houmard J, Drapeau GR: Staphylococcal protease: A proteolytic enzyme specific for glutamoyl bonds. *Proc Natl Acad Sci USA* 1972;**69**:3506.

Jauregui-Adell J, Marti J: Acidic cleavage of the aspartyl-proline bond and the limitations of the reaction. *Anal Biochem* 1975;**69**:468.

Klee WA: Peptides of the central nervous system. *Adv Protein Chem* 1979;**33**:243.

Mahoney WC, Hermodson MA: High-yield cleavage of tryptophanyl peptide bonds by o-iodosobenzoic acid. *Biochemistry* 1979;**18**:3810.

Mahoney WC, Smith PK, Hermodson MA: Fragmentation of proteins with o-iodosobenzoic acid: Chemical mechanism and identification of o-iodosobenzoic acid as a reactive contaminant that modifies tyrosyl residues. *Biochemistry* 1981;**20**:443.

Marglin A, Merrifield RB: Chemical synthesis of peptides and proteins. *Annu Rev Biochem* 1970;**39**:841.

Meister A: *Biochemistry of the Amino Acids,* 2nd ed. Academic Press, 1965.

Needelman SB (editor): *Protein Sequence Determination*. Springer-Verlag, 1970.

Patthy L, Smith EL: Reversible modification of arginine residues: Application to sequence studies by restriction of tryptic hydrolysis to lysine residues. *J Biol Chem* 1975;**250**:557.

Pearson JD et al: Reversed-phase supports for the resolution of large denatured protein fragments. *J Chromatogr* 1981;**207**:325.

Regnier FE, Gooding KM: High performance liquid chromatography of proteins. *Anal Biochem* 1980;**103**:1.

Snyder SH, Innes RB: Peptide neurotransmitters. *Annu Rev Biochem* 1979;**48**:755.

Stewart JM, Young JD: *Solid Phase Peptide Synthesis*. Freeman, 1969.

Storm DR, Rosenthal KS, Swanson PE: Polymyxin antibiotics. *Annu Rev Biochem* 1977;**46**:723.

Touchstone JC: *Practice of Thin Layer Chromatography*. Wiley-Interscience, 1978.

Zweig G, Sherma J: *Handbook of Chromatography*. 2 vols. CRC Press, 1972.

4 | Proteins

Victor W. Rodwell, PhD

All proteins are **high-molecular-weight poly-peptides.** Whether a polypeptide is termed a protein or merely a polypeptide is largely an arbitrary decision, although the dividing line between large polypeptides and small proteins is customarily between MW 8000 and 10,000.

While all proteins are polypeptides, many contain additional, non-amino acid materials such as heme, vitamin derivatives, lipid, or carbohydrate. Historically, these proteins are referred to as **complex proteins** and those which consist solely of amino acids as **simple proteins.** This chapter deals with the properties of simple proteins. While complex proteins share the properties of simple proteins, they possess, in addition, characteristics peculiar to the specific non-amino acid components present. The unique properties of specific complex proteins such as heme proteins (Chapter 5), glycoproteins (Chapter 33), and lipoproteins (Chapter 18) are considered later in this book as are the properties of simple proteins of highly individual structure such as collagen and contractile proteins (Chapter 34).

CLASSIFICATION OF PROTEINS

Since no single, universally satisfactory system of protein classification exists, several mutually contradictory protein classification systems persist in current use. Systems evolved over the years for the classification of proteins are at present of comparatively limited value in terms of their ability to assist us in understanding many key properties of proteins. The persistence of these systems and of the terms used—particularly in the clinical laboratory—dictates, however, brief consideration in a medically oriented text. Discussed below are salient features of protein classification systems based on solubility, shape, function, physical properties, and 3-dimensional structure.

Solubility

A classification system based on solubility developed in 1907–1908 is still in use today, particularly in clinical biochemistry (Table 4–1). The lines of demarcation between the classes are not stringent. For example, a clear distinction between albumins and globulins cannot be made solely on the basis of their solubilities in water or salt solutions. Globulins were therefore subdivided into pseudoglobulins, which are freely water-soluble, and euglobulins, which are insoluble in salt-free water.

Overall Shape

Two broad classes of proteins may be distinguished on the basis of their **axial ratios** (ratios of length to breadth). **Globular proteins** have axial ratios less than 10 and generally not over 3–4 and are characterized by compactly folded and coiled polypeptide chains. Examples include insulin, plasma albumins and globulins, and many enzymes. **Fibrous proteins** have axial ratios greater than 10 and are characterized by polypeptide chains or groups of chains coiled in a spiral or helix and cross-linked by disulfide and hydrogen bonds. Examples include keratin (the major protein of hair, wool, and skin) and myosin (the major contractile protein of muscle).

Function

Proteins may be classified according to their biologic functions—for example, as structural, catalytic, or transport proteins. Catalytic proteins (enzymes), which comprise the majority of protein types, are themselves classified by the type of reaction they catalyze (see Chapter 6).

Physical Properties

For certain proteins of great medical interest, there are specialized systems of classification that distinguish between closely related proteins. This is illustrated for the plasma lipoproteins, which function in transport of dietary and endogenously formed lipids.

Table 4–1. Classification of proteins based on their solubilities.

Albumins	Soluble in water and salt solutions. No distinctive amino acids.
Globulins	Sparingly soluble in water but soluble in salt solutions. No distinctive amino acids.
Protamines	Soluble in 70–80% ethanol but insoluble in water and absolute ethanol. Arginine-rich.
Histones	Soluble in salt solutions.
Scleroproteins	Insoluble in water or salt solutions. Rich in Gly, Ala, Pro.

Two systems of nomenclature are in wide use, and a third is under consideration. The 2 commonly used systems distinguish classes of lipoproteins based on their behavior in electrical or gravitational fields. Thus, we distinguish "origin," α_1-, α_2-, β-, and γ-lipoproteins, on the basis of whether they remain at the origin or migrate to the positions of the corresponding globulins on electrophoresis at pH 8.6. Alternatively, lipoproteins often are classified on the basis of their hydrated densities as chylomicrons (density = 0.94 g/mL), VLDL (very low density lipoproteins [D = 0.94–1.006]), LDL (low-density lipoproteins [D = 1.006–1.063]), HDL (high-density lipoproteins [D = 1.063–1.21]), and VHDL (very high density lipoproteins [D = > 1.21]).

Progress in determination of the primary structures of the various apoproteins of plasma lipoproteins suggests yet another way in which they might be classified, ie, on the basis of the primary structure of the apoproteins present. Six broad classes of plasma lipoproteins might be differentiated, based on whether apoprotein A, B, C, D, E, or F is present in the lipoprotein molecule. Since these apoproteins are antigenic, they may be differentiated by immunologic criteria.

Three-Dimensional Structure

Two broad classes of proteins may be distinguished on the basis of whether or not they possess quaternary structure (see below). In addition, similarities in structure, revealed primarily by x-ray crystallography, provide a potentially valuable basis for protein classification. For instance, proteins that bind nucleotides share a "nucleotide-binding domain" of tertiary structure, and these proteins may be evolutionarily related.

BONDS RESPONSIBLE FOR PROTEIN STRUCTURE

Protein structures are generally stabilized by 2 classes of strong bonds (peptide and disulfide) and 3 classes of weak bonds (hydrogen, hydrophobic, and electrostatic or salt).

The primary structure of proteins derives from covalent linkage of L-α-amino acids by α-peptide bonds. While this was deduced long ago by multiple lines of evidence, the most convincing proof was the synthesis, by chemical means, of insulin and ribonuclease solely by linking amino acids via peptide bonds.

Peptide Bonds

While peptides are written with a single bond connecting α-carboxyl and α-nitrogen atoms, the carbon-nitrogen bond in fact has partial double bond character (Fig 4–1). There thus is no freedom of rotation about the bond that connects the C and N atoms, and all 4 of the atoms shown in Fig 4–1 lie in the same plane (ie, are coplanar). There is, by contrast, ample freedom of rotation about the remaining bonds of the polypeptide backbone. These concepts are sum-

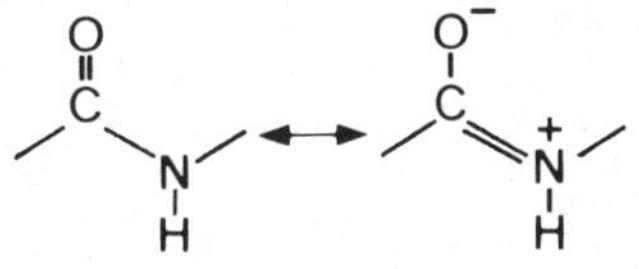

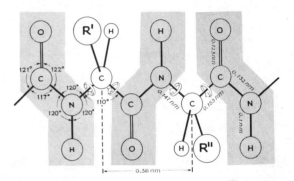

Figure 4–1. Resonance stabilization of the peptide bond confers partial double bond character, and hence rigidity, on the C–N bond.

Figure 4–2. Dimensions of a fully extended polypeptide chain. The 4 atoms grouped in shaded boxes are **coplanar**, ie, they lie in the same plane. These same 4 atoms comprise the polypeptide bond. The unshaded atoms are the α-carbon atom, the α-hydrogen atom, and the α-R group of the particular amino acid. Free rotation can occur about the bonds connecting the α-carbon with the α-nitrogen and α-carbonyl functions (white arrows). The extended polypeptide chain is thus a semirigid structure with two-thirds of the atoms of the backbone held in a fixed planar relationship one to another. The distance between adjacent α-carbon atoms is 0.36 nm. The interatomic distances and bond angles, which are not equivalent, are also shown. (Redrawn and reproduced, with permission, from Pauling L, Corey LP, Branson HR: The structure of proteins: Two hydrogen-bonded helical configurations of the polypeptide chain. *Proc Natl Acad Sci USA* 1951;**37**:205.)

marized in Fig 4–2 where the bonds having freedom of rotation are shown circled by arrows and the coplanar atoms are shown in shaded boxes. This semirigidity has important consequences for orders of protein structure above the primary level.

Disulfide Bonds

The disulfide bond formed between 2 cysteine residues interconnects 2 portions of polypeptide chains through cysteine residues (Fig 4–3). This relatively stable cystine bond is resistant to usual conditions for protein denaturation. Performic acid (oxidizes S–S bonds) or β-mercaptoethanol (reduces the S–S bonds generating 2 cysteine residues) separates polypeptide chains linked by disulfide bonds without affecting primary structure (Fig 4–4).

Hydrogen Bonds

Hydrogen bonds (see Chapter 1) formed between

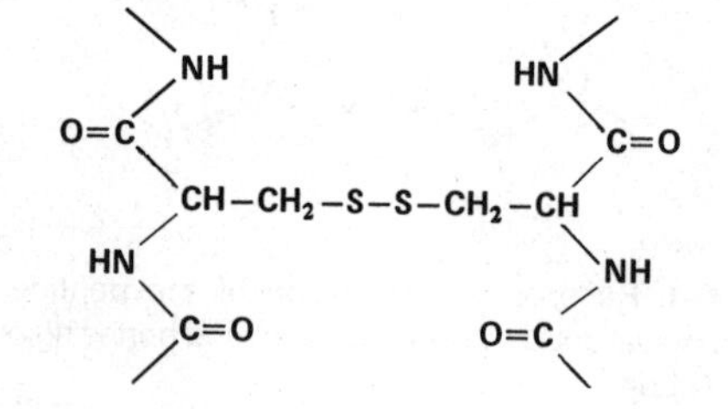

Figure 4–3. Peptide chains united by a disulfide bond.

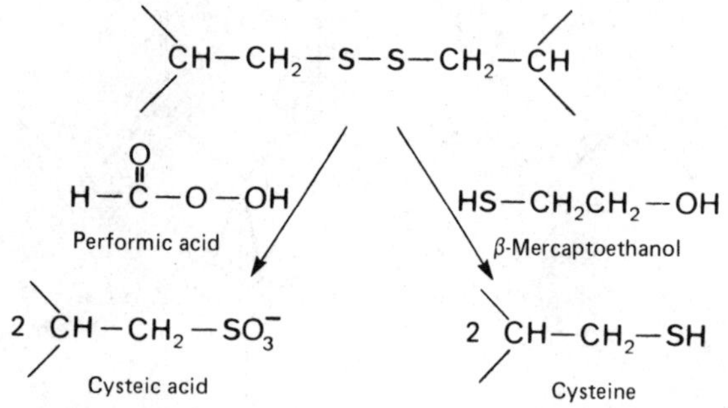

Figure 4–4. Cleavage of disulfide bonds by oxidation with performic acid *(left)* or reduction with β-mercaptoethanol *(right)*.

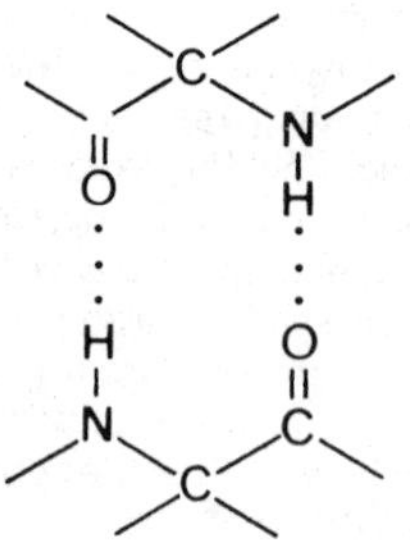

Figure 4–5. Hydrogen bonds between components of peptide bonds.

bonding residues present in the side chains of peptide-linked amino acids and those formed between the hydrogen and oxygen atoms of the peptide bonds themselves all play important roles in the maintenance of protein structure above the primary order. Fig 4–5 illustrates hydrogen bonding between noncontiguous peptide bonds that results in the formation of regular structures such as the α-helix and β-pleated sheet (see below).

Hydrophobic Interactions

The nonpolar side chains of neutral amino acids tend to associate in proteins. The relationship is not stoichiometric; hence, no true bond may be said to exist. Nonetheless, these interactions play a significant role in maintaining protein structure.

Electrostatic Bonds

These are salt bonds formed between oppositely charged groups in the side chains of amino acids. The epsilon-amino group of lysine bears a net charge of $+1$ at physiologic pH and the non-α-carboxyl of aspartate and glutamate a net charge of -1. These may therefore interact electrostatically to stabilize a protein structure.

Bond Stabilities

During denaturation of proteins, hydrogen, hydrophobic, and electrostatic bonds—but not peptide or disulfide bonds—are broken.

ORDERED CONFORMATIONS OF POLYPEPTIDES

The α-Helix

The discovery that polypeptide chains may exist in highly ordered conformations maintained by hydrogen bonds formed between peptide residues constituted a major breakthrough in our understanding of protein structure. Although the existence of these highly ordered structures was subsequently amply confirmed by high-resolutuion x-ray crystallography of crystalline proteins, their existence was first proposed from purely theoretical considerations.

X-ray data obtained in the early 1930s indicated that hair and wool α-keratins possessed repeating units spaced 0.5–0.55 nm along their longitudinal axis. As shown in Fig 4–2, no dimension of the extended polypeptide chain appears to measure 0.5–0.55 nm. This apparent anomaly was resolved by Pauling and Corey, who proposed that the polypeptide chain of α-keratin is arranged as an α-helix (Figs 4–6 and 4–7). In this structure, the R groups on the α-carbon atoms protrude outward from the center of the helix. There are 3.6 amino acid residues per turn of the helix, and the distance traveled per turn is 0.54 nm—a reasonable approximation of the 0.5- to 0.55-nm spacing observed by x-ray diffraction. The spacing per amino acid residue is 0.15 nm, which also corresponds with x-ray data. The main features of the α-helix are as follows:

(1) The α-helix is stabilized by inter-residue hydrogen bonds formed between the H atom attached to a peptide N and the carbonyl O of the residue fourth in line behind in the primary structure.

(2) Each peptide bond participates in the H-bonding. This confers maximum stability.

(3) All of the main chain peptide N and carbonyl O residues are hydrogen-bonded, thus greatly reducing the hydrophilic (increasing the hydrophobic) nature of the α-helical region.

(4) An α-helix forms spontaneously, since it is the lowest energy, most stable conformation for a polypeptide chain.

(5) When the residues are L-amino acids, the right-handed helix that occurs in proteins is significantly more stable than the left-handed helix.

Ball-and-stick model of alpha helix, showing
intrachain hydrogen bonds (small dots)

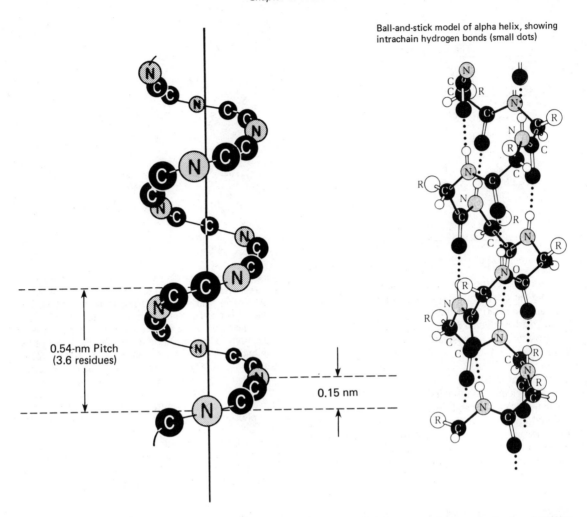

0.54-nm Pitch
(3.6 residues)

0.15 nm

Figure 4–6. Alpha helix structure of a protein. The figure on the left shows the α carbons, α nitrogens, and carboxyl carbons that form the right-handed helical backbone. The structure on the right shows, in addition, the R substituents on the α carbons and the H and O atoms involved in the hydrogen bonds (dots) that hold the protein in the α-helical conformation. (Reprinted [*right*] with permission, from Haggis GH et al: *Introduction to Molecular Biology.* Wiley, 1964.)

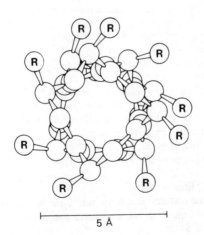

5 Å

Figure 4–7. Cross-sectional view of an α-helix. The side chains (R) are on the outside of the helix. The van der Waals radii of the atoms are larger than shown here; hence, there is almost no free space inside the helix. (Slightly modified and reproduced, with permission, from Stryer L: *Biochemistry,* 2nd ed. Freeman, 1981. Copyright © 1981 by W.H. Freeman and Co.)

Table 4–2. Effect of various amino acid residues on helix formation.

Promote α-Helix	Destabilize α-Helix	Terminate α-Helix
Ala	Arg	Pro
Asn	Asp	Hyp
Cys	Glu	
Gln	Gly	
His	Lys	
Leu	Ile	
Met	Ser	
Phe	Thr	
Trp		
Tyr		
Val		

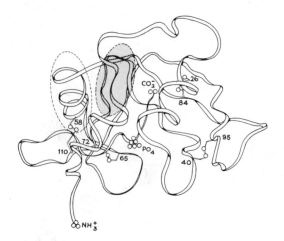

Figure 4–9. Schematic diagram of the main chain folding of bovine pancreatic ribonuclease. This protein is a single chain of 124 amino acid residues starting at the amino end (marked NH_3^+) and ending at the carboxy terminal (marked CO_2^-). The chain is cross-linked at 4 places by disulfide bridges from half cystine residues. The disulfide pairings for these bridges are 26–84, 40–95, 58–110, and 65–72 in the sequence. A region of α-helix is indicated by the dotted oval, and a region of pleated sheet is shaded. Other portions of the molecule are predominantly random coil. The region of the active site (see Chapter 8) is indicated by the binding of the phosphate ion (PO_4^{3-}) in the cleft of the molecule. This model was obtained by x-ray diffraction studies of crystalline bovine pancreatic ribonuclease at 0.2-nm resolution. (Adapted from Kartha G, Bello J, Harker D: Tertiary structure of ribonuclease. *Nature* 1967;213:862.) The protein has been chemically synthesized in its entirety.

Certain amino acids tend to disrupt the α-helix. Among these are proline (the N-atom is part of a rigid ring and no rotation of the N–C bond can occur) and amino acids with charged or bulky R groups that either electrostatically or physically interfere with helix formation (Table 4–2).

The β-Pleated Sheet

Coincident with the deduction of the presence of the α-helix, Pauling and Corey also proposed a second ordered structure, the β-pleated sheet (β because it was their second structure, the α-helix being the first). Whereas in the α-helix the polypeptide chain is coiled and hence condensed, in the β-pleated sheet it is al-

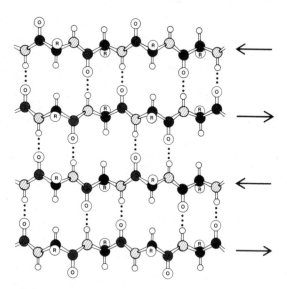

Figure 4–8. Antiparallel β-pleated sheet. Adjacent strands run in opposite directions. Hydrogen bonds between NH and CO groups of adjacent strands stabilize the structure. The side chains (R) are above and below the plane of the sheet. (● Carbon atoms; ◨ nitrogen atoms; ○ hydrogen atoms.) (Modified and reproduced, with permission, from Stryer L: *Biochemistry,* 2nd ed. Freeman, 1981. Copyright © 1981 by W.H. Freeman and Co.)

most fully extended (Fig 4–8). When the adjacent polypeptide chains in a β-pleated sheet run in opposite directions (N to C terminus), the structure is termed an **antiparallel** β-pleated sheet (shown in Fig 4–8). When the chains run in the same direction, it is termed **parallel** (not shown).

Regions of β-pleated structure are present in many proteins, and both parallel and antiparallel forms occur. From 2 to 5 adjacent strands of polypeptide may combine to form these structures. Fig 4–9 illustrates a region of ribonuclease in which 3 sections of polypeptide chain form a β-pleated sheet structure. As may be seen also in Fig 4–9, both α-helix and β-pleated sheet structures commonly occur in many proteins.

While the α-helix is stabilized by hydrogen bonding between peptide bonds 4 residues apart in a primary structural sense, stabilization of the β-pleated sheet results from formation of hydrogen bonds between peptides far removed from one another in a primary structural sense. This is illustrated in Fig 4–9.

The Collagen Helix

The distinctive intertwined triple helices of collagen are unique to that molecule and are discussed in Chapter 34.

LESS HIGHLY ORDERED CONFORMATIONS OF POLYPEPTIDES

Regions of proteins that are not identifiably organized as helices or pleated sheets are said to be present in random coil conformation. As shown in Fig 4–9, a considerable proportion of a protein may be present in this conformation. The term ''random'' is unfortunate, since it may imply less biologic significance than more highly repeating regions. In terms of biologic function, regions of random coil are of equal importance with those of α-helix or β-pleated sheet.

FOUR ORDERS, OR LEVELS, OF PROTEIN STRUCTURE

Primary

Primary structure, already familiar from peptides (see Chapter 3), refers to the order of the amino acids in the polypeptide chain or chains and the location of disulfide bonds, if these are present.

Secondary

Secondary structures, the steric relationship of amino acids close together in a primary structural sense, may be regular (eg, α-helix, β-pleated sheet) and hence give rise to periodic repeating structures. Alternatively, it may exhibit few regularities (eg, random coil).

Tertiary

The overall arrangement and interrelationship of the various regions, or domains, and individual amino acid residues of a single polypeptide chain is called the tertiary structure of the protein. While the division between secondary and tertiary structure is not clear-cut, tertiary structure considers the steric relationship of amino acid residues that are, in general, far apart in a primary structural sense.

Quaternary

Proteins are said to possess quaternary structure if they consist of 2 or more polypeptide chains **united by forces other than covalent bonds** (ie, not peptide or disulfide bonds). The forces that stabilize these aggregates are hydrogen bonds and electrostatic (or salt) bonds formed between residues on the surfaces of the polypeptide chains. Such proteins are termed **oligomers,** and the individual polypeptide chains of which they are composed are variously termed **protomers, monomers,** or **subunits.**

The most commonly encountered oligomeric proteins contain 2 or 4 protomers and are termed dimers or tetramers, respectively. Oligomers containing more than 4 protomers are also common, particularly among regulated enzymes (eg, aspartate transcarbamoylase). Oligomeric proteins play special roles in intracellular regulation, because the protomers can assume different spatial orientations relative to each other with resulting changes in the properties of the oligomer. The best-studied example is hemoglobin (see Chapter 5), in which a variety of conformations exist depending on the degree of oxygenation.

Role of Primary Structures in Determining Higher Levels of Protein Structure

The secondary and tertiary structures of a protein are themselves determined by the primary structure of the polypeptide chain. Once the chain has been formed, the chemical groups that extend from the α carbons direct the specific regional folding (secondary structure) and specific aggregation of the regions (tertiary structure). For example, treatment of the monomeric enzyme ribonuclease with a mild reducing agent (β-mercaptoethanol) and a denaturing agent (urea or guanidine; see below) inactivates it as it assumes a random coil conformation. Slow removal of the denaturing agent and gentle reoxidation to re-form the S–S bonds lead to almost complete reactivation of the enzyme. Thus, the primary structure specifies the secondary, tertiary, and (when present) quarternary structure (ie, conformation) of a protein. The native conformation of a protein such as ribonuclease appears to be that which is thermodynamically most stable for a given environment, eg, a hydrophilic versus hydrophobic one. It is not necessary to postulate independent genetic control of orders of protein structure above the primary level.

The structure of a protein may change during posttranslational processing, such as the conversion of a preproenzyme to the catalytically active form or removal of the ''leader peptide'' that directs exported proteins through membranes (see Chapter 32).

Finally, aggregation of different functional proteins—each of which alone has all 4 orders of structure—into multifunctional macromolecular complexes is encountered in electron transport (see Chapter 12), in fatty acid biosynthesis (see Chapter 17), and in pyruvate metabolism (see Chapter 15).

DENATURATION

The comparatively weak forces responsible for maintaining secondary, tertiary, and quaternary structure of proteins are readily disrupted by a variety of manipulations with a resulting loss of biologic activity. This disruption of native structure is termed **denaturation.** Physically, denaturation may be viewed as randomizing the conformation of a polypeptide chain without affecting its primary structure. For a protomer, the process may be represented as shown in Fig 4–10.

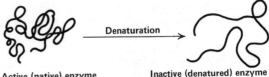

Active (native) enzyme   Inactive (denatured) enzyme

Figure 4–10. Representation of denaturation of a protomer.

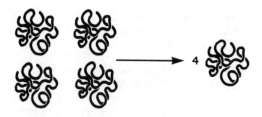

Figure 4–11. Representation of denaturation of an oligomeric protein under conditions not sufficiently severe to alter protomer conformation.

For an oligomeric protein, denaturation may involve dissociation of the protomers with or without accompanying changes in protomer conformation (Fig 4–11).

The biologic activity of most proteins is destroyed by exposure to strong mineral acids or bases, heat, ionic detergents (amphipaths), chaotropic agents (urea, guanidine), heavy metals (Ag, Pb, Hg), or organic solvents at or above room temperature. Denatured proteins generally are less soluble in water, and they often precipitate from aqueous solution. This property is used to advantage in the clinical laboratory. Blood or serum samples to be analyzed for small molecules (eg, glucose, uric acid, drugs) generally are first treated with acids such as trichloroacetic, phosphotungstic, or phosphomolybdic acid to precipitate most of the protein present. This is removed by centrifugation, and the protein-free supernatant liquid is then analyzed.

The heat, acid, and protease lability of most enzymes provides a preliminary test to determine whether a reaction is enzyme-catalyzed. If a cell extract having catalytic activity loses this activity when boiled, acidified and reneutralized, or treated with a protease, the catalyst probably was an enzyme.

Frequently, the denaturation of an enzyme is influenced by the presence of its substrate. The effect is attributed to a conformational change in the enzyme structure occurring when substrate is bound. The new conformation may be either more stable or less stable than before.

DETERMINATION OF PRIMARY STRUCTURE

Methods

Complex proteins are first treated to remove prosthetic groups (eg, heme). Disulfide bonds are oxidized to yield linear polypeptides. The methods used to sequence these polypeptides are discussed in Chapter 3. While most proteins contain only the amino acids listed in Table 3–3, derivatives of these amino acids also occur in certain proteins (Tables 4–3 and 4–4). While discussion of the methods used to identify these amino acid derivatives lies beyond the scope of this chapter, their presence can complicate the determination of primary structure.

Table 4–3. Representative modifications of a-COOH and a-NH$_2$ groups in proteins.*

a-COOH	a-NH$_2$		
Group Modified			
Type of Modification			
Amide	N-Formyl	N-Acetyl	N-Methyl
Amino acid residues subject to modification			
		Ala	Ala
Asp		Asp	Asp
Glu			
Gly	Gly	Gly	Gly
His			
Met	Met	Met	Met
Phe			
Pro			
		Ser	Ser
		Thr	Thr
Tyr			
Val		Val	

*Modified and reproduced, with permission, from Uy R, Wold F: Posttranslational covalent modification of proteins. *Science* 1977;**198**:890. Copyright © 1977 by the American Association for the Advancement of Science.

Table 4–4. Representative modifications of non-a functional groups in proteins.*

—OH	Non-a-N		
Group Modified			
Type of Modification			
PO$_3$H$_2$	N-Methyl	N-Dimethyl	N-Trimethyl
Amino acid residues subject to modification			
	Arg	Arg	
	His		
	Lys	Lys	Lys
Ser			
Thr			
Tyr			

*Modified and reproduced, with permission, from Uy R, Wold F: Posttranslational covalent modification of proteins. *Science* 1977;**198**:890. Copyright © 1977 by the American Association for the Advancement of Science.

Primary Structures of Specific Proteins

A. Insulin: This protein (or large polypeptide) consists of 2 polypeptide chains linked covalently by disulfide bonds (Fig 4–12). The A chain has an N-terminal Gly and a C-terminal Asn; the B chain has Phe and Ala as the N- and C-terminal residues, respectively. When insulin is oxidized with performic acid, the disulfide bonds linking the A and B chains are ruptured. Both chains are biosynthesized as a single polypeptide chain, **proinsulin,** which after formation undergoes proteolytic processing, forming insulin (see Chapter 42).

B. Ribonuclease: The primary structure of performic acid–oxidized ribonuclease, established in 1960 by Hirs, Moore, and Stein, consists of a single chain of 124 residues with Lys N terminus and Val C

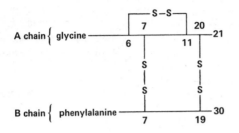

Figure 4–12. Relationship of the A and B chains of human insulin.

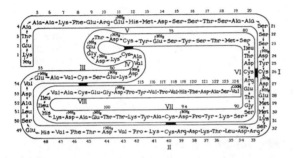

Figure 4–13. Structure of bovine ribonuclease. Two-dimensional schematic diagram showing the arrangement of the disulfide bonds and the sequence of the amino acid residues. Arrows indicate the direction of the peptide chain starting from the amino end. (Reproduced, with permission, from Smyth DG, Stein WH, Moore S: The sequence of amino acid residues in bovine pancreatic ribonuclease: Revisions and confirmations. *J Biol Chem* 1963;**238**:227.)

terminus. Eight cysteine residues are joined by disulfide bonds, forming 4 cross-linkages in the protein (Fig 4–13).

DETERMINATION OF SECONDARY & TERTIARY STRUCTURE

X-Ray Crystallography

While various techniques (eg, optical rotatory dispersion, tritium exchange of labile protons) formerly were much used to infer the presence of helical structures in proteins, these have been largely supplanted by the powerful technique of x-ray crystallography. X-rays are directed at a crystal of protein and generally also at a derivative of that protein which contains a heavy metal ion. The rays are scattered in a pattern that depends upon the electron densities in different parts of the protein. Images, collected on a photographic plate, are translated into electron density maps which, when superimposed one on another, permit the crystallographer to construct a faithful model of the protein in question. Although time-consuming, expensive, and requiring highly specialized training, x-ray crystallography reveals detailed, precise views of the orientations of all the amino acids in many proteins. Its contributions to our present-day concepts of protein structure can hardly be overstated.

Secondary & Tertiary Structure of a Specific Protein—Ribonuclease

X-ray diffraction studies of bovine ribonuclease indicate molecular dimensions of about 3.2 × 2.8 × 2.2 nm. The limited α-helix content is restricted to 2 turns at residues 5–12 and 2 turns near residues 28–35 (Fig 4–9). In contrast to myoglobin (Fig 5–3), ribonuclease has much more of its structure exposed. No portion is shielded by more than one layer of the main chain. A phosphate ion is present at the catalytic site near His residues 119 and 112. Lys 7 and 41 and His 48 also are implicated as being at the catalytic site. The enzyme subtilisin splits ribonuclease into a short S-peptide and a longer S-protein, with loss of enzymic activity. These may be noncovalently reassociated, with restoration of catalytic activity.

DETERMINATION OF QUATERNARY STRUCTURE

Determining the quaternary structure of oligomeric proteins encompasses determining the number and kind of protomers present, their mutual orientation, and the nature of the interactions that unite them.

Determination of the Molecular Weight

As long as oligomers do not undergo denaturation during the procedure used to determine their molecular weight, many methods can yield molecular weight data for oligomers. These same techniques may be used to determine protomer molecular weight if the oligomer is first denatured.

A. Ultracentrifugation: The method developed by Svedberg, which depends upon measurement of sedimentation rate in an ultracentrifugal field of around $10^5 \times g$ has tended in recent years to be replaced by the less complex techniques described below.

B. Sucrose Density Gradient Centrifugation: Unlike the Svedberg technique, which requires an analytic ultracentrifuge, a preparative ultracentrifuge available in most research laboratories is used. Protein standards and unknowns are layered over a 5–20% sucrose gradient in a plastic tube and centrifuged overnight at around $10^5 \times g$. A small hole is then punched in the bottom of the tube, the contents collected in a set of small tubes, the tube location (and thus relative position in the gradient) of the protein determined, and the mobility of the proteins computed.

C. Filtration Through Molecular Sieves: Columns of Sephadex or similar materials are calibrated using proteins of known molecular weight. The molecular weight of an unknown protein is then calculated from its mobility relative to these standards. Large errors may result if the protein is highly asymmetric or interacts strongly with the materials from which the molecular sieve was manufactured.

D. Polyacrylamide Gel Electrophoresis (PAGE): Protein standards are separated by elec-

Table 4—5. Quaternary structures of selected enzymes.*

Enzyme (Oligomer)	Number of Protomers	Molecular Weight of Protomer
Chicken or rabbit muscle creatine kinase (ATP:creatine phosphotransferase, E.C. 2.7.3.2)	2	40,000
Chicken heart aspartate transaminase (L-aspartate:2-oxoglutarate aminotransferase, E.C. 2.6.1.1)	2	50,000
Rabbit liver fructose diphosphatase (D-fructose-1,6-diphosphate 1-phosphohydrolase, E.C. 3.1.3.11)	2†	29,000
	2†	37,000
Rat liver ornithine transaminase (L-ornithine:2-oxoacid aminotransferase, E.C. 2.6.1.13)	4	33,000
Beef heart, liver, or muscle LDH (L-lactate:NAD oxidoreductase, E.C. 1.1.1.27)	4†	35,000
Rabbit muscle glyceraldehyde-3-phosphate dehydrogenase (D-glyceraldehyde-3-phosphate:NAD oxidoreductase [phosphorylating], E.C. 1.2.1.12)	4†	37,000
Rabbit muscle aldolase (ketose-1-phosphate aldehyde-lyase, E.C. 4.1.2.7)	4	40,000
Beef liver catalase (H_2O_2:H_2O_2 oxidoreductase, E.C. 1.11.1.6)	4	57,500
Beef heart mitochondrial ATPase (ATP phosphohydrolase, E.C. 3.6.1.3)	10	26,000
Pigeon liver fatty acid synthase	2	230,000
E coli glutamine synthase (L-glutamate:NH_3 ligase [ADP], E.C. 6.3.1.2)	12	48,500
Pig heart propionyl-CoA carboxylase (propionyl-CoA:CO_2 ligase [ADP], E.C. 6.4.1.2)	4	175,000
Chicken liver acetyl-CoA carboxylase (acetyl-CoA:CO_2 ligase [ADP], E.C. 6.4.1.2)	2†	4,100,000
	10†	409,000

*Adapted from Klotz IM, Langerman NR, Darnall DW: Quaternary structure of enzymes. *Annu Rev Biochem* 1970;**39**:25.
†Nonidentical subunits.

trophoresis in 5–15% cross-linked gels of varying porosity. Gels are stained for protein, generally with Coomassie blue stain or silver, and the molecular weight is estimated relative to the mobility of the standards. By far the most common application of this technique is to determine protomer molecular weight by first denaturing the oligomer (eg, by boiling in a detergent in the presence of β-mercaptoethanol) and separating on gels that contain the ionic detergent sodium dodecyl sulfate (SDS).

Electron Photomicrography

An actual picture of very small objects can be obtained with the electron microscope. Magnifications as high as 100,000 diameters can be obtained with this instrument. This permits the visualization of proteins of high molecular weight, such as virus particles, enzyme complexes, and oligomeric proteins.

Table 4–5 lists examples of the numbers and molecular weights of protomers contributing to the quaternary structures of selected enzymes.

•   •   •

References

Advances in Protein Chemistry. Academic Press, 1944–1983. [Annual publication.]

Aisen P, Listowsky I: Iron transport and storage proteins. *Annu Rev Biochem* 1980;**49**:357.

Amsel M, Poljak RJ: Three-dimensional structure of immunoglobulins. *Annu Rev Biochem* 1979;**48**:961.

Baldwin RL: Intermediates in protein folding. *Annu Rev Biochem* 1975;**44**:453.

Bradbury JH: The structure and chemistry of keratin fibers. *Adv Protein Chem* 1973;**27**:111.

Chou PY, Fassman GD: Empirical predictions of protein structure. *Annu Rev Biochem* 1978;**47**:251.

Croft LR: *Handbook of Amino Acid Sequences of Proteins.* Joynson-Bruvvers Ltd (Oxford, England), 1973.

Dayhoff MO (editor): *Atlas of Protein Structure.* Vol 5. National Biomedical Research Foundation, 1972.

Gurd FN, Rothgeb TM: Motions in proteins. *Adv Protein Chem* 1979;**33**:74.

Haschemeyer RH, deHarven E: Electron microscopy of enzymes. *Annu Rev Biochem* 1974;**43**:279.

Isenberg I: Histones. *Annu Rev Biochem* 1979;**48**:159.

Klotz IM, Langerman NR, Darnall DW: Quaternary structure of enzymes. *Annu Rev Biochem* 1970;**39**:25.

Kuntz ID Jr, Kauzmann W: Hydration of proteins and polypeptides. *Adv Protein Chem* 1974;**28**:239.

Lennarz WJ (editor): *The Biochemistry of Glycoproteins and Proteoglycans.* Plenum Press, 1980.

Lijas A, Rossmann MG: X-ray studies of protein interactions. *Annu Rev Biochem* 1974;**43**:475.

Neurath H, Hill RL (editors): *The Proteins,* 3rd ed. Academic Press, 1975.

Niederwieser A, Pataki G (editors): *New Techniques in Amino Acid, Peptide and Protein Analysis.* Ann Arbor, 1971.

Osborne JC Jr, Brewer HB Jr: The plasma lipoproteins. *Adv Protein Chem* 1977;**31**:253.

Privalov PL: Stability of proteins. *Adv Protein Chem* 1979;**33**:167.

Smith LC, Pownall HJ, Gotto AM Jr: The plasma lipoproteins: Structure and metabolism. *Annu Rev Biochem* 1978;**47**:751.

Wu TT, Fitch WM, Margdiash E: The information content of protein amino acid sequences. *Annu Rev Biochem* 1974;**43**:539.

Structure & Function of a Protein–Hemoglobin | 5

David W. Martin, Jr., MD

Hemoglobin is a readily available major protein in the human body and carries out a well-known function, the **transport of oxygen** from the lungs to the peripheral tissues and CO_2 from the peripheral tissues back to the lungs. Thus, hemoglobin has been an attractive model protein for the study of the structure/function relationships of a macromolecule. However, equally interesting is the observation that when a hemoglobin molecule malfunctions in a human as a result of an inherited defect, it usually induces an illness that may then come to the attention of an astute and inquisitive physician. Subsequently, careful molecular analysis of the abnormal hemoglobin may lead to important deductions concerning the structure/function relationship of both the abnormal and the normal hemoglobin molecule. At present, the structure/function relationship of the hemoglobin molecule is probably better understood than that of any other protein. Accordingly, in this chapter the structure/function relationship of the normal and, when indicated, abnormal molecules will be reviewed as a general model of how protein molecules carry out their important biologic functions.

HEME-OXYGEN INTERACTION

The transport of oxygen is based on a chemical interaction between molecular O_2 and **heme**, a tetrapyrrole porphyrin ring containing ferrous (Fe^{2+}) iron. The porphyrin ring is synthesized in most cells, including plant cells, where it exists as chlorophyll. (Chlorophyll contains magnesium rather than iron.) The four N atoms oriented toward the center of the prophyrin ring help to neutralize the charges on their ferrous ion and thereby hold it in place (Fig 5–1). In solution, heme will bind to oxygen very tightly; in fact, the binding is so tight that it is essentially irreversible. This tight binding is due to the fact that molecular oxygen oxidizes Fe^{2+} to Fe^{3+}, generating superoxide ion, O_2^-.

The **oxidation** of Fe^{2+} to Fe^{3+} in heme involves an intermediate of **one oxygen molecule with 2 heme molecules.** Thus, if heme is to function effectively as a carrier of oxygen molecules, the **hemes must be separated** from one another so as to avoid the oxidation of Fe^{2+} to Fe^{3+}. Furthermore, the ferrous-oxygen bond must be weakened so as to provide **reversible association** of oxygen with the heme moiety.

There are 2 major heme-containing proteins, **myoglobin** and **hemoglobin,** concerned with the transport of oxygen. Both are **red** proteins because of their heme content. Myoglobin and hemoglobin both hold their heme moieties in separated **pockets** and thus avoid the above-described oxidation. In both myoglobin and hemoglobin, the ferrous ion of heme is also attached to the nitrogen atom of a particular **proximal histidine residue,** which by donating electrons to the Fe^{2+} **weakens the ferrous-oxygen bond and thereby confers reversibility.** When oxygen is present in the myoglobin and hemoglobin molecules, the O_2 is bound reversibly and noncovalently to the Fe^{2+} of heme and to a **distal histidine residue** on the side of the molecule opposite the histidine residue to which the Fe^{2+} itself is attached (Fig 5–2). Thus, by attaching the heme moiety to a specific protein molecule and by **separating each of the hemes in different pockets, nature has made the heme-oxygen interaction weaker and reversible.**

MYOGLOBIN

The secondary and tertiary structure of myoglobin was solved by Kendrew using x-ray crystallog-

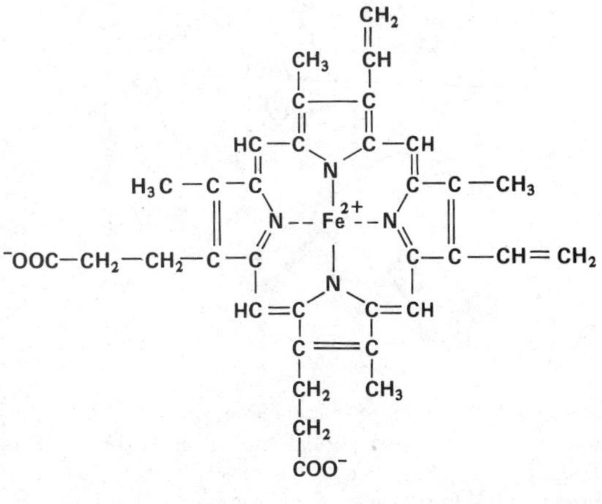

Figure 5–1. The structure of heme.

Proximal His (F8)

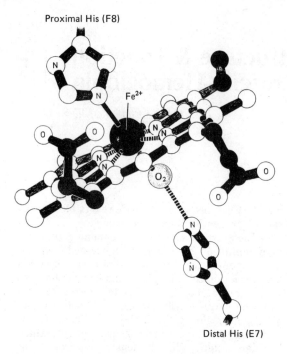

Figure 5–2. Addition of oxygen to heme iron in oxygenation. Shown also are the imidazole side chains of the 2 important histidine residues of globin that attach to the heme iron. (Reproduced, with permission, from Harper HA et al: *Physiologische Chemie.* Springer-Verlag, 1975.)

Distal His (E7)

raphy. This 17,000-MW protein contains **8 α-helical regions** varying from 7 to 20 amino acid residues in length, each separated by interhelical regions (Fig 5–3). Each helical region is given a letter designation A through H, starting with the amino-terminal end of the molecule. The interhelical junctional regions are given the 2 letters denoting the helices between which they reside in the primary structure. The amino-terminal region is referred to as NA and the carboxy-terminal region as HC, since they separate the N terminal from the A helix and the H helix from the carboxy terminal, respectively. The amino acid residues are given designations according to their position within or between helical regions (Fig 5–4). The tenth amino acid of myoglobin, valine, is the eighth residue in the A helix and is designated Val A8 (10). The residue at position 120, proline, is designated Pro GH2 (120).

The heme in myoglobin resides in the pocket **between helix E and helix F** and is attached to the nitrogen atom of **His F8** (the proximal His). The heme moiety is also in contact with the side chains of 15 other amino acid residues from 7 helices.

| H₂ - Val - Leu - Ser - Glu - Gly - Glu - Trp - Gln - Leu - Val - Leu - |
| NA1 NA2 A1 A2 A3 A4 A5 A6 A7 A8 A9 |

His - Val - Trp - Ala - Lys - Val - Glu - Ala - Asp - Val - Ala -
A10 A11 A12 A13 A14 A15 A16 AB1 B1   B2   B3

Gly - His - Gly - Gln - Asp - Ile - Leu - Ile - Arg - Leu - Phe -
B4   B5   B6   B7   B8   B9 B10 B11 B12 B13 B14

Lys - Ser - His - Pro - Glu - Thr - Leu - Glu - Lys - Phe - Asp -
B15 B16 C1   C2   C3   C4   C5   C6   C7 CD1 CD2

Arg - Phe - Lys - His - Leu - Lys - Thr - Glu - Ala - Glu - Met -
CD3 CD4 CD5 CD6 CD7 CD8 D1   D2   D3   D4   D5

Lys - Ala - Ser - Glu - Asp - Leu - Lys - Lys - His - Gly - Val -
D6   D7   E1   E2   E3   E4   E5   E6   E7   E8   E9

Thr - Val - Leu - Thr - Ala - Leu - Gly - Ala - Ile - Leu - Lys -
E10 E11 E12 E13 E14 E15 E16 E17 E18 E19 E20

Lys - Lys - Gly - His - His - Glu - Ala - Glu - Leu - Lys - Pro -
EF1 EF2 EF3 EF4 EF5 EF6 EF7 EF8 F1   F2   F3

Leu - Ala - Gln - Ser - His - Ala - Thr - Lys - His - Lys - Ile -
F4   F5   F6   F7   F8   F9 FG1 FG2 FG3 FG4 FG5

Pro - Ile - Lys - Tyr - Leu - Glu - Phe - Ile - Ser - Glu - Ala -
G1   G2   G3   G4   G5   G6   G7   G8   G9 G10 G11

Ile - Ile - His - Val - Leu - His - Ser - Arg - His - Pro - Gly -
G12 G13 G14 G15 G16 G17 G18 G19 GH1 GH2 GH3

Asn - Phe - Gly - Ala - Asp - Ala - Gln - Gly - Ala - Met - Asn -
GH4 GH5 GH6 H1   H2   H3   H4   H5   H6   H7   H8

Lys - Ala - Leu - Glu - Leu - Phe - Arg - Lys - Asp - Ile - Ala -
H9 H10 H11 H12 H13 H14 H15 H16 H17 H18 H19

Ala - Lys - Tyr - Lys - Glu - Leu - Gly - Tyr - Gln - Gly - COOH
H20 H21 H22 H23 H24 HC1 HC2 HC3 HC4 HC5

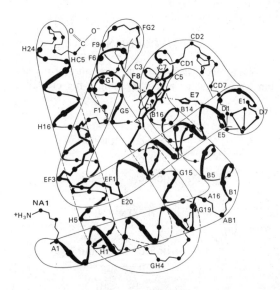

Figure 5–3. A model of myoglobin at low resolution. Only the α-carbon atoms are shown. (Based on Dickerson RE in: *The Proteins,* 2nd ed. Vol 2. Neurath H [editor]. Academic Press, 1964. Reproduced with permission.)

Figure 5–4. Amino acid sequence of sperm whale myoglobin. The labels below each residue in the sequence refer to its position in an α-helical region or a nonhelical region. (Based on Edmundson AE in: *Nature* 1965;**205**:883; and Watson HC in: *Progr Stereochem* 1969;**4**:299.)

The binding of oxygen to the heme moiety of myoglobin increases as the concentration of oxygen in the environment of the molecule increases and decreases as the oxygen concentration decreases. This relationship can be represented graphically as an **oxygen dissociation curve,** in which the fractional O_2 saturation of the myoglobin molecule is compared with the O_2 concentration in its environment, represented by the partial pressure of oxygen (P_{O_2} in millimeters of mercury). The oxygen dissociation curve for myoglobin is hyperbolic, as shown in Fig 5–5. The P_{O_2} in the lung is 100 mm Hg; in venous blood, 40 mm Hg; and in the capillaries of active muscle, 20 mm Hg. Thus, the difference between the P_{O_2} of blood in lungs and that of blood in the capillaries of active muscle tissue would not be sufficient to release more than about 12% of the oxygen being carried by myoglobin (Fig 5–5). Because of the relatively high affinity of myoglobin for oxygen and the hyperbolic shape of the curve, the available oxygen would be released to the peripheral tissues only when the P_{O_2} there dropped below 5 mm Hg.

Myoglobin functions in red muscle to pass oxygen absorbed from the blood on to mitochondria, where the P_{O_2} is quite low. Thus, myoglobin working where the P_{O_2} is in the range of 4–5 mm Hg can effectively discharge most of its O_2 content to mitochondria.

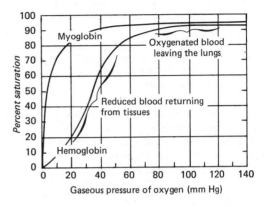

Figure 5–5. Oxygen equilibrium curves of hemoglobin and myoglobin. Arterial oxygen tension is about 100 mm Hg; mixed venous oxygen tension is about 40 mm Hg; capillary (active muscle) oxygen tension is about 20 mm Hg; and the minimum oxygen tension required for the cytochrome enzymes is about 5 mm Hg. The figure illustrates that association of chains into a tetrameric structure (hemoglobin) results in much greater oxygen delivery than would be possible with single chains. (Myoglobin and hemoglobin chains have about the same oxygen affinity.) (Modified, with permission, from Stanbury JB, Wyngaarden JB, Fredrickson DS [editors]: *The Metabolic Basis of Inherited Disease,* 4th ed. McGraw-Hill, 1978.)

THE HEMOGLOBIN MOLECULE

The oxygen carrier molecule in pulmonary venous (lung) blood must be saturated with O_2 at a P_{O_2} of 100 mm Hg but yet discharge a significant quantity, if not most, of this O_2 when it reaches the peripheral tissues, where the capillary P_{O_2} will be no lower than 20 mm Hg. Furthermore, the oxygen carrier molecule of blood must regain maximal O_2 with a limited increase in P_{O_2} (ie, to 100 mm Hg) as it returns to the lung. Such requirements clearly cannot be satisfied by a hyperbolic oxygen dissociation curve but require a **sigmoid oxygen dissociation curve** (Fig 5–5).

A sigmoid oxygen dissociation curve requires an interaction between the heme moieties of a protein. Thus, the oxygen-carrying protein molecule in blood must consist of multiple interacting subunits, each with its own heme moiety. Hemoglobin is such a molecule, containing **4 interacting subunits** that generate a **"cooperative" effect.** The cooperative effect of the tetrameric hemoglobin can be described as follows: **If a hemoglobin molecule takes up one oxygen, it tends to go on and acquire 4 oxygen molecules; and if a hemoglobin molecule saturated with oxygen loses one oxygen, 2 or 3 more oxygens are usually cast off.** Thus, over the range of P_{O_2} values between pulmonary venous blood and peripheral tissue capillary blood, the hemoglobin molecule discharges 35–45% of the oxygen it carries (Fig 5–5). It should be clear that myoglobin is incapable of generating such a cooperative effect, since there is

only one heme moiety per myoglobin molecule, precluding any indirect heme-heme interaction as occurs in the tetrameric hemoglobin molecule.

The greater the sigmoid character of the oxygen dissociation curve, the greater will be the oxygen released per unit drop in P_{O_2}. This effect can be described quantitatively by Hill's number (Chapter 8). The cooperativity of the hemoglobin molecule within the erythrocyte is affected by pH, CO_2, 2,3-diphosphoglycerate (DPG, bisphosphoglycerate), and chloride ion (Fig 43–5); but of course these chemical agents have no effect on myoglobin function, since that molecule does not exhibit any subunit interaction or cooperativity. Hemoglobin is a prototype of **protein molecules that change their structure in response to chemical stimuli,** such as the oxygen molecule.

The Structure of Hemoglobin

The necessity for hemoglobin having multiple subunits has already been described. The hemoglobin molecule consists of 4 protein chains or subunits, 2 designated alpha and 2 designated beta, and is represented as $(\alpha)_2(\beta)_2$. The **alpha chains** contain 141 amino acids; the **beta chains,** 146 amino acids. Each has a distinct but similar amino acid sequence. The alpha subunits, the beta subunits, and the myoglobin molecule are remarkably similar in their tertiary structures. The myoglobin molecule and the beta subunit contain 8 alpha helices; the alpha subunit contains only 7. The hemoglobin molecule and its subunits contain mostly **hydrophobic amino acids internally** and **hy-**

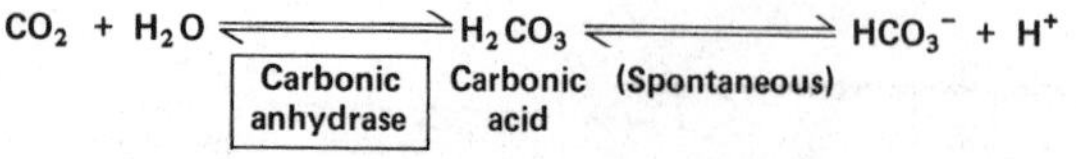

$$CO_2 + H_2O \rightleftharpoons H_2CO_3 \rightleftharpoons HCO_3^- + H^+$$

| Carbonic anhydrase | Carbonic (Spontaneous) acid |

Figure 5–6. The formation of carbonic acid by erythrocyte carbonic anhydrase and the dissociation of carbonic acid to bicarbonate ion and proton.

drophilic amino acids on their surfaces. Thus, the hemoglobin molecule is waxy inside and soapy outside, making it **soluble in water but impermeable to water.** Each subunit contains one **heme moiety hidden within a waxy pocket.**

In addition to transporting oxygen from the lungs to peripheral tissues, hemoglobin facilitates the **transport of CO_2** from tissues to the lungs for exhalation. Hemoglobin can bind CO_2 directly when oxygen is released, and about 15% of the CO_2 carried in blood is carried directly on the hemoglobin molecule. However, as CO_2 is absorbed in blood, the carbonic anhydrase in erythrocytes catalyzes the formation of carbonic acid (Fig 5–6). Carbonic acid rapidly dissociates into bicarbonate and proton; the equilibrium is toward the dissociation. To avoid the extreme danger of increasing the acidity of blood, there must exist a buffering system to absorb this excess proton. **Hemoglobin binds 2 protons for every 4 oxygen molecules lost** and thus provides a major buffering capacity of blood (Fig 5–7). In the lungs, the process is reversed—ie, **as oxygen binds to the deoxygenated hemoglobin, protons are released** and bind with the bicarbonate to drive the bicarbonate toward carbonic acid. With the aid of the very efficient carbonic anhydrase, the carbonic acid forms CO_2, which is exhaled. Thus, the **binding of oxygen forces the exhalation of CO_2.** This reversible phenomenon is called the **Bohr effect.** The Bohr effect is a property of the tetrameric hemoglobin and is dependent upon its heme-heme interaction or cooperative effects. Myoglobin does not exhibit any Bohr effect.

Cooperativity Between Hemoglobin Subunits

The 4 subunits of hemoglobin can be pictured as occupying the apices of a tetrahedron; thus, there are 6 edges of contact. There is a 2-fold symmetry to the hemoglobin molecule, leaving 4 interfaces for subunit interactions. For purposes of discussion, the 2 alpha subunits can be labeled α_1 and α_2, and the 2 beta subunits β_1 and β_2. The α_1/β_1 interaction and the α_2/β_2 interaction each are held together by 17–19 hydrogen bonds and thus are **very rigid;** therefore, these subunit interactions—α_1/β_1 and α_2/β_2—are not affected by the binding of oxygen to heme moieties and there is no **no cooperativity** between them. The α_1/β_2 and α_2/β_1 contacts are less extensive and are therefore weaker. In addition, the contacts between α_1/β_2 and between α_2/β_1 are very **different in oxygenated versus deoxygenated hemoglobin.** These specific contacts act as a "snap action switch" between these 2 states of hemoglobin, ie, the oxygenated and the deoxygenated forms of hemoglobin.

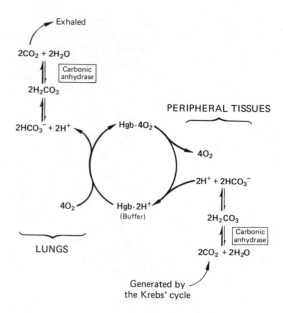

Figure 5–7. The Bohr effect. The carbon dioxide generated in peripheral tissues combines with water to form carbonic acid which dissociates into proton and bicarbonate ions. The deoxygenated hemoglobin acts as a buffer by binding protons and delivering them to the lungs. In the lungs, the binding of oxygen by hemoglobin forces the protons off of the hemoglobin. The protons combine with bicarbonate ion, generating carbonic acid, which with the aid of carbonic anhydrase, becomes carbon dioxide. The carbon dioxide is exhaled from the lungs.

The Two States of Hemoglobin

Based on the allosteric theory of Monod and Changeaux, the 2 states of hemoglobin are designated relaxed (R, oxygenated) and taut (T, deoxygenated). These 2 forms, R and T, are interconvertible, and each form has its own equilibrium constant (K_R and K_T) for the binding of oxygen:

$$R \rightleftharpoons T$$
$$R + O_2 \rightleftharpoons RO_2 \; ; \; K_R = \frac{(RO_2)}{(R)(O_2)}$$
$$T + O_2 \rightleftharpoons TO_2 \; ; \; K_T = \frac{(TO_2)}{(T)(O_2)}$$

The binding of oxygen to the R form is several hundred times more favored than the binding of oxygen to the T structure ($K_R >> K_T$), and the **oxygen affinity of R is thus much greater than the oxygen affinity of T.**

L is defined as the ratio of T to R (L = T/R) and is an index of which form, T or R, is predominant in any solution of hemoglobin. Chemicals such as DPG, protons, chloride, and CO_2, which do not interact directly with the heme moiety of the hemoglobin subunits, all **lower the oxygen affinity by favoring the T structure, ie, by increasing L without changing the equilibrium constants for the association of oxygen with R (K_R) or with T (K_T).**

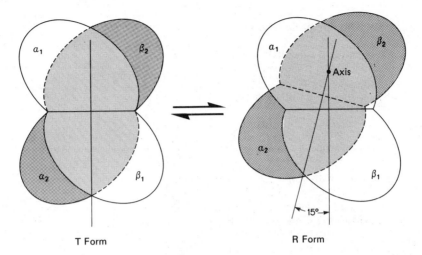

Figure 5–8. During the transition of the T form to the R form of hemoglobin, there occurs a rotation of one pair of rigid subunits (α_2/β_2) through 15 degrees relative to the other rigid pair of subunits (α_1/β_1). The axis of rotation is eccentric, and the α_2/β_2 pair also shifts toward the axis somewhat. In the diagram, the α_1/β_1 pair is unshaded and held fixed, while the shaded α_2/β_2 pair rotates and shifts.

Since the α_1/β_1 dimer and the α_2/β_2 dimer are themselves rigid structures, the transition from R to T and vice versa must involve movement of the α_1/β_1 dimer relative to the α_2/β_2 dimer. By x-ray crystallography, it is apparent that if the α_1/β_1 dimer is fixed, the other dimer, α_2/β_2, rotates 15 degrees about an eccentric axis and shifts a bit along that axis (Fig 5–8). Thus, the hemoglobin molecule can snap back and forth between its 2 structures, R and T. Subtle changes of internal subunit structure that accompany the bind-

ing and dissociation of oxygen are responsible for the switches between the R and T forms.

Salt bridges, defined as ionic bonds between positively charged nitrogen atoms and negatively charged oxygen atoms, play major roles in the switch mechanism. The **T form of the hemoglobin is stabilized by salt bridges,** and **agents that promote oxygen dissociation thus strengthen or add salt bridges** to the T form (increasing the value of L) (Fig 5–9).

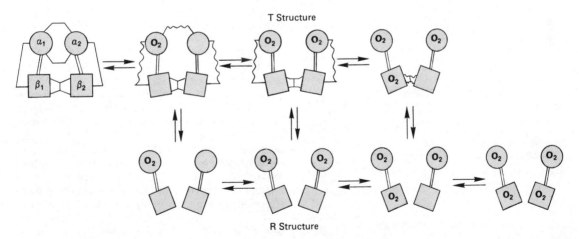

Figure 5–9. Transition from the T structure to the R structure increases in likelihood as each of the 4 heme groups is oxygenated. In this model, salt bridges (thin lines) linking the subunits in the T structure break progressively as oxygen is added, and even those salt bridges that have not yet ruptured are progressively weakened (wavy lines). The transition from T to R does not take place after a fixed number of oxygen molecules have been bound, but it becomes more probable with each successive oxygen bound. The transition between the 2 structures is influenced by several factors, including protons, carbon dioxide, chloride, and DPG. The higher their concentration, the more oxygen must be bound to trigger the transition. Fully oxygenated molecules in the T structure and fully deoxygenated molecules in the R structure are not shown, because they are too unstable to exist in significant numbers. (Modified and redrawn, with permission, from Perutz MF: Hemoglobin structure and respiratory transport. *Sci Am* [Dec] 1978;**239**:92.)

Changes Accompanying Binding of Oxygen to T form of Hemoglobin

The heme pockets in the alpha subunits of hemoglobin are of a size just adequate for the entry of an oxygen molecule, but the entry of oxygen into the heme pockets of the beta subunits is **blocked by a valine residue.**

In the deoxygenated state, or T form, the Fe^{2+} bound to His F8 (87), commonly referred to as proximal His, is **not in the plane of the porphyrin ring.** Instead, as shown in Fig 5–10, the Fe^{2+} is approximately 0.07 nm out of the plane of the porphyrin ring in the direction of the F helix. When oxygen enters the pocket and binds to heme, the Fe^{2+} moves **back into the plane of the porphyrin ring, pulling with it the F8 His** and, of course, the F helix itself (Fig 5–10). This movement of the F helix toward the porphyrin ring is transmitted to the other subunits by a forced breaking of salt bridges. **In the T form, the penultimate tyrosine (HC2) is wedged into a pocket between the H and F helices,** where it is hydrogen-bonded to valine FG5. The C-terminal residue, Arg HC3 in the alpha chain and His HC3 in the beta chain, is constrained by its participation in specific salt bridges, as indicated in Fig 5–11.

The movement of the F helix toward the porphyrin ring upon occupancy of the alpha pocket by oxygen narrows the space between H and F helices, thereby excluding the tyrosyl residues. This rotation of the tyrosyl residues out of the space between the H and F helices forces a loosening of the salt bridges between

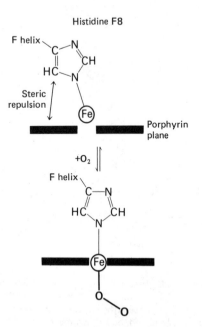

Figure 5–10. The iron atom moves 0.075 nm into the plane of the heme on oxygenation because its diameter becomes smaller. Histidine F8 is pulled along with the iron atom. (Slightly modified and reproduced, with permission, from Stryer L: *Biochemistry,* 2nd ed. Freeman, 1981.)

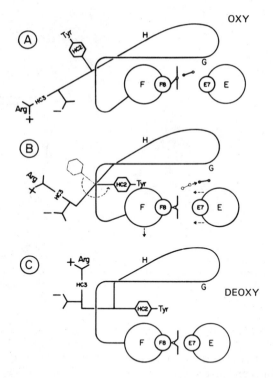

Figure 5–11. The changes in tertiary structure produced by transition from oxy- to deoxyhemoglobin. In oxyhemoglobin *(A),* iron is in the plane of the heme, pulling His F8 upward. Arg HC3 rotates freely. When oxygen moves out *(B),* the E helix moves in and the F helix moves down, forming a pocket between it and the H helix. The phenolic group of Tyr HC2 can occupy this pocket *(C),* and its entry pulls Arg HC3 into position so that it can form the salt bridges indicated in the text. (Reproduced, with permission, from Stanbury JB, Wyngaarden JB, Fredrickson DS [editors]: *The Metabolic Basis of Inherited Disease,* 4th ed. McGraw-Hill, 1978.)

the HC3 residues of α_1 and the α_2 Val NA1 and Asp H9. It is these salt bridges that restrain hemoglobin in its T structure (Fig 5–12). Therefore, **when a sufficient number of salt bridges are broken between and within the subunits, the T structure will snap or click to the R structure.** The R structure has an affinity for oxygen many hundred-fold greater than does the T structure. **Thus, upon the binding of oxygen by the heme moieties in one or 2 subunits of hemoglobin, enough salt bridges are broken to change the structure of the hemoglobin to a form that exhibits a much greater oxygen affinity.** This is the basis of the **cooperative effect.** In the R form, there are no Val residues blocking the heme pockets of the beta subunits. The binding of one or 2 oxygen molecules to the alpha subunits of the hemoglobin molecule, by favoring the R form, makes the binding of subsequent oxygen molecules to the other unoccupied heme moieties much more likely.

Upon removal of an oxygen molecule from oxygenated hemoglobin, the electron being shared by Fe^{3+} and the superoxide oxygen is returned to the Fe^{3+} to reestablish its Fe^{2+} state, and the Fe^{2+} is then again

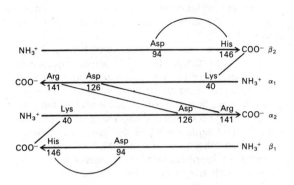

Figure 5–12. Salt-links between different subunits in deoxyhemoglobin. These noncovalent, electrostatic interactions are disrupted on oxygenation. (Slightly modified and reproduced, with permission, from Stryer L: *Biochemistry*, 2nd ed. Freeman, 1981.)

displaced about 0.07 nm above the plane of the porphyrin ring (Fig 5–10). This displacement causes a corresponding displacement of the F helix via the proximal His and reopens the space between the H and F helices for occupancy by the tyrosyl HC2 residue. The reentry of the tyrosyl residue into that space between the H and F helices favors the re-formation of the salt bridges by the C-terminal residues. **When a sufficient number of the salt bridges are re-formed, the hemoglobin molecule will snap or click back into the T state from its R state.** This snapping into the T state will pull the heme ferrous ions of the other subunits out of the plane of the porphyrin ring, **stretching the Fe^{2+}-oxygen bond until it breaks, thus releasing the oxygen.** Again, this **allosteric change** induced by the release of one or two O_2 molecules from the hemoglobin molecule forces oxygen away from the other heme moieties, causing a cooperative release of oxygen—ie, once one or two O_2 molecules have been lost from the oxygenated hemoglobin molecules, the others are effectively pushed out.

Perhaps it is more reasonable to consider the hemoglobin molecule a molecular lung rather than an oxygen tank, since **it changes its structure upon the binding and releasing of oxygen.**

The Bohr Effect at the Submolecular Level

The protons responsible for the Bohr effect are generated by the breaking of salt bridges during the binding of oxygen to the T structure. When oxygen binds to the T structure, salt bridges are broken, and the protons are released from the N atoms of beta chain His residues HC3 (146). These released protons drive the equilibrium with bicarbonate toward carbonic acid, which is then released as CO_2 in alveolar blood (Fig 5–7).

Conversely, upon the release of oxygen, the T structure and its salt bridges are re-formed, requiring

protons to bind to the beta chain HC3 residues. Thus, the presence of protons from peripheral tissues favors the formation of salt bridges by protonating the terminal His residue of the beta subunits. Re-formation of the salt bridges, of course, forces the release of oxygen from oxygenated (R form) hemoglobin. Overall, **an increase in protons causes oxygen release,** while **an increase in oxygen causes proton release.** The former can be represented in an oxygen dissociation curve by a rightward shift in the dissociation curve upon increasing hydrogen ions (protons).

Diphosphoglycerate (DPG, Bisphosphoglycerate) Binding

In peripheral tissues, an oxygen shortage causes an increased accumulation of diphosphoglycerate (DPG). One molecule of DPG is bound per hemoglobin tetramer in a central cavity formed by residues of all 4 subunits. The central cavity is of sufficient size for the entry of DPG only when the hemoglobin molecule is in the **T form,** ie, when the space between the H helices of the beta chains is wide enough. The DPG is bound by salt bridges between its oxygen atoms and both beta chains via their N-terminal amino groups (Val NA1), Lys EF6, and **His H21** residues (Fig 5–13). Thus, **DPG stabilizes the T or deoxygenated form of hemoglobin by cross-linking the beta chains** and contributing additional salt bridges that must be broken for the T form to click into the R form of hemoglobin.

DPG binds more weakly to **fetal hemoglobin** than adult hemoglobin because the **H21** residue of the gamma chain of fetal hemoglobin is **Ser rather than His** and cannot contribute to the salt bridges that hold

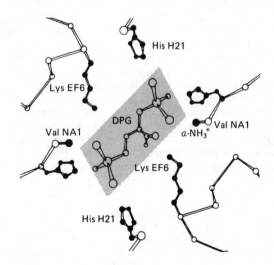

Figure 5–13. Mode of binding of diphosphoglycerate to human deoxyhemoglobin. DPG interacts with 3 positively charged groups on each β chain. (Based on Arnone A: X-ray diffraction study of binding of 2,3-diphosphoglycerate to human deoxyhemoglobin. *Nature* 1972;**237**:146. Reproduced with permission.)

the DPG in the central cavity. Therefore, **DPG has a less profound effect on the stabilization of the T form of fetal hemoglobin** and is responsible for fetal hemoglobin appearing to have a **higher affinity** for oxygen than does adult hemoglobin.

The **trigger** for the transition between the R and T forms of hemoglobin is the **movement of the iron in and out of the plane of the porphyrin ring.** Both steric and electronic factors mediate this trigger with a free energy of about 3000 calories per mole. Thus, a minimal change in the position of Fe^{2+} relative to the porphyrin ring induces very significant switching of the conformations of hemoglobin and crucially affects its biologic function in response to an environmental signal.

INSIGHTS FROM MUTANT HEMOGLOBINS

Because of the intricate relationship between hemoglobin structure and function described above, one might expect that alterations in the primary structure of a hemoglobin subunit would have the potential for greatly affecting its biologic function. An enormous number of abnormal hemoglobins with mutations in the alpha and beta subunits have been described in humans. A few of these will be summarized as illustrative examples.

Hemoglobin M

The **methemoglobinemias** associated with abnormal hemoglobin structure result from the heme iron remaining in the **ferric state.** Hemoglobin with Fe^{3+} in its heme will **not bind oxygen** even though it may be in the R form. Because deoxygenated hemoglobin is less red than oxygenated hemoglobin, clinical cyanosis can result from methemoglobinemia. When oxygen binds to the Fe^{2+} of heme (as described above), the iron donates an electron to oxygen, thus forming Fe^{3+} and superoxide anion (O_2^-) in the heme pockets (Fig 5–14). Upon the removal of oxygen, the superoxide anion returns the electron to the Fe^{3+} to regenerate Fe^{2+} and molecular oxygen. However, the superoxide will return the electron to the Fe^{3+} only so long as **no other electron acceptor is available within the heme pocket.** Of course, **water** is an effective electron acceptor and does occasionally gain access to the heme pocket. This results in the formation of hydrogen

Ferric cation

$$Fe^{2+} + O_2 \rightleftharpoons Fe^{3+} \cdot O_2^-$$

Superoxide anion

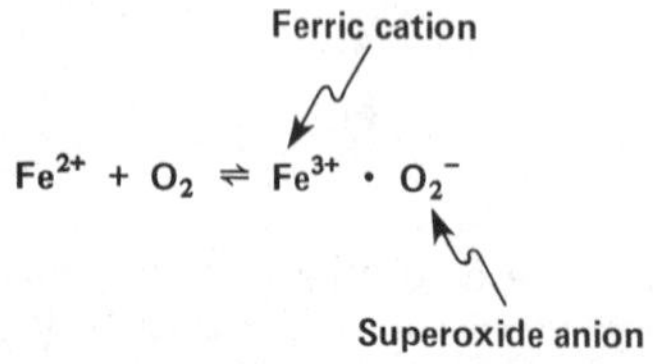

Figure 5–14. When oxygen binds to the ferrous cation of heme, the iron donates an electron to oxygen, forming a ferric cation and a superoxide anion in the heme pocket.

peroxide, Fe^{3+}, and oxygen. However, the erythrocyte contains an enzymatic reducing system with a limited capacity for the reduction of methemoglobin (Fe^{3+}) to hemoglobin (Fe^{2+}).

In the event that the structure of hemoglobin is altered so as to stabilize the Fe^{3+}, increased quantities of methemoglobin are generated and exceed erythrocyte-reducing capacity. Five types of hemoglobin M have been described, and 4 involve the substitution of Tyr for His residues. These latter substitutions involve replacement of the proximal or distal histidines in either alpha or beta units. The Tyr residue, by virtue of its **phenolate ion, forms a very tight complex with the ferric cation,** thereby conferring great stability on ferric hemoglobin and strongly favoring its formation. These new bonds formed between the substituted tyrosines and heme iron are strong enough so that molecular instability is not a component of the M hemoglobinopathies.

The 2 **alpha chain variants,** hemoglobin M Boston and hemoglobin M Iwait, have low oxygen affinity and do not exhibit the Bohr effect. In **hemoglobin M Boston,** the Tyr E7 forms a stronger bond with the iron than does the normal distal His E7. This strong bond allows the F helix to rotate away from the heme, opening the space between the F and H helices sufficiently for the entire HC2 to remain in that space. As described above, this promotes the formation of interchain salt bridges and prevents the abnormal alpha chains from undergoing the switching required for the conversion of the T form to the R form. Thus, the hemoglobin M Boston molecules are **locked in the T conformation with its lower oxygen affinity.** The Bohr effect and the cooperativity of oxygen binding, both of which are dependent upon this switching, accordingly cannot exist.

In **hemoglobin M Iwait,** the alpha chain Tyr F8 binds to the ferric ion and also prevents the T–R transition, thereby conveying the diminished oxygen affinity, absent Bohr effect, and lack of cooperativity.

Hemoglobin M Hyde Park and **hemoglobin M Saskatoon,** both of which contain tyrosine substitutions for His residues in the **beta chains,** do appear to be capable of undergoing R and T interconversion or switching, even though the affected beta subunits contain a stabilized Fe^{3+} in the heme moiety. Accordingly, both hemoglobin M Hyde Park and hemoglobin M Saskatoon exhibit a Bohr effect and relatively normal oxygen affinity by those subunits still containing ferrous heme.

The fifth type of hemoglobin M, **hemoglobin M Milwaukee-1,** has a substitution of Glu for the normal Val residue at E11 (67) of the beta chain. The carboxyl group of the Glu coordinates with Fe^{3+} and causes the quaternary structure to favor the T form. Accordingly, low oxygen affinity results, but the ferric beta subunits of M Milwaukee-1 can undergo the T–R switch upon oxygenation of the alpha chains. Thus, a Bohr effect does exist, but cooperativity is reduced, since only 2 of the oxygen-binding sites are available per abnormal hemoglobin tetramer. In summary, for the **alpha**

chain-substituted hemoglobins M, the R–T equilibrium is greatly in favor of T, so that oxygen affinity is reduced and no Bohr effect is observed. The **beta chain-substituted** hemoglobins M exhibit R–T switching, and a Bohr effect is therefore present.

Hemoglobins With Increased Oxygen Affinities

Hemoglobins that exhibit increased oxygen affinity do not release as much oxygen to the peripheral tissues as does normal hemoglobin. The tissue hypoxia leads to **polycythemia,** an increased number of red cells per unit volume of blood, in order to meet its O_2 needs. Any mutation favoring the R form of hemoglobin will promote an early switch from the T form to the R form and will result in a hemoglobin with high oxygen affinity. **Hemoglobin Chesapeake** has a substitution of Arg for Leu at G4 (92) of the alpha chain. This change stabilizes the R conformation, and hemoglobin Chesapeake thus has a high oxygen affinity and loss of cooperativity, functionally resembling those of myoglobin.

The α_1/β_2 interface is made up of many nonpolar bonds and one H bond (Fig 5–15). In the T form, the H bond exists between Asp G1 (99) β_2 and Tyr C7 (42) α_1; the one H bond in the R form crosses the α_1/β_2 interface between Asn G4 (102) β_2 and Asp G1 (94) α_1. In several mutant hemoglobins, such as Yakima and Upsilanti, Asp G1 (99) β is replaced with a residue that cannot participate in H bonding to stabilize the T structure. Thus, the equilibrium is shifted toward R, greatly increasing oxygen affinity and decreasing cooperativity.

As described above, the penultimate Tyr HC2 is extremely important in the R–T switching. When the Tyr HC2 is absent (hemoglobin McKees Rocks) or replaced by another residue (hemoglobin Bethesda, hemoglobin Osler), the T confirmation is destabilized, generating a hemoglobin with a high oxygen affinity

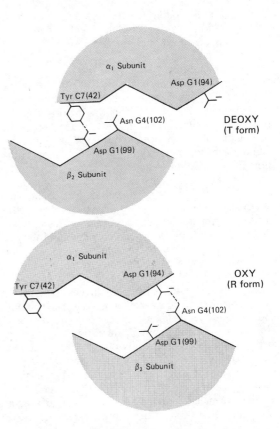

Figure 5–15. Changes at the α_1/β_2 contact on oxygenation. The contact "clicks" from one dovetailing area to another, involving a switch from one hydrogen bond to a second. The other bonds are nonpolar. (Reproduced, with permission, from Perutz MF: Molecular pathology of human hemoglobin: Stereochemical interpretation of abnormal oxygen affinities. *Nature* 1971;**232**:408.)

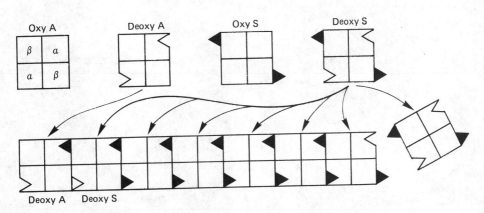

Figure 5–16. Diagrammatic representation of the sticky patch (▲) on hemoglobin S and the sticky patch "receptor" (Δ) present on deoxyhemoglobin A and deoxyhemoglobin S. The complementary surfaces allow deoxyhemoglobin A to polymerize into a fibrous structure, but the presence of deoxyhemoglobin A will terminate the polymerization by failing to provide sticky patches. (Modified and reproduced, with permission, from Stryer L: *Biochemistry,* 2nd ed. Freeman, 1981.)

and lower cooperativity. The C-terminal (HC) portion of the beta chains is also important in the binding of DPG and in generating the Bohr effect; all of these hemoglobins have a reduced Bohr effect, and many of them exhibit reduced binding of DPG.

Sickle Hemoglobin

Hemoglobin S is a substitution of Glu A2 (6) β by a Val residue and was described in 1949 by Linus Pauling and his colleagues. This was the first description of a molecular disease. The A2 residue, whether it be Glu or Val, can be seen to be on the surface of the hemoglobin molecule, exposed to water. The substitution in hemoglobin S replaces the polar glutamate residue with a nonpolar one and thereby generates a **"sticky patch"** on the outside of the beta chain. The sticky patch is present on oxygenated and deoxygenated hemoglobin S but, of course, not on hemoglobin A. On the surface of **deoxygenated hemoglobin,** there exists a **complement to the sticky patch**, but in oxygenated hemoglobin this complementary site is masked (Fig 5–16). When hemoglobin S is deoxygenated, the sticky patch of hemoglobin S can bind to the complementary patch on another deoxygenated hemoglobin molecule. This binding causes a **polymerization of deoxyhemoglobin S, forming long fibrous precipitates** that mechanically distort (sickle) the red cell, causing lysis and multiple secondary clinical effects. Thus, if hemoglobin S can be maintained in an oxygenated state or at least if the concentration of deoxygenated hemoglobin S can be kept at a minimum, formation of these polymers of deoxygen-

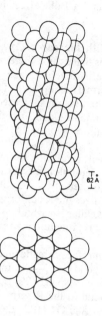

Figure 5–17. Proposed helical structure of a fiber of aggregated deoxyhemoglobin S. (Reproduced, with permission, from Maugh T II: A new understanding of sickle cell emerges. *Science* 1981;211:265. Copyright 1981 by the American Association for the Advancement of Science.)

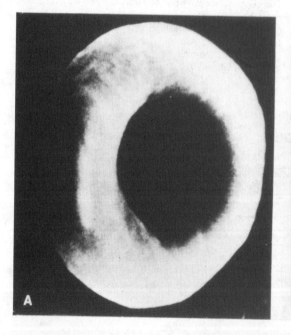
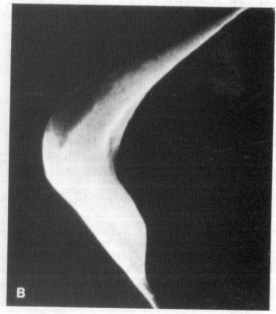

Figure 5–18. Scanning electron micrograph of normal and sickle red cells. *A:* A normal red cell, × 20,000. *B:* A deoxygenated sickle cell, × 15,000. (Reproduced, with permission, from Stanbury JB, Wyngaarden JB, Fredrickson DS [editors]: *The Metabolic Basis of Inherited Disease,* 4th ed. McGraw-Hill, 1978.)

ated hemoglobin S will not occur and "sickling" can be prevented. Clearly, it is the **T form of hemoglobin S that is subject to polymerization.** It is interesting but of no practical use to note that the ferric ion in methemoglobin A remains in the plane of the porphyrin ring and thus stabilizes the R form of hemoglobin. The same occurs in sickle hemoglobin; ie, hemoglobin S in the ferric state (methemoglobin S) will not polymerize into fibers, since it is stabilized in the R form.

Although deoxyhemoglobin A contains the receptor sites for the sticky patch present on oxygenated or deoxygenated hemoglobin S (Fig 5–16), the binding of sticky hemoglobin S to deoxyhemoglobin A cannot extend the polymer, since the latter does not itself have a sticky patch to promote binding to still another hemoglobin molecule. Therefore, the **binding of deoxyhemoglobin A to either the R or the T form of hemoglobin S will terminate the polymerization.**

The polymerization of deoxyhemoglobin S forms a helical fibrous structure, each hemoglobin molecule making contact with 4 neighbors in a tubular helix (Fig 5–17). The formation of these tubular fibers is responsible for the mechanical distortion of the erythrocyte containing them, so that they take on the shape of a sickle (Fig 5–18) and are vulnerable to lysis as they penetrate the interstices of the splenic sinusoids.

• • •

References

Dean J, Schechter AN: Sickle-cell anemia: Molecular and cellular basis of therapeutic approaches. (3 parts.) *N Engl J Med* 1978; **299:**752, 804, 863.

Klotz IM, Haney DN, King LC: Rational approaches to chemotherapy: Antisickling agents. *Science* 1981;**213:**724.

Perutz MF: Hemoglobin structure and respiratory transport. *Sci Am* (Dec) 1978;**239:**92.

Perutz MF: The regulation of oxygen-affinity of hemoglobin: Influence of structure of globin on heme iron. *Annu Rev Biochem* 1979;**48:**327.

Stamatoyannopoulos G: The molecular basis of hemoglobin disease. *Annu Rev Genet* 1972;**6:**47.

Winslow RM, Anderson WF: The hemoglobinopathies. Page 1666 in: *The Metabolic Basis of Inherited Disease,* 5th ed. Stanbury JB et al (editors). McGraw-Hill, 1983.

6 | General Properties of Enzymes

Victor W. Rodwell, PhD

CATALYSIS

Catalysts are substances that accelerate chemical reactions. They undergo physical change during a reaction but revert to their original state when the reaction is complete. **Enzymes** are **protein catalysts** for chemical reactions in biologic systems. Most chemical reactions of living cells would occur extremely slowly were it not for catalysis by enzymes. In contrast to nonprotein catalysts (H^+, OH^-, metal ions), each enzyme catalyzes a small number of reactions, frequently only one. Enzymes are thus **reaction-specific** catalysts. **Essentially all biochemical reactions are enzyme-catalyzed.** For almost every organic compound in nature—and for many inorganic compounds—there is an enzyme in some organism capable of reacting with it and catalyzing a chemical change.

Although enzyme activity was formerly thought to be expressed only in intact cells (hence the term *en-zyme* "in yeast"), enzymes may be extracted from cells without loss of their catalytic activity. Following purification of a specific enzyme, its structure and mechanism of action may be studied in detail. Enzyme-containing extracts are used in studies of metabolic reactions and their regulation and as catalysts for industrial synthesis of hormones and drugs. Since the enzyme content of human serum changes significantly in certain pathologic conditions, serum enzyme levels provide an important diagnostic tool.

ENZYME CLASSIFICATION & NOMENCLATURE

Many enzymes have more than one name, and several hundred different enzymes are referred to by name in this book. For this reason, we shall discuss briefly the historical and mechanistic reasons underlying the naming and classification of enzymes.

When biochemistry was young, the number of known enzymes was small, and most catalyzed hydrolytic reactions. Among the first identified and named were the digestive enzymes that catalyze the hydrolysis of the glycosidic, ester, and amide bonds of carbohydrates, lipids, and proteins. Enzymes initially were named for the substrates on which they acted by adding the suffix **-ase** to the name of the substrate. Thus, enzymes that hydrolyzed starch (amylon) were termed amylases; those that hydrolyzed fat (lipos), lipases; and those that hydrolyzed proteins, proteinases. Somewhat later, groups of enzymes that catalyzed similar reactions were given names that indicated the type of chemical reaction catalyzed. These were termed dehydrogenases, oxidases, decarboxylases, acylases, etc. Many of these names remain in current use. However, the ever-increasing number of known enzymes has brought with it confusion as to which enzyme is actually being referred to, and for this reason, sporadic attempts have been made to evolve more chemically rational systems of classification and nomenclature. The most recent of these is the **International Union of Biochemistry (IUB) Nomenclature System** described briefly below. Initiated in 1972 and periodically updated to incorporate newly discovered enzymes and new knowledge concerning catalytic mechanisms, the IUB system may at first glance appear cumbersome and complex. However, with familiarity it will be appreciated that the system is unambiguous and that its underlying principle, that of naming and classifying enzymes on the basis of chemical reaction type and reaction mechanism, can materially facilitate the student's task of integrating information from widely divergent areas of metabolism. The major features of this system are as follows:

A. Reactions and the enzymes that catalyze them are divided into 6 classes, each with 4–13 subclasses.

B. The enzyme name has 2 parts. The first names the substrate or substrates. The second, ending in **-ase**, indicates the **type of reaction catalyzed.**

C. Additional information, if needed to clarify the reaction, may follow in parentheses. For example, the enzyme catalyzing L-malate + NAD^+ = pyruvate + CO_2 + NADH + H^+ is designated 1.1.1.37 L-malate:NAD oxidoreductase (decarboxylating).

D. Each enzyme has a systematic code number (E.C.). This number characterizes the reaction type as to class (first digit), subclass (second digit), and subsubclass (third digit). The fourth digit is for the specific enzyme. Thus, E.C. 2.7.1.1 denotes class 2 (a transferase), subclass 7 (transfer of phosphate), subsubclass 1 (an alcohol functions as the phosphate acceptor). The final digit denotes the enzyme, hexokinase, or

ATP:D-hexose 6-phosphotransferase, an enzyme catalyzing phosphate transfer from ATP to the hydroxyl group on carbon 6 of glucose.

The 6 classes of enzymes with some illustrative examples are given below. The name in brackets is the trivial (ie, common) name.

1. Oxidoreductases. Enzymes catalyzing oxidoreductions between 2 substrates, S and S'.

$$S_{reduced} + S'_{oxidized} = S_{oxidized} + S'_{reduced}$$

Enzymes catalyzing oxidoreductions of CH–OH, CH–CH, C=O, CH–NH$_2$, and CH=NH groups. Representative subclasses:

1.1 Enzymes acting on the CH–OH group as electron donor. *For example:*
    1.1.1.1 Alcohol:NAD oxidoreductase [alcohol dehydrogenase].

$$Alcohol + NAD^+ = Aldehyde\ or\ ketone + NADH + H^+$$

1.4 Enzymes acting on the CH–NH$_2$ group as electron donor. *For example:*
    1.4.1.3 L-Glutamate:NAD(P) oxidoreductase (deaminating) [glutamic dehydrogenase of animal liver]. NAD(P) means that either NAD$^+$ or NADP$^+$ acts as the electron acceptor.

$$L\text{-Glutamate} + H_2O + NAD(P)^+ =$$
$$\alpha\text{-Ketoglutarate} + NH_4^+ + NAD(P)H + H^+$$

1.11 Enzymes acting on H$_2$O$_2$ as electron acceptor. *For example:*
    1.11.1.6 H$_2$O$_2$:H$_2$O$_2$ oxidoreductase [catalase].

$$H_2O_2 + H_2O_2 = O_2 + 2H_2O$$

2. Transferases. Enzymes catalyzing a transfer of a group, G (other than hydrogen), between a pair of substrates S and S'.

$$S\text{-}G + S' = S'\text{-}G + S$$

Enzymes catalyzing the transfer of one-carbon groups, aldehyde or ketone residues, and acyl, alkyl, glycosyl and phosphorus- or sulfur-containing groups. Representative subclasses:

2.3 Acyltransferases. *For example:*
    2.3.1.6 Acetyl-CoA:choline O-acetyltransferase [choline acyltransferase].

$$Acetyl\text{-}CoA + Choline = CoA + O\text{-}Acetylcholine$$

2.7 Enzymes catalyzing transfer of phosphorus-containing groups. *For example:*
    2.7.1.1 ATP:D-hexose 6-phosphotransferase [hexokinase].

$$ATP + D\text{-Hexose} = ADP + D\text{-Hexose 6-phosphate}$$

3. Hydrolases. Enzymes catalyzing hydrolysis of ester, ether, peptide, glycosyl, acid-anhydride, C–C, C-halide, or P–N bonds. *For example:*

3.1 Enzymes acting on ester bonds. *For example:*
    3.1.1.8 Acylcholine acyl-hydrolase [pseudocholinesterase].

$$An\ acylcholine + H_2O = Choline + An\ acid$$

3.2 Enzymes acting on glycosyl compounds. *For example:*
    3.2.1.23 β-D-Galactoside galactohydrolase [β-galactosidase].

$$A\ \beta\text{-D-Galactoside} + H_2O = An\ alcohol + D\text{-Galactose}$$

3.4 Enzymes acting on peptide bonds. Classification (11 subclasses) distinguishes peptidases from proteases, whether dipeptides or longer peptides are substrates, whether one or more amino acids are removed, and whether attack is from the C- or the N-terminal end. Proteinases are further distinguished by their catalytic mechanism as serine, –SH, or metalloenzyme proteinases.

3.4.21 Serine proteinases. *For example:* Chymotrypsin, trypsin, plasmin, coagulation factors IXa and XIa.

3.4.23 Carboxyl (acid) proteinases. *For example:* Pepsin A, B, and C.

4. Lyases. Enzymes that catalyze removal of groups from substrates by mechanisms other than hydrolysis, leaving double bonds.

$$\begin{array}{cc} X & Y \\ | & | \\ \end{array}$$
$$C\text{-}C = X\text{-}Y + C\text{=}C$$

Enzymes acting on C–C, C–O, C–N, C–S, and C-halide bonds. Representative subgroups:

4.1.2 Aldehyde-lyases. *For example:*
    4.1.2.7 Ketose 1-phosphate aldehyde-lyase [aldolase].

$$A\ ketose\ 1\text{-phosphate} = Dihydroxyacetone\ phosphate$$
$$+ An\ aldehyde$$

4.2 Carbon-oxygen lyases. *For example:*
    4.2.1.2 L-Malate hydro-lyase [fumarase].

$$L\text{-Malate} = Fumarate + H_2O$$

5. Isomerases. Includes all enzymes catalyzing interconversion of optical, geometric, or positional isomers. Two subclasses:

5.2 *Cis-trans* isomerases. *For example:*
    5.2.1.3 All-*trans*-retinene 11-*cis-trans* isomerase [retinene isomerase].

$$All\ trans\text{-retinene} = 11\text{-}cis\text{-retinene}$$

5.3 Enzymes catalyzing interconversion of aldoses and ketoses. *For example:*
    5.3.1.1 D-Glyceraldehyde 3-phosphate ketolisomerase [triosephosphate isomerase].

$$D\text{-Glyceraldehyde 3-phosphate} = Dihydroxyacetone\ phosphate$$

6. Ligases. (*Ligare* = "to bind.") Enzymes catalyzing the linking together of 2 compounds coupled to the breaking of a pyrophosphate bond in ATP or a similar compound. Included are enzymes catalyzing reactions forming C–O, C–S, C–N, and C–C bonds. Representative subclasses are:

6.3 Enzymes catalyzing formation of C–N bonds. *For example:*
    6.3.1.2 L-Glutamate:ammonia ligase (ADP) [glutamine synthase].

$$ATP + L\text{-Glutamate} + NH_4^+ =$$
$$ADP + Orthophosphate + L\text{-Glutamine}$$

6.4 Enzymes catalyzing formation of C–C bonds. *For example:*
    6.4.1.2 Acetyl-CoA:CO$_2$ ligase (ADP) [acetyl-CoA carboxylase].

$$ATP + Acetyl\text{-}CoA + CO_2 = ADP + P_i + Malonyl\text{-}CoA$$

COENZYMES

Many enzymes catalyze reactions of their substrates only in the presence of a specific heat-stable, low-molecular-weight organic molecule, a coenzyme. Where coenzymes are required, the complete catalytic entity or **holoenzyme** consists of the protein part or **apoenzyme** plus bound **coenzyme**. A particular coenzyme may bind covalently or noncovalently to the apoenzyme. The term "prosthetic group" was formerly employed to denote covalently bonded coenzymes. Reactions that require coenzymes include oxidoreductions, group transfer and isomerization reactions, and reactions that form covalent bonds (classes 1, 2, 5, and 6; see above). Lytic reactions, including hydrolytic reactions such as those catalyzed by digestive enzymes, do not require coenzymes (classes 3 and 4; see above).

Second Substrates

It is often helpful to regard the coenzyme as a second substrate or **cosubstrate** for 2 reasons. First, **the chemical changes in the coenzyme exactly counterbalance those taking place in the substrate.** For example, in oxidoreduction (dehydrogenase) reactions, one molecule of substrate is oxidized (dehydrogenated) and one molecule of coenzyme is reduced (hydrogenated) (Fig 6–1).

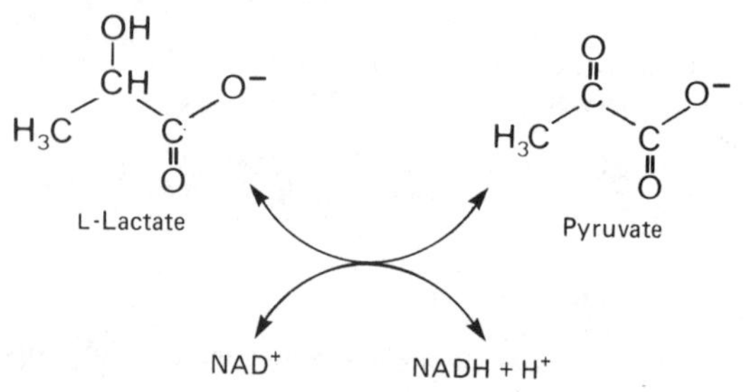

Figure 6–1. NAD^+ acting as cosubstrate in an oxidoreduction reaction.

Similarly, in transamination reactions pyridoxal phosphate acts as a second substrate in 2 concerted reactions and as carrier for transfer of an amino group between different α-keto acids. (See Chapter 10.)

Role of Second Substrates

A second reason to give equal emphasis to the reactions of the coenzyme is that this aspect of the reaction may actually be of greater fundamental physiologic significance. For example, the importance of the ability of muscle working anaerobically to convert pyruvate to lactate does not reside in pyruvate or lactate themselves. The reaction serves merely to convert NADH to NAD^+. Without NAD^+, glycolysis cannot continue and anaerobic ATP synthesis (and hence work) ceases (see Chapter 15). Under anaerobic

Table 6–1. Mechanisms for anaerobic regeneration of NAD^+.

Oxidant	Reduced Product	Life Form
Pyruvate	Lactate	Muscle, homolactic bacteria
Acetaldehyde	Ethanol	Yeast
Dihydroxyacetone phosphate	α-Glycerophosphate	*E coli*
Fructose	Mannitol	Heterolactic bacteria

conditions, reduction of pyruvate to lactate reoxidizes NADH and permits synthesis of ATP. Other reactions can serve this function equally well. This point can best be appreciated by consideration of life forms other than animals. In bacteria or yeast growing anaerobically, substances derived from pyruvate serve as oxidants for NADH and are themselves reduced (Table 6–1).

Role of Coenzymes as Group Transfer Reagents in Intermediary Metabolism

Biochemical group transfer reactions of the type

$$D-G + A \rightleftharpoons A-G + D$$

in which a functional group, G, is transferred from a donor molecule, D–G, to an acceptor molecule, A, usually involve participation of a coenzyme either as the ultimate acceptor (eg, dehydrogenation reactions) or as an intermediate group carrier (eg, transamination reactions). The reaction

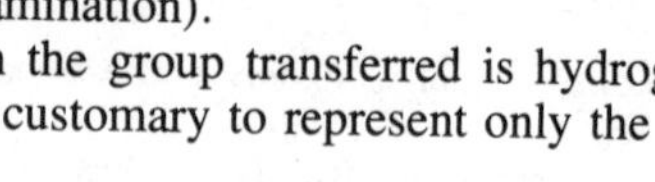

illustrates the latter concept. While this suggests formation of a single CoE–G complex during the course of the overall reaction, several intermediate CoE–G complexes may be involved in a particular reaction (eg, transamination).

When the group transferred is hydrogen, however, it is customary to represent only the left "half reaction":

That this actually represents only a special case of general group transfer can best be appreciated in terms of the reactions that occur in intact cells (Table 6–1). These can be represented as follows:

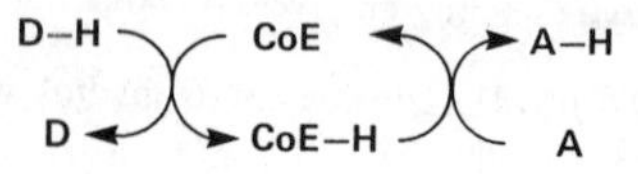

Based on this concept, we might classify coenzymes as follows:

For transfer of groups other than H
    Sugar phosphates
    CoA·SH
    Thiamin pyrophosphate
    Pyridoxal phosphate
    Folate coenzymes
    Biotin
    Cobamide (B_{12}) coenzymes
    Lipoic acid
For transfer of H
    NAD^+, $NADP^+$
    FMN, FAD
    Lipoic acid
    Coenzyme Q

Coenzymes As B-Vitamin Derivatives

B vitamins form part of the structure of many coenzymes, as described in Chapter 10. For example, many enzymes of amino acid metabolism require vitamin B_6. The B vitamins **nicotinamide, thiamin, riboflavin,** and **pantothenic acid** are essential constituents of coenzymes for biologic oxidations and reductions, and **folic acid** and **cobamide** coenzymes function in one-carbon metabolism.

A structural feature common to many coenzymes is an adenine ring joined to D-ribose and inorganic phosphate. Many coenzymes may therefore be regarded as derivatives of adenosine monophosphate (AMP) (Table 6–2).

THREE-POINT ATTACHMENT

Most substrates form at least 3 bonds with enzymes. This **"3-point attachment"** can confer asymmetry on an otherwise symmetric molecule. To explain how this occurs, we shall represent the region of an enzyme that binds a substrate as a planar surface, although as we shall shortly see, the substrate-binding sites of enzymes are rarely, if ever, planar. Fig 6–2 shows a substrate molecule, represented as a carbon atom having 3 different groups, about to attach at 3 points to a planar enzyme site. If the site can be approached only from one side and only complementary atoms and sites can interact (both valid assumptions for actual enzymes), the molecule can bind in only one way. The reaction itself may be confined to the atoms bound at sites 1 and 2 even though atoms 1 and 3 are identical. By mentally turning the substrate molecule in space, note that it can attach at 3 points to one side of the planar site with only one orientation. Consequently, atoms 1 and 3, although identical, become distinct when the substrate is attached to the enzyme. A chemical change thus can involve atom 1 (but not atom 3), or vice versa. Extension of this line of reasoning can explain why the enzyme-catalyzed reduction of the optically inactive pyruvate molecule results in formation of L- and not D,L-lactate.

Table 6–2. Many coenzymes and related compounds are derivatives of adenosine monophosphate.

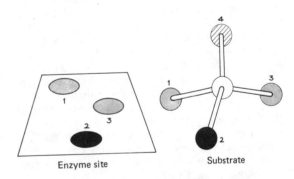

Figure 6–2. Representation of 3-point attachment of a substrate to a planar active site of an enzyme.

Coenzyme	R	R'	R''	n
Active methionine	Methionine*	H	H	0
Amino acid adenylates	Amino acid	H	H	1
Active sulfate	SO_3H_2	H	PO_3H	1
3',5'-Cyclic AMP	H	H	PO_3H	
NAD^+	†	H	H	2
$NADP^+$	†	PO_3H	H	2
FAD	†	H	H	2
CoA—SH	†	H	PO_3H	2

*Replaces phosphate group.
†See Chapters 10 and 12.

ENZYME SPECIFICITY

The ability of an enzyme to catalyze one specific reaction and essentially no others is perhaps its most significant property. The rates of specific metabolic processes may thus be regulated by changes in the catalytic efficiency of specific enzymes (see Chapter 9). However, most enzymes catalyze the same type of reaction (phosphate transfer, oxidation-reduction, etc) with a small number of structurally related substrates. Reactions with alternative substrates tend to take place if these are present in high concentration.

Whether all of the possible reactions will occur in living organisms depends on the relative concentration of alternative substrates in the cell and the relative affinities of the enzyme for those substrates. Some general aspects of enzyme specificity are given below.

Optical Specificity

With the exception of epimerases (racemases), which catalyze interconversion of optical isomers, **enzymes generally show absolute optical specificity for at least a portion of a substrate molecule.** Thus, maltase catalyzes the hydrolysis of α- but not β-glycosides, while enzymes of the glycolytic and direct oxidative pathways catalyze the interconversion of D- but not L-phosphosugars. With a few exceptions, such as the D-amino acid oxidase of kidney, the vast majority of mammalian enzymes act on the L-isomers of amino acids.

Optical specificity may extend to a portion of the substrate molecule or to its entirety. Glycosidases illustrate both extremes. These catalyze hydrolysis of glycosidic bonds between sugars and alcohols, are highly specific for the sugar portion and for the linkage (α or β), but are relatively nonspecific for the aglycone (or alcohol portion).

Group Specificity

Lytic enzymes act on specific chemical groupings, eg, glycosidases on glycosides, pepsin and trypsin on peptide bonds, and esterases on esters. A large number of substrates may be attacked, thus lessening the number of digestive enzymes that might otherwise be required. Many proteases catalyze hydrolysis of esters also. While the ability of proteases to hydrolyze esters is probably of limited physiologic importance, the use of esters as synthetic substrates has been central to the study of the mechanism of action of proteases.

Certain lytic enzymes exhibit a higher order of group specificity. Chymotrypsin preferentially hydrolyzes peptide bonds in which the carboxyl group is contributed by the aromatic amino acids phenylalanine, tyrosine, or tryptophan. Carboxypeptidases and aminopeptidases split off amino acids one at a time from the carboxy- or amino-terminal end of polypeptide chains, respectively.

Although some oxidoreductases utilize either NAD^+ or $NADP^+$ as electron acceptor, most use exclusively one or the other. As a broad generalization, **oxidoreductases functional in biosynthetic processes in mammalian systems (eg, fatty acid or sterol synthesis) tend to use NADPH as reductant, while those functional in degradative processes (eg, glycolysis, fatty acid oxidation) tend to use NAD^+ as oxidant.** Occasionally, a tissue may possess 2 oxidoreductases that differ only in their coenzyme specificity (eg, the NAD^+- and $NADP^+$-specific isocitrate dehydrogenases of rat mitochondria; Table 6-3). In liver, about 90% of the $NADP^+$-specific enzyme occurs extramitochondrially. This may be concerned with biosynthetic processes. The NAD^+-specific enzyme of mitochondria is specifically acti-

Table 6-3. Distribution of NAD^+- and $NADP^+$-specific isocitrate dehydrogenases in mitochondria of rat tissue.*

Organ	Specific Activity (μmol/min/mg) of	
	NAD^+-Specific Enzyme	$NADP^+$-Specific Enzyme
Skeletal muscle	0.84	0.78
Heart	0.57	2.22
Kidney	0.28	1.20
Brain	0.25	0.054
Liver	0.16	0.33

*From Lowenstein JM: The tricarboxylic acid cycle. Page 168 in: *Metabolic Pathways.* Vol 1. Greenberg DM (editor). Academic Press, 1967.

vated by ADP, and since ADP levels rise during depletion of ATP stores, this suggests a degradative role for the NAD^+-specific isocitrate dehydrogenase of mitochondria. High ADP (low ATP) levels would promote carbon flow through the citric acid cycle by activating the NAD^+-specific mitochondrial enzyme.

QUANTITATIVE MEASUREMENT OF ENZYME ACTIVITY

The extremely small quantities of enzymes present in cells introduce problems in determining the amount of an enzyme in tissue extracts or fluids quite different from those of determining the concentration of more abundant organic or inorganic substances. Fortunately, **the catalytic activity of an enzyme provides a sensitive and specific device for its own measurement.** To measure the amount of an enzyme in a sample of tissue extract or other biologic fluid, the **rate of the reaction** catalyzed by the enzyme in the sample is measured. Under appropriate conditions, **the measured rate is proportionate to the quantity of enzyme present.** Where possible, this rate is compared with the rate catalyzed by a known quantity of the highly purified enzyme. Provided that both are assayed under conditions where the enzyme concentration is rate-limiting (high substrate and low product concentration, favorable pH and temperature), the quantity of enzyme in the extract may be calculated. However, it is not easy to determine the number of molecules or mass of enzyme present. Results are therefore expressed in **enzyme units.** Relative amounts of enzyme in different extracts may then be compared. Enzyme units are best expressed in micromoles (μmol; 10^{-6} mol), nanomoles (nmol; 10^{-9} mol), or picomoles (pmol; 10^{-12} mol) of substrate reacting or product produced per minute. The corresponding International Enzyme Units are μU, nU, and pU.

Example of Quantitative Analysis of Enzyme Activity: Assay of a Dehydrogenase

In reactions involving NAD^+ or $NADP^+$ (dehy-

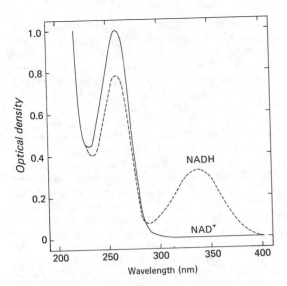

Figure 6–3. Absorption spectra of NAD⁺ and NADH. Densities are for a 44 mg/L solution in a cell of 1-cm light path. NADP⁺ and NADPH have spectra analogous to those of NAD⁺ and NADH, respectively.

drogenases), advantage is taken of the property of NADH or NADPH (but not NAD⁺ or NADP⁺) to absorb light at a wavelength of 340 nm (Fig 6–3).

When NADH is oxidized to NAD⁺ (or vice versa), the optical density (OD) at 340 nm changes. Under specified conditions, the rate of change in OD depends directly on the enzyme activity (Fig 6–4).

A calibration curve (Fig 6–5) is prepared by plot-

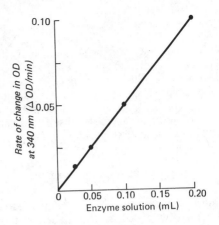

Figure 6–5. Calibration curve for enzymic analysis. The slopes of the lines in Fig 6–4 are plotted versus the quantity of enzyme.

ting the slopes of the lines (velocities) in Fig 6–4 versus the volume of enzyme preparation added. The quantity of enzyme present in an unknown solution may then be calculated from the observed rate of change in OD at 340 nm. If the catalytic activity of a known mass quantity of purified enzyme (assayed under the same conditions) is known, one may then calculate the mass quantity of enzyme present in the unknown solution.

Coupled Enzymic Analyses

In the above example, the rate of formation of a product (NADH) was measured to determine enzyme activity. The activity of enzymes other than dehydrogenases is also determined by measuring the rate of appearance of a product (or, less commonly, the rate of

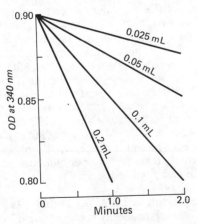

Figure 6–4. Assay of an NADH- or NADPH-dependent dehydrogenase. The rate of change in OD at 340 nm due to conversion of reduced to oxidized coenzyme is observed. Oxidized substrate (S) and reduced coenzyme (NADH) plus buffer are added to a cuvette, and light of 340-nm wavelength is passed through it. Initially, the OD is high, since NADH (or NADPH) absorbs at 340 nm. On addition of 0.025–0.2 mL of a standard enzyme solution, the OD decreases.

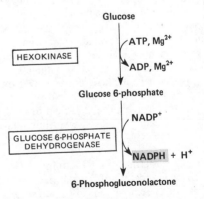

Figure 6–6. Coupled assay for hexokinase activity. The reaction is coupled to that catalyzed by glucose 6-phosphate dehydrogenase. Glucose 6-phosphate dehydrogenase, glucose, ATP, Mg²⁺, and NADP⁺ all are added in excess. The quantity of hexokinase present then determines the rate of the overall coupled reaction and therefore the rate of formation of NADPH, which can be measured directly by increase in absorption at 340 nm.

disappearance of a substrate). The chemical and physical properties of the product or substrate determine the specific method selected for quantitation. It often is convenient to "couple" the product of a reaction to a dehydrogenase for which this product is a substrate. When the dehydrogenase is present in excess, the rate of appearance or disappearance of NAD(P)H may then be used to quantify an enzyme that itself does not use NAD(P)H as a substrate (Fig 6–6).

ISOLATION OF ENZYMES

Knowledge concerning the individual reactions of and chemical intermediates in metabolic pathways and of the regulatory mechanisms that operate at the level of catalysis are derived to a great extent from studies of purified enzymes. Indeed, those areas of metabolism where the enzymes involved have not been purified are exactly those where information is fragmentary and controversial. Reliable information concerning the kinetics, cofactors, active sites, structure, and mechanism of action also requires highly purified enzymes.

The objective of enzyme purification is to isolate a specific enzyme protein from a crude extract of whole cells containing many other components. Small molecules may be removed by dialysis or gel filtration, nucleic acids by precipitation with the antibiotic streptomycin, etc. The problem is to separate the desired enzyme from a mixture of hundreds of chemically and physically similar proteins.

Useful classic purification procedures include precipitation with varying salt concentrations (generally ammonium or sodium sulfate) or solvents (acetone or ethanol), differential heat or pH denaturation, differential centrifugation, gel filtration, and electrophoresis. Selective adsorption and elution of proteins from the cellulose anion exchanger diethylaminoethylcellulose and the cation exchanger carboxymethylcellulose have also been extremely successful for extensive and rapid purification. Separation of proteins on molecular sieves such as Sephadex that segregate proteins on the basis of their size is also widely used. These methods are, however, relatively unselective in the sense that they do not, except in combination, resolve a single protein from all others. This is more readily achieved by affinity chromatography.

Affinity Chromatographic Techniques

The salient feature of this purification technique is its ability to remove selectively from a complex protein mixture one particular protein or, at most, a small number of particular proteins. The basis of the technique is to construct an immobilized ligand that interacts specifically with the enzyme whose purification is desired. When the protein mixture is exposed to this immobilized ligand, the only proteins that bind are those which interact strongly with the ligand. Following removal of the unwanted protein, the desired protein is specifically eluted from the immobilized ligand, generally by competing it off by elution with a high concentration of the soluble form of the ligand. When successful, the purifications achieved by affinity chromatographic techniques are extremely impressive, often surpassing that possible by successive application of numerous classic techniques.

Since enzymes exhibit generally high specificity with respect to their substrates and their coenzymes, the most favored ligands are the substrate and coenzyme of the enzyme. These are covalently attached to a generally inert support such as Sephadex. Attachment may be direct or via a linker molecule about 3–8 carbon atoms in length. Difficulties may arise if the mode of ligand attachment precludes its ability to interact with the enzyme—a difficulty that linker molecules may help to circumvent. Examples of the successful application of affinity chromatographic techniques include purification of many different dehydrogenases on NAD$^+$ affinity supports. While many dehydrogenases may be bound and may be eluted together when the column is treated with soluble NAD$^+$, subsequent application of substrate (rather than coenzyme) affinity supports has been successful in many instances.

Dye ligand chromatography on supports such as blue-, green-, or red-Sepharose and hydrophobic ligand chromatography on supports such as octyl- or phenyl-Sepharose are 2 additional techniques closely related to affinity chromatography. The former employs as the immobilized ligand an organic dye that serves as an analog of a substrate, coenzyme, or allosteric effector. Elution generally is achieved using salt gradients.

In hydrophobic ligand chromatography, an alkyl chain, generally 4–8 carbons in length, is attached to a support such as Sephadex. Retention of proteins on these supports involves hydrophobic interactions between the alkyl chain and hydrophobic regions on the protein. Proteins are applied in solutions that contain a high concentration of a salt (eg, [NH$_4$]$_2$SO$_4$) and are eluted with *decreasing* gradients of the same salt.

The progress of a typical classic enzyme purification for a liver enzyme with good recovery and 490-fold overall purification is shown in Table 6–4. Note how specific activity and recovery of initial activity are calculated. The aim is to achieve the maximum specific activity (enzyme units per milligram of protein) with the best possible recovery of initial activity.

Polyacrylamide Gel (PAGE) Techniques

Protein homogeneity is best assessed by polyacrylamide gel electrophoresis (PAGE) under several sets of conditions. One-dimensional PAGE samples of the native protein will, if sufficient sample is applied, reveal the presence of major and minor protein contaminants. In 2-dimensional (O'Farrell) PAGE, the first dimension separates denatured proteins on the basis of their pI values by equilibrating them in an electrical field that contains urea and a pH gradient maintained by polymerized ampholytes. The second dimension

Table 6–4. Summary of a typical enzyme purification scheme.

Enzyme Fraction	Total Activity (pU)	Total Protein (mg)	Specific Activity (pU/mg)	Overall Recovery (%)
Crude liver homogenate	100,000	10,000	10	(100)
100,000 X g supernatant liquid	98,000	8,000	12.2	98
40–50% $(NH_4)_2SO_4$ precipitate	90,000	1,500	60	90
20–35% acetone precipitate	60,000	250	240	60
DEAE column fractions 80–110	58,000	29	2,000	58
43–48% $(NH_4)_2SO_4$ precipitate	52,000	20	2,600	52
First crystals	50,000	12	4,160	50
Recrystallization	49,000	10	4,900	49

then separates proteins, after denaturation with SDS, on the basis of the molecular sizes of their protomer units (if present).

INTRACELLULAR DISTRIBUTION OF ENZYMES

The naive concept of the cell as a "sack of enzymes" has yielded to recognition of the cardinal significance of spatial arrangement and compartmentalization of enzymes, substrates, and cofactors within the cell. In liver cells, for example, the enzymes of glycolysis are located in the cytoplasm, whereas enzymes of the citric acid cycle are in the mitochondria.

The distribution of enzymes among subcellular organelles may be studied following fractionation of cell homogenates by high-speed centrifugation. The enzyme content of each fraction is then examined.

Localization of a particular enzyme in a tissue or cell in a relatively unaltered state may frequently be accomplished by histochemical procedures ("histoenzymology"). Thin (2–10 μm) frozen sections of tissue, prepared with a low-temperature microtome, are treated with a substrate for a particular enzyme. In regions where the enzyme is present, the product of the enzyme-catalyzed reaction is formed. If the product is colored and insoluble, it remains at the site of formation and serves as a marker for the localization of the enzyme. Histoenzymology provides a graphic and relatively physiologic picture of patterns of enzyme distribution. Histochemical techniques are available for acid and alkaline phosphatases, monoamine oxidase, and many dehydrogenases.

ISOZYMES

While terms such as "malate dehydrogenase" or "glucose 6-phosphatase" may appear to describe a single catalytic entity, they are in fact generic terms that encompass all proteins which catalyze either the oxidation of malate to oxaloacetate or, in the latter instance, the hydrolysis of glucose 6-phosphate to glucose and P_i. When techniques for purification of enzymes were applied to, for example, malate dehydrogenase from different sources (eg, rat liver and *Esche-*

richia coli) in the 1930s, it soon became apparent that while rat liver and *E coli* malate dehydrogenase both catalyze the same reaction, the physical and chemical properties of the proteins concerned exhibited many significant differences. It was not until the late 1950s, however, that it became generally accepted that physically distinct forms of the same catalytic activity may be present in different tissues of the same organism, in different cell types within a tissue, or even within a prokaryotic organism such as *E coli*. This discovery followed from the application of electrophoretic separation procedures, previously exploited to reveal electrophoretically distinct forms of hemoglobin, to separation of electrophoretically distinct forms of a particular enzymic activity.

In a fundamental context, the term "isozyme" (isoenzyme) might be used to encompass all the above examples of physically distinct forms of a given catalytic activity. In practice, and particularly in clinical medicine, "isozyme" has a more restricted meaning, namely, the physically distinct and separable forms of a given enzyme present in different cell types of a specific eukaryote such as the human being. Isozymes are common in sera and tissues of all vertebrates, insects, plants, and unicellular organisms. Both the kind and the number of enzymes involved are equally diverse. Isozymes of numerous dehydrogenases, oxidases, transaminases, phosphatases, transphosphorylases, and proteolytic enzymes have been reported.

Diagnostic Significance of Isozymes

Medical interest in isozymes was stimulated by the discovery in 1957 that **human sera contained several lactate dehydrogenase isozymes and that their relative proportions changed significantly in certain pathologic conditions.** Subsequently, many additional examples of changes in isozyme proportions as a result of disease have been described (see below). For example, serum lactate dehydrogenase isozymes may be visualized by subjecting a serum sample to electrophoresis, usually at pH 8.6, on a starch, agar, or polyacrylamide gel support. The isozymes have different charges at this pH and migrate to 5 distinct regions of the electropherogram. Isozymes are then localized by means of their ability to catalyze reduction of a colorless dye to an insoluble, colored form.

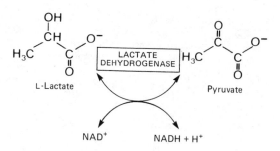

Figure 6–7. The L-lactate dehydrogenase reaction.

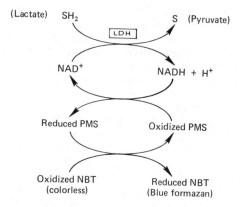

Figure 6–8. Coupled reactions in detection of lactate dehydrogenase activity on an electropherogram.

A typical dehydrogenase isoenzyme reagent contains the following:

(1) Reduced substrate (eg, lactate).

(2) Coenzyme (NAD^+).

(3) Oxidized dye (eg, nitroblue tetrazolium salt [NBT]).

(4) An intermediate electron carrier to transport electrons between NADH and the dye (eg, phenazine methosulfate [PMS]).

(5) Buffer; activating ions if required.

Lactate dehydrogenase catalyzes transfer of 2 electrons and one H^+ from lactate to NAD^+ (Fig 6–7). The reaction proceeds at a measurable rate only in the presence of lactate dehydrogenase. When the assay mixture is spread on the electropherogram and incubated at 37 °C, concerted electron transfer reactions take place only in those regions where lactate dehydrogenase is present (Fig 6–8). The colored bands are visible to the naked eye, and their relative intensities may be quantitated by a suitable scanning photometer (Fig 6–9). The most negative isoenzyme, as detected in an electropherogram, is I_1.

Physical Basis for Isozymes

Oligomeric enzymes with dissimilar protomers can exist in several forms. Frequently, one tissue produces one protomer predominantly and another tissue a different protomer. If these can combine in various ways to construct an active enzyme (eg, a tetramer), **isozymes** of that enzymic activity are said to be formed.

Lactate dehydrogenase isozymes differ at the

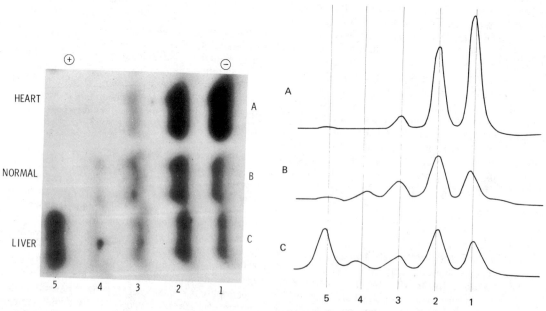

Figure 6–9. Normal and pathologic patterns of lactate dehydrogenase (LDH) isozymes in human serum. LDH isozymes of serum were separated on cellulose acetate at pH 8.6 and stained for enzyme. The photometer scan shows the relative proportion of the isozymes. Pattern A is serum from a patient with a myocardial infarct, B is normal serum, and C is serum from a patient with liver disease. (Courtesy of Dr Melvin Black and Mr Hugh Miller, St Luke's Hospital, San Francisco.)

level of quaternary structure. The oligomeric lactate dehydrogenase molecule (MW 130,000) consists of 4 protomers of 2 types, H and M (MW about 34,000). Only the tetrameric molecule possesses catalytic activity. If order is unimportant, these protomers might be combined in the following 5 ways:

HHHH
HHHM
HHMM
HMMM
MMMM

Markert used conditions known to disrupt and re-form quaternary structure to clarify the relationships between the lactate dehydrogenase isozymes. Splitting and reconstitution of lactate dehydrogenase-I_1 or lactate dehydrogenase-I_5 produces no new isozymes. These therefore consist of a single type of protomer. When a mixture of lactate dehydrogenase-I_1 and lactate dehydrogenase-I_5 is subjected to the same treatment, lactate dehydrogenase-I_2, -I_3, and -I_4 are generated. The proportions of the isozymes found are those which would result if the relationship were:

Lactate Dehydrogenase Isozyme	Subunits
I_1	HHHH
I_2	HHHM
I_3	HHMM
I_4	HMMM
I_5	MMMM

Syntheses of H and M subunits are controlled by distinct genetic loci that are differentially expressed in different tissues, eg, the heart and skeletal muscle.

ENZYMES IN CLINICAL DIAGNOSIS

Distinction Between Functional & Nonfunctional Plasma Enzymes

Certain enzymes and proenzymes are present at all times in the circulation of normal individuals. Their substrates also are present in the circulation either continuously or intermittently, and they perform a physiologic function in blood. Examples of **functional plasma enzymes** include lipoprotein lipase, pseudocholinesterase, and the proenzymes of blood coagulation and of blood clot dissolution. They generally are synthesized in the liver but are present in blood in equivalent or higher concentrations than in tissues.

As the name implies, **nonfunctional plasma enzymes** perform no known physiologic function in blood. Their substrates frequently are absent from plasma, and the enzymes themselves are present in the blood of normal individuals at levels up to a millionfold lower than in tissues. Their presence in plasma at levels elevated above normal values suggests an in-

creased rate of tissue destruction. Measurement of these nonfunctional plasma enzyme levels can thus provide the physician with valuable diagnostic and prognostic clinical evidence.

Nonfunctional plasma enzymes include those present in exocrine secretions and true intracellular enzymes. Exocrine enzymes—pancreatic amylase, lipase, bile alkaline phosphatase, and prostatic acid phosphatase—diffuse passively into the plasma. The true intracellular enzymes are normally absent from the circulation.

Origin of Nonfunctional Plasma Enzymes

Low levels of nonfunctional enzymes found ordinarily in plasma arise apparently from the routine, normal destruction of erythrocytes, leukocytes, and other cells. With accelerated cell death, soluble enzymes enter the circulation. Although elevated plasma enzyme levels are generally interpreted as evidence of cellular necrosis, vigorous exercise also results in release of significant quantities of muscle enzymes.

Diagnostic & Prognostic Value of Specific Enzymes

The present generation of practicing physicians has long made use of the clinical laboratory for quantitation of the levels of certain nonfunctional plasma enzymes. Plasma enzyme analyses, which provide valuable diagnostic and prognostic information, are in most instances performed on fully automated equipment.

The determination of the activity of the following enzymes can provide the physician with valuable diagnostic evidence.

A. Lipase: The plasma lipase level may be low in liver disease, vitamin A deficiency, some malignancies, and diabetes mellitus. It may be elevated in acute pancreatitis and pancreatic carcinoma.

B. Amylase: The plasma amylase level may be low in liver disease and increased in high intestinal obstruction, parotitis, acute pancreatitis, and diabetes.

C. Trypsin: Elevated levels of trypsin in plasma occur during acute pancreatic disease. Elevation of plasma trypsin is probably a more sensitive and reliable indicator of pancreatic disease than plasma amylase or lipase.

D. Cholinesterase: In general, low levels are found in patients ill with liver disease, malnutrition, chronic debilitating and acute infectious diseases, and anemias. High levels occur in nephrotic syndrome. Many drugs produce a temporary decrease in cholinesterase activity, but the alkyl fluorophosphates irreversibly inhibit the enzyme. Some insecticides depress cholinesterase activity, and tests for the activity of this enzyme in the plasma may be useful in detecting overexposure to these agents.

Since the content of cholinesterase in young red blood cells is considerably higher than in the adult red blood cells, the cholinesterase titer of erythrocytes in peripheral blood gives an indication of hematopoietic activity.

E. Alkaline Phosphatase: The level of enzymes capable of catalyzing the hydrolysis of various phosphate esters at alkaline pH (alkaline phosphatase activity) may be increased in rickets, hyperparathyroidism, Paget's disease, osteoblastic sarcoma, obstructive jaundice, and metastatic carcinoma.

Isozymes of alkaline phosphatase are present in body fluids. These include specific isozymes originating from bone, liver, placenta, and intestine. Measurement of specific alkaline phosphatase isozymes may therefore improve the diagnostic value of this test. Alkaline phosphatase isozyme measurements can distinguish liver lesions from bone lesions in cases of metastatic carcinoma.

F. Acid Phosphatase: The level of enzymes capable of catalyzing the hydrolysis of various phosphate esters at acidic pH (acid phosphatase activity) may be elevated in metastatic prostatic carcinoma.

G. Transaminases: Two transaminases are of clinical interest. **Glutamic oxaloacetic transaminase (GOT)** catalyzes the transfer of the amino group of aspartic acid to α-ketoglutaric acid, forming glutamic and oxaloacetic acids; **glutamic pyruvic transaminase (GPT)** transfers the amino group of alanine to α-ketoglutaric acid, forming glutamic and pyruvic acids. Serum transaminase levels in normal subjects are low, but after extensive tissue destruction these enzymes are liberated into the serum. An example is heart muscle, which is rich in transaminases. Consequently, myocardial infarcts are followed by rapid and striking increases in serum transaminase levels. Values decrease toward normal within a few days. Estimation of glutamic oxaloacetic transaminase is widely used to confirm a diagnosis of myocardial infarction.

Liver tissue, rich in both transaminases, contains more GPT than GOT. While both transaminases are elevated in sera of patients with acute hepatic disease, GPT, which is only slightly elevated by cardiac necrosis, is a more specific indicator of liver damage.

Extensive skeletal muscle damage, as in severe trauma, also elevates serum transaminase levels.

H. Lactate Dehydrogenase: In myocardial infarction, the concentration of serum lactate dehydrogenase (LDH) rises within 24 hours after the infarct and returns to the normal range within 5–6 days. High levels of LDH also occur in patients with acute and chronic leukemia in relapse, with generalized carcinomatosis, and, occasionally, with acute hepatitis during its clinical peak, but not in patients with jaundice due to other causes. Serum LDH is normal in patients with acute febrile and chronic infectious diseases as well as those with anemia, pulmonary infarction, localized neoplastic disease, and chronic disease processes.

I. LDH Isozymes: Cardiac muscle contains a preponderance of LDH-I_1. Measurement of the serum isozyme pattern (Fig 6–9) following myocardial infarction is a more sensitive and lasting indication of myocardial necrosis than is simple measurement of the total serum or plasma LDH activity.

J. Isocitrate Dehydrogenase: Measurement of serum **isocitrate dehydrogenase** (ICD) activity is useful in diagnosis of liver disease. The ICD level of cerebrospinal fluid is also elevated in patients with cerebral tumors or meningitis of various types. With tumors, the values are about 10 times normal. With meningitis, the values may be as much as 50 times normal but gradually decrease to normal as the patient recovers.

K. Creatine Phosphokinase: Measurement of serum creatine phosphokinase (CK or CPK) activity is of value in the diagnosis of disorders affecting skeletal and cardiac muscle as well as in studies of families affected with muscular dystrophy. Nonmuscular tissues other than brain do not contain high levels of creatine phosphokinase, so determinations of activity of this enzyme should be more specific to particular tissues than the transaminases or dehydrogenases that are more widely distributed. In human tissue, creatine phosphokinase exists as 3 different dimeric isozymes composed of M (for muscle) and B (for brain) protomers. These are designated CPK_1 (BB), CPK_2 (MB), and CPK_3 (MM). While measurement of creatine phosphokinase levels is relatively routine in confirming a diagnosis of myocardial infarction, determination of differential levels of creatine phosphokinase isozymes—as with LDH—provides valuable additional information. In addition to electrophoretic separation (see Fig 6–9), creatine phosphokinase isozymes may be separated by ion exchange chromatographic techniques.

In normal individuals, the MB isozyme accounts for less than 2% of the total creatine phosphokinase of plasma. By contrast, MB accounts for 4.5–20% of the total creatine phosphokinase in plasma of patients with a recent myocardial infarct, and the total MB isozyme level is elevated up to 20-fold above normal.

L. Ceruloplasmin: This copper-containing serum globulin shows oxidase activity in vitro toward several amines, including epinephrine, 5-hydroxytryptamine, and dihydroxyphenylalanine. Plasma ceruloplasmin levels, determined as oxidase activity, are elevated in several circumstances (cirrhosis, hepatitis, bacterial infections, pregnancy, etc). Decreased levels, however, provide a useful confirmatory test for Wilson's disease (hepatolenticular degeneration).

Diagnostic Applications of Restriction Endonucleases

The diagnosis of genetic diseases has received tremendous impetus from recent developments in recombinant DNA technology. While all molecular diseases have long been known to be a consequence of altered DNA, techniques for direct examination of DNA sequences have only recently become available. For example, development of hybridization probes for DNA fragments (Southern, 1975) has led to techniques of sensitivity sufficient for prenatal screening for hereditary disorders by restriction enzyme mapping of

DNA derived from fetal cells in the amniotic fluid.

DNA probes can, in principle, be constructed for the diagnosis of most genetic diseases. For example, for prenatal detection of thalassemias (characterized by defects in the synthesis of hemoglobin subunits; see Chapter 5), a probe constructed against a portion of the gene for a normal hemoglobin subunit can detect a shortened or absent restriction fragment arising from a deletion in that gene, as occurs in some α-thalassemias and certain rare types of β- and β, δ-thalassemias (Dozy, Forman, and Abuelo, 1979; Kan, Chang, and Dozy, 1982). Alternatively, a synthetic cDNA probe has been constructed that hybridizes to a β-globin sequence that contains a nonsense mutation present in certain β-thalassemias, but not to the normal β-globin gene (Piratsu et al, 1984). Absence of the plasma protease inhibitor α_1-antitrypsin is associated with emphysema and with infantile liver cirrhosis. The presence of inactive α_1-antitrypsin has been detected by a probe constructed against the inactive allele that contains a point mutation in the α_1-antitrypsin gene (Kidd et al, 1983).

Hybridization probes may also be used to detect genetic alterations that lead to the loss of a restriction endonuclease site (see Chapter 28). For example, the point mutation of the Glu codon (GAG) to the Val codon (GTG) characteristic of sickle cell disease can be detected in the β-globin gene from cells in as little as 10 mL of amniotic fluid using the restriction endonuclease *Mst*II or *Sau*I (Orkin et al, 1982).

DNA probes may also be used to detect DNA sequences tightly linked to, but not actually within, the gene of interest. The analyses may be extended to detection of chromosome-specific variations (differences in sequence between homologous chromosomes). Digestion of the DNA with a restriction endonuclease generates different restriction maps (patterns of DNA fragments) from homologous genes that contain different base sequences. This phenomenon is termed "restriction fragment length polymorphism" (RFLP). For a genetic disease linked to a restriction length polymorphism, a human carrier of the disease will bear one chromosome with a normal gene and one with the defective gene. When the restriction fragments are resolved and probed, 2 hybridizing bands are detected (as distinct from a single band where both genes are identical). Offspring who inherit the disease-bearing chromosome exhibit only a single hybridizing band that differs from the band produced by normal chromosomes. The phenomenon of associated RFLP has been applied to the analysis of sickle cell trait (based on an associated *Hpa*I RFLP) and of β-thalassemia (linked to a *Hind*III and a *Bam*HI RFLP) (Little et al, 1980; Woo et al, 1983).

A screen based on RFLPs has been developed for the detection of infant phenylketonuria (Woo et al, 1983) (see Chapter 22). Note, however, that since the RFLP does not cause the disease but is merely located near the defective gene, this general approach is not infallible. The future importance of RFLPs appears to be as points of departure for identification of the gene responsible for linked diseases. This approach has already been applied to a screen for the mutational events involved in formation of retinoblastoma tumors (Cavenee et al, 1983) and Huntington's disease (Gusella et al, 1984).

•   •   •

References

General Enzymology

Boyer PD, Lardy H, Myrbäck K (editors): *The Enzymes,* 3rd ed. 7 vols. Academic Press, 1970–1973.

Nord FF (editor): *Advances in Enzymology.* Interscience. [Issued annually.]

Enzyme Structure

Hirs CHW, Timascheff SN (editors): Enzyme structure. Parts A–H in: *Methods in Enzymology.* Vol 11, 1967; Vols 25 and 26, 1972; Vol 27, 1973; Vol 47, 1977; Vols 48 and 49, 1978; Vol 49, 1979. Academic Press.

Coenzymes

McCormick DB, Wright LD (editors): Vitamins and coenzymes. Parts A–F in: *Methods in Enzymology.* Vol 18A, 1970; Vols 18B and 18C, 1971; Vol 62, 1979; Vols 66 and 67, 1980. Academic Press.

Nomenclature

Enzyme Nomenclature 1978. Recommendations of the Nomenclature Committee of the International Union of Biochemistry on the Nomenclature and Classification of Enzymes. Academic Press, 1979.

Assay & Purification of Enzymes

Bergmeyer H-U (editor): *Methods of Enzymatic Analysis,* 2nd English ed. 4 vols. Academic Press, 1974.

Boyer PD, Lardy H, Myrbäck K (editors): *The Enzymes,* 3rd ed. 7 vols. Academic Press, 1970–1973.

Colowick SP, Kaplan NO (editors): *Methods in Enzymology.* 69 vols. Academic Press, 1955–1980.

Hoffmann-Ostenhoff O et al: *Affinity Chromatography.* Pergamon Press, 1978.

Jacoby WB (editor): Enzyme purification and related techniques. In: *Methods in Enzymology.* Vol 22. Academic Press, 1971.

Jacoby WB, Wilchek M (editors): Affinity techniques. In: *Methods in Enzymology.* Vol 34, 1974; Vol 46, 1977. Academic Press.

Mosbach K (editor): Immobilized enzymes. In: *Methods in Enzymology.* Vol 44. Academic Press, 1976.

Intracellular Distribution of Enzymes

DePierre JW, Ernster L: Enzyme topology of intracellular membranes. *Annu Rev Biochem* 1977;**46**:201.

Clinical Enzymology

Bergmeyer HU: Aspartate aminotransferase. *Test of the Month 6* 1980; No. 2.

Bergström K: Determination of serum alkaline phosphatase activity. *Test of the Month 1* 1974; No. 22.

Cavanee WK et al: Expression of recessive alleles by chromosomal mechanisms in retinoblastomas. *Nature* 1983; **305**:779.

Dozy AM, Forman EN, Abuelo DN: Prenatal diagnosis of homozygous α-thalassemia. *JAMA* 1979;**241**:1610.

Fishinger AF: Creatine phosphokinase and its isoenzymes. *Test of the Month 2* 1976; No. 6.

Gusella JF et al: DNA markers for nervous system diseases. *Science* 1984;**225**:1320.

Kan YW, Chang J, Dozy AM: Pages 275–283 in: *Thalassemia: Recent Advances in Detection and Treatment.* Cao A, Carcassi U, Rowley P (editors). AR Liss, 1982.

Kidd VJ et al: α_1-Antitrypsin deficiency detection by direct analysis of the mutation in the gene. *Nature* 1983;**304**:230.

Little PFR et al: Model for antenatal diagnosis of β-thalassemia and other monogenic disorders by molecular analysis of linked DNA polymorphisms. *Nature* 1980;**285**:144.

McNair RD: Lactate dehydrogenase. *Test of the Month 2* 1976; No. 3.

Orkin SH et al: Improved detection of the sickle mutation by DNA analysis: Application to prenatal diagnosis. *N Engl J Med* 1982;**307**:32.

Pirastu M et al: Multiple mutations produces $S\beta^0$-thalassemia in Sardinia. *Science* 1984;**223**:929.

Southern EM: Detection of specific sequences among DNA fragments separated by gel electrophoresis. *J Mol Biol* 1975;**98**:503.

Wilkinson JH: Clinical applications of isozymes. *Clin Chem* 1970;**16**:733.

Wilkinson JH: Clinical significance of enzyme activity measurements. *Clin Chem* 1970;**16**:733.

Woo SLC et al: Cloned human phenylalanine hydroxylase gene allows prenatal diagnosis and carrier detection of classical phenylketonuria. *Nature* 1983;**306**:151.

Bioenergetics | 7

Peter A. Mayes, PhD, DSc

INTRODUCTION

Bioenergetics, or **biochemical thermodynamics,** is the study of the energy changes accompanying biochemical reactions. These reactions are accompanied by liberation of energy as the reacting system moves from a higher to a lower energy level. Most frequently, the energy is liberated in the form of heat. In nonbiologic systems, heat energy may be transformed into mechanical or electrical energy. Since biologic systems are essentially isothermic, no direct use can be made of heat liberated in biologic reactions to drive the vital processes that require energy. These processes— eg, synthetic reactions, muscular contraction, nerve conduction, and active transport—obtain energy by chemical linkage, or **coupling,** to oxidative reactions. In its simplest form, this type of coupling may be represented as shown in Fig 7–1.

The conversion of metabolite A to metabolite B occurs with release of energy. It is coupled to another reaction, in which energy is required to convert metabolite C to metabolite D. As some of the energy liberated in the degradative reaction is transferred to the synthetic reaction in a form other than heat, the normal chemical terms exothermic and endothermic cannot be applied to these reactions. Rather, the terms **exergonic** and **endergonic** are used to indicate that a process is accompanied by loss or gain, respectively, of free energy, regardless of the form of energy involved. In practice, an endergonic process cannot exist independently but must be a component of a coupled exergonic/endergonic system where the **overall net change is exergonic.** The exergonic reactions are termed **catabolism** (the breakdown or oxidation of fuel molecules), whereas the synthetic reactions that build up substances are termed **anabolism.** The total of all of the catabolic and anabolic processes is **metabolism.**

The Concept of Free Energy

Change in free energy (ΔG)* is that portion of the total energy change in a system which is available for doing work; ie, it is the useful energy.

If the reaction shown in Fig 7–1 is to go from left to right, then the overall process must be accompanied by loss of free energy as heat. One possible mechanism of coupling could be envisaged if a common obligatory intermediate (I) took part in both reactions, ie,

$$A + C \longrightarrow I \longrightarrow B + D$$

Some exergonic and endergonic reactions in biologic systems are coupled in this way. It should be appreciated that this type of system has a built-in mechanism for biologic control of the rate at which oxidative processes are allowed to occur, since the existence of a common obligatory intermediate for both the exergonic and endergonic reactions allows the rate of utilization of the product of the synthetic path (D) to determine by mass action the rate at which A is oxidized. Indeed, these relationships supply a basis for the concept of **respiratory control,** the process that prevents an organism from burning out of control. An extension of the coupling concept is provided by dehydrogenation reactions, which are coupled to hydrogenations by an intermediate carrier (Fig 7–2).

An alternative method of coupling an exergonic to an endergonic process is to synthesize a compound of high-energy potential in the exergonic reaction and to incorporate this new compound into the endergonic reaction, thus effecting a transference of free energy from the exergonic to the endergonic pathway (Fig 7–3).

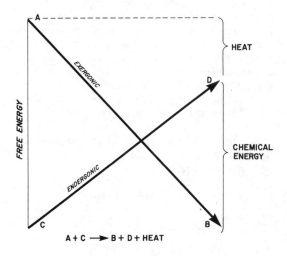

Figure 7–1. Coupling of an exergonic to an endergonic reaction.

*ΔG is the same as ΔF, which is used in some texts.

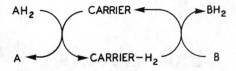

Figure 7-2. Coupling of dehydrogenation and hydrogenation reactions by an intermediate carrier.

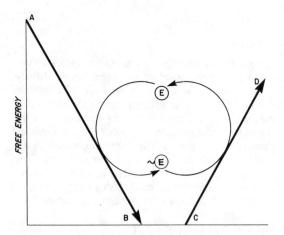

Figure 7-3. Transference of free energy from an exergonic to an endergonic reaction through the formation of a high-energy intermediate compound.

In Fig 7-3, $\sim$Ⓔ is a compound of high potential energy and Ⓔ is the corresponding compound of low potential energy. The biologic advantage of this mechanism is that Ⓔ, unlike I in the previous system, need not be structurally related to A, B, C, or D. This would allow Ⓔ to serve as a transducer of energy from a wide range of exergonic reactions to an equally wide range of endergonic reactions or processes, as shown in Fig 7-4.

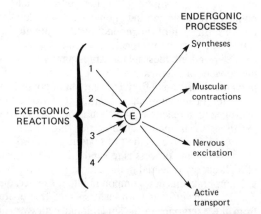

Figure 7-4. Transduction of energy through a common high-energy compound to energy-requiring (endergonic) biologic processes.

In the living cell, the principal high-energy intermediate or carrier compound (designated $\sim$Ⓔ) is **adenosine triphosphate** or **ATP.**

The Laws of Thermodynamics as Applied to Biochemical Systems

The first law of thermodynamics states that **"the total energy of a system, plus its surroundings, remains constant."** This is also the law of conservation of energy. It implies that within the total system, energy is neither lost nor gained during any change. However, within that total system, energy may be transferred from one part to another or may be transformed into another form of energy. For example, chemical energy may be transformed into heat, electrical energy, radiant energy, or mechanical energy.

The second law of thermodynamics states that **"the total entropy of a system must increase if a process is to occur spontaneously."** **Entropy** represents the extent of disorder or randomness of the system and becomes maximum in a system as it approaches true equilibrium. Under conditions of constant temperature and pressure, the relationship between the free energy change (ΔG) of a reacting system and the change in entropy (ΔS) is given by the following equation which combines the 2 laws of thermodynamics:

$$\Delta G = \Delta H - T\Delta S$$

where ΔH is the change in **enthalpy** (heat) and T is the absolute temperature.

Under the conditions of biochemical reactions, because ΔH is approximately equal to ΔE, the total change in internal energy of the reaction, the above relationship may be expressed in the following way:

$$\Delta G = \Delta E - T\Delta S$$

If ΔG is negative in sign, the reaction proceeds spontaneously with loss of free energy; ie, it is **exergonic.** If, in addition, ΔG is of great magnitude, the reaction goes virtually to completion and is essentially irreversible. On the other hand, if ΔG is positive, the reaction proceeds only if free energy can be gained; ie, it is **endergonic.** If, in addition, the magnitude of ΔG is great, the system is stable with little or no tendency for a reaction to occur. If ΔG **is zero,** the system is at **equilibrium** and no net change takes place.

Relationship Between Equilibrium Constant & Standard Free Energy Change

In a model reaction

$$A + B \rightleftharpoons C + D$$

$$\Delta G = \Delta G^0 + RT\ln \frac{[C]\,[D]}{[A]\,[B]}$$

where R is the gas constant and T is the absolute temperature. When the reactants [A], [B], [C], and [D] are present in concentrations of 1.0 mol/L, ΔG^0 is known as the **standard free energy change.**

At equilibrium, $\Delta G = 0$, ie,

$$0 = \Delta G^0 + RT\ln \frac{[C]\ [D]}{[A]\ [B]}$$

and therefore at equilibrium

$$\Delta G^0 = -RT\ln \frac{[C]\ [D]}{[A]\ [B]}$$

For biochemical reactions, a standard state is defined as having a pH of 7.0. The standard free energy change at this standard state is denoted by $\Delta G^{0\prime}$. Since the equilibrium constant under standard conditions is

$$K'_{eq} = \frac{[C]\ [D]}{[A]\ [B]}$$

substitution gives

$$\Delta G^{0\prime} = -RT\ln K'_{eq}$$

or

$$\Delta G^{0\prime} = -2.303\ RT\ \log K'_{eq}$$

Thus, the standard free energy change can be calculated from the equilibrium constant K'_{eq}. It is important to note that ΔG may be larger or smaller than $\Delta G^{0\prime}$ depending on the concentrations of the various reactants.

In a biochemical reaction system, it must be appreciated that an enzyme only speeds up the attainment of equilibrium; *it never alters the final concentrations of the reactants at equilibrium.*

ROLE OF HIGH-ENERGY PHOSPHATES IN BIOENERGETICS & ENERGY CAPTURE

In order to maintain living processes, all organisms must obtain supplies of free energy from their environment. In the case of autotrophic organisms,

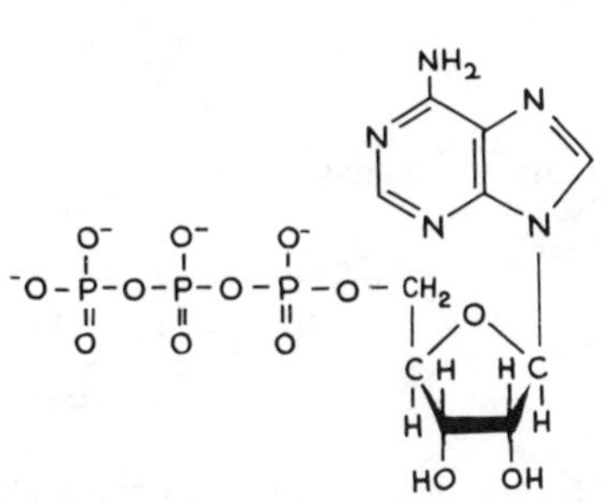

Figure 7–5. Adenosine triphosphate (ATP).

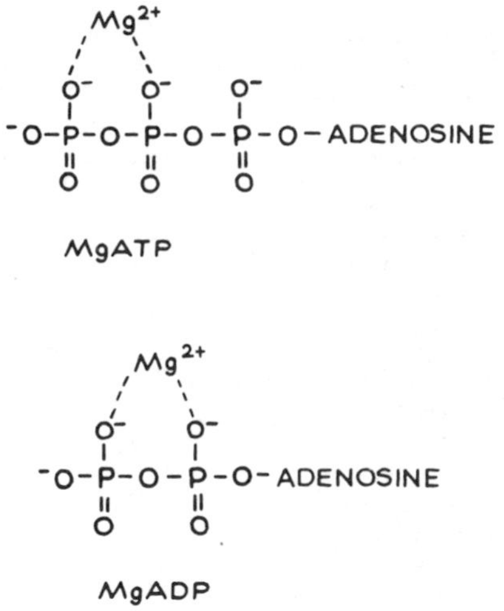

Figure 7–6. The magnesium complexes of ATP and ADP.

this is achieved by coupling their metabolism to some simple exergonic process in their surroundings; eg, green plants utilize the energy of sunlight. On the other hand, heterotrophic organisms obtain free energy by coupling their metabolism to the breakdown of complex organic molecules in their environment. In all of these processes, ATP plays a central role in the transference of free energy from the exergonic to the endergonic processes (Figs 7–3 and 7–4). As can be seen from Fig 7–5, ATP is a specialized nucleotide containing adenine, ribose, and 3 phosphate groups. In its reactions in the cell, it functions as the Mg^{2+} complex (Fig 7–6).

The importance of phosphates in intermediary metabolism became evident in the period between 1930 and 1940 with the discovery of the chemical details of glycolysis and of the role of ATP, ADP, and inorganic phosphate (P_i) in this process. ATP was considered to be a means of transferring phosphate radicals in the process of phosphorylation. The role of ATP in biochemical energetics was indicated in experiments demonstrating that ATP and creatine phosphate were broken down during muscular contraction and that their resynthesis depended on supplying energy from oxidative processes in the muscle. It was not until 1941, when Lipmann introduced the concept of "high-energy phosphates" and the "high-energy phosphate bond," that the role of these compounds in bioenergetics was clearly appreciated.

The Free Energy of Hydrolysis of ATP & Other Organophosphates

The standard free energy of hydrolysis of a number of biochemically important phosphates is shown in Table 7–1. An estimate of the comparative tendency of each of the phosphate groups to transfer to a suitable acceptor may be obtained from the $\Delta G^{0\prime}$ of hydrolysis (measured at 25 °C and pH 7.0). It may be seen from the table that the value for the hydrolysis of

Table 7–1. Standard free energy of hydrolysis of some organophosphates of biochemical importance.

Compound	ΔG⁰′	
	kJ/mol	kcal/mol
Phosphoenolpyruvate	−61.9	−14.8
Carbamoyl phosphate	−51.4	−12.3
1,3-Bisphosphoglycerate (to 3-phosphoglycerate)	−49.3	−11.8
Creatine phosphate	−43.1	−10.3
ATP → ADP + P_i	36.8	−8.8
Glucose 1-phosphate	−20.9	−5.0
Fructose 6-phosphate	−15.9	−3.8
Glucose 6-phosphate	−13.8	−3.3
Glycerol 3-phosphate	−9.2	−2.2

P_i, inorganic orthophosphate

the terminal phosphate of ATP of −8.8 kcal (−36.8 kJ) per mole (−36.0 kJ for the terminal phosphate of ADP) divides the list into 2 groups. One group of "low-energy phosphates," exemplified by the ester phosphates found in the intermediates of glycolysis, has $\Delta G^{0'}$ values which are smaller than that of ATP, while in the other group, designated "high-energy phosphates," the value is equal to or higher than that of ATP. The components of this latter group, including ATP and ADP, are usually anhydrides (eg, the 1-phosphate of 1,3-bisphosphoglycerate), enolphosphates (eg, phosphoenolpyruvate), and phosphoguanidines (eg, creatine phosphate, arginine phosphate). Other biologically important compounds that are classed as "high-energy compounds" are thiol esters involving coenzyme A (eg, acetyl-CoA), acyl carrier protein, amino acid esters involved in protein synthesis, S-adenosylmethionine (active methionine), and UDPG (uridine diphosphate glucose).

High-Energy Phosphates

To indicate the presence of the high-energy phosphate group, Lipmann introduced the symbol ~Ⓟ, indicating **high-energy phosphate bond.** The symbol indicates that the group attached to the bond, on transfer to an appropriate acceptor, results in transfer of the larger quantity of free energy. For this reason, the term **group transfer potential** is preferred by some to "high-energy bond." Thus, ATP contains 2 high-energy phosphate groups and ADP contains one, whereas the phosphate bond in AMP (adenosine monophosphate) is of the low-energy type, since it is a normal ester link (Fig 7–7).

Role of High-Energy Phosphates as the "Energy Currency" of the Cell

As a result of its position midway down the list of standard free energies of hydrolysis (Table 7–1), ATP is able to act as a donor of high-energy phosphate to those compounds below it in the table. Likewise, provided the necessary enzymic machinery is available, ADP can accept high-energy phosphate to form ATP from those compounds above ATP in the table. In

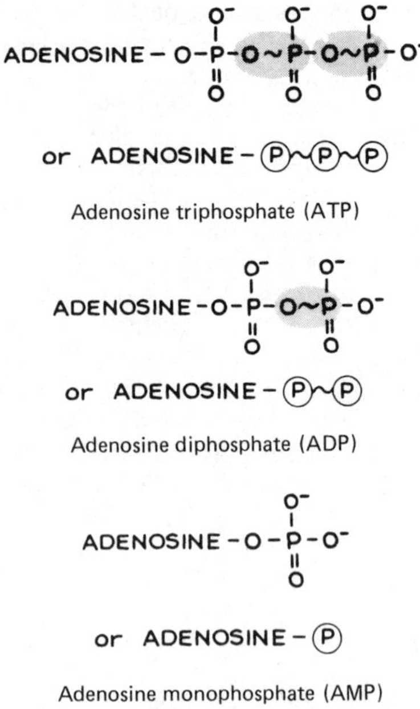

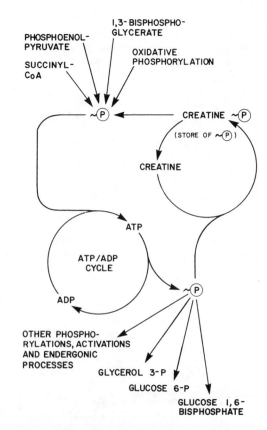

Figure 7–7. Structure of ATP, ADP, and AMP showing the position and the number of high-energy bonds (~).

Figure 7–8. Role of ATP/ADP cycle in transfer of high-energy phosphate. Note that ~Ⓟ does not exist in a free state but is transferred in the reactions shown.

effect, an **ATP/ADP cycle** connects these processes which **generate** $\sim$ ⑦ to those processes that **utilize** $\sim$ ⑦ (Fig 7–8).

The processes that feed $\sim$ ⑦ into this cycle can be divided into 4 main groups. The greatest quantitative source of $\sim$ ⑦ in aerobic organisms is from reactions catalyzed by ATP synthetase. The free energy to drive this process is derived from respiratory chain oxidation within the mitochondria (see p 137). This process, **oxidative phosphorylation,** is part of the mechanism within the cell that operates to achieve **energy conservation** or **energy capture.** Energy capture also results from the catabolism of glucose to lactic acid in the series of reactions known as the Embden-Meyerhof pathway of glycolysis (Fig 15–3), wherein—per mole of glucose catabolized—there is net formation of 2 high-energy phosphate groups, resulting in the formation of 2 mol of ATP from 2 of ADP. The chemical processes resulting in this net formation of ATP involve the incorporation of P$_i$ into 3-phosphoglyceraldehyde, which, after dehydrogenation, forms 1,3-bisphosphoglycerate. This compound contains a high-energy phosphate that in turn reacts with ADP to form ATP. As a result of further molecular changes, another intermediate, phosphoenolpyruvate, is formed that contains a high-energy phosphate which again is transferred to ADP to form ATP (Fig 7–9). Further energy capture occurs at the succinyl thiokinase step of the citric acid cycle (Fig 14–4), where additional high-energy phosphate is liberated.

Another group of compounds (**phosphagens**) represented in Table 7–1 act as storage forms of high-energy phosphate. These include creatine phosphate, occurring in vertebrate muscle and brain, and arginine phosphate, occurring in invertebrate muscle.

Under physiologic conditions, phosphagens permit ATP concentrations to be maintained in muscle while ATP is rapidly being utilized as a source of

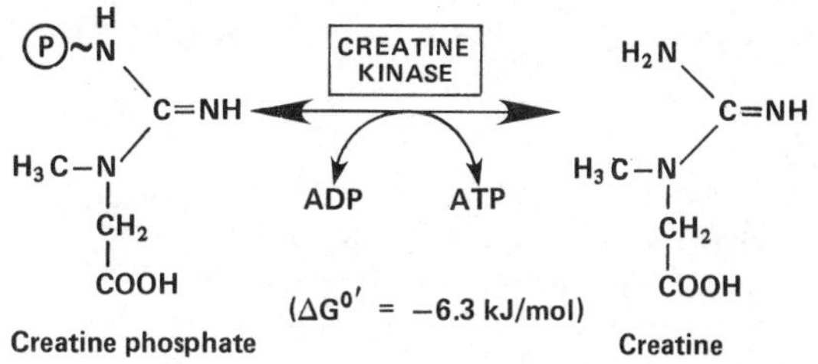

Figure 7–10. Transfer of high-energy phosphate between ATP and creatine.

energy for muscular contraction. On the other hand, when ATP is plentiful, its concentration can build up sufficiently to cause the reverse reaction to occur and allow the concentration of creatine phosphate to increase substantially so as to act as a store of high-energy phosphate. When ATP acts as a phosphate donor to form those compounds of lower free energy of hydrolysis (Table 7–1), the phosphate group is invariably converted to one of low energy, eg,

Glycerol + Adenosine $-$⑦$\sim$⑦$\sim$⑦ $\xrightarrow{\text{GLYCEROKINASE}}$

Glycerol $-$⑦ + Adenosine $-$⑦$\sim$⑦

Bioenergetics of Coupled Reactions

We can now consider in more detail the energetics of coupled reactions, as depicted in Fig 7–1 or 7–3. Such a reaction is the first in the glycolysis pathway (Fig 15–3), the phosphorylation of glucose to glucose 6-phosphate, which is highly endergonic and would not proceed as such under physiologic conditions.

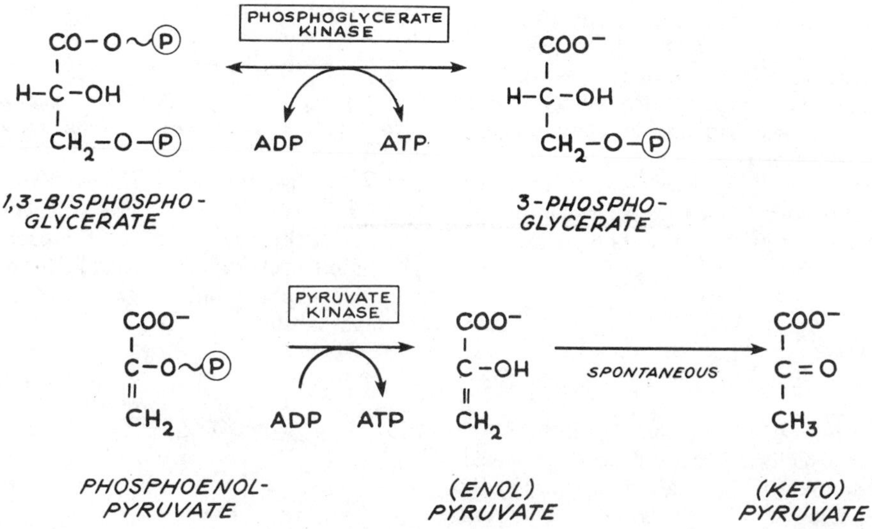

Figure 7–9. Transfer of high-energy phosphate from intermediates of glycolysis to ADP.

(1) Glucose + P$_i$ ⟶ Glucose 6-P + H$_2$O

$$(\Delta G^{0'} = +13.8 \text{ kJ/mol})$$

To take place, the reaction must be coupled with another reaction that is more exergonic than the phosphorylation of glucose is endergonic. Such a reaction is the hydrolysis of the terminal phosphate of ATP.

(2) ATP ⟶ ADP + P$_i$ ($\Delta G^{0'}$ = −36.8 kJ/mol)

When (1) and (2) are coupled in a reaction catalyzed by hexokinase, phosphorylation of glucose readily proceeds in a highly exergonic reaction that under physiologic conditions is far from equilibrium and thus irreversible for practical purposes.

$$\underset{\text{HEXOKINASE}}{\text{Glucose + ATP} \longrightarrow \text{Glucose 6-P + ADP}}$$

$$(\Delta G^{0'} = -23.0 \text{ kJ/mol})$$

Many "activation" reactions follow this pattern.

Interconversion of Adenine Nucleotides

The enzyme **adenylate kinase** (myokinase) is present in most cells. It catalyzes the interconversion of ATP and AMP on the one hand and ADP on the other:

Adenosine −Ⓟ~Ⓟ~Ⓟ + Adenosine −Ⓟ
    (ATP)   (AMP)

$$\underset{\text{ADENYLATE KINASE}}{\rightleftharpoons} \text{ 2 Adenosine} -Ⓟ~Ⓟ$$
                                        (2 ADP)

This reaction has several functions. It allows the high-energy phosphate in ADP to be used in the formation of ATP, and it is also a means whereby AMP, formed as a consequence of several activating reactions involving ATP, can be rephosphorylated to form ADP. Finally, it allows AMP, which increases in concentration when ATP becomes depleted, to act as a metabolic (allosteric) signal to increase the rate of catabolic reactions, which in turn leads to the generation of more ATP (see p 261).

When ATP reacts to form AMP, inorganic pyrophosphate (PP$_i$) is formed, as occurs, for example, in the activation of long-chain fatty acids:

$$\underset{\text{SYNTHETASE}}{\overset{\text{ACYL-CoA}}{\text{ATP + CoA·SH + R·COOH} \longrightarrow}}$$

$$\text{AMP + PP}_i + \text{R·CO~SCoA}$$

This reaction is accompanied by loss of free energy as heat, which ensures that the activation reaction will go to the right; this is further aided by the hydrolytic splitting of PP$_i$, catalyzed by **inorganic pyrophosphatase,** a reaction that itself has a large $\Delta G^{0'}$ of −4.6 kcal/mol. Note that activations via the

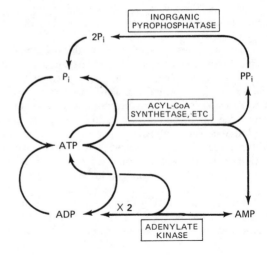

Figure 7–11. Phosphate cycles and interchange of adenine nucleotides.

pyrophosphate pathway result in the loss of 2 ~Ⓟ rather than one ~Ⓟ, as occurs when ADP and P$_i$ are formed.

$$\underset{\text{PYROPHOSPHATASE}}{\overset{\text{INORGANIC}}{\text{PP}_i + \text{H}_2\text{O} \longrightarrow 2 \text{ P}_i}}$$

A combination of the above reactions makes it possible for phosphate to be recycled and the adenine nucleotides to interchange (Fig 7–11).

Nucleoside Phosphates Related to ATP & ADP

By means of the enzyme **nucleoside diphosphate kinase,** nucleoside triphosphates similar to ATP but containing a different base from adenine can be synthesized from their diphosphates, eg:

NUCLEOSIDE DIPHOSPHATE KINASE

ATP + UDP ⇌ ADP + UTP (uridine triphosphate)
ATP + GDP ⇌ ADP + GTP (guanosine triphosphate)
ATP + CDP ⇌ ADP + CTP (cytidine triphosphate)

All of these triphosphates take part in phosphorylations in the cell. Similarly, **nucleoside monophosphate kinases,** specific for each purine or pyrimidine nucleoside, catalyze the formation of nucleoside diphosphates from the corresponding monophosphates

SPECIFIC NUCLEOSIDE MONOPHOSPHATE KINASE

ATP + Nucleoside −Ⓟ ⇌

ADP + Nucleoside −Ⓟ~Ⓟ

Thus, adenylate kinase is a specialized monophosphate kinase.

• • •

References

Florkin M, Stotz EH (editors): *Bioenergetics*. In: *Comprehensive Biochemistry*. Vol 22. Elsevier, 1967.

Kaplan NO, Kennedy EP (editors): *Current Aspects of Biochemical Energetics*. Academic Press, 1966.

Klotz IM: *Energy Changes in Biochemical Reactions*. Academic Press, 1967.

Krebs HA, Kornberg HL: *Energy Transformations in Living Matter*. Springer, 1957.

Lehninger AL: *Biochemistry*, 2nd ed. Worth, 1975.

Lehninger AL: *Bioenergetics: The Molecular Basis of Biological Energy Transformations*, 2nd ed. Benjamin, 1971.

8 | Kinetic Properties of Enzymes

Victor W. Rodwell, PhD

Preceding chapters have reviewed the physical and chemical properties of proteins and the relationship between structure and function of a protein. Chapters 6 and 7 discuss the general properties of enzymes and the energy changes that generally accompany biochemical reactions, most of which are catalyzed by specific enzymes. In this chapter we consider the chemical nature of the catalysis carried out by enzymes and the nature of the enzyme-substrate interaction responsible for the reaction specificity of these biologic catalysts.

ENERGY BARRIERS FOR CHEMICAL REACTIONS; FORMATION OF TRANSITION STATES DURING THE OVERALL REACTION

Shown below is a displacement reaction in which an entering group, Y, displaces a leaving group, X.

$$Y + R-X \rightleftharpoons Y-R + X$$

This overall reaction proceeds via 2 half reactions. The first involves formation of a **transition state** in which Y and X both are attached to R. The second involves decay of the transition state to form products.

$$Y + R-X \rightleftharpoons \underbrace{Y \cdots R \cdots X}_{\substack{\text{Transition} \\ \text{state}}} \rightleftharpoons Y-R + X$$

As with all chemical reactions, characteristic changes in free energy are associated with each of the above half reactions. We shall therefore define ΔG_F as the change in free energy associated with **formation** of the transition state and ΔG_D as the change in free energy associated with **decay** of the transition state to form products

$$\Delta G_F = \Delta G_F^0 + RT \ln \frac{[Y \cdots R \cdots X]}{[Y][R-X]}$$

$$\Delta G_D = \Delta G_D^0 + RT \ln \frac{[Y-R][X]}{[Y \cdots R \cdots X]}$$

where the change in free energy for the **overall** reaction, ΔG, is the sum of the changes in free energy for each of the half reactions.

$$\Delta G = \Delta G_F + \Delta G_D$$

As for any equation with 2 terms, it is not possible by inspection of the algebraic sign and magnitude of ΔG to infer the sign or magnitude of either ΔG_F or ΔG_D. Stated another way, we are unable simply from consideration of the change in free energy for the overall reaction, ΔG, to infer anything whatever concerning the free energy changes associated with the formation and decay of transition states. Since the phenomenon of catalysis is intimately associated with ΔG_F and ΔG_D, it follows that the thermodynamics of the overall reaction (ΔG) can tell us nothing of the **path** a reaction follows (ie, its mechanism). This, as we shall see, is the task of kinetics.

REPRESENTATION OF FREE ENERGY CHANGES ASSOCIATED WITH FORMATION & DECAY OF TRANSITION STATES

Reaction Profiles

The above concepts are represented graphically in Figs 8–1 and 8–2 as "reaction profiles" that illustrate the relationship between ΔG, ΔG_F, and ΔG_D. Note that whereas in Fig 8–1 ΔG is negative ($\Delta G < 0$) and in Fig 8–2 ΔG is positive ($\Delta G > 0$), in both instances, ΔG_F is positive ($\Delta G_F > 0$) and ΔG_D is negative (ΔG_D

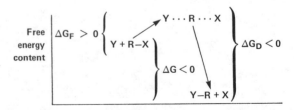

Figure 8–1. Reaction profile for a displacement reaction associated with a negative overall change in free energy, ie, $\Delta G < 0$.

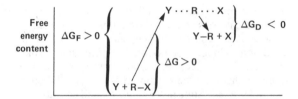

Figure 8–2. Reaction profile for a displacement reaction associated with a positive overall change in free energy, ie, $\Delta G > 0$.

< 0). Therefore, as stated above, **from the sign and magnitude of ΔG we cannot infer the sign or magnitude of either ΔG_F or ΔG_D.**

ROLE OF CATALYSTS IN FORMATION OF PRODUCTIVE TRANSITION STATES

Consider the reaction profiles for 2 different transition states in the same overall reaction (Fig 8–3).

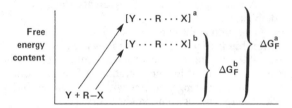

Figure 8–3. Reaction profile for formation of 2 different transition states, $[Y \cdots R \cdots X]^a$ and $[Y \cdots R \cdots X]^b$, and their associated free energies of formation, ΔG_F^a and ΔG_F^b.

In both instances, the magnitude of the free energy of formation of the transition state represents the energy barrier for the overall reaction. The energy barrier for the reaction that proceeds via the transition state $[Y \cdots R \cdots X]^b$ is thus lower than the energy barrier for the reaction that proceeds via the transition state $[Y \cdots R \cdots X]^a$. **Catalysts alter the free energy content of the transition state.** In the above example, $[Y \cdots R \cdots X]^a$ represents the transition state for the **noncatalyzed** reaction, while $[Y \cdots R \cdots X]^b$ represents the transition state for the **catalyzed** reaction. All catalysts, including enzymes, lower the free energy of formation, ΔG_F, of the transition state. Note further that since catalysis has no effect on ΔG, **the change in free energy for the overall reaction is independent of catalysis.** Since, as we have seen in Chapter 7, the equilibrium constant for a chemical reaction is a function of the standard free energy change for a reaction

$$\Delta G^0 = -RT \ln K_{eq}$$

it follows that **enzymes and other catalysts have no effect on the equilibrium constant for a reaction.**

EFFECT OF TEMPERATURE

The **kinetic,** or **collision, theory** for chemical reactions incorporates 2 key concepts:

(1) In order to react, molecules must collide (ie, be within bond-forming distance of one another).

(2) For a collision to be productive (ie, to result in a reaction), the reacting molecules must possess sufficient energy to overcome the energy barrier for the reaction.

It follows that if the reacting molecules have sufficient energy to react, anything that increases the frequency of collision between molecules will increase their rate of reaction. Conversely, factors that decrease either collision frequency or kinetic energy will decrease the rate of reaction.

If some molecules in the population have insufficient energy to react, increased temperature, which increases kinetic energy, will increase the rate of the reaction. These concepts are illustrated diagrammatically in Fig 8–4. In A none, in B a portion, and in C all of the molecules have sufficient kinetic energy to overcome the energy barrier for reaction.

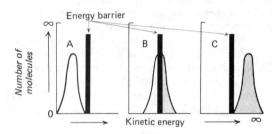

Figure 8–4. The energy barrier for chemical reactions.

In the absence of enzymic catalysis, many chemical reactions proceed exceedingly slowly at the temperature of living cells. However, even at this temperature molecules are in motion and undergo collisions. **They fail to react rapidly, because most possess insufficient kinetic energy to overcome the energy barrier for reaction.** At a considerably higher temperature (and higher kinetic energy), the reaction will occur more rapidly. That the reaction takes place at all shows that it is spontaneous ($\Delta G < 0$). At the lower temperature, it is spontaneous but slow; at the higher temperature, spontaneous and fast. **Enzymes make spontaneous reactions proceed rapidly under the conditions prevailing in living cells.**

ROLE OF ENZYMES IN THE RUPTURE & FORMATION OF COVALENT BONDS

Most chemical reactions of biochemical interest involve breakage or formation of covalent bonds. For example, consider the group transfer reactions introduced in Chapter 6

$$D\text{–}G + A \rightleftharpoons A\text{–}G + D$$

in which a group, G, is transferred from a donor, D–G, to an acceptor, A. The overall reaction involves both rupture of the D–G bond and formation of a new A–G bond. Enzyme-catalyzed group transfer reactions are, however, better represented as follows:

$$
\begin{array}{ccc}
D\text{–}G & Enz & A\text{–}G \\
D & Enz\text{–}G & A
\end{array}
$$

This representation emphasizes 3 important features of enzyme-catalyzed group transfer reactions:

(1) Each half reaction involves both the rupture and formation of a covalent bond.

(2) The enzyme is a reactant coequal with D–G and A.

(3) Whereas in the overall reaction the enzyme acts catalytically (ie, is required only in trace quantities and may be recovered unchanged when the reaction is complete), for each of the half reactions, the enzyme is a stoichiometric reactant (ie, it is required in a 1:1 molar ratio with the other reactants).

Many additional biochemical reactions may be considered as special cases of group transfer in which D, A, or both may be absent. Isomerization reactions (eg, the interconversion of glucose 6-phosphate and glucose 1-phosphate) might be represented as reactions in which both D and A are absent:

$$
\begin{array}{ccc}
S & Enz & P \\
 & Enz\text{–}S &
\end{array}
$$

These representations fail, however, to emphasize yet another key feature of enzyme-catalyzed reactions—**participation in the overall reaction of 2 or more intermediate forms of E–S complex and the consequent participation of a set of several sequential half reactions.** A representation of a group transfer reaction that emphasizes these features might be

$$
\begin{array}{ccc}
D\text{–}G & Enz & A\text{–}G \\
D & & A \\
Enz\text{–}G & & Enz\text{–}G^{**} \\
 & Enz\text{–}G^{*} &
\end{array}
$$

in which Enz–G, Enz–G*, and Enz–G** represent successive E–S complexes in the overall reaction.

It is clear from all of the above representations that for the reaction to occur, all of the reactants must come within bond-forming (or bond-breaking) distance of one another. That is, the reactants must col-

lide. For homogeneous solution chemistry in the absence of catalysts, the concentrations of the reacting molecules are constant throughout the solution. This condition no longer obtains following introduction of a catalyst. To be effective, a catalyst must have surface domains that bind the reacting molecules. While this binding is a reversible process, the overall equilibrium constant for binding strongly favors the bound rather than the free forms of the reacting molecules. Qualitatively, we might represent this as follows:

$$\text{Reactant} + \text{Catalyst} \rightleftharpoons \text{Reactant-catalyst complex}$$

Quantitatively, we might express the tightness of association between a reactant, R, and a catalyst, C, in terms of the dissociation constant, K_d, for the R–C complex, or the equilibrium constant for the reaction:

$$R\text{–}C \rightleftharpoons R + C$$

$$K_d = \frac{[R]\,[C]}{[R\text{–}C]}$$

A low value for K_d thus represents a tight R–C complex.

One important consequence is that when a **reactant binds to a catalyst this raises the concentration of the reactant in a localized area of the solution** well above that of its concentration in free solution. Thus, we are no longer dealing with homogeneous but with heterogeneous solution chemistry.

If the catalyst for a bimolecular (2-reactant) reaction binds both reactants, the local concentration of each reactant is increased by a factor that depends on its individual affinity (K_d value) for the catalyst. Since the rate of the overall bimolecular reaction

$$A + B \rightarrow A\text{–}B$$

is, as we shall see below, proportionate to the concentrations of **both** A and B, binding of both A and B by the catalyst can result in an enormous (several thousand-fold) increase in overall reaction rate.

One key factor in the ability of enzymes to act as catalysts is their ability to bind effectively one or (more frequently) both reactants in a bimolecular reaction with an accompanying increase in local reactant concentration and hence in local reaction rate. That enzymes are, relative to most nonprotein catalysts, both extremely efficient and highly selective catalysts requires further explanation. To understand these distinctive properties of enzymes, we must introduce the concept of the "active" or "catalytic" site.*

---

*While many texts equate the active and catalytic sites of enzymes, there are on enzymes other "active" sites concerned with regulation of enzyme activity rather than with the intermediary enzymology of the catalytic process per se. We therefore use the term "catalytic site" throughout to avoid ambiguity.

THE CATALYTIC SITE

The large size of proteins relative to substrates led to the concept that a restricted region of the enzyme was concerned with catalysis. This region we refer to as the **catalytic site.** Initially, it was extremely puzzling to biochemists why enzymes were so large, when only a portion of their structure appeared to be required for substrate binding and catalysis. Today, we recognize from 3-dimensional models of enzymes that a far greater portion of the protein interacts with the substrate than was formerly supposed. When the need for allosteric sites of equal size also arises (see Chapters 5 and 9), the size of enzymes should no longer be surprising.

"Lock & Key" or "Template" Model of a Catalytic Site

The original model of a catalytic site, proposed by Emil Fischer, visualized interaction between substrate and enzyme in terms of a "lock and key" analogy. This **lock and key,** or **rigid template model** (Fig 8–5), is still useful for understanding certain properties of enzymes—for example, the ordered binding of 2 or more substrates (Fig 8–6) or the kinetics of a simple substrate saturation curve. An unfortunate feature of the Fischer model is the implied rigidity of the catalytic site. A more useful model is the **"induced fit" model** of Koshland discussed below.

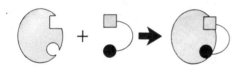

Figure 8–5. Representation of formation of an EnzS complex according to the Fischer template hypothesis.

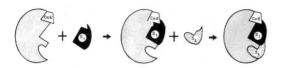

Figure 8–6. Representation of sequential adsorption of a coenzyme (CoE) and of 2 substrates (S_1 and S_2) to an enzyme in terms of the template hypothesis. The coenzyme is assumed to bear a group essential for binding the first substrate (S_1), which in turn facilitates binding of S_2.

"Induced Fit" Model of a Catalytic Site

Originally little more than an attractive hypothesis, this model now has considerable experimental support. An essential feature is the flexibility of the catalytic site. In the Fischer model, the catalytic site is presumed to be preshaped to fit the substrate. In the induced fit model, the substrate induces a conformational change in the enzyme. This aligns amino acid

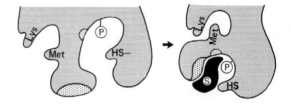

Figure 8–7. Representation of an induced fit by a conformational change in the protein structure. Note the relative positions of key residues before and after the substrate is bound. (After Koshland.)

residues or other groups on the enzyme in the correct spatial orientation for substrate binding, catalysis, or both. At the same time, other amino acid residues may become buried in the interior of the enzyme.

In the example (Fig 8–7), hydrophobic groups (hatched) and charged groups (stippled) both are involved in substrate binding. A phosphoserine (–P) and the –SH of a cysteine residue are involved in catalysis. Other residues involved in neither process are represented by Lys and Met residues. In the absence of substrate, the catalytic and the substrate-binding groups are several bond distances apart. Approach of the substrate induces a conformational change in the enzyme protein, aligning the groups correctly for substrate binding and for catalysis. At the same time, the spatial orientations of other regions are also altered—the Lys and Met are now closer together (Fig 8–7).

Substrate analogs may cause some, but not all, of the correct conformational changes (Fig 8–8). On attachment of the true substrate (A), all groups (shown as closed circles) are brought into correct alignment. Attachment of a substrate analog that is too "bulky" (Fig 8–8B) or too "slim" (Fig 8–8C) induces incorrect alignment. One final feature is the site shown as a small notch on the right. One may visualize a regulatory molecule attaching at this point and "holding down" one of the polypeptide arms bearing a catalytic group. Substrate binding, but not catalysis, might then occur.

The exact sequence of events in a substrate-induced conformational change remains to be established. Several possibilities exist (Fig 8–9).

Even when the complete primary structure of an

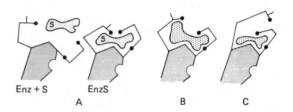

Figure 8–8. Representation of conformational changes in an enzyme protein when binding substrate *(A)* or inactive substrate analogs *(B, C).* (After Koshland.)

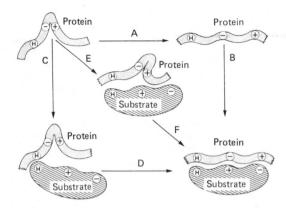

Figure 8–9. Representation of alternative reaction paths for a substrate-induced conformational change. The enzyme may first undergo a conformational change *(A)*, then bind substrate *(B)*. Alternatively, substrate may first be bound *(C)*, whereupon a conformational change occurs *(D)*. Finally, both processes may occur in a concerted manner *(E)* with further isomerization to the final conformation *(F)*. (Adapted from Koshland.)

enzyme is known, it usually is still difficult to decide exactly which residues constitute the catalytic site. As illustrated by the induced fit model, these may be distant one from another in the primary structure but spatially close in the 3-dimensional (tertiary) structure.

In the representation of a catalytic site, several regions of a polypeptide chain each contribute residues to the site. Furthermore, these residues generally are not all sequential within a polypeptide chain, as described for hemoglobin in Chapter 5.

Proenzymes

Many proteins are manufactured and secreted from their cells of origin in the form of inactive precursor proteins known as **"proproteins."** When the proteins are enzymes, the proproteins are termed **"proenzymes"** or **"zymogens."** Conversion of a proprotein to the mature protein involves a process known as limited, selective proteolysis. By this process, the proprotein is converted by one or more successive proteolytic "clips" to a form in which the characteristic activity of the mature protein (its enzymatic activity) is expressed. Examples of proteins manufactured as proproteins include the hormone insulin (proprotein = proinsulin), the digestive enzymes pepsin, trypsin, and chymotrypsin (proproteins = pepsinogen, trypsinogen, and chymotrypsinogen, respectively), several factors of the blood clotting and of the blood clot dissolution cascades (see Chapter 45), and the connective tissue protein collagen (proprotein = procollagen).

Why are certain proteins are secreted in an inactive form? Certain proteins are needed at essentially all times. Others (for example, the enzymes of blood clot formation and dissolution) are needed only intermittently. Furthermore, when these intermittently needed enzymes are required, they are frequently needed rap-

idly. Certain physiologic processes such as digestion are intermittent but fairly regular and predictable (although this may not have been the case for primitive humans). Others (for example, blood clot formation, clot dissolution, and tissue repair) need only to be brought "on line" in response to pressing physiologic or pathophysiologic need. It may be readily appreciated that the processes of blood clot formation and dissolution must be temporally coordinated to achieve homeostasis. In addition, the synthesis of proteases as catalytically inactive precursor proteins serves to protect the tissue of origin (eg, the pancreas) from autodigestion. (Autodigestion can occur in pancreatitis.)

It might be thought that de novo synthesis of the required proteins might be sufficiently rapid to respond to a pressing pathophysiologic demand such as the loss of blood. However, an adequate and complete pool of the precursor amino acids must be available. Furthermore, the secretion process may be slow relative to the physiologic demand.

The example of conversion of a proprotein to its mature, physiologically active form discussed below illustrates the following general principles of proprotein to protein conversions:

(1) The process involves selective proteolysis, which in some instances requires only a single proteolytic clip.

(2) The polypeptide products may separate or may remain associated in the mature protein.

(3) The process may (or may not) be attended by a significant change in molecular weight.

(4) A major consequence of selective proteolysis is the attainment of a new conformation.

(5) If the proprotein is an enzyme, the above conformational change generates the catalytic site of the enzyme. Indeed, selective proteolysis of a proenzyme may be viewed as a process that triggers essential conformational changes that "create" the catalytic site.

Conversion of prochymotrypsin to chymotrypsin. The conversion of prochymotrypsin (pro-CT), a 245-aminoacyl residue polypeptide, to the active enzyme α-chymotrypsin involves 3 proteolytic clips and the formation of an inactive intermediate known as π-chymotrypsin (π-CT) (Fig 8–10).

In α-chymotrypsin, the A, B, and C chains (Fig 8–10) remain associated owing to the presence in α-CT of 2 interchain disulfide bonds (Fig 8–11).

Catalysis by Chymotrypsin

Chymotrypsin catalyzes hydrolysis of peptide bonds in which the carboxyl group is contributed by an aromatic amino acid (Phe, Tyr, or Trp) or by one with a bulky nonpolar R group (Met). Like many other proteases, chymotrypsin also catalyzes the hydrolysis of certain esters. The ability of chymotrypsin to catalyze ester hydrolysis is of no physiologic significance. Rather, it facilitates mechanistic experiments that reveal details of the catalytic mechanism.

A useful ester substrate for chymotrypsin is *p*-nitrophenylacetate:

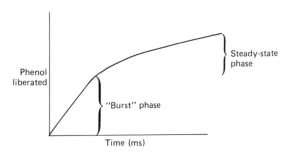

p-Nitrophenylacetate

Use of *p*-nitrophenylacetate as substrate facilitates colorimetric analysis of chymotrypsin activity because hydrolysis of *p*-nitrophenylacetate releases *p*-nitrophenol. In alkali, this converts to the yellow *p*-nitrophenylate anion.

The kinetics of chymotrypsin hydrolysis of *p*-nitrophenylacetate can be studied in a "stop-flow" apparatus. These stop-flow experiments use substrate quantities of enzyme (roughly equimolar quantities of enzyme and of substrate) and measure events that occur in the first few milliseconds after enzyme and substrate are mixed. The stop-flow apparatus has 2 syringes: one for chymotrypsin and the other for *p*-nitrophenylacetate. Instantaneous mixing of enzyme and substrate is achieved by a mechanical device that rapidly and simultaneously expels the contents of both syringes into a single narrow tube that passes through a spectrophotometer. The optical density as a function of time after mixing is displayed on an oscilloscopic screen. Release of *p*-nitrophenylate anion takes place in 2 distinct phases (Fig 8–12): (1) a "burst" phase, characterized by rapid liberation of *p*-nitrophenylate anion; and (2) a subsequent, slower release of additional *p*-nitrophenylate anion.

Figure 8–12. Representation of the kinetics of release of *p*-nitrophenylate anion when chymotrypsin hydrolyzes *p*-nitrophenylacetate in a stop-flow apparatus. In this representation, "phenol liberated" has been calculated from optical density.

The diphasic character of the release of *p*-nitrophenylate anion is comprehensible in terms of the successive steps in catalysis shown in Fig 8–13.

The slow step in overall catalysis is hydrolysis of the chymotrypsin-acetate (CT-Ac) complex. Once all of the available chymotrypsin has been converted to CT-Ac, no further release of *p*-nitrophenylate anion can occur until more free chymotrypsin is liberated by the slow, hydrolytic removal of acetate anion from the CT-Ac complex (Fig 8–13). The "burst" phase of *p*-nitrophenylate anion release (Fig 8–12) corresponds to the conversion of all of the available free chymotrypsin to the CT-Ac complex with simultaneous release of *p*-nitrophenylate anion. The subsequent re-

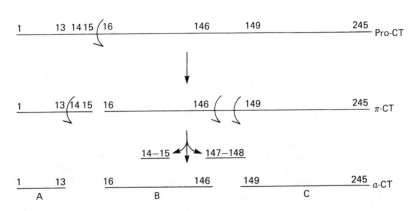

Figure 8–10. Representation of the conversion of prochymotrypsin (pro-CT) to π-chymotrypsin (π-CT) and subsequently to the mature, catalytically active enzyme α-chymotrypsin (α-CT).

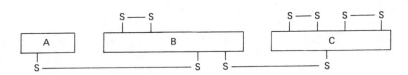

Figure 8–11. Representation of the intra- and interchain polypeptide bonds of α-chymotrypsin (α-CT).

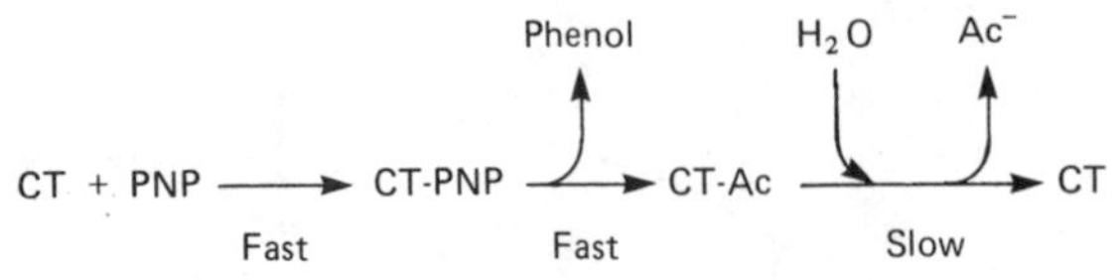

$$CT + PNP \xrightarrow{\text{Fast}} CT\text{-}PNP \xrightarrow[\text{Fast}]{\text{Phenol}} CT\text{-}Ac \xrightarrow[\text{Slow}]{H_2O \quad Ac^-} CT$$

Figure 8–13. Intermediate steps in catalysis of the hydrolysis of *p*-nitrophenylacetate by chymotrypsin. CT, chymotrypsin; PNP, *p*-nitrophenylacetate; CT-PNP, chymotrypsin–*p*-nitrophenylacetate complex; CT-Ac, chymotrypsin-acetate complex; phenol, *p*-nitrophenylate anion; Ac⁻, acetate anion. Formation of the CT-PNP and CT-Ac complexes is fast relative to the hydrolysis of the CT-Ac complex.

lease of *p*-nitrophenylate anion that follows the burst phase results from the slow liberation of free chymotrypsin by hydrolysis of the CT-Ac complex. This free chymotrypsin then is available for further formation of the CT-PNP and CT-Ac complexes with attendant release of *p*-nitrophenylate anion. Indeed, the magnitude of the "burst" phase (ie, moles of *p*-nitrophenylate anion released) is directly proportionate to the number of moles of chymotrypsin present initially.

The acyl group of the acyl-CT intermediate is linked to a highly reactive seryl residue—serine 195—of chymotrypsin. The essential nature and high reactivity of Ser 195 are evidenced by its ability (but not by the ability of the remaining 27 seryl residues of chymotrypsin) to react with diisopropylphosphofluoridate (DIPF) (Fig 8–14). Analogous reactions occur with other serine proteases.

Derivatization of Ser 195 inactivates chymotrypsin. Many other proteases are inactivated by DIFP by an analogous mechanism. These are termed "serine proteases."

A "charge relay network" functions as a proton shuttle during catalysis by chymotrypsin. The charge relay network of chymotrypsin involves 3 aminoacyl residues that are far apart in a primary structural sense but within bond-forming distance of one another in a tertiary structural sense. These residues are Asp 102, His 57, and Ser 195. While most of the charged residues of chymotrypsin are at the surface of the molecule, those of the charge relay network are "buried" in the otherwise nonpolar interior of the molecule. The 3 residues are aligned in the order Asp 102—His 57—Ser 195.

Recall that Ser 195 is the residue that is acylated during catalysis by chymotrypsin. The approach of the acetate anion (derived from *p*-nitrophenylacetate) to the oxygen atom on the R group of Ser 195 triggers sequential proton shifts that "shuttle" protons from Ser 195 through His 57 to Asp 195 (Fig 8–15).

During deacylation of the acyl–Ser 195 intermediate, protons shuttle in the reverse direction. An analogous series of proton shifts is believed to accompany hydrolysis of a physiologic chymotrypsin substrate such as a peptide.

Note that while His 57 and Asp 102 reside on the B peptide of α-chymotrypsin, Ser 195 resides on the C peptide (Fig 8–10). The selective proteolysis of prochymotrypsin (chymotrypsinogen) thus facilitates approximation of the 3 residues concerned with the charge relay network. This illustrates how selective proteolysis can give rise to the catalytic site. Note also that contact and catalytic residues can be located on different peptide chains but still be within bond-forming distance of bound substrate.

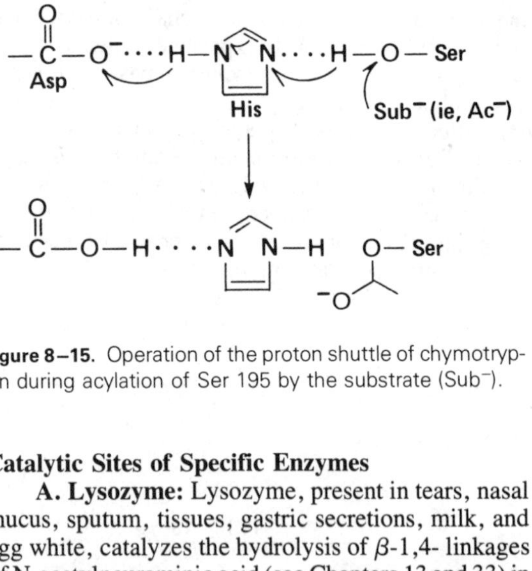

Figure 8–15. Operation of the proton shuttle of chymotrypsin during acylation of Ser 195 by the substrate (Sub⁻).

Catalytic Sites of Specific Enzymes

A. Lysozyme: Lysozyme, present in tears, nasal mucus, sputum, tissues, gastric secretions, milk, and egg white, catalyzes the hydrolysis of β-1,4- linkages of N-acetylneuraminic acid (see Chapters 13 and 33) in proteoglycans and glycosaminoglycans. It performs the function, in tears and nasal mucus, of destroying the cell walls of many airborne gram-positive bacteria. Lysozyme (MW about 15,000) consists of a single polypeptide chain of 129 residues. Since there is no

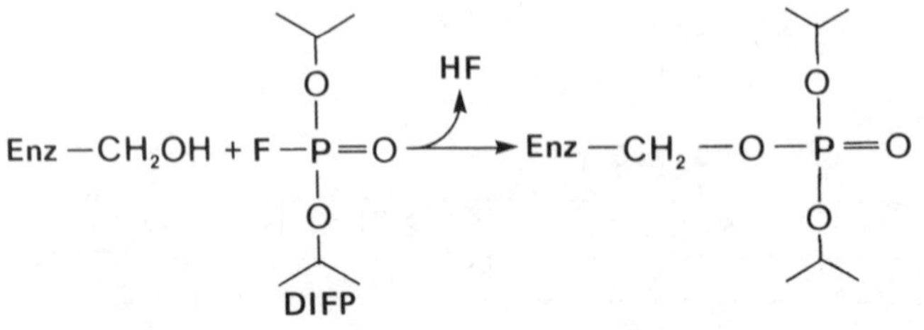

Figure 8–14. Reaction of the primary hydroxyl of Ser 195 of chymotrypsin with diisopropylphosphofluoridate (DIFP).

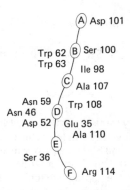

Figure 8–16. Schematic representation of the catalytic site in the cleft region of lysozyme. A to F represent the glycosyl moieties of a hexasaccharide. Some residues in the cleft region are shown with their numbers in the lysozyme sequence. (Adapted from Koshland.)

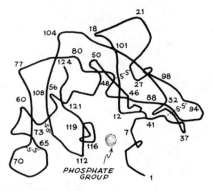

Figure 8–17. Structure of ribonuclease as determined by x-ray diffraction. Numbers refer to specific residues. See also Fig 4–9.

coenzyme or metal ion, catalysis, specificity, and 3-dimensional structure are determined solely by these amino acid residues. There are small regions of pleated sheet, little α-helix, and large regions of random coil. For a model of lysozyme and its substrate, photographed in 3-dimensional color, see *J Biol Chem* 1968;**243**:1663. The molecule bears a deep central cleft which harbors a catalytic site with 6 subsites (Fig 8–16) that bind various substrates or inhibitors. The residues responsible for bond cleavage are thought to lie between sites D and E close to the carboxyl groups of Asp 52 and Glu 35. Glu 35 apparently protonates the acetal bond of the substrate, while the negatively charged Asp 52 stabilizes the resulting carbonium ion from the back side.

B. Ribonuclease: Unlike the case for lysozyme, considerable information about the catalytic site of ribonuclease was available prior to solution of the 3-dimensional structure. The conclusions based on chemical investigations were largely confirmed by crystallography. The structure contains a cleft similar to that of lysozyme across which lie 2 residues, His 12 and His 119. These previously were implicated by chemical evidence as being at the catalytic site. Both residues are near the binding site for uridylic acid (Fig 8–17).

Amino Acid Sequences at Catalytic Sites

Partial decoding of the primary structures of active sites has revealed many similarities between hydrolytic enzymes (Table 8–1). This implies that the number of bond-breaking mechanisms operating in biologic systems is relatively small. In view of these similarities, it is perhaps not surprising that the amino acid sequences near the catalytic sites of the same enzyme from different species bear even greater similarity.

Effect of Temperature

Over a limited range of temperatures, the velocity of enzyme-catalyzed reactions increases as temperature rises. The exact ratio by which the velocity changes for a 10 °C temperature rise is the Q_{10}, **or temperature coefficient.** The velocity of many biologic reactions roughly doubles with a 10 °C rise in temperature ($Q_{10} = 2$), and is halved if the temperature is decreased by 10 °C. Many physiologic processes— eg, the rate of contraction of an excised heart— consequently exhibit a Q_{10} of about 2.

For rates of enzyme-catalyzed reactions measured at several temperatures, Fig 8–18 is typical.

There is an optimal temperature at which the reaction is most rapid. Above this, the reaction rate

Table 8–1. Amino acid sequences in the neighborhood of the catalytic sites of several bovine proteases. Regions shown are those on either side of the catalytic site seryl (S) and histidyl (H) residues. For explanation of single letter abbreviations for amino acids, see Chapter 3. (Reproduced, with permission, from Dayhoff MO [editor]: *Atlas of Protein Sequence and Structure.* Vol 5. National Biomedical Research Foundation, 1972.)

Enzyme	Sequence Around Serine Ⓢ															Sequence Around Histidine Ⓗ									
Trypsin	D	S	C	Q	D	G	Ⓢ	G	G	P	V	V	C	S	G	K	V	V	S	A	A	Ⓗ	C	Y	K	S	G
Chymotrypsin A	S	S	C	M	G	D	Ⓢ	G	G	P	L	V	C	K	K	N	V	V	T	A	A	Ⓗ	G	G	V	T	T
Chymotrypsin B	S	S	C	M	G	D	Ⓢ	G	G	P	L	V	C	Q	K	N	V	V	T	A	A	Ⓗ	C	G	V	T	T
Thrombin	D	A	C	E	G	D	Ⓢ	G	G	P	F	V	M	K	S	P	V	L	T	A	A	Ⓗ	C	L	L	Y	P

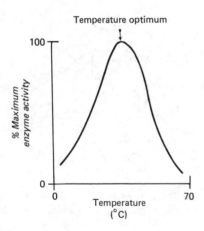

Figure 8–18. Effect of temperature on the velocity of a hypothetical enzyme-catalyzed reaction.

decreases sharply, mainly owing to denaturation of the enzyme by heat.

For most enzymes, optimal temperatures are at or above those of the cells in which they occur. Enzymes from microorganisms adapted to growth in natural hot springs may exhibit optimal temperatures close to the boiling point of water.

The increase in rate below optimal temperature results from the increased kinetic energy of the reacting molecules. As the temperature is raised still further, however, the kinetic energy of the enzyme molecule itself becomes so great that it exceeds the energy barrier for breaking the secondary bonds that hold the enzyme in its native or catalytically active state. There is consequently a loss of secondary and tertiary structure and a parallel loss of catalytic activity.

pH Optima

Moderate pH changes affect the **ionic state of the enzyme** and frequently that of the substrate also. When enzyme activity is measured at several pH values, optimal activity typically is observed between pH values of 5.0 and 9.0. However, a few enzymes, eg, pepsin, are active at pH values well outside this range.

The shape of pH-activity curves is determined by the following factors:

1. Enzyme denaturation at extremely high or low pH.

2. Effects on the charged state of the substrate or enzyme. For the enzyme, charge changes may affect activity either by changing structure or by changing the charge on a residue functional in substrate binding or catalysis. To illustrate, consider a negatively charged enzyme (Enz^-) reacting with a positively charged substrate (SH^+):

$$Enz^- + SH^+ \rightarrow EnzSH$$

At low pH, Enz^- protonates and loses its negative charge:

$$Enz^- + H^+ \rightarrow EnzH$$

Similarly, at high pH, SH^+ ionizes and loses its positive charge:

$$SH^+ \rightarrow S + H^+$$

Since the only forms that will interact are SH^+ and Enz^-, extreme pH values will lower the effective concentration of Enz^- and SH^+, thus lowering the reaction velocity (Fig 8–19). Only in the cross-hatched area are both Enz and S in the appropriate ionic state, and the maximal concentrations of Enz and S are correctly charged at X.

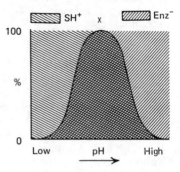

Figure 8–19. Effect of pH on enzyme activity.

Another important factor is a change in conformation of the enzyme when the pH is varied. A charged group distal to the region where the substrate is bound may be necessary to maintain an active tertiary or quaternary structure, as described for hemoglobin (see Chapter 5). As the charge on this group is changed, the protein may unravel, become more compact, or dissociate into protomers—all with resulting loss of activity.

EFFECT OF REACTANT CONCENTRATION

At high reactant concentrations, both the number of molecules with sufficient energy to react and their frequency of collision are high. This is true whether all or only a fraction of the molecules have sufficient energy to react. For reactions involving 2 different molecules, A and B,

$$A + B \rightarrow AB$$

doubling the concentration either of A or of B will double the reaction rate. Doubling the concentration of both A and B will increase the probability of collision 4-fold. The reaction rate therefore increases 4-fold. **The reaction rate is proportionate to the concentrations of the reacting molecules.** Square brackets

([]) are used to denote molar concentrations;* $\propto$ means "proportionate to." The rate expression is

$$\text{Rate} \propto [\text{reacting molecules}]$$

or

$$\text{Rate} \propto [A]\ [B]$$

For the situation represented by

$$A + 2B \rightarrow AB_2$$

the rate expression is

$$\text{Rate} \propto [A]\ [B]\ [B]$$

or

$$\text{Rate} \propto [A]\ [B]^2$$

For the general case where n molecules of A react with m molecules of B

$$nA + mB \rightarrow A_nB_m$$

the rate expression is

$$\text{Rate} \propto [A]^n[B]^m$$

THE EQUILIBRIUM CONSTANT

Since all chemical reactions are reversible, for the reverse reaction where n molecules of A react with m molecules of B

$$A_nB_m \rightarrow nA + mB$$

the appropriate rate expression is

$$\text{Rate} \propto [A_nB_m]$$

We represent reversibility by double arrows,

$$nA + mB \rightleftharpoons A_nB_m$$

This expression reads: "n molecules of A and m molecules of B are in equilibrium with A_nB_m." We may replace the "proportionate to" symbol ($\propto$) with an equality sign by inserting a proportionality constant, k, characteristic of the reaction under study. For the general case

$$nA + mB \rightleftharpoons A_nB_m$$

expressions for the rates of the forward reaction (Rate_1) and back reaction (Rate_{-1}) are

*Strictly speaking, molar activities rather than concentrations should be used.

$$\text{Rate}_1 = k_1 [A]^n[B]^m$$

and

$$\text{Rate}_{-1} = k_{-1} [A_nB_m]$$

When the rates of the forward and back reactions are equal, the system is said to be **at equilibrium,** ie,

$$\text{Rate}_1 = \text{Rate}_{-1}$$

Then

$$k_1 [A]^n[B]^m = k_{-1} [A_nB_m]$$

and

$$\frac{k_1}{k_{-1}} = \frac{[A_nB_m]}{[A]^n[B]^m} = K_{eq}$$

The ratio of k_1 to k_{-1} is termed the **equilibrium constant, K_{eq}.** The following important properties of a system at equilibrium should be kept in mind.

(1) The equilibrium constant is the ratio of the reaction rate **constants** k_1/k_{-1}.

(2) At equilibrium, the reaction **rates** (not the reaction rate constants) of the forward and back reactions are equal.

(3) **Equilibrium is a dynamic state.** Although no **net** change in concentration of reactant or product molecules occurs at equilibrium, A and B are continually being converted to A_nB_m and vice versa.

(4) **The equilibrium constant may be given a numerical value if we know the concentrations of A, B, and A_nB_m at equilibrium.**

Relationship Between Equilibrium Constant & Standard Free Energy Change (ΔG^0) for the Overall Reaction

The equilibrium constant is related to ΔG^0 as follows:

$$\Delta G^0 = -RT \ln K_{eq}$$

R is the gas constant and T the absolute temperature. Since these are known, **knowledge of the numerical value of K_{eq} permits one to calculate a value for ΔG^0.** If the equilibrium constant is greater than 1, the reaction is spontaneous; ie, the reaction as written (from left to right) is favored. If it is less than 1, the opposite is true; ie, the reaction is more likely to proceed from right to left. Note, however, that although the equilibrium constant for a reaction indicates the **direction** in which a reaction is spontaneous, it does not indicate whether it will take place **rapidly.** That is, it does not tell us anything about the **magnitude of the energy barrier** for the reaction (ie, ΔG_F; see above). This follows because K_{eq} determines ΔG^0, previously shown to concern only initial and final states. **Reaction rates depend on the magnitude of the energy barrier, not on the magnitude of ΔG^0.**

Most factors affecting the velocity of enzyme-catalyzed reactions do so by **changing local reactant concentration.**

ENZYME CONCENTRATION

In many situations, is useful to know not only whether a given enzyme is present but also *how much* is present. Under appropriate conditions, the velocity of an enzyme-catalyzed reaction will be directly proportionate to the amount of the enzyme present. (See Figs 6–5 and 6–6.)

That the rate is not always proportionate to enzyme concentration may be seen by considering the forward reaction at equilibrium. Although the forward reaction is proceeding, the rate of the reverse reaction equals it. Accordingly, it would *appear* that the forward reaction velocity is zero. However, when the enzyme-catalyzed reaction *initiates* the conversion of one or more substrates to product (P), there is no P for the reverse reaction to occur. Furthermore, at the *initiation* of the (forward) reaction, the concentration of S will not have been depleted at all. Therefore, at the initiation of the reaction, the velocity, ie, the **initial velocity (v_i)**, will be **directly proportionate to the enzyme concentration** [Enz] (see Fig 6–6).

The enzyme is a reactant that combines with substrate to form an **enzyme-substrate complex, EnzS,** which decomposes to form a product, P, and free enzyme. In its simplest form, this may be represented as

$$Enz + S \underset{k_{-1}}{\overset{k_1}{\rightleftharpoons}} EnzS \underset{k_{-2}}{\overset{k_2}{\rightleftharpoons}} Enz + P$$

Note that although the rate expressions for the forward, back, and *overall* reactions include the term [Enz],

$$Enz + S \underset{k_{-2}}{\overset{k_1}{\rightleftharpoons}} Enz + P$$

$$Rate_1 = k_1 [Enz] [S]$$

$$Rate_{-2} = k_{-2} [Enz] [P]$$

in the expression for the *overall* equilibrium constant, [Enz] cancels out.

$$K_{eq} = \frac{k_1}{k_{-2}} = \frac{[Enz] [P]}{[Enz] [S]} = \frac{[P]}{[S]}$$

The enzyme concentration thus has no effect on the equilibrium constant. Stated another way, since enzymes affect rates, not rate constants, they cannot affect K_{eq}, which is a ratio of rate constants. **The K_{eq} of a reaction is the same regardless of whether equilibrium is approached with or without enzymatic catalysis** (recall ΔG^0). Enzymes change the reaction path but do not affect the initial and final equilibrium concentrations of the reactants and products, the factors that determine K_{eq} and ΔG^0.

SUBSTRATE CONCENTRATION

In the following discussion, enzyme reactions are treated as if they had a single substrate and a single product. While this is the case for some enzyme-catalyzed reactions, most enzyme-catalyzed reactions have 2 or more substrates and products. This consideration does not, however, invalidate the following discussion. What holds for a single substrate is true also for 2 substrates.

If the concentration of a substrate [S] is increased while all other conditions are kept constant, the **measured initial velocity,** v_i (the velocity measured when very little substrate has reacted), increases to a maximum value, V_{max}, and no further (Fig 8–20).

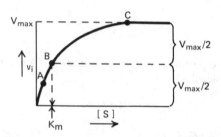

Figure 8–20. Effect of substrate concentration on the velocity of an enzyme-catalyzed reaction.

The velocity increases as the substrate concentration is increased up to a point where the enzyme is said to be "saturated" with substrate. The measured initial velocity reaches a maximal value and is unaffected by further increases in substrate concentration, because substrate is present in large molar excess over the enzyme. For example, if an enzyme with a molecular weight of 100,000 acts on a substrate with a molecular weight of 100 and both are present at a concentration of 1 mg/mL, there are 1000 mol of substrate for every mole of enzyme. More realistic figures might be

$$[Enz] = 0.1 \, \mu g/mL = 10^{-9} \, molar$$
$$[S] = 0.1 \, mg/mL = 10^{-3} \, molar$$

giving a 10^6 molar excess of substrate over enzyme. Even if [S] is decreased 100-fold, substrate is still present in 10,000-fold molar excess over enzyme.

The situations at points A, B, and C in Fig 8–20 are illustrated in Fig 8–21. At points A and B only a portion of the enzyme present is combined with substrate, even though there are many more molecules of substrate than of enzyme. This is because the equilibrium constant for the reaction Enz + S $\rightleftharpoons$ EnzS (formation of the EnzS complex) is not infinitely large. **At point A or B, increasing or decreasing [S] will therefore increase or decrease the amount of Enz associated with S as EnzS, and v_i will thus depend on [S].** At C, essentially all the enzyme is combined with substrate, so that a further increase in [S], al-

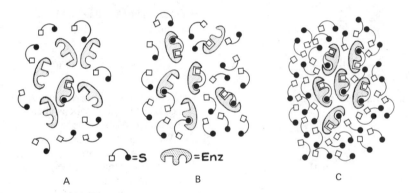

Figure 8–21. Representation of an enzyme at low *(A)*, at high *(C)*, and at the K_m concentration of substrate *(B)*. Points A, B, and C correspond to those of Fig 8–20.

though it increases the frequency of collision between Enz and S, cannot result in increased rates of reaction, since no free enzyme is available to react.

Case B depicts a situation of major theoretical interest where exactly half the enzyme molecules are "saturated with" substrate. The velocity is accordingly **half the maximal velocity** ($V_{max}/2$) attainable at that particular enzyme concentration.

Graphic Evaluation of the Michaelis Constant, K_m

The substrate concentration that produces **half-maximal velocity, termed the K_m value or Michaelis constant,** may be determined experimentally by graphing v_i as a function of [S] (Fig 8–20). Note that K_m has the dimensions of molar concentration.

When [S] is approximately equal to the K_m, v_i is very responsive to changes in [S], and the enzyme is working at precisely half-maximal velocity. In fact, many enzymes possess K_m values that are approximate to the physiologic concentration of their substrates.

The Michaelis-Menten expression

$$v_i = \frac{V_{max}[S]}{K_m + [S]}$$

describes the behavior of many enzymes as substrate concentration is varied. The dependence of the initial velocity of an enzyme-catalyzed reaction on [S] and on K_m may be illustrated by evaluating the Michaelis-Menten equation as follows:

(1) When [S] is very much less than K_m (point A in Figs 8–20 and 8–21). Adding [S] to K_m in the denominator now changes its value very little, so that the [S] term can be dropped from the denominator. Since V_{max} and K_m are both constants, we can replace their ratio by a new constant, K.

$$v_i = \frac{V_{max}[S]}{K_m + [S]} \; ; \; v_i \approx \frac{V_{max}[S]}{K_m} \approx \frac{V_{max}}{K_m}[S] \approx K[S]$$

[≈ means "approximately equal to."]

In other words, **when the substrate concentration is considerably below that required to produce half-maximal velocity (the K_m value), the initial velocity, v_i, depends upon the substrate concentration, [S].**

(2) When [S] is very much greater than K_m (point C, Figs 8–20 and 8–21). Now adding K_m to [S] in the denominator changes the value of the denominator very little, so that the term K_m can be dropped from the denominator.

$$v_i = \frac{V_{max}[S]}{K_m + [S]} \; ; \; v_i \approx \frac{V_{max}[S]}{[S]} \approx V_{max}$$

This states that **when the substrate concentration [S] far exceeds the K_m value, the initial velocity, v_i, is maximal, V_{max}.**

(3) When [S] = K_m (point B, Figs 8–20 and 8–21),

$$v_i = \frac{V_{max}[S]}{K_m + [S]} \; ; \; v_i = \frac{V_{max}[S]}{[S] + [S]} = \frac{V_{max}[S]}{2[S]} = \frac{V_{max}}{2}$$

This states that **when the substrate concentration is equal to the K_m value, the initial velocity, v_i, is half-maximal.** It also tells how **to evaluate K_m,** namely, to **determine experimentally the substrate concentration where the initial velocity is half-maximal.**

Since many enzymes give saturation curves that do not readily permit evaluation of V_{max} (and hence of K_m) when v_i is plotted versus [S], it is convenient to rearrange the Michaelis-Menten expression to simplify evaluation of K_m and V_{max}. The Michaelis-Menten equation may be inverted and factored as follows:

$$v_i = \frac{V_{max}[S]}{K_m + [S]}$$

Invert:

$$\frac{1}{v_i} = \frac{K_m + [S]}{V_{max}[S]}$$

Factor:

$$\frac{1}{v_i} = \frac{K_m}{V_{max}} \cdot \frac{1}{[S]} + \frac{[S]}{V_{max}[S]}$$

Simplify:

$$\frac{1}{v_i} = \frac{K_m}{V_{max}} \cdot \frac{1}{[S]} + \frac{1}{V_{max}}$$

This is the equation for a **straight line**

$$y = a \cdot x + b$$

where

$$y = \frac{1}{v_i} \text{ and } x = \frac{1}{[S]}$$

If y, or $1/v_i$, is plotted as a function of x, or $1/[S]$, the y-intercept, b, is $1/V_{max}$, and the slope, a, is K_m/V_{max}. The negative x-intercept may be evaluated by setting $y = 0$. Then

$$x = -\frac{b}{a} = -\frac{1}{K_m}$$

Such a plot is called a double reciprocal plot; ie, the reciprocal of v_i ($1/v_i$) is plotted versus the reciprocal of $[S]$ ($1/[S]$).

K_m may be estimated from the **double-reciprocal or Lineweaver-Burk plot** (Fig 8–22) using either the slope and y-intercept or the negative x-intercept. Since $[S]$ is expressed in molarity, **the dimensions of K_m are molarity or moles per liter.** Velocity, v_i, may be expressed in any units, since **K_m is independent of [Enz].** The double-reciprocal treatment requires relatively few points to define K_m and is the method most often used to determine K_m.

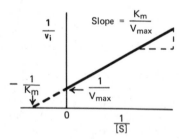

Figure 8–22. Double-reciprocal or Lineweaver-Burk plot of $1/v_i$ versus $1/[S]$ used for graphic evaluation of K_m and V_{max}.

Experimentally, use of the Lineweaver-Burk approach to evaluate K_m can give rise to unwarranted emphasis on data gathered at low substrate concentrations. This is the case if the substrate concentrations selected for study differ by a constant increment. This shortcoming may be circumvented by selecting substrate concentrations the reciprocals of which differ by constant increments.

An alternative approach to the experimental evaluation of K_m and of V_{max} is that of Eadie and

Hofstee. The Michaelis-Menten equation may be rearranged to

$$\frac{v_i}{[S]} = -v_i \cdot \frac{1}{K_m} + \frac{V_{max}}{K_m}$$

To evaluate K_m and V_{max}, plot $v_i/[S]$ (y-axis) versus v_i (x-axis). The y-intercept is then V_{max}/K_m, and the x-intercept is V_{max}. The slope is $-1/K_m$.

While both the Lineweaver-Burk and Eadie-Hofstee approaches are useful in selected instances, rigorous determination of K_m and of V_{max} requires statistical treatment.

Apart from their usefulness in interpretation of the mechanisms of enzyme-catalyzed reactions, K_m values are of considerable practical value. At a substrate concentration of 100 times K_m, the enzyme will act at essentially maximum rate, and therefore the **maximal velocity (V_{max}) will reflect the amount of active enzyme present.** This situation is generally desirable in the assay of enzymes. The **K_m value tells how much substrate to use in order to measure V_{max}.** Double-reciprocal treatments also find extensive application in the evaluation of enzyme inhibitors.

Relationship of K_m to K_d, the Dissociation Constant for the Enzyme-Substrate Complex

The **affinity** of an enzyme for its substrate is equal to the **inverse of the dissociation constant, K_d, for ES.**

$$E + S \underset{k_{-1}}{\overset{k_1}{\rightleftharpoons}} ES$$

$$K_d = \frac{k_{-1}}{k_1}$$

That is, the less the tendency of the substrate and enzyme to dissociate, the greater is the affinity of the enzyme for the substrate.

The K_m value of an enzyme for its substrate may also serve as a measure of its K_d. However, in order for this to be true, an assumption included in the derivation of the Michaelis-Menten expression must be valid. In the derivation, it was assumed that the first step of the enzyme-catalyzed reaction

$$E + S \underset{k_{-1}}{\overset{k_1}{\rightleftharpoons}} ES$$

is fast and always at equilibrium. In other words, the rate of dissociation of ES to E + S must be much faster than its dissociation to enzyme + product

$$ES \underset{k_{-2}}{\overset{k_2}{\rightleftharpoons}} E + P$$

In the Michaelis-Menten expression, the [S] that gives $v_i = V_{max}/2$ is

$$[S] = \frac{k_2 + k_{-1}}{k_1} = K_m$$

But when

$$k_{-1} \gg k_2$$

then

$$k_2 + k_{-1} \approx k_{-1}$$

and

$$[S] = \frac{k_{-1}}{k_1} \equiv K_d$$

Under these conditions, $1/K_m = 1/K_d =$ **affinity**. If $k_2 + k_{-1} \not\approx k_{-1}$, then $1/K_m$ underestimates the affinity, $1/K_d$.

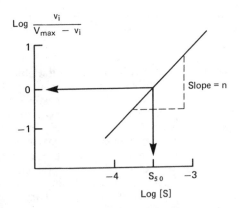

Figure 8–24. Graphic evaluation of the Hill equation to determine the substrate concentration that produces half-maximal velocity when substrate saturation kinetics are sigmoid.

LIMITATIONS OF THE MICHAELIS-MENTEN MODEL

Sigmoidal Saturation Kinetics

Certain enzymes and other ligand-binding proteins, such as hemoglobin (see Chapters 5 and 9), do not exhibit classic Michaelis-Menten saturation kinetics. When [S] is plotted versus v_i, the saturation curve is sigmoid (Fig 8–23). This generally indicates cooperative binding of substrate to multiple sites. Binding at one site affects binding at the others, as described in Chapter 5 for hemoglobin.

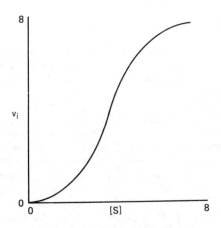

Figure 8–23. Sigmoid saturation kinetics.

For sigmoid substrate saturation kinetics, the methods of graphic evaluation of the substrate concentration that produces half-maximal velocity discussed above are invalid (straight lines are not produced). To evaluate sigmoid saturation kinetics, we employ a graphic representation of the Hill equation, an equation originally derived to describe the cooperative

binding of O_2 to hemoglobin (see Chapter 5). Written in the form of a straight line, the Hill equation is

$$\log \frac{v_i}{V_{max} - v_i} = n\log [S] - \log k'$$

where k' is a complex constant. The equation states that, when [S] is low compared to k', the reaction velocity increases as the nth power of [S]. Fig 8–24 illustrates a Hill plot of kinetic data for an enzyme with cooperative binding kinetics. A plot of $v_i/V_{max} - v_i$ versus log [S] yields a straight line with slope = n, where n is an empirical parameter whose value depends on the number of substrate-binding sites and the number and type of interactions between these binding sites. When n = 1, the binding sites act independently of one another. If n > 1, the sites are cooperative; and the greater the value of n, the stronger is the cooperativity and thus the more "sigmoid" are the saturation kinetics. If n < 1, the sites are said to exhibit negative cooperativity.

At half-maximal velocity ($v_i = V_{max}/2$), $v_i/(V_{max} - v_i) = 1$, and hence log $v_i/(V_{max} - v_i) = 0$. Thus, to determine S_{50} (the concentration of substrate that produces half-maximal velocity), drop a perpendicular line to the x-axis from the point where log $v_i/(V_{max} - v_i) = 0$.

INHIBITION OF ENZYME ACTIVITY

We distinguish 2 broad classes of inhibitors of enzyme activity—competitive and noncompetitive—depending on whether the inhibition is (competitive) or is not (noncompetitive) relieved by increasing the substrate concentration. In practice, many inhibitors do not exhibit the idealized properties of pure competitive or noncompetitive inhibition discussed below. An alternative way to classify inhibitors is by their site of action. Some bind to the enzyme at the same site as does the substrate (the catalytic site); others bind at some site (an allosteric site) away from the catalytic site.

Competitive or Substrate Analog Inhibition

Classic competitive inhibition occurs at the substrate-binding (catalytic) site. The chemical structure of a substrate analog inhibitor (I) generally resembles that of the substrate (S). It may therefore combine reversibly with the enzyme, forming an enzyme inhibitor (EnzI) complex rather than an EnzS complex. When both the substrate and this type of inhibitor are present, they compete for the same binding sites on the enzyme surface. A much studied case of competitive inhibition is that of malonate (I) with succinate (S) for succinate dehydrogenase.

Succinate dehydrogenase catalyzes formation of fumarate by removal of one hydrogen atom from each α-carbon atom of succinate (Fig 8–25).

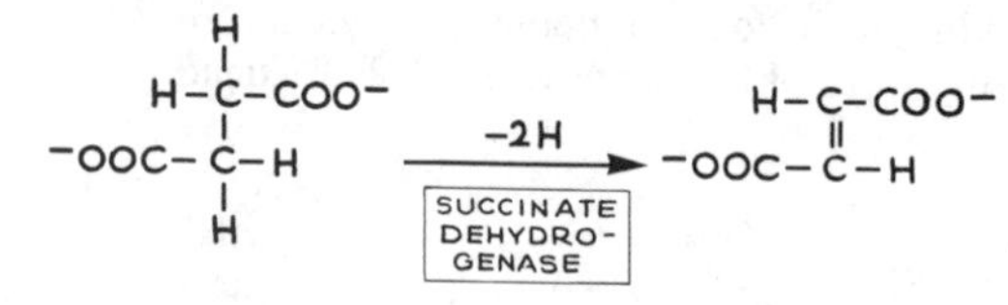

H
|
H–C–COO⁻   H–C–COO⁻
| $\xrightarrow{\text{−2 H}}$ ‖
⁻OOC– C–H $\boxed{\text{SUCCINATE DEHYDRO-GENASE}}$ ⁻OOC– C–H
|
H

Succinate   Fumarate

Figure 8–25. The succinate dehydrogenase reaction.

Malonate ($^-$OOC–CH$_2$–COO$^-$) can combine with the dehydrogenase, forming an EnzI complex. This cannot be dehydrogenated, since there is no way to remove even one H atom from the single α-carbon atom of malonate without forming a pentavalent carbon atom. The only reaction the EnzI complex can undergo is decomposition back to free enzyme plus inhibitor. For the reversible reaction,

$$\text{EnzI} \underset{k_{-1}}{\overset{k_1}{\rightleftharpoons}} \text{Enz + I}$$

the equilibrium constant, K_i, is

$$K_i = \frac{[\text{Enz}] [\text{I}]}{[\text{EnzI}]} = \frac{k_1}{k_{-1}}$$

The action of competitive inhibitors may be understood in terms of the following reactions:

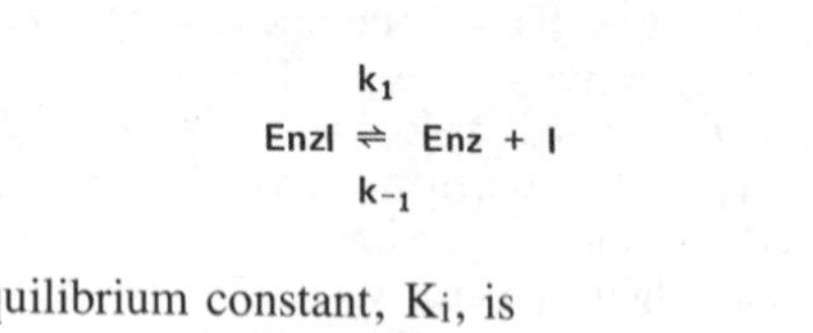

$$\begin{array}{c}
\xrightarrow{\pm I} \quad \text{EnzI (inactive)} \xrightarrow{\quad} \text{Enz + P} \\
\text{Enz} \\
\xrightarrow{\pm S} \quad \text{EnzS (active)} \rightarrow \text{Enz + P}
\end{array}$$

The rate of product formation, which is what generally is measured, depends solely on the concen-

tration of EnzS. Suppose I binds very tightly to the enzyme (K_i = a small number). There now is little free enzyme (Enz) available to combine with S to form EnzS and eventually Enz + P. The reaction rate (formation of P) will thus be slow. For analogous reasons, an equal concentration of a less tightly bound inhibitor (K_i = a larger number) will not decrease the rate of the catalyzed reaction so markedly. Suppose that, at a fixed concentration of I, more S is added. This increases the probability that Enz will combine with S rather than with I. The ratio of EnzS/EnzI and the reaction rate also rise. At a sufficiently high concentration of S, the concentration of EnzI should be vanishingly small. If so, the rate of the catalyzed reaction will be the same as in the absence of I (Fig 8–26).

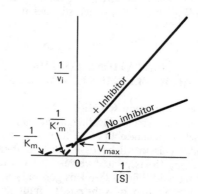

Figure 8–26. Lineweaver-Burk plot of classic competitive inhibition. Note the complete relief of inhibition at high [S] (low 1/[S]).

Graphic Evaluation of Competitive Inhibition Constants

Fig 8–26 represents a typical case of competitive inhibition shown graphically in the form of a Lineweaver-Burk plot. The reaction velocity (v_i) at a fixed concentration of inhibitor was measured at various concentrations of S. The lines drawn through the experimental points coincide at the y-axis. Since the y-intercept is $1/V_{max}$, this states that **at an infinitely high concentration of S (1/S = 0), v_i is the same as in the absence of inhibitor.** However, the intercept on the x-axis (which is related to K_m) varies with inhibitor concentration and becomes a larger number ($-1/K'_m$ is smaller than $-1/K_m$) in the presence of the inhibitor. Thus, **a competitive inhibitor raises the apparent K_m (K'_m) for the substrate.** Since K_m is the substrate concentration where the concentration of free enzyme is equal to the concentration of enzyme as EnzS, substantial free enzyme is available to combine with inhibitor. For simple competitive inhibition, the intercept on the x-axis is

$$x = \frac{1}{K_m \left(1 + \dfrac{[\text{I}]}{K_i} \right)}$$

K_m may be evaluated in the absence of I, and K_i evaluated using the above equation. If the number of moles of I added is much greater than the number of moles of enzyme present, [I] may generally be taken as the added (known) concentration of inhibitor. The K_i values for a series of substrate analog (competitive) inhibitors indicate which are most effective. **At a low concentration, those with the lowest K_i values will cause the greatest degree of inhibition.**

Many clinically efficacious drugs act as competitive inhibitors of important enzyme activities in microbial and animal cells.

Reversible Noncompetitive Inhibition

As the name implies, in this case no competition occurs between S and I. The inhibitor usually bears little or no structural resemblance to S and may be assumed to bind to a different domain on the enzyme. **Reversible noncompetitive inhibitors lower the maximum velocity attainable with a given amount of enzyme (lower V_{max}) but usually do not affect K_m.** Since I and S may combine at different sites, formation of both EnzI and EnzIS complexes is possible. Since EnzIS may break down to form product at a slower rate than does EnzS, the reaction may be slowed but not halted. The following competing reactions may occur:

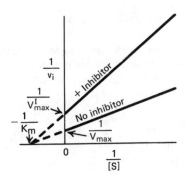

If S has equal affinity both for Enz and for EnzI (I does not affect the affinity of Enz for S), the results shown in Fig 8–27 are obtained when $1/v_i$ is plotted against $1/[S]$ in the presence and absence of inhibitor. (It is assumed that there has been no significant alteration of the conformation of the active site when I is bound.)

Figure 8–27. Lineweaver-Burk plot for reversible noncompetitive inhibition.

Irreversible Noncompetitive Inhibition

A variety of enzyme "poisons," eg, iodoacetamide, heavy metal ions (Ag^+, Hg^{2+}), oxidizing agents, etc, reduce enzyme activity. Since these inhibitors bear no structural resemblance to the substrate, an increase in substrate concentration generally does not relieve this inhibition. The presence of one or more substrates or products may, however, protect the enzyme against inactivation. Kinetic analysis of the type discussed above may not distinguish between enzyme poisons and true reversible noncompetitive inhibitors. Reversible noncompetitive inhibition is, in any case, rare. Unfortunately this is not always appreciated, since both reversible and irreversible noncompetitive inhibition exhibit similar kinetics.

Modulators of Enzyme Activity

The flow of carbon and energy in metabolism is profoundly influenced both by enzyme synthesis and by activation of proenzymes. However, these processes are irreversible. Like all mammalian proteins, enzymes are degraded to amino acids (protein turnover). In bacteria, the activity can be rapidly diluted out among daughter cells on successive divisions. Although both mechanisms effectively reduce enzyme concentration and hence catalytic activity, they are slow, wasteful of carbon and energy, and rather like turning out a light by smashing the bulb and then inserting a new one when light is needed. An "on-off" switch for enzymes clearly would be advantageous. It thus is not surprising that the **catalytic activity** of certain key enzymes can be reversibly decreased or increased by low-molecular-weight intermediary metabolites (see Chapter 5). Small molecule **modulators** that decrease catalytic activity are termed **negative modulators;** those which increase activity are called **positive modulators.** These are discussed further in Chapter 9 and in subsequent chapters.

ORDERED & RANDOM BINDING OF SUBSTRATES

Most enzymes catalyze a reaction between 2 or more substrates, yielding one or more products. For some enzymes, all substrates must be present simultaneously for the reaction to occur. For others, the enzyme first alters one substrate and then catalyzes its reaction with a second substrate. The order in which an enzyme binds its substrates may be **random** or **ordered** (Fig 8–28).

Many reactions that require coenzymes proceed by "ping-pong" mechanisms (so termed because the enzyme alternates between forms E and E') (Figs 8–29 and 8–30).

As stated earlier (see Fig 6–1), the coenzyme frequently may be regarded as a second substrate. In this instance, the comments of the previous section apply equally to substrates and to coenzymes. However, certain coenzymes (eg, pyridoxal phosphate) are covalently bonded to the enzyme or bound noncova-

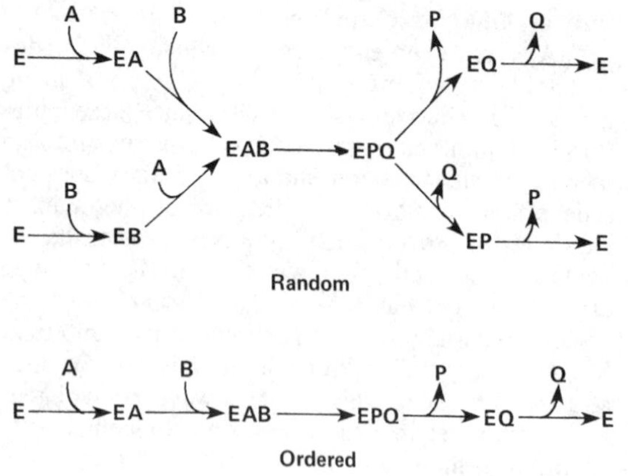

Figure 8–28. Random and ordered addition of substrates A and B and dissociation of products P and Q from an enzyme, E.

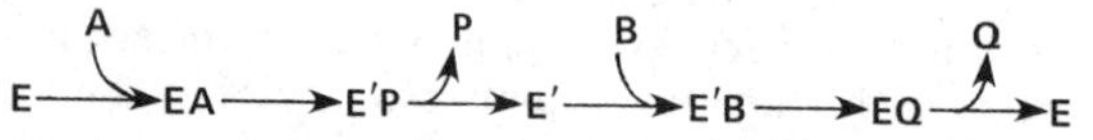

Figure 8–29. Generalized "ping-pong" mechanism for enzymic catalysis.

lently so tightly that dissociation rarely occurs (eg, thiamin pyrophosphate). In these cases, we regard the enzyme-coenzyme complex as the enzyme.

ENZYMES AS GENERAL ACID OR GENERAL BASE CATALYSTS

Once the substrate has bound at the catalytic site, the charged (or chargeable) functional groups of the side chains of nearby aminoacyl residues (for examples, see Table 3–1) may participate in catalysis by functioning as acidic or basic catalysts.

We recognize 2 broad categories of acid-base catalysis by enzymes: **general** acid (or base) catalysis and **specific** acid (or base) catalysis.

Reactions whose rates vary in response to changes in H+ or H_3O^+ concentration but are independent of the concentrations of other acids or bases present in the solution are said to be subject to **specific acid** or **specific base catalysis**. Reactions whose rates are responsive to all the acids (proton donors) or bases

(proton acceptors) present in solution are said to be subject to **general acid** or **general base catalysis.**

To determine whether a given enzyme-catalyzed reaction is subject to general or specific acid or base catalysis, one measures the rate of the reaction under 2 sets of conditions: (1) at various pH values but at a constant buffer concentration; (2) at constant pH but at various buffer concentrations.

If the rate of the reaction changes as a function of pH at constant buffer concentration, the reaction is said to be **specific base–catalyzed** (if the pH is above 7) or **specific acid–catalyzed** (if the pH is below 7). If the reaction rate at constant pH increases as the buffer concentration increases, the reaction is said to be subject to **general base catalysis** (if the pH is above 7) or **general acid catalysis** (if the pH is below 7).

As an example of specific acid catalysis, consider the conversion of a substrate (S) to a product (P). This occurs in 2 steps—a rapid, reversible proton transfer step,

$$S + H_3O^+ \rightleftharpoons SH^+ + H_2O$$

followed by a slower, and therefore rate-determining, step of rearrangement of the protonated substrate to product

$$SH^+ + H_2O \rightarrow P + H_3O^+$$

Increasing the concentration of hydronium ion $[H_3O^+]$ increases the reaction rate by elevating the concentration of SH^+, the conjugate acid of the substrate, which is the substrate for the rate-determining step in the overall reaction. Stated mathematically,

$$Rate = \frac{d[P]}{dt} = k[SH^+]$$

where P = the product, t = time, k = the specific rate constant, and $[SH^+]$ = the concentration of the conjugate acid of the substrate.

Since the concentration of SH^+ depends upon both the concentration of S and the concentration of H_3O^+, the general rate expression for specific acid–catalyzed reactions is

$$\frac{d[P]}{dt} = k'[S][H_3O^+]$$

Note that it is a requirement of specific acid catalysis that the rate expression contain *only* terms for S and for H_3O^+.

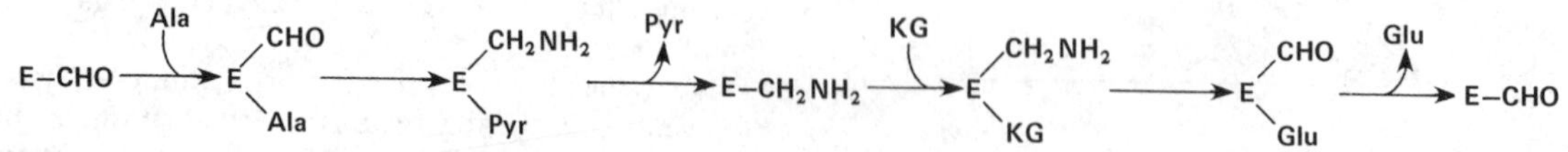

Figure 8–30. "Ping-pong" mechanism for transamination. E—CHO and E—CH_2NH_2 represent the enzyme–pyridoxal phosphate and enzyme–pyridoxamine phosphate complexes, respectively. (Ala, alanine; Pyr, pyruvate; KG, α-ketoglutarate; and Glu, glutamate.)

Next consider that, in addition to the specific acid catalysis described above, there is also catalysis by imidazolium ion of an imidazole buffer. Since imidazole is a weak acid (pK_a about 7), it is a poor proton donor; hence the reaction

$$S + Imidazole \cdot H^+ \rightarrow SH^+ + Imidazole$$

is slow and is rate-determining for the overall reaction. Note that the fast and slow steps are reversed when the mechanism changes from specific to general acid catalysis. The rate expressions for general acid catalysis frequently are complex and for this reason are not discussed here.

Role of Metal Ions

Over 25% of all enzymes contain tightly bound metal ions or require them for activity. The functions of these metal ions are studied by x-ray crystallography, nuclear magnetic resonance (NMR), and electron spin resonance (ESR). Coupled with knowledge of the formation and decay of metal complexes and of reactions within the coordination spheres of metal ions, this provides insight into the roles of metal ions in enzymic catalysis. These roles are considered below.

Metalloenzymes and Metal-Activated Enzymes. Metalloenzymes contain a definite quantity of functional metal ion that is retained throughout purification. **Metal-activated enzymes** bind metals less tightly but require added metals. The distinction between metalloenzymes and metal-activated enzymes thus rests on the affinity of a particular enzyme for its metal ion. The mechanisms whereby metal ions perform their functions appear to be similar both in metalloenzymes and metal-activated enzymes.

Ternary Enzyme-Metal-Substrate Complexes. For ternary (3-component) complexes of the catalytic site (Enz), a metal ion (M), and substrate (S) that exhibit 1:1:1 stoichiometry, 4 schemes are possible:

Enz–S–M	M–Enz–S
Substrate-bridge complex	**Enzyme-bridge complex**

Enz–M–S	Enz$\diagup^M_{\diagdown S}$
Simple metal-bridge complex	**Cyclic metal-bridge complex**

All 4 are possible for metal-activated enzymes. Metalloenzymes cannot form the Enz–S–M complex, because they retain the metal throughout purification (ie, are already as Enz–M). Three generalizations can be stated:

(1) Most but not all kinases (ATP:phosphotransferases) form substrate-bridge complexes of the type Enz–nucleotide–M.

(2) Phosphotransferases using pyruvate or phosphoenolpyruvate as substrate, enzymes catalyzing other reactions of phosphoenolpyruvate, and carboxylases form metal-bridge complexes.

(3) A given enzyme may form one type of bridge complex with one substrate and a different type with another.

Enzyme-Bridge Complexes (M–Enz–S). The metals in enzyme-bridge complexes are presumed to perform structural roles maintaining an active conformation (eg, glutamine synthase) or to form a metal bridge to a substrate (eg, pyruvate kinase). In addition to its structural role, the metal ion in pyruvate kinase appears to hold one substrate (ATP) in place and to activate it.

$$\text{Pyruvate kinase} \diagup^{\displaystyle \overset{M}{\diagup\!|}}_{\diagdown \text{Creatine}}\!\!\!\text{ATP}$$

Substrate-Bridge Complexes (Enz–S–M). The formation of ternary substrate-bridge complexes of nucleoside triphosphates with enzyme, metal, and substrate appears attributable to displacement of H_2O from the coordination sphere of the metal by ATP:

$$ATP^{4-} + M(H_2O)_6{}^{2+} \rightleftharpoons ATP-M(H_2O)_3{}^{2-} + 3H_2O$$

Substrate then binds, forming the ternary complex:

$$ATP-M(H_2O)_3{}^{2-} + Enz \rightleftharpoons Enz-ATP-M(H_2O)_3{}^{2-}$$

In phosphotransferase reactions, metal ions are thought to activate the phosphorus atoms and form a rigid, polyphosphate-adenine complex of appropriate conformation in the active, quaternary complex.

Metal-Bridge Complexes:

$$\text{Enz–M–S or Enz}\diagup^{\displaystyle \overset{M}{|}}_{\diagdown S}$$

Crystallographic and sequencing data have established that a His residue is concerned with metal binding at the active site of many proteins (eg, carboxypeptidase A, cytochrome c, rubredoxin, metmyoglobin, and methemoglobin; see Chapter 5). For binary (2-component) Enz–M complexes, the rate-limiting step is in many cases the departure of water from the coordination sphere of the metal ion. For many peptidases, activation by metal ions is a slow process requiring many hours. The slow reaction probably is conformational rearrangement of the binary Enz–M complex to an active conformation, eg,

Metal binding:

$$Enz + M(H_2O)_6 \xrightarrow{\text{Rapid}} Enz-M(H_2O)_{6-n} + nH_2O$$

Rearrangement to active conformation (Enz*):

$$Enz-M(H_2O)_{6-n} \xrightarrow{\text{Slow}} Enz^*-M(H_2O)_{6-n}$$

For metalloenzymes, however, the ternary metal-bridge complex must be formed by combination of the substrate (S) with the binary Enz–M complex:

$$\text{Enz–M} + \text{S} \rightleftharpoons \text{Enz–M–S} \text{ or } \text{Enz} \diagdown^{\text{M}}_{\text{S}}$$

Role of Metal Ions in Catalysis

Metal ions may participate in each of the 4 mechanisms by which enzymes are known to accelerate the rates of chemical reactions: (1) general acid-base catalysis, (2) covalent catalysis, (3) approximation of reactants, and (4) induction of strain in the enzyme or substrate.

Metal ions, like protons, are Lewis acids (electrophiles) and can share an electron pair forming a sigma bond. Metal ions may also be considered "super acids," since they exist in neutral solution, frequently have a positive charge of > 1, and may form pi bonds. In addition (and unlike protons), metals can serve as 3-dimensional templates for orientation of basic groups on the enzyme or substrate.

Metal ions can also accept electrons via sigma or pi bonds to activate electrophiles or nucleophiles (general acid-base catalysis). By donating electrons, metals can activate nucleophiles or act as nucleophiles themselves. The coordination sphere of a metal may bring together enzyme and substrate (approximation) or form chelate-producing distortion in either the enzyme or substrate (strain). A metal ion may also

Table 8–2. Selected examples of the roles of metal ions in the mechanism of action of enzymes.*

Enzyme	Role of Metal Ion
Histidine deaminase	Masking a nucleophile
Kinases, lyases, pyruvate decarboxylase	Activation of an electrophile
Carbonic anhydrase	Activation of a nucleophile
Cobamide enzymes	Metal acts as a nucleophile
Pyruvate carboxylase, carboxypeptidase, alcohol dehydrogenase	π-Electron withdrawal
Nonheme iron proteins	π-Electron donation
Pyruvate kinase, pyruvate carboxylase, adenylate kinase	Metal ion gathers and orients ligands
Phosphotransferase, D-xylose isomerase, hemoproteins	Strain effects

*Adapted from Mildvan AS: Metals in enzyme catalysis. Vol 2. Page 456 in: *The Enzymes.* Boyer PD, Lardy H, Myrbäck K (editors). Academic Press, 1970.

"mask" a nucleophile and thus prevent an otherwise likely side-reaction. Finally, stereochemical control of the course of an enzyme-catalyzed reaction may be achieved by the ability of the metal coordination sphere to act as a 3-dimensional template to hold reactive groups in a specific steric orientation (Table 8–2).

The mechanisms of catalysis mediated by the coenzyme of some of the B vitamins are discussed in Chapter 10.

• • •

References

Kinetics

Christensen HN: *Dissociation, Enzyme Kinetics, Bioenergetics.* Saunders, 1975.

Engle PC: *Enzyme Kinetics.* Wiley, 1977.

Piszkiwicz D: *Kinetics of Chemical and Enzyme-Catalyzed Reactions.* Oxford Univ Press, 1977.

Purich DL (editor): Enzyme kinetics and mechanisms. Parts A and B in: *Methods in Enzymology.* Vol 63, 1979; Vol 64, 1980. Academic Press.

Segel IH: *Enzyme Kinetics.* Wiley, 1975.

Van Tamlen EE (editor): *Bioorganic Chemistry.* Vol 1, *Enzyme Action,* 1977. Vol 2, *Macro- and Multimolecular systems,* 1977. Vol 3, *Substrate Behavior,* 1978. Academic Press.

The Active Site

Sigman DS, Mooser G: Chemical studies of enzyme active sites. *Annu Rev Biochem* 1975;**44:**889.

Mechanism of Enzyme Action

Crane F: Hydroquinone dehydrogenases. *Annu Rev Biochem* 1977;**46:**439.

Kraut J: Serine proteases: Structure and mechanism of catalysis. *Annu Rev Biochem* 1977;**46:**331.

Mildvan AS: Mechanism of enzyme action. *Annu Rev Biochem* 1974;**43:**357.

Wimmer MJ, Rose IA: Mechanisms of enzyme-catalyzed group transfer reactions. *Annu Rev Biochem* 1978;**47:**1031.

Wood HG, Barden RE: Biotin enzymes. *Annu Rev Biochem* 1977;**46:**385.

Regulation of Enzyme Activity | 9

Victor W. Rodwell, PhD

In this chapter, mechanisms by which metabolic processes are regulated via enzymes are illustrated by selected examples. The intent is to characterize overall patterns of regulation. Throughout this book, reference is made to many other specific examples to illustrate these diverse features of metabolic regulation.

METABOLIC REGULATION

Homeostasis

The concept of homeostatic regulation of the internal milieu advanced by Claude Bernard in the late 19th century stressed the ability of animals to maintain the constancy of their intracellular environments. This implies that all the necessary enzyme-catalyzed reactions proceed at rates responsive to changes in the internal and external environment. A cell or organism might be defined as diseased when it responds inadequately or incorrectly to an internal or external stress. Knowledge of factors affecting the rates of enzyme-catalyzed reactions is essential both to understand the mechanism of homeostasis in normal cells and to comprehend the molecular basis of disease.

All chemical reactions, including enzyme-catalyzed reactions, are to some extent reversible.* Within living cells, however, reversibility may not obtain, because reaction products are promptly removed by additional enzyme-catalyzed reactions. Metabolite flow in living cells is analogous to the flow of water in a pipe. Although the pipe can transfer water in either direction, in practice the flow is unidirectional. Metabolite flow in living cells also is largely unidirectional. True equilibrium, far from being characteristic of life, is approached only when cells die. The living cell is a dynamic steady-state system maintained by a unidirectional flow of metabolites (Fig 9–1). In mature cells, the mean concentrations of metabolites remain relatively constant over considerable periods of time.† The flexibility of the steady-

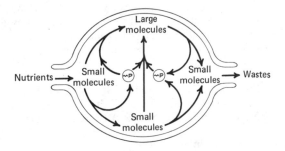

Figure 9–1. An idealized cell in steady state.

state system is well illustrated in the delicate shifts and balances by which organisms maintain the constancy of the internal environment despite wide variations in food, water, and mineral intake, work output, or external temperature.

Scope of Metabolic Regulation

For life to proceed in orderly fashion, metabolite flow through anabolic and catabolic pathways must be regulated. All requisite chemical events must proceed at rates consistent with the requirements of the intact organism in relation to its environment. ATP production, synthesis of macromolecular precursors, transport, secretion, and tubular reabsorption all must respond to subtle changes in the environment of the cell, organ, or intact animal. These processes must be coordinated and must respond to short-term changes in the external environment (eg, addition or removal of a nutrient) as well as to periodic intracellular events (eg, DNA replication). The mechanisms by which cells and intact organisms regulate and coordinate overall metabolism are of concern to biochemists with as seemingly diverse research interests as cancer, heart disease, aging, microbial physiology, differentiation and metamorphosis, or the mechanism of hormone action. Until recently, the molecular details of regulation were best understood in bacteria, which lack the complexities of rapid protein turnover or of hormonal or neural control and in which genetic studies can readily be conducted to analyze molecular events. Our understanding of molecular regulation in animal cells is, however, presently in a state of rapid expansion.

While knowledge of cellular regulatory processes

---

*A readily reversible reaction has a small numerical value of ΔG. One with a large negative value for ΔG ($\Delta G < -5$ kcal) might be termed "effectively irreversible" in most biochemical situations.
†Short-term oscillations of metabolite concentrations and of enzyme levels do occur, however, and are of profound physiologic importance.

in humans is central to an understanding and therapy of metabolic diseases, the molecular events in regulation of many metabolic processes in mammals are still poorly understood. It is clear that metabolic regulation in mammals differs significantly from superficially similar phenomena in bacteria. Regulation of metabolic processes in bacteria will be discussed because it provides a conceptual framework for considering regulation in humans.

Available Options for Regulation of Enzymes

Net flow of carbon through any enzyme-catalyzed reaction might be influenced (1) by changing the absolute quantity of enzyme present, (2) by altering the pool size of reactants other than enzyme, and (3) by altering the catalytic efficiency of the enzyme. All 3 options are exploited in most forms of life.

REGULATION OF ENZYME QUANTITY BY CONTROL OF THE RATES OF ENZYME SYNTHESIS & DEGRADATION

General Principles

The absolute quantity of an enzyme present is determined by its rate of synthesis (k_s) and rate of degradation (k_{deg}) (Fig 9–2). The quantity of an enzyme in a cell may be raised either by an increase in its rate of synthesis (increase in k_s), by a decrease in its rate of degradation (decrease in k_{deg}), or by both. Similarly, a lower quantity of enzyme can result from a decrease in k_s, an increase in k_{deg}, or both. Examples of changes in both k_s and k_{deg} occur in human subjects. In all forms of life, enzyme (protein) synthesis from amino acids and enzyme (protein) degradation to amino acids are distinct processes catalyzed by entirely different sets of enzymes. Independent regulation of enzyme synthesis and enzyme degradation is thus readily achieved.

Figure 9–2. Enzyme quantity is determined by the net balance between enzyme synthesis and enzyme degradation.

Enzyme Synthesis a Result of Information Stored in DNA

The primary structure of an enzyme, like that of all proteins, is dictated by the trinucleotide (triplet) code of its messenger RNA (mRNA). The sequence of nucleotide bases of the mRNA is in turn dictated by a complementary base sequence in a DNA template or gene (see Chapters 28 and 30). Information for protein synthesis, stored in DNA, thus determines a cell's ability to synthesize a particular enzyme.

Mutations alter the nucleotide sequence of DNA and result in synthesis of proteins with modified primary structures. This may alter structure at higher levels of organization if the new amino acid has properties significantly different from the original. Mutations may cause partial or complete loss of catalytic activity or, rarely, enhanced catalytic activity. Since mutations at various genetic loci can produce enzymes with impaired activity, a large number of human molecular diseases are possible.

Induction

Cells can synthesize specific enzymes in response to the presence of specific low-molecular-weight inducers. Enzyme induction is illustrated by the following experiment: *Escherichia coli* grown on glucose will not ferment lactose owing to the absence of the enzyme β-galactosidase, which hydrolyzes lactose to galactose and glucose. If lactose or certain other β-galactosides are added to the growth medium, synthesis of the β-galactosidase is induced and the culture can now ferment lactose.

The inducer (lactose) is a substrate for the induced protein (β-galactosidase). Although many inducers are substrates for the enzymes they induce, compounds structurally similar to the substrate may be inducers but not substrates. These are termed **gratuitous inducers.** Conversely, a compound may be a substrate but not an inducer. Frequently, a compound induces several enzymes of a catabolic pathway (eg, β-galactoside permease and β-galactosidase are both induced by lactose). Where the structural genes that specify a group of catabolic enzymes comprise an **operon,** all enzymes of that operon are induced by a single inducer (**coordinate induction**). The ability to regulate the synthesis of enzymes dependent upon the availability of a nutrient permits the bacterium to use its available nutrients to maximum advantage; ie, it does not synthesize "unnecessary enzymes."

Enzymes whose concentration in a cell is independent of added inducer are termed **constitutive.** A particular enzyme may be constitutive in one strain, inducible in another, and absent in a third. Cells capable of being induced for a particular enzyme or other protein usually contain a small measurable **basal level** of that protein even when grown in the absence of added inducer. The extent to which a particular organism responds to an inducer is genetically determined (see Chapter 31). Increases in enzyme content from 2- to 1000-fold may be observed on induction in different strains. The genetic heritage of the cell thus determines both the nature and magnitude of the response to an inducer. The terms "constitutive" and "inducible" are therefore relative terms, like "hot" and "cold," that represent the extremes of a spectrum of responses.

Enzyme induction also occurs in eukaryotes. Examples of inducible enzymes in animals are tryptophan pyrrolase, threonine dehydrase, tyrosine-α-ketoglutaric transaminase, invertase, enzymes of the urea cycle, and HMG-CoA reductase.

Repression & Derepression

In bacteria capable of synthesizing a biosynthetic metabolite, its presence in the medium may curtail new synthesis of that metabolite via **repression.** A small molecule such as a purine or amino acid, acting as a **corepressor,** can ultimately block synthesis of the enzymes involved in its own biosynthesis. For example, in *Salmonella typhimurium,* addition of histidine (His) represses synthesis of all the enzymes of His biosynthesis, and addition of leucine (Leu) represses synthesis of the first 3 enzymes unique to Leu biosynthesis. In both cases, these biosynthetic enzymes comprise **operons; coordinate repression** occurs following addition of the end products His or Leu. Coordinate repression is not general for all biosynthetic pathways. Following removal or exhaustion of an essential biosynthetic intermediate from the medium, enzyme biosynthesis again occurs. This constitutes **derepression.** Derepression may be coordinate or noncoordinate.

The above examples illustrate **product feedback repression** characteristic of biosynthetic pathways in bacteria. **Catabolite repression,** a related phenomenon, refers to the ability of an intermediate in a sequence of **catabolic** enzyme-catalyzed reactions to repress synthesis of catabolic enzymes. This effect was first noted in cultures of *E coli* growing on a carbon source (X) other than glucose. Addition of glucose repressed synthesis of the enzymes concerned with catabolism of X. This phenomenon was initially termed the "glucose effect." Since oxidizable nutrients other than glucose produce similar effects, the term **catabolite repression** was adopted. Catabolite repression is mediated by cAMP. The molecular mechanisms of induction, repression, and derepression are discussed in Chapter 31.

In multiply branched biosynthetic pathways such as those generating the branched-chain amino acids or the aspartate family of amino acids, early enzymes function in the biosynthesis of several amino acids (Fig 9–3). Following addition of lysine (Lys) to the medium of growing bacteria, synthesis of the enzymes unique to Lys biosynthesis (Enz_L) are repressed. Repression of the enzymes unique to threonine (Thr) biosynthesis (Enz_T) follows addition of Thr to the medium. These effects illustrate simple product feedback repression. Enzymes Enz_1 and Enz_2, however, function both in Lys and Thr biosynthesis. Product feedback repression of their synthesis by Lys or Thr alone would starve the bacterium of the other amino acid. If, however, both Lys and Thr are added to the medium, Enz_1 and Enz_2 become redundant, and repression of synthesis of Enz_1 and Enz_2 could be advantageous to survival, since it would permit more efficient use of available nutrients.

In the presence of all necessary end products of a branched or multiple-branched biosynthetic pathway, **multivalent repression** may occur. This occurs only when all end products of a particular set of biosynthetic enzymes are present in ample supply. Complete repression of aspartokinase (Enz_1) should therefore re-

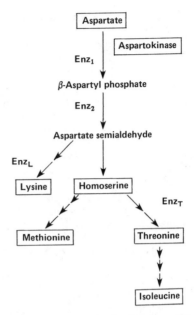

Figure 9–3. The aspartate family of amino acids. Enz_L and Enz_T denote groups of enzymes involved in lysine and threonine biosynthesis, respectively. Multiple arrows indicate multiple reactions.

quire methionine (Met) and isoleucine (Ile) in addition to Lys and Thr.

Enzyme Turnover

In rapidly growing bacteria, the overall rate of protein degradation is about 2% per hour, and control of enzyme levels is achieved primarily by increases or decreases in k_S. This is not true for starving bacteria or for bacteria transferred to fresh medium providing a poorer source of carbon for growth ("stepdown culture"). Under these conditions, bacteria degrade protein at 7–10% per hour.

The combined processes of enzyme synthesis and degradation constitute **enzyme turnover.** While turnover occurs both in bacteria and mammals, the importance of enzyme degradation as a device by which enzyme levels are regulated in bacteria has received little emphasis. Turnover of protein was recognized as a characteristic property of all mammalian cells long before it was shown also to occur in bacteria. The existence of protein (enzyme) turnover in humans was deduced from dietary experiments well over a century ago. It was, however, Schoenheimer's classic work, just prior to and during World War II, that conclusively established that turnover of cellular protein occurred throughout life. By measuring the rates of incorporation of ^{15}N-labeled amino acids into protein and the rates of loss of ^{15}N from protein, Schoenheimer deduced that body proteins are in a state of "dynamic equilibrium," a concept since extended to other body constituents, including lipids and nucleic acids.

In mammals, control of intracellular enzyme levels involves regulation both of enzyme synthesis

and degradation. While the major events in protein synthesis are well understood, those in enzyme degradation are not. Enzyme degradation involves hydrolysis by proteolytic enzymes, but little is known of the processes by which proteolytic activity is regulated other than that it requires ATP. The susceptibility of an enzyme to proteolytic degradation depends upon its conformation. The presence or absence of substrates, coenzymes, or metal ions, which can alter protein conformation, alters proteolytic susceptibility. The concentrations of substrates, coenzymes, and possibly ions in cells may thus determine the rates at which specific enzymes are degraded. Arginase and tryptophan oxygenase (tryptophan pyrrolase) illustrate these concepts. Regulation of liver arginase levels can involve a change either in k_s or in k_{deg}. Following ingestion of a protein-rich diet, liver arginase levels rise owing to an increased rate of arginase synthesis. Liver arginase levels also rise in starved animals. Here, however, it is arginase degradation that is decreased, while k_s remains unchanged. In a second example, injection of glucocorticoids and ingestion of Trp both elevate levels of tryptophan oxygenase in mammals. The hormone raises the rate of oxygenase synthesis (raises k_s). Trp, however, has no effect on k_s but lowers k_{deg} by stabilizing the oxygenase toward proteolytic digestion. Contrast these 2 examples with enzyme induction in bacteria. For arginase, the increased intake of nitrogen on a high-protein diet may elevate liver arginase levels (see Chapter 21). The increased rate of arginase synthesis thus superficially resembles that of substrate induction in bacteria. For tryptophan pyrrolase, however, even though Trp may act as an inducer in bacteria (affects k_s), its effect in mammals is solely on the enzyme degradative process (lowers k_{deg}).

Enzyme levels in mammalian tissues may be altered by a wide range of physiologic, hormonal, or dietary manipulations. Examples are known for a variety of tissues and metabolic pathways (Table 9–1), but our knowledge of the molecular details that account for these changes is fragmentary.

Glucocorticoids increase the concentration of tyrosine transaminase by stimulating k_s. This was the first clear case of a hormone regulating the synthesis of a mammalian enzyme. Insulin and glucagon—despite their mutually antagonistic physiologic effects—both independently increase k_s 4- to 5-fold. The effect of glucagon probably is mediated via cAMP, which mimics the effect of the hormone in organ cultures of rat liver.

Proenzymes

Enzyme activity can be regulated by converting an inactive proenzyme to a catalytically active form. To become catalytically active, the proenzyme must undergo limited proteolysis, a process accompanied by conformational changes that either reveal or "create" the catalytic site (see Chapter 8). Synthesis as a catalytically inactive proenzyme is characteristic of diges-

Table 9–1. Selected examples of rat liver enzymes that adapt to an environmental stimulus by changes in activity.*

Enzyme	$t\frac{1}{2}$ (hours)	Stimulus	Fold Change
Amino acid metabolism			
Arginase	100–120	Starvation or glucocorticoids.	+2
		Change from high- to low-protein diet.	−2
Serine dehydratase	20	Glucagon or dietary amino acids.	+100
Histidase	60	Change from low- to high-protein diet.	+20
Carbohydrate metabolism			
Glucose 6-P dehydrogenase	15	Thyroid hormone; fasted rats re-fed a high-carbohydrate diet.	+10
a-Glycerophosphate dehydrogenase	100	Thyroid hormone.	+10
Fructose 1,6-phosphatase		Glucose.	+10
Lipid metabolism			
Citrate cleavage enzyme		Starved rats re-fed a high-carbohydrate, low-fat diet.	+30
Fatty acid synthase		Starvation.	−10
		Starved animals re-fed a fat-free diet.	+30
HMG-CoA reductase	2–3	Fasting or 5% cholesterol diet.	−10
		Twenty-four-hour diurnal variation.	±5
		Insulin or thyroid hormone.	+2 to 10
Purine or pyrimidine metabolism			
Xanthine oxidase		Change to high-protein diet.	−10
Aspartate transcarbamoylase	60	One percent orotic acid diet.	+2
Dihydroorotase	12	One percent orotic acid diet.	+3

*Data, with the exception of those for HMG-CoA reductase, from Schimke RT, Doyle D: Control of enzyme levels in animal tissues. *Annu Rev Biochem* 1970;39:929.

tive enzymes and enzymes of blood coagulation and of blood clot dissolution. This phenomenon is discussed in Chapters 4, 44, and 45.

REGULATION OF THE CATALYTIC EFFICIENCY OF ENZYMES

Definition of Terms

If a physiologic manipulation alters the level of enzyme activity, we have no way of knowing whether the quantity of enzyme has changed or whether the enzyme is a more efficient or less efficient catalyst. **We shall refer to all changes in enzyme activity that occur without change in the quantity of enzyme present as "effects on catalytic efficiency."**

Availability of Reactants

A. General Principles: The kinetic and regulatory properties of enzymes provide insights into physiologic processes in intact cells, tissues, and organisms. However, most information was obtained by studying enzymes in vitro under conditions that differ substantially from those in living cells. Application of this knowledge to the in vivo situation therefore requires considerable caution. For instance, the concentrations of substrates studied in vitro differ significantly from those in vivo.

B. Enzyme Compartmentation: The importance of compartmentation of metabolic processes in eukaryotic cells, including those of mammals, cannot be overemphasized. Localization of specific metabolic processes in the cytosol or in cellular organelles facilitates regulation of these processes independent of processes proceeding elsewhere. The extensive compartmentalization of metabolic processes characteristic of higher forms of life thus confers the potential for finely tuned regulation of metabolism. At the same time, it poses problems with respect to translocation of metabolites across compartmental barriers. This is achieved via "shuttle mechanisms" that convert the metabolite to a form permeable to the compartmental barrier. This is followed by transport and conversion back to the original form on the other side of the barrier. Consequently, these interconversions require, for example, cytosolic and mitochondrial forms of the same catalytic activity. Since these 2 forms of the enzyme are physically separated, their independent regulation is facilitated. The role of shuttle mechanisms in achieving equilibration of metabolic pools of reducing equivalents, of citric acid cycle, and of other amphibolic intermediates is discussed in Chapter 14.

C. Macromolecular Complexes: Organization of a set of enzymes that catalyze a protracted sequence of metabolic reactions as a macromolecular complex coordinates the enzymes and channels intermediates along a metabolic path. Appropriate alignment of the enzymes can facilitate transfer of product between enzymes without prior equilibration with metabolic pools. This permits a finer level of metabolic control than is possible with the isolated components of the complex. In addition, conformational changes in one component of the complex may be transmitted by protein-protein interactions to other enzymes of the complex. Amplification of regulatory effects thus is possible.

D. Effective Concentrations of Substrates, Coenzymes, and Cations: The **mean** intracellular concentration of a substrate, coenzyme, or metal ion may have little meaning for the in vivo behavior of an enzyme. Information on the concentrations of essential metabolites **in the immediate neighborhood of the enzyme in question** is needed. However, even measuring metabolite concentrations in different cellular compartments does not account for local discontinuities in metabolite concentrations within compartments brought about by factors such as proximity to the site of entry or production of a metabolite. Finally, little consideration generally is given to the discrepancy between total and free metabolite concentrations. For example, while the total concentration of 2,3-bisphosphoglycerate in erythrocytes is extremely high, the concentration of free bisphosphoglycerate is comparable to that of other tissues. Erythrocytes contain approximately 5 mmol of hemoglobin, which binds 1 mol of bisphosphoglycerate per mol of deoxygenated tetramer. A **total** concentration of 4 mmol of bisphosphoglycerate would therefore result in a minuscule concentration of **free** bisphosphoglycerate in venous erythrocytes. Similar considerations apply to other metabolites in the presence of proteins that bind them effectively and reduce their concentrations in the free state.

An assumption of the Michaelis-Menten kinetic approach was that the concentration of total substrate was essentially equal to the concentration of free substrate. As noted above, this assumption may well be invalid in vivo, where concentrations of free substrates often are of the same order of magnitude as those of enzyme concentrations.

Metal ions, which perform catalytic and structural roles in over one-fourth of all known enzymes, may also fulfill regulatory roles, particularly for reactions where ATP is a substrate. Where the ATP-metal ion complex is the substrate for the reaction, maximal activity typically is observed at molar ratio of ATP to metal of about unity. Excess metal or excess ATP is inhibitory. Since nucleoside di- and triphosphates form stable complexes with divalent cations, intracellular concentrations of the nucleotides can influence intracellular concentrations of free metal ions and hence the activity of certain enzymes. For example, in the absence of metal ions, *E coli* glutamine synthase assumes a "relaxed" configuration that is catalytically inactive. Mg^{2+} or Mn^{2+} converts the synthase to the active, "tightened" form. In addition, adenylylation of the synthase changes the divalent cation specificity from Mg^{2+} to Mn^{2+}. The activity of the adenylylated enzyme is, furthermore, sensitive to the $ATP:Mg^{2+}$ ratio, whereas that of the unadenylylated form is not.

Allosteric Regulation

The catalytic activity of certain **regulatory enzymes** is modulated by low-molecular-weight **allosteric effectors** that generally have little or no structural similarity to the substrates or coenzymes for the regulated enzyme. **Feedback inhibition** refers to the inhibition of the activity of an enzyme in a biosynthetic pathway by an end product of that pathway. For biosynthesis of D from A, catalyzed by enzymes Enz_1 through Enz_3,

$$A \xrightarrow{Enz_1} B \xrightarrow{Enz_2} C \xrightarrow{Enz_3} D$$

a high concentration of D typically inhibits conversion of A to B. This involves not simple "backing up" of intermediates but the ability of D to bind to and inhibit Enz_1. D thus acts as a **negative allosteric effector** or **feedback inhibitor** of Enz_1. **Feedback inhibition** of Enz_1 by D therefore regulates the synthesis of D. Typically, D binds to the sensitive enzyme at an **allosteric site** remote from the catalytic site.

The kinetics of feedback inhibition may be competitive, noncompetitive, partially competitive, uncoupled, or mixed. Feedback inhibition is commonest in biosynthetic pathways. **Frequently the feedback inhibitor is the last small molecule before a macromolecule** (eg, amino acids before proteins, nucleotides before nucleic acids). **Feedback regulation generally occurs at the earliest functionally irreversible* step unique to a particular biosynthetic sequence.**

Examples of feedback inhibition in microorganisms include inhibition by His of phosphoribosyl:ATP pyrophosphorylase, by Trp of anthranilate synthase, and by CTP of aspartate transcarbamoylase. In each case the regulated enzyme is involved in biosynthesis of a single end product—His, Trp, or CTP.

Frequently a biosynthetic pathway may be branched, with the initial portion serving for synthesis of 2 or more essential metabolites. Fig 9–4 shows

probable sites of simple feedback inhibition in a branched biosynthetic pathway (eg, for amino acids, purines or pyrimidines). S_1, S_2, and S_3 are precursors of all 4 end products (A, B, C, and D), S_4 is a precursor of B and C, and S_5 a precursor solely of D. The sequences:

$$S_3 \longrightarrow A$$
$$S_4 \longrightarrow B$$
$$S_4 \longrightarrow C$$
$$S_3 \longrightarrow S_5 \longrightarrow D$$

thus constitute linear reaction sequences that might be expected to be feedback-inhibited by their end products.

Multiple feedback loops (Fig 9–5) provide additional fine control. For example, if B is present in excess, the requirement for S_2 decreases. The ability of B to decrease production of S_2 thus confers a biologic advantage. However, if excess B inhibits not only the portion of the pathway unique to its own synthesis but also portions common to that for synthesis of A, C, or D, excess B should curtail synthesis of all 4 end products. Clearly, this is undesirable. Mechanisms have, however, evolved to circumvent this difficulty.

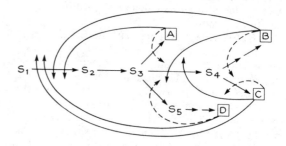

Figure 9–5. Multiple feedback inhibition in a branched biosynthetic pathway. Superimposed on simple feedback loops (dashed, curved arrows) are multiple feedback loops (solid, curved arrows) that regulate enzymes common to biosynthesis of several end products.

In **cumulative feedback inhibition,** the inhibitory effect of 2 or more end products on a single regulatory enzyme is strictly additive.

In **concerted** or **multivalent feedback inhibition,** complete inhibition occurs only when 2 or more end products both are present in excess.

In **cooperative feedback inhibition,** a single end product present in excess inhibits the regulatory enzyme, but **the inhibition when 2 or more end products are present far exceeds the additive effects of cumulative feedback inhibition.**

The aspartate family provides yet another variant—**multiple enzymes** each with distinct regulatory characteristics. E coli produces 3 aspartokinases. One (AK_L) is specifically and completely inhibited by Lys, a second (AK_T) by Thr, and the third

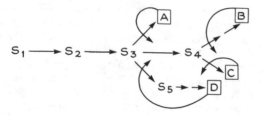

Figure 9–4. Sites of feedback inhibition in a branched biosynthetic pathway. S_1–S_5 are intermediates in the biosynthesis of end products A–D. Straight arrows represent enzymes catalyzing the indicated conversions. Curved arrows represent feedback loops and indicate probable sites of feedback inhibition by specific end products.

---

*One strongly favored (in thermodynamic terms) in a single direction, ie, one with a large negative ΔG.

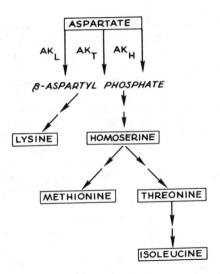

Figure 9–6. Regulation of aspartokinase (AK) activity in *E coli*. Multiple enzymes are subject to end product inhibition by lysine (AK_L), threonine (AK_T), or homoserine (AK_H).

Table 9–2. Patterns of allosteric regulation of aspartokinase.

Organism	Feedback Inhibitor	Repressor
E coli (kinase I)	Homoser	...
E coli (kinase II)	Lys	Lys
E coli (kinase III)	Thr	...
R rubrium	Thr	...
B subtilis	Thr + Lys	...

(AK_H) by homoserine, a precursor of Met, Thr, and Ile (Fig 9–6). In the presence of excess Lys, AK_L is inhibited and β-aspartyl phosphate production decreases. This alone would not suffice to channel metabolites toward synthesis of homoserine and its products. Channeling is achieved by feedback inhibition at secondary sites further along the pathway. Lys also inhibits the first enzyme in the sequence leading from β-aspartyl phosphate to Lys. This facilitates unrestricted synthesis of homoserine, and hence of Thr and Ile. Additional control points exist at the branch point where homoserine leads both to Met and to Thr and Ile.

That all these variations can regulate metabolism is suggested by the persistence in different bacteria of distinctive patterns of feedback inhibition of a single biosynthetic pathway (Table 9–2).

The most extensively studied allosteric enzyme, **aspartate transcarbamoylase,** catalyzes the first reaction unique to pyrimidine biosynthesis (Fig 9–7). Aspartate transcarbamoylase (ATCase) is **feedback-inhibited by cytidine triphosphate (CTP).** Following treatment with mercurials, ATCase loses its sensitivity to inhibition by CTP but retains its full activity for carbamoyl aspartate synthesis. This suggests that CTP is bound at a different (allosteric) site from either substrate. ATCase consists of 2 catalytic and 3 or 4 regulatory protomers. Each catalytic protomer contains 4 aspartate (substrate) sites and each regulatory protomer at least 2 CTP (regulatory) sites. Each type of protomer is subject to independent genetic control, as shown by the production of mutants lacking normal feedback control of CTP and, from these, of revertants with essentially normal regulatory properties.

A. Evidence for Allosteric Sites on Regulated Enzymes: About 1963, Monod noted the lack of structural similarity between a feedback inhibitor and the substrate for the enzyme whose activity it regulated. Since the effectors are not isosteric with a substrate but **allosteric** ("occupy another space"), he proposed that enzymes whose activity is regulated by **allosteric effectors** (eg, feedback inhibitors) bind the effector at an **allosteric site** that is physically distinct from the catalytic site. **Allosteric enzymes** thus are enzymes whose activity at the catalytic site may be modulated by the presence of allosteric effectors at an allosteric site. Lines of evidence that support the existence of physically distinct allosteric sites on regulated enzymes include the following:

(1) Regulated enzymes modified by chemical or physical techniques frequently become insensitive to their allosteric effectors without alteration of their catalytic activity. Selective denaturation of allosteric sites has been achieved by treatment with mercurials, urea, x-rays, proteolytic enzymes, extremes of ionic strength or pH, aging at 0–5 °C, by freezing, or by heating.

(2) Allosteric effectors frequently protect the

Carbamoyl phosphate + L-Aspartate

ASPARTATE TRANSCARBAMOYLASE

P_i

Carbamoyl aspartate

Figure 9–7. The aspartate transcarbamoylase (ATCase) reaction.

catalytic site from denaturation under conditions where the substrates themselves do not protect. Since it seems unlikely that an effector bound at the catalytic site would protect when substrates do not, this suggests a second, allosteric site elsewhere on the enzyme molecule.

(3) In certain bacterial and mammalian cell mutants, the regulated enzymes have altered regulatory properties but identical catalytic properties to those of the wild-type from which the mutant derived. The structure of the allosteric and catalytic sites thus are genetically distinct.

(4) Binding studies of substrates and of allosteric effectors to regulated enzymes show that each may bind independently of the other.

(5) In certain cases (eg, ATCase), the allosteric site is present on a different protomer from the catalytic site.

B. Kinetics: Fig 9–8 illustrates the rate of a reaction catalyzed by a typical allosteric enzyme measured at several concentrations of substrate in the presence and absence of an allosteric inhibitor. In the absence of the allosteric inhibitor, hyperbolic saturation kinetics are observed. In its presence, the substrate saturation curve is distorted from a hyperbola into a sigmoid, which at high substrate concentrations may merge with the hyperbola. Note the analogy to the relationship between the O_2 saturation curves for myoglobin and hemoglobin (see Chapter 5).

On kinetic analysis, feedback inhibition may appear to be competitive, noncompetitive, partially competitive, or of other types. If, at high concentrations of S, comparable activity is observed in the presence or absence of the allosteric inhibitor, the kinetics superficially resemble those of competitive inhibition. However, since the substrate saturation curve is sigmoid rather than hyperbolic, it is not possi-

ble to obtain meaningful results by graphing data for the allosteric inhibition by the double-reciprocal technique. This method of analysis was developed for substrate competitive inhibition **at the catalytic site.** Since allosteric inhibitors act at a different (allosteric) site, that kinetic model is invalid.

The sigmoid character of the V versus S curve in the presence of an allosteric inhibitor reflects the phenomenon of **cooperativity.** At low concentrations of S, the activity in the presence of the inhibitor is low relative to that in its absence. However, as S is increased, the extent of inhibition becomes relatively less severe. The kinetics are consistent with the presence of 2 or more interacting substrate-binding sites, where the presence of a substrate molecule at one catalytic site facilitates binding of a second substrate molecule at a second site. Cooperativity of substrate binding has been described in Chapter 5 for hemoglobin. The sigmoid O_2 saturation curve results from cooperative interactions between four O_2 binding sites located on different protomers.

C. Models: Reference to the kinetics of allosteric inhibition as "competitive" or "noncompetitive" with substrate carries mechanistic implications which are misleading. We refer instead to 2 classes of regulated enzymes, K-series and V-series enzymes. For K-series allosteric enzymes, the substrate saturation kinetics are competitive in the sense that K_m is raised (decreased affinity for substrate) without effect on V_{max}. For V-series allosteric enzymes, the allosteric inhibitor lowers V_{max} (lowered catalytic efficiency) without affecting the apparent K_m. Alterations in K_m or V_{max} probably result from conformational changes at the catalytic site induced by binding of the allosteric effector at the allosteric site. For a K-series allosteric enzyme, this conformational change may weaken the bonds between substrate and substrate-binding residues. For a V-series allosteric enzyme, the primary effect may be to alter the orientation of catalytic residues so as to lower V_{max}. Intermediate effects on K_m and V_{max} may, however, be observed consequent to these conformational changes.

While various models have been proposed for regulation of allosteric enzymes, it is unlikely that a single model can explain the behavior of all regulatory enzymes. Since sigmoidicity of the substrate saturation curve confers a regulatory advantage, any mutation that gives rise to sigmoidicity should tend to be retained. To expect that these mutations would involve identical mechanisms is unrealistic. The presence of sigmoid kinetics does not, therefore, imply a particular mechanism of inhibition.

D. Physiologic Consequences of Cooperativity: The consequences of cooperative substrate-binding kinetics are analogous to those resulting from the cooperative binding of O_2 to hemoglobin. At low substrate concentrations, the allosteric effector is an effective inhibitor. It thus regulates most effectively at the time of greatest need, ie, when intracellular concentrations of substrates are low. As more substrate becomes available, stringent regulation is less neces-

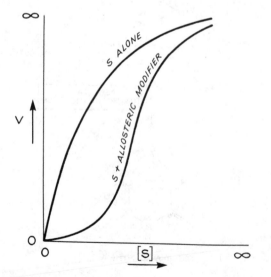

Figure 9–8. Sigmoid saturation curve for substrate in the presence of an allosteric inhibitor.

sary. As substrate concentration rises, the degree of inhibition therefore lessens, and more product is formed. As with hemoglobin, the sigmoid substrate saturation curve in the presence of inhibitor also means that relatively small changes in substrate concentration result in large changes in activity. Sensitive control of catalytic activity thus is achieved by small changes in substrate concentration. Finally, by analogy with the differing O_2 saturation curves of hemoglobins from different species, regulatory enzymes from different sources may have sigmoid saturation curves shifted to the left or right to accommodate to the range of prevailing in vivo concentrations of substrate.

Feedback Regulation in Mammalian Cells

In both mammalian and bacterial cells, end products "feed back" and control their own synthesis. In some instances (eg, ATCase), this involves feedback inhibition of an early biosynthetic enzyme. We must, however, distinguish between **feedback regulation,** a phenomenologic term devoid of mechanistic implications, and **feedback inhibition,** a mechanism for regulation of many bacterial and mammalian enzymes. For example, dietary cholesterol restricts the synthesis of cholesterol from acetate in mammalian tissues. This feedback regulation does not, however, appear to involve feedback inhibition of an early enzyme of cholesterol biosynthesis. An early enzyme (HMG-CoA reductase) is affected, but the mechanism involves curtailment by cholesterol or a cholesterol metabolite of the expression of the genes that code for the formation of HMG-CoA reductase. Cholesterol added directly to HMG-CoA reductase has no effect on its catalytic activity.

Covalent Modification

A. General Principles: Reversible modulation of the catalytic activity of enzymes can occur by covalent attachment of a phosphate group (predominates in mammals) or a nucleotide (predominates in bacteria). Enzymes that undergo covalent modification with attendant modulation of their activity are termed "interconvertible enzymes" (Fig 9–9).

Interconvertible enzymes exist in 2 activity states, one of high and the other of low catalytic efficiency. Depending on the enzyme concerned, the

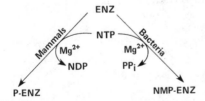

Figure 9–9. Regulation of enzyme activity by covalent modification. *Left:* phosphorylation. *Right:* nucleotidylation. For both processes the nucleoside triphosphate (NTP) generally is ATP.

Table 9–3. Examples of mammalian enzymes whose catalytic activity is altered by covalent phosphorylation-dephosphorylation. E = dephosphoenzyme; EP = phosphoenzyme.

Enzyme	Activity State	
	Low	High
Acetyl-CoA carboxylase	EP	E
Glycogen synthase	EP	E
Pyruvate dehydrogenase	EP	E
HMG-CoA reductase	EP	E
Glycogen phosphorylase	E	EP
Citrate lyase	E	EP
Pyruvate dehydrogenase	E	EP
Phosphorylase b kinase	E	EP
HMG-CoA reductase kinase	E	EP

phospho- or the dephosphoenzyme may be the more active catalyst (Table 9–3).

B. Phosphorylation Site: A specific Ser residue is phosphorylated, forming O-phosphoseryl residue, or, in rarer cases, a tyrosyl residue is phosphorylated to form O-phosphotyrosyl. While an interconvertible enzyme may contain many Ser or Tyr residues, phosphorylation is highly selective and occurs at only a small number (1–3) of possible sites (Table 9–4). These sites probably do not form part of the catalytic site, at least in a primary structural sense, and thus constitute another example of an allosteric site.

C. Converter Proteins: Phosphorylation and dephosphorylation are catalyzed by protein kinases and protein phosphatases (converter proteins), respec-

Table 9–4. Primary structure in the neighborhood of the seryl residue of proteins phosphorylated by protein kinases. (Z, glutamate or glutamine.)

Phosphorylase kinase (α-subunit)	S	G	Ⓢ	V	Y	E	P	L	K	
Phosphorylase kinase (β-subunit)		L	Ⓢ	I	S	T	E	S	Z	P
Glycogen synthase (site 1)	S	N	Ⓢ	V	D	T	S	S	L	S
Glycogen synthase (site 2)		A	Ⓢ							
Glycogen synthase (site 3)		Z	I	Ⓢ	V	R				
Pyruvate kinase (pig liver)		A	Ⓢ	L	G					
Pyruvate kinase (rat liver)		A	S	Ⓢ	V	A	Z	L		
Phosphorylase (rat or rabbit muscle)	Q	I	S	Ⓢ	V	R				
Phosphorylase (human muscle)	E	I	S	Ⓢ	V	R				
Phosphorylase (pig or rabbit liver)	Q	I	S	Ⓢ	V	R				
Fructose 1,6-bisphosphatase	P	Ⓢ	L	P	L	P				

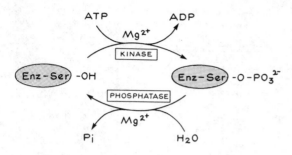

Figure 9–10. Covalent modification of a regulated enzyme by phosphorylation-dephosphorylation of a Ser residue.

tively (Fig 9–10). In specific instances, the converter proteins themselves may be interconvertible enzymes (Table 9–3). Thus, there are protein kinase kinases and protein kinase phosphatases that catalyze the interconversion of these converter proteins. Evidence that protein phosphatases are also interconvertible proteins is less convincing, although their activity is regulated. The activity of both protein kinases and protein phosphatases is under hormonal and neural control, although the precise details by which these agents act are in most instances far from clear.

D. Energetics: The reactions of Fig 9–10 resemble those for interconversion of glucose and glucose 6-phosphate or of fructose 6-phosphate and fructose 1,6-bisphosphate (see Chapter 15). The net result of phosphorylating and then dephosphorylating 1 mol of substrate (enzyme or sugar) is the hydrolysis of 1 mol of ATP.

The activity of the kinases (catalyzing reactions 1 and 3) and of the phosphatases (catalyzing reactions 2 and 4) should themselves be regulated, for if not, they would act together to catalyze uncontrolled hydrolysis of ATP.

1.	Glucose + ATP $\longrightarrow$ ADP + Glucose 6-P
2.	H_2O + Glucose 6-P $\longrightarrow$ P_i + Glucose
Net:	H_2O + ATP $\longrightarrow$ ADP + P_i
3.	Enz–Ser–OH + ATP $\longrightarrow$ ADP + Enz–Ser–O–P
4.	H_2O + Enz–Ser–O–P $\longrightarrow$ P_i + Enz–Ser–OH
Net:	H_2O + ATP $\longrightarrow$ ADP + P_i

E. Analogies to Feedback Inhibition: Regulation of enzyme activity by phosphorylation-dephosphorylation has analogies to regulation by feedback inhibition. Both provide for short-term regulation of metabolite flow in response to specific physiologic signals; both act without altering gene expression, both act at early enzymes of a protracted (often biosynthetic) metabolic sequence; and both act at allosteric rather than catalytic sites. Feedback inhibition, however, involves a single protein and lacks hormonal and neural features. By contrast, regulation of mammalian enzymes by phosphorylation-dephosphorylation involves several proteins and ATP or another nucleoside triphosphate and is under direct neural and hormonal control.

• • •

References

Gumaa KA, McLean P, Greenbaum AL: Compartmentation in relation to metabolic control in liver. *Essays Biochem* 1971; **7**:39.

Kun E, Grisolia S: *Biochemical Regulatory Mechanisms in Eukaryotic Cells.* Wiley, 1972.

Nestler EJ, Greengard P: Protein phosphorylation in the brain. *Nature* 1983;**305**:583.

Newsholme EA, Stuart C: *Regulation in Metabolism.* Wiley, 1973.

Schimke RT, Doyle D: Control of enzyme levels in animal tissues. *Annu Rev Biochem* 1970;**39**:929.

Soderling TR: Role of hormones and protein phosphorylation in metabolic regulation. *Fed Proc* 1982;**41**:2615.

Sols A, Marco R: Concentrations of metabolites and binding sites: Implications in metabolic regulation. *Curr Top Cell Regul* 1970;**2**:227.

Stanbury JB et al (editors): *The Metabolic Basis of Inherited Disease,* 5th ed. McGraw-Hill, 1983.

Umbarger HE: Amino acid biosynthesis and its regulation. *Annu Rev Biochem* 1978;**47**:533.

Weber G (editor): *Advances in Enzyme Regulation.* Vols 1–9. Pergamon Press, 1963–1982.

Water-Soluble Vitamins | 10

David W. Martin, Jr., MD

The water-soluble vitamins have chemical structures that are remarkably diverse, but they do share the property of being polar molecules and therefore are soluble in water.

Of the water-soluble vitamins, all but one—**cobalamin** (vitamin B_{12})—can be synthesized by plants and are therefore provided by legumes, whole grains, leafy green vegetables, and yeast, as well as meat and milk. Because of their water-solubility, the B complex vitamins and vitamin C have no stable storage form and must be **provided continuously** in the diet. Vitamin B_{12} is an exception in that the normal human liver can store several years' supply of cobalamin. All of the water-soluble vitamins serve as **coenzymes or cofactors in enzymatic reactions.**

THE VITAMINS OF THE B COMPLEX

The recognized B vitamins important for human nutrition are as follows:

(1) Thiamin (vitamin B_1)
(2) Riboflavin (vitamin B_2)
(3) Pantothenic acid (vitamin B_5)
(4) Niacin (nicotinic acid)
(5) Pyridoxine (vitamin B_6)
(6) Biotin
(7) Cobalamin (vitamin B_{12})
(8) Folic acid (pteroylglutamic acid)

Because of their water-solubility, these vitamins can be excreted in urine and thus rarely accumulate in toxic concentrations. Deficiencies of the water-soluble vitamins are not uncommon and frequently occur in the setting of a multiple vitamin deficiency state.

THIAMIN*

Thiamin consists of a substituted pyrimidine joined by a methylene bridge to a substituted thiazole (Fig 10–1).

*The word thiamin is derived from thi(o + vit)amin; more commonly but inappropriately spelled thiamine.

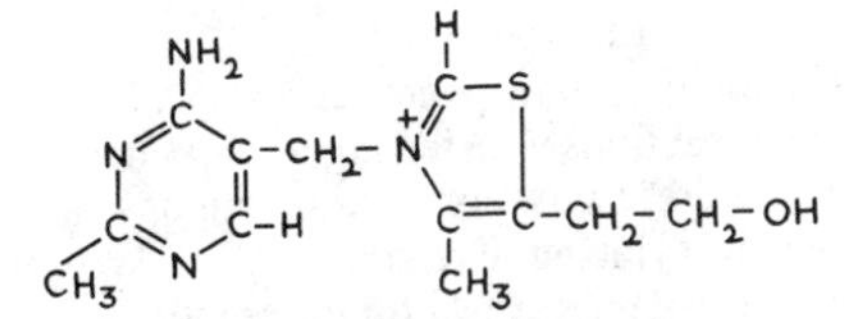

2,5,Dimethyl-6-aminopyrimidine

4-Methyl-5-hydroxyethylthiazole

Figure 10–1. Thiamin.

Sources

Thiamin is present in almost all plant and animal tissues commonly used as food, but the content is usually small. Among the more abundant sources are unrefined cereal grains and meat. Enrichment of flour, bread, corn, and macaroni products with thiamin has increased the availability of this vitamin in the diet. Deficiencies of thiamin are likely to occur not only in persons with poor dietary habits or in the indigent but also in many patients suffering from organic disease, particularly alcoholism. In addition, certain raw fish contain a heat-labile enzyme (thiaminase) that destroys thiamin. Attention was drawn to this "thiaminase" by the appearance of "Chastek paralysis" in foxes fed a diet containing 10% or more of uncooked fish. The disease is characterized by anorexia, weakness, progressive ataxia, spastic paraplegia, and hyperesthesia. The similarities between the focal lesions of the nervous system in this paralysis in the fox and the lesions seen in Wernicke's syndrome in humans have lent support to the concept that the syndrome is in part attributable to thiamin deficiency.

Thiamin is readily absorbed from the intestines but cannot be stored in the body to a significant degree. Any excess of thiamin is promptly excreted in the urine, and there is no evidence for thiamin toxicity.

Metabolism

An ATP-dependent thiamin pyrophosphotransferase (thiamin pyrophosphokinase) present in at least the brain and liver is responsible for the conversion of thiamin to its active form, **thiamin pyrophosphate** (Fig 10–2). Phosphatases in food sources, the gastrointestinal tract, and other human tissues are ca-

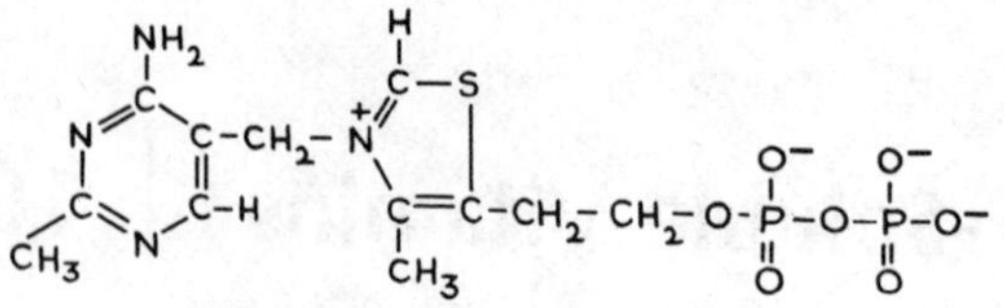

Figure 10–2. Thiamin pyrophosphate (thiamin diphosphate).

pable of removing the pyrophosphate from thiamin pyrophosphate.

Biochemical Function

Thiamin pyrophosphate serves as a coenzyme in enzymatic reactions transferring an activated aldehyde unit. There are 2 types of such reactions—an **oxidative decarboxylation** of α-keto acids (α-ketoglutarate and pyruvate) and **transketolase** reactions, in which aldehyde groups are removed from a molecule. In each case, the thiamin pyrophosphate provides a reactive carbon on the thiazole that forms a carbanion,

stabilized by the positively charged ring nitrogen of thiamin pyrophosphate (Fig 10–3). This carbanion is then free to add to the carbonyl group of—for instance—pyruvate (Fig 10–3). The addition compound then decarboxylates, eliminating CO_2 and generating the 2 resonance forms of ionized hydroxyethyl thiamin pyrophosphate (Fig 10–4). This reaction occurs in a multi-enzyme complex known as the **pyruvate dehydrogenase complex** (see Chapter 15). The hydroxyethyl thiamin pyrophosphate, as an integral part of the enzyme complex, transfers the acetaldehyde moiety to lipoamide (Fig 10–5). This

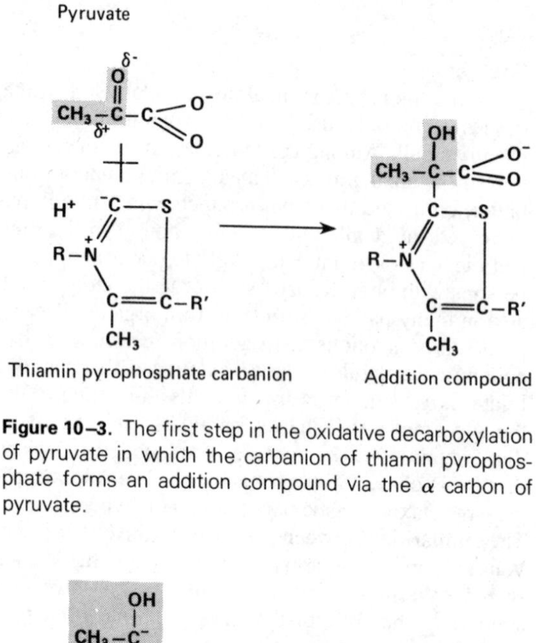

Figure 10–3. The first step in the oxidative decarboxylation of pyruvate in which the carbanion of thiamin pyrophosphate forms an addition compound via the α carbon of pyruvate.

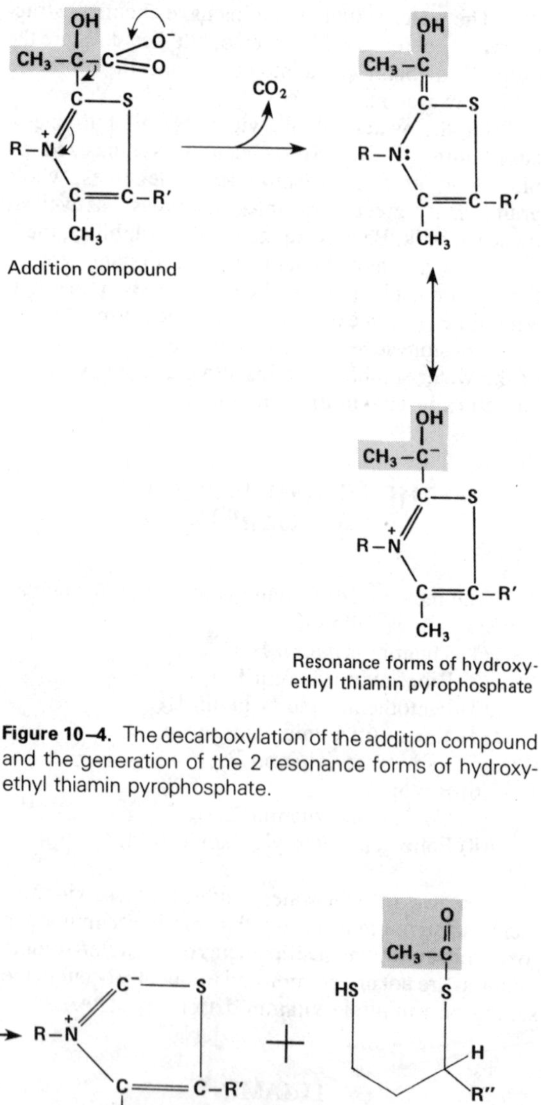

Figure 10–4. The decarboxylation of the addition compound and the generation of the 2 resonance forms of hydroxyethyl thiamin pyrophosphate.

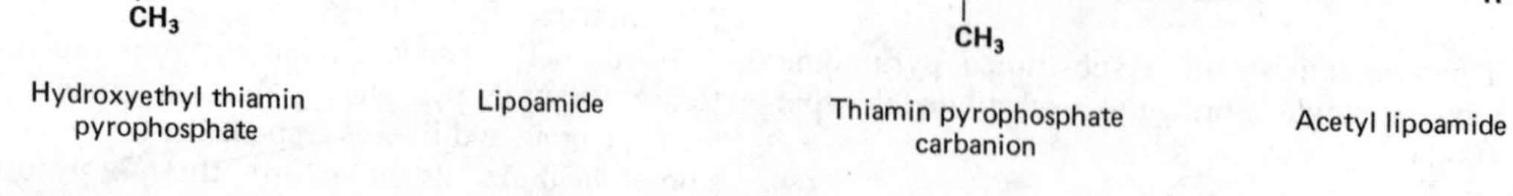

Figure 10–5. The transfer of the acetaldehyde moiety to lipoamide, a reaction catalyzed by the dihydrolipoyl transacetylase portion of the enzyme complex.

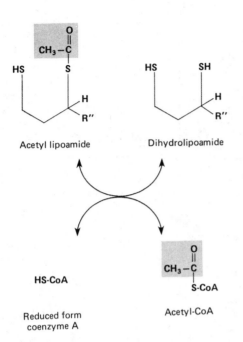

Figure 10–6. The acetyl group of acetyl lipoamide is transferred to the reduced form of coenzyme A to form acetyl-CoA.

phase of the reaction is catalyzed by the dihydrolipoyl transacetylase portion of the complex, yielding acetyl lipoamide. The dihydrolipoyl transacetylase also catalyzes the transfer of the acetyl group from acetyl lipoamide to reduced coenzyme A (Fig 10–6).

The oxidized form of lipoamide is regenerated by a dihydrolipoyl dehydrogenase of which flavin adenine dinucleotide is a prosthetic group.

The role of thiamin pyrophosphate as a coenzyme in the transketolase reactions is very similar to that described above for the oxidative decarboxylations. However, the glycolaldehyde moiety of glycolaldehyde thiamin pyrophosphate is transferred to a ribose 5-phosphate to form sedoheptulose 7-phosphate (see Chapter 15) rather than to lipoamide, as in the pyruvate dehydrogenase reaction above.

The oxidative decarboxylation of α-ketoglutarate to succinyl-CoA and CO_2 (see Chapter 14) is catalyzed by an enzyme complex structurally very similar to the pyruvate dehydrogenase complex. Again, the thiamin pyrophosphate provides a stable carbanion to react with the alpha carbon of α-ketoglutarate. A similar oxidative decarboxylation of the α-ketocarboxylic acid derivatives of the branched-chain amino acids (Chapter 22) utilizes thiamin pyrophosphate.

Accordingly, in the thiamin-deficient human, these thiamin pyrophosphate–dependent reactions are prevented or severely limited, leading to accumulation of the substrates of the reactions, eg, pyruvate, pentosugars, and the α-ketocarboxylate derivatives of the branched-chain amino acids leucine, isoleucine, and valine.

RIBOFLAVIN

Riboflavin consists of a heterotricyclic structure to which is attached ribitol (Fig 10–7). The ring structure is conjugated; thus, riboflavin is a colored and fluorescent pigment. It is relatively heat-stable but sensitive to irreversible decomposition upon exposure to visible light. Riboflavin is synthesized by all plants and many microorganisms but not by higher animals. The absorption of riboflavin in the intestine occurs concomitantly with its phosphorylation by the intestinal mucosa to form riboflavin phosphate, or riboflavin mononucleotide (Fig 10–8). The enzyme flavokinase, which phosphorylates riboflavin, is competitively inhibited by chlorpromazine, a widely used phenothiazine drug. Riboflavin is excreted in urine, particularly when ingested in excess; thus, there is no known toxicity of riboflavin. Free riboflavin does not cross the placenta, but in pregnant animals estrogen induces the formation of a riboflavin carrier protein that transports the vitamin across the placenta to the fetal circulation.

Riboflavin is a component of the flavin nucleotides. **Flavin mononucleotide (FMN)** is formed by

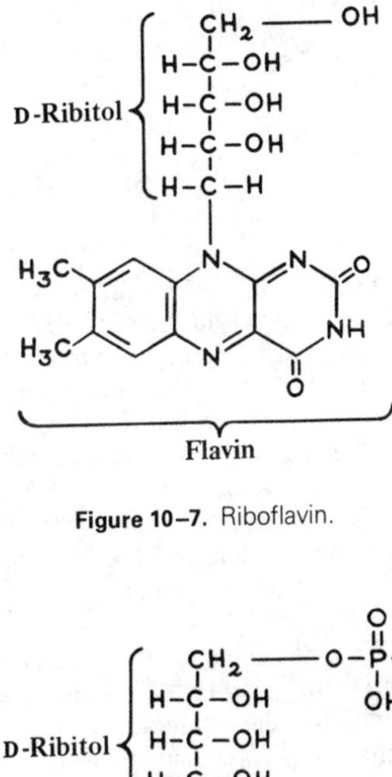

Figure 10–7. Riboflavin.

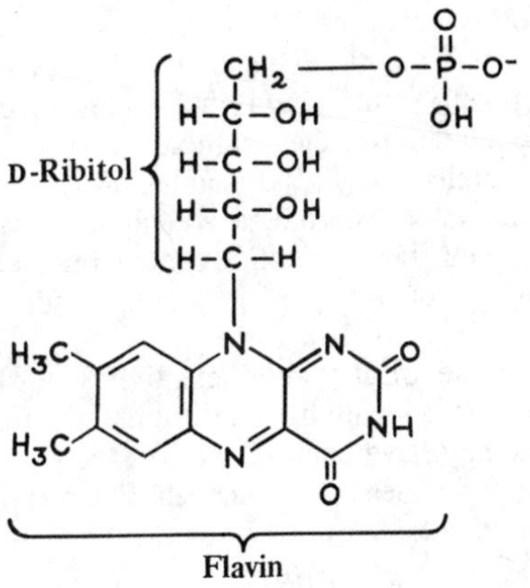

Figure 10–8. Riboflavin phosphate (flavin mononucleotide, FMN).

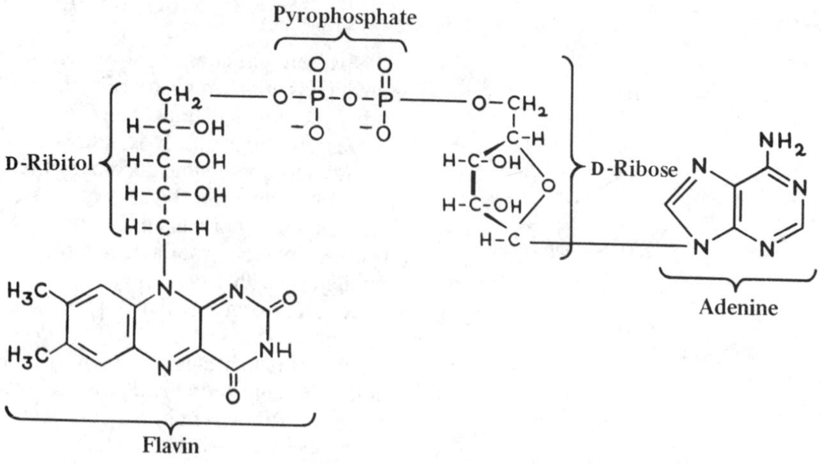

Figure 10–9. Flavin adenine dinucleotide (FAD).

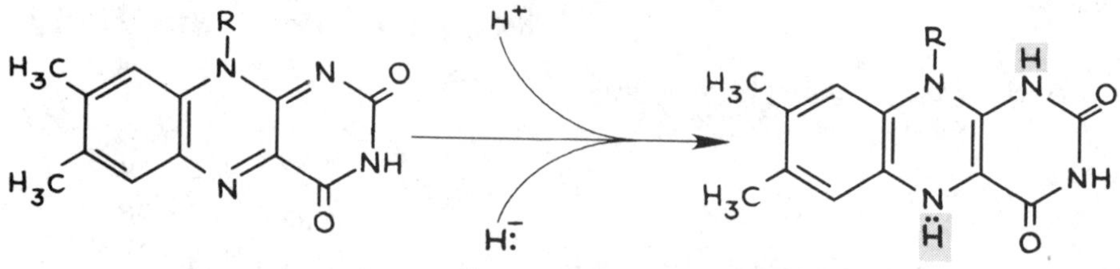

Figure 10–10. Reduction of isoalloxazine ring in flavin nucleotides.

the ATP-dependent phosphorylation of riboflavin. **Flavin adenine dinucleotide (FAD)** is formed by the transfer of an AMP moiety from another ATP molecule to the FMN (Fig 10–9). These reactions seem to occur in most tissues. The FMN and FAD serve as prosthetic groups of oxidation-reduction enzymes, known as **flavoenzymes** or **flavoproteins.** They are usually tightly but not covalently bound to the protein. Many flavoproteins contain one or more metals as additional cofactors and are referred to as **metalloflavoproteins.**

In the catalytic cycle of the flavoproteins, the flavin moiety of the flavin nucleotides undergoes reversible reduction of the isoalloxazine ring to yield the reduced nucleotides $FMNH_2$ and $FADH_2$ (Fig 10–10). The oxidized flavoproteins are highly colored as a result of their flavonucleotide content but bleach when the conjugation through the 3 rings is disrupted by reduction (Fig 10–10).

Because of the light-sensitivity of riboflavin, newborn infants with hyperbilirubinemia treated with phototherapy have been shown to have signs of riboflavin deficiencies even when riboflavin supplements were provided.

NIACIN & NIACINAMIDE

Niacin, or nicotinic acid, is a **pyridine derivative** that is a nontoxic component of the toxic alkaloid nicotine of tobacco. Plants and most animals can synthesize nicotinic acid from the amino acid **tryptophan** by the rearrangement shown in Fig 10–11. Note that this pathway to nicotinic acid requires **pyridoxal phosphate,** the active coenzyme form of vitamin B_6, or pyridoxine. Thus, the major sources of niacin are tryptophan-containing proteins such as meat and those foodstuffs containing nicotinic acid per se (unrefined grains and cereals, yeasts, milk, leafy vegetables, etc). Of note is the fact that **corn is very poor in tryptophan and available niacin.** Thus, diets in which corn is a major source of protein can result in a niacin deficiency syndrome called **pellagra.** For every 60 mg of tryptophan, only 1 mg of nicotinic acid can be generated in the presence of an active pathway. Thus, pellagra is usually associated with a deficiency of not only niacin but also tryptophan and pyridoxine. Rarely, in specific diseases of tryptophan metabolism such as carcinoid syndrome and Hartnup disease, pellagra can occur as an isolated entity.

Nicotinic acid is absorbed in the intestines as nicotinate but is not excreted unmodified in the urine. The largest portion of niacin is excreted as the N-methyl derivative N-methylnicotinamide.

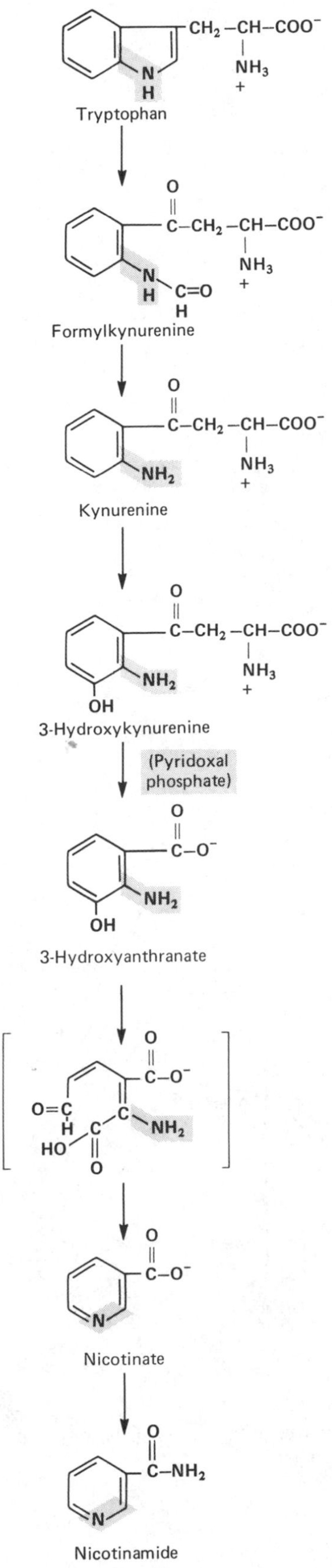

Tryptophan

Formylkynurenine

Kynurenine

3-Hydroxykynurenine

(Pyridoxal phosphate)

3-Hydroxyanthranate

Nicotinate

Nicotinamide

In the cellular cytosol, nicotinate is phosphoribosylated by PPriboseP to form **nicotinate mononucleotide** (NMN). The latter compound is then adenylylated by ATP to form desamidonicotinamide dinucleotide (desamido-NAD^+) (Fig 10–12). The amido group of glutamine then contributes its amide to form the coenzyme **nicotinamide adenine dinucleotide (NAD^+).** A phosphorylated derivative of NAD, **nicotinamide dinucleotide phosphate ($NADP^+$),** also acts as an important coenzyme (see legend, Fig 10–12).

The niacin nucleotides, NAD^+ and $NADP^+$, serve as coenzymes in a large number of reversible oxidation-reduction reactions, as shown in Fig 10–13. The property of these pyridine nucleotides that is responsible for their effectiveness as coenzymes for the oxidation-reduction reactions is the ability of the pyridine ring to serve as an **electron sink**—ie, the hydride or reduced form can exist in multiple resonant forms and therefore is relatively stable.

One group of oxidation-reduction enzymes can utilize either NAD^+ or $NADP^+$; another group can utilize only NAD^+; and a third group can utilize only $NADP^+$.

Nicotinic acid (but not nicotinamide) in high doses can induce skin flushing, pruritus, and gastrointestinal distress and also has demonstrated efficacy for lowering serum cholesterol levels by mechanisms that are not understood.

In the deficiency of niacin, the dermatitis, diarrhea, dementia, etc, of pellagra respond rapidly to niacin, frequently within 1 day. The metabolic abnormalities associated with pellagra are difficult to define, because, as mentioned above, a deficiency of niacin is usually accompanied by the deficiencies of multiple vitamins and by other specific diseases.

PYRIDOXINE

Vitamin B_6 consists of 3 closely related naturally occurring pyridine derivatives: **pyridoxine, pyridoxal,** and **pyridoxamine** (Fig 10–14). All 3 appear to be equally active as precursors for the coenzyme pyridoxal phosphate. Seeds, grains, liver, and to some extent milk, eggs, and leafy green vegetables are good sources of vitamin B_6.

Pyridoxine and its analogs are readily absorbed in the intestines. In the cellular cytoplasm, all 3 serve as substrate for the enzyme pyridoxal kinase, which utilizes ATP to phosphorylate all 3 derivatives to their respective **phosphate esters** (Fig 10–15). Only pyridoxal phosphate and pyridoxamine phosphate are active as coenzymes. Pyridoxal phosphate is the major metabolite present in plasma, while the major metabolite excreted in urine is 4-pyridoxic acid, which can be measured by a fluorometric method.

The coenzyme pyridoxal phosphate binds to its apoenzyme via a **Schiff base** between its 4-aldehyde

Figure 10–11 (at left). The synthesis of nicotinic acid and nicotinamide from tryptophan.

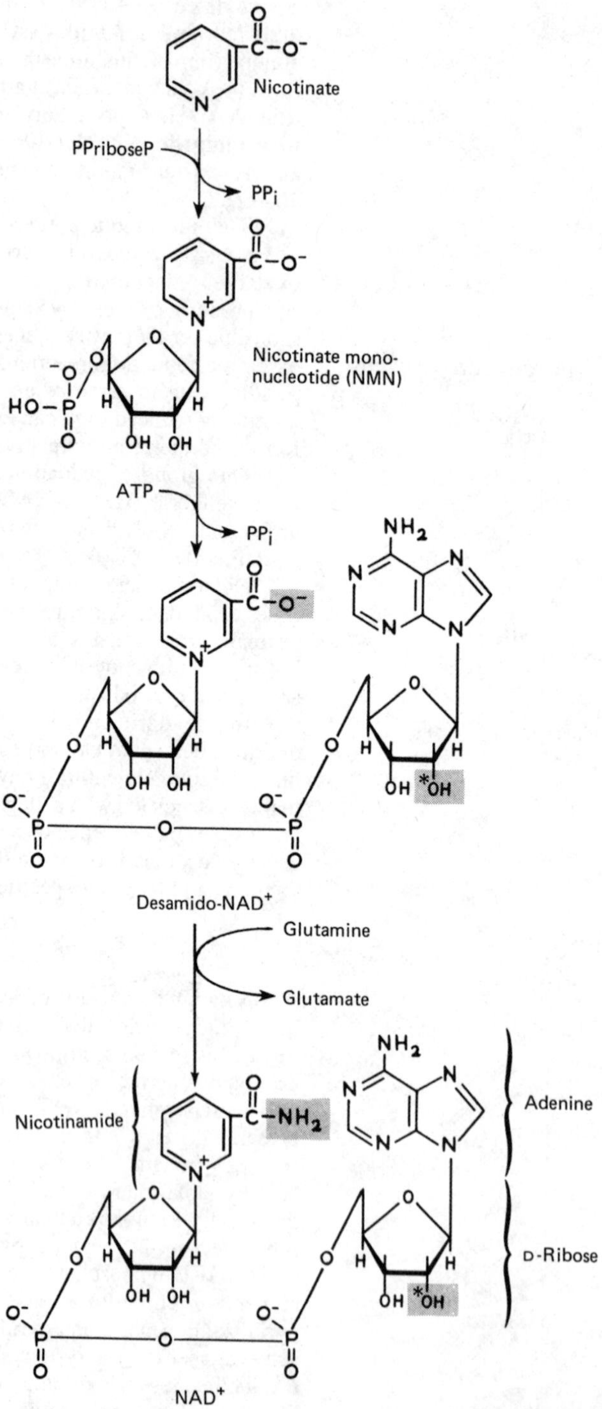

Figure 10–12. The synthesis of nicotinamide adenine dinucleotide (NAD⁺) from nicotinate. The 2′-hydroxyl group (*) of the adenosine moiety is phosphorylated in nicotinamide dinucleotide phosphate (NADP⁺).

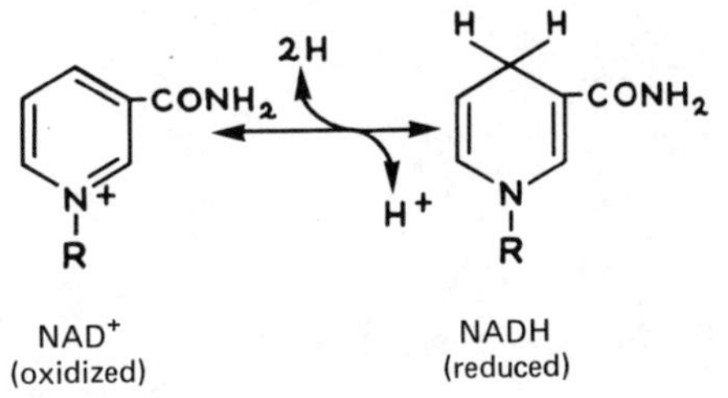

Figure 10–13. Reduction of NAD+.

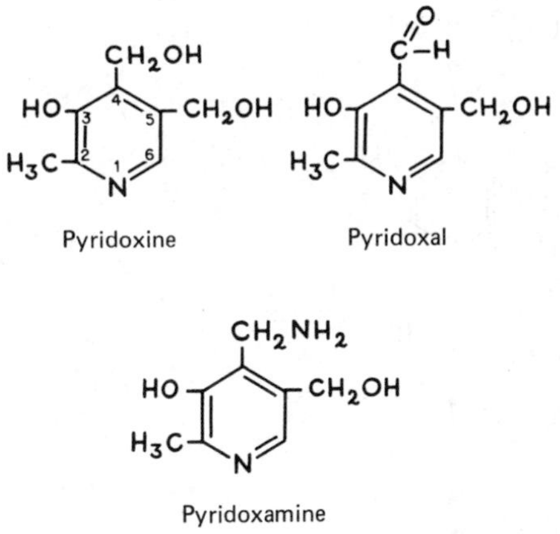

Pyridoxine   Pyridoxal

Pyridoxamine

Figure 10–14. Naturally occurring forms of vitamin B6.

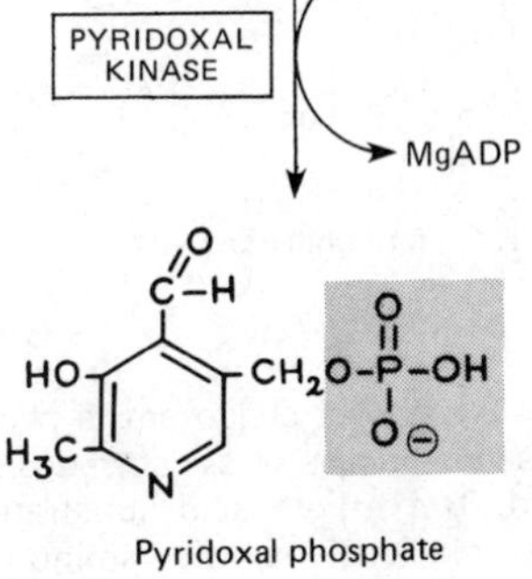

Pyridoxal

PYRIDOXAL KINASE

MgATP

MgADP

Pyridoxal phosphate

Figure 10–15. The phosphorylation of pyridoxal by pyridoxal kinase to form pyridoxal phosphate.

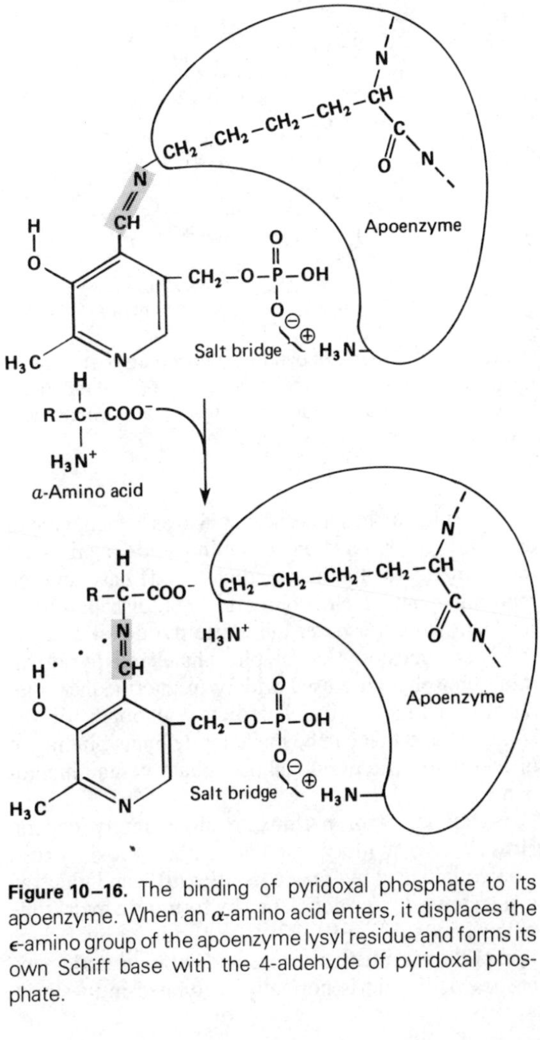

group and an ϵ-amino group of a lysine residue in the enzyme and via an ionic bond (salt bridge) between its phosphate and the enzyme (Fig 10–16). The ability of pyridoxal phosphate to form the Schiff base with an amine is of utmost importance for its function as a coenzyme in **transamination** and **decarboxylation reactions.** In the absence of substrate, the 4-aldehyde group of pyridoxal phosphate remains in the Schiff base linkage with the lysyl residue of the enzyme-active site. Upon the entry of an α-amino group of a substrate, such as an amino acid, the α-amino group displaces the ϵ-amino group of the lysyl residue, forming a new Schiff base; but the coenzyme remains bound to the enzyme by the salt bridge (Fig 10–16). By a series of electron shifts and rearrangements, the pyridoxal phosphate becomes **pyridoxamine phosphate** as the substrate is oxidatively deaminated (Fig 10–17) to form the corresponding α-keto acid. Subsequently, the α-keto acid substrate of the transamination reaction forms a Schiff base with the pyridoxamine phosphate (Fig 10–18), and the α-amino group removed from the amino acid is transferred to the α-keto acid, completing the transamination cycle.

Figure 10–16. The binding of pyridoxal phosphate to its apoenzyme. When an α-amino acid enters, it displaces the ϵ-amino group of the apoenzyme lysyl residue and forms its own Schiff base with the 4-aldehyde of pyridoxal phosphate.

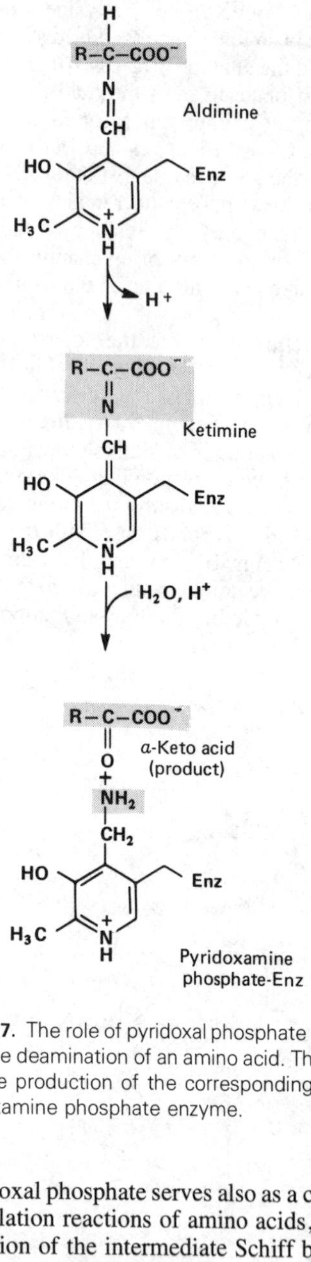

Figure 10–17. The role of pyridoxal phosphate coenzyme in the oxidative deamination of an amino acid. The first phase involves the production of the corresponding α-keto acid and pyridoxamine phosphate enzyme.

Pyridoxal phosphate serves also as a coenzyme in decarboxylation reactions of amino acids, again with the formation of the intermediate Schiff base and the rearrangement of electrons and their distribution in resonant structures over the entire pyridoxal moiety. As coenzymes, pyridoxal phosphate and pyridoxamine phosphate are used widely in intermediary metabolism. Figure 10–19 depicts the bonds of the α-amino acid that can be made labile by its binding to different specific pyridoxal phosphate–containing enzymes.

Deficiency of pyridoxine alone rarely occurs. However, a widely used antituberculosis drug, isonicotinic acid hydrazide **(isoniazid)**, can induce an isolated pyridoxine deficiency by forming a hydrazone with pyridoxal (Fig 10–20). The pyridoxal-hydrazone is rapidly excreted in urine, and vitamin deficiency ensues. Isoniazid is normally acetylated in the liver,

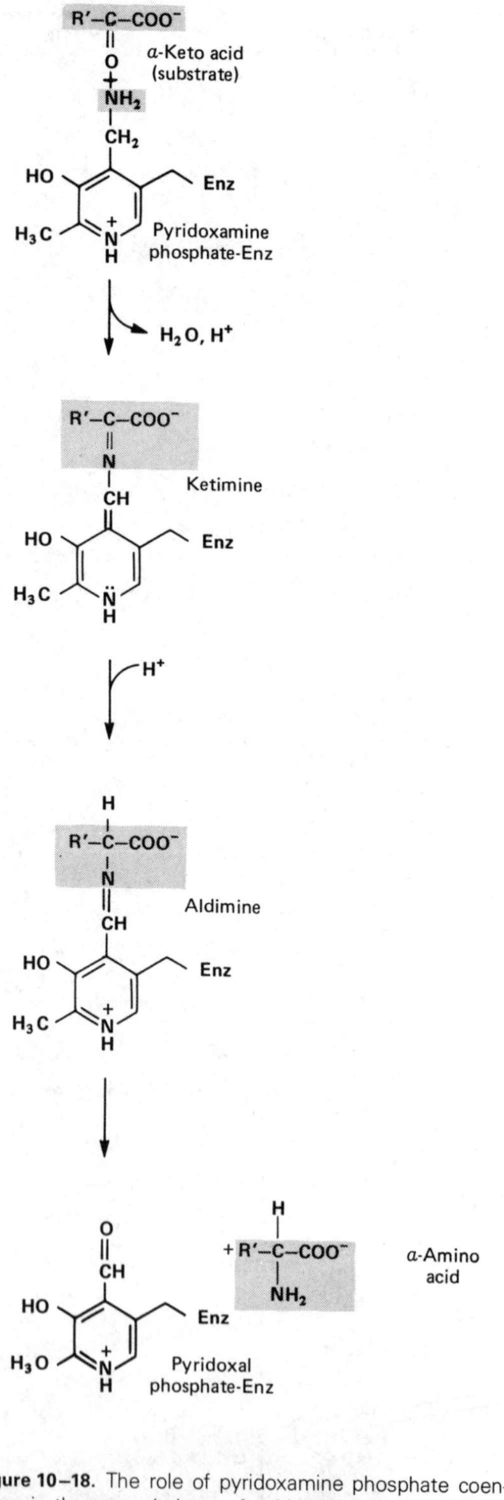

Figure 10–18. The role of pyridoxamine phosphate coenzyme in the second phase of oxidative deamination of an α-amino acid. The α-keto acid substrate (frequently α-ketoglutarate) receives the amino group from pyridoxamine phosphate to generate the corresponding α-amino acid (glutamate) and pyridoxal phosphate, completing the transamination cycle.

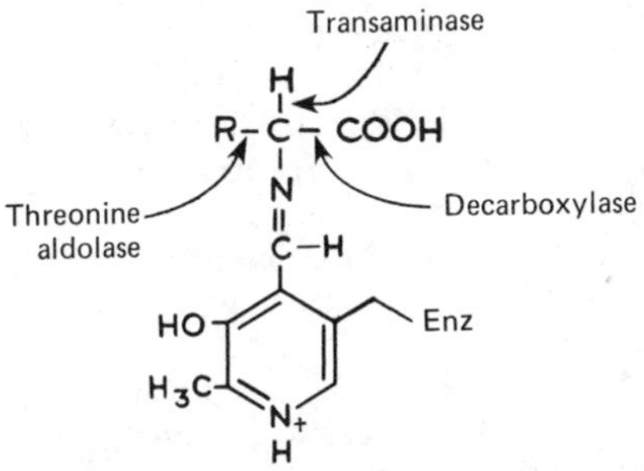

Figure 10–19. The covalent bonds of an α-amino acid that can be made labile by its binding to specific pyridoxal phosphate–containing enzymes.

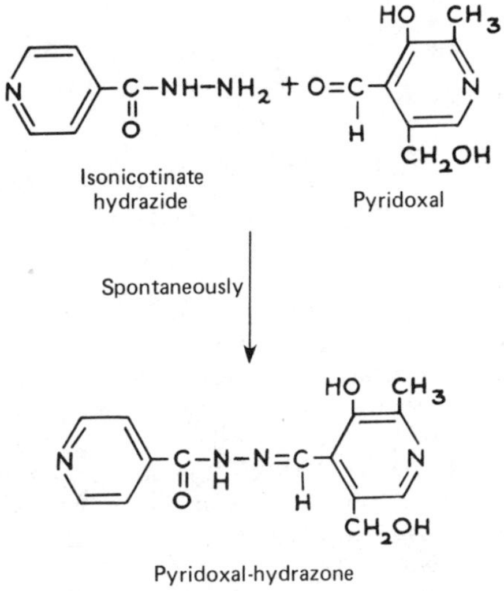

Figure 10–20. The formation of the rapidly excreted pyridoxal-hydrazone from pyridoxal and isonicotinate hydrazine (isoniazid).

but a significant fraction of the population of most racial groups consists of genetically slow acetylators of isoniazid. Only in **slow acetylators** does isoniazid have the opportunity to form the hydrazone of pyridoxal. There is some evidence that in renal failure, pyridoxal kinase is inhibited and there ensues a deficiency of the coenzyme pyridoxal phosphate in spite of adequate intake of vitamin B_6.

As mentioned above in the discussion of niacin, the generation of nicotinic acid from tryptophan is dependent upon pyridoxal phosphate as coenzyme. Hence, **pellagra is a frequent accompaniment of pyridoxine deficiency.**

Pyridoxine is also necessary in the transulfuration reactions that convert methionine to cysteine (Chapter 22). Homocystinuria and cystathioninuria are metabolic indicators of pyridoxine deficiency.

A number of genetic diseases in humans result from the inability of specific apoenzymes to bind pyridoxal phosphate with adequate avidity. Some of those diseases will respond to pharmacologic doses of vitamin B_6 (see Chapter 47).

Nerve toxicity associated with daily doses exceeding 1–2 g of vitamin B_6 is now recognized.

PANTOTHENIC ACID

Pantothenic acid is an amide of pantoic acid and β-alanine (Fig 10–21). It is widely distributed in foods, being particularly abundant in animal tissues, whole-grain cereals, and legumes. A specific pantothenate deficiency syndrome in humans has been recognized only experimentally after the administration of specific antagonists. Deficiency of pantothenate is usually associated with deficiencies of other B complex vitamins. There is no known toxicity of pantothenic acid.

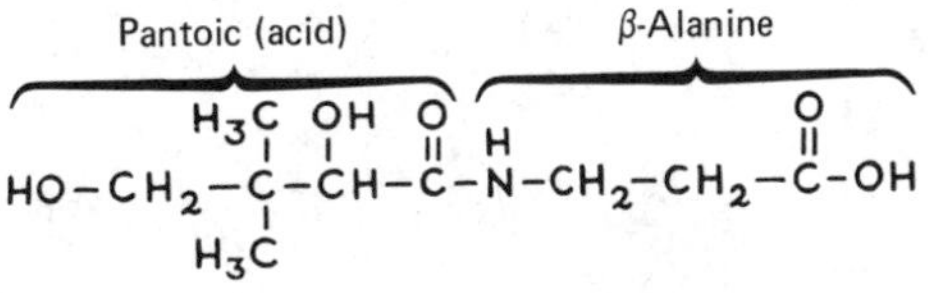

Figure 10–21. Pantothenic acid.

Pantothenic acid is absorbed readily in the intestines and subsequently phosphorylated by ATP to form 4′-phosphopantothenic acid (Fig 10–22). On the path to conversion to the active coenzyme, **coenzyme A,** cysteine is added to the phosphopantothenic acid, and the carboxyl group of cysteine is subsequently removed, resulting in the net addition of thioethanolamine to phosphopantothenic acid, generating 4′-phosphopantetheine. Like the active coenzymes of so many other water-soluble vitamins, the active coenzyme of pantothenate contains an adenine nucleotide. Thus, 4′-phosphopantetheine is adenylylated by ATP to form dephospho-coenzyme A. The final phosphorylation occurs with ATP adding phosphate to the 3′-hydroxyl group of the ribose moiety to generate coenzyme A (Fig 10–22). Coenzyme A contains adenine at one pole and a thiol at the opposite pole of the molecule. This latter **thiol group acts as a carrier of acyl groups** in reactions involving fatty acid oxidation and synthesis, acetylation reactions, and (as discussed above) oxidative decarboxylations in which thiamin pyrophosphate also participates. The acyl-sulfur bond formed from coenzyme A and a transferred acyl moiety is a **high-energy bond,** equivalent to the high-energy bond of ATP. Formation of these high-energy bonds therefore requires a source of energy, either from a coupled exergonic reaction or from the transfer of energy from a high-energy phosphate or a high-energy sulfur bond. It is customary to abbreviate the structure of the free (ie, reduced) coenzyme A as CoA·SH, in which the reactive SH group of the coenzyme is designated.

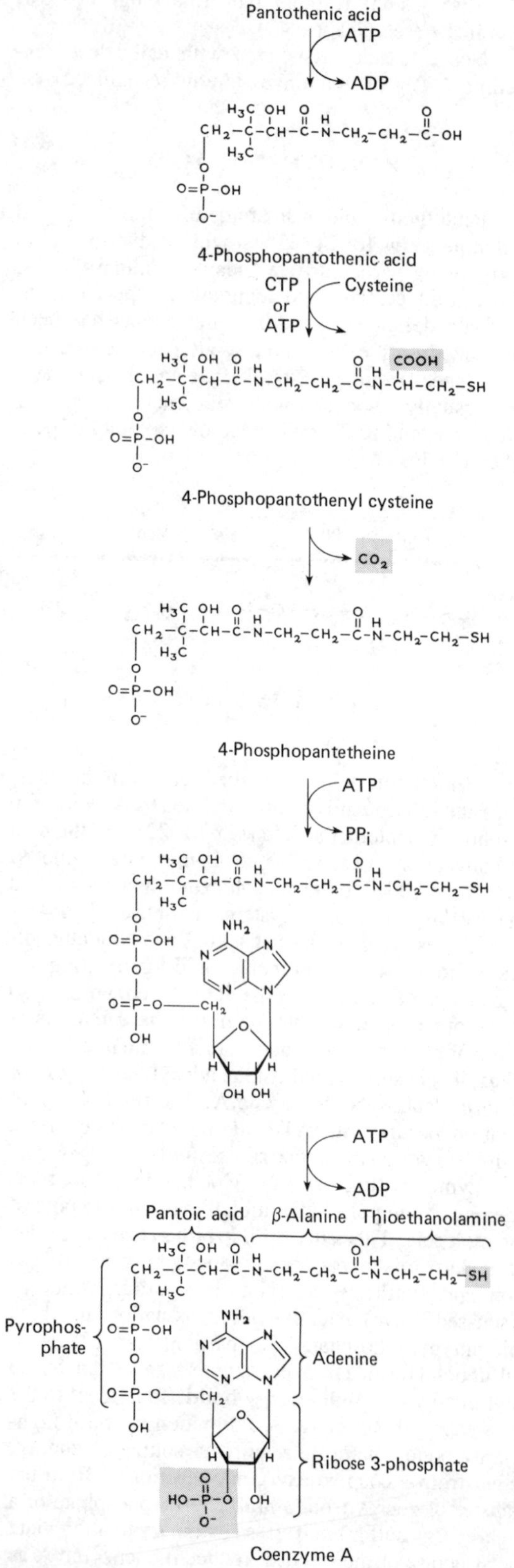

Pantothenic acid

4-Phosphopantothenic acid

4-Phosphopantothenyl cysteine

4-Phosphopantetheine

Pantoic acid   β-Alanine   Thioethanolamine

Pyrophos-
phate

Adenine

Ribose 3-phosphate

Coenzyme A

Figure 10–22. The synthesis of coenzyme A from pantothenic acid.

BIOTIN

Biotin is an imidazole derivative widely distributed in natural foods (Fig 10–23). A large portion of the human biotin requirement is probably **supplied from the intestinal bacteria.** Careful balance studies in humans have shown that in many instances urinary excretion of biotin exceeded dietary intake and fecal excretion was 3–6 times greater than dietary intake. Biotin deficiency can be induced more readily in animals fed antibacterial drugs to reduce the intestinal bacterial flora to a minimum. Biotin is absorbed in the ileum.

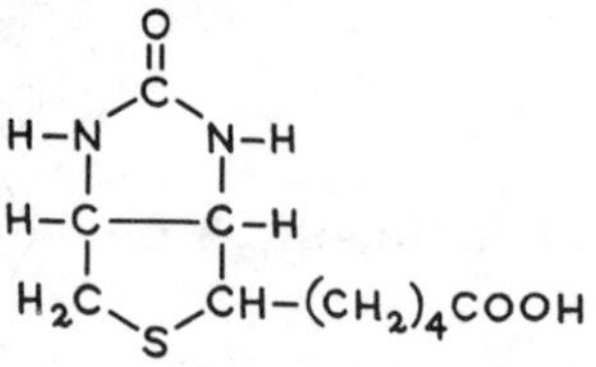

Figure 10–23. Biotin.

The bioavailability of biotin differs widely in various foodstuffs. For example, while the biotin of corn and soy meals is completely available, that of wheat is almost unavailable. Egg yolk, animal tissues, tomatoes, and yeast are excellent sources of biotin. Egg white contains a heat-labile protein, **avidin,** which combines very tightly with biotin, thereby preventing its absorption from the intestine and inducing an isolated biotin deficiency.

Biotin functions as a component of specific multisubunit enzymes (Table 10–1) that catalyze carboxylation reactions. It is attached to the apoenzyme by an amide linkage to the ε-amino group of a lysyl residue.

In the first step of the reaction of pyruvate carboxylase, a carboxylate ion is attached to the N^1 of the biotin, generating an activated intermediate, **carboxybiotin-enzyme** (Fig 10–24). This step requires HCO_3^-, ATP, Mg^{2+}, and acyl-CoA (as an allosteric effector). The activated carboxyl group is then

Table 10–1. Biotin-dependent enzymes in animals.

Enzyme	Role
Pyruvate carboxylase	First reaction in pathway that converts 3-carbon precursors to glucose (gluconeogenesis)
	Replenishes oxaloacetate for citric acid cycle
Acetyl-CoA carboxylase	Commits acetate units to fatty acid synthesis by forming malonyl-CoA
Propionyl-CoA carboxylase	Converts proprionate to succinate, which can then enter citric acid cycle
β-Methylcrotonyl-CoA carboxylase	Catabolism of leucine and certain isoprenoid compounds

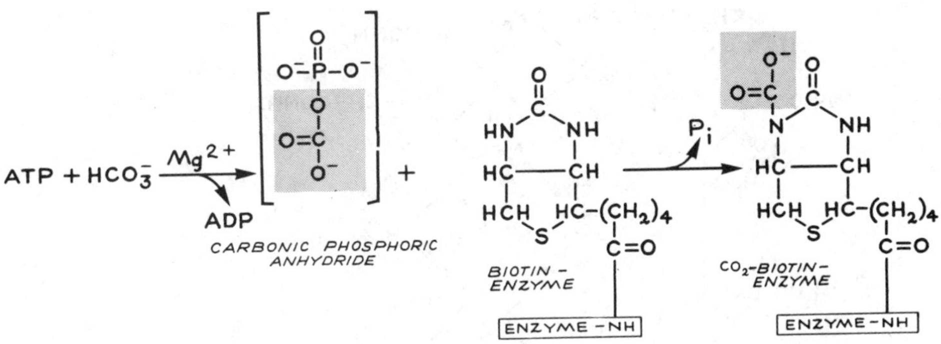

Figure 10—24. Formation of the CO_2-biotin enzyme complex.

transferred from the carboxybiotin-enzyme intermediate to pyruvate to form oxaloacetate and the biotin-holoenzyme. The long flexible arm between the biotin and the enzyme probably enables this prosthetic group (biotin) to move from one active site of the multisubunit enzyme (eg, the phosphocarbonate-forming component) to the other site (eg, that possessing the pyruvate).

There appears to be a single enzyme responsible for attaching biotin to the proper lysyl residue of all the carboxylase apoenzymes. This enzyme is called holocarboxylase synthetase. In the absence of holocarboxylase synthetase activity, substrates of the biotin-dependent carboxylase enzymes accumulate and can be detected in urine. These metabolites include lactate, β-methylcrotonate, β-hydroxyisovalerate, and β-hydroxypropionate. Children with this enzyme deficiency exhibit dermatitis, retarded growth, alopecia, loss of muscular control, and, in some cases, immune deficiency diseases.

There is no known toxicity of biotin.

VITAMIN B_{12}

Vitamin B_{12}, or cobalamin, consists of a corrin ring similar to the porphyrins that includes a **cobalt ion** at its center (Fig 10–25). A cyano group is usually attached to the cobalt as an artifact of isolation and must be removed in the body before cobalamin can be converted to its active form. Cobalamin is **synthesized exclusively by bacteria** but is present in normal animal liver, where it exists as methylcobalamin, adenosylcobalamin, and hydroxocobalamin. The cyanocobalamin is the most stable form and therefore that form in which the vitamin is commercially produced from bacterial fermentation. It is water-soluble and heat-stable.

The intestinal absorption of vitamin B_{12} is mediated by receptor sites in the ileum that require cobalamin to be bound by the highly specific glycoprotein **intrinsic factor,** secreted by parietal cells of the gastric mucosa. Other cobalamin-binding proteins, known collectively as R proteins, are secreted by sali-

vary glands and stomach and bind cobalamin much (50-fold) more tightly at an acid pH than does intrinsic factor. The R proteins are normally degraded by pancreatic proteases, while intrinsic factor is not protease-sensitive. In pancreatic insufficiency, cobalamin molecules are not released from the R proteins and thus cannot bind to intrinsic factor for normal absorption.

As the cobalamin–intrinsic factor complex crosses the ileal mucosa, intrinsic factor is released and the vitamin is transferred to a plasma transport protein, **transcobalamin II.** Other cobalamin-binding proteins, such as transcobalamin I, exist in the plasma and liver and in the latter provide an effective storage form of cobalamin, a unique situation for water-soluble vitamins. Cobalamin is secreted in bile and participates in enterohepatic circulation; thus, there is an enhanced requirement for exogenous cobalamin whenever the enterohepatic circulatory system is disturbed. Once the cobalamin is bound to transcobalamin II in the portal blood, it disappears from the plasma in a few hours. The major circulating vitamin is **methylcobalamin,** with a trace of hydroxocobalamin detectable. However, in the liver, **5′-deoxyadenosylcobalamin** accounts for 70% of the total cobalamins, whereas methylcobalamin contributes only 3%.

The transcobalamin II complex delivers cobalamin to the tissues. It binds to specific cell surface receptors and enters the cell by way of an endocytotic process, ultimately releasing free cobalamin as **hydroxocobalamin in the cytosol.** There it is either converted to methylcobalamin or enters the **mitochondria,** where the cobalt is **reduced** and **5′-deoxyadenosylcobalamin** subsequently formed (Fig 10–26).

There are in humans only 2 enzymatic reactions for which cobalamin serves as a coenzyme. **Methylation of homocysteine to methionine** occurs in the cytoplasm and utilizes methylcobalamin as coenzyme and N^5-methyltetrahydrofolate as methyl source (Fig 10–27). The methyltransferase apoenzyme binds cobalamin, and the N^5**-methyltetrahydrofolate** transfers its methyl group to the cobalamin prosthetic group. The methyl group bound to the cobalamin is then transferred to homocysteine, generating

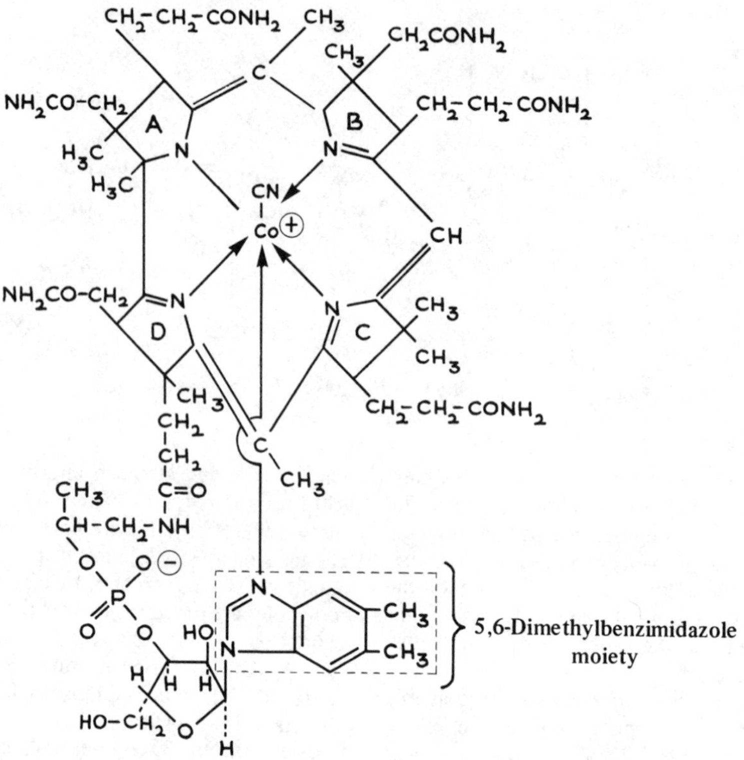

Figure 10–25. Cyanocobalamin; vitamin B_{12} ($C_{63}H_{88}O_{14}N_{14}PCo$).

methionine. As will be discussed below, absence of cobalamin effects a block in this reaction and an accumulation of N^5-methyltetrahydrofolate. Thus, a deficiency of cobalamin generates a **trap for tetrahydrofolate,** an important cofactor discussed below.

The second enzymatic reaction that utilizes cobalamin is isomerization of L-methylmalonyl-CoA to succinyl-CoA by the enzyme L-**methylmalonyl-CoA mutase** and the coenzyme **5′-deoxyadenosyl-cobalamin** (Fig 10–27). As described above, the deoxyadenosylcobalamin is formed from ATP and reduced cobalamin in mitochondria, and the isomerization likewise occurs in the **mitochondria** (Fig 10–26).

In the cobalamin-deficient states, whether they be due to malabsorption of vitamin B_{12} or to defective delivery of cobalamin to the peripheral tissues, homocystinuria and methylmalonic aciduria occur.

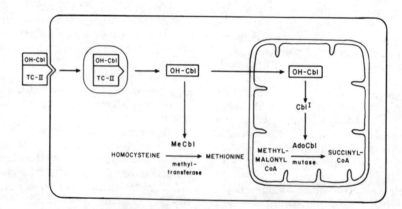

Figure 10–26. Pathway of cellular uptake and subcellular compartmentation of cobalamin and cobalamin coenzymes. (OH-Cbl, hydroxocobalamin; TC-II, transcobalamin II; MeCbl, methylcobalamin; AdoCbl, 5′-deoxyadenosylcobalamin.) (Reproduced, with permission, from Stanbury JB, Wyngaarden JB, Fredrickson DS: *The Metabolic Basis of Inherited Disease,* 4th ed. McGraw-Hill, 1978.)

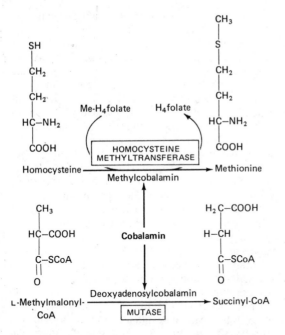

Figure 10–27. Reactions catalyzed by cobalamin coenzymes in mammalian tissues. Note the specificity of deoxyadenosylcobalamin for the isomerization of methylmalonyl-CoA and of methylcobalamin for the methylation of homocysteine. (Me-H$_4$folate, N^5-methyltetrahydrofolate; H$_4$folate, tetrahydrofolate.) (Redrawn, with permission, from Stanbury JB, Wyngaarden JB, Fredrickson DS: *The Metabolic Basis of Inherited Disease,* 4th ed. McGraw-Hill, 1978.)

Although in some bacteria vitamin B$_{12}$ derivatives are necessary for the reduction of ribonucleotides to the 2'-deoxyribonucleotide substrates of DNA synthesis, there is no evidence for direct involvement of cobalamin coenzymes in the formation of the substrates for DNA synthesis in humans. As discussed below with folates, the megaloblastic anemia characteristic of vitamin B$_{12}$ deficiency is probably due to a secondary deficiency of reduced folate, a consequence of the accumulation of excessive N^5-methyltetrahydrofolate (see above). The neurologic disorder associated with cobalamin deficiency may be secondary to a relative deficiency of methionine.

In some inherited diseases discussed in Chapter 44, massive quantities of vitamin B$_{12}$—1000 times the normal requirement—are administered to effect a functional cure of an inherited metabolic disease.

Four inherited disorders of cobalamin metabolism have been described in humans. Two affect the synthesis of deoxyadenosylcobalamin only; in the other 2, patients are unable to synthesize either deoxyadenosylcobalamin or methylcobalamin.

FOLATE OR FOLACIN

The term folic is derived from Latin *folium* "leaf." Chemically, folic acid or folate consists of the heterobicyclic pteridine, para-aminobenzoic acid (PABA), and glutamic acid (Fig 10–28). Animal cells are not capable of synthesizing PABA or of attaching the first glutamate to pteroic acid. Thus, unlike bacteria and plants, they require folic acid in their diets. The major source of folic acid is, of course, leafy vegetables. **Folate deficiency is probably the most common vitamin deficiency in the USA.**

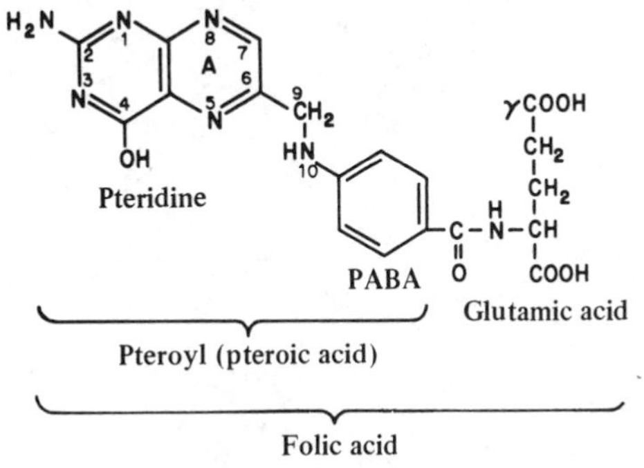

Figure 10–28. The structure and numbering of atoms of folic acid.

In plants, folic acid exists as a polyglutamate conjugate with an unusual gamma-linked polypeptide chain of 7 glutamic acids. In the liver, the major folate is a pentaglutamyl conjugate. These unusual gamma-linked glutamyl peptide chains are resistant to hydrolysis by the usual proteolytic enzymes present in the intestine. However, they are cleaved by a specific group of intestinal enzymes, folyl polyglutamate hydrolases.

The hydrolysis of pteroylheptaglutamate to pteroylmonoglutamate by intestinal enzymes is rapid and not rate-limiting for the absorption of the folates into the mesenteric circulation. Only the monoglutamyl form is absorbed, and a major portion of that is reduced to tetrahydrofolate (H$_4$folate) and methylated to N^5-methyl-H$_4$folate within the intestinal cell as an integral part of the absorption process. After the oral administration of folic acid to normal humans, there is a transitory rise in the plasma concentration of N^5-methyltetrahydrofolate regardless of the form in which folates are administered. Folate absorption is impaired in idiopathic steatorrhea and tropical sprue and in various other disorders of the small intestine.

In the blood plasma, approximately two-thirds of the folate is bound to a protein. Of the folates filtered by the kidney glomerulus, only a negligible fraction is reabsorbed by the tubules when the plasma folate concentration exceeds 10 μg/L. Some folate cleavage products may be excreted in bile.

This rather complex molecule folic acid, after being **reduced to tetrahydrofolate** (H$_4$folate), serves

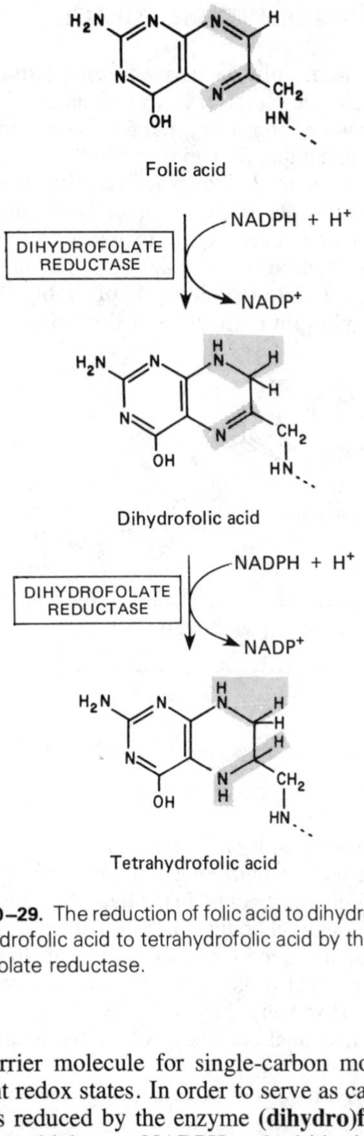

Folic acid

Dihydrofolic acid

Tetrahydrofolic acid

Figure 10–29. The reduction of folic acid to dihydrofolic acid and dihydrofolic acid to tetrahydrofolic acid by the enzyme dihydrofolate reductase.

as a carrier molecule for single-carbon moieties of different redox states. In order to serve as carrier, the folate is reduced by the enzyme **(dihydro)folate reductase,** which uses NADPH as hydride donor (Fig 10–29). **Trimethoprim** is a selective inhibitor of dihydrofolate reductase from gram-negative bacteria and has little efficacy as inhibitor of the mammalian enzyme. However, the inhibitor methotrexate (amethopterin) binds more strongly to dihydrofolate reductase from both bacteria and mammalian sources than do the naturally occurring substrates. These folate antagonists are important tools for treatment of infections and cancers.

The one-carbon moiety carried on H_4folate may be a **methyl, methylene, methenyl, formyl,** or **formimino moiety.** All are metabolically interconvertible.

Folate metabolism is complex, because of the interconversions, the number of one-carbon moieties carried by tetrahydrofolate, and the many reactions in which they participate.

Serine is the major source of the one-carbon moiety for the H_4folates. Serine transfers its hydroxy-

methylene group to H_4folate, generating glycine and N^5,N^{10}-methylene-H_4folate (Fig 10–30, reaction 1). The N^5,N^{10}-methylene-H_4folate plays a central role in the metabolism of H_4folates. It can be reduced to N^5-methyl-H_4folate (Fig 10–30, reaction 2), the folate derivative mentioned above, which plays an important role in the function of cobalamin. The N^5,N^{10}-methylene-H_4folate can be dehydrogenated to N^5,N^{10}-methenyl-H_4folate (Fig 10–30, reaction 3). The N^5,N^{10}-methenyl-H_4folate, without changing its redox state, can be hydrated to N^{10}-formyl-H_4folate (Fig 10–30, reaction 4) or to N^5-formyl-H_4folate (Fig 10–30, reaction 5). The latter, also referred to as **folinic acid,** is a stable form of H_4folate that can be administered orally or parenterally to provide reduced folate; ie, folinic acid does not need to be acted upon by folate reductase in order to function as a carrier for the one-carbon moiety. However, before its absorption, the N^5-formyl moiety is mostly removed and replaced by a methyl moiety in the intestinal mucosal cell.

Formiminoglutamate can transfer its formimino group to H_4folate to form N^5-formimino-H_4folate, which in turn can be deaminated to form folinic acid (Fig 10–30), reaction 6). Formiminoglutamic acid (Figlu) is a catabolite of histidine, an α-amino acid. In folate deficiency, Figlu will accumulate when oral histidine is administered.

The N^5,N^{10}-methylene-H_4folate provides the methyl group to deoxyuridylate to form thymidylate, a necessary precursor of DNA synthesis (Fig 10–31). Note that the redox state of the methylene changes as the methyl group is added to deoxyuridylate. Thus, concomitant with the reduction of the methylene to the methyl moiety is oxidation of tetrahydrofolate to dihydrofolate. This is the only one-carbon transfer reaction that results in the oxidation of H_4folate. Therefore, cells synthesizing thymidylate (for DNA) are particularly vulnerable to inhibitors of dihydrofolate reductase.

N^5-Methyl-H_4folate acts as methyl donor to homocysteine, discussed above under cobalamin metabolism. The N^5,N^{10}-methenyl-H_4folate provides the carbon at position 8 of purines (see Chapter 26), whereas the N^{10}-formyl-H_4folate provides the carbon at position 2 of the purine ring.

As depicted in Fig 10–30, N^5,N^{10}-methylene-H_4folate can also provide a hydroxymethylene group to glycine, forming serine, a reversal of the serine hydroxymethyl transferase reaction (Fig 10–30, reaction 1).

Because of the close interrelationship between folic acid and cobalamin metabolism and the presence of a megaloblastic anemia when either one of these vitamins is deficient, the clinical distinction between the 2 deficiency states is sometimes difficult. However, in a truly folic acid–deficient patient, the administration of 300–500 μg of folate per day will produce a positive hematologic response. This small dose will achieve no response in a patient with pernicious anemia, ie, vitamin B_{12} deficiency. The use of this conservative but adequate dose of folate can serve as a

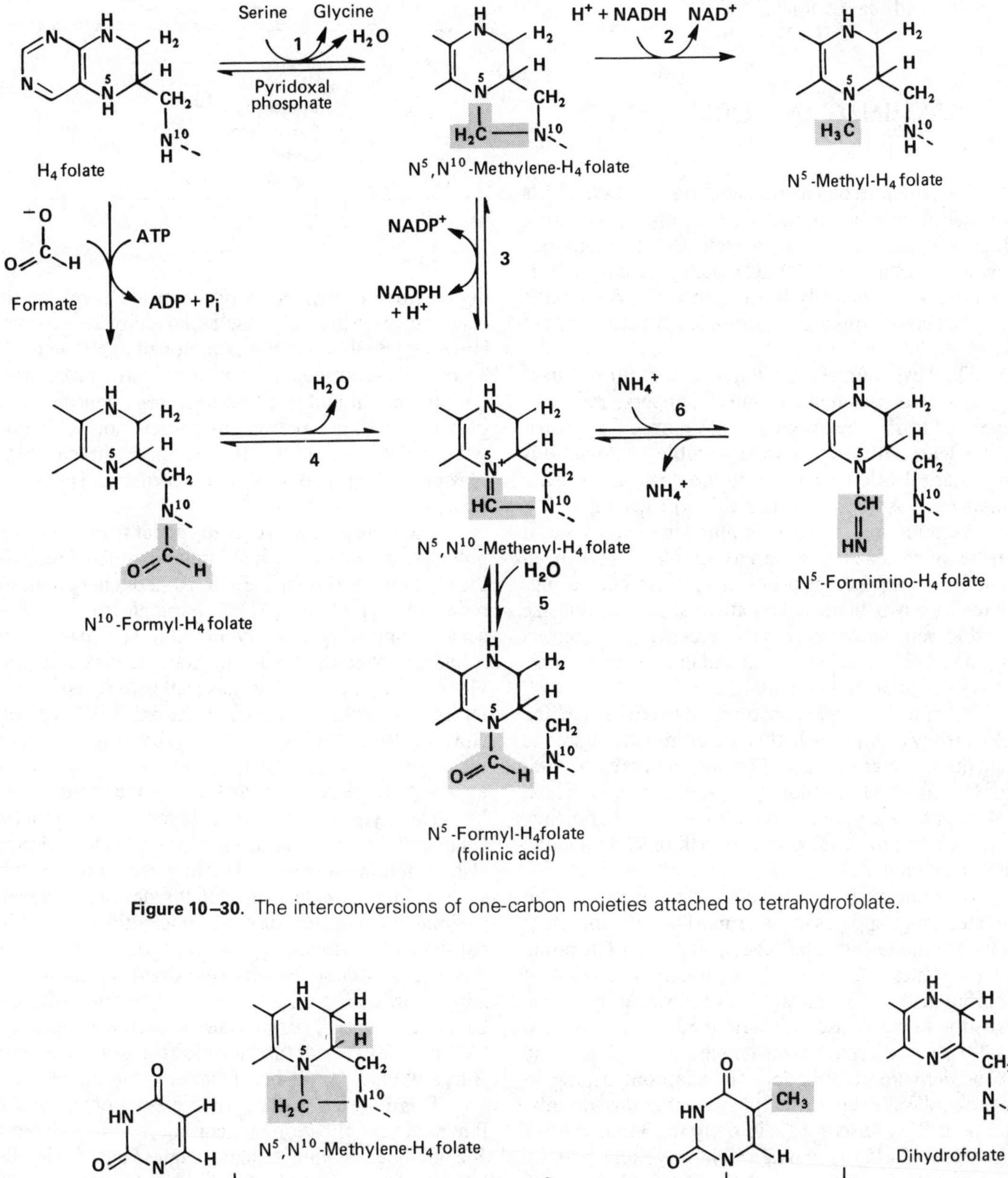

Figure 10–30. The interconversions of one-carbon moieties attached to tetrahydrofolate.

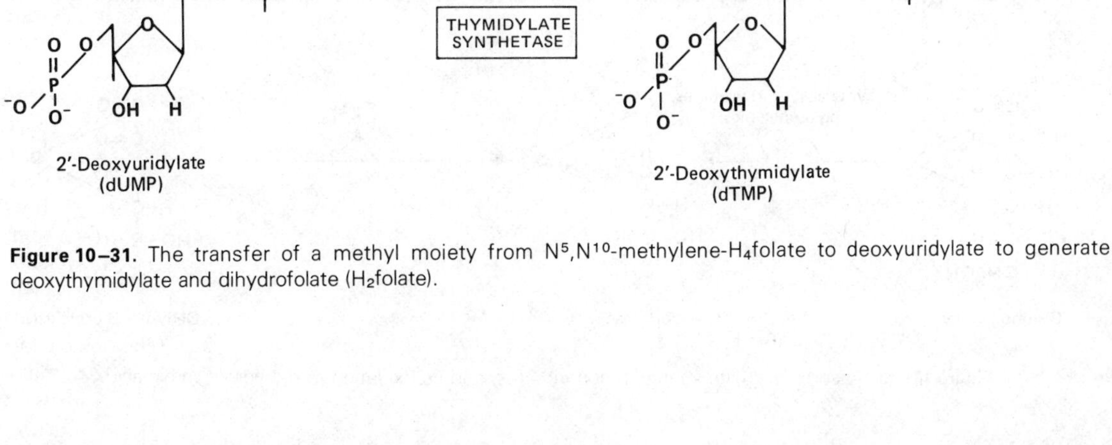

Figure 10–31. The transfer of a methyl moiety from N^5,N^{10}-methylene-H_4folate to deoxyuridylate to generate deoxythymidylate and dihydrofolate (H_2folate).

means of differentiating between the deficiency of vitamin B_{12} and that of folate.

VITAMIN C (ASCORBIC ACID)

The structure of ascorbic acid resembles that of a monosaccharide but contains an enediol group from which the removal of a hydrogen occurs to produce dehydroascorbate (Fig 10–32). Dehydroascorbate is generated spontaneously from vitamin C by oxidation in air, but both forms are physiologically active and are found in body fluids.

The best sources of vitamin C are citrus fruits, berries, melons, tomatoes, green peppers, raw cabbage, and leafy green vegetables. Vitamin C is probably the **least stable** of the water-soluble vitamins. It is particularly labile to **heating** in the presence of trace metals such as copper. It is stable to freezing.

Ascorbic acid is widely required in metabolism. It can be synthesized in a variety of plants and in all animals studied except primates and the guinea pig. Animals such as humans that are unable to synthesize ascorbic acid lack the enzyme necessary to convert L-gulonic acid to ascorbic acid and thus require ascorbic acid in their diet (Fig 10–32).

Vitamin C is readily absorbed in the intestine, and a deficiency of this nutrient is therefore attributable to inadequate dietary intake. The normal stores of vitamin C in the body cannot be rapidly depleted. Thus, 3–4 months are required for a vitamin C deficiency state, **scurvy,** to develop in a human placed on a diet free of vitamin C.

Ascorbic acid can be converted in humans to oxalate, which appears in the urine. The calcium salt of oxalate is quite insoluble and is capable of forming kidney stones. A study of the urinary excretion of ascorbic acid and its metabolites following daily oral ingestion of 3 g of ascorbic acid for 2 weeks revealed that 90% was excreted as unchanged ascorbic acid and 6% as dehydroascorbic acid. In addition, 31 mg of oxalic acid was excreted daily. Even after the administration of 9 g of ascorbic acid daily for 3 consecutive days, only 40–45 mg of oxalic acid was excreted daily in urine, the normal value being approximately 20

Table 10–2. Compounds that can be reduced by ascorbic acid.

$\frac{1}{2}O_2$
NO_3^-
Cytochrome a Fe^{3+}
Cytochrome c Fe^{3+}
Crotonyl-CoA
Methemoglobin

mg/d. Thus, the major excretory products of ascorbic acid are ascorbic acid itself and dehydroascorbate. However, doubling of the excretion of oxalic acid after 9 g of oral ascorbic acid is not an insignificant change.

In animal and plant tissues, large concentrations of vitamin C are present in comparison with other water-soluble vitamins. For example, human blood plasma contains about 1 mg of ascorbic acid per deciliter.

Ascorbic acid is a reducing agent with a hydrogen potential of +0.08 V, making it capable of reducing the compounds shown in Table 10–2 but not capable of reducing NAD^+ to NADH, pyruvate to lactate, or acetoacetate to β-hydroxybutyrate. The oxidation of p-hydroxyphenylpyruvate to homogentisate requires vitamin C and copper for maximal activity (see Chapter 22). The subsequent step in the oxidative **degradation of tyrosine** is catalyzed by homogentisate dioxygenase, a ferrous iron–containing enzyme that also requires ascorbic acid for maximal activity.

The hydroxylation of proline in collagen (see Chapter 34) requires ascorbic acid. Ascorbic acid may also function in other oxidation-reduction systems such as that coupled with glutathione, cytochrome c, pyridine nucleotides, or flavin nucleotides. The adrenal cortex contains large amounts of vitamin C, and this is rapidly depleted when the gland is stimulated by adrenocorticotropic hormone. The function of ascorbate in the adrenal cortex is not known with certainty, but it does serve as a cofactor for dopamine β-hydroxylase, probably as an electron donor.

There are no known toxic effects of vitamin C. Potential complications of chronic massive overdosage include calcium oxalate stones and detrimental effects of ascorbate on the biotransformation or ab-

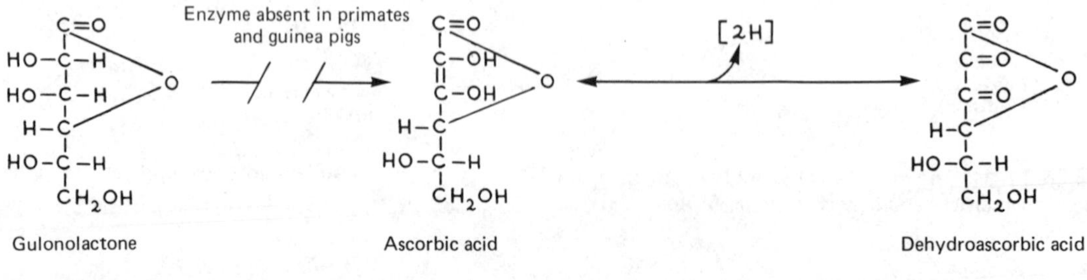

Gulonolactone   Ascorbic acid   Dehydroascorbic acid

Figure 10–32. Ascorbic acid, its source in nonprimates, and its oxidation to dehydroascorbic acid.

sorption of other vitamins (eg, vitamin B_{12}) and drugs present simultaneously in the gastrointestinal tract. Ascorbic acid is capable of acidifying urine, at times a useful and at other times a detrimental effect. The

intestinal absorption of iron is significantly enhanced by the simultaneous presence of ascorbate, and the mobilization of iron from tissue depositories (see Chapter 46) is also increased by vitamin C.

• • •

References

Benkovic SJ: On the mechanism of action of folate and biopterin-requiring enzymes. *Annu Rev Biochem* 1980;**49:**227.

Erbe R: Inborn errors of folate metabolism. *N Engl J Med* 1975;**293:**753.

Katz M, Lee SK, Cooper BA: Vitamin B_{12} malabsorption due to a biologically inert intrinsic factor. *N Engl J Med* 1972; **287:**425.

Rivlin RS: Hormones, drugs and riboflavin. *Nutr Rev* 1979; **37:**241.

Rosenberg IH: Folate absorption and malabsorption. *N Engl J Med* 1975;**293:**1303.

Rosenberg L: Disorders of propionate, methylmalonate, and

cobalamin metabolism. Pages 474–497 in: *The Metabolic Basis of Inherited Disease,* 5th ed. Stanbury JB et al (editors). McGraw-Hill, 1983.

Rubin RH, Swartz MN: Trimethroprim-sulfamethoxazole. *N Engl J Med* 1980;**303:**426.

Saunders M et al: Biotin-responsive organicaciduria. *J Clin Invest* 1979;**64:**1695.

Sebrell WH Jr: History of pellagra. *Fed Proc* 1981;**40:**1520.

Seetharam B, Alpers DH: Absorption and transport of cobalamin (vitamin B_{12}). *Annu Rev Nutr* 1982;**2:**343.

Wood HG, Barden RE: Biotin enzymes. *Annu Rev Biochem* 1977;**46:**385.

11 | Fat-Soluble Vitamins

David W. Martin, Jr., MD

As is apparent from the name, the fat-soluble (lipid-soluble) vitamins are **apolar hydrophobic** molecules, all of which are **isoprene derivatives** (Fig

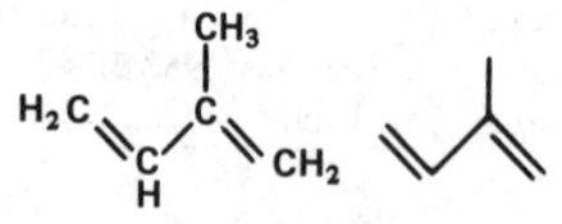

Figure 11–1. Two representations of the isoprene unit.

11–1). All are handled by the gastrointestinal system in the same manner as dietary fat. In general, the lipid-soluble vitamins require **normal fat absorption** to be absorbed themselves. Therefore, steatorrhea and biliary system disorders can result in malabsorption of the fat-soluble vitamins. Once absorbed, the lipid-soluble vitamins are transported to the liver in chylomicrons and stored either in the liver (vitamins A, D, K) or in adipose tissue (vitamin E) for varying periods of time. These vitamins are transported in blood by **lipoproteins** or **specific binding proteins,** since they are not directly soluble in plasma water, as are the water-soluble vitamins. Accordingly, lipid-soluble vitamins are not excreted in urine but are more likely to appear in bile and are thus excreted in feces. Because of the body's ability to store excess fat-soluble vitamins, toxicity occurs at least from vitamin A and D overdosage.

Although once thought to be a vitamin in the true sense, **vitamin D (cholecalciferol) is a hormone** intimately involved in regulation of calcium and phosphate metabolism.

VITAMIN A
(Retinoids)

Vitamin A, or retinol, is a polyisoprenoid compound containing a cyclohexenyl ring (Fig 11–2). Vitamin A is a generic term referring to all compounds other than the carotenoids that exhibit the biologic activity of retinol. In recent years, the term retinoids has been used to describe both the natural forms and the synthetic analogs of retinol. Vitamin A is necessary in higher animals to support growth and health and is particularly necessary for **vision, reproduction, mucus secretion,** and the maintenance of differentiated **epithelia.**

Although the retinoids are required for normal function of many tissues in humans and experimental animals, the **loss of night vision** is an early sign of vitamin A deficiency. The full syndrome of vitamin A deficiency includes xeroderma, xerophthalmia, keratomalacia, severe growth retardation (including that of the nervous system), glandular degeneration, and sterility. Because vitamin A can be stored in the liver, both acute and chronic toxicity may result from excessive intake. The excessive intake of the provitamin β-carotene from plants results only in a benign yellow discoloration of the skin. Because β-carotene is not efficiently metabolized to vitamin A, one molecule is only one-sixth as effective a source of vitamin A as an equivalent amount of oral retinol.

In animal products, dietary vitamin A exists as long-chain fatty acid **esters of retinol.** In vegetables, dietary vitamin A exists as a provitamin in the form of **β-carotenes,** which are yellow pigments (Fig 11–3).

β-Carotene is an unusual type of lipid antioxidant that may play an important role in reducing the concentration of chain-carrying peroxyl radicals in tissues and organelles at low partial pressures of oxygen. The ability of β-carotene to act as an antioxidant results from its ability to stabilize carbon-centered radicals within its conjugated alkyl structure, as shown in Fig 11–3. Although β-carotene also has some capacity to quench singlet oxygen, this property does not seem to account for its antioxidant activity. Since β-carotene is effective at low oxygen concentrations, it can complement the antioxidant properties of vitamin E, which is effective at high oxygen concentrations. The antioxidant properties of these 2 lipid-soluble vitamins may well account for their possible anticancer activity.

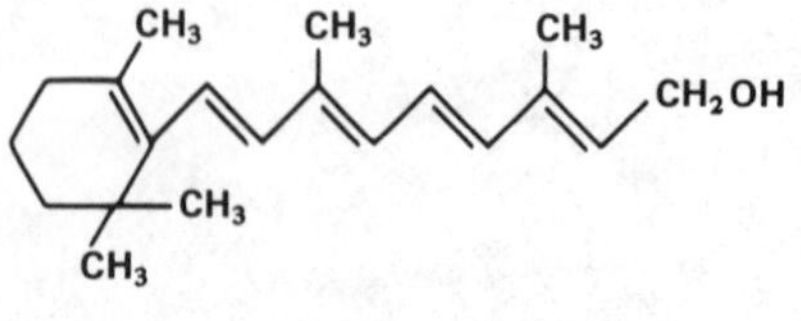

Figure 11–2. Retinol (vitamin A).

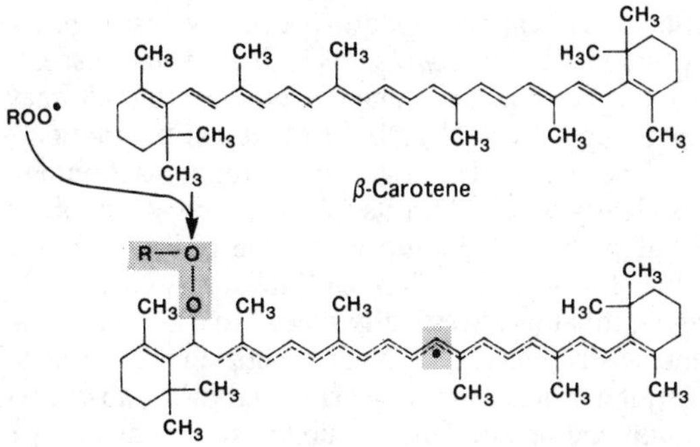

Figure 11–3. The formation of a resonance-stabilized carbon-centered radical from a peroxyl radical (ROO•) and β-carotene. (Slightly modified and reproduced, with permission, from Burton GW, Ingold KU: β-Carotene: An unusual type of lipid antioxidant. *Science* 1984;**224**:569. Copyright © 1984 by The American Association for the Advancement of Science.)

The retinol esters digested as components of animal products are hydrolyzed within the intestinal lumen and absorbed directly in the intestines. The ingested β-carotenes can be oxidatively cleaved by β-carotene dioxygenase (Fig 11–4). This cleavage utilizes molecular oxygen and requires bile salts (and lecithin in vitro) to generate 2 molecules of **retinaldehyde (retinal).** Also in the **intestinal mucosa,** the retinaldehyde is reduced by a specific reductase utilizing NADPH to form retinol (Fig 11–4). A small fraction of the retinal generated from the β-carotene is oxidized to **retinoic acid** in the intestines. The retinoic acid is absorbed through the portal system and does not generally accumulate in the liver or other tissues. Retinoic acid can be metabolized to more polar compounds, such as epoxides, and excreted in urine and bile.

The absorbed retinol is reesterified with long-chain saturated fatty acids, incorporated into lymph chylomicrons, and then enters the bloodstream. These retinyl esters are eventually removed from the circulation, almost exclusively by the **liver.** In hepatocytes, the retinyl esters are hydrolyzed and subsequently reesterified as retinyl palmitate to be stored in hepatic lipid droplets. Hence, vitamin A depletion occurs in liver injury including that due to alcohol.

Stored retinol is mobilized from the liver by hydrolysis of its ester and by binding of retinol to **aporetinol-binding protein,** which is synthesized in the hepatocyte. The retinol-binding protein complex, called **holoretinol-binding protein,** then enters the circulation and delivers retinol to the target tissues.

Aporetinol-binding protein is also capable of binding retinal and retinoic acid, even though the

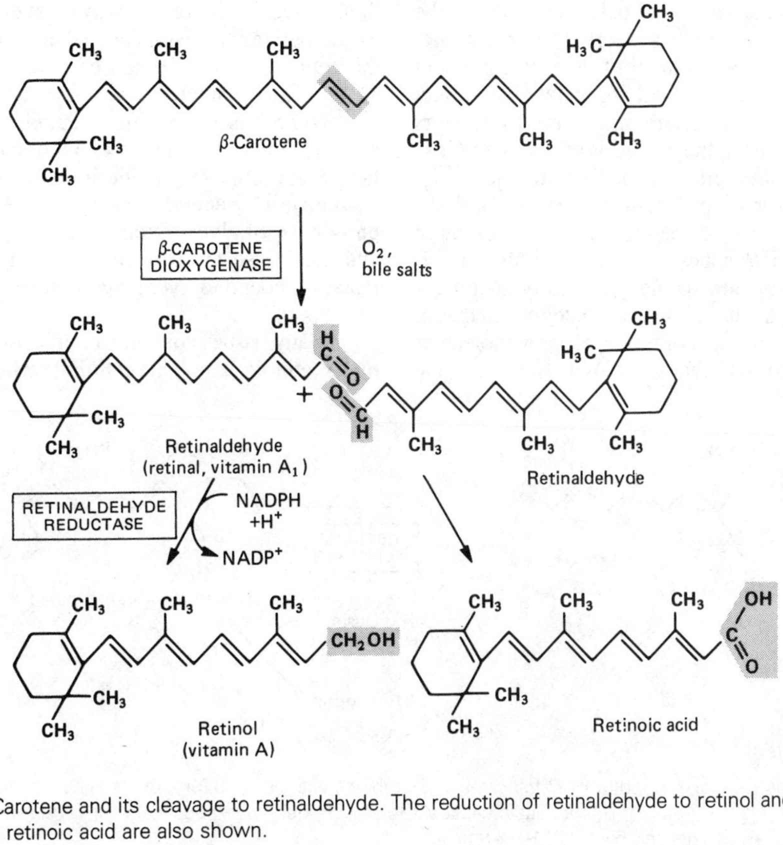

Figure 11–4. β-Carotene and its cleavage to retinaldehyde. The reduction of retinaldehyde to retinol and the oxidation of retinaldehyde to retinoic acid are also shown.

majority of retinoic acid in the circulation is transported bound to serum albumin. The holoretinol-binding protein has a high affinity for **prealbumin** in a strong protein-protein interaction that is dependent upon the presence of retinol. The prealbumin complex also carries thyroxine at an independent site. Leaving the aporetinol-binding protein behind, the retinol enters its target cell.

It appears that **vitamin A toxicity** occurs in vivo only after the capacity of the retinol-binding protein has been exceeded and the cells exposed to unbound retinol. Thus, the nonspecific and unregulated delivery of free vitamin A to tissues may lead to vitamin A toxicity.

Most target cells for vitamin A are capable of metabolizing the retinol to retinal and retinoic acid. However, within the cellular environment, retinoic acid cannot be reduced back to retinal or to retinol. Retinol can satisfy all of the requirements for vitamin A, but retinoic acid has only selective vitamin A-like biologic activity. Experimental animals provided with retinoic acid as the only source of retinoids will become blind and sterile but otherwise remain in good general health. Thus, **retinoic acid can support the normal rate of growth and differentiation but cannot replace retinal as a visual pigment precursor or support normal function of the reproductive system in males or females.**

Each of the 3 major retinoids—retinol, retinal, and retinoic acid—appears to have its own unique biologic function, as discussed below. Retinol, in the lowest oxidation state, probably serves as a **hormone.** Retinal is a necessary precursor of the visual pigment **rhodopsin.** Retinoic acid and its metabolites affect differentiation of epithelia and may serve as **carriers** for oligosaccharides in the synthesis of glycoproteins.

When retinol enters its target cell, it is promptly bound to a **cellular retinol-binding protein (CRBP)** distinct from the retinol-binding protein present in serum. The CRBP transports the retinol within the cell, where the latter appears to bind specifically to **nuclear proteins,** perhaps with a function analogous to that of the intracellular steroid hormone receptor molecules (see Chapter 35). Of the 2 biologic functions that

retinoic acid cannot support, one, the visual pigment precursor, can be provided by retinal. Thus, it seems that the reproductive function of the retinoids may depend upon **retinol acting as a sterol hormone.**

The next oxidation state of the retinoids is retinal. It is clearly required for its role as a component of the **visual pigment, rhodopsin,** of the rod cells in the retina. In rod cells, **11-*cis*-retinal,** an isomer of all-*trans*-retinal, is **specifically bound to the visual protein, opsin** (Fig 11–5). When rhodopsin is exposed to light, it dissociates as it bleaches and forms **all-*trans*-retinal** and **opsin.** This reaction is accompanied by a conformational change that induces a **calcium ion channel** in the membrane of the rod cell. The rapid influx of the calcium ions triggers a nerve impulse, allowing light to be perceived by the brain. The all-*trans*-retinal, generated from rhodopsin by the absorption of photons of light, is incompletely converted back to the 11-*cis*-retinal (Fig 11–5). Hence, in order to regenerate rhodopsin for vision, a **constant supply** of all-*trans*-retinal is required from the diet.

The third distinct biochemical function of the retinoids involves the participation of retinoic acid or a polar metabolite such as phosphorylated retinoic acid in the **synthesis of glycoproteins** (see Chapter 33). Oligosaccharide retinoyl phosphate is a minor product of the microsomal systems that use mostly the polyisoprenoid derivative dolichol phosphate as carrier. It has been proposed that the retinoyl phosphate functions as a carrier of the oligosaccharides across the lipid bilayer of the cell by way of an enzymatic *trans-cis* isomerization analogous to that described above in the *trans-cis* isomerization of rhodopsin generation. The evidence that retinoic acid is involved in glycoprotein synthesis is compelling. A deficiency of vitamin A results in the accumulation of abnormal, low-molecular-weight oligosaccharide-lipid intermediates, eg, (mannose)$_5$(N-acetylglucosamine)$_2$-dolichoylpyrophosphate, of glycoprotein synthesis (see Chapter 33) and can cause an 80% reduction in the amount of mannose bound to liver glycoproteins in experimental animals.

Many tissues contain an intracellular protein that binds retinoic acid. This **cellular retinoic acid–bind-**

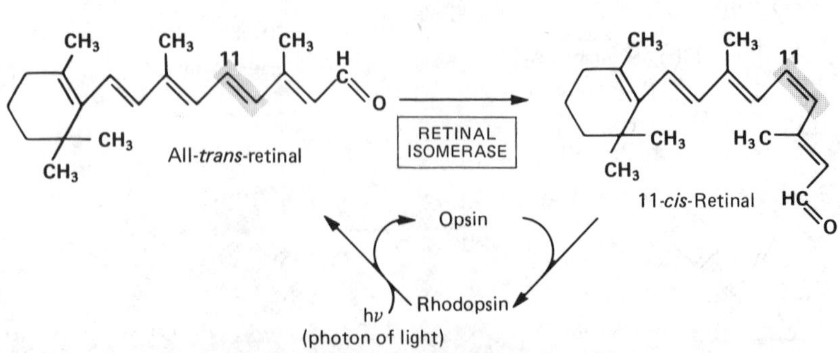

Figure 11–5. 11-*cis*-Retinal, formed from all-*trans*-retinal, combines with opsin to form rhodopsin in the rod cell of the eye. The absorption of a photon of light by rhodopsin causes it to bleach, generating opsin and all-*trans*-retinal. The all-*trans*-retinal is incompletely isomerized back to 11-*cis*-retinal.

ing protein (**CRABP**) shows no affinity for retinol or retinal. The tissue distribution of CRABP is different from that of CRBP, even though the proteins are similar in structure. The retinoic acid–CRABP complex does not have an affinity for the cell nucleus, as does the retinol-CRBP complex.

Retinoic acid elicits many biologic and biochemical responses from cells in vitro, including increasing the number of receptors for epidermal growth factor on surfaces of cultured cells and for 1,25-dihydroxyvitamin D_3 in the cytosol of cultured cells, stimulation of differentiation of embryonal carcinoma cells, prevention of the expression of the Epstein-Barr virus in virus-infected cells, enhancement of cAMP-dependent protein kinase, inhibition of collagenase, changing the positional information of vertebrate limbs, and the reversible inhibition of growth of human breast cancer cell lines in long-term tissue culture. All of the listed biologic effects are clearly not mediated by the involvement of retinoids in glycoprotein synthesis. It is likely that retinoids affect the expression of genes involved in the proliferation and differentiation of many types of normal and malignant cells.

VITAMIN D

Only in humans **not exposed to sunlight** is vitamin D a necessary organic nutrient, thereby satisfying the classic criteria for vitamin status. Vitamin D is a legitimate prohormone of a sterol type. Thus, the D vitamins are a group of sterol compounds that occur in nature chiefly in animals but also in plants and yeasts.

The D vitamins are generated from the provitamins **ergosterol** and **7-dehydrocholesterol** in plants and animals, respectively. Ergosterol and 7-dehydrocholesterol differ chemically only in the side chains at position 21 (Fig 11–6). Ultraviolet irradiation spontaneously cleaves the B ring of ergosterol or of 7-dehydrocholesterol. In plants, the irradiation of ergosterol leads to the production of ergocalciferol (vitamin D_2). In animals, the 7-dehydrocholesterol is converted to cholecalciferol (vitamin D_3) by irradiation of skin (Fig 11–6). Ergocalciferol and cholecalciferol are of equal biologic potency as D vitamins, and the rest of this discussion will deal only with cholecalciferol.

Humans have 2 main sources of vitamin D: ingestion in the diet and photolysis of 7-dehydrocholesterol in skin.

Dietary vitamin D_2 or D_3 mixes with intestinal micelles and is absorbed through the proximal small intestine. Bound to a specific globulin, it is transported in blood to the liver. In the **liver,** vitamin D_3 is **hydroxylated on the 25 position** by a specific vitamin D_3 25-hydroxylase (Fig 11–7). This 25-hydroxylation occurs in microsomes and can be rate-limiting. At physiologic concentrations, 25-hydroxy-D_3 (or calcifediol) has no direct action in any of the vitamin D target tissues. Regulation of the 25-hydroxylation step is dependent upon the hepatic level of 25-hydroxy-D_3.

25-Hydroxy-D_3 is the major form of vitamin D in the circulation and the **major storage form.** A signifi-

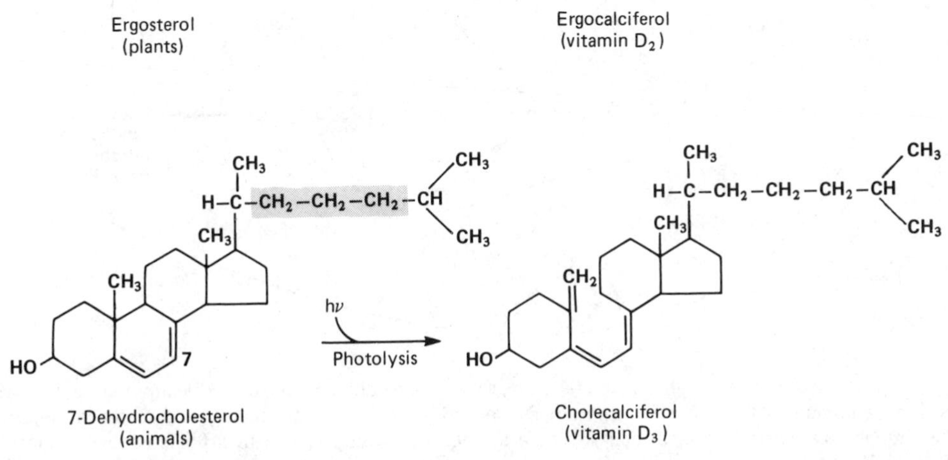

Figure 11–6. Ergosterol and 7-dehydrocholesterol and their conversion by photolysis to ergocalciferol and cholecalciferol, respectively.

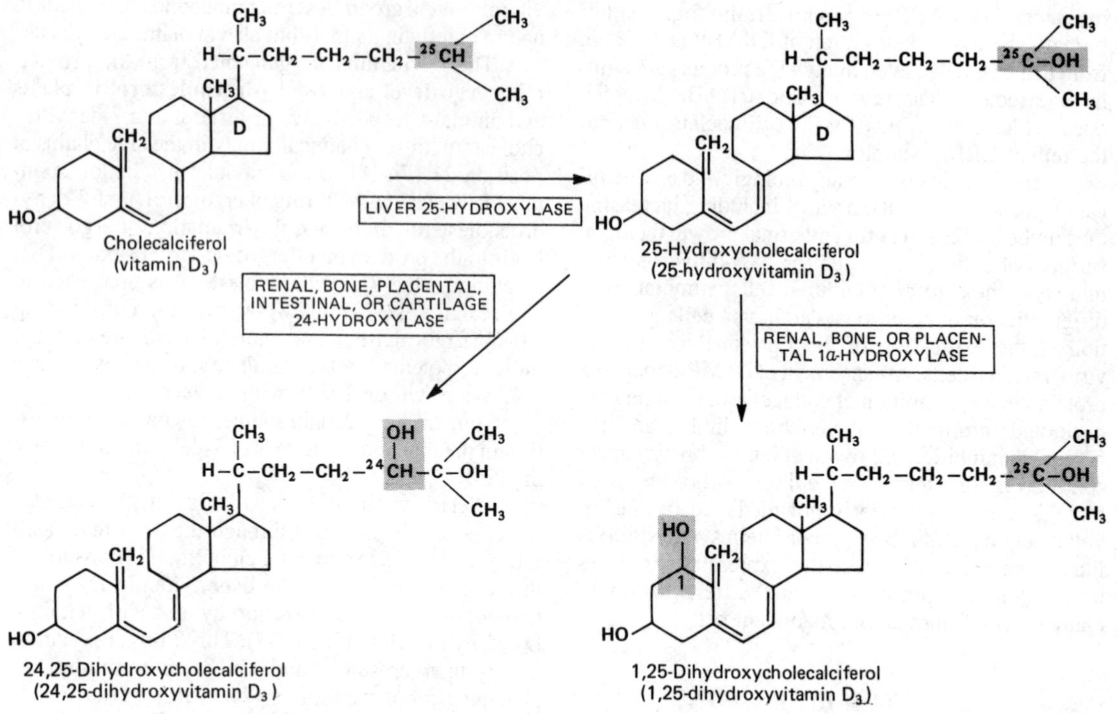

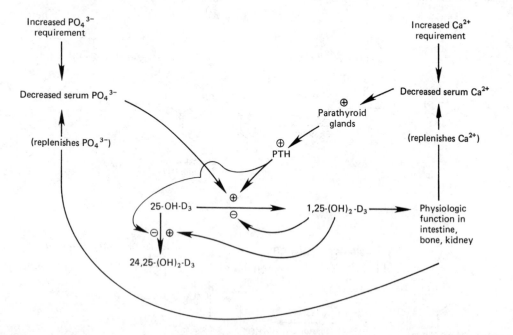

Figure 11–7. Cholecalciferol can be hydroxylated at the C_{25} position by a liver enzyme. The 25-hydroxycholecalciferol is further metabolized to $1\alpha,25$-dihydroxycholecalciferol or to 24,25-dihydroxycholecalciferol. The levels of 24,25-dihydroxycholecalciferol and 1,25-dihydroxycholecalciferol are regulated in a reciprocal manner.

Figure 11–8. Summary of regulation of vitamin D_3 hydroxylation. Increased phosphate or calcium requirement will cause diminished concentrations of these ions in the serum. Decreased serum phosphate (directly) and decreased serum calcium (indirectly through parathyroid hormone) both increase the activity of the renal 1α-hydroxylase activity to increase the formation of 1,25-dihydroxy-D_3. The 1,25-dihydroxy-D_3 has 3 effects: It inhibits its own production, it stimulates the 24-hydroxylase to generate 24,25-dihydroxy-D_3, and it has physiologic functions in the intestine, bone, and kidney. All of the physiologic functions of 1,25-dihydroxy-D_3 operate in the direction of replenishing serum phosphate and serum calcium.

cant fraction of 25-hydroxy-D₃ undergoes enterohepatic circulation, and a disturbance in that process can therefore lead to a vitamin D-deficient state.

The 25-hydroxy-D₃ can be further hydroxylated on the 1 position by a specific 25-hydroxy-D₃ 1α-**hydroxylase** that exists in the **renal tubules,** bone, and the placenta (Fig 11–7). The production of 1α,25-dihydroxy-D₃, the **most potent vitamin D** metabolite, is tightly regulated by **parathyroid hormone, serum phosphate,** and **its own level.** 1α,25-Dihydroxy-D₃ is the only naturally occurring form of vitamin D that in physiologic amounts can maintain normal serum calcium in animals without kidneys or without parathyroid glands. 25-Hydroxy-D₃ 1α-hydroxylase is a **mitochondrial** enzyme.

25-Hydroxy-D₃ can also be hydroxylated at the 24 position by a mitochondrial enzyme present in renal tubules, cartilage, intestine, and placenta (Fig 11–7). The level of 24,25-dihydroxy-D₃ seems to be reciprocally related to the level of 1,25-hydroxy-D₃ in serum. In fact, the levels of 1,25-dihydroxy-D₃ and 24,25-dihydroxy-D₃ are approximately equal in the presence of a normal serum Ca²⁺ level.

Hypocalcemia induces the parathyroid glands to excrete more parathyroid hormone, which in turn increases the activity of the renal 1α-hydroxylase, generating more 1,25-dihydroxy-D₃ (Fig 11–8). Concomitantly, parathyroid hormone reduces the 24-hydroxylase pathway, thus diminishing the level of 24,25-dihydroxy-D₃. As discussed below, the 1,25-dihydroxy-D₃ **increases intestinal absorption of calcium and enhances calcium reabsorption from both the kidney and bone.** These effects cause a normalization of serum Ca²⁺, a reduction in parathyroid hormone and 1α-hydroxylase activity, and a concomitant increase in the 24-hydroxylation of 25-hydroxy-D₃ (Fig 11–8). Thus, regulation of the level on 1,25-dihydroxy-D₃ and 24,25-dihydroxy-D₃ is intimately related to the level of parathyroid hormone and indirectly to the level of serum calcium.

Hypophosphatemia directly stimulates the synthesis of 1,25-dihydroxy-D₃. 1,25-Dihydroxy-D₃ also increases the absorption of **phosphate** by the intestine and, in the absence of parathyroid hormone, enhances the **reabsorption of phosphate** by the kidney tubules. Thus, plasma phosphate levels also regulate the level of 1,25-dihydroxy-D₃ (Fig 11–8).

Accordingly, in the presence of a high plasma phosphate (hyperphosphatemia) or in a disorder such as uremia, the production of 1,25-dihydroxy-D₃ will be inhibited and calcium absorption from the intestine will thus be minimal. Once the serum phosphate is lowered, such as by chelating phosphate in the intestine, the 1,25-dihydroxy-D₃ will increase and calcium absorption will follow.

The mechanism of action of 1,25-dihydroxy-D₃ resembles that of the steroid hormones. The target tissues include the **intestine, bone, kidney, pancreas, gonads,** and perhaps pituitary and thymus. In the intestine, 1,25-dihydroxy-D₃ enters the cell and is bound to a specific **cytoplasmic receptor molecule.** The 1,25-dihydroxy-cholecalciferol-receptor complex is then translocated to the nucleus, where, by poorly defined mechanisms, it effects an increase in the synthesis of the intestinal **calcium-binding protein** necessary for intestinal absorption of calcium. The phosphorylation of this calcium-binding protein may also be stimulated by 1,25-dihydroxy-D₃.

In the intestine, 1,25-dihydroxy-D₃ also increases intestinal phosphate absorption by mechanisms that have not been defined. In the kidney, 1,25-dihydroxy-D₃ enhances the reabsorption of filtered tubular phosphate, but **this effect of the active vitamin D metabolite is usually masked by the inhibition of phosphate reabsorption by parathyroid hormone.** 1,25-Dihydroxy-D₃ seems to affect the cross-linking of bone collagen and increases the synthesis of the vitamin K-dependent calcium-binding protein (osteocalcin; see below) of bone, thereby influencing the **mineralization** of bone tissues. The active metabolite of vitamin D₃ also seems to prevent a **myopathy** that occurs in the vitamin D-deficient states, but the mechanism is unknown.

24,25-Dihydroxy-D₃ also has an effect of increasing intestinal calcium absorption but decreases the serum concentrations of both calcium and phosphorus. 24,25-Dihydroxy-D₃ **promotes normal bone mineralization** and the synthesis of hydroxyapatite, the major form of calcium in mineralized bone and cartilage.

The 26-hydroxylation of 1,25-dihydroxy-D₃ appears to be on the pathway of vitamin D oxidative degradation.

25-Hydroxy-D₃ is degraded by hepatic microsomes, and these enzymes can be induced by numerous pharmacologic agents, including phenytoin and phenobarbital. Glucocorticosteroids in large pharmacologic doses result in a decrease in 25-hydroxy-D₃ levels.

The major biochemical abnormalities of vitamin D deficiency are **hypocalcemia and hypophosphatemia.** Vitamin D-deficient states were common during the industrial revolution in England, when air pollution and the urban environment prevented adequate exposure of children to sunlight, and vitamin D supplementation of foodstuffs was nonexistent. There is now some evidence that the ability to photolyse 7-dehydrocholesterol to vitamin D₃ in the skin diminishes with age and may contribute to the age-related disorders of calcium metabolism. The vitamin D-deficient clinical states are beyond the scope of this chapter.

VITAMIN E
(α-Tocopherol)

α-Tocopherol is an oil present in plants, particularly wheat germ, rice, and cotton seeds. Although fish liver oils are rich in vitamins A and D, they are devoid of vitamin E. Vitamin E is required in higher animals such as poultry and cattle for **fertility.** (The word

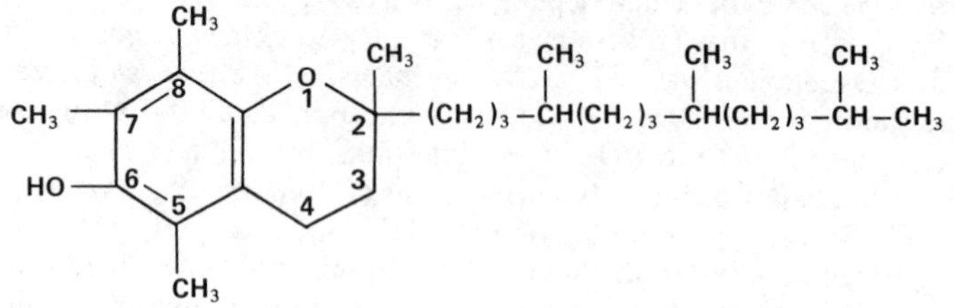

Figure 11–9. α-Tocopherol.

tocopherol is derived from Greek *tokos,* "childbirth," and *pherein,* "to bear.") There are 6 naturally occurring tocopherols (Table 11–1). All are isoprenoid substituted 6-hydroxychromanes or tocols (Fig 11–9).

Table 11–1. The naturally occurring tocopherols.

Tocopherol	Substituents
Alpha	5,7,8-Trimethyl tocol
Beta	5,8-Dimethyl tocol
Gamma	7,8-Dimethyl tocol
Delta	8-Methyl tocol
Eta	7-Methyl tocol
Zeta	5,7-Dimethyl tocol

α-Tocopherol has the widest natural distribution and the greatest biologic activity as a vitamin. Although there is no reliable evidence that vitamin E is necessary for fertility in humans, it is clear that a vitamin E–deficient state exists in humans with severely **impaired intestinal fat absorption.** The signs of vitamin E deficiency in humans are muscular weakness, creatinuria, and fragile erythrocytes. All disappear after the administration of α-tocopherol. α-Tocopherol is readily absorbed through the small intestine, transported to the liver probably in chylomicrons, and delivered in lipoproteins to peripheral tissues. The phospholipids of mitochondria, endoplasmic reticulum, and plasma membranes possess specific affinities for α-tocopherol, and the vitamin appears to concentrate at these sites.

Vitamin E has at least 2 metabolic roles: It acts as nature's most potent fat-soluble **antioxidant,** and it plays a specific but incompletely understood role in **selenium metabolism.** The level of vitamin E in plasma lipoproteins and organelle phospholipids depends on 4 factors: (1) the amount of α-tocopherol being consumed, (2) the level of pro-oxidants and antioxidants in the diet, (3) the adequacy of dietary selenium, and (4) the dietary intake of sulfur-containing amino acids.

Vitamin E appears to be the first line of defense against peroxidation of cellular and subcellular membrane phospholipids. The tocopherols act as chain-breaking antioxidants as a result of their ability to transfer a phenolic hydrogen to a peroxyl radical (Fig 11–10). The phenoxy radical is resonant-stabilized

$$ROO^{\cdot} + TocOH \longrightarrow ROOH + TocO^{\cdot}$$

$$ROO^{\cdot} + TocO^{\cdot} \longrightarrow ROOH + \text{Nonradical product}$$

Figure 11–10. The chain-breaking antioxidant activity of tocopherols (TocOH) toward peroxyl radicals (ROO·).

and relatively unreactive, except toward other peroxyl radicals. Thus, α-tocopherol does not readily engage in reversible oxidation; in humans, the chromane ring and the side chain of α-tocopherol are oxidized to produce the nonradical product shown in Fig 11–11.

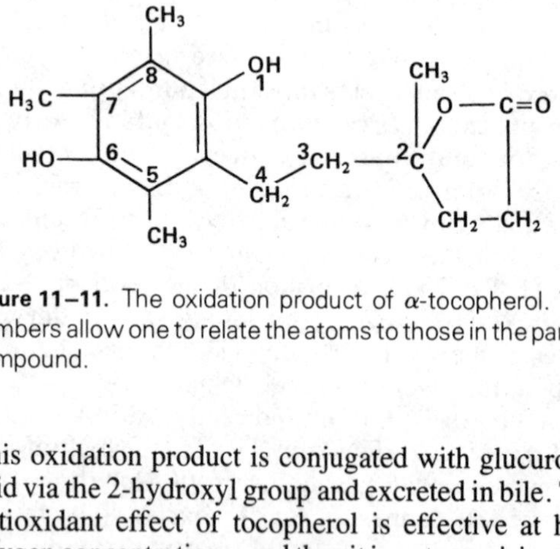

Figure 11–11. The oxidation product of α-tocopherol. The numbers allow one to relate the atoms to those in the parent compound.

This oxidation product is conjugated with glucuronic acid via the 2-hydroxyl group and excreted in bile. The antioxidant effect of tocopherol is effective at high oxygen concentrations, and thus it is not surprising that vitamin E tends to be concentrated in those lipid regions which are exposed to the highest partial pressures of oxygen, such as the erythrocyte membrane and membranes of the respiratory tree.

However, even in the presence of adequate vitamin E, some peroxides are formed. **Glutathione peroxidase,** of which selenium is an integral component, provides a second line of defense to destroy the peroxides before they cause damage to the membranes. Thus, the biochemical action of vitamin E and selenium seems to be prevention of peroxidative damage to cellular and subcellular elements, which thereby preserves the organelles necessary to cope with disease, physical and chemical environmental insults, and other stresses.

Selenium spares vitamin E or reduces the vitamin

E requirements in at least 3 ways: (1) Selenium is required for normal pancreatic function and thus the digestion and absorption of lipids, including vitamin E. (2) As a component of glutathione peroxidase, selenium helps destroy peroxides and thereby reduces the peroxidation of polyunsaturated acids of lipid membranes. This diminished peroxidation greatly reduces the vitamin E requirement for the maintenance of membrane integrity. (3) In some unknown way, selenium aids in the retention of vitamin E in the blood plasma lipoproteins.

Conversely, vitamin E appears to reduce the selenium requirement, at least in experimental animals, by preventing loss of selenium from the body or maintaining it in an active form. By preventing auto-oxidation of membrane lipids from within, vitamin E reduces the amount of glutathione peroxidase needed to destroy peroxides formed in the cell.

There is reliable experimental evidence for the need of supplemental vitamin E in the diets of pregnant and lactating women and for newborn infants, particularly premature infants. Other evidence suggests that vitamin E is efficacious for older persons suffering from circulatory disturbances, particularly intermittent claudication. In experimental animals, a reversible muscular dystrophy is associated with vitamin E deficiency.

VITAMIN K

The K vitamins (Danish *Koagulation*) are polyisoprenoid substituted naphthoquinones (Fig 11–12). They were the last of the 4 fat-soluble vita-

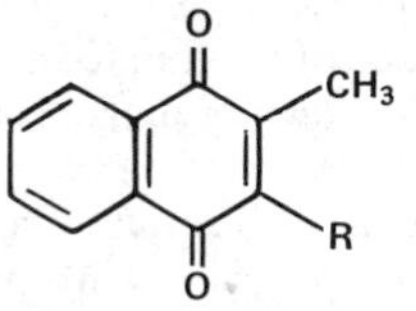

2-Methyl-1,4-naphthoquinone

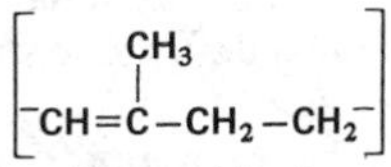

Figure 11–12. Substituted naphthoquinone and the isoprenoid unit. In the vitamins K, the R substitutions are polyisoprenoids.

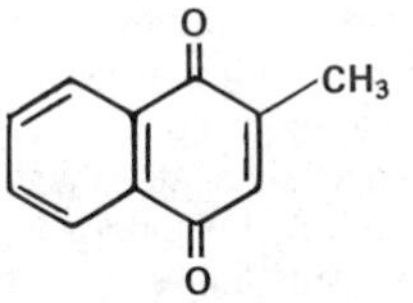

mins to be discovered and characterized. However, the metabolic role of vitamin K can be described in more molecular detail than is the case with any other fat-soluble vitamin. **Menadione,** the parent compound of the vitamin K series, exhibits biologic activity in vivo after it has been alkylated to one of the menaquinones by animal tissues (Fig 11–13). Phylloquinone (vitamin K_1) is the major form of vitamin K found in plants. Menaquinone-7 is one of the series of polyprenoid unsaturated forms of vitamin K found in animal tissues and bacteria. Vitamin K_1 is abundant in vegetable oils, leafy green vegetables, and wheat bran. Menaquinones (vitamin K_2) are synthesized by the intestinal bacterial flora, and vitamin K is therefore not required in the diet.

Absorption of vitamin K from the intestines requires normal fat absorption. Thus, the most common causes of vitamin K deficiency are the **fat malabsorption syndromes** associated with pancreatic dysfunction, biliary disease, intestinal mucosal atrophy, or any other cause of steatorrhea. In addition, **sterilization of**

Menadione (vitamin K_3)

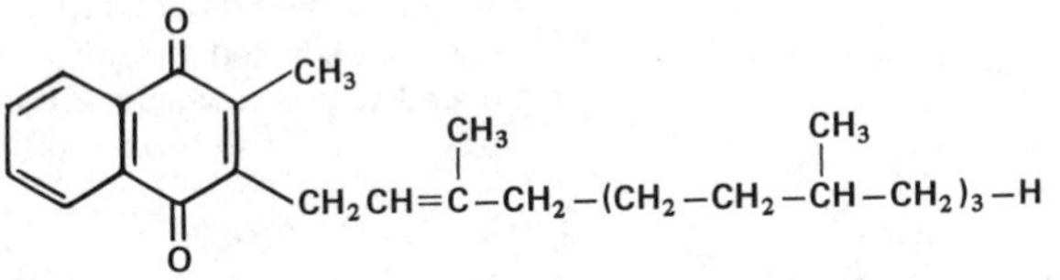

Phylloquinone (vitamin K_1, phytonadione, Mephyton)

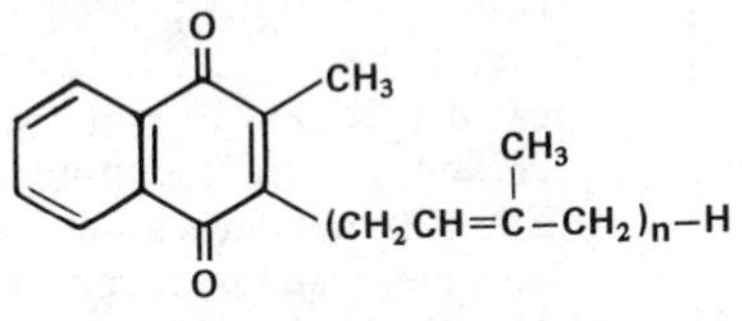

Menaquinone-n (vitamin K_2; n = 6, 7, or 9)

Figure 11–13. The naturally occurring vitamins K.

the large intestine by eliminating the bacterial flora removes the most reliable source of vitamin K and can result in a deficiency state when dietary intake is limited.

The **menaquinones** are absorbed only in the presence of bile salts and via the lymphatics. **Menadione** and its water-soluble derivatives are absorbed **even in the absence of bile salts** and go directly into the bloodstream.

Although vitamin K accumulates initially in the liver, its hepatic concentration declines rapidly. Little vitamin K accumulates in peripheral tissues. A deficiency state, indicated by hypoprothrombinemia, can occur within several weeks when acute biliary disease halts its absorption.

Vitamin K has been known to be required for the maintenance of normal levels of blood clotting factors II, VII, IX, and X, all of which are synthesized in the liver (see Chapter 45). Each of these specific clotting factor proteins is synthesized by the liver in an **inactive precursor** form that is dependent upon vitamin K for conversion to the biologically active clotting factors. Generation of these mature clotting factors involves the vitamin K–dependent **posttranslational modification** of glutamic acid (Glu) residues to γ-**carboxyglutamic acid** (Gla), a previously unrecognized amino acid (Fig 11–14). The Gla residues, of which pro-

Initially, only these clotting factors (II, VII, IX, X) were thought to contain vitamin K-dependent Gla residues, but now it has been recognized that other proteins in bones (''osteocalcin''), kidney, placenta, plasma, lung, and spleen contain them. These modifications have also been described in both bacterial and mammalian ribosomal proteins. However, physiologic roles for the Gla residues have not been defined for any of the nonclotting-factor, vitamin K-dependent proteins.

The major—if not the only—function of vitamin K is to serve as an essential cofactor for the carboxylase enzyme that forms the Gla residues from the Glu residues in the specific protein molecules. The vitamin K-dependent carboxylase reaction occurs in **microsomes** of many tissues and requires molecular oxygen, carbon dioxide, and the **hydroquinone form of vitamin K.** In liver microsomes, there exists a **vitamin K cycle** (Fig 11–16), in which the hydroquinone form can be converted by a monooxygenase to its

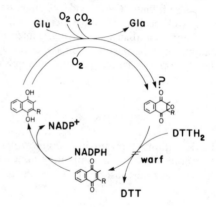

Figure 11–16. Vitamin K–related metabolic activities in liver microsomes. The pathway crossed and indicated warf is sensitive to the action of the coumarin anticoagulants. The (?) in the figure indicates that the product of the involvement of vitamin K hydroquinone in the carboxylation reaction is not known. The figure indicates that the epoxide is reduced by a warfarin-sensitive pathway that used dithiothreitol (DTT) as a reducing agent, and that the quinone form of the vitamin can be reduced to the hydroquinone by a pyridine nucleotide-linked dehydrogenase. (Modified and reproduced, with permission, from Suttie JW: The metabolic role of vitamin K. *Fed Proc* 1980;**39**:2730.)

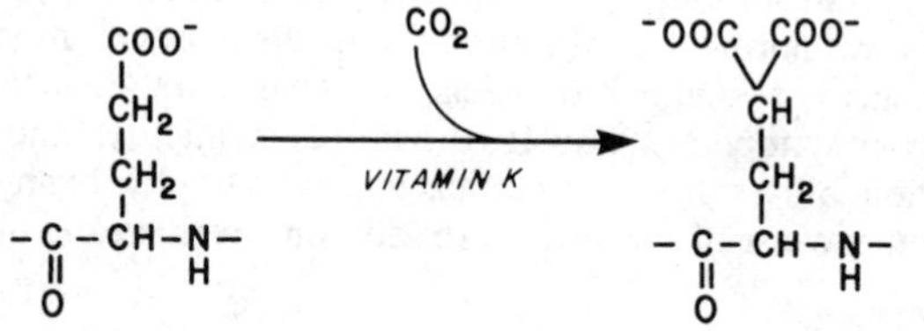

Figure 11–14. Carboxylation of a glutamic acid residue catalyzed by vitamin K.

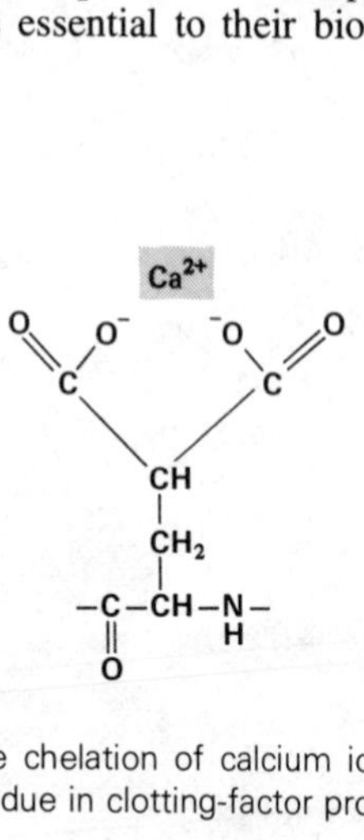

thrombin contains 10, allow these proteins to **chelate calcium** in a specific protein-calcium-phospholipid interaction that is essential to their biologic role (Fig 11–15).

Figure 11–15. The chelation of calcium ion by the γ-carboxyglutamyl residue in clotting-factor proteins.

2,3-epoxide. It is not yet clear whether this specific reaction is an obligatory one in which the hydroquinone of vitamin K participates in the carboxylase reaction, but it appears to be so. This uncertainty is indicated in Fig 11–16 by the question mark of the upward curved arrow representing that carboxylation reaction. The 2,3-epoxide is a substrate for another microsomal enzyme, an epoxide reductase, that utilizes a still unidentified sulfhydryl reducing compound to form the quinone. This **epoxide reductase** is sensitive to **inhibition by the 4-hydroxydicoumarin** compounds (Fig

11–17) and thus is the target for the pharmacologic action of these **anticoagulants.** Subsequent reduction of the quinone form to the hydroquinone form by NADH completes the vitamin K cycle by regenerating the active form of vitamin K.

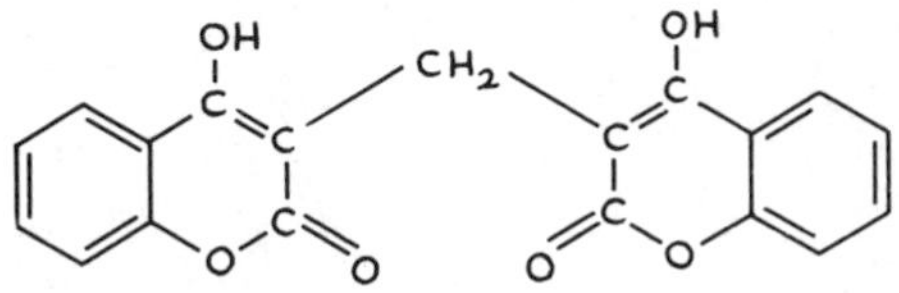

Figure 11–17. Dicumarol (bishydroxycoumarin; 3,3′-methylene-bishydroxycoumarin).

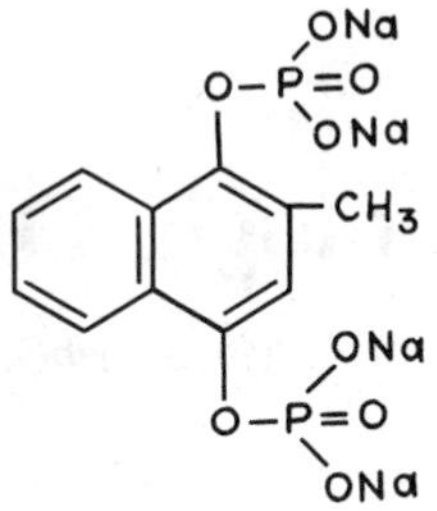

Figure 11–18. Menadiol sodium diphosphate (Synkayvite)—a form of vitamin K for clinical use.

An important therapeutic use of vitamin K is as an antidote to the 4-hydroxycoumarin anticoagulant drugs. The quinone forms of vitamin K will bypass the inhibited epoxide reductase and provide a potential source of the active hydroquinone form of vitamin K. For these purposes, large oral doses of vitamin K_1 will suffice, but there are also available synthetic water-soluble vitamin K analogs such as menadiol sodium

diphosphate (Synkayvite) and menadione sodium bisulfite (Fig 11–18). These water-soluble vitamin K analogs may be administered parenterally. If liver function is adequate to manufacture active prothrombin, the prothrombin time (a laboratory index of the presence of mature prothrombin; see Chapter 45) will usually return to normal 12–36 hours after the administration of vitamin K.

There is the potential of toxicity of large doses of vitamin K; menadione in particular can cause hemolysis in infants and aggravate hyperbilirubinemia.

● ● ●

References

Vitamin D

Adams JS et al: Vitamin-D synthesis and metabolism after ultraviolet irradiation of normal and vitamin-D-deficient subjects. *N Engl J Med* 1982;**306:**722.

DeLuca HF: Regulation of vitamin D metabolism. *Life Sci* 1976;**17:**1351.

DeLuca HF, Schnoes HK: Metabolism and mechanism of action of vitamin D. *Annu Rev Biochem* 1976;**45:**631.

Favus M: Vitamin D physiology and some clinical aspects of the vitamin D endocrine system. *Med Clin North Am* 1978; **62:**1291.

Feldman D, Colston K: Nuclear translocation of the 1,25-dihydroxy cholicalciferol receptor in mouse kidney. *J Biol Chem* 1980;**255:**7510.

Jacobs MD: Vitamin D deficient states. *West J Med* 1979; **131:**305.

Norman AW, Roth J, Orci L: The vitamin D endocrine system. *Endocr Rev* 1982;**3:**331.

Vitamin A

Goodman DS: Vitamin A and retinoids in health and disease. *N Engl J Med* 1984;**310:**1023.

Goodman DS et al: Vitamin A and retinoids: Recent advances. *Fed Proc* 1979;**38:**2501.

Jetten AM: Retinoids specifically enhance the number of epidermal growth factor receptors. *Nature* 1980;**284:**626.

LaCroix A, Lippman ME: Binding of retinoids to human breast cancer cell lines and their effects on cell growth. *J Clin Invest* 1980;**65:**586.

Leo MA, Lieber CS: Hepatic vitamin A depletion in alcoholic

liver injury. *N Engl J Med* 1982;**307:**597.

Maden M: Vitamin A and pattern formation in the regenerating limb. *Nature* 1982;**295:**672.

Sporn MB, Roberts AB: Role of retinoids in differentiation and carcinogenesis. *Cancer Res* 1983;**43:**3034.

Vitamin E

Bieri JG, Corash L, Hubbard VS: Medical uses of vitamin E. *N Engl J Med* 1983;**308:**1063.

Corash L et al: Reduced chronic hemolysis during high dose vitamin E administration in Mediterranean-type glucose 6-phosphate dehydrogenase deficiency. *N Engl J Med* 1980;**303:**416.

Scott ML: Advances in our understanding of vitamin E. *Fed Proc* 1980;**39:**2736.

Vitamin K

Jackson CM, Nemerson Y: Blood coagulation. *Annu Rev Biochem* 1980;**49:**767.

Suttie JW: The metabolic role of vitamin K. *Fed Proc* 1980; **39:**2730.

Suttie JW, Jackson CM: Prothrombin structure, activation, and biosynthesis. *Physiol Rev* 1977;**57:**1.

Wessler S, Gitel SN: Warfarin: From bedside to bench. *N Engl J Med* 1984;**311:**645.

Whitlon DS et al: Mechanism of coumarin action: Significance of vitamin K epoxide reductase inhibition. *Biochemistry* 1978;**17:**1371.

Wolf IL, Babior BM: Vitamin K and warfarin. Metabolism, function and interaction. *Am J Med* 1972;**53:**261.

12 | Biologic Oxidation

Peter A. Mayes, PhD, DSc

Historical Review

Chemically, **oxidation is defined as the removal of electrons** and **reduction as the gain of electrons,** as illustrated by the oxidation of ferrous to ferric ion.

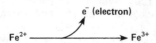

It follows that oxidation is always accompanied by reduction of an electron acceptor. The above definition covers a much wider range of reactions than did the older restricted definition, which covered only the addition of oxygen or removal of hydrogen.

Modern concepts of oxidation in biologic systems may be traced back to Lavoisier, who demonstrated that animals utilize oxygen from the air and replace it with carbon dioxide and water. He showed that respiration was similar in this respect to the burning of a candle. However, Pasteur, in his studies of the fermentation of glucose by yeast, firmly established that living organisms could respire in the absence of oxygen, ie, under **anaerobic** conditions. In the period around 1930, two diametrically opposed concepts of biologic oxidation prevailed. Warburg advocated the view that a widely distributed enzyme (**Atmungsferment**) catalyzed the activation of oxygen and its combination with substrate molecules. Opposed to this concept was the thesis of Wieland, that substrate molecules were activated and oxidized by removal of hydrogen in reactions catalyzed by specific enzymes called **dehydrogenases.** With the discovery by Keilin of a group of respiratory catalysts designated the **cytochrome system,** the 2 concepts were reconciled, as it became clear that most substrates were in fact oxidized by a combination of both processes. Dehydrogenation initiated oxidation, and the reducing equivalents were transported via the cytochrome system to react ultimately with molecular oxygen in the presence of Warburg's enzyme, the last member of the cytochrome system, now renamed **cytochrome oxidase.** The sequence of enzymes and carriers responsible for the transport of reducing equivalents from substrates to molecular oxygen is known as the **respiratory chain.** Further elucidation by Warburg and others of the role of **nicotinamide nucleotides** and **flavoproteins** made it possible by 1940 to construct the following sequence of components of the respiratory chain. The arrows indicate the direction of flow of reducing equivalents (H or electrons).

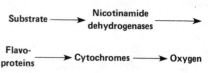

The respiratory chain is localized within **mitochondria.**

Oxidation-Reduction Equilibria; Redox Potential

In reactions involving oxidation and reduction, the free energy exchange is proportionate to the tendency of reactants to donate or accept electrons. Thus, in addition to expressing free energy change in terms of $\Delta G^{0'}$ (see p 67), it is possible, in an analogous manner, to express it numerically as an **oxidation-reduction** or **redox potential** (E_0'). It is usual to compare the redox potential of a system (E_0) against the potential of the hydrogen electrode, which at pH 0 is designated as 0.0 volts. However, for biologic systems it is normal to express the redox potential (E_0') at pH 7.0, at which pH the electrode potential of the hydrogen electrode is -0.42 volts. The redox potentials of some redox systems of special interest in mammalian physiology are shown in Table 12–1. The list of redox potentials shown in the table allows prediction of the direction of

Table 12–1. Some redox potentials of special interest in mammalian oxidation systems.

System	E_0' volts
Oxygen/water	+0.82
Cytochrome a; Fe^{3+}/Fe^{2+}	+0.29
Cytochrome c; Fe^{3+}/Fe^{2+}	+0.22
Ubiquinone; ox/red	+0.10
Cytochrome b; Fe^{3+}/Fe^{2+}	+0.08
Fumarate/succinate	+0.03
Flavoprotein-old yellow enzyme; ox/red	−0.12
Oxaloacetate/malate	−0.17
Pyruvate/lactate	−0.19
Acetoacetate/β-hydroxybutyrate	−0.27
Lipoate; ox/red	−0.29
$NAD^+/NADH$	−0.32
H^+/H_2	**−0.42**
Succinate/α-ketoglutarate	−0.67

flow of electrons from one redox couple to another. The reduced member of a redox couple can potentially reduce the oxidized member of a redox couple **above** it (ie, with a larger E_0') in Table 12–1.

ENZYMES & COENZYMES INVOLVED IN OXIDATION & REDUCTION

All enzymes concerned in oxidative processes are designated **oxidoreductases.** In the following account, they are classified into 5 groups.

(1) Oxidases: Enzymes that catalyze the removal of hydrogen from a substrate but use **only oxygen** as a hydrogen acceptor.* They invariably contain **copper** and form water as a reaction product (with the exception of uricase and monoamine oxidase, which form H_2O_2) (Fig 12–1).

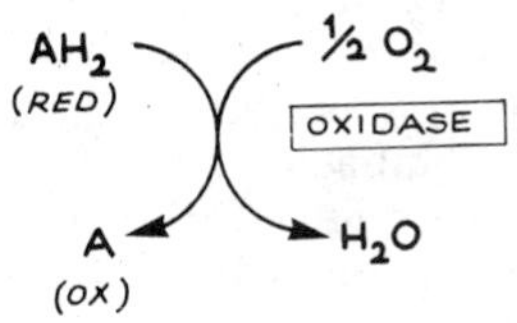

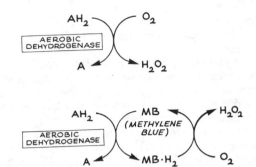

Figure 12–2. Oxidation of a metabolite catalyzed by an aerobic dehydrogenase.

drogenases are specific for their substrates but often utilize the same coenzyme or hydrogen carrier as other dehydrogenases. As the reactions are reversible, these properties enable reducing equivalents to be freely transferred within the cell. This type of reaction, which enables a substrate to be oxidized at the expense of another, is particularly useful in enabling oxidative processes to occur in the **absence of oxygen.**

Figure 12–1. Oxidation of a metabolite catalyzed by an oxidase.

(2) Aerobic dehydrogenases: Enzymes catalyzing the removal of hydrogen from a substrate but which, as distinct from oxidases, can use **either oxygen or artificial substances** such as methylene blue as hydrogen acceptor. Characteristically, these dehydrogenases are **flavoproteins.** Hydrogen peroxide rather than water is formed as a product (Fig 12–2).

(3) Anaerobic dehydrogenases: Enzymes catalyzing the removal of hydrogen from a substrate but **not able to use oxygen** as hydrogen acceptor. There are a large number of enzymes in this class. They perform 2 main functions:

(a) Transfer of hydrogen from one substrate to another in a coupled oxidation-reduction reaction not involving a respiratory chain (Fig 12–3). These dehy-

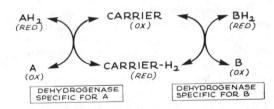

Figure 12–3. Oxidation of a metabolite catalyzed by anaerobic dehydrogenases, not involving a respiratory chain.

(b) As components in a respiratory chain of electron transport from substrate to oxygen (Fig 12–4).

(4) Hydroperoxidases: Enzymes utilizing hydrogen peroxide or an organic peroxide as a substrate. Two types of enzymes fall into this category: **peroxidases,** found in milk, plants, leukocytes, platelets, and erythrocytes, etc; and **catalase,** found in animals and plants.

(5) Oxygenases: Enzymes that catalyze the direct transfer and **incorporation of oxygen** into a substrate molecule.

*Sometimes the term "oxidase" is used collectively to denote all enzymes that catalyze reactions involving molecular oxygen.

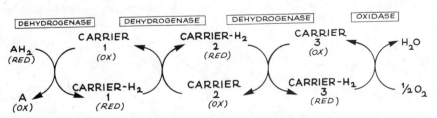

Figure 12–4. Oxidation of a metabolite by anaerobic dehydrogenases and finally by a true oxidase in a respiratory chain.

Oxidases

True oxidases are conjugated proteins that contain copper.

Cytochrome oxidase is a hemoprotein widely distributed in many plant and animal tissues. It is the terminal component of the chain of respiratory carriers found in mitochondria and is therefore responsible for the reaction whereby electrons resulting from the oxidation of substrate molecules by dehydrogenases are transferred to their final acceptor, oxygen. The enzyme is poisoned by carbon monoxide (only in the dark), cyanide, and hydrogen sulfide. It is considered to be identical with Warburg's respiratory enzyme and with what has also been termed cytochrome a_3. It was formerly assumed that cytochrome a and cytochrome a_3 were separate compounds, since each has a distinct spectrum and different properties with respect to the effects of carbon monoxide and cyanide. More recent studies show that the 2 cytochromes are combined with the same protein, and the complex is known as **cytochrome aa$_3$**. It contains 2 molecules of heme, each having one Fe atom that oscillates between Fe^{3+} and Fe^{2+} during oxidation and reduction. Also, 2 atoms of Cu are present, each associated with a heme unit.

Phenolase (tyrosinase, polyphenol oxidase, catechol oxidase) is a copper-containing enzyme that is specific for more than one type of reaction. It is able to convert monophenols or o-diphenols to o-quinones. Other enzymes containing copper are **laccase,** which is widely distributed in plants and animals (converts p-hydroquinones to p-quinones), and **ascorbic acid oxidase,** found only in plants. Copper has been claimed to be present in a number of other enzymes such as **uricase,** which catalyzes the oxidation of uric acid to allantoin, and **monoamine oxidase,** an enzyme that oxidizes epinephrine and tyramine in mitochondria.

Aerobic Dehydrogenases

Aerobic dehydrogenases are flavoprotein enzymes containing **flavin mononucleotide (FMN)** or **flavin adenine dinucleotide (FAD)** (Figs 10–8 and 10–9). The flavin groups vary in their affinity for their respective apoenzyme protein, some being detached easily and others not detached without destroying the enzyme. Many of these flavoprotein enzymes contain, in addition, a metal that is essential for the functioning of the enzyme; these are known as **metalloflavoproteins.**

Enzymes belonging to this group of aerobic dehydrogenases include D-**amino acid dehydrogenase** (D-amino acid oxidase), an FAD-linked enzyme, found particularly in liver and kidney, that catalyzes the oxidative deamination of the unnatural (D-) forms of amino acids. Other substrates include glycine, D-lactate, and L-proline, demonstrating that the enzyme is not completely specific for D-amino acids. L-**Amino acid dehydrogenase** (L-amino acid oxidase) is an FMN-linked enzyme found in kidney with general specificity for the oxidative deamination of the naturally occurring L-amino acids. **Xanthine dehydrogenase** (xanthine oxidase) has a wide distribution, occurring in milk, small intestine, kidney, and liver. It contains molybdenum and plays an important role in the conversion of purine bases to uric acid. It is of particular significance in the liver and kidneys of birds, which excrete uric acid as the main nitrogenous end product not only of purine metabolism but also of protein and amino acid catabolism.

Aldehyde dehydrogenase (aldehyde oxidase) is an FAD-linked enzyme present in mammalian livers. It is a metalloflavoprotein containing molybdenum and nonheme iron and acts upon aldehydes and N-heterocyclic substrates.

Of interest because of its use in estimating glucose is **glucose oxidase,** an FAD-specific enzyme prepared from fungi.

All of the above-mentioned aerobic dehydrogenases contain 2 molecules of the flavin nucleotide per mole. The metalloflavoproteins also have a fixed stoichiometry with regard to the number of atoms of metal per molecule, usually Mo:Fe as 2:8. The mechanisms of oxidation and reduction of these enzymes are complex. There seem to be different detailed mechanisms for each enzyme with the possible involvement of free radicals. However, evidence points to reduction of the isoalloxazine ring taking place in 2 steps via a semiquinone (free radical) intermediate (Fig 12–5).

Anaerobic Dehydrogenases

A. Dehydrogenases Dependent on Nicotinamide Coenzymes: A large number of dehydrogenase enzymes fall into this category. They are linked as coenzymes either to **nicotinamide adenine dinucleotide (NAD)** or to **nicotinamide adenine dinucleotide phosphate (NADP).** The coenzymes are reduced by the specific substrate of the dehydrogenase and reoxidized by a suitable electron acceptor. They may freely and reversibly dissociate from their respective apoenzymes. The nicotinamide nucleotides are synthesized from the vitamin niacin (see Chapter 10). The

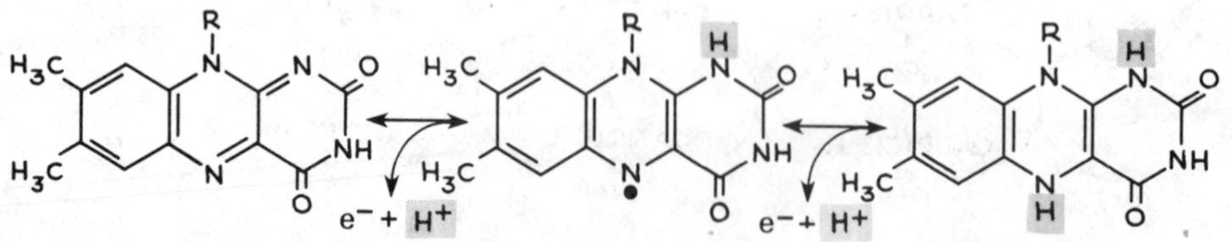

Figure 12–5. Reduction of isoalloxazine ring in flavin nucleotides.

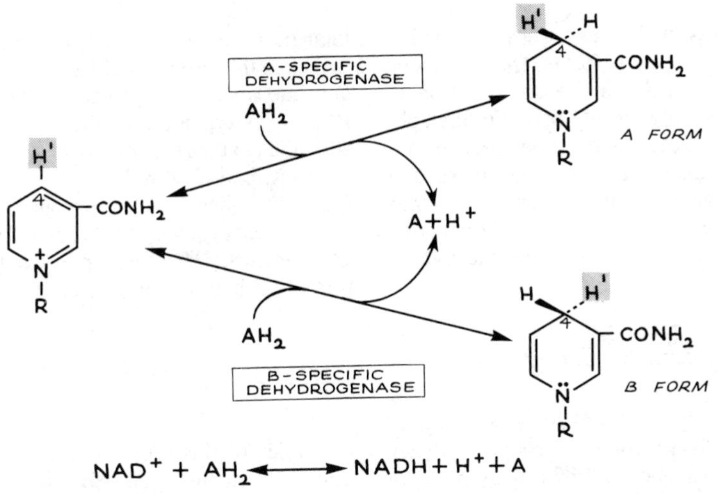

Figure 12–6. Mechanism of oxidation of nicotinamide coenzymes.

mechanism of oxidation of the coenzymes is as shown in Fig 12–6.

There is stereospecificity about position 4 of nicotinamide when it is reduced by a substrate AH_2. One of the hydrogen atoms is removed from the substrate as a hydrogen nucleus with 2 electrons (hydride ion, H^-) and is transferred to the 4 position, where it may be attached in either the A- or B-position according to the specificity determined by the particular dehydrogenase catalyzing the reaction. The remaining hydrogen of the hydrogen pair removed from the substrate remains free as a hydrogen ion. Deuterium-labeled substrates have been used in elucidating these mechanisms.

Generally, **NAD-linked dehydrogenases** catalyze oxidoreduction reactions in the **oxidative pathways** of metabolism, particularly in glycolysis, in the citric acid cycle, and in the respiratory chain of mitochondria. **NADP-linked dehydrogenases** are found characteristically in **reductive syntheses,** as in the extramitochondrial pathway of fatty acid synthesis and steroid synthesis. They are also to be found as coenzymes to the dehydrogenases of the hexose monophosphate shunt. Some nicotinamide coenzyme-dependent dehydrogenases have been found to contain zinc, notably alcohol dehydrogenase from liver and glyceraldehyde 3-phosphate dehydrogenase from skeletal muscle. The zinc ions are not considered to take part in the oxidation and reduction.

B. Dehydrogenases Dependent on Riboflavin: The flavin groups associated with these dehydrogenases are similar to those of the aerobic dehydrogenase group, namely FMN and FAD. They are in the main more tightly bound to their apoenzymes than the nicotinamide coenzymes. Most of the riboflavin-linked anaerobic dehydrogenases are concerned with electron transport in (or to) the respiratory chain. **NADH dehydrogenase** is a member of the respiratory chain acting as a carrier of electrons between NADH and the more electropositive components. Other dehydrogenases such as **succinate dehydrogenase, acyl-CoA dehydrogenase,** and **mitochondrial glycerol 3-phosphate dehydrogenase** transfer reducing equivalents directly from the substrate to the respiratory chain. Another role of the flavin-dependent dehydrogenases is in the dehydrogenation (by dihydrolipoyl dehydrogenase) of reduced lipoate, an intermediate in the oxidative decarboxylation of pyruvate and α-ketoglutarate (Fig 14–5). In this particular instance, owing to the low redox potential, the flavoprotein (FAD) acts as a hydrogen carrier from reduced lipoate to NAD^+. The **electron-transferring flavoprotein** is an intermediary carrier of electrons between acyl-CoA dehydrogenase and the respiratory chain (Fig 12–12).

C. The Cytochromes: Except for cytochrome oxidase (previously described), the cytochromes are classified as anaerobic dehydrogenases. Their identification and study are facilitated by the presence in the reduced state of characteristic absorption bands that disappear on oxidation. In the respiratory chain, they are involved as **carriers of electrons from flavoproteins on the one hand to cytochrome oxidase on the other.** The cytochromes are iron-containing hemoproteins in which the iron atom oscillates between Fe^{3+} and Fe^{2+} during oxidation and reduction. Several identifiable cytochromes occur in the respiratory chain, ie, cytochromes b, c_1, c, a, and a_3 (cytochrome oxidase). Of these, only cytochrome c is soluble. Study of its structure has revealed that the iron porphyrin group is attached to the apoprotein by 2 thioether bridges derived from condensation of cysteine residues of the protein with vinyl groups of the heme. Besides the respiratory chain, cytochromes are found in other locations, eg, the endoplasmic reticulum (cytochromes P-450 and b_5), plant cells, bacteria, and yeasts.

Hydroperoxidases

A. Peroxidase: Although originally considered to be plant enzymes, peroxidases are found in milk and in leukocytes, platelets, and other tissues involved in eicosanoid metabolism (see p 221). The prosthetic group is protoheme, which, unlike the situation in most hemoproteins, is only loosely bound to the apoprotein. In the reaction catalyzed by peroxidase, hydrogen peroxide is reduced at the expense of several substances that will act as electron acceptors, such as ascorbate, quinones, and cytochrome c. The reaction catalyzed by peroxidase is complex, but the overall reaction is as follows:

$$H_2O_2 + AH_2 \xrightarrow{\boxed{PEROXIDASE}} 2 H_2O + A$$

In erythrocytes, the enzyme **glutathione peroxidase,** containing selenium as a prosthetic group, catalyzes the destruction of H_2O_2 and lipid hydroperoxides by reduced glutathione, protecting membrane lipids and hemoglobin against oxidation by peroxides (see pp 183 and 659).

B. Catalase: Catalase is a hemoprotein containing 4 heme groups. In addition to possessing peroxidase activity, it is able to use one molecule of H_2O_2 as a substrate electron donor and another molecule of H_2O_2 as oxidant or electron acceptor. Under most conditions in vivo, the peroxidase activity of catalase seems to be favored.

$$2 H_2O_2 \xrightarrow{\boxed{CATALASE}} 2 H_2O + O_2$$

Catalase is found in blood, bone marrow, mucous membranes, kidney, and liver. Its function is assumed to be the **destruction of hydrogen peroxide** formed by the action of aerobic dehydrogenases. Microbodies or **peroxisomes** are found in many tissues, including liver. They are rich in aerobic dehydrogenases and in catalase, which suggests that there may be a biologic advantage in grouping the enzymes which produce H_2O_2 with the enzyme that destroys it (Fig 12–7). In addition to the peroxisomal enzymes, mitochondrial and microsomal electron transport systems must be considered as sources of H_2O_2.

Oxygenases

Oxygenases are concerned with the synthesis or degradation of many different types of metabolites rather than with taking part in reactions that have as their purpose the provision of energy to the cell. Enzymes in this group catalyze the incorporation of oxygen into a substrate molecule. This takes place in 2 steps: (1) oxygen binding to the enzyme at the active site, and (2) the reaction in which the bound oxygen is reduced or transferred to the substrate. Oxygenases may be divided into 2 subgroups:

A. Dioxygenases (Oxygen Transferases, True Oxygenases): These enzymes catalyze the incorporation of both atoms of oxygen into the substrate:

$$A + O_2 \longrightarrow AO_2$$

Examples of this type include enzymes that contain iron such as **homogentisate dioxygenase** and **3-hydroxyanthranilate dioxygenase** from the supernatant fraction of the liver, and enzymes utilizing heme such as L-**tryptophan dioxygenase** (tryptophan pyrrolase) from the liver.

B. Monooxygenases (Mixed Function Oxidases, Hydroxylases): These enzymes catalyze the incorporation of only one atom of the oxygen molecule into a substrate. The other oxygen atom is reduced to water, an additional electron donor or cosubstrate being necessary for this purpose.

Example:

$$A{-}H + O_2 + ZH_2 \longrightarrow A{-}OH + H_2O + Z$$

Hayaishi has subdivided the monooxygenases into subgroups according to the nature of the cosubstrate electron donor involved. For example, many of the enzymes involved in steroid syntheses or transformations are monooxygenases utilizing NADPH as a cosubstrate. These are found mainly in the endoplasmic reticulum (microsomes) of the liver and in both the mitochondria and the endoplasmic reticulum of the adrenal glands and other steroidogenic tissues.

Microsomal Cytochrome P-450 Monooxygenase Systems

The enzymes involved in the metabolism of many drugs by hydroxylation belong to this group. They are found in the microsomes of the liver together with cytochrome P-450 and cytochrome b_5. Both NADH and NADPH donate reducing equivalents for the reduction of these cytochromes (Fig 12–8), which in turn are oxidized by substrates in a series of enzymic reactions collectively known as the hydroxylase cycle (Fig 12–9).

Example:

$$DRUG{-}H + O_2 + 2 Fe^{2+} + 2 H^+ \xrightarrow{\boxed{HYDROXYLASE}}$$
$$(P{-}450)$$

$$DRUG{-}OH + H_2O + 2 Fe^{3+}$$
$$(P{-}450)$$

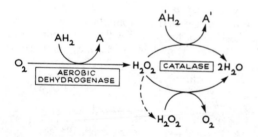

Figure 12–7. Role of catalase in oxidative reactions.

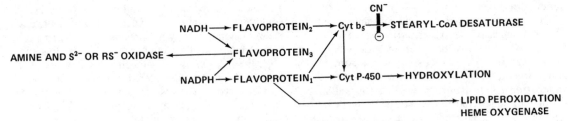

Figure 12–8. Electron transport chain in microsomes. Cyanide (CN⁻) inhibits the indicated step.

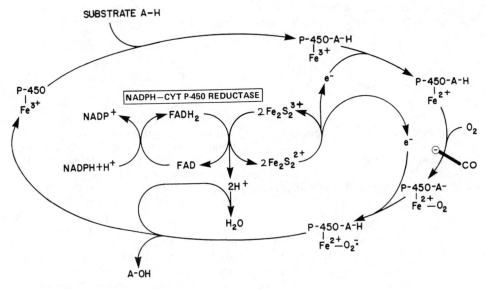

Figure 12–9. Cytochrome P-450 hydroxylase cycle in microsomes. The system shown is typical of steroid hydroxylases of the adrenal cortex. Liver microsomal cytochrome P-450 hydroxylase does not require the iron-sulfur protein Fe₂S₂. Carbon monoxide (CO) inhibits the indicated step.

Among the drugs metabolized by this system are benzpyrene, aminopyrine, aniline, morphine, and benzphetamine. Many drugs such as phenobarbital have the ability to induce the formation of microsomal enzymes and of cytochrome P-450.

Mitochondrial Cytochrome P-450 Monooxygenase Systems

These systems are found in steroidogenic tissues such as adrenal cortex, testis, ovary, and placenta and are concerned with the biosynthesis of steroid hormones from cholesterol (hydroxylation at C_{22} and C_{20} in side-chain cleavage and at 11β and 18 positions). Renal systems catalyze 1α- and 24-hydroxylations of 25-hydroxycholecalciferol, and the liver catalyzes 26-hydroxylation in bile acid biosynthesis. In the adrenal cortex, mitochondrial cytochrome P-450 is 6 times more abundant than cytochromes of the respiratory chain. The monooxygenase system consists of 3 components situated on the inside of the inner mitochondrial membrane: an NADP-specific FAD containing flavoprotein, an Fe₂S₂ protein (adrenodoxin), and cytochrome P-450 (Fig 12–10).

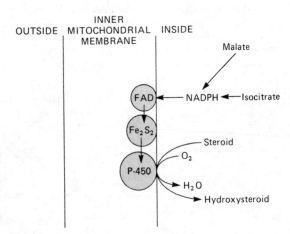

Figure 12–10. Mitochondrial cytochrome P-450 monooxygenase system. Fe₂S₂, iron-sulfur protein (adrenodoxin). Note that because NADP(H) cannot penetrate the mitochondrial membrane, sources of reducing equivalents are confined to substrates such as malate and isocitrate for which there are intramitochondrial NADP-specific dehydrogenases.

Superoxide Metabolism

Oxygen is a potentially toxic substance, the toxicity of which has hitherto been attributed to the formation of H_2O_2. Recently, however, the ease with which oxygen can be reduced in tissues to the superoxide anion free radical ($O_2^{\cdot-}$) and the occurrence of **superoxide dismutase** in aerobic organisms (although not in obligate anaerobes) have suggested that the toxicity of oxygen is due to its conversion to superoxide (Friedovich, 1975). However, no direct evidence of superoxide toxicity has yet been obtained.

Superoxide is formed when reduced flavins, eg, xanthine dehydrogenase, are reoxidized univalently by molecular oxygen. It is also formed during univalent oxidations with molecular oxygen in the respiratory chain.

$$EnzH_2 + O_2 \longrightarrow EnzH + O_2^{\cdot-} + H^+$$

Superoxide can reduce oxidized cytochrome c

$$O_2^{\cdot-} + Cyt\ c\ (Fe^{3+}) \longrightarrow O_2 + Cyt\ c\ (Fe^{2+})$$

or be removed by the presence of the specific enzyme superoxide dismutase.

$$O_2^{\cdot-} + O_2^{\cdot-} + 2H^+ \xrightarrow{\text{SUPEROXIDE DISMUTASE}} H_2O_2 + O_2$$

Superoxide acts as both oxidant and reductant; the chemical effects are amplified by free-radical chain reactions. It has been proposed that $O_2^{\cdot-}$ bound to cytochrome P-450 is an intermediate in the activation of oxygen in hydroxylation reactions (Fig 12–9).

The function of superoxide dismutase seems to be that of protecting aerobic organisms against the potential deleterious effects of superoxide. The cytosolic enzyme is composed of 2 similar subunits, each one containing one equivalent of Cu^{2+} and Zn^{2+}, whereas the mitochondrial enzyme contains Mn^{2+}, being similar to the enzyme found in bacteria. This finding supports the hypothesis that mitochondria have evolved from a prokaryote that entered into symbiosis with a protoeukaryote. The distribution of the dismutase is widespread, being present in all major aerobic tissues. Although exposure of animals to an atmosphere of 100% oxygen causes an adaptive increase of the enzyme, particularly in the lungs, prolonged exposure leads to lung damage and death. Antioxidants, eg, α-tocopherol (vitamin E), act as scavengers of free radicals such as $O_2^{\cdot-}$ and reduce the toxicity of oxygen.

THE RESPIRATORY CHAIN

The mitochondrion has appropriately been termed the "powerhouse" of the cell, since it is within the mitochondria that most of the useful energy derived from oxidation within the tissues is captured in the form of the high-energy intermediate ATP. All of the useful energy liberated during the oxidation of fatty acids and amino acids and nearly all of that from the oxidation of carbohydrate is made available within the mitochondria as reducing equivalents (–H or electrons). To accomplish this, the mitochondria contain the series of catalysts known as the respiratory chain, which are concerned with the transport of reducing equivalents and their final reaction with oxygen to form water, together with the machinery for trapping the liberated free energy as high-energy phosphate. Mitochondria also contain the enzyme systems responsible for producing most of the reducing equivalents in the first place, ie, the enzymes of β-oxidation and of the citric acid cycle. The latter is the final common metabolic pathway for the oxidation of all the major foodstuffs. These relationships are shown in Fig 12–11.

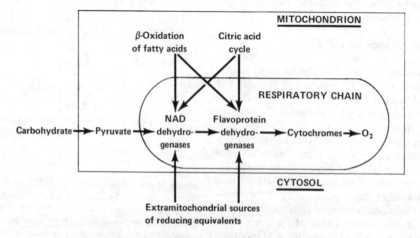

Figure 12–11. The major sources of reducing equivalents and their relationship to the mitochondrial respiratory chain. The main extramitochondrial source is NADH formed in glycolysis.

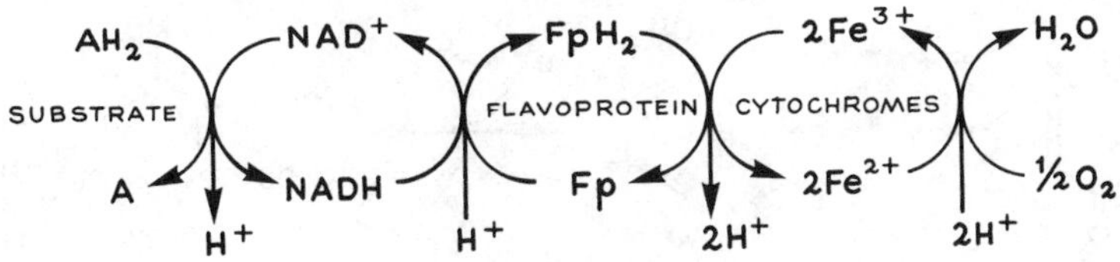

$$AH_2 \quad NAD^+ \quad FpH_2 \quad 2Fe^{3+} \quad H_2O$$

SUBSTRATE   FLAVOPROTEIN   CYTOCHROMES

$$A \quad NADH \quad Fp \quad 2Fe^{2+} \quad \tfrac{1}{2}O_2$$

$$H^+ \qquad H^+ \qquad 2H^+ \qquad 2H^+$$

Figure 12–12. Transport of reducing equivalents through the respiratory chain.

Organization of the Respiratory Chain in Mitochondria

The major components of the respiratory chain (Fig 12–12) are arranged sequentially in order of increasing redox potential (Table 12–1). Hydrogen or electrons flow through the chain in a stepwise manner **from the more electronegative components to the more electropositive oxygen** through a redox span of 1.1 volts from $NAD^+/NADH$ to $O_2/2H_2O$ (Table 12–1). Thus, the redox potential of a component of the respiratory chain contributes to the information necessary to assign it a tentative position in the chain. Several other approaches have been used to identify components and their relative positions. Sophisticated techniques for following the absorption spectra of the individual components in intact mitochondria have been developed, or the chain has been broken down into separate components or complexes and reconstructed from the separate parts. Inhibitors that block specific reactions in the chain are frequently employed with artificial electron acceptors and donors. Chance and Williams introduced the concept of "crossover" to locate the site of action of inhibitors. The concept is based upon the assumption that when an inhibitor is introduced into an active series of redox components of the respiratory chain in the steady state, those components on the electronegative side of the block become more reduced while those on the electropositive side become more oxidized.

The main respiratory chain in mitochondria proceeds from the NAD-linked dehydrogenase systems on the one hand, through flavoproteins and cytochromes, to molecular oxygen on the other. Not all substrates are linked to the respiratory chain through NAD-specific dehydrogenases; some, because their redox potentials are more positive (eg, fumarate/succinate; see Table 21–1), are linked directly to flavoprotein dehydrogenases, which in turn are linked to the cytochromes of the respiratory chain (Fig 12–13).

In recent years it has become clear that an additional carrier is present in the respiratory chain linking the flavoproteins to cytochrome b, the member of the cytochrome chain of lowest redox potential. This substance, which has been named **ubiquinone** or **Q** (**coenzyme Q;** see Fig 12–14), exists in mitochondria in the oxidized quinone form under aerobic conditions and in the reduced quinol form under anaerobic conditions. Q is a constituent of the mitochondrial lipids, the

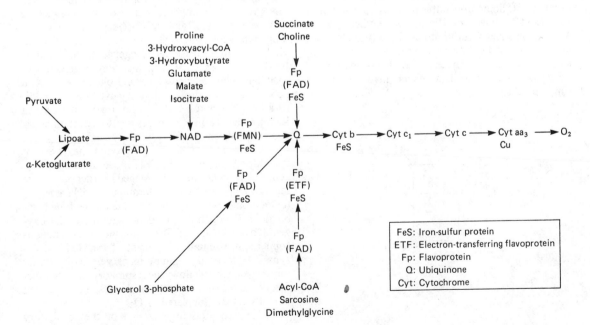

Figure 12–13. Components of the respiratory chain in mitochondria. FeS occurs in the sequences on the O_2 side of Fp or Cyt b.

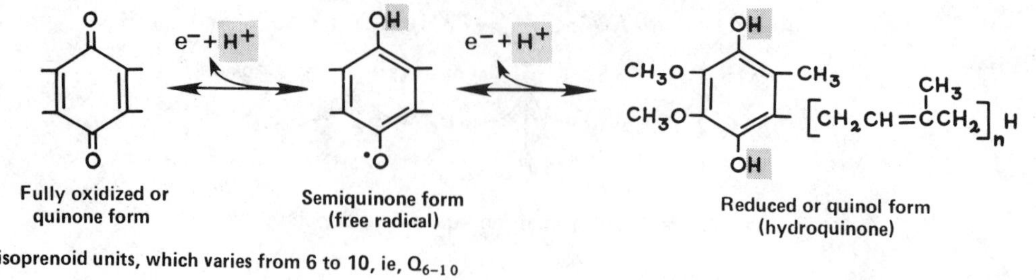

n = number of isoprenoid units, which varies from 6 to 10, ie, Q_{6-10}

Figure 12–14. Structure of ubiquinone (Q).

other lipids being predominantly phospholipids that constitute part of the mitochondrial membrane. Its structure is very similar to those of vitamin K and vitamin E (see Chapter 11). It is also similar to plastoquinone, found in chloroplasts. All of these substances are characterized by the possession of a polyisoprenoid side chain. In mitochondria there is a large stoichiometric excess of Q compared with other members of the respiratory chain, leading to the idea that it is a mobile component of the respiratory chain which collects reducing equivalents from the more fixed flavoprotein complexes and passes them on to the cytochromes.

An additional component found in respiratory chain preparations is the **iron-sulfur protein (FeS;** nonheme iron). It is associated with the flavoproteins (metalloflavoproteins) and with cytochrome b. The iron-sulfur-protein complex (Fig 12–15) is similar to the ferredoxins of bacteria and to iron proteins present in plants. On denaturation with acid or heat, H_2S is liberated in an amount stoichiometrically related to the iron present. Some iron-sulfur proteins contain 2 iron atoms and 2 sulfur atoms (Fe_2S_2) while others contain 4 iron atoms and 4 sulfur atoms (Fe_4S_4), both structures connected by 4 cysteine residues to the apoprotein. The sulfur and iron are thought to take part in the oxidoreduction mechanism, which involves only a single e^- change.

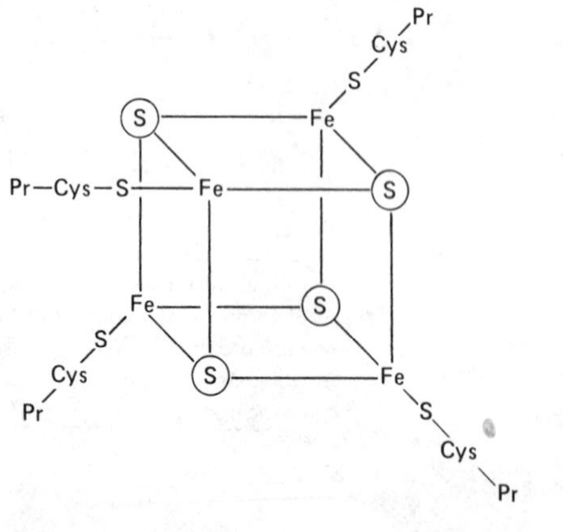

Figure 12–15. Iron-sulfur-protein complex (Fe_4S_4). Ⓢ, acid-labile sulfur; Pr, apoprotein; Cys, cysteine residue.

A current view of the principal components of the respiratory chain is shown in Fig 12–13. At the electronegative end of the chain, dehydrogenase enzymes catalyze the transfer of electrons from substrates to NAD of the chain. Several differences exist in the manner in which this is carried out. The α-keto acids pyruvate and ketoglutarate have complex dehydrogenase systems involving lipoate and FAD prior to the passage of electrons to NAD of the respiratory chain. Electron transfers from other dehydrogenases such as L(+)-3-hydroxyacyl-CoA, D(−)-3-hydroxybutyrate, proline, glutamate, malate, and isocitrate dehydrogenases appear to couple directly with NAD of the respiratory chain.

The reduced NADH of the respiratory chain is in turn oxidized by a metalloflavoprotein enzyme— **NADH dehydrogenase.** This enzyme contains FeS and FMN and is tightly bound to the respiratory chain. Q is the collecting point in the respiratory chain for reducing equivalents derived from other substrates that are linked directly to the respiratory chain through flavoprotein dehydrogenases. These substrates include succinate, choline, glycerol 3-phosphate, sarcosine, dimethylglycine, and acyl-CoA (Fig 12–13). The flavin moiety of all these dehydrogenases appears to be FAD, and those catalyzing the dehydrogenation of succinate, choline, and glycerol 3-phosphate contain FeS. In the dehydrogenation of acyl-CoA, an additional flavoprotein, the **electron-transporting flavoprotein (ETF),** is necessary to effect transference of electrons to the respiratory chain.

Electrons flow from Q, through the series of cytochromes shown in Fig 12–13, to molecular oxygen. The cytochromes are arranged in order of increasing redox potential. The terminal cytochrome aa_3 (cytochrome oxidase) is responsible for the final combination of reducing equivalents with molecular oxygen. It has been noted that this enzyme system contains copper, an essential component of true oxidase enzymes. Cytochrome oxidase has a very high affinity for oxygen, which allows the respiratory chain to function at the maximum rate until the tissue has become virtually anoxic (depleted of O_2).

The structural organization of the respiratory chain has been the subject of considerable speculation. Of significance is the finding of nearly constant molar proportions between the components. The cytochromes are present in approximate molar proportions, one with another. These findings, together with the fact that many of the components appear to be structurally integrated with the mitochondrial membranes, have suggested that these components have a definite spatial orientation in the membranes. Cytochrome c is the only soluble cytochrome and seems to be a more mobile component of the respiratory chain.

THE ROLE OF THE RESPIRATORY CHAIN IN ENERGY CAPTURE

ADP is envisaged as a molecule that captures, in the form of **high-energy phosphate,** some of the free energy resulting from catabolic processes. The resulting **ATP** passes on this free energy to drive those processes requiring energy. Thus, ATP has been called the **energy "currency"** of the cell.

As indicated in Chapter 15, under anaerobic conditions there is a net capture of 2 high-energy phosphate groups in the glycolytic reactions equivalent to approximately 74 kJ/mol of glucose. Since 1 mol of glucose yields approximately 2870 kJ on complete combustion, the energy captured by phosphorylation in glycolysis is small. The reactions of the citric acid cycle, the final pathway for the complete oxidation of glucose, include only one phosphorylation step, the conversion of succinyl-CoA to succinate, which allows the capture of 2 more high-energy phosphates per mol of glucose. All of the phosphorylations described so far occur **at the substrate level.** Examination of intact respiring mitochondria reveals that when substrates are oxidized via an NAD-linked dehydrogenase, 3 mol of inorganic phosphate are incorporated into 3 mol of ADP to form 3 mol of ATP per ½ mol of O_2 consumed; ie, the P:O ratio = 3. On the other hand, when a substrate is oxidized via a flavoprotein-linked dehydrogenase, only 2 mol of ATP are formed; ie, P:O = 2. These reactions are known as **oxidative phosphorylation at the respiratory chain level.** Taking into account dehydrogenations in the pathway of catabolism of glucose in both glycolysis and the citric acid cycle, plus phosphorylations at the substrate level, it is now possible to account for at least 46% of the free energy resulting from the combustion of glucose, captured in the form of high-energy phosphate.

If phosphorylation is coupled to certain reactions in the respiratory chain, it is pertinent to inquire what sites could support phosphorylation. There must be a redox potential of approximately 0.2 volts or a free energy change of approximately 37 kJ between components of the respiratory chain if that particular site is to support the coupled formation of 1 mol of ATP. Location of these sites has been elucidated by experiments in which the P:O ratio is measured in the presence of inhibitors of known reactions in the chain and in the presence of artificial electron acceptors.

The rate of respiration of mitochondria can be controlled by the concentration of ADP. This is because **oxidation and phosphorylation are tightly coupled;** ie, oxidation cannot normally proceed without phosphorylation. Thus, ADP is an essential component of the phosphorylation process. When ADP is deficient in the presence of excess substrate, 3 crossover points can be identified, since the component at the substrate side of the crossover point becomes more reduced and that on the oxygen side becomes more oxidized. These crossover points coincide with 3 of the possible sites previously identified on thermodynamic grounds. The 3 sites that could support phosphorylation have been designated I, II, and III (Fig 12–16). The above findings explain why oxidation of succinate via the respiratory chain produces a P:O ratio of only 2, as site I would be bypassed by the flavoprotein-linked succinate dehydrogenase (Fig 12–13).

Respiratory Control

As stated above, oxidation and phosphorylation are tightly coupled in mitochondria. Thus, respiration cannot occur via the respiratory chain without concomitant phosphorylation of ADP. Chance and Williams have defined 5 conditions that can control the rate of respiration in mitochondria. These are listed in Table 12–2.

Table 12–2. States of respiratory control.

	Conditions Limiting the Rate of Respiration
State 1	Availability of ADP and substrate
State 2	Availability of substrate only
State 3	The capacity of the respiratory chain itself, when all substrates and components are present in saturating amounts
State 4	Availability of ADP only
State 5	Availability of oxygen only

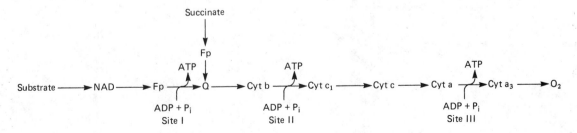

Figure 12–16. Sites supporting phosphorylation in the respiratory chain.

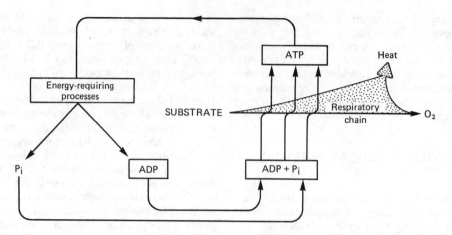

Figure 12–17. The role of ADP in respiratory control.

Generally most cells in the resting state seem to be in state 4, respiration being controlled by the availability of ADP. When work is performed, ATP is converted to ADP, allowing more respiration to occur, which in turn replenishes the store of ATP (Fig 12–17). It would appear that under certain conditions the concentration of inorganic phosphate could also affect the rate of functioning of the respiratory chain. As respiration increases (as in exercise), the cell approaches state 3 or state 5 when either the capacity of cytochrome a_3 becomes saturated or the P_{O_2} decreases below the K_m for cytochrome a_3. There is also the possibility that the ADP/ATP transporter (see p 145), which facilitates entry of cytosolic ADP into the mitochondrion, becomes rate-limiting.

Thus, the manner in which biologic oxidative processes allow the free energy resulting from the oxidation of foodstuffs to become available and to be captured is stepwise, efficient (40–50%), and controlled—rather than explosive, inefficient, and uncontrolled. The remaining free energy that is not captured as high-energy phosphate is liberated as **heat.** This need not be considered as ''wasted,'' since in the warm-blooded animal it contributes to maintenance of body temperature.

Inhibitors of the Respiratory Chain & of Oxidative Phosphorylation

Much information about the respiratory chain has been obtained by the use of inhibitors, and their proposed loci of action are shown in Fig 12–18. For descriptive purposes, they may be divided into inhibitors of the respiratory chain proper, inhibitors of oxidative phosphorylation, and uncouplers of oxidative phosphorylation.

Inhibitors that arrest respiration by blocking the respiratory chain appear to act at 3 loci that may be identical to the energy transfer sites I, II, and III. Site I is inhibited by **barbiturates** such as **amobarbital,** by the antibiotic **piericidin A,** and by the fish poison **rotenone.** Some steroids and mercurials also affect this site. The crossover point induced by these inhibitors lies on the O_2 side of all the FeS proteins (Fig 12–12). These inhibitors prevent the oxidation of substrates that communicate directly with the respiratory chain via an NAD-linked dehydrogenase, eg, 3-hydroxybutyrate.

Dimercaprol and **antimycin A** inhibit the respiratory chain at or around site II, between cytochrome b and cytochrome c; and the inhibitors of cytochrome oxidase, **H₂S, carbon monoxide,** and **cyanide,** that

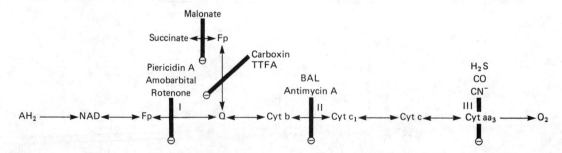

Figure 12–18. Proposed sites of inhibition (⊝) of respiratory chain by specific drugs, chemicals, and antibiotics. The energy transfer sites (I, II, and III) are indicated. BAL, dimercaprol. TTFA is an iron-chelating agent.

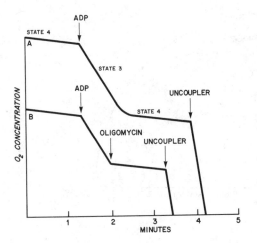

Figure 12–19. Respiratory control in mitochondria. Experiment A shows the basic state of respiration in state 4 that is accelerated upon addition of ADP. When the exogenous ADP has been phosphorylated to ATP, respiration reverts to state 4. The addition of uncoupler, eg, dinitrophenol, releases respiration from phosphorylation. In experiment B, addition of oligomycin blocks phosphorylation of added ADP and therefore of respiration as well. Addition of uncoupler again releases respiration from phosphorylation.

have been known for many years are considered to act at or near site III. **Carboxin** and **TTFA** specifically inhibit transfer of reducing equivalents from succinate dehydrogenase to Q, whereas **malonate** is a competitive inhibitor of succinate dehydrogenase.

The antibiotic **oligomycin** completely blocks oxidation and phosphorylation in intact mitochondria. However, in the additional presence of the uncoupler **dinitrophenol,** oxidation proceeds without phosphorylation, indicating that oligomycin does not act directly on the respiratory chain but subsequently on a step in phosphorylation (Fig 12–19).

Atractyloside inhibits oxidative phosphorylation, which is dependent on the transport of adenine nucleotides across the inner mitochondrial membrane. It is considered to inhibit the transporter of ADP into the mitochondrion and of ATP out of the mitochondrion (Fig 12–27).

The action of **uncouplers** is to dissociate oxidation in the respiratory chain from phosphorylation. This results in respiration becoming uncontrolled, the concentration of ADP or P_i no longer limiting the rate of respiration. The uncoupler that has been used most frequently is 2,4-dinitrophenol, but other compounds act in a similar manner, including dinitrocresol, pentachlorophenol, and CCCP (*m*-chlorocarbonyl cyanide phenylhydrazone). The latter, compared with dinitrophenol, is about 100 times as active.

Reversal of Electron Transport

Mitochondria catalyze the energy-dependent reversal of electron transport through the respiratory chain. The energy is provided either by ATP, where

the effect is mediated by a complete reversal of oxidative phosphorylation, or by some other intermediate. Although these experiments demonstrate the reversibility of electron transport, the physiologic significance of the process is unknown.

Energy-Linked Transhydrogenase

There is evidence for an energy-linked transhydrogenase that can catalyze the transfer of hydrogen from NADH to NADP. The energy required for the reaction is provided either directly by the respiratory chain in an oligomycin-insensitive process or by ATP, in which case it is blocked by oligomycin.

MECHANISMS OF OXIDATIVE PHOSPHORYLATION

Two principal hypotheses have been advanced to account for the coupling of oxidation and phosphorylation. The **chemical hypothesis** postulated direct chemical coupling at all stages of the process, as in the reactions that generate ATP in glycolysis. The **chemiosmotic theory** postulates that oxidation of components in the respiratory chain generates hydrogen ions, which are ejected to the outside of a coupling membrane in the mitochondrion. The electrochemical potential difference resulting from the asymmetric distribution of the hydrogen ions (protons, H^+) is used to drive the mechanism responsible for the formation of ATP.

Other hypotheses have been advanced in which it is envisaged that energy from oxidation is conserved in conformational changes of molecules, which in turn lead to the generation of high-energy phosphate bonds.

The chemical hypothesis postulated the existence of an energy-rich intermediate $(I \sim X)$ linking oxidation with phosphorylation. Because this has never been isolated, the hypothesis has become discredited and will no longer be described in detail in this text. For an account of the chemical hypothesis, see Harper, Rodwell, and Mayes (1979).

THE CHEMIOSMOTIC THEORY

According to Mitchell, the primary event in oxidative phosphorylation is the translocation of protons (H^+) to the exterior of a coupling membrane (ie, the mitochondrial inner membrane), driven by oxidation in the respiratory chain. It is also postulated that the membrane is impermeable to ions in general but particularly to protons which accumulate outside the membrane, creating an **electrochemical potential difference across the membrane** $(\Delta\mu_{H^+})$. This consists of a chemical potential (difference in pH) and an electrical potential. The electrochemical potential difference is used to drive a **membrane-located ATP synthetase** (or the reversal of a membrane-located ATP hydrolase) which in the presence of P_i + ADP forms ATP (Fig 12–20). Thus, there is no high-energy

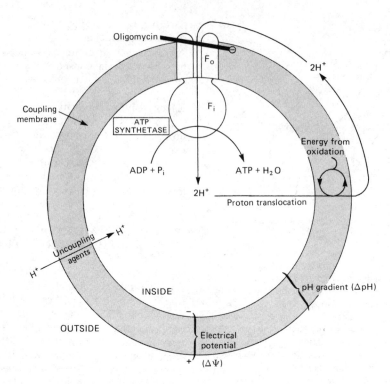

Figure 12-20. Principles of the chemiosmotic theory of oxidative phosphorylation. F_i, F_o, protein subunits responsible for phosphorylation. The main proton circuit is created by the coupling of oxidation to proton translocation from the inside to the outside of the membrane. Uncoupling agents such as dinitrophenol allow leakage of H^+ across the membrane, thus collapsing the electrochemical proton gradient. Oligomycin specifically blocks conduction of H^+ through F_o.

intermediate that is common to both oxidation and phosphorylation as in the chemical hypothesis.

It is proposed that the respiratory chain is folded into 3 oxidation/reduction (**o/r**) loops in the membrane, each loop corresponding functionally to site I, site II, and site III of the respiratory chain. An idealized single loop consisting of a hydrogen carrier and an electron carrier is shown in Fig 12-21. A possible configuration of the respiratory chain folded into 3 functional o/r loops is shown in Fig 12-22.

In this scheme, each electron pair transferred from NADH to oxygen causes 6 protons to be translocated from the inside to the outside of the mitochondrial membrane. NADH first donates one proton and 2 electrons, which, together with another proton from the internal medium, reduce FMN to $FMNH_2$. FMN is part of a large protein complex that is considered to extend the full width of the membrane, enabling it to release 2 protons to the outside of the membrane and then to return 2 electrons to the inside surface via FeS proteins, which become reduced. Each reduced FeS complex donates one electron to an ubiquinone (Q) molecule which, upon taking up a proton from inside the membrane, forms QH_2. Being lipid-soluble and a small molecule, QH_2 is free to move to the outside of the membrane, where it discharges a proton pair into the cytosol and donates 2 electrons to 2 molecules of

the next carrier in the respiratory chain, cytochrome b. This electron carrier is thought to span the mitochondrial membrane (as cytochromes b_{566} and b_{562}), enabling the electrons to join another molecule of ubiquinone together with 2 more protons from the internal medium. The resulting QH_2 shuttles to the outer surface, where 2 protons are liberated and 2 electrons passed to 2 molecules of cytochrome c. The more recently proposed "Q" cycle, for which there is convincing evidence, obviates the necessity of QH_2 operating the H-transporting limbs of 2 separate o/r loops. The electrons then pass through the remainder of the cytochrome chain, traversing the membrane to cytochrome a_3, which lies on the inside of the membrane. At this site, 2 electrons combine with two H^+ from the internal medium and an oxygen atom to form water.

The inner membrane contains the enzyme proteins of the respiratory chain arranged in a sided manner as indicated in Fig 12-22. Scattered over the surface of the inner membrane are the phosphorylating subunits responsible for the production of ATP (Fig 12-23). These consist of several proteins, collectively known as an F_i subunit, which project into the matrix and which contain the ATP synthetase (Fig 12-20). These subunits are attached, possibly by a stalk, to a membrane protein subunit known as F_o, which probably extends through the membrane (Fig 12-20). For

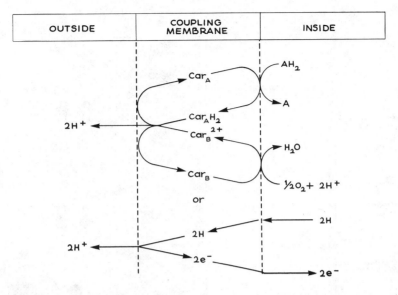

Figure 12–21. Proton-translocating oxidation/reduction (o/r) loop (chemiosmotic theory).

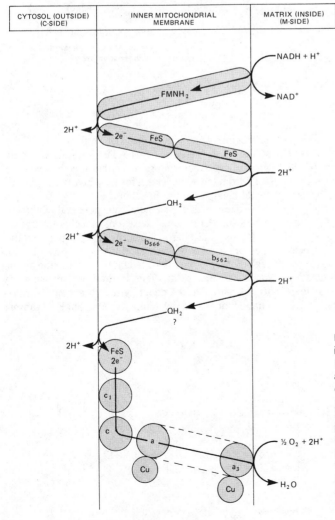

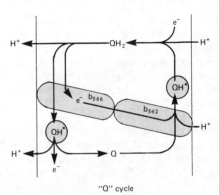

"Q" cycle

Figure 12–22. Possible configuration of o/r loops in the respiratory chain (chemiosmotic theory). Much of this scheme is still tentative, particularly around the Q/cytochrome b region, where the exact nature and relative positions of the intermediates are not known with certainty. It is possible that the semiquinone (QH·) is involved in a protonmotive "Q" cycle as indicated on the right, QH· being anchored on each side of the membrane by attachment to a Q-binding protein, whereas QH_2 and Q are mobile. Cytochromes are shown respectively as b, c_1, c, a, and a_3. (The last is part of cytochrome aa_3, which traverses the membrane.) FeS, iron-sulfur protein.

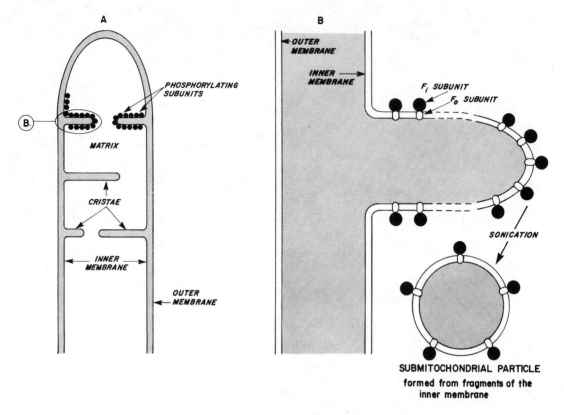

Figure 12–23. Structure of the mitochondrial membranes.

every proton pair passing through the F_o–F_i complex, one ATP molecule is formed from ADP and P_i. It is of interest that similar phosphorylating units are found inside the plasma membrane of bacteria but outside the thylakoid membrane of chloroplasts. It is significant that the proton gradient is from outside to inside in mitochondria and bacteria but in the reverse direction in chloroplasts.

The mechanism of coupling of proton translocation to the anisotropic (vectorial) ATP synthetase system is conjectural. One model suggested by Mitchell is shown in Fig 12–24. A proton pair attacks one oxygen of P_i to form H_2O and an active form of P_i, which immediately combines with ADP to form ATP. Other studies have suggested that ATP synthesis is not the main energy-requiring step—rather it is the release of ATP from the active site. This may involve conformational changes in the F_i subunit.

The existence of a membrane potential required to synthesize ATP would cause ions of a charge opposite to the internal phase to leak in through the coupling membrane. To prevent swelling and lysis, the ion leakage would have to be balanced by extrusion of ions against the electric gradient. It was therefore necessary to postulate that the coupling membrane contains exchange diffusion systems for exchange of anions

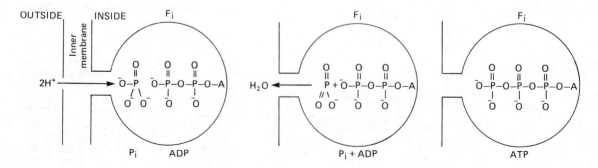

Figure 12–24. Proton-translocating ATP synthetase (Mitchell).

against OH⁻ ions and of cations against H⁺ ions. Such systems would be necessary for uptake of ionized metabolites through the membrane.

The chemiosmotic theory can account for the phenomenon of respiratory control. The electrochemical potential difference across the membrane, once built up as a result of proton translocation, would inhibit further transport of reducing equivalents through the o/r loops unless it was discharged by back-translocation of protons across the membrane through the vectorial ATP synthetase system. This in turn depends on the availability of ADP and P$_i$.

Several corollaries arise from the chemiosmotic theory that have experimental support. These are as follows:

(1) Mitochondria are generally impermeable to protons and other ions. There is, however, evidence for the existence of specific transport systems that enable ions to penetrate the inner mitochondrial membrane.

(2) Uncouplers such as dinitrophenol are amphipathic (see p 206) and increase the permeability of mitochondria to protons, thus reducing the electrochemical potential and short-circuiting the anisotropic ATP synthetase system for the generation of ATP (Fig 12–20).

(3) Addition of acid to the external medium, establishing a proton gradient, leads to the generation of ATP.

(4) The P/H⁺(transported out) quotient of the ATP synthetase is 1/2, and the H⁺ (transported out)/O quotients for succinate and 3-hydroxybutyrate oxidation are 4 and 6, respectively, conforming with the expected P/O ratios of 2 and 3, respectively. These ratios are compatible with the postulated existence of 3 o/r loops in the respiratory chain.

(5) Oxidative phosphorylation does not occur in soluble systems, where there is no possibility of a vectorial ATP synthetase. Some structural element involving a closed membrane must be present in the system in order to obtain oxidative phosphorylation.

The respiratory chain does contain components organized in a sided manner (transverse asymmetry) as required by the chemiosmotic theory (Fig 12–22).

Mitochondrial Membranes

Mitochondria have an outer membrane that is permeable to most metabolites, an inner membrane which is selectively permeable and which is thrown into folds or cristae, and a matrix within the inner membrane (Fig 12–23). The outer membrane may be removed by treatment with digitonin and is characterized by the presence of monoamine oxidase and a few other enzymes (eg, acyl-CoA synthetase, glycerophosphate acyltransferase, monoacyl glycerophosphate acyltransferase, phospholipase A$_2$). Adenylate kinase and creatine kinase are found in the intermembrane space. Cardiolipin is concentrated in the inner membrane, where most of the lipid is phospholipid. The exact relationship of the lipid to the protein of the membranes is not understood. Delipidation of the inner membrane does not lead to its disruption.

Sonication of the inner mitochondrial membrane leads to the formation of vesicles (submitochondrial particles) that are "inside-out," as it were, so that the phosphorylating units are located on the outside rather than on the inside of the membrane (Fig 12–23). Studies on submitochondrial particles have been useful in determining the properties of the inner surface of the inner mitochondrial membrane.

The soluble enzymes of the citric acid cycle and the enzymes of β-oxidation of fatty acids are found in the matrix, necessitating mechanisms for transporting ions and fatty and other organic acids, as well as nucleotides, across the inner membrane. Succinate dehydrogenase is found on the inner surface of the inner mitochondrial membrane, where it transports reducing equivalents into the respiratory chain at ubiquinone, bypassing the first o/r loop. 3-Hydroxybutyrate dehydrogenase is also bound to the matrix side of the inner mitochondrial membrane. Glycerol 3-phosphate dehydrogenase is found on the outer surface of the inner membrane, where it is suitably located to participate in the glycerophosphate shuttle (Fig 12–25).

TRANSPORT OF SUBSTANCES INTO & OUT OF MITOCHONDRIA

Oxidation of Extramitochondrial NADH

Although NADH cannot penetrate the mitochondrial membrane, it is produced continuously in the cytosol by 3-phosphoglyceraldehyde dehydrogenase,

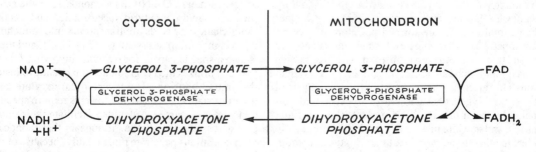

Figure 12–25. Glycerophosphate shuttle for transfer of reducing equivalents from the cytosol into the mitochondrion.

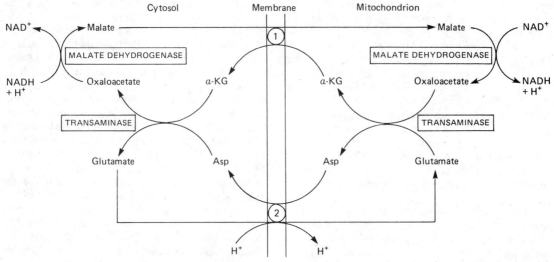

Figure 12–26. Malate shuttle for transfer of reducing equivalents from the cytosol into the mitochondrion. ① , ketoglutarate transporter; ② , glutamate-aspartate transporter (note the proton symport).

an enzyme in the Embden-Meyerhof glycolysis sequence (p 168). However, under aerobic conditions, extramitochondrial NADH does not accumulate and is presumed to be oxidized by the respiratory chain in mitochondria. Several possible mechanisms have been considered to permit this process. These involve transfer of reducing equivalents through the mitochondrial membrane via substrate pairs, linked by suitable dehydrogenases. Substrate pairs that have been considered include acetoacetate/3-hydroxybutyrate, lactate/pyruvate, dihydroxyacetone phosphate/glycerol 3-phosphate, and malate/oxaloacetate. It is necessary that the specific dehydrogenase be present on both sides of the mitochondrial membrane. However, 3-hydroxybutyrate dehydrogenase is found only in mitochondria and lactate dehydrogenase only in the cytosol, ruling out these substrate pairs. Glycerol 3-phosphate dehydrogenase is NAD-linked in the cytosol, whereas the enzyme found in the mitochondria is a flavoprotein enzyme. In some species, the activity of the latter enzyme decreases after thyroidectomy and increases after administration of thyroxine. The mechanism of transfer using this system is shown in Fig 12–25. It is to be noted that since the mitochondrial enzyme is linked to the respiratory chain via a flavoprotein rather than NAD, only 2 rather than 3 mol of ATP are formed per atom of oxygen consumed. Thus, if more reducing equivalents are passed through the **glycerophosphate shuttle,** oxygen consumption must increase to maintain ATP production. This mechanism may account for at least part of the extra oxygen consumption of hyperthyroid animals. Although this shuttle is present in insect flight muscle and in white muscle and might be important in liver, in other tissues (eg, heart muscle) the mitochondrial glycerol 3-phosphate dehydrogenase is deficient. It is therefore believed that a transport system involv-

ing malate and malate dehydrogenase is of more universal utility. The malate "shuttle" system is shown in Fig 12–26. The complexity of this system is due to the impermeability of the mitochondrial membrane to oxaloacetate. However, even the other anions are not freely permeable, requiring specific transport systems for passage across the membrane.

Energy-Linked Ion Transport in Mitochondria

Actively respiring mitochondria in which oxidative phosphorylation is taking place maintain or accumulate cations such as K^+, Na^+, Ca^{2+}, and Mg^{2+}, and P_i. Uncoupling with dinitrophenol leads to loss of ions from the mitochondria, but the ion uptake is not inhibited by oligomycin, suggesting that the energy need not be supplied by phosphorylation of ADP. It is envisaged that a primary proton pump drives cation exchange.

Mitochondrial Transporter Systems
(Fig 12–27)

The inner bilipoid mitochondrial membrane is freely permeable to uncharged small molecules such as oxygen, water, CO_2, NH_3, and monocarboxylic acids such as 3-hydroxybutyric, acetoacetic, and acetic. Long-chain fatty acids are transported into mitochondria via the carnitine system (see Fig 17–2), and there is also a special carrier for pyruvate involving a symport that utilizes the H^+ gradient from outside to inside the mitochondrion. However, dicarboxylate and tricarboxylate anions and amino acids require specific transporter or carrier systems to facilitate their transport across the membrane. It appears that monocarboxylate anions penetrate more readily, because of the lesser degree of dissociation of these acids. It is the undissociated and more lipid-soluble acid that is

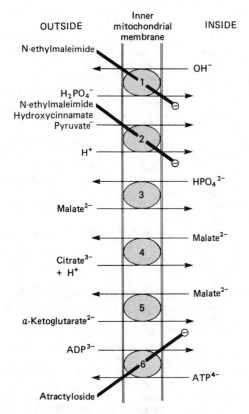

Figure 12–27. Transporter systems in the mitochondrial membrane. 1. Phosphate transporter. 2. Pyruvate symport. 3. Dicarboxylate transporter. 4. Tricarboxylate transporter. 5. α-Ketoglutarate transporter. 6. Adenine nucleotide transporter. N-ethylmaleimide, hydroxycinnamate, and atractyloside inhibit (⊖) the indicated systems. Also present (but not shown) are transporter systems for glutamate/aspartate (Fig 12–26), glutamine, ornithine, and carnitine (Fig 17–2).

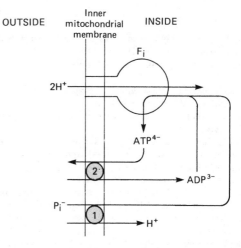

Figure 12–28. Combination of phosphate transporter ① with the adenine nucleotide transporter ② in ATP synthesis. The H^+/P_i symport shown is equivalent to the P_i/OH^- antiport shown in Fig 12–27. Three protons are taken into the mitochondrion for each ATP exported. However, only 2 protons are taken in when ATP is used inside the mitochondrion. This model conforms with a stoichiometry of 3 protons transported per electron pair at each coupling site instead of 2 protons (Cross), or it agrees with the original Mitchell hypothesis (Fig 12–22) of 2 protons per electron pair at each coupling site and revised values for the P/O ratio of 2 for NADH-linked oxidations and 1.3 for succinate oxidation (Hinkle).

thought to be the molecular species that penetrates the lipid membrane.

The transport of di- and tricarboxylate anions is closely linked to that of inorganic phosphate, which penetrates readily as the $H_2PO_4^-$ ion in exchange for OH^-. The net uptake of malate by the dicarboxylate transporter requires inorganic phosphate for exchange in the opposite direction. The net uptake of citrate, isocitrate, or cis-aconitate by the tricarboxylate transporter requires malate in exchange. α-Ketoglutarate transport also requires an exchange with malate. Thus, by the use of exchange mechanisms, osmotic balance is maintained. It will be appreciated that citrate transport across the mitochondrial membrane depends not only on malate transport but on the transport of inorganic phosphate as well. The adenine nucleotide transporter allows the exchange of ATP and ADP but not AMP. It is inhibited by the poison atractyloside. Na^+

can be exchanged for H^+, driven by the proton gradient. It is believed that active uptake of Ca^{2+} by mitochondria is facilitated by the membrane potential and that it occurs with a net charge transfer of 1 (Ca^+ uniport), possibly through a Ca^{2+}/H^+ antiport. Calcium release from mitochondria is facilitated by exchange with Na^+.

Action of Ionophores

These substances are so termed because of their ability to complex specific cations and thus to facilitate cation transport through biologic membranes (see Fig 32–17). This property of ionophoresis is due to their lipophilic character, which allows penetration of lipoid membranes such as the mitochondrial membrane. An example is the antibiotic **valinomycin,** which allows penetration of K^+ through the mitochondrial membrane and then discharges the membrane potential between the inside and the outside of the mitochondrion. **Nigericin** also acts as an ionophore for K^+ but in exchange for H^+. It therefore abolishes the pH gradient across the membrane. In the presence of both valinomycin and nigericin, both the membrane potential and the pH gradient are eliminated, and phosphorylation is therefore completely inhibited. The classic uncouplers such as dinitrophenol are, in fact, proton ionophores.

• • •

References

Amzel LM, Pedersen PL: Proton ATPases: Structure and mechanism. *Annu Rev Biochem* 1983;**52**:801.

Bonnett R: Oxygen activation and tetrapyrroles. *Essays Biochem* 1981;**17**:1.

Boyd GS, Smellie RMS (editors): *Biological Hydroxylation Mechanisms.* Academic Press, 1972.

Crane FL: Hydroquinone dehydrogenases. *Annu Rev Biochem* 1977;**46**:439.

Cross RL: The mechanism and regulation of ATP synthesis by F$_i$-ATPases. *Annu Rev Biochem* 1981;**50**:681.

DePierre JW, Ernster L: Enzyme topology of intracellular membranes. *Annu Rev Biochem* 1977;**46**:201.

Fleisher S, Packer L (editors): Biological oxidations, microsomal, cytochrome P-450, and other hemoprotein systems. In: *Methods in Enzymology.* Vol 52. Biomembranes, part C. Academic Press, 1978.

Friedovich I: Superoxide dismutases. *Annu Rev Biochem* 1975; **44**:147.

Gunsalus IC, Pederson TC, Sligar SG: Oxygenase-catalyzed biological hydroxylations. *Annu Rev Biochem* 1975;**44**:377.

Harper HA, Rodwell VW, Mayes PA: Page 276 in: *Review of Physiological Chemistry,* 17th ed. Lange, 1979.

Hayaishi O (editor): *Oxygenases.* Academic Press, 1972.

Hinkle PC, McCarty RE: How cells make ATP. *Sci Am* (March) 1978;**238**:104.

Hinkle PC, Yu ML: The phosphorus/oxygen ratio of mitochondrial oxidative phosphorylation. *J Biol Chem* 1979;**254**:2450.

LaNoue KF, Schoolwerth AC: Metabolite transport in mitochondria. *Annu Rev Biochem* 1979;**48**:871.

Lemberg R, Barrett J: *Cytochromes.* Academic Press, 1973.

Mitchell P: *Chemiosmotic Coupling and Energy Transduction.* Glynn Research, Bodmin, United Kingdom, 1968.

Mitchell P: Keilin's respiratory chain concept and its chemiosmotic consequences. *Science* 1979;**206**:1148.

Nicholls DG: *Bioenergetics: An Introduction to the Chemiosmotic Theory.* Academic Press, 1982.

Racker E: From Pasteur to Mitchell: A hundred years of bioenergetics. *Fed Proc* 1980;**39**:210.

Salemme FR: Structure and function of cytochromes c. *Annu Rev Biochem* 1977;**46**:299.

Schenkman JB, Jansson I, Robie-Suh KM: The many roles of cytochrome b$_5$ in hepatic microsomes. *Life Sci* 1976;**19**:611.

Singer TP (editor): *Biological Oxidations.* Interscience, 1968.

Sund H (editor): *Pyridine Nucleotide Dependent Dehydrogenases.* Springer, 1970.

Tolbert NE: Metabolic pathways in peroxisomes and glyoxysomes. *Annu Rev Biochem* 1981;**50**:133.

Tyler DD: The mitochondrial ATP synthase. Page 117 in: *Membrane Structure and Function.* Vol 5. Bittar EE (editor). Wiley, 1984.

Tyler DD, Sutton CM: Mitochondrial transporting systems. Page 181 in: *Membrane Structure and Function.* Vol 5. Bittar EE (editor). Wiley, 1984.

Tyler DD, Sutton CM: Respiratory enzyme systems in mitochondrial membranes. Page 33 in: *Membrane Structure and Function.* Vol 5. Bittar EE (editor). Wiley, 1984.

White RE, Coon MJ: Oxygen activation by cytochrome P-450. *Annu Rev Biochem* 1980;**49**:315.

Wickström M, Krab K, Saraste M: Proton-translocating cytochrome complexes. *Annu Rev Biochem* 1981;**50**:623.

Carbohydrates | 13

Peter A. Mayes, PhD, DSc

The carbohydrates are widely distributed both in animal and in plant tissues. In plants, they are produced by photosynthesis and include the cellulose of the plant framework as well as the starch of the plant cells. In animal tissues, carbohydrate in the form of glucose and glycogen serves as an important source of energy for vital activities. Some carbohydrates have highly specific functions (eg, ribose in the nucleic acids of the cells, galactose in certain lipids, and the mannose of glycoproteins).

Carbohydrates may be defined chemically as aldehyde or ketone derivatives of the polyhydric (more than one OH group) alcohols or as compounds that yield these derivatives on hydrolysis.

Classification

(1) **Monosaccharides** (often called "simple sugars") are those carbohydrates that cannot be hydrolyzed into a simpler form. They may be subdivided into **trioses, tetroses, pentoses, hexoses, heptoses, or octoses,** depending upon the number of carbon atoms they possess; and as **aldoses** or **ketoses,** depending upon whether the aldehyde or ketone group is present. Examples are

		Aldoses	Ketoses
Trioses	$(C_3H_6O_3)$	Glycerose	Dihydroxyacetone
Tetroses	$(C_4H_8O_4)$	Erythrose	Erythrulose
Pentoses	$(C_5H_{10}O_5)$	Ribose	Ribulose
Hexoses	$(C_6H_{12}O_6)$	Glucose	Fructose

(2) **Disaccharides** yield 2 molecules of the same or of different monosaccharide(s) when hydrolyzed. Examples are sucrose, lactose, and maltose.

(3) **Oligosaccharides** yield 3–6 monosaccharide units on hydrolysis. Maltotriose* is an example.

(4) **Polysaccharides** yield more than 6 molecules of monosaccharides on hydrolysis. Examples of polysaccharides, which may be linear or branched, are the starches and dextrins. These are sometimes designated as hexosans, pentosans, homopolysaccharides, or heteropolysaccharides depending upon the identity of the monosaccharides they yield on hydrolysis.

Structure of Glucose

Glucose is the principal sugar in blood, serving

*Note that this is not a true triose but a trisaccharide containing 3 α-glucose residues.

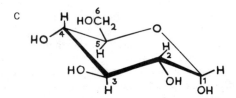

A

B

C

Figure 13–1. α-D-glucose.

the tissues as a major metabolic fuel. Although the straight chain structural formula (aldohexose, Fig 13–1[A]) can account for some of its properties, a cyclic structure is favored on thermodynamic grounds and accounts completely for its chemical properties. For most purposes, the structural formula may be represented as a simple ring in perspective as proposed by Haworth (Fig 13–1[B]). X-ray diffraction analysis shows that the 6-membered ring containing one oxygen atom is actually in the form of a chair (Fig 13–1[C]).

Isomerism

Compounds that have the same structural formula but differ in spatial configuration are known as **stereoisomers.** The presence of asymmetric carbon atoms (carbon atoms attached to 4 different atoms or groups) allows the formation of isomers. The number of possible isomers of a compound depends on the

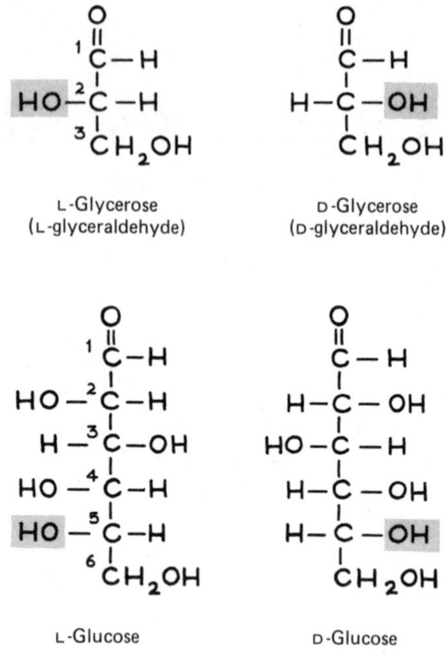

L-Glycerose
(L-glyceraldehyde)

D-Glycerose
(D-glyceraldehyde)

Pyran

Furan

L-Glucose

D-Glucose

Figure 13–2. D- and L-isomerism of glycerose and glucose.

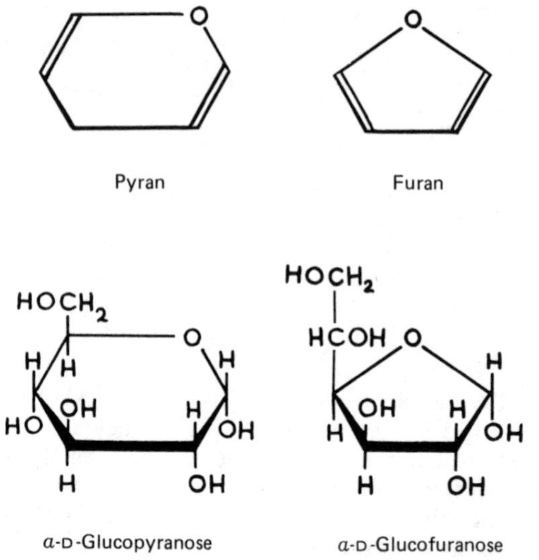

a-D-Glucopyranose

a-D-Glucofuranose

Figure 13–3. Pyranose and furanose forms of glucose.

number of asymmetric carbon atoms (n) and is equal to 2^n. Glucose, with 4 asymmetric carbon atoms, therefore has 16 isomers. The more important types of isomerism found with glucose are as follows:

(1) **D and L:** The designation of an isomer as D- or of its mirror image as the L- form is determined by its spatial relationship to the parent compound of the carbohydrate family, the 3-carbon sugar glycerose. The L and D forms of this sugar are shown in Fig 13–2 together with the corresponding isomers of glucose. The orientation of the H and OH groups around the carbon atom **adjacent** to the terminal primary alcohol carbon (eg, carbon atom 5 in glucose) determines whether the sugar belongs to the D or L series. When the OH group on this carbon is on the right (as seen in Fig 13–2), the sugar is a member of the D series; when it is on the left, it is a member of the L series. Most of the monosaccharides occurring in mammalian metabolism are of the D configuration.

The presence of asymmetric carbon atoms also confers **optical activity** on the compound. When a beam of plane-polarized light is passed through a solution of an **optical isomer**, it will be rotated either to the right, dextrorotatory (+), or to the left, levorotatory (−). A compound may be designated D(−), D(+), L(−), or L(+), indicating structural relationship to D or L glycerose but not necessarily exhibiting the same optical rotation. For example, the naturally occurring form of fructose is the D(−) isomer.

When equal amounts of D and L isomers are present, the resulting mixture has no optical activity, since the activities of each isomer cancel one another. Such a mixture is said to be a **racemic,** or DL, mixture. Synthetically produced compounds are necessarily

racemic because the opportunities for the formation of each optical isomer are identical.

(2) **Pyranose and Furanose Ring Structures:** On the basis of the ring structures known to exist in glycosides (see below), Haworth proposed similar structures for the sugars. The terminology was based on the fact that the stable ring structures of monosaccharides are similar to the ring structures of either pyran or furan (Fig 13–3). Ketoses may also show ring formation (eg, D-fructofuranose or D-fructopyranose) (Fig 13–4). In the case of glucose in solution, more than 99% is in the pyranose form; thus, less than 1% is in the furanose form.

(3) **α and β Anomers:** The ring structure of an aldose is a hemiacetal, since it is formed by combina-

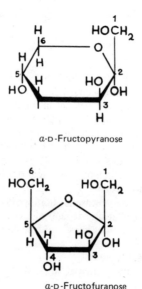

a-D-Fructopyranose

a-D-Fructofuranose

Figure 13–4. Pyranose and furanose forms of fructose.

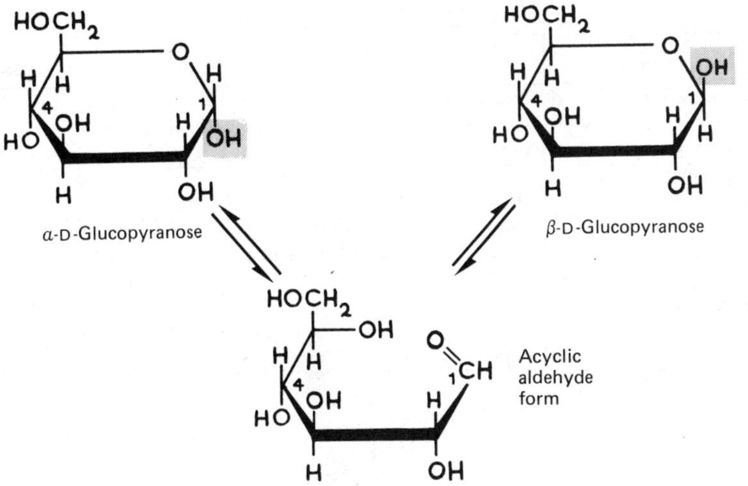

Figure 13–5. Mutarotation of glucose.

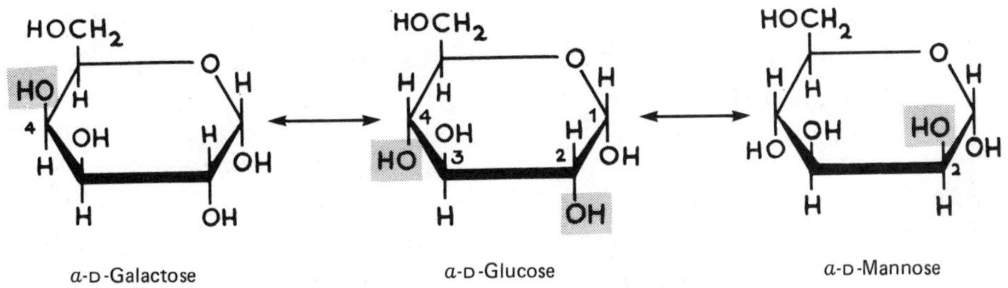

Figure 13–6. Epimerization of glucose.

tion of an aldehyde and an alcohol group (Fig 13–5). Similarly, the ring structure of a ketose is a hemiketal. Crystalline glucose is α-D-glucopyranose. The cyclic structure is retained in solution, but isomerism takes place about position 1, the carbonyl or anomeric carbon atom, to give a mixture of α-glucopyranose (36%) and β-glucopyranose (63%), the remaining 1% represented mainly by α- and β-isomers of glucofuranose. This equilibration is accompanied by optical rotation (**mutarotation**) as the hemiacetal ring opens and reforms with change of position of the –H and –OH groups on carbon 1. The change probably takes place via a hydrated straight-chain acyclic molecule, although polarography has indicated that glucose exists only to the extent of 0.0025% in the acyclic form.

(4) **Epimers:** Isomers differing as a result of variations in configuration of the –OH and –H on carbon atoms 2, 3, and 4 of glucose are known as epimers. Biologically, the most important epimers of glucose are mannose and galactose, formed by epimerization at carbons 2 and 4, respectively (Fig 13–6).

(5) **Aldose-Ketose Isomerism:** Fructose has the same molecular formula as glucose but differs in its structural formula, since there is a potential keto group in position 2, whereas there is a potential aldehyde group in position 1 of glucose (Figs 13–3 and 13–4).

MONOSACCHARIDES

The monosaccharides include trioses, tetroses, pentoses, hexoses, heptoses, and octoses (3, 4, 5, 6, 7, 8 carbon atoms). Derivatives of trioses are formed in the course of the metabolic breakdown of glucose by the glycolysis pathway, while derivatives of trioses, tetroses, pentoses, of a 7-carbon sugar, sedoheptulose, and of an 8-carbon sugar, glycero-ido octulose, are formed in the breakdown of glucose via the hexose monophosphate shunt. Pentose sugars are important constituents of nucleotides, nucleic acids, and many coenzymes (Table 13–1). Of the hexoses, glucose, galactose, fructose, and mannose are physiologically the most important (Table 13–2).

The structures of the aldo sugars of biochemical significance are shown in Fig 13–7. Five keto sugars which are important in metabolism are shown in Fig 13–8.

HEXOSES

The hexoses are most important physiologically (Table 13–2). Examples are D-glucose, D-fructose, D-galactose, and D-mannose. Of additional signifi-

Table 13—1. Examples of pentoses.

Sugar	Where Found	Importance	Reactions
D-Ribose	Nucleic acids.	Structural elements of nucleic acids and coenzymes, eg, ATP, NAD, NADP, flavoproteins.	Reduces Benedict's, Fehling's, Barfoed's, and Haynes' solutions. Forms distinctive osazones with phenylhydrazine.
D-Ribulose	Formed in metabolic processes.	Intermediates in hexose monophosphate shunt.	
D-Arabinose	Gum arabic. Plum and cherry gums.	These sugars are used in studies of bacterial metabolism, as in fermentation tests for identification of bacteria.	With orcinol-HCl reagent gives colors: violet, blue, red, and green.
D-Xylose	Wood gums, proteoglycans, glycosaminoglycans.		With phloroglucinol-HCl gives a red color.
D-Lyxose	Heart muscle.	A constituent of a lyxoflavin isolated from human heart muscle.	

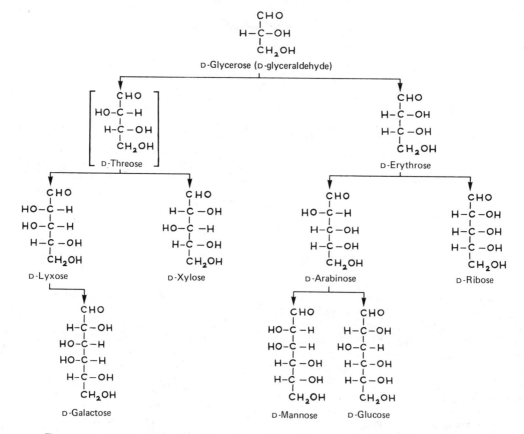

Figure 13–7. The structural relations of the aldoses, D series. D-Threose is not of physiologic significance. The series is built up by the theoretical addition of a CH_2O unit to the —CHO group of the sugar.

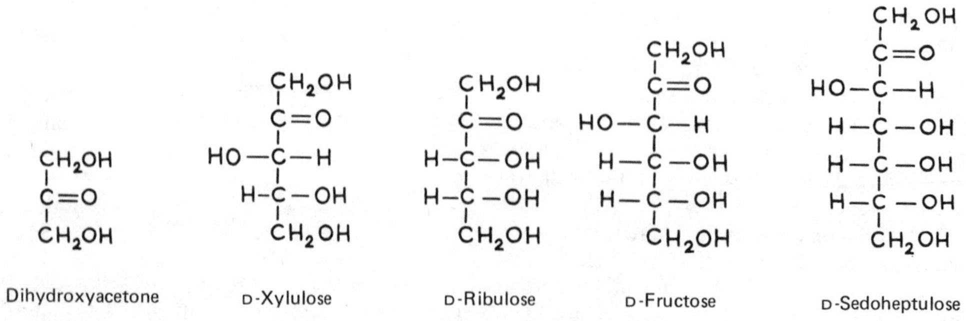

Figure 13–8. Examples of ketoses.

Table 13–2. Hexoses of physiologic importance.

Sugar	Source	Importance	Reactions
D-Glucose	Fruit juices. Hydrolysis of starch, cane sugar, maltose, and lactose.	The "sugar" of the body. The sugar carried by the blood, and the principal one used by the tissues. Glucose is usually the "sugar" of the urine when glycosuria occurs.	Reduces Benedict's, Haynes', Barfoed's reagents (a reducing sugar). Gives osazone with phenylhydrazine. Fermented by yeast. With HNO_3, forms soluble saccharic acid.
D-Fructose	Fruit juices. Honey. Hydrolysis of cane sugar and of inulin (from the Jerusalem artichoke).	Can be changed to glucose in the liver and intestine and so used in the body.	Reduces Benedict's, Haynes', Barfoed's reagents (a reducing sugar). Forms osazone identical with that of glucose. Fermented by yeast. Cherry-red color with Seliwanoff's resorcinol-HCl reagent.
D-Galactose	Hydrolysis of lactose.	Can be changed to glucose in the liver and metabolized. Synthesized in the mammary gland to make the lactose of milk. A constituent of glycolipids and glycoproteins.	Reduces Benedict's, Haynes', Barfoed's reagents (a reducing sugar). Forms osazone, distinct from above. Phloroglucinol-HCl reagent gives red color. With HNO_3, forms insoluble mucic acid. Not fermented by yeast.
D-Mannose	Hydrolysis of plant mannans and gums.	A constituent of prosthetic polysaccharide of albumins, globulins, mucoproteins. A sugar frequently occurring in glycoproteins.	Reduces Benedict's, Haynes', Barfoed's reagents (a reducing sugar). Forms same osazone as glucose.

cance are carboxylic acid derivatives of glucose such as D-glucuronate (important in glucuronide formation and present in glycosaminoglycans) and its metabolic derivatives, L-iduronate (present in glycosaminoglycans) (Fig 13–9) and L-gulonate (a member of the uronic acid pathway; see p 188).

GLYCOSIDES

Glycosides are compounds formed from a condensation between a monosaccharide, or monosaccharide residue, and the hydroxyl group of a second compound that may, or may not (in the case of an **aglycone**), be another monosaccharide. The **glycosidic bond** is an **acetal** link, because it results from a reaction between a hemiacetal group (formed from an aldehyde and an –OH group) and another –OH group. If the hemiacetal portion is glucose, the resulting compound is a **glucoside;** if galactose, a **galactoside,** etc.

A simple example is the methyl glucoside formed when a solution of glucose in boiling methyl alcohol is treated with 0.5% hydrogen chloride as a catalyst. The

reaction proceeds with the formation of anomeric α- and β-glucosides (Fig 13–10).

Glycosides are found in many drugs and spices and in the constituents of animal tissues. The aglycone may be methanol, glycerol, a sterol, or a phenol. The glycosides which are important in medicine because of their action on the heart (**cardiac glycosides**) all contain steroids as the aglycone component. These include derivatives of digitalis and strophanthus such as ouabain, an inhibitor of the Na^+/K^+-ATPase of cell membranes. Other glycosides include antibiotics such as streptomycin (Fig 13–11).

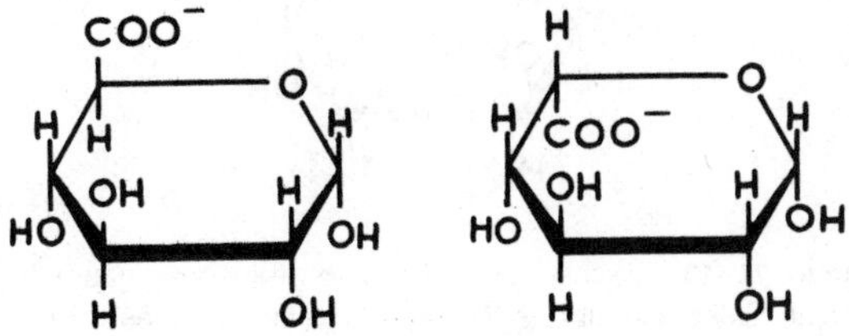

DEOXY SUGARS

Deoxy sugars are those in which a hydroxyl group attached to the ring structure has been replaced by a hydrogen atom. They are obtained on hydrolysis of certain substances that are important in biologic processes. An example is the deoxyribose (Fig 13–12) occurring in nucleic acids (DNA).

Also found as a carbohydrate of glycoproteins is L-fucose (see p 156), and of importance as an inhibitor of glucose metabolism is 2-deoxyglucose.

AMINO SUGARS (HEXOSAMINES)

Sugars containing an amino group are called **amino sugars.** Examples are D-glucosamine (Fig 13–13), D-galactosamine, and D-mannosamine, all of which have been identified in nature. Glucosamine is a constituent of hyaluronic acid. Galactosamine (chondrosamine) is a constituent of chondroitin. (See Chapter 33.)

Several antibiotics (erythromycin, carbomycin) contain amino sugars. Erythromycin contains a dimethylamino sugar. Carbomycin contains the first

Figure 13–9. α-D-Glucuronate *(left)* and β-L-Iduronate *(right)*.

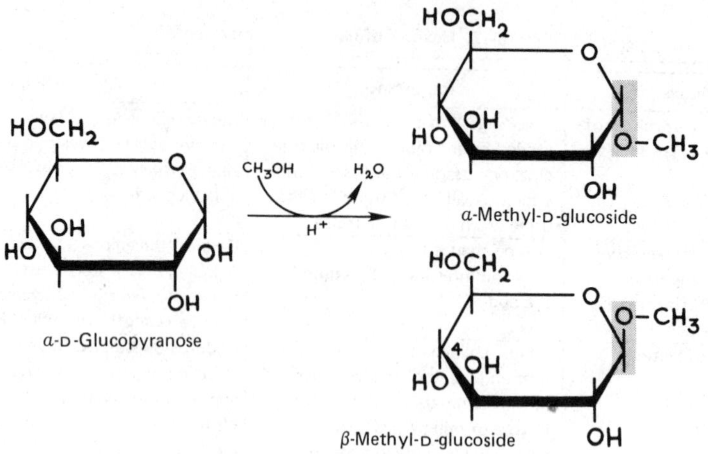

Figure 13–10. Formation of methyl glucosides.

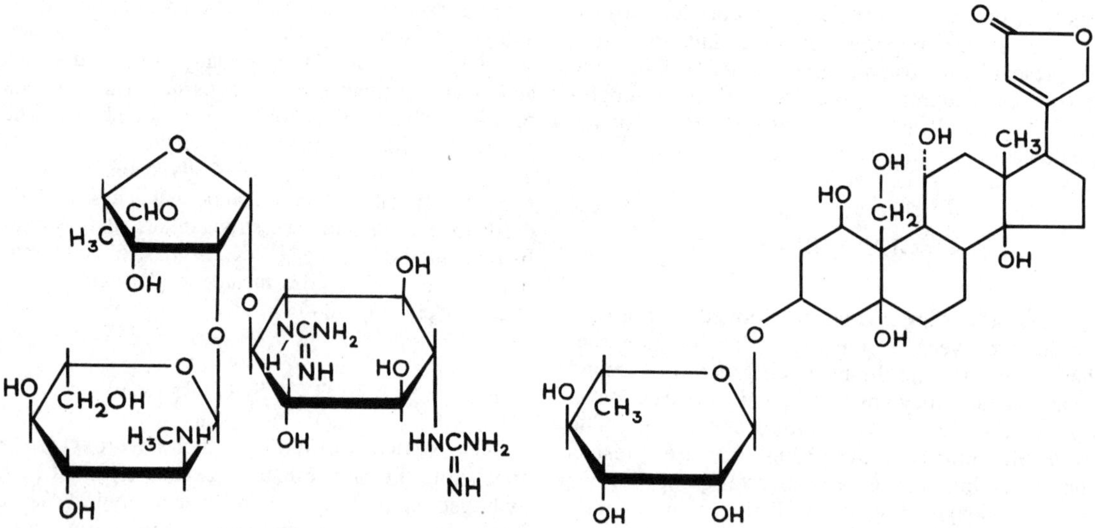

Figure 13–11. Streptomycin *(left)* and ouabain *(right).*

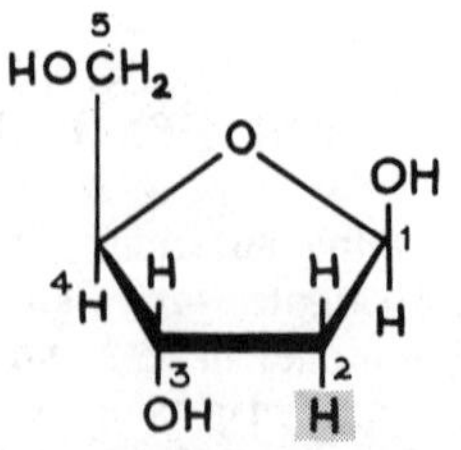

Figure 13–12. 2-Deoxy-D-ribofuranose (β form).

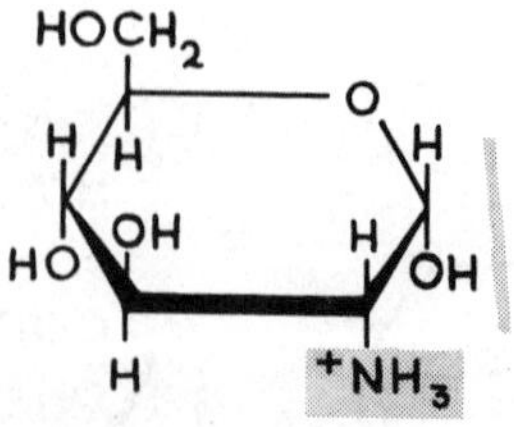

Figure 13–13. Glucosamine (2-amino-D-glucopyranose) (α form). Galactosamine is 2-amino-D-galactopyranose. Both glucosamine and galactosamine often occur as N-acetyl derivatives in more complex carbohydrates, eg, glycoproteins (see Fig 13–20).

MALTOSE

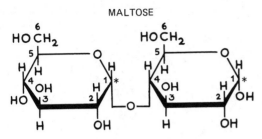

O-α-D-Glucopyranosyl-(1→4)-α-D-glucopyranose

TREHALOSE

O-α-D-Glucopyranosyl-(1→1)-α-D-glucopyranoside

SUCROSE

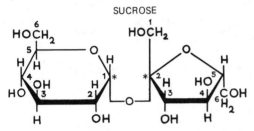

O-α-D-Glucopyranosyl-(1→2)-β-D-fructofuranoside

CELLOBIOSE

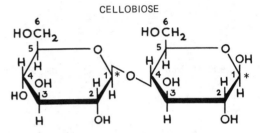

O-β-D-Glucopyranosyl-(1→4)-β-D-glucopyranose

LACTOSE

O-β-D-Galactopyranosyl-(1→4)-β-D-glucopyranose

Figure 13–14. Structures of representative disaccharides. The -α and -β refer to the configuration at the anomeric carbon atom (*). When the anomeric carbon of the second residue takes part in the formation of the glycosidic bond to form a nonreducing sugar, the residue becomes a glycoside known as a furanoside or pyranoside.

known 3-amino sugar, 3-amino-D-ribose. The amino sugars are believed to be related to the antibiotic activity of these drugs.

DISACCHARIDES

The disaccharides are sugars composed of 2 monosaccharide residues united by a glycosidic linkage (Fig 13–14). They are named chemically according to the structures of their component monosac-

charides. The suffix **-furan** or **-pyran** refers to the structural resemblances to these compounds. The physiologically important disaccharides are maltose, sucrose, lactose, and trehalose (Table 13–3).

Since sucrose has no potential carbonyl group, as the anomeric carbon atoms in both glucose and fructose residues are joined together through the acetal bond linking the 2 residues, it gives none of the reactions characteristic of "reducing" sugars. Thus, it fails to reduce alkaline copper solutions, form an

Table 13–3. Disaccharides.

Sugar	Source	Reactions
Maltose	Digestion by amylase or hydrolysis of starch. Germinating cereals and malt.	Reducing sugar. Forms osazone with phenylhydrazine. Fermentable. Hydrolyzed to D-glucose.
Lactose	Milk. May occur in urine during pregnancy.	Reducing sugar. Forms osazone with phenylhydrazine. Not fermentable by yeasts. Hydrolyzed to glucose and galactose.
Sucrose	Cane and beet sugar. Sorghum. Pineapple. Carrot roots.	Nonreducing sugar. Does not form osazone. Fermentable. Hydrolyzed to fructose and glucose.
Trehalose	Fungi and yeasts. The major sugar of insect hemolymph.	Nonreducing sugar. Does not form an osazone. Hydrolyzed to glucose.

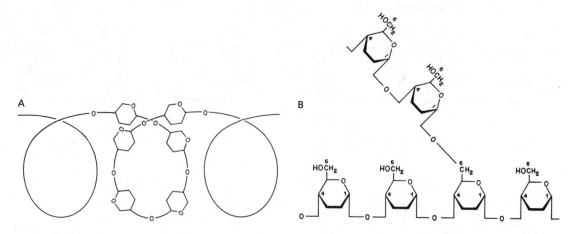

Figure 13–15. Structure of starch. *A:* Amylose, showing helical coil structure. *B:* Amylopectin, showing 1:6 branch point.

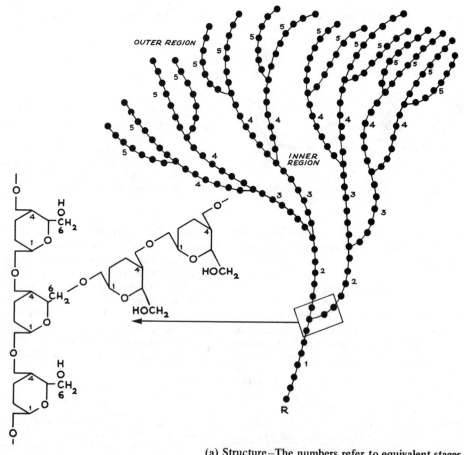

(b) Enlargement of struc-
ture at a branch point.

(a) Structure—The numbers refer to equivalent stages in
the growth of the macromolecule. R, primary glucose
residue with free reducing-CHO group (carbon No. 1).
The branching is more variable than shown, the ratio of
1,4 to 1,6 bonds being from 12 to 18.

Figure 13–16. The glycogen molecule.

osazone, or exhibit mutarotation. Hydrolysis of sucrose yields a crude mixture often called "invert sugar" because the strongly levorotatory fructose thus produced changes (inverts) the previous dextrorotatory action of the sucrose. Trehalose is also a nonreducing sugar, for similar reasons.

POLYSACCHARIDES

Polysaccharides include the following physiologically important substances:

Starch is formed of an α-glucosidic chain. Such a compound, yielding only glucose on hydrolysis, is a homopolymer called a **glucosan** or **glucan.** It is the most important food source of carbohydrate and is found in cereals, potatoes, legumes, and other vegetables. Natural starch is insoluble in water and gives a blue color with iodine solution. The microscopic form of the granules is characteristic of the source of the starch. The 2 chief constituents are **amylose** (15–20%), which is a nonbranching helical structure responsible for the color with iodine (Fig 13–15), and **amylopectin** (80–85%), which consists of branched chains that give only a red color with iodine because they do not coil effectively. Each chain is composed of 24–30 glucose residues. The glucose residues are united by 1→4 linkages in the chains and by 1→6 linkages at the branch points.

Glycogen is the storage polysaccharide of the animal body. It is often called animal starch. It is a more highly branched structure than amylopectin with chains of 11-18-α-D-glucopyranose residues (in $\alpha[1{\to}4]$-glucosidic linkage) with branching by means of $\alpha(1{\to}6)$-glucosidic bonds. Glycogen is nonreducing (but see Fig 13–16) and gives a red color with iodine.

Inulin is a starch found in tubers and roots of dahlias, artichokes, and dandelions. It is hydrolyzable to fructose, and hence it is a fructosan. No color is given when iodine is added to inulin solutions. This starch is easily soluble in warm water. It is used in physiologic investigation for determination of the rate of glomerular filtration.

Dextrins are substances formed in the course of the hydrolytic breakdown of starch. The partially digested starches are amorphous. Limit dextrins that give a red color when tested with iodine are the first formed products as hydrolysis reaches a certain degree of branching. These are called **erythrodextrins.** As hydrolysis proceeds, the iodine color is no longer produced. These are the so-called **achroodextrins.** Finally, only reducing sugars remain.

Cellulose is the chief constituent of the framework of plants. It gives no color with iodine and is not soluble in ordinary solvents. It consists of β-D-glucopyranose units linked by β (1→4) bonds to form long, straight chains strengthened by cross-linked hydrogen bonds. Cellulose cannot be digested by many mammals, including humans, because of the absence of a hydrolase that attacks the β linkage. Thus, it is an important source of "bulk" in the diet. Ruminants and other herbivores have microorganisms in their gut that can attack the β linkage, making cellulose available as a major calorigenic source.

Chitin is an important structural polysaccharide of invertebrates. It is found, for example, in the shells of crustaceans and exoskeletons of insects. Structurally, chitin consists of N-acetyl-D-glucosamine units joined by $\beta(1{\to}4)$-glucosidic linkages (Fig 13–17).

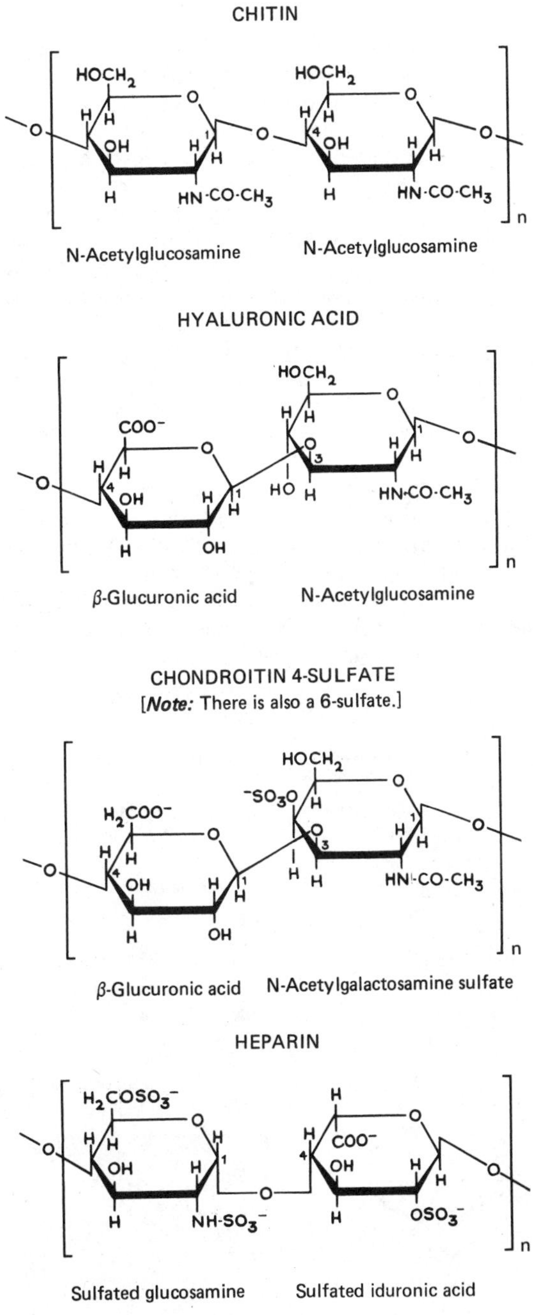

Figure 13–17. Structure of some complex polysaccharides.

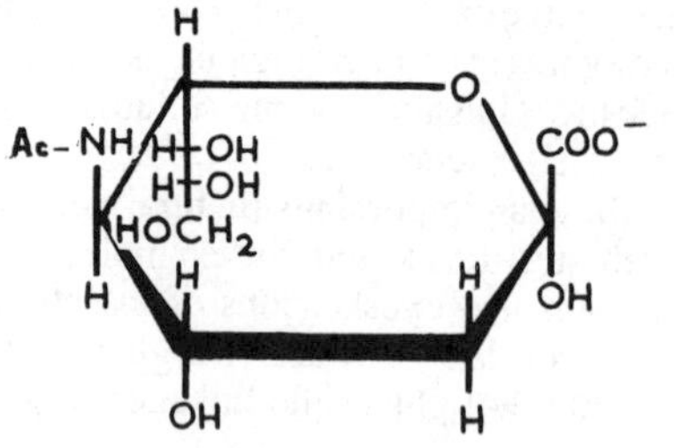

Figure 13–18. Structure of sialic acids. (Ac = CH_3 –CO– in N-acetylneuraminic acid.)

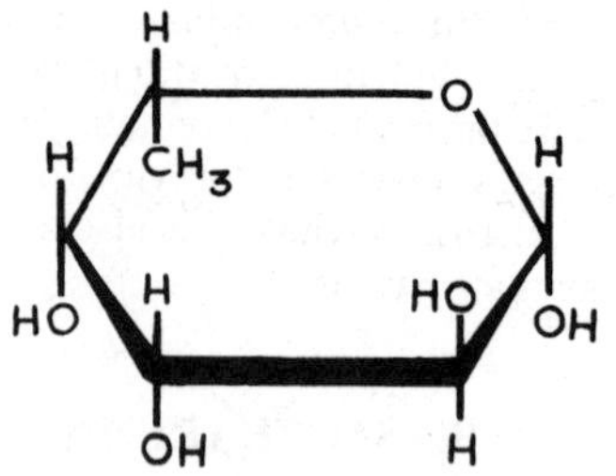

Figure 13–19. β-L-Fucose (6-deoxy-β-L-galactose).

Glycosaminoglycans (mucopolysaccharides) consist of chains of complex carbohydrates characterized by their content of amino sugars and uronic acids. When these chains are attached to a protein molecule, the compound is known as a **proteoglycan.** As the ground or packing substance, they are associated with the structural elements of the tissues such as bone, elastin, and collagen. Their property of holding large quantities of water and occupying space, thus cushioning or lubricating other structures, is assisted by the large number of –OH groups and negative charges on the molecules, which, by repulsion, keep the carbohydrate chains apart. Examples are shown in Fig 13–17, and all are discussed in detail in Chapter 33.

Glycoproteins (mucoproteins) occur in many different situations in fluids and tissues, including the cell membranes (see Chapters 32 and 33 for detailed discussions). They are proteins containing carbohydrates in varying amounts attached as short or long (up to 15 units) branched or unbranched chains. Constituent carbohydrates include

Glucose is not found in glycoproteins apart from collagen, and, in contrast to the glycosaminoglycans, uronic acids are absent.

The **sialic acids** are N-acyl derivatives of neuraminic acid. They are widely distributed in vertebrate tissues and have also been isolated from certain strains of bacteria. **N-Acetylneuraminic acid,** the structure of which is shown in Fig 13–18, is an example of a sialic acid.

Nature of Carbohydrate-Polypeptide Linkage in Glycoproteins

Fucose (Fig 13–19) and sialic acid (Fig 13–18) always occupy distal positions to the polypeptide chain, whereas acetylglucosamine and galactose are usually found nearest the protein, often forming part of the carbohydrate-protein linkage. The amino acids of glycoproteins that participate in the linkage with carbohydrate are asparagine, serine, threonine, hydroxylysine, and hydroxyproline. Two examples are shown in Fig 13–20.

Hexoses
  Mannose (Man)   Galactose (Gal)
Acetyl hexosamines
  N-Acetylglucosamine   N-Acetylgalactosamine
  (GlcNAc)   (GalNAc)
Pentoses
  Arabinose (Ara)   Xylose (Xyl)
Methyl pentose
  L-Fucose (Fuc; see Fig 13–19)
Sialic acids
  N-Acyl derivatives of neuraminic acid, eg, N-acetyl-
  neuraminic acid (Nana; see Fig 13–18).

CARBOHYDRATES OF CELL MEMBRANES

The lipid structure of the cell membrane is described in Chapters 16 and 32. However, analysis of mammalian cell membrane components indicates that approximately 5% are carbohydrates, present in glycoproteins and glycolipids. Their presence on the outer surface of the plasma membrane has been shown with the use of plant **lectins,** protein agglutinins that bind specifically with certain glycosyl residues. For

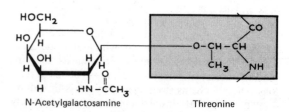

Figure 13–20. Types of linkage between carbohydrate and amino acid residues in glycoproteins.

example, **concanavalin A** has a specificity towards α-glucosyl and α-mannosyl residues.

Glycophorin is a major integral membrane glycoprotein of human erythrocytes. It has 130 amino acid residues and spans the lipid membrane, having free polypeptide portions outside both the external and internal (cytoplasmic) surfaces. Carbohydrate chains are only attached to the N-terminal portion outside the external surface, via asparagine, serine, and threonine residues (see Chapter 32).

•   •   •

References

Advances in Carbohydrate Chemistry. Academic Press, 1945–current.

Conn EE, Stumpf PK: *Outlines of Biochemistry,* 4th ed. Wiley, 1976.

Cook GMW, Stoddart RW: *Surface Carbohydrates of the Eukaryotic Cell.* Academic Press, 1973.

Davidson EA: *Carbohydrate Chemistry.* Holt, 1967.

Ferrier RJ, Collins PM: *Monosaccharide Chemistry.* Penguin Books, 1972.

Florkin M, Stotz E: *Comprehensive Biochemistry; Carbohydrates.* Section 2, vol 5. Elsevier, 1963.

Hughes RC: The complex carbohydrates of mammalian cell surfaces and their biological roles. *Essays Biochem* 1975;**11**:1.

Lindahl U, Höök M: Glycosaminoglycans and their binding to biological macromolecules. *Annu Rev Biochem* 1978;**47**:385.

McGilvery RW: *Biochemistry,* 3rd ed. Saunders, 1983.

Percival EGV, Percival E: *Structural Carbohydrate Chemistry.* Prentice-Hall, 1962.

Pigman WW, Horton D (editors): *The Carbohydrates.* Vols 1A and 1B. Academic Press, 1972.

Sharon N: Lectins. *Sci Am* (June) 1977;**236**:108.

Smith EL et al: *Principles of Biochemistry,* 7th ed. McGraw-Hill, 1983.

The Citric Acid Cycle–
The Catabolism of Acetyl-CoA

Peter A. Mayes, PhD, DSc

The citric acid cycle (Krebs cycle, tricarboxylic acid cycle) is a series of reactions in mitochondria that bring about the catabolism of acetyl residues, liberating hydrogen equivalents, which, upon oxidation, lead to the release of most of the free energy of tissue fuels. The acetyl residues are in the form of **acetyl-CoA** ($CH_3-CO \sim S-CoA$, active acetate), an ester of coenzyme A (see Chapter 10) which with other acyl thio esters of CoA is classified as a high-energy compound.

An Overview of Acetyl-CoA Metabolism

Acetyl-CoA is at the confluence of the major metabolic pathways (Fig 14–1). Nearly all carbohydrate and fat molecules form acetyl-CoA during oxidative catabolism, as do many of the amino acids resulting from the degradation of proteins. In addition, acetyl-CoA serves as the source of acetyl units in the anabolic processes responsible for the synthesis of long-chain fatty acids, cholesterol and other steroids, and ketone bodies (acetoacetate, 3-hydroxybutyrate, and acetone). These metabolic pathways will be the subjects of following chapters. The present chapter is concerned solely with the catabolism of acetyl-CoA and the role of the citric acid cycle.

SIGNIFICANCE OF THE CITRIC ACID CYCLE

Essentially, the cycle comprises the combination of a molecule of acetyl-CoA with the 4-carbon dicarboxylic acid oxaloacetate, resulting in the formation of a **6-carbon tricarboxylic acid, citrate.** There follows a series of reactions in the course of which 2 molecules of CO_2 are released and oxaloacetate is regenerated (Fig 14–2). Since only a small quantity of oxaloacetate is needed to facilitate the conversion of a large quantity of acetyl units to CO_2, oxaloacetate may be considered to play a **catalytic role.**

The major function of the cycle is to act as the final common pathway for the oxidation of carbohydrate, lipids, and protein, since glucose, fatty acids, and many amino acids are all metabolized to acetyl-CoA (Figs 14–1 and 14–3). Furthermore, the citric acid cycle is the mechanism by which much of the free energy liberated during the oxidation of carbohydrate, lipids, and amino acids is made available. During the course of oxidation of acetyl-CoA in the cycle, reducing equivalents in the form of hydrogen or of electrons are formed as a result of the activity of specific dehydrogenases. These reducing equivalents then enter the respiratory chain, where large amounts of ATP are

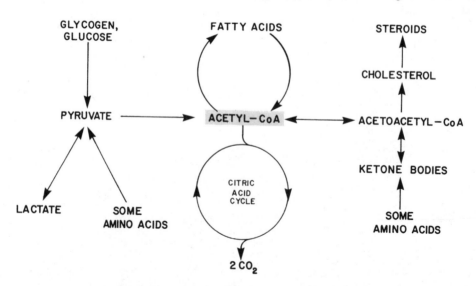

Figure 14–1. Overview of acetyl-CoA metabolism.

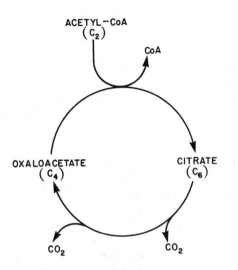

ACETYL–CoA
(C_2)

CoA

OXALOACETATE
(C_4)

CITRATE
(C_6)

CO_2 CO_2

Figure 14–2. Citric acid cycle, illustrating the catalytic role of oxaloacetate.

generated in the process of oxidative phosphorylation (Fig 14–3; see also Chapter 12).

The enzymes of the citric acid cycle are located in the **mitochondrial matrix,** either free or attached to the inner surface of the inner mitochondrial membrane, which facilitates the **transfer of reducing equivalents to the adjacent enzymes of the respiratory chain,** situated in the inner mitochondrial membrane.

It is of further significance that the citric acid cycle has a dual or **amphibolic** role, as it is a source of molecules for anabolic processes such as fatty acid and amino acid synthesis and gluconeogenesis.

Historical Aspects

By 1935, it was known that certain dicarboxylic and tricarboxylic acids were actively oxidized by respiring aerobic tissues. Szent-Györgyi had established that succinate was converted to oxaloacetate via fumarate and malate, and Martius and Knoop showed that succinate could be formed from citrate via α-ketoglutarate. In 1937, Krebs supplied a conceptual basis for these reactions by suggesting that they were arranged in a cyclic sequence termed the "citric acid cycle." Krebs came to this conclusion in the course of investigations on pigeon breast muscle, an actively respiring tissue, in which he showed that oxidation of pyruvate or of endogenous carbohydrate was stimulated by only small amounts of citric acid cycle intermediates, ie, in a catalytic manner. In other experiments where malonate was added as an inhibitor of succinate dehydrogenase, succinate accumulated after addition of pyruvate or any of the other intermediates of the citric acid cycle. The block in pyruvate utilization could be relieved by the addition of oxaloacetate on a mole-for-mole basis, thus establishing the existence of the initial condensation reaction that forms citrate.

REACTIONS OF THE CITRIC ACID CYCLE
(See Fig 14–4)*

Acetyl-CoA + Oxaloacetate + H_2O ⟶ Citrate + CoA·SH

The initial condensation of acetyl-CoA with oxaloacetate to form citrate is catalyzed by a condensing enzyme, **citrate synthase,** which effects synthesis of a carbon-to-carbon bond between the methyl carbon of acetyl-CoA and the carbonyl carbon of oxaloacetate. The condensation reaction, which forms citryl-CoA, is followed by hydrolysis of the thioester bond of CoA, accompanied by considerable loss of free energy as heat, ensuring that the reaction goes to completion.

Citrate is converted to isocitrate by the enzyme **aconitase** (aconitate hydratase), which contains iron in the Fe^{2+} state. This conversion takes place in 2 steps: dehydration to *cis*-aconitate, some of which remains bound to the enzyme, and rehydration to isocitrate.

Citrate ⟷ *Cis*-aconitate ⟷ Isocitrate
(enzyme bound)
H_2O H_2O

The reaction may be inhibited by **fluoroacetate,** which, in the form of fluoroacetyl-CoA, condenses with oxaloacetate to form fluorocitrate. The latter inhibits aconitase, causing citrate to accumulate.

Experiments using ^{14}C-labeled intermediates indicate that citrate reacts with aconitase in an asymmetric manner, with the result that aconitase always acts on that part of the citrate molecule that is derived from oxaloacetate. Ogston suggested that this was due to a 3-point attachment of the enzyme to the substrate. The 3-point attachment would enable aconitase to differentiate the two –CH_2COOH groups in citrate, thus conferring asymmetry on an apparently symmetric molecule. However, the 3-point attachment hypothesis is not necessary to explain the asymmetric action of aconitase. It is now realized that the two –CH_2COOH groups are not identical in space with respect to the –OH and –COOH groups. The consequences of the asymmetric action of aconitase may be appreciated by reference to the fate of labeled acetyl-CoA in the citric acid cycle as shown in Fig 14–4. It is possible that *cis*-aconitate may not be an obligatory intermediate between citrate and isocitrate but may in fact be a side branch from the main pathway.

Isocitrate undergoes dehydrogenation in the presence of **isocitrate dehydrogenase** to form oxalosuccinate. Three different isocitrate dehydrogenases have been described. One, which is NAD^+-specific, is found only in mitochondria. The other 2 enzymes are

*From Circular No. 200 of the Committee of Editors of Biochemical Journals Recommendations (1975): "According to standard biochemical convention, the ending *ate* in, eg, palmitate, denotes any mixture of free acid and the ionized form(s) (according to pH) in which the cations are not specified." The same convention is adopted in this text for all carboxylic acids.

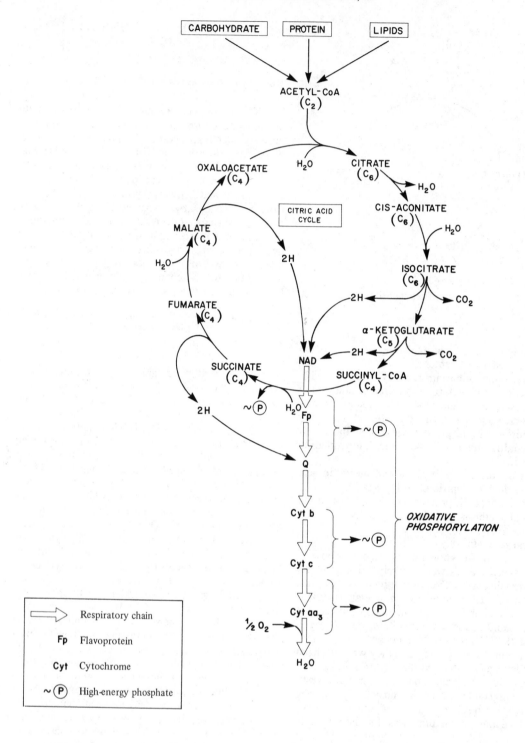

Figure 14–3. The citric acid cycle: the major catabolic pathway for acetyl-CoA in aerobic organisms. Acetyl-CoA, the product of carbohydrate, protein, and lipid catabolism, is taken up into the cycle, together with H_2O, and oxidized to CO_2 with the release of reducing equivalents (2H). Subsequent oxidation of 2H in the respiratory chain leads to coupled phosphorylation of 2–3 ADP to 2–3 ATP. For one turn of the cycle, 11 ~ Ⓟ are generated via oxidative phosphorylation and one ~ Ⓟ arises at substrate level from the conversion of succinyl-CoA to succinate.

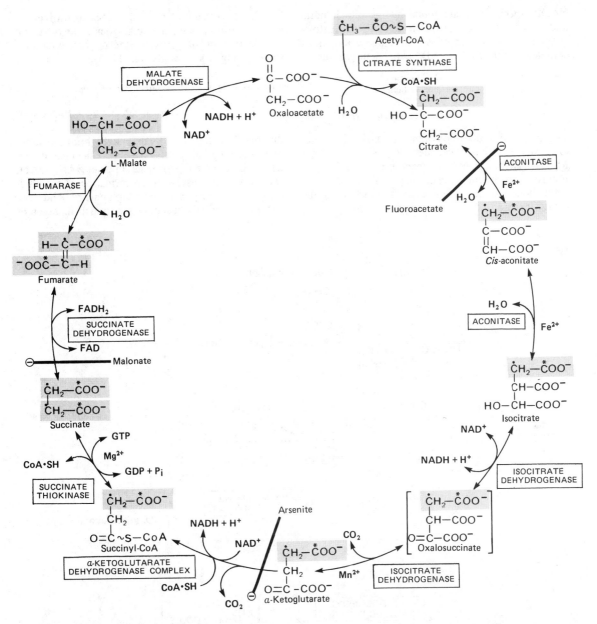

Figure 14–4. The citric acid (Krebs) cycle. Oxidation of NADH and FADH$_2$ in the respiratory chain leads to the generation of ATP via oxidative phosphorylation. In order to follow the passage of acetyl-CoA through the cycle, the 2 carbon atoms of the acetyl radical are shown labeled on the carboxyl carbon (using the designation [*]) and on the methyl carbon (using the designation [•]). Although 2 carbon atoms are lost as CO$_2$ in one revolution of the cycle, these atoms are not derived from the acetyl-CoA that has immediately entered the cycle but from that portion of the citrate molecule which derived from oxaloacetate. However, on completion of a single turn of the cycle, the oxaloacetate that is regenerated is now labeled, which leads to labeled CO$_2$ being evolved during the second turn of the cycle. Because succinate is a symmetric compound and because succinate dehydrogenase does not differentiate between its 2 carboxyl groups, "randomization" of label occurs at this step such that all 4 carbon atoms of oxaloacetate appear to be labeled after one turn of the cycle. During gluconeogenesis, some of the label in oxaloacetate is incorporated into glucose and glycogen (see p 186). In this process, oxaloacetate is decarboxylated by release of the carboxyl group adjacent to the CH$_2$ group. As a result of recombination of the resulting 3-carbon residues in a process that is essentially a reversal of glycolysis, the eventual location of label from acetate in glucose (or glycogen) is distributed in a characteristic manner. Thus, if oxaloacetate leaves the citric acid cycle after only one turn from the entry of labeled acetyl-CoA (acetate), label from the carboxyl carbon of acetate is found in carbon atoms 3 and 4 of glucose, whereas label from the methyl carbon of acetate is found in carbon atoms 1, 2, 5, and 6. For a discussion of the stereochemical aspects of the citric acid cycle, see Greville (1968). The sites of inhibition (⊖) by fluoroacetate, malonate, and arsenite are indicated.

NADP⁺-specific and are found in the mitochondria and the cytosol, respectively. Respiratory chain-linked oxidation of isocitrate proceeds almost completely through the NAD⁺-dependent enzyme.

Isocitrate + NAD⁺ ⟷ **Oxalosuccinate** ⟷
(enzyme bound)

α-Ketoglutarate + CO₂ + NADH + H⁺

There follows a decarboxylation to α-ketoglutarate, also catalyzed by isocitrate dehydrogenase. Mn²⁺ (or Mg²⁺) is an important component of the decarboxylation reaction. It would appear that oxalosuccinate remains bound to the enzyme as an intermediate in the overall reaction.

Next, α-ketoglutarate undergoes **oxidative decarboxylation** in a manner analogous to the oxidative decarboxylation of pyruvate (see p 172), both substrates being α-keto acids (Fig 14–5).

α-Ketoglutarate + NAD⁺ + CoA·SH ⟶

Succinyl-CoA + CO₂ + NADH + H⁺

The reaction, catalyzed by an **α-ketoglutarate dehydrogenase** complex, also requires identical cofactors—eg, thiamin diphosphate, lipoate, NAD⁺, FAD, and CoA—and results in the formation of succinyl-CoA, a thioester containing a high-energy bond. The equilibrium of this reaction is so much in favor of

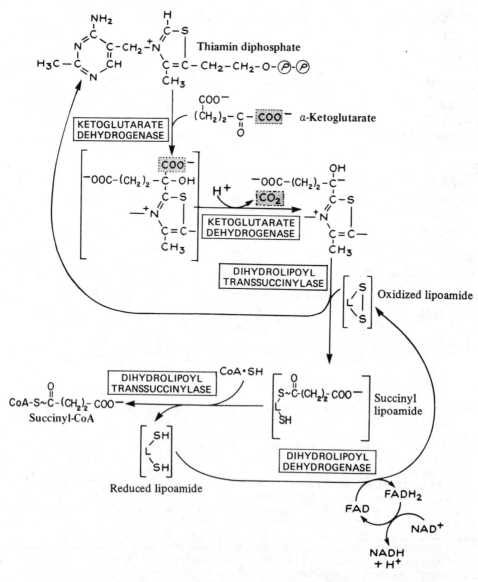

Figure 14–5. Oxidative decarboxylation of α-ketoglutarate by the α-ketoglutarate dehydrogenase complex. This series of reactions is analogous to those described for the oxidative decarboxylation of pyruvate, discussed in greater detail on pp 102 and 171.

succinyl-CoA formation that the reaction must be considered as physiologically unidirectional. As in the case of pyruvate oxidation (see p 171), arsenite inhibits the reaction, causing the substrate, α-**ketoglutarate,** to accumulate.

To continue the cycle, succinyl-CoA is converted to succinate by the enzyme **succinate thiokinase (succinyl-CoA synthase).**

$$\text{Succinyl-CoA} + P_i + \text{GDP} \longleftrightarrow \text{Succinate} + \text{GTP} + \text{CoA} \cdot \text{SH}$$

This reaction requires GDP or IDP, which is converted in the presence of inorganic phosphate to either GTP or ITP. This is the only example in the citric acid cycle of the **generation of a high-energy phosphate at the substrate level** and arises because the release of free energy from the oxidative decarboxylation of α-ketoglutarate is sufficient to generate a high-energy bond in addition to the formation of NADH (equivalent to 3 ~ ⓟ). By means of a phosphokinase, ATP may be formed from either GTP or ITP,

$$\text{eg, GTP} + \text{ADP} \longleftrightarrow \text{GDP} + \text{ATP}$$

An alternative reaction in extrahepatic tissues, which is catalyzed by **succinyl-CoA-acetoacetate-CoA transferase (thiophorase),** is the conversion of succinyl-CoA to succinate coupled with the conversion of acetoacetate to acetoacetyl-CoA (see p 247). In liver there is also deacylase activity, causing some hydrolysis of succinyl-CoA to succinate plus CoA.

Succinate is metabolized further by undergoing a dehydrogenation followed by the addition of water, and subsequently by a further dehydrogenation which regenerates oxaloacetate.

$$\text{Succinate} + \text{FAD} \longleftrightarrow \text{Fumarate} + \text{FADH}_2$$

The first dehydrogenation reaction is catalyzed by **succinate dehydrogenase,** which is bound to the inner surface of the inner mitochondrial membrane. It is the only dehydrogenation in the citric acid cycle that involves the **direct transfer of hydrogen from the substrate to a flavoprotein without the participation of NAD$^+$.** The enzyme contains FAD and iron-sulfur (Fe:S) protein. Fumarate is formed as a result of the dehydrogenation. Isotopic experiments have shown that the enzyme is stereospecific for the *trans* hydrogen atoms of the methylene carbons of succinate. Addition of malonate or oxaloacetate inhibits succinate dehydrogenase competitively, resulting in succinate accumulation.

Fumarase (fumarate hydratase) catalyzes the addition of water to fumarate to give malate.

$$\text{Fumarate} + \text{H}_2\text{O} \longleftrightarrow \text{L-Malate}$$

In addition to being specific for the L-isomer of malate, fumarase catalyzes the addition of the elements of water to the double bond of fumarate in the *trans* configuration. Malate is converted to oxaloace-

tate by **malate dehydrogenase,** a reaction requiring NAD$^+$.

$$\text{L-Malate} + \text{NAD}^+ \longleftrightarrow \text{Oxaloacetate} + \text{NADH} + \text{H}^+$$

Although the equilibrium of this reaction strongly favors malate, the net flux is toward the direction of oxaloacetate because this compound, together with the other product of the reaction (NADH), is removed continuously in further reactions.

The enzymes of the citric acid cycle, except for the α-ketoglutarate and succinate dehydrogenases, are also found outside the mitochondria. While they may catalyze similar reactions, some of the enzymes, eg, malate dehydrogenase, may not in fact be the same proteins as the mitochondrial enzymes of the same name.

ENERGETICS OF THE CITRIC ACID CYCLE

As a result of oxidation catalyzed by dehydrogenase enzymes of the citric acid cycle, **3 molecules of NADH** and **one of FADH$_2$** are produced for each molecule of acetyl-CoA catabolized in one revolution of the cycle. These reducing equivalents are transferred to the respiratory chain in the inner mitochondrial membrane (Fig 14–3). During passage along the chain, reducing equivalents from NADH generate 3 high-energy phosphate bonds by the esterification of ADP to ATP in the process of oxidative phosphorylation (see Chapter 12). However, FADH$_2$ produces only 2 high-energy phosphate bonds because it transfers its reducing power to Q, thus bypassing the first site for oxidative phosphorylation in the respiratory chain (Fig 12–15). A further high-energy phosphate is generated at the level of the cycle itself (ie, at substrate level) during the conversion of succinyl-CoA to succinate. Thus, **12 new high-energy phosphate bonds are generated for each turn of the cycle** (Table 14–1).

Table 14–1. Generation of high-energy phosphate bonds by the citric acid cycle.

Reaction Catalyzed By	Method of ~ ⓟ Production	Number of ~ ⓟ Formed
Isocitrate dehydrogenase	Respiratory chain oxidation of NADH	3
α-Ketoglutarate dehydrogenase	Respiratory chain oxidation of NADH	3
Succinate thiokinase	Oxidation at substrate level	1
Succinate dehydrogenase	Respiratory chain oxidation of FADH$_2$	2
Malate dehydrogenase	Respiratory chain oxidation of NADH	3
		Net 12

AMPHIBOLIC ROLE OF THE CITRIC ACID CYCLE

Some metabolic pathways end in a constituent of the cycle while other pathways originate from the cycle. These pathways concern the processes of gluconeogenesis, transamination, deamination, and fatty acid synthesis. Although these will be discussed in greater detail in subsequent chapters, their relationships with the cycle are summarized below.

Gluconeogenesis, Transamination, & Deamination

All major members of the cycle, from citrate to oxaloacetate, are potentially glucogenic, since they can give rise to a net production of glucose in the liver or kidney, the organs that contain a complete set of enzymes necessary for gluconeogenesis (see p 185). The key enzyme that facilitates the net transfer out of the cycle into the main pathway of gluconeogenesis is **phosphoenolpyruvate carboxykinase,** which catalyzes the decarboxylation of oxaloacetate to phosphoenolpyruvate, GTP acting as the source of high-energy phosphate (Fig 14–6).

$$\text{Oxaloacetate} + \text{GTP} \longrightarrow \text{Phosphoenolpyruvate} + CO_2 + \text{GDP}$$

Net transfer into the cycle (anaplerotic reactions) occurs as a result of several different reactions. Among the most significant is the formation of oxaloacetate by the carboxylation of pyruvate, catalyzed by **pyruvate carboxylase.**

$$\text{ATP} + CO_2 + H_2O + \text{Pyruvate} \longrightarrow \text{Oxaloacetate} + \text{ADP} + P_i.$$

This reaction is considered important in maintaining adequate concentrations of oxaloacetate for the condensation reaction with acetyl-CoA. If acetyl-CoA accumulates, it acts as an allosteric activator of pyruvate carboxylase, thereby ensuring a supply of oxaloacetate. Lactate, an important substrate for gluconeogenesis, enters the cycle via conversion to pyruvate and oxaloacetate.

Transaminase reactions produce pyruvate from alanine, oxaloacetate from aspartate, and α-ketoglutarate from glutamate. Because these reactions are reversible, the cycle also serves as a source of carbon skeletons for the synthesis of nonessential amino acids, eg,

$$\text{Aspartate} + \text{Pyruvate} \longleftrightarrow \text{Oxaloacetate} + \text{Alanine}$$

$$\text{Glutamate} + \text{Pyruvate} \longleftrightarrow \alpha\text{-Ketoglutarate} + \text{Alanine}$$

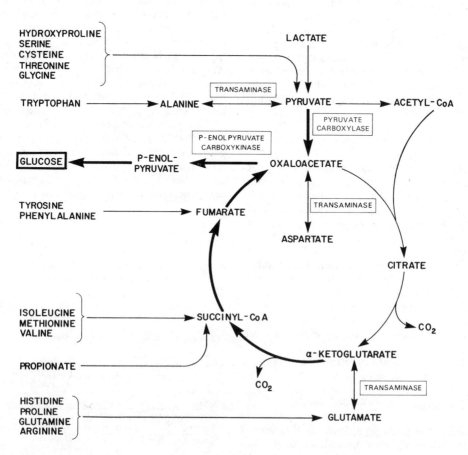

Figure 14–6. Involvement of the citric acid cycle in transamination and gluconeogenesis. The bold arrows indicate the main pathway of gluconeogenesis.

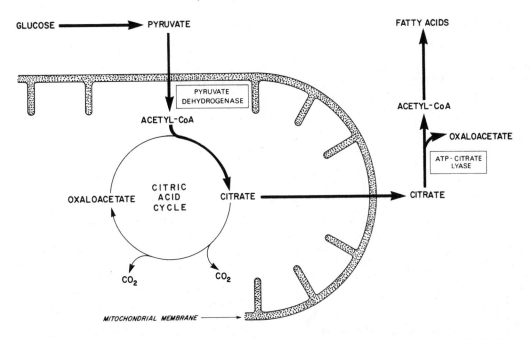

Figure 14–7. Participation of the citric acid cycle in fatty acid synthesis from glucose. See also Fig 17–9.

Other amino acids contribute to gluconeogenesis because all or part of their carbon skeletons enter the citric acid cycle after deamination or transamination. Examples are alanine, cysteine, glycine, hydroxyproline, serine, threonine, and tryptophan, which form pyruvate; arginine, histidine, glutamine, and proline, which form α-ketoglutarate via glutamate; isoleucine, methionine, and valine, which form succinyl-CoA; and tyrosine and phenylalanine, which form fumarate (see Fig 14–6). Substances forming pyruvate have the option of complete oxidation to CO_2 if they follow the pyruvate dehydrogenase pathway to acetyl-CoA, or they may follow the gluconeogenic pathway via carboxylation to oxaloacetate.

Of particular significance to ruminants is the conversion of propionate, the major glucogenic product of rumen fermentation, to succinyl-CoA via the methylmalonyl-CoA pathway (see p 187).

Fatty Acid Synthesis (See Fig 14–7.)

Acetyl-CoA formed from pyruvate by the action of pyruvate dehydrogenase is the major building block for long-chain fatty acid synthesis in nonruminants. (In ruminants, acetyl-CoA is derived directly from acetate.) As pyruvate dehydrogenase is a mitochondrial enzyme and the enzymes responsible for fatty acid synthesis are extramitochondrial, the cell needs to transport acetyl-CoA through the mitochondrial membrane, which is impermeable to acetyl-CoA. This is accomplished by allowing **acetyl-CoA to form citrate** in the citric acid cycle, **transporting citrate** out of the mitochondria, and finally making acetyl-CoA available in the cytosol by **cleaving citrate** in a reaction catalyzed by the enzyme **ATP-citrate lyase.**

Citrate + ATP + CoA → Acetyl-CoA + Oxaloacetate + ADP + P$_i$

Regulation of the Citric Acid Cycle

This is discussed in Chapter 19.

• • •

References

Boyer PD (editor): *The Enzymes,* 3rd ed. Academic Press, 1971.

Goodwin TW (editor): *The Metabolic Roles of Citrate.* Academic Press, 1968.

Greville GD: Vol 1, p 297, in: *Carbohydrate Metabolism and Its Disorders.* Dickens F, Randle PJ, Whelan WJ (editors). Academic Press, 1968.

Lowenstein JM: Vol 1, p 146, in: *Metabolic Pathways,* 3rd ed. Greenberg DM (editor). Academic Press, 1967.

Lowenstein JM (editor): *Citric Acid Cycle: Control and Compartmentation.* Dekker, 1969.

Lowenstein JM (editor): *Citric Acid Cycle.* Vol 13 in: *Methods in Enzymology.* Academic Press, 1969.

15 | Metabolism of Carbohydrate

Peter A. Mayes, PhD, DSc

Although animal diets are variable, in most instances carbohydrate accounts for a large proportion of the daily intake. However, some of the dietary carbohydrate is converted to fat and consequently is metabolized as fat. The extent of this process (lipogenesis) depends on the species and whether or not the animal is a "meal eater" or a more continual feeder. It is possible that in humans the frequency of taking meals and the extent to which carbohydrates are converted to fat could have a bearing on disease states such as atherosclerosis, obesity, and diabetes mellitus. In herbivores, especially ruminants, much of the intake of carbohydrate is fermented by microorganisms to lower-molecular-weight fatty acids prior to absorption from the alimentary tract.

The major function of carbohydrate in metabolism is as a fuel to be oxidized and provide energy for other metabolic processes. In this role, carbohydrate is utilized by cells mainly in the form of glucose. The 3 principal monosaccharides resulting from the digestive processes are **glucose, fructose,** and **galactose.** Fructose may assume considerable quantitative importance if there is a large intake of sucrose. Galactose is of major quantitative significance only when lactose is the principal carbohydrate of the diet. Both fructose and galactose are readily converted to glucose by the liver.

Pentose sugars such as xylose, arabinose, and ribose may be present in the diet, but their fate after absorption is obscure. D-Ribose is synthesized in the tissues for incorporation into nucleotides.

INTERMEDIARY METABOLISM OF CARBOHYDRATE

The metabolism of carbohydrate in the mammalian organism may be subdivided as follows:

(1) Glycolysis: The oxidation of glucose or glycogen to pyruvate and lactate by the Embden-Meyerhof pathway (Fig 15–1).

(2) Glycogenesis: The synthesis of glycogen from glucose.

(3) Glycogenolysis: The breakdown of glycogen. Glucose is the main end product of glycogenolysis in the liver, and pyruvate and lactate are the main products in muscle.

(4) The oxidation of pyruvate to acetyl-CoA: This is a necessary step prior to the entrance of the products of glycolysis into the citric acid cycle, which is the final common pathway for the oxidation of carbohydrate, fat, and protein.

(5) The hexose monophosphate shunt (pentose phosphate pathway, phosphogluconate oxidative pathway): An alternative pathway to the Embden-Meyerhof pathway for the oxidation of glucose. Its primary function is the synthesis of important intermediates such as NADPH and ribose.

(6) Gluconeogenesis: The formation of glucose or glycogen from noncarbohydrate sources. The pathways involved in gluconeogenesis are mainly the citric acid cycle and the reversal of glycolysis. The principal substrates for gluconeogenesis are glucogenic amino acids, lactate, and glycerol, and, in the ruminant, propionate (Fig 15–2).

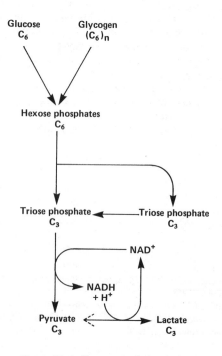

Figure 15–1. Summary of glycolysis.

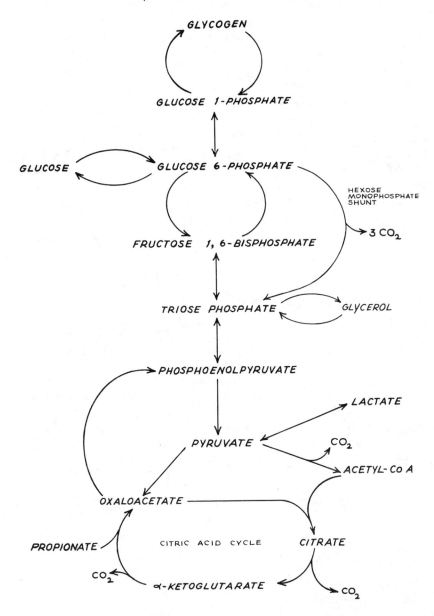

Figure 15–2. Major pathways of carbohydrate metabolism.

GLYCOLYSIS

At an early period in the course of investigations on carbohydrate metabolism it was realized that the process of fermentation in yeast was similar to the breakdown of glycogen in muscle. Although many of the early investigations of the glycolytic pathway were carried out on these 2 systems, the process is now known to occur in virtually **all tissues.**

In many of the first studies on the biochemical changes that occur during muscular contraction it was noted that when a muscle contracts in an anaerobic medium, ie, one from which oxygen is excluded, glycogen disappears and pyruvate and lactate appear as the principal end products. When oxygen is admitted, aerobic recovery takes place and glycogen reappears, while pyruvate and lactate disappear. However, if contraction takes place under aerobic conditions, lactate does not accumulate and pyruvate is oxidized further to CO_2 and water. As a result of these observations, it has been customary to separate carbohydrate metabolism into anaerobic and aerobic phases. However, this distinction is arbitrary, since the reactions in glycolysis are the same in the presence of oxygen as in its absence except in extent and end products. When oxygen is in short supply, reoxidation of NADH formed during glycolysis is impaired. Under these circumstances, NADH is reoxidized by being coupled to the reduction of pyruvate to lactate, the NAD so formed being used to allow further glycolysis to proceed (Fig 15–1).

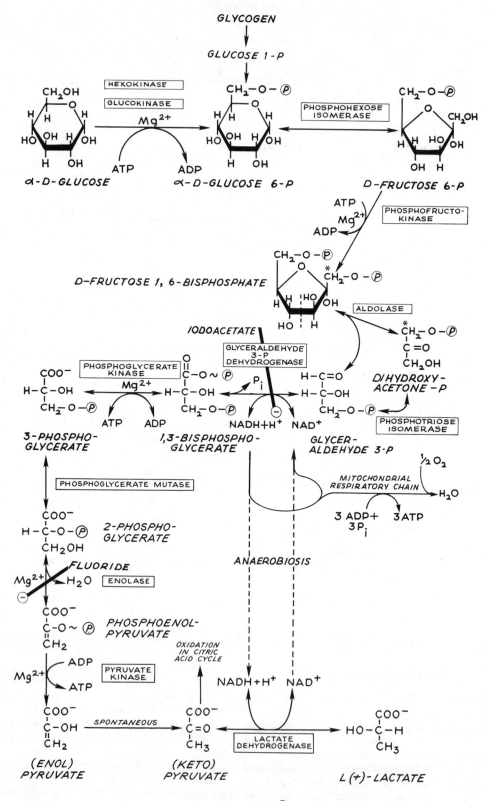

Figure 15–3. Embden-Meyerhof pathway of glycolysis. ($\textcircled{P}$, $-PO_3^{2-}$; P_i, $HOPO_3^{2-}$; $\ominus$, inhibition.)

Thus, glycolysis can take place under anaerobic conditions, but this limits the amount of energy liberated per mole of glucose oxidized. Consequently, **to provide a given amount of energy, more glucose must undergo glycolysis under anaerobic as compared with aerobic conditions.**

The overall equation for glycolysis to lactate is

Glucose + 2 ADP + 2 P_i → 2 L-Lactate + 2 ATP + 2 H_2O

Sequence of Reactions in Glycolysis

All of the enzymes of the Embden-Meyerhof pathway (Fig 15–3) are found in the extramitochondrial soluble fraction of the cell, the cytosol. They catalyze the reactions involved in the glycolysis of glucose to pyruvate and lactate, as follows:

Glucose enters into the glycolytic pathway by phosphorylation to glucose 6-phosphate. This is accomplished by the enzyme **hexokinase** and in liver parenchymal cells by **glucokinase,** whose activity is inducible and affected by changes in the nutritional state. The reaction is accompanied by considerable loss of free energy as heat and therefore, under physiologic conditions, may be regarded as irreversible. ATP is required as phosphate donor, and, as in many reactions involving phosphorylation, it reacts as the Mg-ATP complex. One high-energy phosphate bond of ATP is utilized, and ADP is produced. Hexokinase is inhibited in an allosteric manner by the product, glucose 6-phosphate.

$$\alpha\text{-D-Glucose} + \text{ATP} \xrightarrow{\text{Mg}^{2+}} \alpha\text{-D-Glucose 6-phosphate} + \text{ADP}$$

Hexokinase, present in all cells except those of the liver parenchyma, has a high affinity (low K_m) for its substrate, glucose. Its function is to ensure a supply of glucose for the tissues, even in the presence of low blood glucose concentrations, by phosphorylating all the glucose that enters the cell, thereby maintaining a large glucose concentration gradient between the blood and the intracellular environment. It acts on both the α- and β-anomer of glucose and will also catalyze the phosphorylation of other hexoses but at a much slower rate than glucose.

The function of glucokinase is to remove glucose from the blood following a meal. In contrast to hexokinase, it has a high K_m for glucose and operates optimally at blood glucose concentrations above 100 mg/dL. It is specific for glucose.

Glucose 6-phosphate is an important compound, being at the junction of several metabolic pathways (glycolysis, gluconeogenesis, the hexose monophosphate shunt, glycogenesis, and glycogenolysis) (Fig 15–2). In glycolysis it is converted to fructose 6-phosphate by **phosphohexose isomerase,** which involves an aldose-ketose isomerization. Only the α-anomer of glucose 6-phosphate is acted upon.

α-D-Glucose 6-phosphate ⟷ α-D-Fructose 6-phosphate

This reaction is followed by another phosphorylation with ATP catalyzed by the enzyme **phosphofructokinase (phosphofructokinase-1)** to produce fructose 1,6-bisphosphate. Phosphofructokinase is another inducible enzyme whose activity is considered to play a major role in the regulation of the rate of glycolysis. The phosphofructokinase reaction is another that may be considered to be functionally irreversible under physiologic conditions.

D-Fructose 6-phosphate + ATP → D-Fructose 1,6-bisphosphate

The hexose phosphate, fructose 1,6-bisphosphate, is split by **aldolase** (fructose 1,6-bisphosphate aldolase) into 2 triose phosphates, glyceraldehyde 3-phosphate and dihydroxyacetone phosphate.

D-Fructose 1,6-bisphosphate ⟷ D-Glyceraldehyde 3-phosphate + Dihydroxyacetone phosphate

Several different aldolases have been described, all of which contain 4 subunits. Aldolase A occurs in most tissues, and, in addition, aldolase B occurs in liver and kidney. The fructose phosphates exist in the cell mainly in the furanose form, but they react with phosphohexose isomerase, phosphofructokinase, and aldolase in the open chain configuration.

Glyceraldehyde 3-phosphate and dihydroxyacetone phosphate are interconverted by the enzyme **phosphotriose isomerase.**

D-Glyceraldehyde 3-phosphate ⟷ Dihydroxyacetone phosphate

Glycolysis proceeds by the oxidation of glyceraldehyde 3-phosphate to 1,3-bisphosphoglycerate, and, because of the activity of phosphotriose isomerase, the dihydroxyacetone phosphate is also oxidized to 1,3-diphosphoglycerate via glyceraldehyde 3-phosphate.

D-Glyceraldehyde 3-phosphate + NAD^+ + P_i ⟷ 1,3-Bisphosphoglycerate + NADH + H^+

The enzyme responsible for the oxidation, **glyceraldehyde-3-phosphate dehydrogenase,** is NAD-dependent. Structurally, it consists of 4 identical polypeptides (monomers) forming a tetramer. Four SH groups are present on each polypeptide, probably derived from cysteine residues within the polypeptide chain. One of the SH groups is found at the active site of the enzyme. It is believed that the SH group participates in the reaction in which glyceraldehyde 3-phosphate is oxidized. The substrate initially combines with a cysteinyl moiety on the dehydrogenase forming a thiohemiacetal that is converted to a thiol ester by oxidation, the hydrogens removed in this oxidation being transferred to NAD bound to the enzyme. The NADH produced on the enzyme is not so firmly bound to the enzyme as is NAD. Consequently, NADH is easily displaced by another molecule of NAD. Finally, by phosphorolysis, inorganic phosphate (P_i) is added, forming 1,3-bisphosphoglycerate, and the free en-

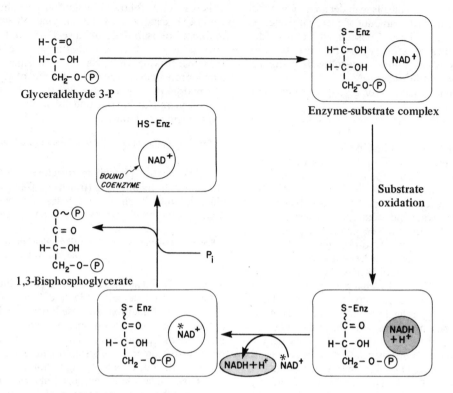

Figure 15–4. Oxidation of glyceraldehyde 3-phosphate. (Enz, glyceraldehyde 3-phosphate dehydrogenase.) The enzyme is inhibited by the —SH poison **iodoacetate**, which is thus able to inhibit glycolysis.

zyme with a reconstituted SH group is liberated (Fig 15–4). Energy released during the oxidation is retained by the formation of a high-energy sulfur bond that becomes, after phosphorolysis, a high-energy phosphate bond in position 1 of 1,3-bisphosphoglycerate. This high-energy phosphate is captured as ATP in a further reaction with ADP catalyzed by **phosphoglycerate kinase,** leaving 3-phosphoglycerate.

1,3-Bisphosphoglycerate + ADP ⟷ 3-Phosphoglycerate + ATP

Since 2 molecules of triose phosphate are formed per molecule of glucose undergoing glycolysis, 2 molecules of ATP are generated at this stage per molecule of glucose, an example of phosphorylation "at the substrate level."

If arsenate is present, it will compete with inorganic phosphate (P_i) in the above reactions to give 1-arseno-3-phosphoglycerate, which hydrolyzes spontaneously to give 3-phosphoglycerate plus heat, without generating ATP. This is an important example of the ability of arsenate to accomplish uncoupling of oxidation and phosphorylation.

3-Phosphoglycerate arising from the above reactions is converted to 2-phosphoglycerate by the enzyme **phosphoglycerate mutase.** It is likely that 2,3-bisphosphoglycerate (diphosphoglycerate, DPG) is an intermediate in this reaction.

3-Phosphoglycerate ⟷ 2-Phosphoglycerate

The subsequent step is catalyzed by **enolase** and involves a dehydration and redistribution of energy within the molecule, raising the phosphate on position 2 to the high-energy state, thus forming phosphoenolpyruvate. Enolase is inhibited by **fluoride,** a property that can be made use of when it is required to prevent glycolysis prior to the estimation of blood glucose. The enzyme is also dependent on the presence of either Mg^{2+} or Mn^{2+}.

2-Phosphoglycerate ⟷ Phosphoenolpyruvate + H_2O

The high-energy phosphate of phosphoenolpyruvate is transferred to ADP by the enzyme **pyruvate kinase** to generate, at this stage, 2 mol of ATP per mol of glucose oxidized. Enolpyruvate formed in this reaction is converted spontaneously to the keto form of pyruvate. This is another nonequilibrium reaction that is accompanied by considerable loss of free energy as heat and must be regarded as physiologically irreversible.

Phosphoenolpyruvate + ADP → Pyruvate + ATP

The redox state of the tissue now determines which of 2 pathways is followed. If **anaerobic** conditions prevail, the reoxidation of NADH by transfer of reducing equivalents through the respiratory chain to oxygen is prevented. Pyruvate is reduced by the NADH to lactate, the reaction being catalyzed by **lactate dehydrogenase.** Several isozymes of this enzyme have been described and have clinical significance (see p 60).

$$\text{Pyruvate} + \text{NADH} + \text{H}^+ \longleftrightarrow \text{L-Lactate} + \text{NAD}^+$$

The reoxidation of NADH via lactate formation allows glycolysis to proceed in the absence of oxygen by **regenerating sufficient NAD**$^+$ for another cycle of the reaction catalyzed by glyceraldehyde 3-phosphate dehydrogenase. Thus, tissues that function under **hypoxic circumstances tend to produce lactate** (Fig 15–3). This is particularly true of skeletal muscle, where the rate at which the organ performs work is not limited by its capacity for oxygenation. The additional quantities of lactate produced may be detected in the tissues and in the blood and urine. Glycolysis in erythrocytes, even under aerobic conditions, always terminates in lactate, because mitochondria that contain the enzymatic machinery for the aerobic oxidation of pyruvate are absent. The mammalian erythrocyte is unique in that about 90% of its total energy requirement is provided by glycolysis. Besides skeletal muscle and erythrocytes, other tissues that normally produce lactate include brain, gastrointestinal tract, renal medulla, and skin. The liver, kidneys, and heart usually take up lactate but will produce it under hypoxic conditions.

Although most of the glycolytic reactions are reversible, 3 of them are markedly exergonic and must therefore be considered physiologically irreversible. These reactions are catalyzed by **hexokinase** (and glucokinase), **phosphofructokinase,** and **pyruvate kinase.** Cells that are capable of effecting a net movement of metabolites in the synthetic direction of the glycolytic pathway (gluconeogenesis) do so because of the presence of different enzyme systems which provide alternative routes around the irreversible reactions catalyzed by the above-mentioned enzymes. These will be discussed under gluconeogenesis.

2,3-Bisphosphoglycerate Cycle

In the erythrocytes of many mammalian species, the step catalyzed by phosphoglycerate kinase is bypassed by a process that effectively dissipates as heat the free energy associated with the high-energy phosphate of 1,3-bisphosphoglycerate (Fig 15–5). An extra enzyme, **bisphosphoglycerate mutase,** catalyzes the conversion of 1,3-bisphosphoglycerate to 2,3-bisphosphoglycerate. The latter is converted to 3-phosphoglycerate by **2,3-bisphosphoglycerate phosphatase,** an activity also attributed to phosphoglycerate mutase. The loss of a high-energy phosphate, which means that there is no net production of ATP when glycolysis takes this route, may be of advantage to the economy of the red cell, since it would allow glycolysis to proceed when the need for ATP was minimal. However, 2,3-bisphosphoglycerate

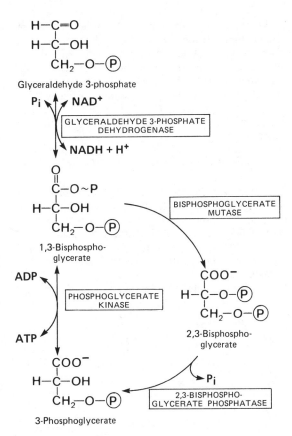

Figure 15–5. 2,3-Bisphosphoglycerate cycle in erythrocytes.

combines with hemoglobin, causing a decrease in affinity for oxygen and a displacement of the oxyhemoglobin dissociation curve to the right. Thus, its presence in the red cells aids oxyhemoglobin to unload oxygen (see Chapter 5).

OXIDATION OF PYRUVATE TO ACETYL-CoA

Before pyruvate can enter the citric acid cycle, it must be transported into the mitochondrion via a special pyruvate transporter that aids its passage across the inner mitochondrial membrane. This involves a symport mechanism whereby one proton is cotransported (Fig 12–28). Within the mitochondrion, pyruvate is oxidatively decarboxylated to acetyl-CoA. This reaction is catalyzed by several different enzymes working sequentially in a multienzyme complex. They are collectively designated as the **pyruvate dehydrogenase** complex and are analogous to the α-ketoglutarate dehydrogenase complex of the citric acid cycle (see p 162). Pyruvate is decarboxylated in the presence of thiamin diphosphate to a hydroxyethyl derivative of the thiazole ring of enzyme-bound thiamin diphosphate, which in turn reacts with oxidized lipoamide to form acetyl lipoamide (Fig 15–6). In the presence of **dihydrolipoyl transacetylase,** acetyl lipoamide reacts with coenzyme A to form acetyl-CoA and reduced lipoamide. The cycle of reaction is completed when the latter is reoxidized by a flavoprotein in the presence of **dihydrolipoyl dehydrogenase.** Finally, the reduced flavoprotein is oxidized by NAD, which in turn transfers reducing equivalents to the respiratory chain.

$$\text{Pyruvate} + NAD^+ + CoA \rightarrow \text{Acetyl-CoA} + NADH + H^+ + CO_2$$

The pyruvate dehydrogenase complex consists of about 29 mol of pyruvate dehydrogenase and about 8 mol of flavoprotein (dihydrolipoyl dehydrogenase) distributed around 1 mol of transacetylase. Movement of the individual enzymes appears to be restricted, and the metabolic intermediates do not dissociate freely but remain bound to the enzymes.

It is to be noted that the pyruvate dehydrogenase

system is sufficiently electronegative with respect to the respiratory chain that, in addition to generating a reduced coenzyme (NADH), it also generates a high-energy thio ester bond in acetyl-CoA.

Arsenite or mercuric ions complex the –SH groups of lipoic acid and inhibit pyruvate dehydrogenase, as does a dietary deficiency of thiamin, allowing pyruvate to accumulate. Nutritionally deprived alcoholics are thiamin-deficient and if administered glucose exhibit rapid accumulation of pyruvate and **lactic acidosis,** which is frequently lethal. Patients with inherited pyruvate dehydrogenase deficiency present with a similar lactic acidosis, particularly after glucose load. Mutations have been reported for virtually all of the enzymes of carbohydrate metabolism, each associated with human disease (Stanbury et al, 1983).

Energetics of Carbohydrate Oxidation

When 1 mol of glucose is combusted in a calorimeter to CO_2 and water, approximately 2870 kJ

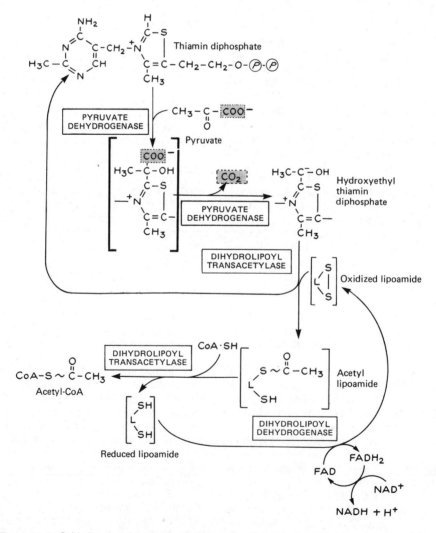

Figure 15–6. Oxidative decarboxylation of pyruvate by the pyruvate dehydrogenase complex.

Table 15—1. Generation of high-energy bonds in the catabolism of glucose.

Pathway	Reaction Catalyzed By	Method of ~ⓅProduction	Number of ~ Ⓟ Formed per Mole of Glucose
Glycolysis	Glyceraldehyde 3-phosphate dehydrogenase	Respiratory chain oxidation of 2 NADH	6*
	Phosphoglycerate kinase	Oxidation at substrate level	2
	Pyruvate kinase	Oxidation at substrate level	2
			10
	Allow for consumption of ATP by reactions catalyzed by hexokinase and phosphofructokinase		−2
			Net 8
Citric acid cycle	Pyruvate dehydrogenase	Respiratory chain oxidation of 2 NADH	6
	Isocitrate dehydrogenase	Respiratory chain oxidation of 2 NADH	6
	α-Ketoglutarate dehydrogenase	Respiratory chain oxidation of 2 NADH	6
	Succinate thiokinase	Oxidation at substrate level	2
	Succinate dehydrogenase	Respiratory chain oxidation of 2 FADH$_2$	4
	Malate dehydrogenase	Respiratory chain oxidation of 2 NADH	6
			Net 30
	Total per mole of glucose under aerobic conditions		38
	Total per mole of glucose under anaerobic conditions		2

*It is assumed that NADH formed in glycolysis is transported into mitochondria via the malate shuttle (see p 144). If the glycerophosphate shuttle is used, only 2 ~ Ⓟ would be formed per mole of NADH, the total net production being 36 instead of 38. The calculation ignores the small loss of ATP due to a transport of H$^+$ into the mitochondrion with pyruvate and a similar transport of H$^+$ in the operation of the malate shuttle, totaling about 1 mol of ATP.

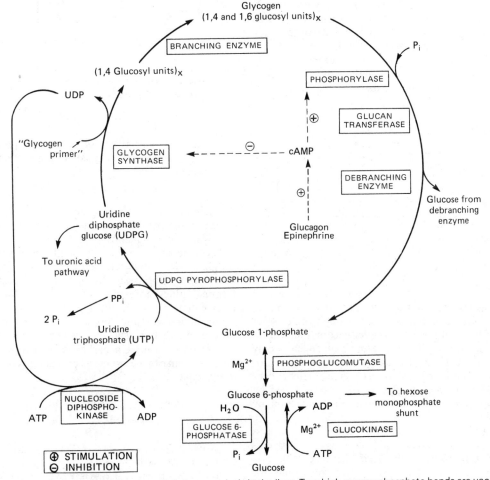

Figure 15—7. Pathway of glycogenesis and of glycogenolysis in the liver. Two high-energy phosphate bonds are used in the incorporation of 1 mol of glucose into glycogen.

are liberated as heat. When oxidation occurs in the tissues, some of this energy is not lost immediately as heat but is "captured" in high-energy phosphate bonds. On the order of 38 high-energy phosphate bonds are generated per molecule of glucose oxidized to CO_2 and water. Assuming each high-energy bond to be equivalent to 36.8 kJ, the total energy captured in ATP per mole of glucose oxidized is 1398 kJ, or approximately 48.7% of the energy of combustion. Most of the ATP is formed as a consequence of oxidative phosphorylation resulting from the reoxidation of reduced coenzymes by the respiratory chain. The remainder is generated by phosphorylation at the "substrate level." (See Chapter 12.) Table 15–1 indicates the reactions responsible for the generation of high-energy phosphate during oxidation of glucose and the net production under aerobic and anaerobic conditions.

GLYCOGEN FORMATION & DEGRADATION

The synthesis (glycogenesis) and degradation of glycogen (glycogenolysis) are not simply the reversal of one series of reactions. Instead, each process is an entirely separate metabolic pathway catalyzed by a different set of enzymes (Fig 15–7).

The formation of glycogen occurs in practically every tissue of the body but chiefly in liver and muscle (Table 15–2). In humans, the liver may contain as

Table 15–2. Storage of carbohydrate in postabsorptive normal adult humans (70 kg).

Liver glycogen	4.0% =	72 g*
Muscle glycogen	0.7% =	245 g†
Extracellular glucose	0.1% =	10 g‡
		327 g

*Liver weight, 1800 g.
†Muscle mass, 35 kg.
‡Total volume, 10 L.

much as 6% of its wet weight as glycogen when analyzed shortly after a meal high in carbohydrate. After 12–18 hours of fasting, the liver becomes almost totally depleted of glycogen. Muscle glycogen is only rarely elevated above 1% and is only depleted significantly after prolonged vigorous exercise. Higher concentrations of muscle glycogen can be induced by feeding high-carbohydrate diets after depletion by exercise.

The function of muscle glycogen is to act as a readily available source of hexose units for glycolysis **within the muscle itself.** Liver glycogen is largely concerned with export of hexose units for maintenance of the **blood glucose,** particularly between meals.

GLYCOGENESIS

Glucose is phosphorylated to glucose 6-phosphate, a reaction that is common to the first reaction in the pathway of glycolysis from glucose. Glucose 6-phosphate is then converted to glucose 1-phosphate in a reaction catalyzed by the enzyme **phosphoglucomutase.** The enzyme itself is phosphorylated, and the phospho- group takes part in a reversible reaction in which glucose 1,6-bisphosphate is an intermediate.

Enz-P + Glucose 6-phosphate ⟷ Enz + Glucose 1,6-bisphosphate ⟷ Enz-P + Glucose 1-phosphate

Next, glucose 1-phosphate reacts with uridine triphosphate (UTP) to form the active nucleotide **uridine diphosphate glucose (UDPG).***

Uridine diphosphate glucose (UDPG)

The reaction between glucose 1-phosphate and uridine triphosphate is catalyzed by the enzyme **UDPG pyrophosphorylase.**

UTP + Glucose 1-phosphate ⟷ UDPG + PPi

The subsequent hydrolysis of inorganic pyrophosphate by **inorganic pyrophosphatase** pulls the reaction to the right of the equation.

By the action of the enzyme **glycogen synthase** (or **glucosyltransferase**), the C_1 of the activated glucose of UDPG forms a glycosidic bond with the C_4 of a terminal glucose residue of glycogen, liberating uridine diphosphate (UDP) (Fig 15–7). A preexisting glycogen molecule, or "primer," must be present to initiate this reaction. The glycogen primer may in turn be formed on a protein backbone, which may be a process similar to the synthesis of other glycoproteins (see Chapter 33).

UDPG + $(C_6)_n$ ⟶ UDP + $(C_6)_{n+1}$
glycogen   glycogen

*Other nucleoside diphosphate sugar compounds are known, eg, UDPGal. In addition, the same sugar may be linked to different nucleotides. For example, glucose may be linked to uridine (as shown above) as well as to guanosine, thymidine, adenosine, or cytidine nucleotides.

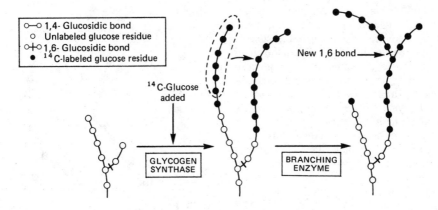

(a) Synthesis—The mechanism of branching as revealed by the addition of ^{14}C-labeled glucose.

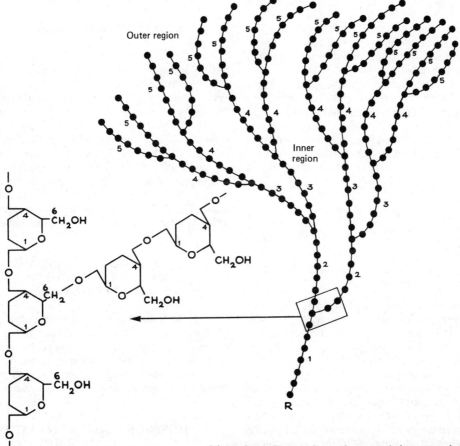

(c) Enlargement of structure at a branch point.

(b) Structure—The numbers refer to equivalent stages in the growth of the macromolecule. Thus, primary chain 1 branched into chains 2, which were synthesized simultaneously before branching into chains 3, etc. R, primary glucose residue. The branching is, in fact, more variable than shown, the ratio of 1,4 to 1,6 bonds being from 12 to 18.

Figure 15–8. The glycogen molecule.

The addition of a glucose residue to a preexisting glycogen chain, or "primer," occurs at the nonreducing, outer end of the molecule so that the "branches" of the glycogen "tree" become elongated as successive **-1,4- linkages** occur (Fig 15–8). When the chain has been lengthened to a minimum of 11 glucose residues, a second enzyme, the **branching enzyme (amylo-1,4→1,6-transglucosidase)**, acts on the glycogen. This enzyme transfers a part of the -1,4-chain (minimum length 6 glucose residues) to a neighboring chain to form a **-1,6- linkage,** thus establishing a **branch point** in the molecule. The branches grow by further additions of 1,4- glucosyl units and further branching.

The action of the branching enzyme has been studied in the living animal by feeding ^{14}C-labeled glucose and examining the liver glycogen at intervals thereafter. At first only the outer branches of the chain are labeled, indicating that the new glucose residues are added at this point. Later, some of these outside chains are transferred to the inner portion of the molecule, appearing as labeled -1,6- linked branches (Fig 15–8). Thus, under the combined action of glycogen synthase and branching enzyme, the glycogen molecule is assembled.

Liver glycogen consists of single spheres (β particles) and clusters of spheres (α particles), which are covalently joined. A β particle has a molecular weight of about 10^7, whereas an α particle can approach a weight of 2×10^9. Muscle glycogen consists only of β particles. The maximum size of the β particle is limited because the molecule becomes more dense toward the periphery.

GLYCOGENOLYSIS

It is the step catalyzed by **phosphorylase** that is rate-limiting in glycogenolysis.

$$(C_6)_n + P_i \rightarrow (C_6)_{n-1} + \text{Glucose 1-phosphate}$$

glycogen   glycogen

This enzyme is specific for the phosphorylytic breaking (phosphorolysis) of the -1,4- linkages of glycogen to yield glucose 1-phosphate. Glucosyl residues from the outermost chains of the glycogen molecule are removed until approximately 4 glucose residues remain on either side of a -1,6- branch (Fig 15–9). Another enzyme (α**-1,4→** α**-1,4 glucan transferase**) transfers a trisaccharide unit from one branch to the other, exposing the -1,6- branch points. The **hydrolytic** splitting of the -1,6- linkages requires the action of a specific **debranching enzyme (amylo-1,6-glucosidase),** which appears to be a second activity of the glucan transferase.* With the removal of the branch,

---

*Because the -1,6- linkage is hydrolytically split, 1 mol of free glucose is produced rather than 1 mol of glucose 1-phosphate. In this way, it is possible for some rise in the blood glucose to take place even in the absence of glucose 6-phosphatase, as occurs in type I glycogen storage disease (von Gierke's disease; see p 179) after glucagon or epinephrine is administered.

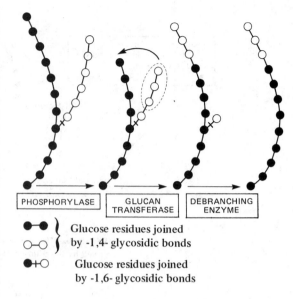

PHOSPHORYLASE | GLUCAN TRANSFERASE | DEBRANCHING ENZYME

●—● } Glucose residues joined
○—○ } by -1,4- glycosidic bonds

●—○ Glucose residues joined
by -1,6- glycosidic bonds

Figure 15–9. Steps in glycogenolysis.

further action by phosphorylase can proceed. The combined action of phosphorylase and these other enzymes leads to the complete breakdown of glycogen. The reaction catalyzed by phosphoglucomutase is reversible, so that glucose 6-phosphate can be formed from glucose 1-phosphate. In **liver** and **kidney** (but not in muscle), there is a specific enzyme, **glucose 6-phosphatase,** that removes phosphate from glucose 6-phosphate, enabling the free glucose to diffuse from the cell into the extracellular spaces, including the blood. This is the final step in hepatic glycogenolysis, which is reflected by a rise in the blood glucose.

CONTROL MECHANISMS OF GLYCOGENOLYSIS & GLYCOGENESIS

The principal enzymes controlling glycogen metabolism—glycogen phosphorylase and glycogen synthase—are themselves controlled by a complex series of reactions involving both allosteric mechanisms and covalent modifications owing to phosphorylation and dephosphorylation of enzyme protein.

PHOSPHORYLASE ACTIVATION & INACTIVATION
(Fig 15–10.)

In liver, the enzyme exists in both an active and an inactive form. Active phosphorylase (**phosphorylase a)** has one of its serine hydroxyl groups phosphorylated in an ester linkage. By the action of a specific phosphatase (**protein phosphatase-1),** the enzyme is inactivated to **phosphorylase b** in a reaction that involves hydrolytic removal of the phosphate from the

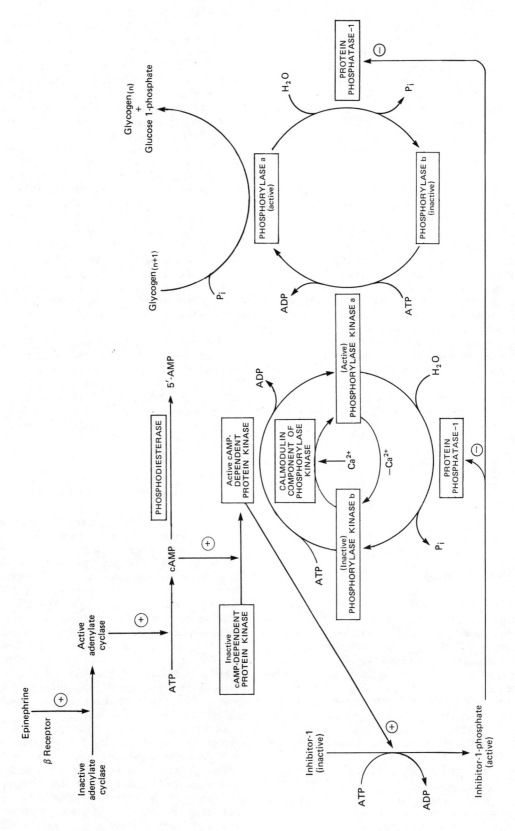

Figure 15–10. Control of phosphorylase in muscle (n = number of glucose residues).

serine residue. Reactivation requires rephosphorylation with ATP and a specific enzyme, **phosphorylase kinase.**

Muscle phosphorylase is immunologically and genetically distinct from that of liver. It is present in 2 forms: **phosphorylase a,** which is phosphorylated and active in either the presence or absence of AMP (its allosteric modifier), and **phosphorylase b,** which is dephosphorylated and active only in the presence of AMP. Phosphorylase a is the normal physiologically active form of the enzyme. It is a dimer, each monomer containing 1 mol of pyridoxal phosphate.

Activation via cAMP

Phosphorylase in **muscle** is activated by epinephrine (Fig 15–10). However, this occurs not as a direct effect but rather by way of the action of cAMP (3',5'-cyclic adenylic acid; cyclic AMP). cAMP is the intracellular intermediate compound (second messenger) through which many hormones act. It is formed from ATP by an enzyme, **adenylate cyclase,** occurring in the inner surface of cell membranes. Adenylate cyclase is activated by hormones such as **epinephrine** and **norepinephrine** acting through β-adrenergic receptors on the cell membrane and additionally in liver by **glucagon** acting through an independent receptor. cAMP is destroyed by a **phosphodiesterase,** and it is the activity of this enzyme that maintains the level of cAMP at its normally low level. Insulin has been reported to increase its activity in liver. Thyroid hormones may increase the synthesis of adenylate cyclase, thus potentiating the effects of epinephrine in stimulating the formation of cAMP.

3',5'-Adenylic acid (cyclic AMP; cAMP)

Increasing concentration of cAMP activates an enzyme of rather wide specificity, **cAMP-dependent protein kinase.** This kinase catalyzes the phosphorylation by ATP of inactive **phosphorylase kinase b** to active **phosphorylase kinase a,** which in turn, by means of a further phosphorylation, activates phosphorylase b to phosphorylase a (Fig 15–10).

Inactive cAMP-dependent protein kinase comprises 2 pairs of subunits, each pair consisting of a regulatory subunit (R), which binds 2 mol of cAMP, and a catalytic subunit (C), which contains the active site. Combination with cAMP causes the R_2C_2 complex to dissociate, releasing active C monomers

$$R_2C_2 + 4\ cAMP \leftrightarrow 2\ C + (cAMP)_4R_2$$

| Inactive enzyme | | Active enzyme | |

Activation by Ca²⁺ & Synchronization With Muscle Contraction

Glycogenolysis increases in muscle several hundred-fold immediately after the onset of contraction. This involves the rapid activation of phosphorylase owing to activation of phosphorylase kinase by Ca^{2+}, the same signal that initiates contraction. Muscle phosphorylase kinase has 4 types of subunits, α, β, γ, and δ, in a structure represented as $(\alpha\beta\gamma\delta)_4$. The α and β subunits contain serine residues that are phosphorylated by cAMP-dependent protein kinase. The β subunit binds 4 Ca^{2+} and is identical to the Ca^{2+} binding protein **calmodulin.** The binding of Ca^{2+} activates the catalytic site of the γ subunit while the molecule remains in the dephosphorylated b configuration. However, the phosphorylated a form is only fully activated in the presence of Ca^{2+}. It is of significance that calmodulin is similar in structure to TpC, the Ca^{2+} binding protein in muscle (see p 485). A second molecule of calmodulin or TpC can interact with the phosphorylase kinase, causing further activation. Thus, activation of muscle contraction and glycogenolysis are carried out by the same Ca^{2+} binding protein (Cohen, 1983).

Inactivation of Phosphorylase

Both phosphorylase a and phosphorylase kinase a are dephosphorylated and inactivated by protein phosphatase-1. Protein phosphatase-1 is inhibited by a protein called **inhibitor-1,** which is active only after it has been phosphorylated by cAMP-dependent protein kinase. Thus, cAMP controls both the activation and inactivation of phosphorylase (Fig 15–10).

GLYCOGEN SYNTHASE ACTIVATION & INACTIVATION

Like phosphorylase, glycogen synthase exists in either a phosphorylated or nonphosphorylated state. However, unlike phosphorylase, the active form is dephosphorylated (**glycogen synthase a**) and may be inactivated to **glycogen synthase b** by phosphorylation on 7 serine residues by no less than 6 different protein kinases. All 7 phosphorylation sites are contained on each of 4 identical subunits. Two of the protein kinases are Ca^{2+}-calmodulin-dependent (one of these is phosphorylase kinase). Another kinase is cAMP-dependent protein kinase, which allows cAMP-mediated hormonal action to inhibit glycogen synthesis synchronously with the activation of glycogenolysis. The remaining kinases are known as glycogen synthase kinase-3, -4, and -5.

Glucose 6-phosphate is an allosteric activator of glycogen synthase b, causing a decrease in K_m for UDP-glucose and allowing glycogen synthesis by the phosphorylated enzyme. Glycogen also exerts an inhibition on its own formation, and insulin also stimulates glycogen synthesis in muscle by promoting dephosphorylation and activation of glycogen synthase b. Normally, dephosphorylation of glycogen synthase b

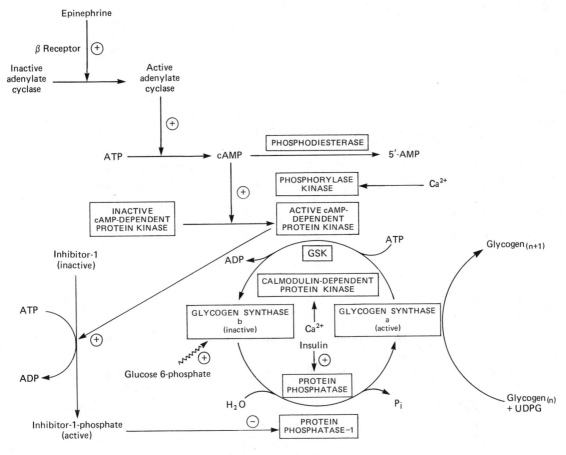

Figure 15–11. Control of glycogen synthase in muscle (n = number of glucose residues). The sequence of reactions arranged in a cascade allows amplification at each step, allowing only nanomole quantities of hormone to cause major changes in glycogen concentration. GSK, glycogen synthase kinase –3, –4, and –5.

is carried out by protein phosphatase-1, which is under the control of cAMP-dependent protein kinase (Fig 15–11).

Studies on **liver** (Exton) have shown that α_1 **receptors** are the major mediators of catecholamine stimulation of glycogenolysis. This involves a **cAMP-independent** mobilization of Ca^{2+} from mitochondria into the cytosol, followed by the stimulation of a Ca^{2+}**-calmodulin-sensitive phosphorylase kinase.** Skeletal muscle phosphorylase is not affected by glucagon, although heart muscle is. Another important difference is that liver protein phosphatase-1 is inhibited by the active form of phosphorylase (see p 263).

Further aspects of the regulation of glycogen metabolism are discussed on p 261.

Diseases of Glycogen Storage

The term "glycogen storage disease" is a generic one intended to describe a group of inherited disorders characterized by deposition of an abnormal type or quantity of glycogen in the tissues.

In **type I glycogenosis (von Gierke's disease),** both the liver cells and the cells of the renal convoluted tubules are characteristically loaded with glycogen. However, these glycogen stores are unavailable, as evidenced by the occurrence of hypoglycemia and a lack of glucose release under stimulus by epinephrine or glucagon. Ketosis and hyperlipemia are also present in these patients, as would be characteristic of an organism deprived of carbohydrate. In liver, kidney, and intestinal tissue, the activity of glucose 6-phosphatase is either extremely low or entirely absent.

Other types of glycogen storage disease include the following: **type II (Pompe's disease),** which is fatal and is characterized by a deficiency of lysosomal α-1,4- and 1,6-glucosidase (acid maltase) whose function is to degrade glycogen, which otherwise accumulates in the lysosomes; **type III (limit dextrinosis; Forbes', or Cori's, disease),** characterized by the absence of debranching enzyme, which causes the accumulation of a polysaccharide of the limit dextrin type; and **type IV (amylopectinosis; Andersen's disease),** characterized by the absence of branching enzyme, with the result that a polysaccharide having few branch points accumulates. Death due to cardiac or

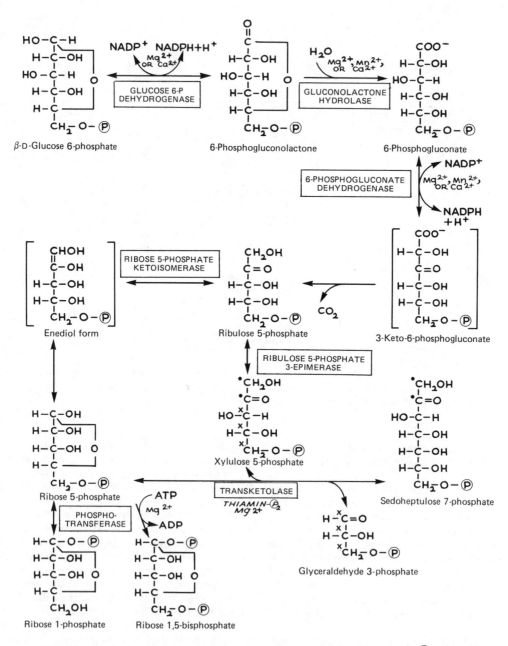

Figure 15–12. The hexose monophosphate shunt (pentose phosphate pathway). (Ⓟ, $-PO_3^{2-}$.)

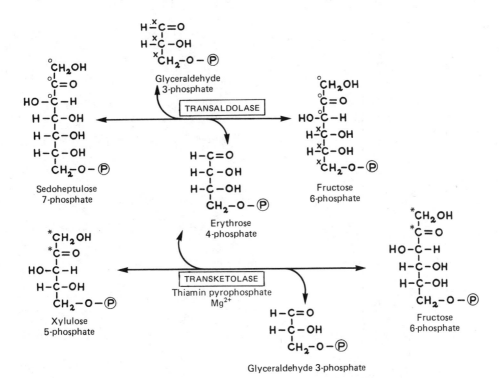

Figure 15–12 (cont'd). The hexose monophosphate shunt.

liver failure usually occurs in the first year of life.

An absence of muscle phosphorylase (myophosphorylase) is the cause of **type V glycogenosis (myophosphorylase deficiency glycogenosis; McArdle's syndrome).** Patients with this disease exhibit a markedly diminished tolerance to exercise. Although their skeletal muscles have an abnormally high content of glycogen (2.5–4.1%), little or no lactate is detectable in their blood after exercise. A rise in blood sugar does occur, however, after administration of glucagon or epinephrine, which indicates that hepatic phosphorylase activity is normal. In some of the reported cases, myoglobinuria has been an associated finding.

Also described among the glycogen storage diseases are phosphorylase deficiency in the liver **(type VI)**, a deficiency of phosphofructokinase in the muscles and erythrocytes **(type VII; Tarui's disease)**, and a glycogenosis in which liver phosphorylase kinase is deficient. Deficiencies of adenylate kinase and cAMP-dependent protein kinase have also been reported.

THE HEXOSE MONOPHOSPHATE SHUNT, OR PENTOSE PHOSPHATE PATHWAY

Major functions of the hexose monophosphate shunt are to provide NADPH for reductive syntheses outside the mitochondria and to provide ribose for nucleotide and nucleic acid synthesis.

Sequence of Reactions

This pathway for the oxidation of glucose occurs in certain tissues, notably liver, lactating mammary gland, and adipose tissue, in addition to the Embden-Meyerhof pathway of glycolysis. It is in effect a multicyclic process whereby 3 molecules of glucose 6-phosphate give rise to 3 molecules of CO_2 and three 5-carbon residues. The latter are rearranged to regenerate 2 molecules of glucose 6-phosphate and one molecule of glyceraldehyde 3-phosphate. Since 2 molecules of glyceraldehyde 3-phosphate can regenerate a molecule of glucose 6-phosphate by reactions that are essentially a reversal of glycolysis, the pathway can account for the complete oxidation of glucose. As in the Embden-Meyerhof glycolysis pathway, oxidation is achieved by dehydrogenation; but in the case of the shunt pathway, NADP and not NAD is used as a hydrogen acceptor. The enzymes of the shunt pathway are found in the **extramitochondrial** soluble portion of the cell.

A summary of the reactions of the hexose monophosphate shunt is shown below.

3 Glucose 6-P + 6 NADP$^+$ → 3 CO_2 + 2 Glucose 6-P +

Glyceraldehyde 3-P + 6 NADPH + 6 H$^+$

The sequence of reactions of the shunt pathway may be divided into 2 phases. In the first, glucose 6-phosphate undergoes dehydrogenation and decarboxylation to give the pentose, ribulose 5-phosphate. In the second phase, ribulose 5-phosphate is converted back to glucose 6-phosphate by a series of reactions

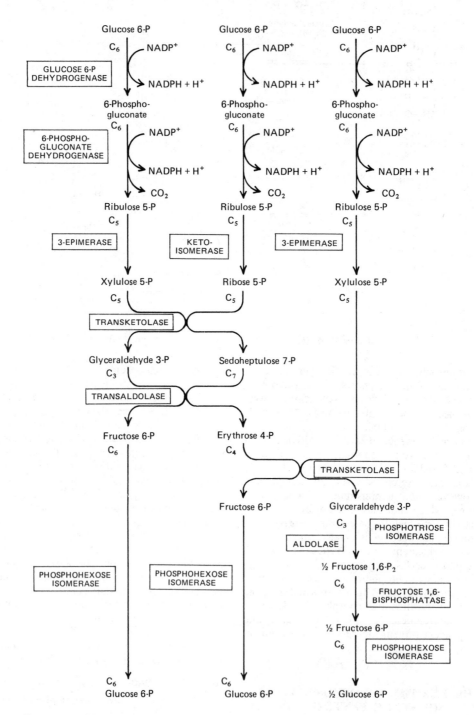

Figure 15–13. Flow chart of hexose monophosphate shunt (F-type pathway) and its connections with the Embden-Meyerhof pathway of glycolysis.

involving mainly 2 enzymes: **transketolase** and **transaldolase** (Fig 15–12).

Dehydrogenation of glucose 6-phosphate to 6-phosphogluconate occurs via the formation of 6-phosphogluconolactone catalyzed by **glucose 6-phosphate dehydrogenase,** an NADP-dependent enzyme. The hydrolysis of 6-phosphogluconolactone is accomplished by the enzyme **gluconolactone hydrolase.** A second oxidative step is catalyzed by **6-phosphogluconate dehydrogenase,** which also requires $NADP^+$ as hydrogen acceptor. Decarboxylation follows with the formation of the ketopentose, ribulose 5-phosphate. The reaction probably takes place in 2 steps through the intermediate 3-keto-6-phosphogluconate.

Ribulose 5-phosphate now serves as substrate for 2 different enzymes. **Ribulose 5-phosphate 3-epimerase** alters the configuration about carbon 3, forming the epimer xylulose 5-phosphate, another ketopentose. **Ribose 5-phosphate ketoisomerase** converts ribulose 5-phosphate to the corresponding aldopentose, ribose 5-phosphate. This reaction is analogous to the interconversion of fructose 6-phosphate and glucose 6-phosphate in the Embden-Meyerhof pathway.

Transketolase transfers the 2-carbon unit comprising carbons 1 and 2 of a ketose to the aldehyde carbon of an aldose sugar. It therefore effects the conversion of a ketose sugar into an aldose with 2 carbons less, and simultaneously converts an aldose sugar into a ketose with 2 carbons more. In addition to the enzyme transketolase, the reaction requires thiamin diphosphate as coenzyme and Mg^{2+} ions. The 2-carbon moiety transferred is probably glycolaldehyde bound to thiamin diphosphate, ie, "active glycolaldehyde." In the hexose monophosphate shunt, transketolase catalyzes the transfer of the 2-carbon unit from xylulose 5-phosphate to ribose 5-phosphate, producing the 7-carbon ketose sedoheptulose 7-phosphate and the aldose glyceraldehyde 3-phosphate. These 2 products then enter another reaction known as transaldolation. Transaldolase allows the transfer of a 3-carbon moiety, "active dihydroxyacetone" (carbons 1–3), from the ketose sedoheptulose 7-phosphate to the aldose glyceraldehyde 3-phosphate to form the ketose fructose 6-phosphate and the 4-carbon aldose erythrose 4-phosphate.

A further reaction takes place, again involving transketolase, in which xylulose 5-phosphate serves as a donor of "active glycolaldehyde." In this case the erythrose 4-phosphate formed above acts as acceptor, and the products of the reaction are fructose 6-phosphate and glyceraldehyde 3-phosphate.

In order to oxidize glucose completely to CO_2 via the shunt pathway, it is necessary that the enzymes are present in the tissue to convert glyceraldehyde 3-phosphate to glucose 6-phosphate. This involves the enzymes of the Embden-Meyerhof pathway working in a reverse direction and, in addition, the enzyme **fructose 1,6-diphosphatase.** A summary of the reactions is shown in Fig 15–13. Most of the reactions shown in that illustration are reversible, but the complete pathway is probably irreversible at the gluconolactone hydrolase step.

F-Type & L-Type Pathways

Williams has claimed that the pathway described above is found only in fat tissue (ie, F type), whereas a different pathway is found in liver and other tissues (L type). The L-type pathway is characterized by the actions of aldolase in a reaction involving arabinose 5-phosphate, dihydroxyacetone phosphate, and the 8-carbon sugar phosphate D-glycero D-ido octulose 1,8-bisphosphate. In addition, an octulose monophosphate and a sedoheptulose bisphosphate take part, together with 2 new enzyme activities—an epimerase and a phosphotransferase (Fig 15–14). However, the claims of Williams have been denied by several laboratory workers (eg, Landau), who state that the pathway in the liver is the classic pathway (ie, the F type).

Metabolic Significance of the Hexose Monophosphate Shunt

It is clear that this is markedly different from the Embden-Meyerhof pathway of glycolysis. Oxidation occurs in the first reactions, and CO_2, which is not produced at all in the Embden-Meyerhof pathway, is a characteristic product.

Estimates of the activity of the shunt pathway in various tissues give an indication of its metabolic significance. It is active in liver, adipose tissue, adrenal cortex, thyroid, erythrocytes, testis, and lactating mammary gland. It is not active in nonlactating mammary gland, and its activity is low in skeletal muscle. Most of the tissues in which the pathway is active use NADPH from the shunt in the synthesis of fatty acids or steroids and in the synthesis of amino acids via glutamate dehydrogenase. It is probable that the presence of active lipogenesis or of a system which utilizes NADPH stimulates an active degradation of glucose via the shunt pathway. The synthesis of glucose 6-phosphate dehydrogenase and 6-phosphogluconate dehydrogenase may also be induced during conditions associated with the "fed state."

The hexose monophosphate shunt in the erythrocyte provides NADPH for the reduction of oxidized glutathione (G–S–S–G) to reduced glutathione (2G–SH), catalyzed by **glutathione reductase.** In turn, reduced glutathione removes H_2O_2 from the erythrocyte in a reaction catalyzed by **glutathione peroxidase**

$$2G\text{–}SH + H_2O_2 \longrightarrow G\text{–}S\text{–}S\text{–}G + 2H_2O$$

This reaction is important, since accumulation of H_2O_2 may decrease the life span of the erythrocyte by increasing the rate of oxidation of hemoglobin to methemoglobin. An inverse correlation has been

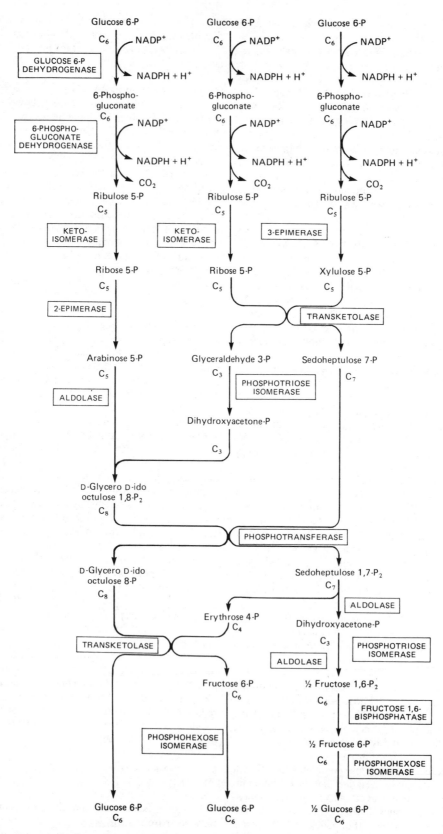

Figure 15–14. Flow chart of hexose monophosphate shunt (L-type pathway) and its connections with the Embden-Meyerhof pathway of glycolysis.

found between the activity of glucose 6-phosphate dehydrogenase and the fragility of red cells (susceptibility to hemolysis). A mutation present in some populations causes a deficiency in this enzyme that is manifested as red cell hemolysis when the susceptible individual is subjected to oxidants such as the antimalarial primaquine, aspirin, or sulfonamides, or when the susceptible individual has eaten fava beans (*Vicia fava*—favism).

The hexose monophosphate shunt provides pentoses for nucleotide and nucleic acid synthesis (Fig 15–12). The source of the ribose is the ribose 5-phosphate intermediate. This compound may be isomerized to the 1-phosphate (cf glucose 6-phosphate $\longleftrightarrow$ glucose 1-phosphate interconversion, p 174), or it can react with ATP to give ribose 1,5-bisphosphate (cf fructose 6-phosphate $\rightarrow$ fructose 1,6-bisphosphate). Muscle tissue contains very small amounts of glucose 6-phosphate dehydrogenase and 6-phosphogluconate dehydrogenase. Nevertheless, skeletal muscle is capable of synthesizing ribose. This is probably accomplished by a reversal of the shunt pathway utilizing fructose 6-phosphate. Thus, it is not necessary to have a completely functioning shunt pathway in order that a tissue may synthesize ribose. In human tissues, ribose seems to be derived primarily by way of the oxidative reactions of the shunt pathway, whereas in the rat and mouse—except in muscle—the nonoxidative reactions appear to play a larger role than the oxidative.

GLUCONEOGENESIS

The Basal Requirement for Glucose

Gluconeogenesis meets the needs of the body for glucose when carbohydrate is not available in sufficient amounts from the diet. A continual supply of glucose is necessary as a source of energy, especially for the nervous system and the erythrocytes. Below a critical blood glucose concentration, which varies among individuals and is dependent upon nutritional status, there is brain dysfunction, which under conditions of severe hypoglycemia can lead to coma and death. Glucose is also required in adipose tissue as a source of glyceride-glycerol, and it probably plays a role in maintaining the level of intermediates of the citric acid cycle in many tissues. It is clear that even under conditions where fat may be supplying most of the caloric requirement of the organism, there is always a certain basal requirement for glucose. In addition, glucose is the only fuel that will supply energy to skeletal muscle under anaerobic conditions. It is the precursor of milk sugar (lactose) in the mammary gland, and it is taken up actively by the fetus. It is not surprising, therefore, to find that enzymatic pathways have been developed in certain specialized tissues for the conversion of **noncarbohydrates to glucose,** ie, **gluconeogenesis.** In addition, these gluconeogenic mechanisms are used to clear the products of the metabolism of other tissues from the blood, eg, lactate, produced by muscle and erythrocytes, and glycerol,

which is continuously produced by adipose tissue. Propionate, the principal glucogenic fatty acid produced in the digestion of carbohydrates by ruminants, is a major substrate for gluconeogenesis in these species.

In mammals, the **liver** and the **kidney** are the principal organs responsible for gluconeogenesis. As the main pathway for gluconeogenesis is essentially a reversal of glycolysis, this can explain why the glycolytic activity of liver and kidney is low when there is active gluconeogenesis.

Metabolic Pathways Involved in Gluconeogenesis (Fig 15–15.)

These pathways are modifications and adaptations of the Embden-Meyerhof pathway and the citric acid cycle. They are concerned with the conversion of glucogenic amino acids, lactate, glycerol, and, in ruminants, propionate, to glucose or glycogen. It has been pointed out by Krebs that energy barriers obstruct a simple reversal of glycolysis (1) between pyruvate and phosphoenolpyruvate, (2) between fructose 1,6-bisphosphate and fructose 6-phosphate, (3) between glucose 6-phosphate and glucose, and (4) between glucose 1-phosphate and glycogen. These barriers are circumvented by special reactions described below:

(1) Present in mitochondria is an enzyme, **pyruvate carboxylase,** which in the presence of ATP, biotin, and CO_2 converts pyruvate to oxaloacetate. The function of the biotin is to bind CO_2 from bicarbonate onto the enzyme prior to the addition of the CO_2 to pyruvate (Fig 10–24). In the extramitochondrial part of the cell is found a second enzyme, **phosphoenolpyruvate carboxykinase,** which catalyzes the conversion of oxaloacetate to phosphoenolpyruvate. High-energy phosphate in the form of GTP or ITP is required in this reaction, and CO_2 is liberated. Thus, with the help of these 2 enzymes and lactate dehydrogenase, lactate can be converted to phosphoenolpyruvate.

However, oxaloacetate does not diffuse readily from mitochondria. Alternative means are available to achieve the same end by converting oxaloacetate into compounds that can diffuse from the mitochondria, followed by their reconversion to oxaloacetate in the extramitochondrial portion of the cell. Such a compound is malate, but conversion via aspartate, α-ketoglutarate, glutamate, and citrate has also been proposed. Their formation from oxaloacetate within mitochondria and their conversion back to oxaloacetate in the extramitochondrial compartment involve citric acid cycle reactions and transaminations. There are species differences with regard to the distribution of phosphoenolpyruvate carboxykinase. The extramitochondrial location is true for the rat and mouse; but in the rabbit and chicken the enzyme is located in the mitochondria, and in the guinea pig and human it is found in both the mitochondria and cytosol.

(2) The conversion of fructose 1,6-bisphosphate to fructose 6-phosphate, necessary to achieve a reversal of glycolysis, is catalyzed by a specific enzyme,

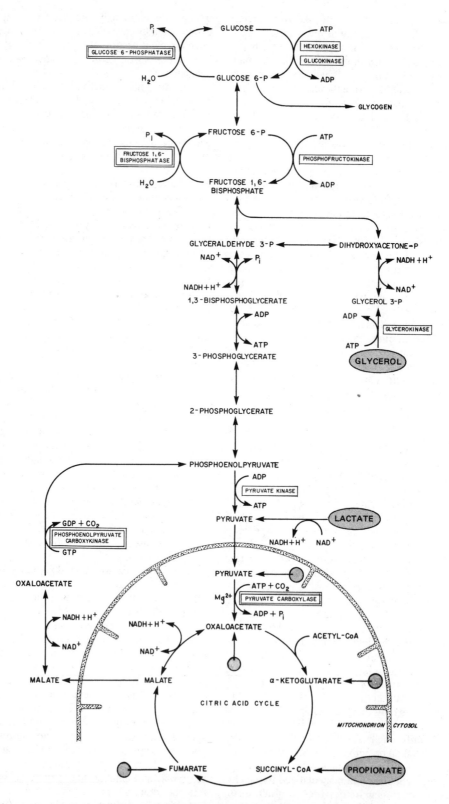

Figure 15–15. Major pathways of gluconeogenesis in the liver. Entry points of glucogenic amino acids after transamination are indicated by ◯→. (See also Fig 14–6.) The key gluconeogenic enzymes are shown thus ▭. The ATP required for gluconeogenesis is supplied by the oxidation of acetyl-CoA derived mainly from long-chain fatty acids or lactate (via pyruvate and pyruvate dehydrogenase). Propionate is of quantitative importance only in ruminants.

fructose 1,6-bisphosphatase. This is a key enzyme in the sense that its presence determines whether or not a tissue is capable of resynthesizing glycogen from pyruvate and triosephosphates. It is present in liver and kidney and has been demonstrated in striated muscle. It is held to be absent from heart muscle and smooth muscle.

(3) The conversion of glucose 6-phosphate to glucose is catalyzed by another specific phosphatase, **glucose 6-phosphatase.** It is present in intestine, platelets, liver, and kidney. Its presence allows a tissue to add glucose to the blood. The enzyme, which is microsomal, also possesses pyrophosphatase activity. It is absent from muscle and adipose tissue.

(4) The breakdown of glycogen to glucose 1-phosphate is carried out by phosphorylase. The synthesis of glycogen involves an entirely different pathway through the formation of uridine diphosphate glucose and the activity of **glycogen synthase** (Fig 15–7).

The relationships between these key enzymes of gluconeogenesis and the Embden-Meyerhof glycolytic pathway are shown in Fig 15–15. After transamination or deamination, glucogenic amino acids form either pyruvate or members of the citric acid cycle. Therefore, the reactions described above can account for the conversion of both glucogenic amino acids and lactate to glucose or glycogen. Thus, lactate forms pyruvate and enters the mitochondria before conversion to oxaloacetate and ultimate conversion to glucose. Propionate, which is a major source of glucose in ruminants, enters the main gluconeogenic pathway via the citric acid cycle after conversion to succinyl-CoA. Propionate is first activated with ATP and CoA by an appropriate **acyl-CoA synthetase.** Propionyl-CoA, the product of this reaction, undergoes a CO_2 fixation reaction to form D-methylmalonyl-CoA, catalyzed by **propionyl-CoA carboxylase** (Fig 15–16). This reaction is analogous to the fixation of CO_2 in acetyl-CoA by acetyl-CoA carboxylase (see Chapter 17) in that it forms a malonyl derivative and requires biotin as a

coenzyme. D-Methylmalonyl-CoA must be converted to its stereoisomer, L-methylmalonyl-CoA, by **methylmalonyl-CoA racemase** before its final isomerization to succinyl-CoA by the enzyme **methylmalonyl-CoA isomerase,** which requires vitamin B_{12} as a coenzyme (see Chapter 10). Vitamin B_{12} deficiency in humans and animals results in the excretion of large amounts of methylmalonate (**methylmalonic aciduria**).

Although the pathway to succinate is its main route of metabolism, propionate may also be used as the priming molecule for the synthesis—in adipose tissue and mammary gland—of fatty acids that have an odd number of carbon atoms in the molecule. C_{15} and C_{17} fatty acids are found particularly in the lipids of ruminants.

Glycerol is a product of the metabolism of adipose tissue, and only tissues that possess the activating enzyme, **glycerokinase,** can utilize it. This enzyme, which requires ATP, is found in liver and kidney, among other tissues. Glycerokinase catalyzes the conversion of glycerol to glycerol 3-phosphate. This pathway connects with the triosephosphate stages of the Embden-Meyerhof pathway, because glycerol 3-phosphate may be oxidized to dihydroxyacetone phosphate by NAD^+ in the presence of **glycerol 3-phosphate dehydrogenase** (Fig 17–17). Although the equilibrium constant is very much in favor of glycerol 3-phosphate formation, liver and kidney are able to convert glycerol to blood glucose by making use of the above enzymes, some of the enzymes of the Embden-Meyerhof pathway, and the specific enzymes of the gluconeogenic pathway, fructose 1,6-bisphosphatase and glucose 6-phosphatase (Fig 15–15).

METABOLISM OF HEXOSES

Phosphorylation

The hexoses of metabolic importance—glucose, fructose, and galactose—enter most metabolic path-

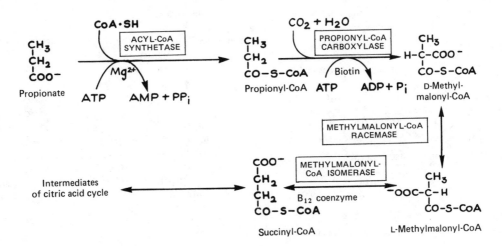

Figure 15–16. Metabolism of propionate.

ways, including glycolysis, after phosphorylation. As mentioned previously, glucose is phosphorylated by ATP in the presence of the enzyme **hexokinase;** but in liver parenchymal cells there is a more specific **glucokinase.** Most studies indicate that only glucokinase, and not hexokinase, is present in these hepatic cells. Hexokinase differs from glucokinase in that it is inhibited by glucose 6-phosphate (allosteric inhibition); it does not change in activity as a response to the nutritional or hormonal state of the animal; and it has a high affinity for glucose (low K_m). When glucose is the substrate, the product of the reaction with glucokinase or hexokinase is glucose 6-phosphate.

Fructose and galactose are not phosphorylated in the presence of glucokinase, but they have their own specific enzymes, **fructokinase** and **galactokinase,** which carry out phosphorylation in the liver. These

enzymes always convert the hexose to the corresponding hexose 1-phosphate.

MINOR PATHWAYS OF GLUCOSE METABOLISM

THE URONIC ACID PATHWAY

Besides the major pathways of metabolism of glucose 6-phosphate that have been described, there exists a pathway for the conversion of glucose to glucuronic acid, ascorbic acid, and pentoses that is referred to as the **uronic acid pathway.** It is also an alternative oxidative pathway for glucose, but like the

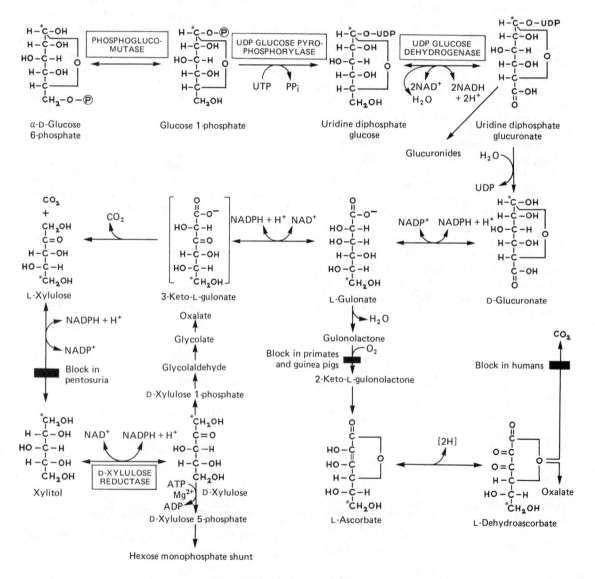

Figure 15–17. Uronic acid pathway.

hexose monophosphate shunt, it does not lead to the generation of ATP.

In the uronic acid pathway, glucuronic acid is formed from glucose by the reactions shown in Fig 15–17. Glucose 6-phosphate is converted to glucose 1-phosphate, which then reacts with uridine triphosphate (UTP) to form the active nucleotide, uridine diphosphate glucose (UDPG). This latter reaction is catalyzed by the enzyme **UDPG pyrophosphorylase.** All of the steps up to this point are those previously indicated as in the pathway of glycogenesis in the liver. UDPG is oxidized at carbon 6 by a 2-step process to glucuronate. The product of the oxidation, which is catalyzed by an NAD-dependent **UDPG dehydrogenase,** is **UDP-glucuronate.**

UDP-glucuronate is the "active" form of glucuronate for reactions involving incorporation of glucuronic acid into chondroitin sulfate or for reactions in which glucuronate is conjugated to such substrates as steroid hormones, certain drugs, or bilirubin (Fig 24–15).

In an NADPH-dependent reaction, glucuronate is reduced to L-gulonate (Fig 15–17). This latter compound is the direct precursor of ascorbate in those animals capable of synthesizing this vitamin. In humans and other primates as well as in guinea pigs, ascorbic acid cannot be synthesized. Gulonate is oxidized to 3-keto-L-gulonate, which is then decarboxylated to the pentose, L-xylulose.

Xylulose is a constituent of the hexose monophosphate shunt pathway; but in the reactions shown in Fig 15–17, the L-isomer of xylulose is formed from ketogulonate. If the 2 pathways are to connect, it is therefore necessary to convert L-xylulose to the D-isomer. This is accomplished by an NADPH-dependent reduction to xylitol, which is then oxidized in an NAD-dependent reaction to D-xylulose; this latter compound, after conversion to D-xylulose 5-phosphate, is further metabolized in the hexose monophosphate shunt. Parenteral administration of xylitol may lead to **oxalosis** involving calcium oxalate deposition in brain and kidneys. This results from the conversion of D-xylulose to oxalate via xylulose 1-phosphate, glycolaldehyde, and glycolate formation (James et al, 1982).

In the rare hereditary disease termed **"essential pentosuria,"** considerable quantities of L-xylulose appear in the urine. It is now believed that this may be explained by the absence in pentosuric patients of the enzyme necessary to accomplish reduction of L-xylulose to xylitol.

Various drugs markedly increase the rate at which glucose enters the uronic acid pathway. For example, administration of barbital or of chlorobutanol to rats results in a significant increase in the conversion of glucose to glucuronate, L-gulonate, and ascorbate. This effect on L-ascorbic acid biosynthesis is shown by many drugs, including various barbiturates, aminopyrine, and antipyrine. It is of interest that these last 2 drugs have also been reported to increase the excretion of L-xylulose in pentosuric subjects.

METABOLISM OF FRUCTOSE

Fructose may be phosphorylated to form fructose 6-phosphate, catalyzed by the same enzyme, hexokinase, that accomplishes the phosphorylation of glucose (or mannose). (See Fig 15–18.) However, the affinity of the enzyme for fructose is very low compared with its affinity for glucose. It is unlikely, therefore, that this is a major pathway for fructose utilization.

Another enzyme, **fructokinase,** is present in liver and effects the transfer of phosphate from ATP to fructose, forming fructose 1-phosphate. It has also been demonstrated in kidney and intestine. This enzyme will not phosphorylate glucose, and, unlike glucokinase, its activity is not affected by fasting or by insulin, which may explain why fructose disappears from the blood of diabetic patients at a normal rate. The K_m for fructose of the enzyme in liver is very low, indicating a very high affinity of the enzyme for its substrate. It seems probable that this is the major route for the phosphorylation of fructose. **Essential fructosuria** results from a lack of hepatic fructokinase.

Fructose 1-phosphate is split into D-glyceraldehyde and dihydroxyacetone phosphate by **aldolase B,** an enzyme found in the liver. The enzyme also attacks fructose 1,6-bisphosphate. Absence of this enzyme leads to a **hereditary fructose intolerance.** D-Glyceraldehyde may gain entry to the glycolysis sequence of reactions via 3 possible routes. One is by the action of **alcohol dehydrogenase** to form glycerol, which, in the presence of **glycerokinase,** forms glycerol 3-phosphate. A second alternative involves **aldehyde dehydrogenase** which forms D-glycerate from D-glyceraldehyde. In rat liver, **D-glycerate kinase** catalyzes the formation of 2-phosphoglycerate, but this enzyme is not active in human liver. Another enzyme present in liver, **triokinase,** catalyzes the phosphorylation of D-glyceraldehyde to glyceraldehyde 3-phosphate. This appears to be the major pathway for the further metabolism of D-glyceraldehyde. The 2 triose phosphates, dihydroxyacetone phosphate and glyceraldehyde 3-phosphate, may be degraded via the Embden-Meyerhof pathway or they may combine under the influence of aldolase and be converted to glucose. The latter is the fate of much of the fructose metabolized in the liver.

One consequence of hereditary fructose intolerance and of another condition due to **fructose 1,6-bisphosphatase deficiency** is a fructose-induced hypoglycemia despite the presence of high glycogen reserves. Apparently, the accumulation of fructose 1-phosphate and fructose 1,6-bisphosphate inhibits the activity of liver phosphorylase.

If the liver and intestines of an experimental animal are removed, the conversion of injected fructose to glucose does not take place and the animal succumbs to hypoglycemia unless glucose is administered. However, according to a recent report (Björkman), the human kidney can convert fructose to glucose and lactate. In humans but not in the rat, a significant

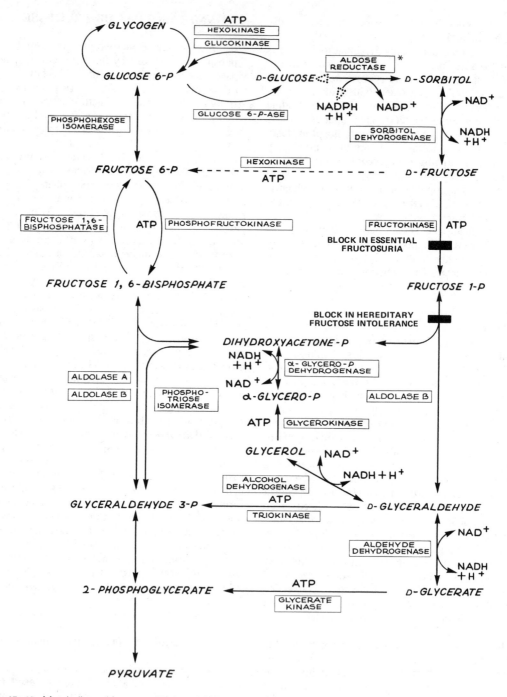

Figure 15–18. Metabolism of fructose. Aldolase A is found in all tissues except the liver, where only aldolase B is present. (*Not found in liver.)

amount of the fructose resulting from the digestion of sucrose is converted to glucose in the intestinal wall prior to passage into the portal circulation. Fructose is more rapidly glycolyzed by the liver than glucose. This is due most probably to the fact that it bypasses the step in glucose metabolism catalyzed by phosphofructokinase, at which point metabolic control is exerted on the rate of catabolism of glucose.

Studies have indicated that fructose is metabolized by adipose tissue and that it is metabolized independently of glucose. At low concentrations, fructose is utilized by epididymal adipose tissue of the rat more slowly than glucose; at high concentrations, fructose is metabolized at a faster rate than glucose.

Free fructose is found in seminal plasma and is secreted in quantity into the fetal circulation of ungulates and whales, where it accumulates in the amniotic and allantoic fluids. Both fructose and **sorbitol** are found in the human lens, where they increase in concentration in diabetes and may be involved in the pathogenesis of diabetic cataract. The **sorbitol (polyol) pathway** (not found in liver) is responsible for fructose formation from glucose (Fig 15–18) and increases in activity as the glucose concentration rises in diabetes. Sorbitol does not diffuse through cell membranes easily and therefore accumulates. Glucose undergoes reduction by NADPH to sorbitol catalyzed by **aldose reductase,** followed by oxidation of sorbitol to fructose in the presence of NAD and **sorbitol dehydrogenase** (polyol dehydrogenase). Aldose reductase is found in the placenta of the ewe and is responsible for the secretion of sorbitol into the fetal blood. As in adult liver, the presence of sorbitol dehydrogenase in fetal liver is responsible for the conversion of sorbitol into fructose. When sorbitol is administered intravenously, it is converted to fructose rather than to glucose, although if given by mouth, much escapes absorption from the gut and is fermented in the colon by bacteria to products such as acetate and H_2. Abdominal pain **(sorbitol intolerance)** may be caused by ''sugar-free'' sweeteners containing sorbitol.

METABOLISM OF GALACTOSE

Galactose is derived from the hydrolysis in the intestine of the disaccharide **lactose** (Fig 13–14), the sugar of milk. It is readily converted in the liver to glucose. The ability of the liver to accomplish this conversion may be used as a test of hepatic function in the galactose tolerance test. The pathway by which galactose is converted to glucose is shown in Fig 15–19.

In reaction ①, galactose is phosphorylated with the aid of **galactokinase,** using ATP as phosphate donor. The product, galactose 1-phosphate, reacts with **uridine diphosphate glucose** (UDPG) to form **uridine diphosphate galactose** and glucose 1-phosphate. In this step (reaction ②), which is catalyzed by an enzyme called **galactose 1-phosphate uridyl transferase,** galactose is transferred to a position on UDPG, replacing glucose. The conversion of galactose to glucose takes place (reaction ③) in a reaction of the galactose-containing nucleotide that is catalyzed by an **epimerase.** The product is uridine diphosphate glucose, UDPG. Epimerization probably involves an oxidation and reduction at carbon 4 with NAD as coenzyme. Finally (reaction ④), glucose is liberated

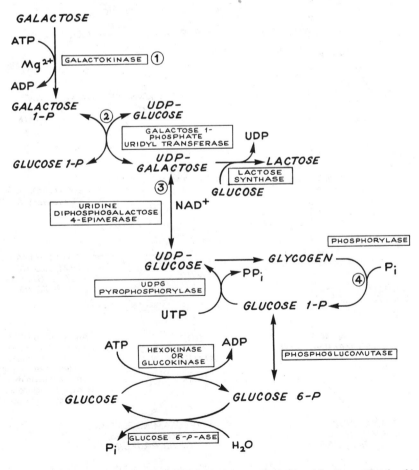

Figure 15–19. The pathway for conversion of galactose to glucose and for the synthesis of lactose.

from UDPG as glucose 1-phosphate, probably after incorporation into glycogen followed by phosphorolysis.

Reaction ③ is freely reversible. In this manner, glucose can be converted to galactose, so that preformed galactose is not essential in the diet. It will be recalled that galactose is required in the body not only in the formation of milk but also as a constituent of glycolipids (cerebrosides), proteoglycans, and glycoproteins.

Galactokinase is an adaptive enzyme, responding with an increased activity upon the feeding of galactose. Young animals show higher activity than adults.

In the synthesis of lactose in the mammary gland, glucose is converted to UDP-galactose by the enzymes described above. UDP-galactose condenses with glucose to yield lactose, catalyzed by **lactose synthase.**

Inability to metabolize galactose occurs in the **galactosemias,** which may be caused by inherited defects in any of the 3 enzymes marked ①, ②, and ③ in Fig 15–19, although a deficiency in the uridyl transferase (②) is the best known. Galactose, which increases in concentration in the blood, is reduced by aldose reductase in the eye to the corresponding polyol (galactitol), which accumulates, causing cataract. The general condition is more severe if it is due to a defect in the uridyl transferase, since galactose 1-phosphate accumulates and depletes the liver of inorganic phosphate. Ultimately, liver failure and mental deterioration result.

In inherited galactose 1-phosphate uridyl transferase deficiency in the liver and red blood cells (reaction ②), the epimerase (reaction ③) is, however, present in adequate amounts, so that the galactosemic

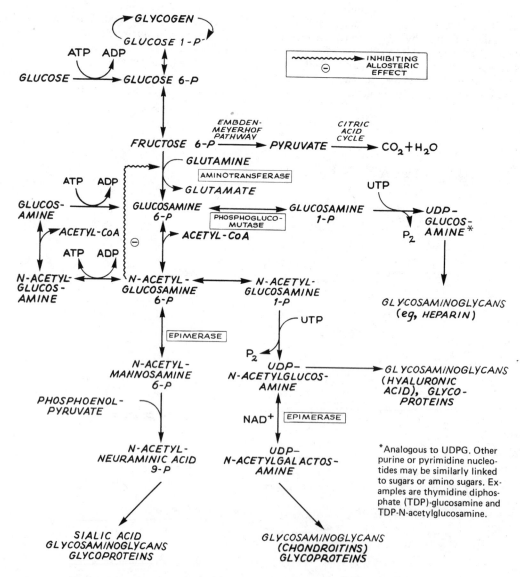

Figure 15–20. A summary of the interrelationships in metabolism of amino sugars.

individual can still form UDP-galactose from glucose. This explains how it is possible for normal growth and development of affected children to occur regardless of the galactose-free diets used to control the symptoms of the disease. Several different genetic defects have been described that cause reduced rather than total transferase deficiency. As the enzyme is normally present in excess, a reduction in activity to 50% or even less does not cause clinical manifestation of the disease, which is apparent only in homozygotes. The epimerase has been found deficient in erythrocytes but present in liver and elsewhere, and this third condition appears to be symptom-free.

Metabolism of Amino Sugars (Hexosamines)
(See Fig 15–20.)

Amino sugars are important components of the carbohydrates that are widely distributed throughout the body as a part of the structural elements of the tissues. The glycosaminoglycans (mucopolysaccharides; see Chapter 33) are examples of these ''structural'' carbohydrates. In contrast to glycogen, in which each unit of the polysaccharide is identical (a glucosyl unit), the glycosaminoglycans consist of units of 2 monosaccharides, one of which is an amino sugar.

A summary of the interrelationships in the metabolism of the amino sugars is shown in Fig 15–20. Note the pathways for the synthesis from glucose of N-acetylglucosamine and N-acetylgalactosamine as their active uridine diphosphate derivatives. Also note the pathway of synthesis of N-acetylneuraminic acid, another important amino sugar in glycoproteins and mucopolysaccharides.

• • •

References

Blass JP: Disorders of pyruvate metabolism. *Neurology* 1979; **29**:280.

Boyer PD (editor): *The Enzymes,* 3rd ed. Vols 5–9. Academic Press, 1972.

Brown DH, Brown BI: Some inborn errors of carbohydrate metabolism. Page 391 in: *MTP International Review of Science.* Vol 5. Whelan WJ (editor). Butterworth, 1975.

Busby JW, Radda GK: Page 89 in: *Current Topics in Cellular Regulation.* Vol 10. Academic Press, 1976.

Cohen P: *Control of Enzyme Activity,* 2nd ed. Chapman & Hall, 1983.

Dickens F, Randle PJ, Whelan WJ (editors): *Carbohydrate Metabolism and Its Disorders.* 2 vols. Academic Press, 1968.

Exton JH: Molecular mechanisms involved in α-adrenergic responses. *Mol Cell Endocrinol* 1981;**23**:233.

Geddes R et al: The molecular size and shape of liver glycogen. *Biochem J* 1977;**163**:201.

Greenberg DM (editor): *Metabolic Pathways,* 3rd ed. Vol 1. Academic Press, 1967.

Hers HG: The control of glycogen metabolism in the liver. *Annu Rev Biochem* 1976;**45**:167.

Hers HG: *Rev Int d'Hépatol* 1959;**9**:35.

Huijing F: Textbook errors: Galactose metabolism and galactosemia. *Trends Biochem Sci* 1978;**3**:N129.

James HM et al: Models for the metabolic production of oxalate from xylitol in humans. *Aust J Exp Biol Med Sci* 1982;**60**:117.

Krebs EG: Page 99 in: *Current Topics in Cellular Regulation.* Vol 5. Academic Press, 1972.

Krebs HA: Gluconeogenesis. *Proc R Soc Lond [Biol]* 1964; **159**:545.

Landau BR, Wood HG: The pentose cycle in animal tissues: Evidence for the classical and against the ''L-type'' pathway. *Trends Biochem Sci* 1983;**8**:292.

Lindahl U, Höök M: Glycosaminoglycans and their binding to biological macromolecules. *Annu Rev Biochem* 1978;**47**:385.

Marshall RD: Glycoproteins. *Annu Rev Biochem* 1972;**41**:673.

Randle PJ, Steiner DF, Whelan WJ (editors): *Carbohydrate Metabolism and Its Disorders.* Vol 3. Academic Press, 1981.

Rapoport S: Page 69 in: *Essays in Biochemistry.* Vol 4. Campbell PN, Greville GD (editors). Academic Press, 1968.

Sperling O, de Vries A (editors): *Inborn Errors of Metabolism in Man.* Karger, 1978.

Stanbury JB et al (editors): *The Metabolic Basis of Inherited Disease,* 5th ed. McGraw-Hill, 1983.

Weber G: Page 263 in: *The Biological Basis of Medicine.* Vol 2. Bittar EE, Bittar N (editors). Academic Press, 1968.

Whelan WJ: On the origin of primer for glycogen synthesis. *Trends Biochem Sci* 1976;**1**:13.

Williams JF: A critical examination of the evidence for the reactions of the pentose pathway in animal tissues. *Trends Biochem Sci* 1980;**5**:315.

16 | Lipids

Peter A. Mayes, PhD, DSc

The lipids are a heterogeneous group of compounds related, either actually or potentially, to the fatty acids. They have the common property of being (1) relatively insoluble in water and (2) soluble in nonpolar solvents such as ether, chloroform, and benzene. Thus, the lipids include fats, oils, waxes, and related compounds.

A lipoid is a "fatlike" substance that may not actually be related to the fatty acids, although occasionally the terms "lipid" and "lipoid" are used synonymously.

Lipids are important dietary constituents not only because of their high energy value but also because of the fat-soluble vitamins and the essential fatty acids contained in the fat of natural foods. In the body, fat serves as an efficient source of energy—both directly and potentially, when stored in adipose tissue. It serves as a thermal insulator in the subcutaneous tissues and around certain organs, and nonpolar lipids act as electrical insulators allowing rapid propagation of depolarization waves along myelinated nerves. The fat content of nerve tissue is particularly high. Combinations of fat and protein (lipoproteins) are important cellular constituents, occurring both in the cell membrane and in the mitochondria within the cytoplasm, and serving also as the means of transporting lipids in the blood.

Classification

The following classification of lipids has been proposed by Bloor:

A. Simple Lipids: Esters of fatty acids with various alcohols.

1. Fats–Esters of fatty acids with glycerol. A fat in the liquid state is known as an oil.

2. Waxes–Esters of fatty acids with higher molecular weight monohydric alcohols.

B. Compound Lipids: Esters of fatty acids containing groups in addition to an alcohol and a fatty acid.

1. Phospholipids–Lipids containing, in addition to fatty acids and an alcohol, a phosphoric acid residue. They also have nitrogen-containing bases and other substituents. In many phospholipids—eg, the glycerophospholipids—the alcohol is glycerol, but in others—eg, the sphingophospholipids—it is sphingosine.

2. Glycolipids–Compounds of the fatty acids with carbohydrate, containing nitrogen but no phosphoric acid.

3. Other compound lipids, such as sulfolipids and aminolipids. Lipoproteins may also be placed in this category.

C. Derived Lipids: Substances derived from the above groups by hydrolysis. These include fatty acids (both saturated and unsaturated), glycerol, steroids, alcohols in addition to glycerol and sterols, fatty aldehydes, and ketone bodies (see Ketosis, p 268).

Because they are uncharged, glycerides (acylglycerols), cholesterol, and cholesteryl esters are termed **neutral lipids.**

FATTY ACIDS

Fatty acids are carboxylic acids obtained from the hydrolysis of esters of mainly glycerol and cholesterol. Fatty acids that occur in natural fats usually contain an **even number** of carbon atoms (because they are synthesized from 2-carbon units) and are straight-chain derivatives. The chain may be saturated (containing no double bonds) or unsaturated (containing one or more double bonds).

Nomenclature

The most frequently used systematic nomenclature is based on naming the fatty acid after the hydrocarbon with the same number of carbon atoms, **-oic** being substituted for the final **e** in the name of the hydrocarbon (Genevan system). Thus, saturated acids end in **-anoic,** eg, octanoic acid, and unsaturated acids with double bonds end in **-enoic,** eg, octadecenoic acid (oleic acid). Carbon atoms are numbered from the carboxyl carbon (carbon No. 1). The carbon atom adjacent to the carboxyl carbon (No. 2) is also known as the α-carbon. Carbon atom No. 3 is the β-carbon, and the end methyl carbon is known as the ω-carbon or n-carbon. Various conventions are in use for indicating the number and position of the double bonds; eg, Δ^9 indicates a double bond between carbon atoms 9 and 10 of the fatty acid. A widely used convention is to indicate the number of carbon atoms, the number of double bonds, and the positions of the double bonds as shown in Figs 16–1 and 16–2.

A closer examination of the position of the double

18:1; 9

$$\overset{18}{CH_3}(CH_2)_7\overset{10}{CH}=\overset{9}{CH}(CH_2)_7\overset{1}{COOH}$$

or

ω9,C18:1

$$\overset{\omega}{CH_3}\overset{2}{CH_2}\overset{3}{CH_2}\overset{4}{CH_2}\overset{5}{CH_2}\overset{6}{CH_2}\overset{7}{CH_2}\overset{8}{CH_2}\overset{9}{CH}=CH(CH_2)_7COOH$$

Figure 16–1. Oleic acid.

18:2; 9, 12

$$\overset{18}{CH_3}(CH_2)_4\overset{13}{CH}=\overset{12}{CH}CH_2\overset{10}{CH}=\overset{9}{CH}(CH_2)_7\overset{1}{COOH}$$

or

ω6,C18:2

$$\overset{\omega}{CH_3}\overset{2}{CH_2}\overset{3}{CH_2}\overset{4}{CH_2}\overset{5}{CH_2}\overset{6}{CH}=CHCH_2\,CH=CH(CH_2)_7COOH$$

Figure 16–2. Linoleic acid.

bonds in naturally occurring fatty acids reveals that they are related to the –CH$_3$ or ω-end of the fatty acid rather than the carboxyl group. Thus, a series of fatty acids of increasing chain length or increasing desaturation based on oleic acid are ω9 or n−9 (n minus 9) acids, series based on linoleic acid are ω6 or n−6 acids, and a series based on linolenic acid are ω3 or n−3 acids. In animals, additional double bonds are introduced only **between the existing double bond (eg, ω9, ω6, or ω3, respectively) and the carboxyl carbon** (Figs 16–1 and 16–2).

Table 16–1. Saturated fatty acids.

	Number of C Atoms	
Acetic	2	Major end product of carbohydrate fermentation by rumen organisms
Propionic	3	An end product of carbohydrate fermentation by rumen organisms
Butyric	4	In certain fats in small amounts
Valeric	5	(especially butter). An end product
Caproic	6	of carbohydrate fermentation by rumen organisms.
Caprylic (octanoic)	8	In small amounts in many fats (including butter), especially those of
Decanoic (capric)	10	plant origin
Lauric	12	Spermaceti, cinnamon, palm kernel, coconut oils, laurels
Myristic	14	Nutmeg, palm kernel, coconut oils, myrtles
Palmitic	16	Common in all animal and plant
Stearic	18	fats
Arachidic	20	Peanut (arachis) oil
Behenic	22	Seeds
Lignoceric	24	Cerebrosides, peanut oil

Saturated Fatty Acids

Saturated fatty acids may be envisaged as based on acetic acid as the first member of the series. Examples of the acids in this series are shown in Table 16–1.

Other higher members of the series are known to occur, particularly in waxes. A few branched-chain fatty acids have also been isolated from both plant and animal sources.

Unsaturated Fatty Acids (Table 16–2)

These may be further subdivided according to degree of unsaturation.

A. Monounsaturated (Monoethenoid, Monoenoic) Acids.

B. Polyunsaturated (Polyethenoid, Polyenoic) Acids.

C. Eicosanoids: These compounds, derived from eicosapolyenoic fatty acids, comprise the **prostanoids** and **leukotrienes (LT).** Prostanoids include **prostaglandins (PG), prostacyclins (PGI),** and **thromboxanes (TX).** The term "prostaglandins" is often used loosely to include all prostanoids.

Prostaglandins were originally discovered in seminal plasma but are now known to exist in virtually every mammalian tissue and have important physiologic and pharmacologic activities. They are synthesized in vivo by cyclization of the center of the carbon chain of 20-C (eicosanoic) polyunsaturated fatty acids (eg, arachidonic acid) to form a cyclopentane ring (Fig 16–3). A related series of compounds, the **thromboxanes,** discovered in platelets, have the cyclopentane ring interrupted with an oxygen atom (oxane ring) (Fig 16–4). Three different eicosanoic fatty acids give rise to 3 groups of eicosanoids characterized by the number of double bonds in the acyl side chains, eg, PG$_1$, PG$_2$, PG$_3$. Variations in the substituent groups attached to the rings give rise to different types in each series of prostaglandins and thromboxanes, labeled A, B, etc. For example, the "E" type of prostaglandin (as in PGE$_2$) has a keto group in position 9, whereas the "F" type has a hydroxyl group in this position. PGI$_2$ is known as **prostacyclin.** The **leukotrienes** are a third group of eicosanoid derivatives formed via the lipoxygenase pathway (p 223) rather than cyclization of the fatty acid chain (Fig 16–5). First described in leukocytes, they are characterized by the presence of 3 conjugated double bonds.

D. Many other fatty acids have been detected in biologic material. Various structures, such as hydroxy groups (ricinoleic acid) or cyclic groups, have been

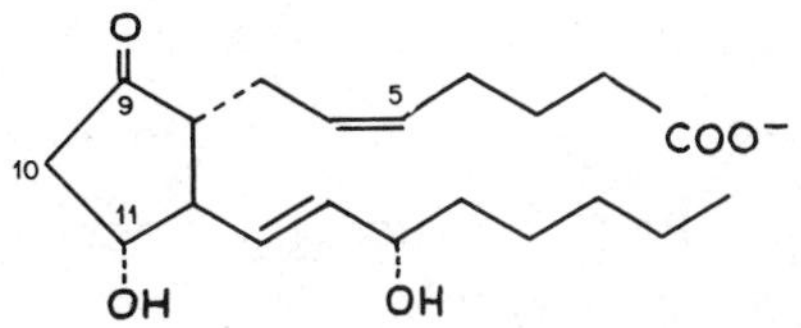

Figure 16–3. Prostaglandin E$_2$ (PGE$_2$).

Table 16–2. Unsaturated fatty acids.

Number of C Atoms and Position of Double Bonds	Series	Common Name	Systematic Name	Occurrence
Monoenoic acids (one double bond)				
16:1;9	ω7	Palmitoleic	*cis*-9-Hexadecenoic	In nearly all fats.
18:1;9	ω9	Oleic	*cis*-9-Octadecenoic	Possibly the most common fatty acid in natural fats.
18:1;9	ω9	Elaidic	*trans*-9-Octadecenoic	Hydrogenated and ruminant fats.
18:1;11	ω7	Vaccenic	*cis*-11-Octadecenoic	Synthesized by bacteria.
22:1;13	ω9	Erucic	*cis*-13-Docosenoic	Rape and mustard seed oils.
Dienoic acids (2 double bonds)				
18:2;9,12	ω6	Linoleic	all-*cis*-9,12-Octadecadienoic	Corn, peanut, cottonseed, soybean, and many plant oils.
Trienoic acids (3 double bonds)				
18:3;6,9,12	ω6	γ-Linolenic	all-*cis*-6,9,12-Octadecatrienoic	Some plants, eg, oil of evening primrose; minor fatty acid in animals.
18:3;9,12,15	ω3	α-Linolenic	all-*cis*-9,12,15-Octadecatrienoic	Frequently found with linoleic acid but particularly in linseed oil.
Tetraenoic acids (4 double bonds)				
20:4;5,8,11,14	ω6	Arachidonic	all-*cis*-5,8,11,14-Eicosatetraenoic	Found with linoleic acid particularly in peanut oil; important component of phospholipids in animals.
Pentaenoic acids (5 double bonds)				
20:5;5,8,11,14,17	ω3	Timnodonic	all-*cis*-5,8,11,14,17-Eicosapentaenoic	Important component of fish oils, eg, cod liver oil.
22:5;7,10,13,16,19	ω3	Clupanodonic	all-*cis*-7,10,13,16,19-Docosapentaenoic	Fish oils, phospholipids in brain.
Hexaenoic acids (6 double bonds)				
22:6;4,7,10,13,16,19	ω3		all-*cis*-4,7,10,13,16,19-Docosahexaenoic	Fish oils, phospholipids in brain.

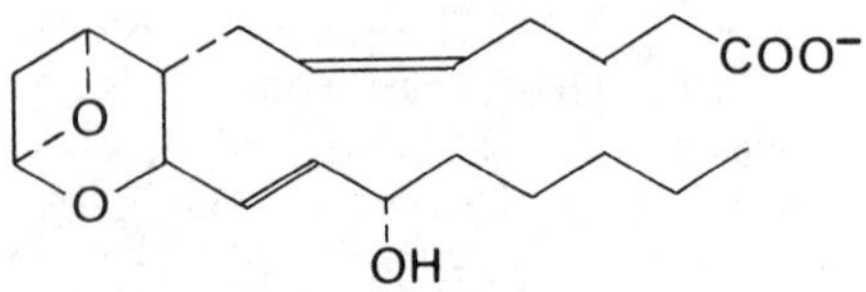

Figure 16–4. Thromboxane A_2 (TXA$_2$).

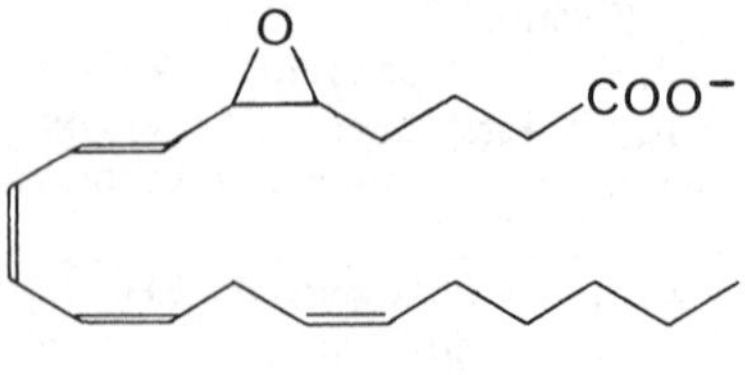

Figure 16–5. Leukotriene A_4 (LTA$_4$).

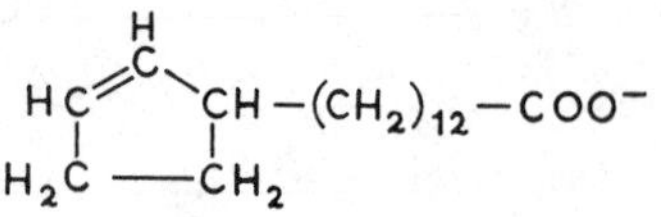

Figure 16–6. Chaulmoograte.

found. An example of the latter is chaulmoograte (Fig 16–6).

Isomerism in Unsaturated Fatty Acids

Variations in the location of the double bonds in unsaturated fatty acid chains produce isomers. Thus, oleic acid could have 15 different positional isomers.

Geometric isomerism depends on the orientation of atoms or groups around the axis of double bonds. Some compounds differ only in the orientation of their parts around this axis. This is noteworthy in the chemistry of steroids. If the radicals that are being considered are on the same side of the bond, the compound is called *cis*; if on opposite sides, *trans*. This can be illustrated with oleic and elaidic acids or with dicarboxylic acids such as fumarate and maleate (Fig 16–7).

In acids with a greater degree of unsaturation, there are, of course, more geometric isomers. Naturally occurring unsaturated long-chain fatty acids are nearly all of the *cis* **configuration,** the molecule being "bent" at the position of the double bond, as in Fig 16–7. Thus, arachidonic acid, having 4 double bonds, is U-shaped.

Alcohols

Alcohols associated with lipids include glycerol, cholesterol, and higher alcohols (eg, cetyl alcohol,

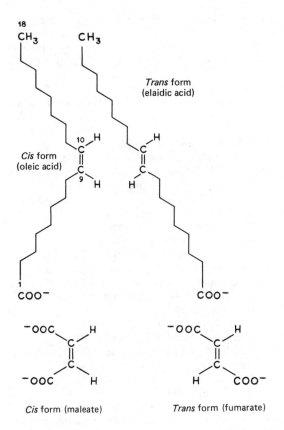

Figure 16–7. Geometric isomerism of oleic and elaidic acids and of maleate and fumarate.

$C_{16}H_{33}OH$), usually found in the waxes, and the polyisoprenoid alcohol dolichol (see p 202).

Among the unsaturated alcohols found in fats are a number of important pigments. These include phytol (phytyl alcohol), which is also a constituent of chlorophyll, and lycophyll ($C_{40}H_{56}O_2$), a polyunsaturated dihydroxy alcohol that occurs in tomatoes as a purple pigment.

Fatty Aldehydes

The fatty acids may be reduced to fatty aldehydes. These compounds are found either combined or free in natural fats.

TRIACYLGLYCEROLS*
(Triglycerides)

The triacylglycerols, or so-called neutral fats, are esters of the alcohol glycerol and fatty acids. In natu-

*According to the current standardized terminology of the International Union of Pure and Applied Chemistry (IUPAC) and the International Union of Biochemistry (IUB), the monoglycerides, diglycerides, and triglycerides are to be designated monoacylglycerols, diacylglycerols, and triacylglycerols, respectively. The older terminology may be used occasionally in this book.

rally occurring fats, the proportion of triacylglycerol molecules containing the same fatty acid residue in all 3 ester positions is very small. They are nearly all **mixed acylglycerols.**

In Fig 16–8, if all 3 fatty acids were the same and if R were $C_{17}H_{35}$, the fat would be known as tristearin, since it consists of 3 stearic acid residues esterified with glycerol. In a mixed acylglycerol, more than one fatty acid is involved (Figs 16–9 and 16–10).

Nomenclature

The numbering system has largely superseded the older α-, β- nomenclature. When it is required to number the carbon atoms of glycerol unambiguously, the -sn- (stereochemical numbering) system is used, eg, 1,2-distearyl-3-palmityl-sn-glycerol (as below, or more generally as a projection formula shown in Fig 16–11). It is important to realize that carbons 1 and 3 of glycerol are not identical when viewed in 3 dimensions (Fig 16–11). Enzymes readily distinguish between them and are nearly always specific for one or the other carbon; eg, glycerol is always phosphorylated on sn-3 by glycerokinase to give glycerol 3-phosphate and not glycerol 1-phosphate.

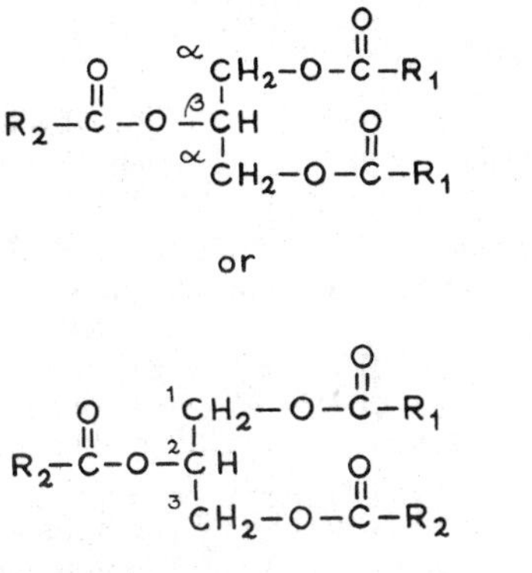

$$R_2-\overset{\overset{\displaystyle O}{\|}}{C}-O-\overset{\beta}{\underset{|}{C}}H\;\begin{matrix}\overset{\alpha}{C}H_2-O-\overset{\overset{\displaystyle O}{\|}}{C}-R_1\\[4pt]\overset{\alpha}{C}H_2-O-\overset{\overset{\displaystyle O}{\|}}{C}-R_1\end{matrix}$$

or

$$R_2-\overset{\overset{\displaystyle O}{\|}}{C}-O-\overset{2}{\underset{|}{C}}H\;\begin{matrix}{}^1CH_2-O-\overset{\overset{\displaystyle O}{\|}}{C}-R_1\\[4pt]{}^3CH_2-O-\overset{\overset{\displaystyle O}{\|}}{C}-R_2\end{matrix}$$

Figure 16–8. Triacylglycerols.

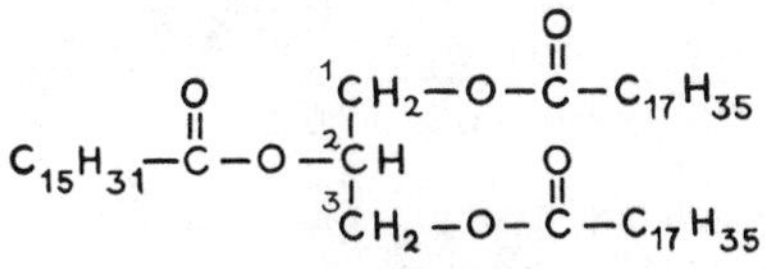

$$C_{15}H_{31}-\overset{\overset{\displaystyle O}{\|}}{C}-O-\overset{2}{\underset{|}{C}}H\;\begin{matrix}{}^1CH_2-O-\overset{\overset{\displaystyle O}{\|}}{C}-C_{17}H_{35}\\[4pt]{}^3CH_2-O-\overset{\overset{\displaystyle O}{\|}}{C}-C_{17}H_{35}\end{matrix}$$

Figure 16–9. 1,3-Distearopalmitin (or α,α'-distearopalmitin).

$$C_{17}H_{35}-\overset{\overset{\displaystyle O}{\|}}{C}-O-\overset{2}{\underset{|}{C}}H\;\begin{matrix}{}^1CH_2-O-\overset{\overset{\displaystyle O}{\|}}{C}-C_{17}H_{35}\\[4pt]{}^3CH_2-O-\overset{\overset{\displaystyle O}{\|}}{C}-C_{15}H_{31}\end{matrix}$$

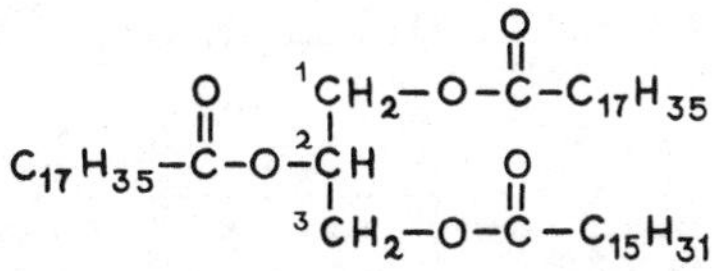

Figure 16–10. 1,2-Distearopalmitin (or α,β-distearopalmitin).

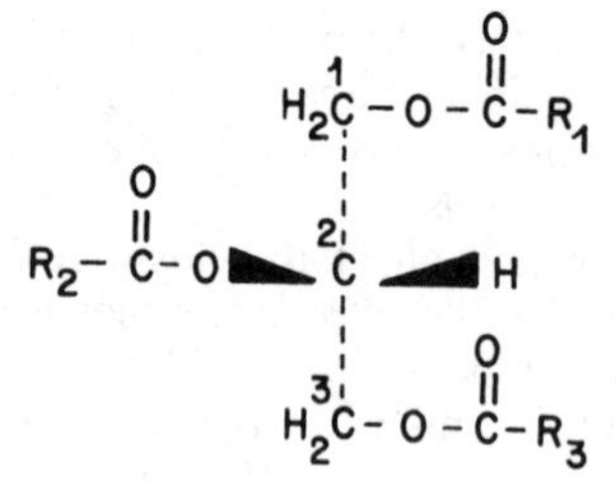

Figure 16–11. Triacyl-*sn*-glycerol.

Partial acylglycerols consisting of mono- and diacylglycerols wherein a single fatty acid or 2 fatty acids are esterified with glycerol are also found in the tissues. These are of particular significance in the synthesis and hydrolysis of triacylglycerols.

Waxes

If the fatty acid is esterified with a monohydric alcohol of high molecular weight instead of with glycerol, the resulting compound has a high melting point and is called a wax.

PHOSPHOLIPIDS

The phospholipids include the following: (1) phosphatidic acid and phosphatidylglycerols, (2) phosphatidylcholine, (3) phosphatidylethanolamine, (4) phosphatidylinositol, (5) phosphatidylserine, (6) lysophospholipids, (7) plasmalogens, and (8) sphingomyelins.

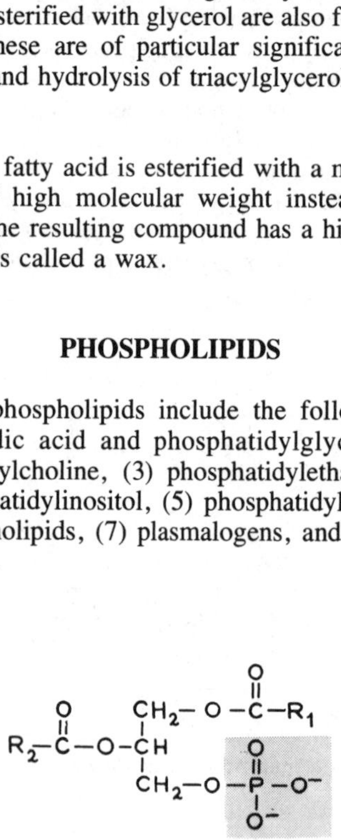

Figure 16–12. Phosphatidic acid.

Phosphatidic Acid & Phosphatidylglycerols

Phosphatidic acid is important as an intermediate in the synthesis of triacylglycerols and phospholipids but is not found in any great quantity in tissues (Fig 16–12).

Cardiolipin is a phospholipid that is found in membranes of mitochondria. It is formed from **phosphatidylglycerol** (Fig 16–13).

Phosphatidylcholine (Lecithin)

The lecithins contain glycerol and fatty acids, as do the simple fats, but they also contain phosphoric acid and choline. The lecithins are widely distributed in the cells of the body, having both metabolic and structural functions in membranes. Dipalmityl lecithin is a very effective surface active agent, preventing adherence, due to surface tension, of the inner surfaces of the lungs. Its absence from the lungs of premature infants causes respiratory distress syndrome. However, most phospholipids have a saturated acyl radical in the C_1 position and an unsaturated radical in the C_2 position (Fig 16–14).

Phosphatidylethanolamine (Cephalin)

The cephalins differ from lecithins only in that ethanolamine replaces choline (Fig 16–15).

Phosphatidylinositol

Inositol as a constituent of lipids was first discovered in acid-fast bacteria. Later it was found to occur in phospholipids of brain tissue and of soybeans as well as in other plant phospholipids. The inositol is present as the stereoisomer, myo-inositol (Fig 16–16). **Phosphatidylinositol 4,5-bisphosphate** is an important constituent of cell membrane phospholipids; upon stimulation by a suitable hormone agonist, it is cleaved into **diacylglycerol** and **inositol triphosphate,** both of which act as internal signals or second messengers.

Phosphatidylserine (See Fig 16–17.)

A cephalinlike phospholipid, phosphatidylserine, which contains the amino acid serine rather than ethanolamine, has been found in tissues. In addition, phospholipids containing threonine have been isolated from natural sources.

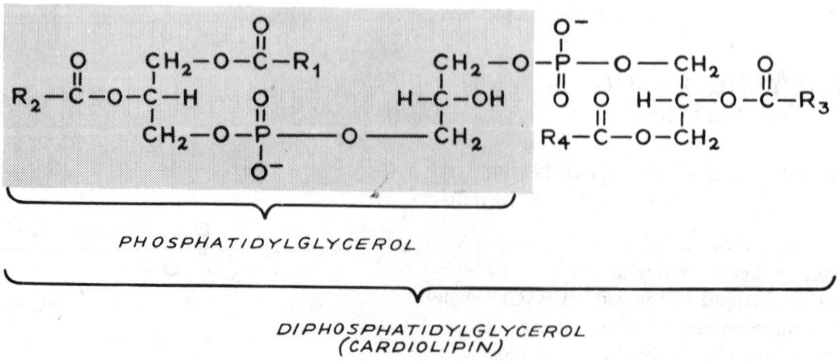

Figure 16–13. Diphosphatidylglycerol (cardiolipin).

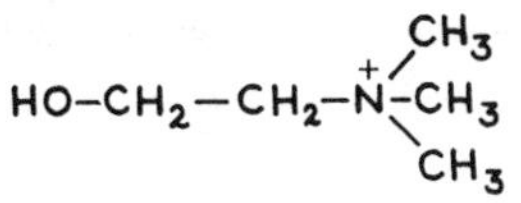

Choline

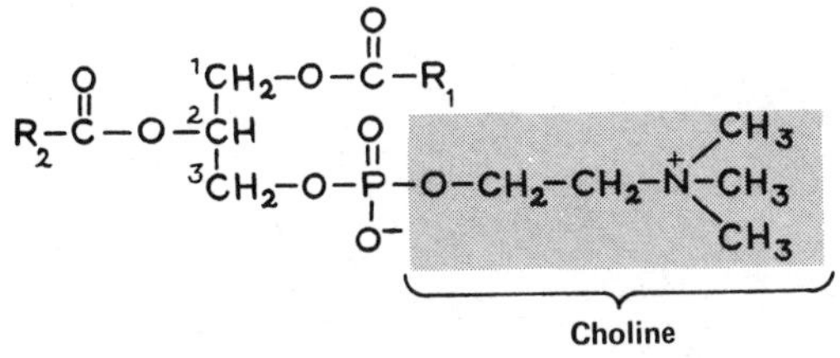

$$HO-CH_2-CH_2-\overset{+}{\underset{\underset{CH_3}{|}}{\overset{\overset{CH_3}{|}}{N}}}-CH_3$$

$$R_2-\overset{O}{\overset{||}{C}}-O-\overset{2}{\underset{\underset{3CH_2-O-\overset{O}{\underset{\underset{O^-}{|}}{\overset{||}{P}}}-O-CH_2-CH_2-\overset{+}{\underset{\underset{CH_3}{|}}{\overset{\overset{CH_3}{|}}{N}}}-CH_3}{|}}{\overset{\overset{1CH_2-O-\overset{O}{\overset{||}{C}}-R_1}{|}}{CH}}}$$

Choline

Figure 16–14. 3-Phosphatidylcholine.

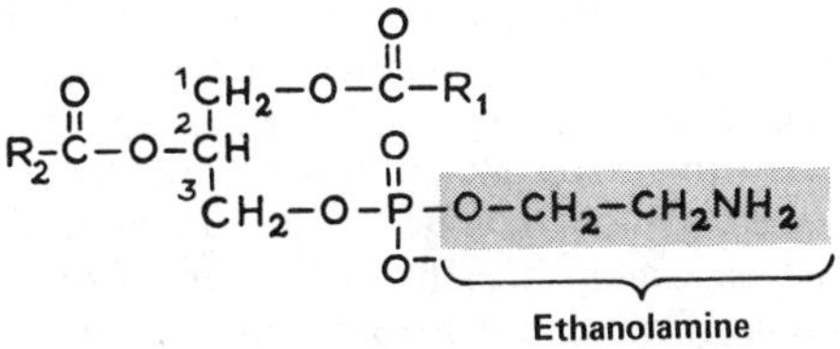

$$R_2-\overset{O}{\overset{||}{C}}-O-\overset{2}{\underset{\underset{3CH_2-O-\overset{O}{\underset{\underset{O^-}{|}}{\overset{||}{P}}}-O-CH_2-CH_2NH_2}{|}}{\overset{\overset{1CH_2-O-\overset{O}{\overset{||}{C}}-R_1}{|}}{CH}}}$$

Ethanolamine

Figure 16–15. 3-Phosphatidylethanolamine.

$$R_2-\overset{O}{\overset{||}{C}}-O-\overset{2}{\underset{\underset{3CH_2-O-\overset{O}{\underset{\underset{O^-}{|}}{\overset{||}{P}}}-O}{|}}{\overset{\overset{1CH_2-O-\overset{O}{\overset{||}{C}}-R_1}{|}}{CH}}}$$

Myo-inositol

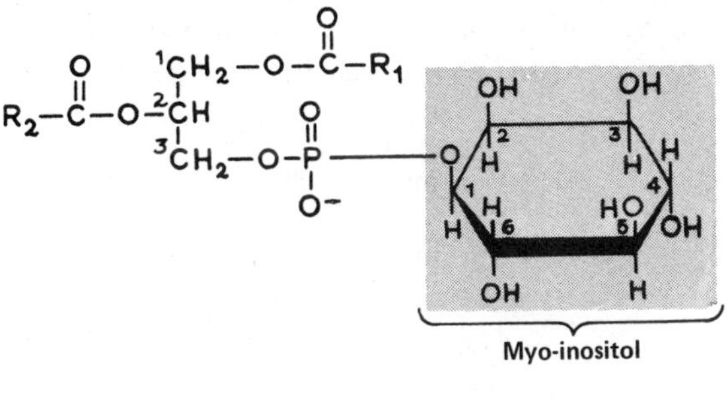

Figure 16–16. 3-Phosphatidylinositol.

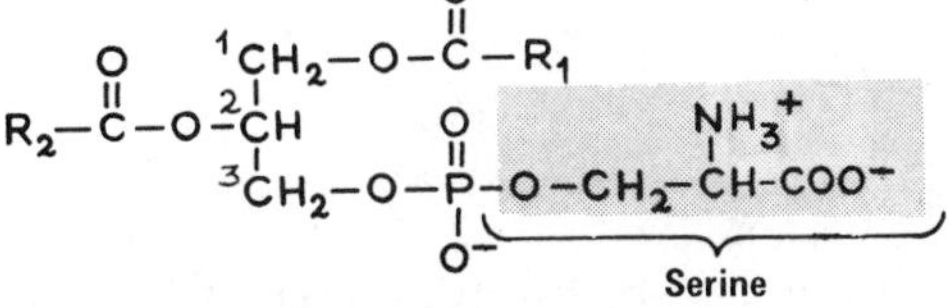

$$R_2-\overset{O}{\overset{||}{C}}-O-\overset{2}{\underset{\underset{3CH_2-O-\overset{O}{\underset{\underset{O^-}{|}}{\overset{||}{P}}}-O-CH_2-\overset{\overset{NH_3^+}{|}}{CH}-COO^-}{|}}{\overset{\overset{1CH_2-O-\overset{O}{\overset{||}{C}}-R_1}{|}}{CH}}}$$

Serine

Figure 16–17. 3-Phosphatidylserine.

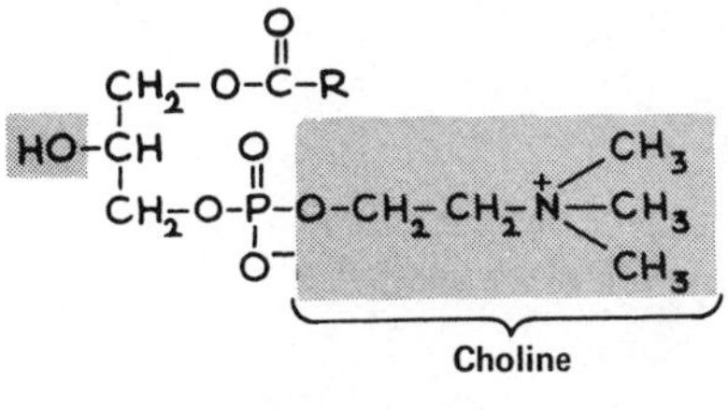

$$HO-\overset{\overset{CH_2-O-\overset{O}{\overset{||}{C}}-R}{|}}{\underset{\underset{CH_2-O-\overset{O}{\underset{\underset{O^-}{|}}{\overset{||}{P}}}-O-CH_2-CH_2-\overset{+}{\underset{\underset{CH_3}{|}}{\overset{\overset{CH_3}{|}}{N}}}-CH_3}{|}}{CH}}$$

Choline

Figure 16–18. Lysolecithin.

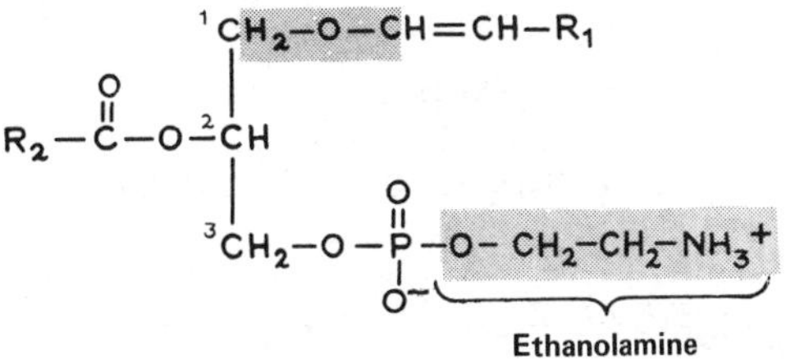

$$R_2-\overset{O}{\overset{||}{C}}-O-\overset{2}{\underset{\underset{3CH_2-O-\overset{O}{\underset{\underset{O^-}{|}}{\overset{||}{P}}}-O-CH_2-CH_2-NH_3^+}{|}}{\overset{\overset{1CH_2-O-CH=CH-R_1}{}}{CH}}}$$

Ethanolamine

Figure 16–19. Structure of plasmalogen (phosphatidal ethanolamine).

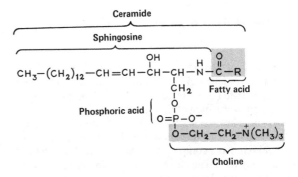

Figure 16–20. Structure of a sphingomyelin.

Lysophospholipids

These are phosphoacylglycerols containing only one acyl radical, eg, lysolecithin (Fig 16–18).

Plasmalogens (See Fig 16–19.)

These compounds constitute as much as 10% of the phospholipids of brain and muscle. Structurally, the plasmalogens resemble phosphatidylethanolamine but possess an ether link on the C_1 carbon instead of the normal ester link found in most acylglycerols. Typically, the alkyl radical is an unsaturated alcohol.

In some instances, choline, serine, or inositol may be substituted for ethanolamine.

Sphingomyelins

Sphingomyelins are found in large quantities in brain and nerve tissue (see Chapter 17). On hydrolysis, the sphingomyelins yield a fatty acid, phosphoric acid, choline, and a complex amino alcohol, sphingosine (Fig 16–20). No glycerol is present. The combination sphingosine plus fatty acid is known as **ceramide,** a structure also found in the glycolipids (see below).

GLYCOLIPIDS
(Glycosphingolipids)

Glycolipids contain **ceramide** plus **galactose.** Therefore, they may also be classified with the sphingomyelins as **sphingolipids.** Simple glycolipids contain only galactose, a high-molecular-weight fatty acid, and sphingosine. They are known as **cerebrosides.** Individual cerebrosides are differentiated by

$$CH_3-(CH_2)_{22}-COO^-$$

Lignocerate

$$CH_3-(CH_2)_{21}-CH(OH)-COO^-$$

Cerebronate

$$CH_3-(CH_2)_7-CH=CH-(CH_2)_{13}-COO^-$$

Nervonate

$$CH_3-(CH_2)_7-CH=CH-(CH_2)_{12}-CH(OH)-COO^-$$

Oxynervonate

Figure 16–21. Characteristic fatty acids of cerebrosides.

the type of fatty acid in the molecule. These are **kerasin,** containing lignocerate; **cerebron,** with a hydroxy lignocerate (cerebronate); **nervon,** containing an unsaturated homolog of lignocerate called nervonate; and **oxynervon,** having the hydroxy derivative of nervonate as its constituent fatty acid (Fig 16–21). Stearic acid is a major component of the fatty acids of rat brain cerebrosides. The cerebrosides are found in many tissues besides brain and the myelin of nerve fibers.

Sulfatides are cerebrosides in which the galactose residue is sulfated (Fig 16–22). They are representative of a subgroup of the **sulfolipids** known as **sulfosphingolipids.** Two other subgroups of the sulfolipids are the **sulfoglycerolipids,** which are sulfogalactoalkyl derivatives of glycerol, and the **steroid sulfates** such as cholesterol sulfate.

Gangliosides (Fig 16–23) are more complex glycolipids that occur in the brain. They contain **sialic acid,** eg, N-acetylneuraminic acid (Nana; see p 156), **ceramide** (containing fatty acids of which 80–90% are of C-18 chain length), and **3 molecules of hexose** (glucose and galactose). Hexosamine is a common constituent of virtually all naturally occurring gangliosides; the N-acetylneuraminic acid (Nana) content varies between 1 and 5 molecules per molecule of ganglioside, giving rise to di-, trisialogangliosides, etc.

Ceramide–Glucose–Galactose–N–Acetylgalactosamine–Galactose
(Acyl-
sphingo-
sine)   Nana

or

Cer–Glc–Gal–GalNAc–Gal
                    |
                  Nana

Figure 16–23. G_{M1} ganglioside, a monosialoganglioside.

STEROIDS

The steroids are often found in association with fat. They may be separated from the fat after saponification (see p 204), since they occur in the "unsaponifiable residue." All of the steroids have a similar cyclic nucleus resembling phenanthrene (rings A, B, and C) to which a cyclopentane ring (D) is attached. However, the rings are not uniformly saturated, so the parent (completely saturated) substance is better designated as cyclopentanoperhydrophenanthrene. The carbon positions on the steroid nucleus are numbered as shown in Fig 16–24.

It is important to realize that in structural formulas of steroids, a simple hexagonal ring denotes a completely saturated 6-carbon ring with all valences satisfied by hydrogen bonds unless shown otherwise; ie, it is not a benzene ring. All double bonds are shown as

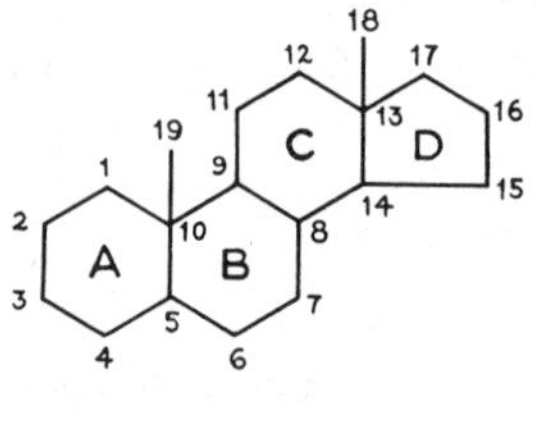

Figure 16–24. Cyclopentanoperhydrophenanthrene nucleus.

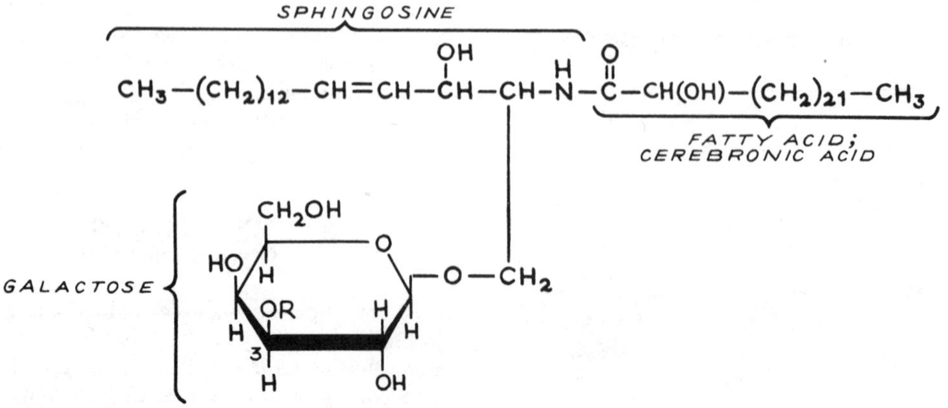

Figure 16–22. Structure of a cerebroside (R=H) and a sulfatide (cerebroside sulfate, R=SO$_4^{2-}$).

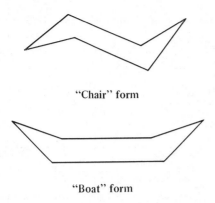

"Chair" form

"Boat" form

Figure 16–25. Conformations of stereoisomers.

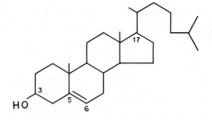

Figure 16–27. Cholesterol.

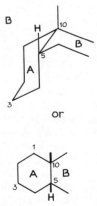

Figure 16–28. Ergosterol.

such. Methyl side chains are shown as single bonds unattached at the farther (methyl) end. These occur typically at positions 10 and 13 (constituting C atoms 19 and 18). A side chain at position 17 is usual (as in cholesterol). If the compound has one or more hydroxyl groups and no carbonyl or carboxyl groups, it is a **sterol,** and the name terminates in -ol.

Stereochemical Aspects

Because of their complexity and the possibilities of asymmetry in the molecule, steroids have many potential stereoisomers. Each of the 6-carbon rings of the steroid nucleus is capable of existing in the 3-dimensional conformation either of a "chair" or a "boat" (Fig 16–25).

In naturally occurring steroids, virtually all the rings are in the "chair" form, which is the more stable conformation. With respect to each other, the rings can be either -*cis* or -*trans* (Fig 16–26).

The junction between the A and B rings can be -*cis* or -*trans* in naturally occurring steroids. That between B and C is -*trans* and the C/D junction is -*trans* except in cardiac glycosides and toad poisons. Bonds attaching substituent groups above the plane of the rings are shown with bold solid lines (β), whereas

those bonds attaching groups below are indicated with broken lines (α). The A ring of a 5α steroid is always -*trans* to the B ring, whereas it is -*cis* in a 5β steroid. The methyl groups attached to C_{10} and C_{13} are invariably in the β configuration.

Cholesterol (See Fig 16–27.)

Cholesterol is widely distributed in all cells of the body, but particularly in nervous tissue. It is the parent compound of all steroids synthesized in the body. It occurs in animal fats but not in plant fats. The metabolism of cholesterol is discussed on p 249. Cholesterol is designated as 3-hydroxy-5,6-cholestene.

Ergosterol (See Fig 16–28.)

Ergosterol occurs in plants and yeast. It is im-

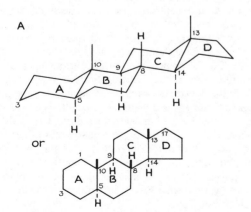

Figure 16–26. Generalized steroid nucleus, showing *(A)* an all-*trans* configuration between adjacent rings and *(B)* a *cis* configuration between rings A and B.

portant as a precursor of vitamin D. When irradiated with ultraviolet light, it acquires antirachitic properties consequent to the opening of ring B.

Coprosterol

Coprosterol (coprostanol) occurs in feces as a result of the reduction of the double bond of cholesterol between C_5 and C_6 by bacteria in the intestine. The orientation of rings A and B (between carbon atoms 5 and 10), which is *trans* in cholesterol, is *cis* in coprosterol.

Other Important Sterols & Steroids

These include the bile acids, adrenocortical hormones, sex hormones, D vitamins, cardiac glycosides, sitosterols of the plant kingdom, and some alkaloids.

Polyprenoid Compounds

Although not steroids, these compounds are related because they are synthesized, like cholesterol (see p 252), from 5-carbon isoprene units (Fig 16–29). They include **ubiquinone** (see p 135), a member of the respiratory chain in mitochondria, and the long-chain alcohol **dolichol** (Fig 16–30), which takes part in glycoprotein synthesis by transferring carbohydrate residues to asparagine residues of the polypeptide (see Chapter 33). Plant-derived isoprenoid compounds include rubber, camphor, the fat-soluble vitamins (see Chapter 11), and β-carotene (provitamin A).

$$\begin{array}{c} CH_3 \\ | \\ -CH=C-CH=CH- \end{array}$$

Figure 16–29. Isoprene unit.

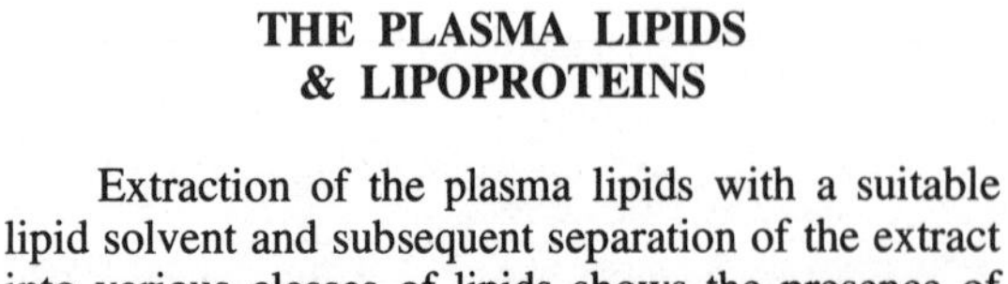

Figure 16–30. Dolichol—a C_{95} alcohol.

THE PLASMA LIPIDS & LIPOPROTEINS

Extraction of the plasma lipids with a suitable lipid solvent and subsequent separation of the extract into various classes of lipids shows the presence of triacylglycerols, phospholipids, cholesterol and cholesteryl esters, and, in addition, the existence of a much smaller fraction of unesterified long-chain fatty acids (free fatty acids) that accounts for less than 5% of the total fatty acid present in the plasma. This latter fraction, the **free fatty acids (FFA)**, is now known to be metabolically the most active of the plasma lipids. An analysis of blood plasma showing the major lipid

Table 16–3. Lipids of the blood plasma in humans.

Lipid	mg/dL	
	Mean	Range
Total lipid	570	360–820
Triacylglycerol	142	80–180*
Total phospholipid†	215	123–390
Lecithin		50–200
Cephalin		50–130
Sphingomyelins		15–35
Total cholesterol	200	107–320
Free cholesterol (nonesterified)	55	26–106
Free fatty acids (nonesterified)	12	6–16*

Total fatty acids (as stearic) range from 200–800 mg/dL; 45% are triacylglycerols, 35% phospholipids, 15% cholesteryl ester, and less than 5% free fatty acids.

*Varies with nutritional state.

†Analyzed as lipid phosphorus; mean lipid phosphorus = 9.2 mg/dL (range, 6.1–14.5). Lipid phosphorus × 25 = phospholipid as lecithin (4% phosphorus).

classes is given in Table 16–3.

Since lipids account for much of the energy expenditure of the body, the problem is presented of transporting a large quantity of hydrophobic material (lipid) in an aqueous environment (blood plasma). This is solved by associating the more insoluble lipids (triacylglycerols and cholesteryl esters) with more polar ones (phospholipids and cholesterol) and then combining them with protein to form a **hydrophilic lipoprotein complex.** It is in this way that triacylglycerols derived from intestinal absorption of fat or from the liver are transported in the blood as chylomicrons or very low density lipoproteins. Fat is released from adipose tissue in the form of free fatty acids and carried in the unesterified state in the plasma as an albumin-free fatty acid complex. Many classes of lipids are, therefore, transported in the blood as lipoproteins.

Pure fat is less dense than water; it follows that as the proportion of lipid to protein in lipoproteins increases, the density decreases. Use is made of this property in separating the various lipoproteins in plasma by ultracentrifugation. The rate at which each lipoprotein floats through a solution of NaCl (specific gravity 1.063) may be expressed in Svedberg (Sf) units of flotation. One Sf unit is equal to 10^{-13} cm/s/dyne/g at 26 °C. The composition of the various lipoprotein fractions obtained by centrifugation is shown in Table 16–4; the density of lipoproteins increases as the protein content rises and the lipid content falls and as the size of the particle becomes smaller. The various chemical classes of lipids are seen to occur in varying amounts in most of the lipoprotein fractions. Since the fractions represent the physiologic entities present in the plasma, mere chemical analysis of the plasma lipids (apart from FFA) yields little information on their physiology.

In addition to the use of techniques depending on their density, lipoproteins may be separated according to their electrophoretic properties (Fig 16–31) and may

Table 16—4. Composition of the lipoproteins in plasma of humans.

| | | | | | | | Composition | | | | |
| | | | | | | | Percentages of Total Lipid | | | | |
Fraction	Source	Diameter (nm)	Density	Sf	Protein (%)	Total Lipid (%)	Triacyl-glycerol	Phospho-lipid	Choles-teryl Ester	Choles-terol (Free)	Free Fatty Acids
Chylomicrons	Intestine	100–1000	< 0.96	> 400	1–2	98–99	88	8	3	1	...
Very low density lipoproteins (VLDL)	Liver and intestine	30–80	0.96–1.006	20–400	7–10	90–93	56	20	15	8	1
Low-density lipoproteins LDL$_1$ or IDL	VLDL and chylomi-crons	25–30	1.006–1.019	12–20	11	89	29	26	34	9	1
LDL$_2$		20–25	1.019–1.063	2–12	21	79	13	28	48	10	1
High-density lipoproteins HDL$_1$ *	Liver and intestine VLDL? Chylomi-crons?	20	1.063	0–2							
HDL$_2$		10–20	1.063–1.125		33	67	16	43	31	10	...
HDL$_3$		7.5–10	1.125–1.210		57	43	13	46	29	6	6
Albumin-FFA	Adipose tissue		> 1.2810		99	1	0	0	0	0	100

IDL, intermediate density lipoprotein; FFA, free fatty acids.

*This fraction is quantitatively insignificant.

be identified more accurately by means of im-munoelectrophoresis. Apart from FFA, 4 major groups of lipoproteins have been identified that are important physiologically and in clinical diagnosis. These are **chylomicrons,** very low density lipopro-teins (**VLDL** or pre-β-lipoproteins), low-density lipo-proteins (**LDL** or β-lipoproteins), and high-density lipoproteins (**HDL** or α-lipoproteins). Triacylglycerol is the predominant lipid in chylomicrons and VLDL, whereas cholesterol and phospholipid are the predom-inant lipids in LDL and HDL, respectively (Table 16-4).

The protein moiety of lipoproteins is known as apolipoprotein or apoprotein, constituting nearly 60%

of some HDL and as little as 1% of chylomicrons. Many lipoproteins contain more than one type of apo-protein polypeptide. They differ in their amino acid content and may be identified from their terminal amino acid residues or by polyacrylamide gel elec-trophoresis or by immunochemical methods. Apopro-teins are prepared by delipidation of isolated lipopro-teins. The lipid-free apoproteins may be purified by gel filtration, ion-exchange chromatography, or elec-trophoresis.

The larger lipoproteins—such as chylomicrons and VLDL—consist of a **lipid core** of **nonpolar triacylgylcerol** and **cholesteryl ester** surrounded by more polar phospholipid, cholesterol, and apoproteins that can solubilize the particle in the surrounding aque-ous plasma.

PROPERTIES & REACTIONS OF LIPIDS

Physical Properties

The physical properties of body lipids depend to a large extent on the lengths of the carbon chains and degree of unsaturation of their constituent fatty acids. Thus, the melting points of even-numbered–carbon fatty acids increase with chain length and decrease according to unsaturation. A triacylglycerol contain-ing all saturated fatty acids of 12 C or more is solid at body temperature, whereas if all 3 fatty acid residues are 18:2, it is liquid to below 0 °C. In practice, natural acylglycerols contain a mixture of fatty acids tailored to suit their functional roles. The membrane lipids,

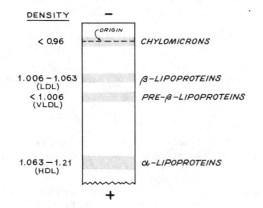

Figure 16–31. Separation of plasma lipoproteins by elec-trophoresis.

which must be fluid, are more unsaturated than storage lipids. Lipids in tissues that are subject to cooling, eg, in hibernators or in the extremities of animals, are more unsaturated.

Hydrolysis

Hydrolysis of a lipid such as a triacylglycerol may be accomplished enzymatically through the action of lipases, yielding fatty acids and glycerol. Use may be made of the property of pancreatic lipase to attack the ester bonds in positions 1 and 3 preferentially to position 2 of triacylglycerols. **Phospholipases** attack the various ester linkages in phospholipids. Their specificity may be used to analyze the components of phospholipids. The sites of action of the various phospholipases are discussed on p 227.

Saponification

Hydrolysis of a fat by alkali is called **saponification.** The products are glycerol and the alkali salts of the fatty acids, which are called **soaps.** Acid hydrolysis of a fat yields the free fatty acids and glycerol. Soaps are cleansing agents because of their emulsifying action. Some soaps of high molecular weight and a considerable degree of unsaturation are selective germicides. Others, such as sodium ricinoleate, have detoxifying activity against diphtheria and tetanus toxins.

Unsaponifiable Matter

Unsaponifiable matter includes substances in natural fats that cannot be saponified by alkali but are soluble in ether or petroleum ether. Since soaps are not ether-soluble, they may be separated from lipid mixtures by extraction with these solvents following saponification of the fat. Ketones, hydrocarbons, high-molecular-weight alcohols, and the steroids are examples of unsaponifiable residues of natural fats.

Hydrogenation

Hydrogenation of unsaturated fats in the presence of a catalyst (nickel) is known as "hardening." It is commercially valuable as a method of converting these liquid fats, usually of plant origin, into solid fats as lard substitutes or margarines.

Peroxidation

Peroxidation (**auto-oxidation**) of lipids exposed to oxygen is responsible not only for deterioration of foods (**rancidity**) but also for damage to tissues in vivo, where it may be a cause of cancer. The deleterious effects are initiated by free radicals ($ROO^{\bullet}$, $RO^{\bullet}$, $OH^{\bullet}$) produced during peroxide formation from fatty acids containing methylene-interrupted double bonds, ie, those found in the naturally occurring polyunsaturated fatty acids (Fig 16–32). Lipid peroxidation is a chain reaction providing a continuous supply of free radicals that initiate further peroxidation. The whole process can be depicted as follows:

(1) Initiation: Production of $R^{\bullet}$ from a precursor.
(2) Propagation:

$$R^{\bullet} + O_2 \rightarrow ROO^{\bullet}$$

$$ROO^{\bullet} + RH \rightarrow ROOH + R^{\bullet}, \text{ etc.}$$

(3) Termination:

$$ROO^{\bullet} + ROO^{\bullet} \rightarrow \text{Non-free radical product.}$$

Since the molecular precursor for the initiation process is generally the hydroperoxide product ROOH, lipid peroxidation is a branching chain reaction with potentially devastating effects. To control and reduce lipid peroxidation both humans and nature invoke the use of **antioxidants.** Propyl gallate, butylated hydroxyanisole (BHA), and butylated hydroxytoluene (BHT) are antioxidants used as food additives. Naturally occurring antioxidants include vitamin E (tocopherol), which is lipid-soluble, and urate and vitamin C, which are water-soluble. β-Carotene is an antioxidant at low P_{O_2} (Burton and Ingold, 1984). Antioxidants fall into 2 classes: (1) preventive antioxidants, which reduce the rate of chain initiation, and (2) chain-breaking antioxidants, which interfere with chain propagation. Preventive antioxidants include catalase and other peroxidases that react with ROOH. Chain-breaking antioxidants are often phenols or aromatic amines. In vivo, the principal chain-breaking antioxidants are superoxide dismutase (p 134), which acts in the aqueous phase to trap superoxide free radicals (O_2^{-}); perhaps urate; and vitamin E, which acts in the lipid phase to trap $ROO^{\bullet}$ radicals.

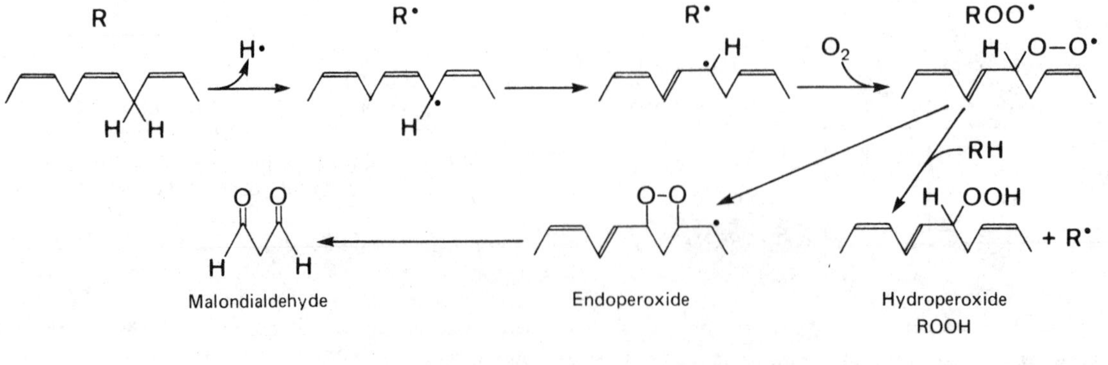

Figure 16–32. Lipid peroxidation. The reaction is initiated by light or by metal ions.

Peroxidation is also catalyzed in vivo by heme compounds and by **lipoxygenases** found in platelets and leukocytes, etc (p 223).

Spontaneous Oxidation

Oils that contain highly unsaturated fatty acids (eg, linseed oil) are spontaneously oxidized by atmospheric oxygen at ordinary temperatures and form a hard, waterproof material. Such oils are added for this purpose to paints and shellacs. They are then known as "drying oils."

METHODS FOR SEPARATING & IDENTIFYING LIPIDS IN BIOLOGIC MATERIAL

The older methods of separation and identification of lipids, based on classic chemical procedures of crystallization, distillation, and solvent extraction, have now been largely supplanted by chromatographic procedures. Particularly useful for the separation of the various lipid classes is **thin layer chromatography** (TLC) and for the separation of the individual fatty acids, **gas-liquid chromatography** (GLC; Fig 16–33). Before these techniques are applied to wet tissues, the lipids are extracted by a solvent system based usually on a mixture of chloroform and methanol (2:1).

Gas-liquid chromatography involves the physical separation of a moving gas phase by adsorption onto a stationary phase consisting of an inert solid such as silica gel or inert granules of ground firebrick coated with a nonvolatile liquid (eg, lubricating grease or silicone oils). In practice, a glass or metal column is packed with the inert solid, and a mixture of th methyl esters of fatty acids is evaporated at one end of the column, the entire length of which is kept at temperatures of 170–225 °C (Fig 16–33). A constantly flowing stream of an inert gas such as argon or helium keeps the volatilized esters moving through the column. As with other types of chromatography, separation of the vaporized fatty acid esters is dependent upon the different affinities of the components of the gas mixture for the stationary phase. Gases that are strongly attracted to the stationary phase move through the column at a slower rate and therefore emerge at the end of the column later than those that are relatively less attracted. As the individual fatty acid esters emerge from the column, they are detected by physical or chemical means and recorded automatically as a series of peaks that appear at different times according to the tendency of each fatty acid ester to be retained by the stationary phase (Fig 16–33). The area under each peak is proportionate to the concentration of a particular component of the mixture. The identity of each component is established by comparison with the gas chromatographic pattern of a related standard mixture of known composition. A detector of radioactivity may also be incorporated into the gas stream, together with the mass detector. Thus, a measure of the specific radioactivity of each component separated is obtained.

The advantages of gas-liquid chromatography are its extreme sensitivity, which allows very small quantities of mixtures to be separated, and the fact that the columns may be used repeatedly. Application of the technique has shown that natural fats contain a wide variety of hitherto undetected fatty acids.

Thin layer chromatography (TLC) is carried out on glass plates coated with a thin slurry of adsorbent, usually silica gel. This is allowed to dry and is then heated in an oven at a standard temperature and for a standard time. After cooling, the "activated" plate is "spotted" with the lipid mixture contained in a suitable solvent. The solvent is evaporated, the edge of the plate nearest the spots is dipped in an appropriate solvent mixture, and the plate is run inside a closed tank until the solvent front arrives near the top edge of

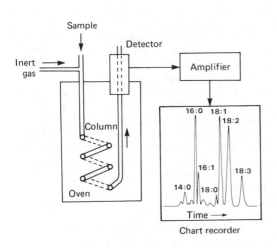

Figure 16–33. Diagrammatic representation of a gas-liquid chromatography apparatus and the separation of long-chain fatty acids (as methyl esters). (A section of the record of a chromatogram is shown at right.)

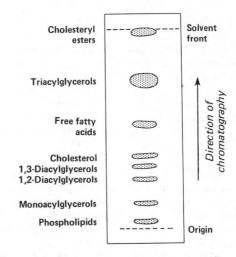

Figure 16–34. Separation of major lipid classes by thin layer chromatography. A suitable solvent system for the above would be hexane–diethyl ether–formic acid (80:20:2 v/v/v).

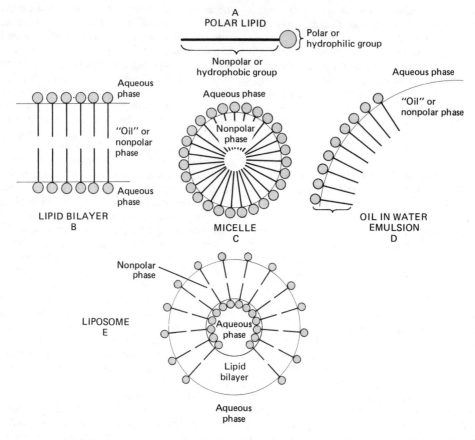

Figure 16–35. Formation of lipid membranes, micelles, emulsions, and liposomes from polar lipids, eg, phospholipids.

the plate. The plate is dried of solvent, and the position of the spots is determined by "charring" (spraying with sulfuric acid followed by heating) or by fluorescence (with dichlorofluorescein) or by reacting with iodine vapor (Fig 16–34). Greater resolution of mixtures can be achieved by 2-dimensional development, using first one solvent in one direction and then, after drying, running the plate in a second solvent in a direction at right angles to the first. As well as being used for analytic purposes, thin layer chromatography may be used in purifying lipids; milligram quantities of lipid may be applied as a band to one plate. For reviews of general analytic methods applicable to lipids, see Lowenstein (1969) and Christie (1973).

Membranes, Micelles, Liposomes, & Emulsions

In general, lipids are insoluble in water, since they contain a predominance of nonpolar (hydrocarbon) groups. However, fatty acids, some phospholipids, sphingolipids (the polar lipids) and, to a lesser extent, cholesterol contain polar groups. Therefore, part of the molecule is **hydrophobic,** or water-insoluble, and part is **hydrophilic,** or water-soluble. Such molecules are described as **amphipathic** (Fig 16–35). They become oriented at oil-water interfaces with the **polar group in the water phase** and the **nonpolar group in the oil phase,** as in a typical plasma lipoprotein. A bilayer of such polar lipids has been regarded as a basic structure in biologic membranes, being some 5–10 nm in thickness. When a critical concentration of polar lipids is present in an aqueous medium, they form **micelles.** Aggregations of bile salts into micelles and the formation of mixed micelles with the products of fat digestion are important in facilitating absorption of lipids from the intestine. **Liposomes** are formed by sonicating a lipid in an aqueous medium. They consist of spheres of lipid bilayers that enclose part of the aqueous medium. **Emulsions** are much larger particles, formed usually by nonpolar lipids in an aqueous medium. These are stabilized by emulsifying agents such as polar lipids (eg, lecithin), which form a surface layer separating the main bulk of the nonpolar material from the aqueous phase (Fig 16–35).

THE CELL MEMBRANES
(See Chapter 32.)

The plasma membrane of the living cell is a permeability barrier controlling the transfer of water and solutes between the external and internal environments. Overton recognized that the penetration of the cell by many classes of compounds was proportionate to their solubility in lipids rather than to molecular size. This led to the concept that the cell membrane is lipoid in nature. Gorter and Grendel observed in experiments using the Langmuir trough that the area occupied by lipids extracted from erythrocytes and spread as a monomolecular film on water was twice the surface area of the cells before extraction. This finding suggested that the membrane lipids were arranged in a bimolecular layer (bilayer), with the nonpolar ends of the molecules toward each other within the membrane and the polar ends oriented toward the aqueous phase inside and outside the cell (Fig 16–35).

To overcome thermodynamic objections to the traditional concept of the simple lipid bilayer model of the plasma membrane, Singer and Nicolson (1972) proposed a **fluid mosaic model** (see Fig 32–13). This consists of a mosaic of globular proteins in a bilayer of phospholipids, all of which are in a dynamic and fluid state.

● ● ●

References

Burton GW, Ingold KU: β-Carotene: An unusual type of lipid antioxidant. *Science* 1984;**224**:569.

Christie WW: *Lipid Analysis.* Pergamon Press, 1973.

Gunstone FD: *An Introduction to the Chemistry and Biochemistry of Fatty Acids and Their Glycerides,* 2nd ed. Chapman & Hall, 1967.

Gurr AI, James AT: *Lipid Biochemistry: An Introduction,* 3rd ed. Wiley, 1980.

Hanahan DJ: *Lipide Chemistry.* Wiley, 1960.

Hawthorne JN, Ansell GB (editors): *Phospholipids.* Elsevier, 1982.

Hilditch TP, Williams PN: *The Chemical Constitution of Natural Fats,* 4th ed. Chapman & Hall, 1964.

Johnson AR, Davenport JB: *Biochemistry and Methodology of Lipids.* Wiley, 1971.

Klyne W: *The Chemistry of the Steroids.* Methuen, 1965.

Lowenstein JM (editor): *Methods in Enzymology.* Vol 14. Academic Press, 1969.

Marsh D: Spectroscopic studies of membrane structure. *Essays Biochem* 1975;**11**:139.

Nelson NA, Kelly RC, Johnson RA: Prostaglandins and the arachidonic acid cascade. *Chemical and Engineering News* (Aug 16) 1982;**60**:30.

Pecsok RL (editor): *Principles and Practice of Gas Chromatography.* Wiley, 1959.

Ralston AW: *Fatty Acids and Their Derivatives.* Wiley, 1948.

Rothfield LI (editor): *Structure and Function of Biological Membranes.* Academic Press, 1971.

Singer SJ, Nicolson GL: The fluid mosaic model of the structure of cell membranes. *Science* 1972;**175**:720.

17 | Metabolism of Lipids: I. Fatty Acids

Peter A. Mayes, PhD, DSc

The lipids of metabolic significance in the mammalian organism include triacylglycerols (triglycerides,* neutral fat), phospholipids, and steroids, together with products of their metabolism such as long-chain fatty acids (free fatty acids), glycerol, and ketone bodies. An overview of their metabolic interrelationships and their relationship to carbohydrate metabolism is shown in Fig 17–1.

For many years the tissue lipids were considered to be inactive storehouses of calorigenic material, called upon only in times of shortage of energy-yielding foods. However, Schoenheimer and Rittenberg showed by experiments in which deuterium-labeled fatty acids were fed to mice in caloric equilibrium that in only 4 days a considerable proportion of the depot lipid had been formed from the dietary lipid. Since the total mass of triacylglycerol in the depots

*See explanatory note on p 197.

remained constant, a corresponding quantity of triacylglycerol must have been mobilized during this period. These investigations demonstrated the dynamic state of body fat, a concept that forms the basis of present understanding of lipid metabolism.

A variable amount of the carbohydrate of the diet is converted to triacylglycerol before it is utilized for the purpose of providing energy. As a result, fatty acids derived from triacylglycerol may be the major source of energy for many tissues; indeed, there is evidence that in certain organs fatty acids may be used as fuel in preference to carbohydrate.

As the principal form in which energy is stored in the body, triacylglycerol has definite advantages over carbohydrate or protein. Its caloric value per unit mass is over twice as great (38.9 kJ/g), and it is associated with less water in storage. Triacylglycerol is therefore the most concentrated form in which potential energy can be stored. In addition, fatty acids provide more

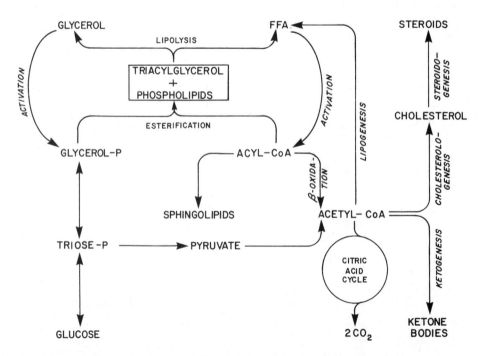

Figure 17–1. Overview of the principal pathways of lipid metabolism and their relationship to glucose metabolism. FFA, free fatty acids (nonesterified long-chain fatty acids).

metabolic water upon oxidation than other metabolic fuels, which is advantageous to mammals occupying dry environments.

A minimal amount of lipid is essential in the diet to provide an adequate supply of certain polyunsaturated fatty acids (the essential fatty acids) and of fat-soluble vitamins that cannot be synthesized in adequate amounts for optimal body function. As well as acting as a carrier of these essential compounds, dietary lipid is necessary for their efficient absorption from the gastrointestinal tract. Apart from these functions, it is not certain how essential lipid is as a constituent of the diet. As a source of energy, it can be replaced completely by either carbohydrate or protein, although the efficiency with which foodstuffs are utilized may suffer as a consequence.

OXIDATION OF FATTY ACIDS

Activation of Fatty Acids

As in the metabolism of glucose, fatty acids must first be converted in a reaction with ATP to an active intermediate before they will react with the enzymes responsible for their further metabolism. This is the only step in the complete degradation of a fatty acid that requires energy from ATP. In the presence of ATP and coenzyme A, the enzyme **acyl-CoA synthetase (thiokinase)** catalyzes the conversion of a fatty acid (or free fatty acid) to an "active fatty acid" or acyl-CoA, accompanied by the expenditure of one high-energy phosphate bond.

$$\text{Fatty acid} + \text{ATP} + \text{CoA} \rightarrow \text{Acyl-CoA} + \text{PP}_i + \text{AMP}$$

The presence of **inorganic pyrophosphatase** ensures that activation goes to completion by facilitating the loss of the additional high-energy phosphate bond of pyrophosphate. Thus, in effect, 2 high-energy phosphate bonds are expended during the activation of each fatty acid molecule.

$$\text{PP}_i + \text{H}_2\text{O} \rightarrow 2 \text{ P}_i$$

Acyl-CoA synthetases are found both inside and outside the mitochondria. Several acyl-CoA synthetases have been described, each specific for fatty acids of different chain length. In addition, there is a GTP-specific mitochondrial acyl-CoA synthetase that, unlike the ATP-specific enzyme, forms GDP + P$_i$ as products and not pyrophosphate.

Role of Carnitine in Fatty Acid Oxidation

Carnitine (β-hydroxy-γ-trimethylammonium butyrate), $(\text{CH}_3)_3\text{N}^+\text{-CH}_2\text{-CH(OH)-CH}_2\text{-COO}^-$, stimulates the oxidation of long-chain fatty acids by mitochondria. It is widely distributed, being particularly abundant in muscle. Activation of long-chain fatty acids to acyl-CoA occurs in microsomes and on the outer membranes of mitochondria. Activation of

Acyl-CoA + Carnitine ⟷ Acylcarnitine + CoA

> CARNITINE PALMITOYL TRANSFERASE

lower fatty acids may occur within the mitochondria, independently of carnitine. Long-chain acyl-CoA **will not penetrate mitochondria** and become oxidized unless carnitine is present. An enzyme, **carnitine palmitoyl transferase I,** is associated with the outer side of the inner mitochondrial membrane and allows long-chain acyl groups (as acylcarnitine) to penetrate the mitochondria and gain access to the β-oxidation system of enzymes. A possible mechanism to account for the action of carnitine in facilitating the oxidation of fatty acids by mitochondria is shown in Fig 17–2. In addition, another enzyme, **carnitine-acetyl acyltransferase,** is present within mitochondria and catalyzes the transfer of short-chain acyl groups between CoA and carnitine. The function of this enzyme is obscure, but it may facilitate transport of acetyl groups out through the mitochondrial membrane, acetyl-

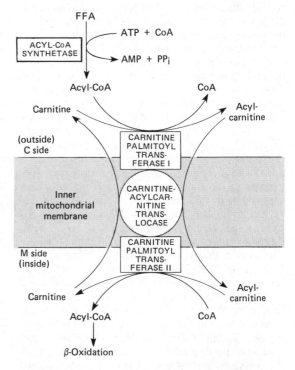

Figure 17–2. Role of carnitine in the transport of long-chain fatty acids through the inner mitochondrial membrane (Pande and Parvin, 1980). Long-chain acyl-CoA cannot pass through the inner mitochondrial membrane, but its metabolic product, acylcarnitine, formed by the action of **carnitine palmitoyl transferase I,** can. **Carnitine-acylcarnitine translocase** acts as a membrane carnitine exchange transporter. Acylcarnitine is transported in, coupled with the transport out of one molecule of carnitine. The acylcarnitine then reacts with CoA, catalyzed by **carnitine palmitoyl transferase II,** attached to the inside of the inner membrane. Acyl-CoA is re-formed in the mitochondrial matrix, and carnitine is liberated.

Acetyl-CoA + Carnitine ⟷ Acetyl-carnitine + CoA

CARNITINE-ACETYL
ACYLTRANSFERASE

carnitine exchanging with carnitine, allowing all of the carnitine of the cell to buffer acetyl groups formed in fatty acid oxidation. This releases CoA for further reactions within the mitochondrion. A deficiency of carnitine impairs fatty acid oxidation, and triacylglycerol accumulates. Carnitine is synthesized from lysine in liver and kidney.

β-Oxidation of Fatty Acids

Several enzymes, known collectively as "fatty acid oxidase," are found in the mitochondrial matrix adjacent to the respiratory chain (which is found in the inner membrane). These catalyze the oxidation of acyl-CoA to acetyl-CoA, the system being coupled with the phosphorylation of ADP to ATP (Fig 17–3).

After the formation of acyl-CoA and the penetration of the acyl moiety through the mitochondrial membrane via the carnitine transporter system, there follows the removal of 2 hydrogen atoms from the $2(\alpha)$- and $3(\beta)$-carbon atoms, catalyzed by **acyl-CoA dehydrogenase.** This results in the formation of α,β-unsaturated or Δ^2-unsaturated acyl-CoA. The coenzyme for the dehydrogenase is a flavoprotein, containing FAD as prosthetic group, whose reoxidation by the respiratory chain requires the mediation of another flavoprotein, termed **electron-transferring flavoprotein** (see p 131). Water is added to saturate the double bond and form β-hydroxyacyl-CoA, catalyzed by the enzyme Δ^2-**enoyl-CoA hydratase** (crotonase). The β-hydroxy derivative undergoes further dehydrogenation on the β-carbon (β-**hydroxyacyl-CoA dehydrogenase**) to form the corresponding β-ketoacyl-CoA compound. In this case, NAD is the coenzyme involved in the dehydrogenation. Finally, β-ketoacyl-CoA is split at the β-position by **thiolase** (β-ketothiolase or acetyl-CoA acyltransferase), which catalyzes a thiolytic cleavage involving another molecule of CoA. The products of this reaction are acetyl-CoA and an acyl-CoA derivative containing 2 carbons less than the original acyl-CoA molecule that underwent oxidation. The acyl-CoA formed in the cleavage reaction reenters the oxidative pathway at reaction 2 (Fig 17–3). In this way, a long-chain fatty acid may be degraded completely to acetyl-CoA (C_2-units). As acetyl-CoA can be oxidized to CO_2 and water via the citric acid cycle (which is also found within the mitochondria), the complete oxidation of fatty acids is achieved.

Fatty acids with an odd number of carbon atoms are oxidized by the pathway of β-oxidation until a 3-carbon (propionyl-CoA) residue remains. This compound is converted to succinyl-CoA, a constituent of the citric acid cycle (see also p 187).

Energetics of Fatty Acid Oxidation

Transport in the respiratory chain of electrons from reduced flavoprotein and NAD will lead to the synthesis of 5 high-energy phosphate bonds (see Chapter 12) for each of the first 7 acetyl-CoA molecules formed by β-oxidation of palmitate ($7 \times 5 = 35$). A total of 8 mol of acetyl-CoA is formed, and each will give rise to 12 high-energy bonds on oxidation in the citric acid cycle, making $8 \times 12 = 96$ high-energy bonds derived from the acetyl-CoA formed from palmitate, minus 2 for the initial activation of the fatty acid, yielding a net gain of 129 high-energy bonds/mol, or $129 \times 36.8 = 4747$ kJ. As the free energy of combustion of palmitic acid is 9791 kJ/mol, the process captures as high-energy phosphate on the order of 48% of the total energy of combustion of the fatty acid.

Peroxisomal Fatty Acid Oxidation

A modified form of β-oxidation is found in peroxisomes and leads to the formation of acetyl-CoA and H_2O_2 (from the flavoprotein-linked dehydrogenase step). The system is not linked directly to phosphorylation and the generation of ATP but aids the oxidation of very long chain fatty acids (eg, C_{20}, C_{22}) and is induced by high-fat diets and hypolipidemic drugs such as clofibrate.

The enzymes in peroxisomes do not attack shorter-chain fatty acids; the β-oxidation sequence ends at octanoyl-CoA. Octanoyl and acetyl groups are subsequently removed from the peroxisomes in the forms of octanoyl and acetyl carnitine, and both are further oxidized in mitochondria.

α- & ω-Oxidation of Fatty Acids

Quantitatively, β-oxidation is the most important pathway for fatty acid oxidation. However, α-oxidation, ie, the removal of one carbon at a time from the carboxyl end of the molecule, has been detected in brain tissue. It does not require CoA intermediates and does not generate high-energy phosphates. Phytanic acid formed from phytol present in plant foodstuffs contains a $-CH_3$ group on the 3-carbon that blocks β-oxidation. Normally, an initial α-oxidation removes the methyl group, but persons with **Refsum's disease** have an inherited defect in α-oxidation that prevents the oxidizing of phytanic acid.

ω-Oxidation is brought about by hydroxylase enzymes involving cytochrome P-450 in microsomes (see p 131). The $-CH_3$ group is converted to a $-CH_2OH$ group that subsequently is oxidized to $-COOH$, thus forming a dicarboxylic acid. This is β-oxidized usually to adipic and suberic acids, which are found in the urine of ketotic patients (**ketotic dicarboxylic aciduria**). The sources of the dicarboxylic acids are the C_{10}–C_{14} monocarboxylic acids of adipose tissue, which are mobilized to the liver under conditions of ketosis (see p 268).

Oxidation of Unsaturated Fatty Acids

The CoA esters of these acids are degraded by the enzymes normally responsible for β-oxidation until either a Δ^3-*cis*-acyl-CoA compound or a Δ^2-*cis*-acyl-CoA compound is formed, depending upon the position of the double bonds (Fig 17–4). The former

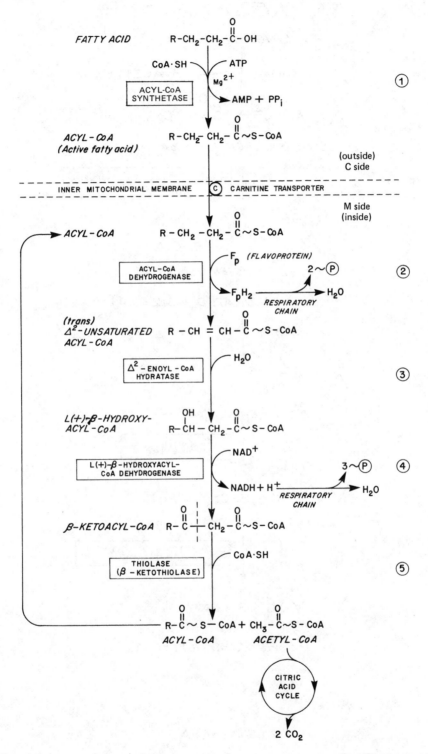

Figure 17–3. β-Oxidation of fatty acids. Long-chain acyl-CoA is cycled through reactions ②–⑤, acetyl-CoA being split off each cycle by thiolase (reaction ⑤). When the acyl radical is only 4 carbon atoms in length, 2 acetyl-CoA molecules are formed in reaction ⑤.

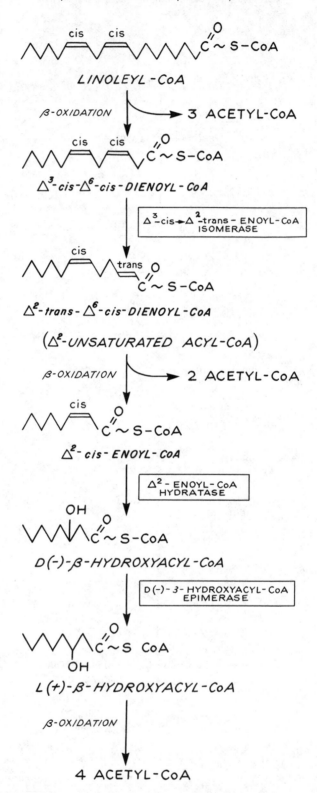

Figure 17–4. Sequence of reactions in the oxidation of unsaturated fatty acids, eg, linoleic acid.

compound is isomerized (Δ^3-*cis*→Δ^2-*trans*-enoyl-CoA isomerase) to the corresponding Δ^2-*trans*-CoA stage, which in turn is hydrated by Δ^2-enoyl-CoA hydratase to L(+)-β-hydroxyacyl-CoA. The Δ^2-*cis*-acyl-CoA compound is first hydrated by Δ^2-enoyl-CoA hydratase to the D(−)-β-hydroxyacyl-CoA derivative. This undergoes epimerization (D[−]-β-hydroxyacyl-CoA epimerase) to give the normal L(+)-β-hydroxyacyl-CoA stage in β-oxidation.

Microsomal Peroxidation of Polyunsaturated Fatty Acids

Lipid peroxidation results in vivo in the destruction of polyunsaturated fatty acids in membrane lipids. Initially, a hydrogen atom is removed, leaving a lipid-free radical. After rearrangement of the double bonds, molecular oxygen is added to form a lipid hydroperoxide or endoperoxide. If the original fatty acid contained at least 3 double bonds, malondialdehyde may be detected as a final product. NADPH-dependent peroxidation of unsaturated fatty acids is catalyzed by microsomal enzymes (see p 133). The antioxidants BHT (butylated hydroxytoluene) and α-tocopherol (vitamin E) inhibit microsomal lipid peroxidation.

BIOSYNTHESIS OF SATURATED FATTY ACIDS

Like many other degradative and synthetic processes (eg, glycogenolysis and glycogenesis), fatty acid synthesis was formerly considered to be merely the reversal of oxidation. However, it now seems clear that a mitochondrial system for fatty acid synthesis, involving some modification of the β-oxidation sequence, is responsible only for elongation of existing fatty acids of moderate chain length, whereas a radically different and highly active **extramitochondrial** system is responsible for the complete synthesis of palmitate from acetyl-CoA. An active system for chain elongation is also present in liver microsomes.

Extramitochondrial System for De Novo Synthesis of Fatty Acids (Lipogenesis)

This system has been found in the soluble (cytosol) fraction of many tissues, including liver, kidney, brain, lung, mammary gland, and adipose tissue. Its cofactor requirements include NADPH, ATP, Mn^{2+}, and HCO_3^- (as a source of CO_2). Acetyl-CoA is the substrate, and free palmitate is the end product. These characteristics contrast markedly with those of β-oxidation.

Bicarbonate as a source of CO_2 is required in the initial reaction for the carboxylation of acetyl-CoA to **malonyl-CoA** in the presence of ATP and **acetyl-CoA carboxylase.** Acetyl-CoA carboxylase has a requirement for the vitamin **biotin** (Fig 17–5). The enzyme contains a variable number of identical subunits, each monomer containing biotin, biotin carboxylase, biotin carboxyl carrier protein, and transcarboxylase, as well as a regulatory allosteric site. It is therefore a multienzyme protein. The reaction takes place in 2 steps: (1) carboxylation of biotin (involving ATP) and (2) transfer of the carboxyl to acetyl-CoA to form malonyl-CoA. Acetyl-CoA carboxylase is activated by citrate and inhibited by long-chain acyl-CoA. The activated form readily polymerizes into filaments containing 10–20 protomers. Since acyl-CoA derivatives are inactive in the system—unlike the situation in the mitochondria—it was concluded that acyl derivatives of CoA were not intermediates in the extramitochondrial pathway during the synthesis of palmitate, and it was proposed that the acyl moiety remained attached to the enzyme as an acyl-S-enzyme complex.

There appear to be 2 types of **fatty acid synthase** systems found in the soluble portion of the cell. In bacteria, plants, and lower forms such as *Euglena,* the individual enzymes of the system may be separate, and the acyl radicals are found in combination with a protein called the **acyl carrier protein (ACP).** However, in yeast, mammals, and birds, the synthase system is a multienzyme complex that may not be subdivided without loss of activity, and ACP is part of this complex. Both ACP of bacteria and the multienzyme complex contain the vitamin pantothenic acid in the form of 4'-phosphopantetheine (see p 109).

Recent investigations have shown that the fatty acid synthase complex is a dimer, each monomer having a molecular weight of 267,000 (Fig 17–6). In animals, it would appear that each monomer is identical, consisting of one remarkable polypeptide chain containing all the 7 enzymes of fatty acid synthase and an ACP with a 4'-phosphopantetheine –SH group. In close proximity is another thiol of a cysteine residue attached to β-**ketoacyl synthase (condensing enzyme)** of the other monomer (Fig 17–6). Since both thiols participate in the synthase activity, only the dimer is active.

Initially, a priming molecule of acetyl-CoA combines with the cysteine –SH group catalyzed by **acetyl**

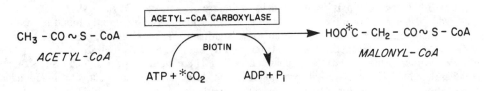

Figure 17–5. Biosynthesis of malonyl-CoA.

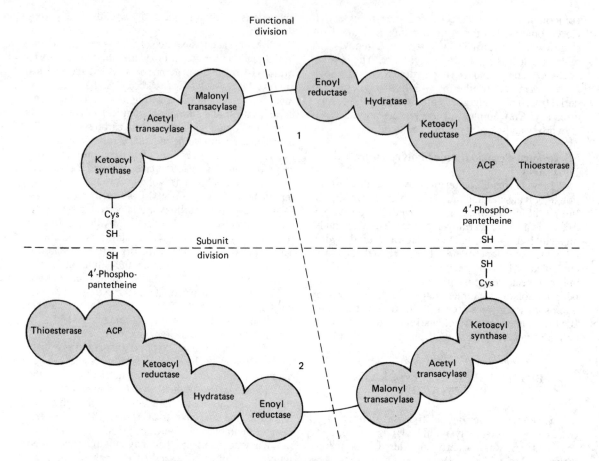

Figure 17–6. Fatty acid synthase multienzyme complex. The complex is a dimer of 2 identical polypeptide monomers, 1 and 2, each consisting of 7 separate enzyme activities and the acyl carrier protein (ACP). Cys –SH, cysteine thiol. The –SH of the 4'-phosphopantetheine of one monomer is in close proximity to the –SH of the cysteine residue of the ketoacyl synthase of the other monomer, suggesting a "head-to-tail" arrangement of the 2 monomers. The detailed sequence of the enzymes in each monomer is tentative (based on Tsukamoto). Though each monomer contains all the partial activities of the reaction sequence, the actual functional unit consists of one-half of a monomer interacting with the complementary half of the other. Thus, 2 acyl chains are produced simultaneously.

transacylase (Fig 17–7). Malonyl-CoA combines with the adjacent –SH on the 4'-phosphopantetheine of ACP of the other monomer, catalyzed by **malonyl transacylase** to form **acetyl (acyl)-malonyl enzyme.** The acetyl group attacks the methylene group of the malonyl residue, catalyzed by β**-ketoacyl synthase,** and liberates CO_2, forming β-ketoacyl enzyme (acetoacetyl enzyme). This frees the cysteine –SH group, hitherto occupied by the acetyl group. Decarboxylation allows the reaction to go to completion, acting as a pulling force for the whole sequence of reactions. The β-ketoacyl group is reduced, dehydrated, and reduced again to form the corresponding saturated acyl-S-enzyme. These reactions are analogous to those in β-oxidation, except that the β-hydroxy acid is the $D(-)$ isomer instead of the $L(+)$ isomer and NADPH rather than NADH serves as hydrogen donor for both reductions. A new malonyl-CoA molecule combines with the –SH of 4'-phosphopantetheine, displacing the saturated acyl residue onto the free cys-

teine –SH group. The sequence of reactions is repeated 6 more times, a new malonyl residue being incorporated during each sequence, until a saturated 16-carbon acyl radical (palmityl) has been assembled. It is liberated from the enzyme complex by the activity of a seventh enzyme in the complex, **thioesterase** (deacylase). The free palmitate must be activated to acyl-CoA before it can proceed via any other metabolic pathway. Its usual fate is esterification into acylglycerols (Fig 17–8).

In mammary gland, there is a separate thioesterase enzyme specific for acyl residues of C_8, C_{10}, or C_{12}, which are subsequently found in milk lipids. In ruminant mammary gland, this enzyme is part of the fatty acid synthase complex.

There would appear to be 2 centers of activity in one dimer complex that function independently and simultaneously.

The aggregation of all the enzymes of a particular pathway into one multienzyme functional unit offers

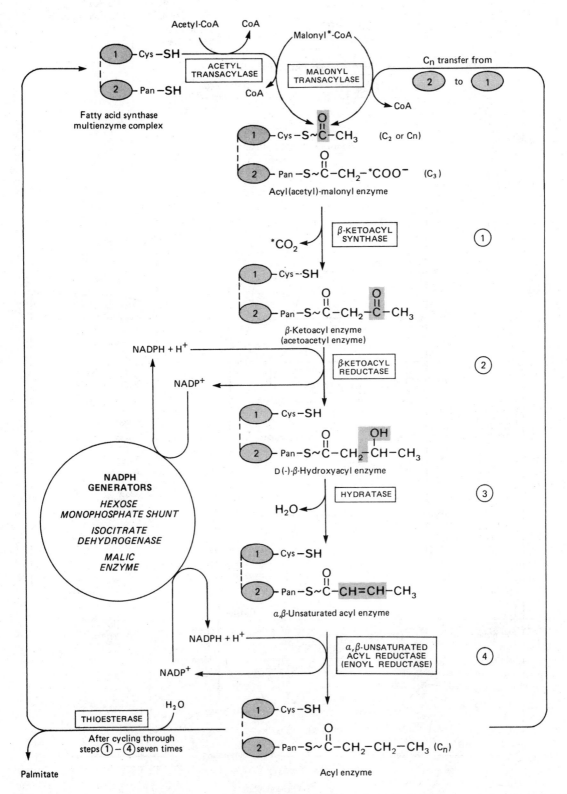

Figure 17-7. Biosynthesis of long-chain fatty acids. Details of how addition of a malonyl residue causes the acyl chain to grow by 2 carbon atoms. (Cys-, cysteine residue; pan, 4'-phosphopantetheine.) Details of the fatty acid synthase dimer are shown in Fig 17-6. ① and ② represent the individual monomers of fatty acid synthase.

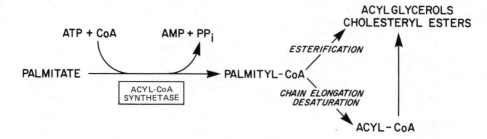

Figure 17–8. Fate of palmitate.

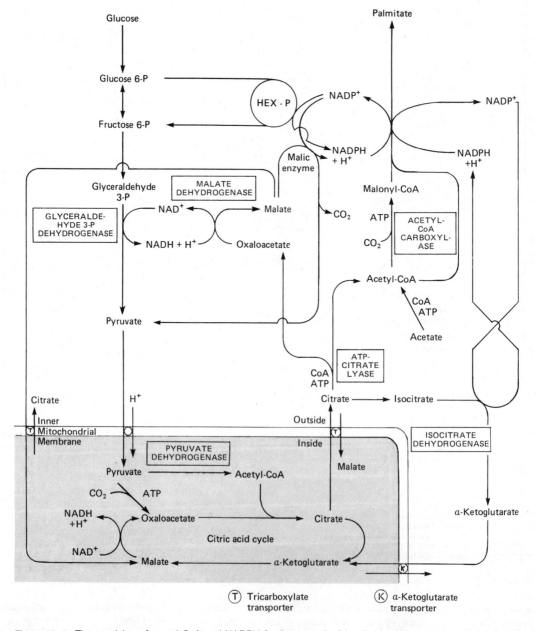

Figure 17–9. The provision of acetyl-CoA and NADPH for lipogenesis. (Hex-P, hexose monophosphate shunt.)

great efficiency and freedom from interference by competing processes, thus achieving the effect of compartmentalization of the process within the cell, without the erection of permeability barriers.

The equation for the overall synthesis of palmitate from acetyl-CoA and malonyl-CoA is shown below:

$$CH_3CO \cdot S \cdot CoA + 7HOOC \cdot CH_2CO \cdot S \cdot CoA + 14NADPH + 14H^+$$

$$\longrightarrow CH_3(CH_2)_{14}COOH + 7CO_2 + 6H_2O + 8CoA \cdot SH + 14NADP^+$$

The acetyl-CoA used as a primer forms carbon atoms 15 and 16 of palmitate. The addition of all the subsequent C_2 units is via malonyl-CoA formation. Butyryl-CoA may act as a primer molecule in mammalian liver and mammary gland. If propionyl-CoA acts as primer, long-chain fatty acids having an odd number of carbon atoms result. These are found particularly in ruminants, where propionate is formed by microbial action in the rumen.

Source of reducing equivalents and acetyl-CoA. NADPH is involved as coenzyme in both the reduction of the β-ketoacyl and of the α,β-unsaturated acyl derivatives. The oxidative reactions of the **hexose monophosphate shunt** are the chief source of the hydrogen required for the reductive synthesis of fatty acids. It is significant that tissues which possess an active hexose monophosphate shunt are also the tissues specializing in active lipogenesis, ie, liver, adipose tissue, and the lactating mammary gland. Moreover, both metabolic pathways are found in the extramitochondrial region of the cell, so that there are no membranes or permeability barriers for the transfer of NADPH/NADP from one pathway to the other. Other sources of NADPH include the extramitochondrial **isocitrate dehydrogenase** reaction (probably not a substantial source) and the reaction that converts malate to pyruvate catalyzed by the **"malic enzyme"** (NADP malate dehydrogenase) (Fig 17-9).

Acetyl-CoA, the main building block for fatty acids, is formed from carbohydrate via the oxidation of pyruvate within the mitochondria, but acetyl-CoA does not diffuse readily into the extramitochondrial compartment, the principal site of fatty acid synthesis. The activity of the extramitochondrial **ATP-citrate lyase (citrate cleavage enzyme),** like the "malic enzyme," increases in activity in the well-fed state, closely paralleling the activity of the fatty acid synthesizing system. It is now believed that utilization of pyruvate for lipogenesis is by way of citrate. The pathway involves glycolysis followed by the oxidative decarboxylation of pyruvate to acetyl-CoA, catalyzed by pyruvate dehydrogenase, within the mitochondria, and subsequent condensation with oxaloacetate to form citrate, as part of the citric acid cycle. This is followed by the translocation of citrate into the extramitochondrial compartment, where in the presence of CoA and ATP, it undergoes cleavage to acetyl-CoA and oxaloacetate catalyzed by ATP-citrate lyase. The

acetyl-CoA is then available for malonyl-CoA formation and synthesis to palmitate (Fig 17-9). The oxaloacetate can form malate via NADH-linked malate dehydrogenase, followed by the generation of NADPH via the malic enzyme. In turn, the NADPH becomes available for lipogenesis. This pathway is a means of transferring reducing equivalents from extramitochondrial NADH to NADP. Alternatively, malate can be transported into the mitochondrion,

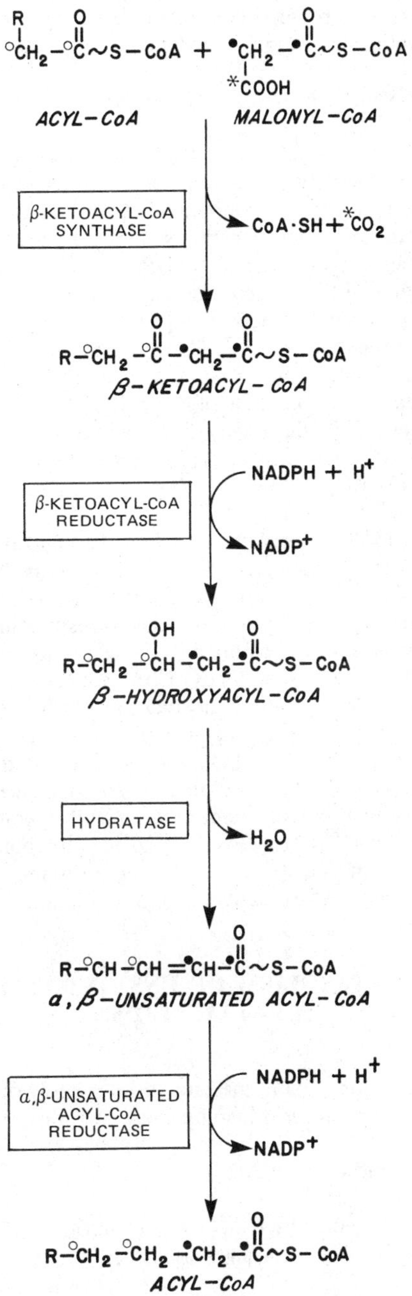

Figure 17-10. Microsomal system for chain elongation.

where it is able to re-form oxaloacetate. It is to be noted that the citrate (tricarboxylate) transporter in the mitochondrial membrane requires malate to exchange with citrate (see p 145).

There is little ATP-citrate lyase or malic enzyme in ruminants, probably because in these species acetate (derived from the rumen) is the main source of acetyl-CoA. Since the acetate is activated to acetyl-CoA extramitochondrially, there is no necessity for it to enter mitochondria and form citrate prior to incorporation into long-chain fatty acids. Generation of NADPH via extramitochondrial isocitrate dehydrogenase is more important in these species, because of the deficiency in malic enzyme.

Microsomal System for Chain Elongation (Elongase)

This is probably the main site for the elongation of existing long-chain fatty acid molecules. The pathway converts acyl-CoA compounds of fatty acids to acyl derivatives having 2 carbons more, using malonyl-CoA as acetyl donor and NADPH as reductant. Intermediates in the process are the CoA thioesters. The acyl groups that may act as a primer molecule include the saturated series from C_{10} upward, as well as unsaturated fatty acids. Fasting largely abolishes chain elongation. Elongation of stearyl-CoA in brain increases rapidly during myelination in order to provide C_{22} and C_{24} fatty acids that are present in sphingolipids (Fig 17–10).

Mitochondrial System for Chain Elongation

The enzymes are probably the same as those involved in β-oxidation except for the conversion of the α,β-unsaturated acyl-CoA to the corresponding saturated compound catalyzed by **α,β-unsaturated acyl-CoA reductase** (enoyl-CoA reductase), requiring NADPH. Pyridoxal phosphate has been suggested as a coenzyme for the enzyme condensing acetyl-CoA with acyl-CoA; thus, thiolase may not be used in this synthetic pathway. The physiologic significance of this pathway is uncertain, since it will operate only when the [NADH]/[NAD$^+$] ratio in mitochondria is high, ie, under anaerobic conditions, or in the liver, in the presence of excessive ethanol oxidation.

METABOLISM OF UNSATURATED FATTY ACIDS

The long-chain unsaturated fatty acids of metabolic significance in mammals are as follows:

Nonessential Fatty Acids

$$CH_3(CH_2)_5 CH=CH(CH_2)_7 COOH$$
Palmitoleic acid (16:1)

$$CH_3(CH_2)_7 CH=CH(CH_2)_7 COOH$$
Oleic acid (18:1)

Essential Fatty Acids

$$CH_3(CH_2)_4 CH=CHCH_2 CH=CH(CH_2)_7 COOH$$
Linoleic acid (18:2)

$$CH_3 CH_2 CH=CHCH_2 CH=CHCH_2 CH=CH(CH_2)_7 COOH$$
α-Linolenic acid (18:3)

$$CH_3(CH_2)_4 (CH=CHCH_2)_4 (CH_2)_2 COOH$$
Arachidonic acid (20:4)

Other C_{20}, C_{22}, and C_{24} polyenoic fatty acids may be detected by gas-liquid chromatography. These are derived from linoleic and α-linolenic acids by chain elongation. It is to be noted that all double bonds present in naturally occurring unsaturated fatty acids of mammals are of the *cis* configuration.

Palmitoleic and oleic acids are not essential in the diet, because the tissues are capable of introducing one double bond into the corresponding saturated fatty acid. Experiments with labeled palmitate have demon-

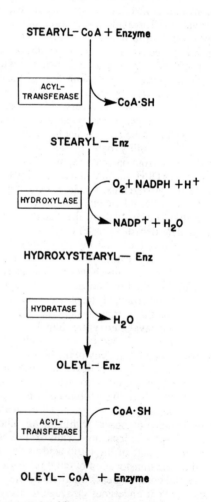

Figure 17–11. Microsomal Δ^9 desaturase system.

strated that the label enters freely into palmitoleic and oleic acids but is absent from linoleic, α-linolenic, and arachidonic acids. Linoleic, α-linolenic, and arachidonic acids are the only fatty acids known to be essential for the complete nutrition of many species of animals, including the human, and must therefore be supplied in the diet; as a consequence, they are known as the **nutritionally essential fatty acids.** Although linoleic acid cannot be synthesized and therefore must be supplied preformed in the diet, arachidonic acid can be formed from linoleic acid in the animal body (Fig 17–13). In animals, double bonds can be introduced at the Δ^4, Δ^5, Δ^6, Δ^8, and Δ^9 positions but never beyond the Δ^9 position.

Synthesis of Monounsaturated Fatty Acids
(Fig 17–11.)

It is a common finding in the husbandry of animals that the degree of saturation of the fat laid down in the depots can be altered by dietary means. If, for example, an animal is fed a diet containing a large quantity of vegetable oil (ie, a high proportion of the unsaturated fatty acids), the animal lays down a soft type of depot fat. The converse situation is found in ruminants, where a characteristic hard, saturated fat is laid down as a result of the action of microorganisms in the rumen, which saturate the unsaturated fatty acids of the diet. As far as the nonessential monounsaturated fatty acids are concerned, the liver is considered to be the main organ responsible for their interconversion with the saturated fatty acids. An enzyme system (Δ^9 desaturase) in liver microsomes (endoplasmic reticulum) will catalyze the conversion of stearyl-CoA to oleyl-CoA. Oxygen and either NADPH or NADH are necessary for the reaction. The enzymes appear to be those of a typical monooxygenase system involving cytochrome b_5 (hydroxylase). They are specific for introducing a double bond in the Δ^9 position of saturated fatty acids, eg, palmitic and stearic acids.

Synthesis of Polyunsaturated Fatty Acids

Additional double bonds introduced into existing

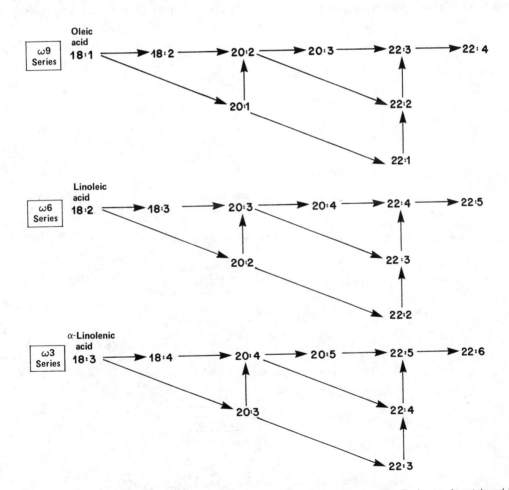

Figure 17–12. Biosynthesis of the ω9, ω6, and ω3 series of polyunsaturated fatty acids. Each step is catalyzed by the microsomal chain elongation or desaturase system. ω9 Polyunsaturated fatty acids only become quantitatively significant when linoleic and α-linolenic acids are withheld from the diet. This is because each series competes for the same enzyme systems, and affinities decrease from the ω3 to ω9 series.

monounsaturated fatty acids are always separated from each other by a methylene group (methylene interrupted), except in bacteria. In animals, the additional double bonds are **all introduced between the existing double bond and the carboxyl group,** but in plants they may also be introduced between the existing double bond and the ω carbon. Thus, since animals have a Δ^9 desaturase, they are able to completely synthesize the ω9 (oleic acid) series of unsaturated fatty acids by a combination of chain elongation and desaturation. However, since they are unable to synthesize either linoleic (ω6) or α-linolenic (ω3) acids, the required desaturases being absent, these acids must be supplied in the diet to accomplish the synthesis of the other members of the ω6 and ω3 series of polyunsaturated fatty acids (Fig 17–12). Linoleate may be converted to arachidonate (Fig 17–13). The pathway is first by dehydrogenation of the CoA ester through γ-linolenate followed by the addition of a 2-carbon unit via malonyl-CoA in the microsomal system for chain elongation, to give eicosatrienoate (dihomo γ-linolenate). The latter forms arachidonate by a further dehydrogenation. The dehydrogenating system is similar to that described above for saturated fatty acids. The nutritional requirement for arachidonate may thus be dispensed with if there is adequate linoleate in the diet.

The desaturation and chain elongation system is greatly diminished in the fasting state and in the absence of insulin.

THE ESSENTIAL FATTY ACIDS (EFA)

In 1928, Evans and Burr noticed that rats fed on a purified nonlipid diet to which vitamins A and D were added exhibited a reduced growth rate and a reproductive deficiency. Later work showed that the deficiency syndrome was cured by the addition of linoleic, α-linolenic, and arachidonic acids to the diet. Further diagnostic features of the syndrome include scaly skin, necrosis of the tail, and lesions in the urinary system, but the condition is not fatal. These fatty acids are found in high concentrations in various vegetable oils (see p 195 and Table 18–2) and in small amounts in animal carcasses.

The functions of the essential fatty acids appear to

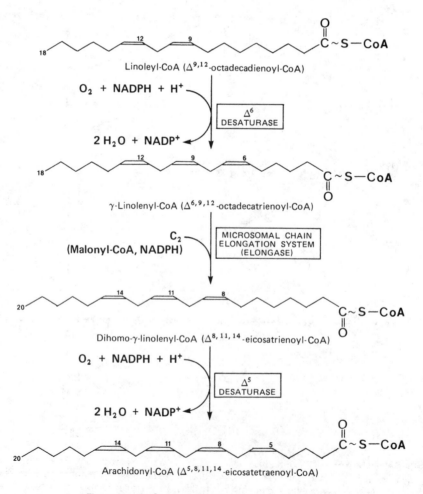

Figure 17–13. Conversion of linoleate to arachidonate.

be various, though not well defined, apart from prostaglandin and leukotriene formation (see below). Essential fatty acids are found in the structural lipids of the cell, are concerned with the structural integrity of the mitochondrial membrane, and occur in high concentration in the reproductive organs. In many of their structural functions, essential fatty acids are present in phospholipids, mainly in the 2 position. In essential fatty acid deficiency, nonessential polyenoic acids of the $\omega 9$ series replace the essential fatty acids in phospholipids, other complex lipids, and membranes. The roles of essential fatty acids in the genesis of fatty livers and in the metabolism of cholesterol are discussed later.

A deficiency of essential fatty acids has been produced in animals as well as in humans using diets restricted in essential fatty acids. In experimental animals, signs of the deficiency include poor growth, dermatitis, decreased capacity to reproduce, lessened resistance to stress, and impaired transport of lipids. The skin symptoms and impairment of lipid transport have also been noted in human subjects ingesting a diet lacking in essential fatty acids. In adults subsisting on ordinary diets, no signs of essential fatty acid deficiencies have been reported. However, infants receiving formula diets low in fat developed skin symptoms that were cured by giving linoleate. Deficiencies attributable to a lack of essential fatty acids, including α-linolenic acid, also occur among patients maintained for long periods exclusively by intravenous nutrition low in essential fatty acids.

Deficiency can be prevented by an essential fatty acid intake of 1–2% of the total caloric requirement. This quantity is obtained in the diet in all but the most extraordinary circumstances.

Trans-Fatty Acids

The presence of *trans*-unsaturated fatty acids in partially hydrogenated vegetable oils (eg, margarine) raises the question of their safety as food additives. Their long-term effects in humans are not known, but up to 15% of tissue fatty acids have been found at autopsy to be in the *trans* configuration. To date, no serious effects have been substantiated. They are metabolized more like saturated than like the *cis*-unsaturated fatty acids. This may be due to their similar straight-chain conformation (see Chapter 16). *Trans*-polyunsaturated fatty acids do not possess essential fatty acid activity and may antagonize the metabolism of essential fatty acids and exacerbate essential fatty acid deficiency.

Eicosanoids

Isotopic experiments have indicated that arachidonate and some other C_{20} fatty acids with methylene-interrupted bonds give rise to **eicosanoids,** physiologically and pharmacologically active compounds known as **prostaglandins (PG), thromboxanes (TX),** and **leukotrienes (LT)** (see pp 195–196). Their physiologic roles are under intensive investigation.

There are 3 groups of eicosanoids (each comprising PG, TX, and LT) that are synthesized from each of the essential fatty acids, respectively, **linoleate, arachidonate,** and α-**linolenate** (Fig 17–14).

Arachidonate, usually derived from the 2-position of phospholipids in the plasma membrane as a result of phospholipase A_2 activity (Fig 17–21), is the substrate for the synthesis of the PG_2, TX_2, and LT_4 compounds. The pathways of arachidonate metabolism are divergent, the synthesis of the PG_2 and TX_2 series **(prostanoids)** competing with the synthesis of LT_4 for the arachidonate substrate. These 2 pathways are known as the **cyclooxygenase** and **lipoxygenase pathways,** respectively (Fig 17–14).

Prostanoid synthesis (Fig 17–15) involves the consumption of 2 molecules of O_2 catalyzed by **prostaglandin endoperoxide synthase,** which possesses 2 separate enzyme activities, **cyclooxgenase** and **peroxidase.** Aspirin inhibits the cyclooxygenase, as does indomethacin. The product of the cyclooxygenase pathway, an endoperoxide (PGH), is converted to prostaglandins D, E, and F as well as to the thromboxane (TXA_2) and prostacyclin (PGI_2). **Thromboxanes** are synthesized in platelets and upon release cause vasoconstriction and platelet aggregation. **Prostacyclins (PGI_2)** are produced by blood vessel walls and are potent inhibitors of platelet aggregation. Thus, thromboxanes and prostacyclins are antagonistic in their actions. The low incidence of heart disease, diminished platelet aggregation, and prolonged clotting times in Greenland Eskimos have been attributed to their high intake of fish oils containing $20:5 \, \omega 3$ (EPA, or eicosapentaenoic acid), which gives rise to the series 3 prostaglandins (PG_3) and thromboxane TX_3. PG_3 and TX_3 inhibit the release of arachidonate from phospholipids and the formation of PG_2 and TX_2. PGI_3 is as potent an antiaggregator of platelets as PGI_2, but TXA_3 is a weaker aggregator than TXA_2; thus, the balance of activity is shifted towards nonaggregation. In addition, the plasma concentrations of cholesterol, triacylglycerol, and low-density and very low density lipoproteins are all low in Eskimos, whereas the high-density lipoprotein is raised—all factors considered to militate against atherosclerosis and myocardial infarction.

The prostaglandins are potent biologically active substances. As little as 1 ng/mL causes contraction of smooth muscle in animals. Potential therapeutic uses include prevention of conception, induction of labor at term, termination of pregnancy, prevention or alleviation of gastric ulcers, control of inflammation and of blood pressure, and relief of asthma and nasal congestion.

Prostaglandins increase cAMP in platelets, thyroid, corpus luteum, fetal bone, adenohypophysis, and lung but lower cAMP in adipose tissue (see p 227).

Although there is a marked correlation between essential fatty acid activity of various fatty acids and their ability to be converted to prostaglandins, it does not seem that essential fatty acids exert all of their physiologic effects via prostaglandin synthesis. The

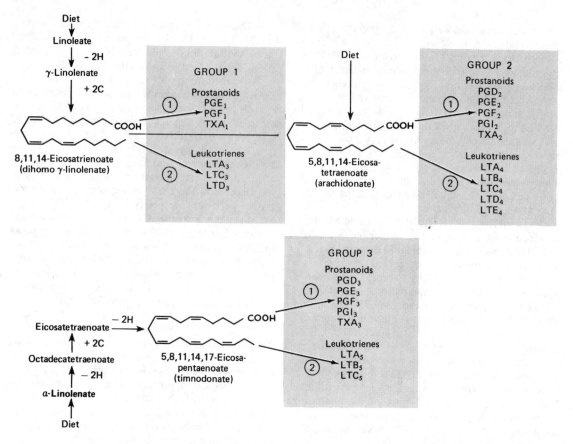

Figure 17–14. The 3 groups of eicosanoids and their biosynthetic origins. (PG, prostaglandin; PGI, prostacyclin; TX, thromboxane; LT, leukotriene; ①, cyclooxygenase pathway; ②, lipoxygenase pathway.) The subscript denotes the total number of double bonds in the molecule and the series to which the compound belongs.

role of essential fatty acids in membrane formation is unrelated to prostaglandin formation. Prostaglandins do not relieve symptoms of essential fatty acid deficiency, and an essential fatty acid deficiency syndrome is not caused by chronic inhibition of prostaglandin synthesis.

The inactivation of prostaglandins is rapid, over 90% being removed in one passage through the pulmonary capillaries. The presence of the enzyme **15-hydroxyprostaglandin dehydrogenase** in most mammalian tissues is probably the principal cause of the rapid metabolism by the pathway shown in Fig 17–16. It has been shown that blocking the action of this enzyme can prolong the half-life of prostaglandins in the body.

The **leukotrienes** are a newly discovered family of conjugated trienes formed from eicosanoic acids in leukocytes, mastocytoma cells, and macrophages by the **lipoxygenase pathway,** in response to both immunologic and nonimmunologic stimuli. The immediate product of **5-lipoxygenase** is 5-HPETE, which is converted to leukotriene A_4, which in turn is metabolized to either leukotriene B_4 or leukotriene C_4 (Fig 17–15). Leukotriene C_4 is formed by the addition of the peptide glutathione via a thioether bond. The

subsequent removal of glutamate and glycine generates leukotriene D_4 and leukotriene E_4, sequentially. The slow-reacting substance of anaphylaxis **(SRS-A)** is a mixture of leukotrienes C_4, D_4, and E_4. This mixture of leukotrienes is 100–1000 times more potent than histamine or prostaglandins as a constrictor of the bronchial airway musculature. These leukotrienes also cause vascular permeability and attraction and activation of leukocytes and seem to be important regulators in many diseases involving inflammatory or immediate hypersensitivity reactions.

METABOLISM OF ACYLGLYCEROLS

Catabolism of Triacylglycerol

Triacylglycerols must be hydrolyzed by lipases to their constituent fatty acids and glycerol before further catabolism can proceed. Much of this hydrolysis occurs in adipose tissue (see p 232) with release of free fatty acids into the plasma, where they are found combined with serum albumin. This is followed by free fatty acid uptake into tissues and subsequent oxidation. Many tissues (including liver, heart, kidney, muscle, lung, testis, brain, and adipose tissue) have the ability

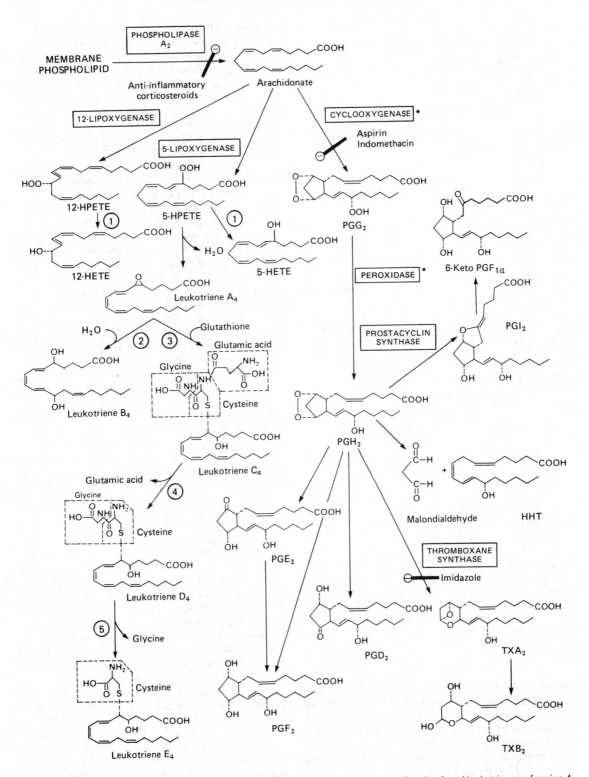

Figure 17–15. Conversion of arachidonic acid to prostaglandins and thromboxanes of series 2 and leukotrienes of series 4. (PG, prostaglandin; TX, thromboxane; PGI, prostacyclin; HPETE, hydroperoxyeicosatetraenoate; HETE, hydroxyeicosatetraenoate; HHT, hydroxyheptadecatrienoate.) *Both of these activities are attributed to one enzyme—prostaglandin endoperoxide synthase. Some similar conversions occur in series 1 and 3 prostaglandins and thromboxanes and in series 3 and 5 leukotrienes. The figure explains why steroids, which inhibit the production of leukotrienes as well as of prostaglandins, are better anti-inflammatory agents than aspirinlike drugs and why they are effective in diseases such as asthma while selective inhibitors of cyclooxygenase are not. ①, Peroxidase; ②, leukotriene A₄ epoxide hydrolase; ③, glutathione S-transferase; ④, γ-glutamyltransferase; ⑤, cysteinyl-glycine dipeptidase.

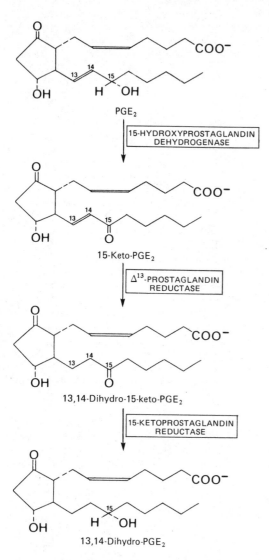

Figure 17–16. Catabolism of prostaglandins. This pathway is responsible for the inactivation of prostaglandins. These metabolites, together with their oxidation products due to β- and ω-oxidation, are found in urine. Sulfasalazine inhibits PG inactivation, as does the inhibitor of cyclooxygenase, indomethacin.

to oxidize long-chain fatty acids, although brain cannot extract them from the blood. The utilization of glycerol depends upon whether such tissues possess the necessary activating enzyme, **glycerokinase** (Fig 17–17). The enzyme has been found in significant amounts in liver, kidney, intestine, brown adipose tissue, and lactating mammary gland.

Biosynthesis of Acylglycerols

Although reactions involving the hydrolysis of triacylglycerols by lipase can be reversed, this is not the mechanism by which acylglycerols are synthesized in tissues. Both glycerol and fatty acids must be acti-

vated by ATP before they become incorporated into acylglycerols. Glycerokinase will catalyze the activation, by phosphorylation, of glycerol to sn-glycerol 3-phosphate. If this enzyme is absent—or low in activity, as it is in muscle or adipose tissue—most of the glycerol 3-phosphate must be derived from an intermediate of the glycolytic system, dihydroxyacetone phosphate, which forms glycerol 3-phosphate by reduction with NADH catalyzed by **glycerol 3-phosphate dehydrogenase** (Fig 17–17).

A. Triacylglycerol: Fatty acids are activated to acyl-CoA by the enzyme **acyl-CoA synthetase,** utilizing ATP and CoA. Two molecules of acyl-CoA combine with glycerol 3-phosphate to form 1,2-diacylglycerol phosphate (phosphatidate). This takes place in 2 stages via lysophosphatidate, catalyzed first by **glycerol 3-phosphate acyltransferase** and then by **1-acylglycerol 3-phosphate acyltransferase** (lysophosphatidate acyltransferase). Phosphatidate is converted by **phosphatidate phosphohydrolase** to a 1,2-diacylglycerol. In intestinal mucosa, a monoacylglycerol pathway exists whereby monoacylglycerol is converted to 1,2-diacylglycerol as a result of the presence of **monoacylglycerol acyltransferase.** A further molecule of acyl-CoA is esterified with the diacylglycerol to form a triacylglycerol, catalyzed by **diacylglycerol acyltransferase.** Most of the activity of these enzymes resides in the microsomal fraction of the cell, but some is found also in mitochondria, eg, glycerol 3-phosphate acyltransferase. Phosphatidate phosphohydrolase activity is found mainly in the particle-free supernatant fraction but also is membrane-bound. Dihydroxyacetone phosphate may be acylated and converted to lysophosphatidate after reduction by NADPH. The quantitative significance of this pathway remains in dispute. The pathway appears to be more important in peroxisomes, where it is involved in ether lipid synthesis, than in microsomes.

B. Phospholipids: Phospholipids are synthesized either from phosphatidate, eg, phosphatidylinositol, or from 1,2-diacylglycerol, eg, phosphatidylcholine or phosphatidylethanolamine. In the synthesis of phosphatidylinositol, cytidine triphosphate (CTP) reacts with phosphatidate to form a cytidine-diphosphate-diacylglycerol (CDP-diacylglycerol). Finally, this compound reacts with inositol, catalyzed by the enzyme **CDP-diacylglycerol inositol transferase,** to form a phosphatidylinositol (Fig 17–17).

In the biosynthesis of phosphatidylcholine and phosphatidylethanolamine (lecithins and cephalins) (Fig 17–17), choline or ethanolamine must first be converted to "active choline" or "active ethanolamine," respectively. This is a 2-stage process involving, first, a reaction with ATP to form the corresponding monophosphate, followed by a further reaction with CTP to form either cytidine diphosphocholine (CDP-choline) or cytidine diphosphoethanolamine (CDP-ethanolamine). In this form, choline or ethanolamine reacts with 1,2-diacylglycerol so that a phosphorylated base (either phosphocholine or phosphoethanolamine) is transferred to the diacylglycerol to

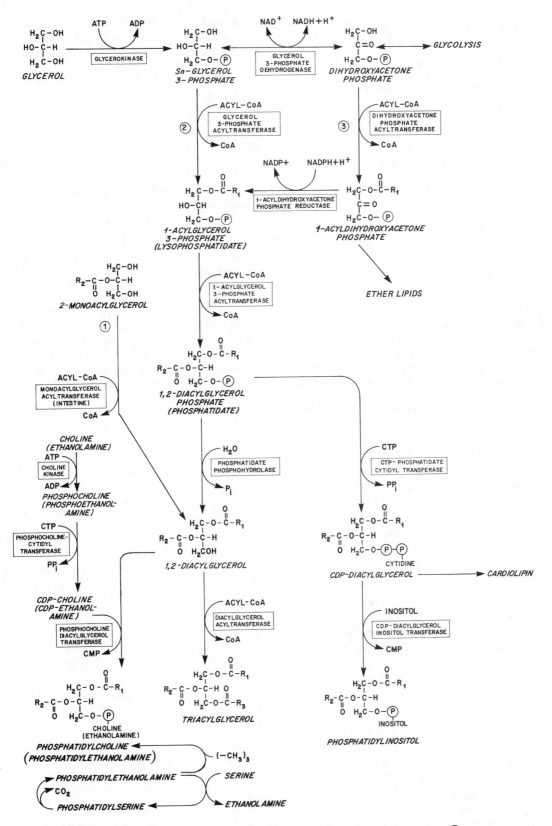

Figure 17–17. Biosynthesis of triacylglycerol and phospholipids. ① Monoacylglycerol pathway. ② Glycerol phosphate pathway. ③ Dihydroxyacetone phosphate pathway.

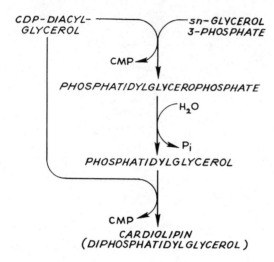

Figure 17–18. Biosynthesis of cardiolipin.

form either phosphatidylcholine or phosphatidylethanolamine, respectively. The activating enzyme, choline kinase, appears to be the regulatory enzyme of the phosphatidylcholine pathway. The enzyme responsible for the formation of phosphatidylethanolamine, **phosphoethanolamine-diacylglycerol transferase,** is not present in liver. Phosphatidylserine is formed from phosphatidylethanolamine directly by reaction with serine. Phosphatidylserine may re-form phosphatidylethanolamine by decarboxylation. An alternative pathway enables phosphatidylethanolamine to give rise directly to phosphatidylcholine by progressive methylation of the ethanolamine residue utilizing S-adenosylmethionine as the methyl donor.

A phospholipid present in mitochondria is **cardiolipin** (diphosphatidylglycerol). It is formed from phosphatidylglycerol, which in turn is synthesized from CDP-diacylglycerol (Fig 17–17) and glycerol 3-phosphate according to the scheme shown in Fig 17–18.

C. Glycerol Ether Phospholipids and Plasmalogens: A plasmalogenic diacylglycerol is one in which the 1 (or 2) position has an alkenyl residue containing the vinyl ether aldehydogenic linkage ($-CH_2-O-CH=CH-R'$). It appears that dihydroxyacetone phosphate is the precursor of the glycerol moiety (Fig 17–19). This compound combines with acyl-CoA to give 1-acyldihydroxyacetone phosphate. An exchange reaction takes place between the acyl group and a long-chain alcohol to give a 1-alkyldihydroxyacetone phosphate (containing the ether link) which in the presence of NADPH is converted to 1-alkylglycerol 3-phosphate. After further acylation in the 2 position, the resulting 1-alkyl, 2-acyl glycerol 3-phosphate (analogous to phosphatidate in Fig 17–17) is hydrolyzed to give the free glycerol derivative. Plasmalogens are formed by desaturation

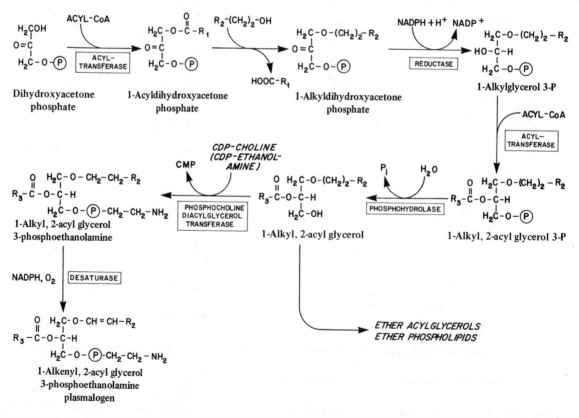

Figure 17–19. Biosynthesis of ether lipids and plasmalogens.

of the analogous glycerol ether lipid (Fig 17–19). Much of the phospholipid in mitochondria consists of plasmalogens.

Degradation & Turnover of Phospholipids

Degradation of many complex molecules in tissues is complete, eg, proteins. Thus, a turnover time can be determined for such a molecule. Although phospholipids are actively degraded, each portion of the molecule turns over at a different rate; eg, the turnover time of the phosphate group is different from that of the 1-acyl group. This is due to the presence of enzymes that allow partial degradation followed by resynthesis (Fig 17–21). **Phospholipase A_2** catalyzes the hydrolysis of the ester bond in position 2 of glycerophospholipids to form a free fatty acid and lysophospholipid, which in turn may be reacylated by acyl-CoA in the presence of an acyltransferase. Alternatively, lysophospholipid (eg, lysolecithin) is attacked by **lysophospholipase** (phospholipase B), removing the remaining 1-acyl group and forming the corresponding glyceryl phosphoryl base, which in turn

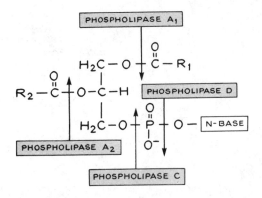

Figure 17–21. Sites of the hydrolytic activity of phospholipases on a phospholipid substrate.

may be split by a hydrolase liberating glycerol 3-phosphate plus base (Fig 17–20). **Phospholipase A_1** attacks the ester bond in position 1 of phospholipids. **Phospholipase C** attacks the ester bond in position 3, liberating 1,2-diacylglycerol plus a phosphoryl base. **Phospholipase D** is an enzyme, described mainly in plants, that hydrolyzes the nitrogenous base from phospholipids (Fig 17–21).

Lysolecithin may be formed by an alternative route involving **lecithin:cholesterol acyltransferase (LCAT).** This enzyme, found in plasma and possibly in liver, catalyzes the transfer of a fatty acid residue from the 2 position of lecithin to cholesterol to form cholesteryl ester and is considered to be responsible for much of the cholesteryl ester in plasma lipoproteins.

Lecithin + Cholesterol ⟶ Lysolecithin + Cholesteryl ester

LECITHIN:
CHOLESTEROL
ACYLTRANSFERASE

Long-chain saturated fatty acids are found predominantly in the 1 position of phospholipids, whereas the polyunsaturated acids (eg, the precursors of prostaglandins) are incorporated more into the 2 position. The incorporation of fatty acids into lecithin occurs by complete synthesis of the phospholipid, by transacylation between cholesteryl ester and lysolecithin, and by direct acylation of lysolecithin by acyl-CoA. Thus, a continuous exchange of the fatty acids is possible, particularly with regard to introducing essential fatty acids into phospholipid molecules.

METABOLISM OF SPHINGOLIPIDS

The **sphingomyelins** are phospholipids containing a fatty acid, phosphoric acid, choline, and a complex amino alcohol, sphingol (sphingosine). No glycerol is present.

The synthesis of **sphingosine** (Fig 17–22) has been studied in microsomes. Following activation by combination with pyridoxal phosphate, the amino acid

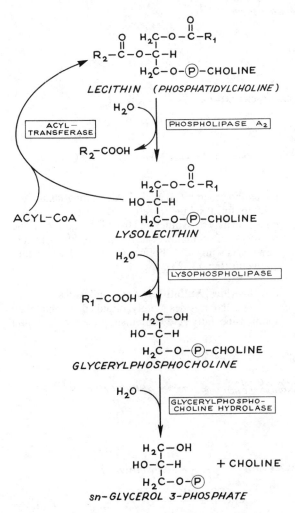

Figure 17–20. Metabolism of lecithin (phosphatidylcholine).

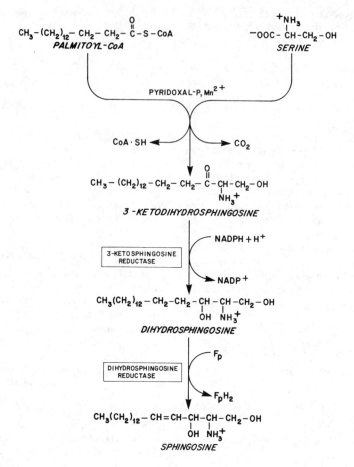

Figure 17–22. Biosynthesis of sphingosine. (Fp, flavoprotein.)

serine combines with palmitoyl-CoA to form 3-keto-dihydrosphingosine after loss of CO_2. Sphingosine itself is formed after 2 reductive steps, one of which is known to utilize NADPH as H donor and the other to involve a flavoprotein enzyme, analogous to the acyl-CoA dehydrogenase step in β-oxidation.

In vivo, sphingomyelin is synthesized from sphingosine phosphorylcholine (Fig 17–23). This is formed by the reaction of sphingosine with CDP-choline. Sphingosine phosphorylcholine is acylated at the amino group by an acyl-CoA of a long-chain fatty acid to form sphingomyelin. Alternatively, sphingomyelin may be synthesized from sphingosine via the formation of ceramide (N-acyl sphingosine), which in turn reacts with CDP-choline, giving CMP and sphingomyelin (Fig 17–23).

Cerebrosides, Sulfatides, & Gangliosides

The cerebrosides are glycolipids that contain the sphingosine–fatty acid combination (ceramide) found

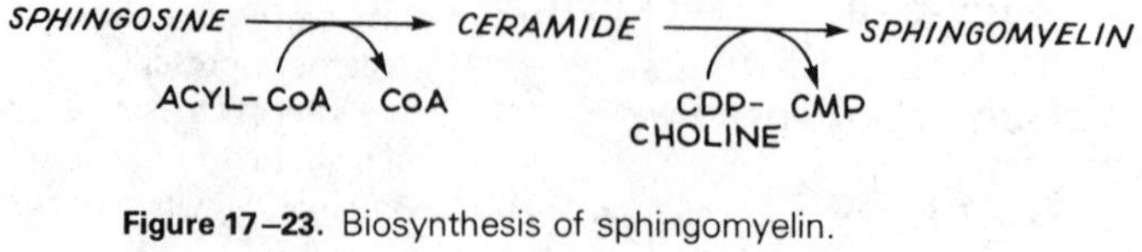

Figure 17–23. Biosynthesis of sphingomyelin.

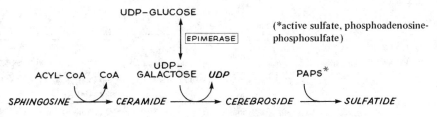

Figure 17-24. Biosynthesis of cerebrosides and sulfatides.

in the sphingomyelins, but a **galactose** moiety is attached to the ceramide in the place of the phosphorylcholine residue found in sphingomyelin. Characteristically, C_{24} fatty acids occur in cerebrosides (lignoceric, cerebronic, and nervonic acids). Lignoceric acid ($C_{23}H_{47}COOH$) is completely synthesized from acetate. Cerebronic acid, the 2-hydroxy derivative of lignoceric acid, is formed from it. Nervonic acid ($C_{23}H_{45}COOH$), a monounsaturated acid, is formed by elongation of oleic acid.

The requirement for galactose in the formation of cerebrosides, chondromucoids, and mucoproteins is the only known physiologic role of this sugar other than in the formation of lactose in milk.

The biosynthesis of the complete cerebroside molecule is catalyzed by an enzyme preparation obtained from young rat brain (Fig 17-24). **Uridine diphosphogalactose epimerase** utilizes uridine diphosphate glucose as substrate and accomplishes epimerization of the glucose moiety to galactose, thus

forming uridine diphosphogalactose. The reaction in brain is similar to that described on p 191 for the liver and mammary gland.

In one reaction sequence shown in Fig 17-24, acyl-CoA represents the CoA derivative of a fatty acid that is to be incorporated into the cerebroside. Examples would be lignoceric, cerebronic, and nervonic acids or stearic acid, which is a major component among the fatty acids of the cerebrosides in rat brain. The cerebrosides are found in high concentration in the myelin sheaths of nerves. **Sulfatides** are formed from cerebrosides after reaction with 3'-phosphoadenosine-5'-phosphosulfate (PAPS; "active sulfate"). PAPS is also involved in the biosynthesis of the other sulfolipids, ie, the **sulfo(galacto)glycerolipids** and the **steroid sulfates.** Gangliosides are synthesized from ceramide (acylsphingosine) by the stepwise addition of the activated sugars (eg, UDPG and UDPGal) and N-acetylneuraminic acid (Fig 17-25). A large number of gangliosides of increasing molecular weight may be formed.

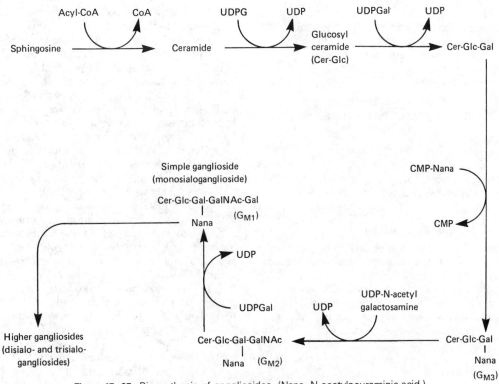

Figure 17-25. Biosynthesis of gangliosides. (Nana, N-acetylneuraminic acid.)

Table 17—1. Summary of the sphingolipidoses.
(Adapted from Brady, 1978.)

Disease	Enzyme Deficiency	Lipid Accumulating; Site of Deficient Enzymatic Reaction	Clinical Symptoms
Fucosidosis	α-Fucosidase	Cer – Glc – Gal – GalNAc – Gal $\div$ Fucose H-Isoantigen	Cerebral degeneration, muscle spasticity, thick skin.
Generalized gangliosidosis	G_{M1}-β-galactosidase	Cer – Glc – Gal(Nana)* – GalNAc $\div$ Gal G_{M1} Ganglioside	Mental retardation, liver enlargement, skeletal deformation.
Tay-Sachs disease	Hexosaminidase A	Cer – Glc – Gal(Nana) $\div$ GalNAc G_{M2} Ganglioside	Mental retardation, blindness, muscular weakness.
Tay-Sachs variant	Hexosaminidase A and B	Cer – Glc – Gal – Gal $\div$ GalNAc Globoside plus GM_2 ganglioside	Same as Tay-Sachs but progressing more rapidly.
Fabry's disease	Ceramide trihexosid-ase	Cer – Glc – Gal $\div$ Gal Ceramide trihexoside	Skin rash, kidney failure (full symptoms only in males; X-linked recessive).
Ceramide lacto-side lipidosis	Ceramide lactosidase (β-galactosidase)	Cer – Glc $\div$ Gal Ceramide lactoside	Progressing brain damage, liver and spleen enlargement.
Metachromatic leukodystrophy	Arylsulfatase A	Cer – Gal $\div$ OSO_3 Sulfatide	Mental retardation and psychologic disturbances in adults; demyelination.
Krabbe's disease	Galactocerebrosidase	Cer $\div$ Gal Galactocerebroside	Mental retardation; myelin almost absent.
Gaucher's disease	Glucocerebrosidase	Cer $\div$ Glc Glucocerebroside	Enlarged liver and spleen, erosion of long bones, mental retardation in infants.
Niemann-Pick disease	Sphingomyelinase	Cer $\div$ P – choline Sphingomyelin	Enlarged liver and spleen, mental retardation; fatal in early life.
Farber's disease	Ceramidase	Acyl $\div$ Sphingosine Ceramide	Hoarseness, dermatitis, skeletal deformation, mental retardation.

*Nana, N-acetylneuraminic acid; Cer, ceramide; Glc, glucose; Gal, galactose.

Although glycosphingolipids are recognized as constituents of cell membranes, it is now realized that they are involved as determinants in immunologic reactions such as in blood group substances.

PHOSPHOLIPIDS & SPHINGOLIPIDS IN DISEASE (Lipidoses)

Certain diseases are characterized by abnormal quantities of these lipids in the tissues, often in the nervous system. They may be classified into 3 groups: (1) true demyelinating diseases, (2) sphingolipidoses, and (3) leukodystrophies.

In **multiple sclerosis,** which is a demyelinating disease, there is loss both of phospholipids, particularly ethanolamine plasmalogen, and of sphingolipids from white matter, such that an analysis of it resembles more the composition of gray matter. Cholesteryl esters are also found, though normally absent. The cerebrospinal fluid shows raised phospholipid levels.

The **sphingolipidoses** are a group of inherited diseases that are often manifested in childhood. These diseases are part of a larger group of lysosomal disorders (Neufeld, 1975).

Lipid storage diseases exhibit several constant features: (1) In various tissues, there is an accumulation of complex lipids that have a portion of their structure in common. This portion is **ceramide** (an N-fatty acyl derivative of sphingosine, Fig 17–23). (2) The rate of **synthesis** of the stored lipid is comparable to that in normal humans. (3) The enzymatic defect in each of these diseases is **a deficiency of a specific hydrolytic enzyme necessary to break down the lipid.** (4) The extent to which the activity of the affected enzyme is decreased is similar in all of the tissues of the affected individual. As a result of these unifying basic considerations, procedures for the diagnosis of patients with these disorders have been developed. It has also become possible to detect heterozygous carriers of the genetic abnormalities responsible for these diseases as well as to discover in the unborn fetus the fact that a sphingolipodystrophy is present. A summary of the more important lipidoses is shown in Table 17–1.

In **metachromatic leukodystrophy,** there is general demyelination characterized by the accumulation of sulfatides containing galactose. **Multiple sulfatase deficiency** results in accumulation of cerebroside sulfate, steroid sulfates, and mucopolysaccharides owing to a combined deficiency of arylsulfatases A, B, and C and steroid sulfatase (see p 477).

• • •

References

Bell RM, Coleman RA: Enzymes of glycerolipid synthesis in eukaryotes. *Annu Rev Biochem* 1980;**49**:459.

Boyer PD (editor): *The Enzymes,* 3rd ed. Vol 16: *Lipid Enzymology.* Academic Press, 1983.

Brady RO: Sphingolipidoses. *Annu Rev Biochem* 1978;**47**:687.

Buege JA, Aust SD: Microsomal lipid peroxidation. Page 302 in: *Methods in Enzymology.* Vol 52. Biomembranes, part C. Fleischer S, Packer L (editors). Academic Press, 1978.

Buisseret PD: Allergy. *Sci Am* (Aug) 1982;**247**:86.

Farooqui AA: Metablism of sulfolipids in mammalian tissues. *Adv Lipid Res* 1981;**18**:159.

Gurr MI, James AT: *Lipid Biochemistry: An Introduction,* 3rd ed. Wiley, 1980.

Hammarström S: Leukotrienes. *Annu Rev Biochem* 1983;**52**:355.

Harris RH, Ramwell PW: Cellular mechanisms of prostaglandin action. *Annu Rev Physiol* 1979;**41**:553.

Hawthorne JN, Ansell GB (editors): *Phospholipids.* Elsevier, 1982.

Henderson LM, Hulse JD, Henderson LL: Page 35 in: *Carnitine Biosynthesis, Metabolism, and Functions.* Frenkel RA, McGarry JD (editors). Academic Press, 1980.

Holub BJ, Kuksis A: Metabolism of molecular species of diacylglycerophospholipids. *Adv Lipid Res* 1978;**16**:1.

Houtsmuller UMT: Biochemical aspects of fatty acids with *trans* double bonds. *Fette Seifen Anstrichmittel* 1978;**80**:162.

Jeffcoat R: The physiological role and control of mammalian fatty acyl-coenzyme A desaturases. *Biochem Soc Trans* 1977; **5**:811.

Lewis RA, Austen KF: The biologically active leukotrienes: Biosynthesis, metabolism, receptors, functions, and pharmacology. *J Clin Invest* 1984;**73**:889.

Marx JL: Blood clotting: The role of the prostaglandins. *Science* 1977;**196**:1072.

Moncada S (editor): Prostacyclin, thromboxane and leukotrienes. *Br Med Bull* 1983;**39**:209.

Neufeld EF, Lim TW, Shapiro LJ: Inherited disorders of lysosomal metabolism. *Annu Rev Biochem* 1975;**44**:357.

Pande SV, Parvin R: Page 143 in: *Carnitine Biosynthesis, Metabolism, and Functions.* Frenkel RA, McGarry JD (editors). Academic Press, 1980.

Piper P: Formation and actions of leukotrienes. *Physiol Rev* 1984;**64**:744.

Ramwell PW (editor): *The Prostaglandins.* Vols 1–3. Plenum Press, 1973–1978.

Rivers JPW, Frankel TL: Essential fatty acid deficiency. *Br Med Bull* 1981;**37**:59.

Rosenberg RN: Biochemical genetics of neurologic disease. *N Engl J Med* 1981;**305**:1181.

Samuelsson B et al: Prostaglandins and thromboxanes. *Annu Rev Biochem* 1978;**47**:997.

Tsukamoto Y et al: The architecture of the animal fatty acid synthetase complex. *J Biol Chem* 1983;**258**:15312.

Willis AL: Nutritional and pharmacological factors in eicosanoid biology. *Nutr Rev* 1981;**39**:289.

Various authors: Disorders characterized by evidence of abnormal lipid metabolism. In: *The Metabolic Basis of Inherited Disease,* 5th ed. Stanbury JB et al (editors). McGraw-Hill, 1983.

18 | Metabolism of Lipids: II. Role of the Tissues

Peter A. Mayes, PhD, DSc

In the previous chapter, the metabolism of the fatty acids was described from a mainly chemical viewpoint. However, while certain metabolic sequences, eg, β-oxidation, are common to many tissues, some tissues have distinct and specialized functions in the transport and utilization of lipids in the mammalian organism. The major routes for the disposition of fatty acids between the intestinal tract, the liver, adipose tissue, and the extrahepatic tissues are

shown in Fig 18–1. Lipoprotein triacylglycerol in chylomicrons or in very low density lipoprotein (VLDL) cannot be taken up intact by tissues but must first undergo hydrolysis by lipoprotein lipase, an enzyme situated on the capillary endothelium of extrahepatic tissues. The released free fatty acids are then taken up into the tissues where they are reesterified to triacylglycerol or oxidized as fuel. Free fatty acids are also released from adipose tissue and taken up by the

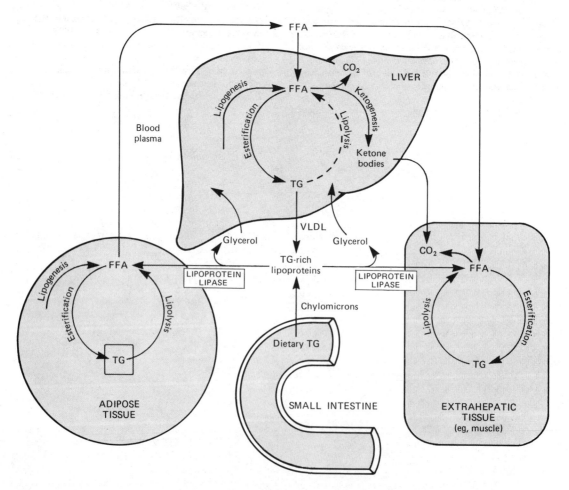

Figure 18–1. Overview of lipid metabolism in the whole animal. (VLDL, very low density lipoproteins; FFA, free fatty acids; TG, triacylglycerol.)

liver and other tissues and oxidized as fuel or esterified. In the liver, an additional pathway (ketogenesis) allows fatty acids to form ketone bodies, which in turn are transported via the circulation to other tissues for oxidation to CO_2.

As shown in Fig 18–1, there are 2 main entry points for fatty acids in this system. One is from chylomicrons, resulting from digestion and absorption of dietary triacylglycerol; the other is from de novo synthesis of fatty acids (lipogenesis) in the liver and adipose tissue.

Before their ultimate oxidation to CO_2, fatty acids may undergo several journeys through the circulation, either as free fatty acids or esterified as lipoprotein acylglycerol. This involves alternation of lipolysis (hydrolysis) and esterification. Both processes may take place in the same tissue; thus, the balance in activities between lipolysis and esterification determines the rate of release of free fatty acids from adipose tissue.

METABOLISM OF ADIPOSE TISSUE & MOBILIZATION OF FAT

The triacylglycerol stores in adipose tissue are continually undergoing lipolysis (hydrolysis) and reesterification (Fig 18–2). These 2 processes are not the forward and reverse phases of the same reaction. Rather, they are entirely different pathways involving different reactants and enzymes. Many of the nutritional, metabolic, and hormonal factors that regulate the metabolism of adipose tissue act either upon the process of esterification or on lipolysis. The resultant of these 2 processes determines the magnitude of the free fatty acid pool in adipose tissue, which in turn is the source and determinant of the level of free fatty acids circulating in the plasma. Since the level of plasma free fatty acids has most profound effects upon the metabolism of other tissues, particularly liver and muscle, the factors operating in adipose tissue that regulate the outflow of free fatty acids exert an influence far beyond the tissue itself.

Metabolic Pathways

In adipose tissue, triacylglycerol is synthesized from acyl-CoA and glycerol 3-phosphate according to the mechanism shown in Fig 17–17. Because the enzyme **glycerokinase** is low in activity in adipose tissue, glycerol cannot be utilized to any great extent in the esterification of acyl-CoA. For the provision of glycerol 3-phosphate needed in this reaction, the tissue is dependent on a supply of glucose.

Triacylglycerol undergoes hydrolysis by a **hormone-sensitive lipase*** or **mobilizing lipase** to form free fatty acids and glycerol. Since glycerol cannot be utilized readily in this tissue, it diffuses out into

the plasma, from where it is utilized by such tissues as liver and kidney, which possess an active glycerokinase. The free fatty acids formed by lipolysis can be reconverted in the tissue to acyl-CoA by **acyl-CoA synthetase** and reesterified with glycerol 3-phosphate to form triacylglycerol. Thus, there is a continual cycle of lipolysis and reesterification within the tissue. However, when the rate of reesterification is not sufficient to match the rate of lipolysis, free fatty acids accumulate and diffuse into the plasma, where they bind to albumin and raise the concentration of plasma **free fatty acids** (nonesterified fatty acids). These are a most important source of fuel for many tissues.

When the utilization of glucose by adipose tissue in vitro is increased, the free fatty acid outflow decreases. However, the release of glycerol continues, demonstrating that the effect of glucose is not mediated by reducing the rate of lipolysis. It is believed that the effect is due to the provision of glycerol 3-phosphate, which enhances esterification of free fatty acids via acyl-CoA.

Glucose can take several pathways in adipose tissue, including oxidation to CO_2 via the citric acid cycle, oxidation in the hexose monophosphate shunt, conversion to long-chain fatty acids, and formation of acylglycerol via glycerol 3-phosphate (Fig 18–2). When glucose utilization is high, a larger proportion of the uptake is oxidized to CO_2 and converted to fatty acids. However, as total glucose utilization decreases, the greater proportion of the glucose is directed to the formation of glycerol 3-phosphate and acylglycerol, which helps to minimize the efflux of free fatty acids.

There is more than one free fatty acid pool within adipose tissue. Dole has shown that the free fatty acid pool (Fig 18–2, pool 1) formed by lipolysis of triacylglycerol is the same pool that supplies fatty acids for reesterification; also, it releases them into the external medium (plasma). This latter process is not reversible, since labeled fatty acids taken up from the external medium do not label pool 1 before they are incorporated into triacylglycerol. It is necessary to postulate the existence of a second free fatty acid pool (pool 2) through which free fatty acids pass after uptake by the adipose cell before they are incorporated into triacylglycerol or oxidized to CO_2. This second pool must be small and have a high turnover rate.

Role of Hormones in Fat Mobilization

Insulin. The rate of release of free fatty acids from adipose tissue is affected by many hormones that influence either the rate of esterification or the rate of lipolysis. Insulin administration is followed by a fall in circulating plasma free fatty acids. In vitro, insulin inhibits the release of free fatty acids from adipose tissue, enhances lipogenesis and the synthesis of acylglycerol, and increases the oxidation of glucose to CO_2 via the hexose monophosphate shunt. All of these effects are dependent on the presence of glucose in the medium and can be explained, to a large extent, on the basis of the ability of insulin to enhance the uptake of glucose into adipose cells. This is achieved by insulin

*This lipase is distinct from lipoprotein lipase that catalyzes lipoprotein triacylglycerol hydrolysis prior to its uptake into extrahepatic tissues (see p 240).

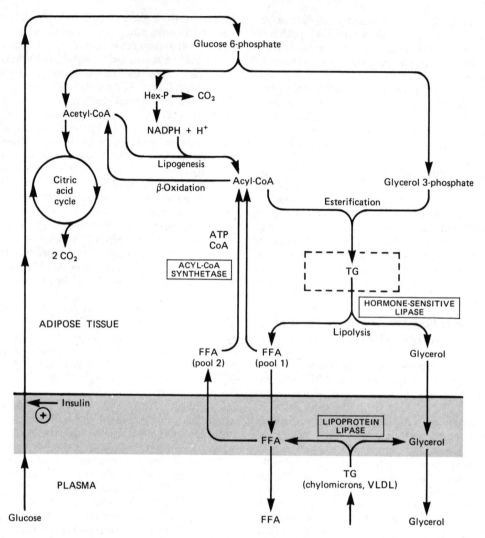

Figure 18–2. Metabolism of adipose tissue. Hormone-sensitive lipase is activated by ACTH, TSH, glucagon, epinephrine, norepinephrine, and vasopressin and inhibited by insulin, prostaglandin E_1, and nicotinic acid. Shaded area represents lipoprotein lipase region of the capillary wall. Details of the formation of glycerol 3-phosphate from intermediates of glycolysis are shown in Fig 17–17. (Hex-P, hexose monophosphate shunt; TG, triacylglycerol; FFA, free fatty acids; VLDL, very low density lipoproteins.)

causing the translocation of glucose transporters from the Golgi complex to the plasma membrane. Insulin has also been shown to increase the activity of pyruvate dehydrogenase, acetyl-CoA carboxylase, and glycerol phosphate acyltransferase, which could explain the enhancement of fatty acid and acylglycerol synthesis. These 3 enzymes are now known to be regulated by covalent modification, ie, by phosphorylation-dephosphorylation mechanisms. A principal action of insulin in adipose tissue is to inhibit the activity of the hormone-sensitive lipase, reducing the release not only of free fatty acids but of glycerol as well. Adipose tissue is much more sensitive to insulin than are many other tissues, which points to adipose tissue as a major site of insulin action in vivo. Both glucose oxidation

and lipogenesis are reduced to the extent of 80–90% in adipose tissue from alloxan-diabetic rats. These metabolic effects are reversed by the addition of insulin in vivo.

Lipolytic hormones. Other hormones accelerate the release of free fatty acids from adipose tissue and raise the plasma free fatty acid concentration by increasing the rate of lipolysis of the triacylglycerol stores. These include epinephrine, norepinephrine, glucagon, adrenocorticotropic hormone (ACTH), α- and β-melanocyte-stimulating hormones (MSH), thyroid-stimulating hormone (TSH), growth hormone (GH), and vasopressin. Many of these activate the hormone-sensitive lipase and increase glucose utilization as well. The latter process has been attributed to stimulation of esterification by the increased production of free fatty acids. For an optimum effect, most of these lipolytic processes require the presence of glucocorticoids and thyroid hormones. On their own, these particular hormones do not increase lipolysis markedly but act in a facilitatory or permissive capacity with respect to other lipolytic endocrine factors.

Adipose tissue contains a number of lipases, one of which is a hormone-sensitive triacylglycerol lipase. In addition, there is present a diacylglycerol lipase (which may be the same enzyme, since it is hormone-sensitive) and a monoacylglycerol lipase (which is not hormone-sensitive in mammals). The hormone-sensitive triacylglycerol lipase is considered to catalyze the rate-limiting step in lipolysis (Fig 18–3). All of these hydrolase enzymes may be part of an enzyme complex together with a hormone-sensitive cholesteryl ester hydrolase. The hormones that act rapidly in promoting lipolysis, ie, catecholamines, do so by stimulating the activity of adenylate cyclase, the enzyme that converts ATP to cAMP. The mechanism is analogous to that responsible for hormonal stimulation of glycogenolysis (see p 176). Hormones, upon occupying their membrane receptor, activate adenyl-

ate cyclase through a GTP-dependent process occurring in the cellular membrane. It appears that cAMP, by stimulating **cAMP-dependent protein kinase,** converts inactive hormone-sensitive triacylglycerol lipase into active lipase. Lipolysis is controlled largely by the amount of cAMP present in the tissue. It follows that processes which destroy or preserve cAMP have an effect on lipolysis. cAMP is degraded to 5'-AMP by the enzyme **cyclic 3',5'-nucleotide phosphodiesterase.** This enzyme is inhibited by methyl xanthines such as caffeine and theophylline. Thus, at concentrations at which caffeine itself does not cause any increase in cAMP in isolated fat cells, and in the presence of a lipolytic hormone such as epinephrine, caffeine acts synergistically to cause a considerable increase in cAMP over that which would be caused by the epinephrine alone. It is significant that the drinking of coffee or the administration of caffeine causes marked and prolonged elevation of plasma free fatty acids in humans.

Insulin has a pronounced antilipolytic effect both in vivo and in vitro and antagonizes the effect of the lipolytic hormones. It is now considered that lipolysis may be more sensitive to changes in concentration of

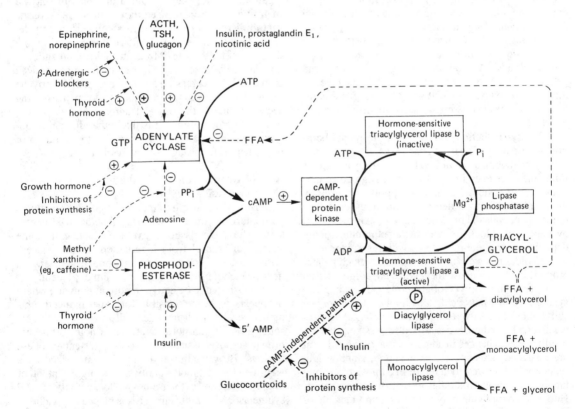

Figure 18–3. Control of adipose tissue lipolysis. (TSH, thyroid-stimulating hormone; FFA, free fatty acids.) Note the cascade sequence of reactions affording amplification at each step. The lipolytic stimulus is "switched off" by the action of lipase phosphatase, the inhibition of the lipase and adenylate cyclase by high concentrations of FFA, the inhibition of adenylate cyclase by adenosine, and the removal of cAMP by the action of phosphodiesterase. ACTH, TSH, and glucagon may not activate adenylate cyclase in vivo, since the concentration of each hormone required in vitro is much higher than is found in the circulation. Positive $(\oplus)$ and negative $(\ominus)$ regulatory effects are represented by broken lines and substrate flow by solid lines.

insulin than are glucose utilization and esterification. The antilipolytic effects of insulin, nicotinic acid, and prostaglandin E_1 may be accounted for by inhibition of the synthesis of cAMP, possibly at the adenylate cyclase site or by stimulating phosphodiesterase. In addition, insulin inhibits a cAMP-independent pathway for the activation of lipolysis. Prostaglandin synthesis in adipose tissue is increased by lipolytic hormones and is reduced by essential fatty acid deficiency. When infused in vivo at low concentration, prostaglandin E_1 causes the release of catecholamines with consequent increase in free fatty acid mobilization. However, when infused at high concentration, it inhibits mobilization, as it does in vitro. Possible mechanisms for the action of thyroid hormones include an augmentation of the level of cAMP by facilitation of the passage of the stimulus from the receptor site on the outside of the cell membrane to the adenylate cyclase site on the inside of the membrane and an inhibition of phosphodiesterase activity. The effect of growth hormone in promoting lipolysis is slow. It is dependent on new formation of proteins involved in the formation of cAMP. Glucocorticoids promote lipolysis via synthesis of new lipase protein by a cAMP-independent pathway. These findings help to explain the role of the pituitary gland and the adrenal cortex in enhancing fat mobilization.

Besides the recognized hormones, certain other adipokinetic principles have been isolated from pituitary glands. A "fat-mobilizing substance" can be isolated from the urine of several fasting species, including humans, provided the pituitary gland is intact. This substance is highly active both in vivo and in vitro.

The sympathetic nervous system, through liberation of norepinephrine in adipose tissue, plays a central role in the mobilization of free fatty acids by exerting a tonic influence even in the absence of augmented nervous activity. Thus, the increased lipolysis caused by many of the factors described previously can be reduced or abolished by denervation of adipose tissue, by ganglionic blockade with hexamethonium, or by depleting norepinephrine stores with reserpine.

In older rats weighing over 350 g, a much greater proportion of the glucose metabolized in adipose tissue is converted to acylglycerol glycerol, and much less is synthesized into fatty acids; this implies that there is a shift in lipogenesis from adipose to other tissues such as the liver. The adipose tissue is also less sensitive to insulin. These changes in adipose tissue of the older rat are related to adiposity rather than age, since weight reduction is followed by a return in adipose tissue metabolism to a pattern similar to that of the young rat. Human adipose tissue may not be an important site of lipogenesis. This is indicated by the observation that there is not significant incorporation of label into long-chain fatty acids from labeled glucose or pyruvate and that ATP-citrate lyase, a key enzyme in lipogenesis, does not appear to be present and has extremely low activity in liver. Other enzymes—eg, glucose 6-phosphate dehydrogenase, the malic enzyme—which in the rat undergo adaptive changes coincident with increased lipogenesis, do not undergo similar changes in human adipose tissue. Indeed, it has been suggested that in humans there is a "carbohydrate excess syndrome" due to a unique limitation in ability to dispose of excess carbohydrate by lipogenesis (Björntorp and Sjöström, 1978). In birds, lipogenesis is confined to the liver, where it is particularly important in providing lipids for egg formation.

Human adipose tissue is unresponsive to most of the lipolytic hormones apart from the catecholamines. Of further interest is the lack of lipolytic response to epinephrine in the rabbit, guinea pig, pig, and chicken; the pronounced lipolytic effect of glucagon in birds, together with an absence of any antilipolytic effect of insulin; and the lack of acylglycerol glycerol synthesis from glucose in the pigeon. It would appear that, in the various species studied, a variety of mechanisms have been evolved for fine control of adipose tissue metabolism.

On consideration of the profound derangement of metabolism in diabetes mellitus (which is due mainly to increased release of free fatty acids from the depots) and the fact that insulin to a large extent corrects the condition, it must be concluded that **insulin plays a prominent role in the regulation of adipose tissue metabolism.** To reach as firm a conclusion with respect to the role of the pituitary hormones is more difficult, since the rate of free fatty acid mobilization is only slightly depressed in fasting hypophysectomized animals. This depression could be accounted for by the reduced facilitatory or potentiating influence of the secretion of the thyroid and adrenal glands. Under physiologic conditions, it is likely that the main lipolytic stimulus in adipose tissue is due to liberation of norepinephrine through sympathetic activity.

Role of Brown Adipose Tissue in Thermogenesis

Brown adipose tissue is involved in metabolism particularly at times when heat generation is necessary. Thus, the tissue is extremely active in some species in arousal from hibernation, in animals exposed to cold (nonshivering thermogenesis), and in heat production in the newborn animal. Recently, it has been shown to be active in normal humans, where it appears to be responsible for "diet-induced thermogenesis," which may account for how some persons can "eat and not get fat." It is noteworthy that brown adipose tissue is reduced or absent in obese persons. Brown adipose tissue is characterized by a well-developed blood supply and a high content of mitochondria and cytochromes but low activity of ATP synthetase. Metabolic emphasis is placed on oxidation of both glucose and fatty acids.

Norepinephrine liberated from sympathetic nerve endings is important in increasing lipolysis in the tissue. Experiments indicate that oxidation and phosphorylation are not coupled in mitochondria of this tissue, since dinitrophenol has no effect and there is no respiratory control by ADP. The phosphorylation that does occur appears to be at the substrate level, eg, at the succinate thiokinase step and in glycolysis. Thus, oxidation produces much heat, and little free energy is trapped in ATP. In terms of the **chemiosmotic theory** (see p 139), it would appear that the proton gradient normally present across the inner mitochondrial membrane of coupled mitochondria is continually dissipated in brown adipose tissue by a thermogenic protein, **thermogenin,** which acts as a proton conductance pathway through the membrane. This would explain the apparent lack of effect of uncouplers (Fig 18–4).

Glycerol 3-phosphate is oxidized readily via the mitochondrial flavoprotein-linked glycerol 3-phos-

phate dehydrogenase. If substrate level phosphorylation is important in brown adipose tissue, this pathway would be a means of maintaining glycolysis by transporting reducing equivalents generated in glycolysis into the mitochondria for oxidation in the respiratory chain. The presence of glycerokinase would enable free glycerol resulting from lipolysis to be converted to glycerol 3-phosphate and be oxidized directly in the tissue. It does not appear that much heat is generated by the energy-consuming futile cycle of lipolysis followed by resynthesis of triacylglycerol.

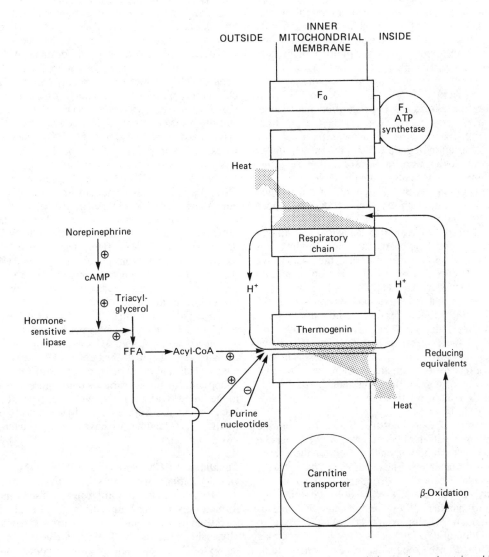

Figure 18–4. Thermogenesis in brown adipose tissue. Activity of the respiratory chain produces heat in addition to translocating protons (see p 137). These protons dissipate heat when returned to the inner mitochondrial compartment via thermogenin, instead of generating ATP when returning via the F_1 ATP synthetase. The passage of H^+ via thermogenin is inhibited by purine nucleotides when brown adipose tissue is unstimulated. Under the influence of norepinephrine, the inhibition is removed by the production of free fatty acids (FFA) and acyl-CoA. Note the dual role of acyl-CoA in both facilitating the action of thermogenin and in supplying reducing equivalents for the respiratory chain.

METABOLISM OF THE PLASMA LIPOPROTEINS

For the chemistry and composition of lipoproteins, see p 202.

Five groups of lipoproteins having major roles in the transport and metabolism of lipids are present in plasma: (1) **chylomicrons,** derived from intestinal absorption of triacylglycerol; (2) **very low density lipoproteins** (VLDL, or pre-β-lipoproteins), derived from the liver for the export of triacylglycerol; (3) **low-density lipoproteins** (LDL, or β-lipoproteins), representing a final stage in the catabolism of VLDL and possibly chylomicrons; (4) **high-density lipoproteins** (HDL, or α-lipoproteins), involved in VLDL and chylomicron metabolism and also in cholesterol metabolism; and (5) **free fatty acids** (FFA), not generally classified with the other plasma lipoproteins since their structure is different, consisting of long-chain fatty acids bound to serum albumin.

Free Fatty Acids

The free fatty acids (nonesterified fatty acids, unesterified fatty acids) arise in the plasma from lipolysis of triacylglycerol in adipose tissue or as a result of the action of lipoprotein lipase during uptake of plasma triacylglycerols into tissues. They are found in combination with serum albumin in concentrations varying between 0.1 and 2 μeq/mL of plasma and comprise the long-chain fatty acids found in adipose tissue, ie, palmitic, stearic, oleic, palmitoleic, linoleic, and other polyunsaturated acids, and smaller quantities of other long-chain fatty acids. Binding sites on albumin of varying affinity for the fatty acids have been described. Low levels of free fatty acids are recorded in the fully fed condition, rising to about 0.5 μeq/mL in the postabsorptive and between 0.7 and 0.8 μeq/mL in the fully fasting state. In uncontrolled diabetes mellitus, the level may rise to as much as 2 μeq/mL. In meal eaters, the level falls just after eating and rises again prior to the next meal, whereas in such continual feeders as ruminants—where there is a continual influx of nutrient from the intestine—the free fatty acids remain relatively constant and at a low level.

The rate of removal of free fatty acids from the blood is extremely rapid. Estimates suggest that the free fatty acids supply about 25–50% of the energy requirements in fasting. The remainder of the uptake is esterified and, according to evidence using radioactive free fatty acids, eventually recycled. In starvation, the respiratory quotient (RQ) would indicate that considerably more fat is being oxidized than can be traced to the oxidation of free fatty acids. This difference may be accounted for by the oxidation of esterified lipids from the circulation or of those present in tissues. The latter are thought to occur particularly in heart and skeletal muscle, where considerable stores of lipid are to be found in the muscle cells. The free fatty acid turnover is related directly to free fatty acid concentration. Thus, the rate of free fatty acid production in adipose tissue controls the free fatty acid concentration in plasma, which in turn determines the free fatty acid uptake by other tissues. The nutritional condition does not appear to have a great effect on the fractional uptake of free fatty acids by tissues. It does, however, alter the proportion of the uptake which is oxidized to CO_2 compared to the fraction which is esterified, more being oxidized in the fasting than in the fed state.

A **fatty acid-binding protein** or **Z-protein** has been reported to occur in the cytosol of many of the major tissues. It presumably fulfills a similar role, intracellularly, to serum albumin in the extracellular transport of long-chain fatty acids.

The Apolipoproteins (Apoproteins)

The lipoproteins are characterized by the presence of one or more proteins or polypeptides known as apoproteins. According to the ABC nomenclature, the 2 major apoproteins of HDL are designated A-I and A-II, respectively. The main apoprotein of LDL is apoprotein B, which is found also in VLDL and chylomicrons. However, apo-B of chylomicrons (B-48) is smaller than apo-B of LDL or VLDL (B-100) and has a different amino acid composition. B-48 is synthesized in the intestine and B-100 in the liver. (In the rat, the liver appears to form both B-100 and B-48.) Apoproteins C-I, C-II, and C-III are smaller polypeptides found in VLDL, HDL, and chylomicrons (Table 18-1). Carbohydrates account for approximately 5% of apo-B and include mannose, galactose, fucose, glucose, glucosamine, and sialic acid. Thus, some lipoproteins are also glycoproteins (Table 18–1). The C apoproteins seem to be freely transferable between VLDL and chylomicrons on the one hand and HDL on the other. C-II is an important activator of extrahepatic lipoprotein lipase, involved in the clearance of triacylglycerol from the circulation.

Several apoproteins other than apo-A, -B, or -C have been found in plasma lipoproteins. One is the arginine-rich apoprotein E isolated from VLDL; it contains arginine to the extent of 10% of the total amino acids and accounts for 5–10% of total VLDL apoproteins in normal subjects but is present in excess in the broad β-VLDL of patients with type III hyperlipoproteinemia. Animals made hypercholesterolemic by cholesterol feeding also have increased quantities of this apoprotein.

Formation of Chylomicrons & Very Low Density Lipoproteins (VLDL)

By definition, **chylomicrons** are found in chyle formed only by the lymphatic system **draining the intestine.** Smaller and denser particles having the physical characteristics of VLDL are also to be found in chyle. However, their apoprotein composition resembles chylomicrons rather than VLDL, indicating that they should be regarded as small chylomicrons. Their formation is more constant and occurs even in the fasting state, in which they are responsible for transporting 50% of lymphatic triacylglycerol and cholesterol, their lipids being derived mainly from bile

Table 18–1. Apoproteins of human plasma lipoproteins.

Apoprotein	Lipoprotein	C-Terminal Amino Acid	Number of Amino Acid Residues	Molecular Weight	Presence of Carbohydrate Residues	Additional Remarks
A-I	HDL, chylomicrons	Glutamine	245	28,300	+	Activator of lecithin:cholesterol acyltransferase (LCAT).
A-II	HDL, chylomicrons	Glutamine	77 × 2	17,000	−	Structure is 2 identical monomers joined by a disulfide bridge
A-IV	HDL, chylomicrons	?	?	46,000	?	?
B-100	LDL, VLDL, IDL	?	?	?	+	Synthesized in liver.
B-48	Chylomicrons, chylomicron remnants	?	?	?	+	Synthesized in intestine.
C-I	VLDL, HDL, chylomicrons	Serine	57	6631	−	Possible activator of LCAT.
C-II	VLDL, HDL, chylomicrons	Glutamic acid	?	8837	−	Activator of extrahepatic lipoprotein lipase.
C-III	VLDL, HDL, chylomicrons	Alanine	79	8764	+	Several polymorphic forms depending on content of sialic acids.
D	Subfraction of HDL	?	?	20,000	+	Possibly identical to the cholesteryl ester transfer protein.
E (arginine-rich)	VLDL, HDL, chylomicrons, chylomicron remnants	Histidine	?	34,000	+	Present in excess in the β-VLDL of patients with type III hyperlipoproteinemia and exclusively in HDL$_C$.

and intestinal secretions. Chylomicron formation increases with the load of triacylglycerol absorbed. The bulk of the plasma **VLDL** is of hepatic origin, being the vehicle of transport of **triacylglycerol from the liver to the extrahepatic tissues.**

There are many similarities in the mechanism of formation of chylomicrons by intestinal cells and of VLDL by hepatic parenchymal cells (Fig 18–5). Apoprotein B is synthesized by ribosomes in the rough endoplasmic reticulum and is incorporated into lipo-

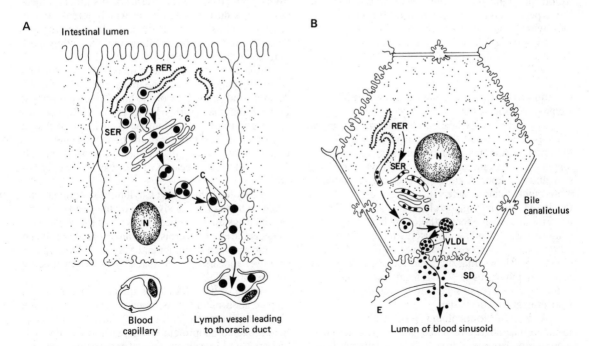

Figure 18–5. The formation and secretion of *(A)* chylomicrons by an intestinal cell and *(B)* very low density lipoproteins by a hepatic cell. (RER, rough endoplasmic reticulum; SER, smooth endoplasmic reticulum; G, Golgi complex; N, nucleus; C, chylomicrons; VLDL, very low density lipoproteins; E, endothelium; SD, space of Disse, containing blood plasma.) The figure is a diagrammatic representation of events that can be seen with electron microscopy.

proteins in the smooth endoplasmic reticulum, which is the main site of synthesis of triacylglycerol, phospholipids, and cholesterol. Apo A-I and A-II are also synthesized by intestinal cells and incorporated into chylomicrons. Lipoproteins are also found in the Golgi apparatus, where, it is thought, carbohydrate residues are added to the lipoprotein. The chylomicrons and VLDL are released from either the intestinal or hepatic cell by fusion of the secretory vacuole with the cell membrane (reverse pinocytosis). Chylomicrons pass into the spaces between the intestinal cells, eventually making their way into the lymphatic system (lacteals) draining the intestine. VLDL are secreted by hepatic parenchymal cells into the space of Disse and then into the hepatic sinusoids. The similarities between the 2 processes and the anatomic mechanisms are striking, for—apart from the mammary gland—the intestine and liver are the only tissues from which particulate lipid is secreted. The inability of particulate lipid to pass through endothelial cells of the capillaries without prior hydrolysis is probably the reason dietary fat enters the circulation via the lymphatics (thoracic duct) and not via the hepatic portal system.

Apoprotein B is essential for chylomicron and VLDL formation. In abetalipoproteinemia (a rare disease), apoprotein B is not synthesized; lipoproteins containing this apoprotein are not formed, and lipid droplets accumulate in the intestine and liver. Although both chylomicrons and VLDL isolated from blood contain apoproteins C and E, the newly secreted or "nascent" lipoproteins contain little or none, and it would appear that the complement of apoprotein C and E polypeptides is taken up by transfer from HDL once the chylomicrons and VLDL have entered the circulation (Figs 18–6 and 18–7). A more detailed account of the factors controlling hepatic VLDL secretion is given on p 243.

Catabolism of Chylomicrons & Very Low Density Lipoproteins

The clearance of labeled chylomicrons from the blood is rapid, the half-time of disappearance being on the order of minutes in small animals (eg, rats) but longer in larger animals (eg, humans), in whom it is still under 1 hour. Larger particles are catabolized more quickly than smaller ones. When chylomicrons labeled in the triacylglycerol fatty acids are administered intravenously, some 80% of the label is found in adipose tissue, heart, and muscle and approximately 20% in the liver. As experiments with the perfused organ have shown that the liver does not metabolize native chylomicrons or VLDL significantly, the label in the liver must result secondarily from their metabolism in extrahepatic tissues.

A. Role of Lipoprotein Lipase: There is a significant correlation between the ability of a tissue to incorporate lipoprotein triacylglycerol fatty acids and the activity of the enzyme **lipoprotein lipase.** It is located on the **walls of blood capillaries,** anchored by proteoglycan chains of heparan sulfate, and has been found in extracts of heart, adipose tissue, spleen, lung,

renal medulla, aorta, diaphragm, and lactating mammary gland. Normal blood does not contain appreciable quantities of the enzyme; however, following injection of heparin, lipoprotein lipase is released from its heparan sulfate binding into the circulation and is accompanied by the clearing of lipemia. A lipase is also released from the liver by large quantities of heparin **(heparin-releasable hepatic lipase),** but this enzyme has properties different from those of lipoprotein lipase and does not react readily with chylomicrons.

Both phospholipids and apolipoprotein C-II are required as cofactors for lipoprotein lipase activity. Apo C-II contains a specific phospholipid binding site through which it is attached to the lipoprotein. Thus, chylomicrons and VLDL provide the enzyme with both its substrate and cofactors. Hydrolysis takes place while the lipoproteins are attached to the enzyme on the endothelium. The triacylglycerol is hydrolyzed progressively through a diacylglycerol to a monoacylglycerol that is finally hydrolyzed to free fatty acid plus glycerol. Some of the released free fatty acids return to the circulation, attached to albumin, but the bulk are transported into the tissue (Figs 18–6 and 18–7). Heart lipoprotein lipase has a low K_m for triacylglycerol, whereas the K_m of the enzyme in adipose tissue is 10 times greater. As the concentration of plasma triacylglycerol decreases in the transition from the fed to the starved condition, the heart enzyme remains saturated with substrate but the saturation of the enzyme in adipose tissue diminishes, thus redirecting uptake from adipose tissue toward the heart. A similar redirection occurs during lactation, in which adipose tissue activity diminishes and mammary gland activity increases, allowing uptake of lipoprotein triacylglycerol long-chain fatty acid for milk fat synthesis.

Reaction with lipoprotein lipase results in the loss of approximately 90% of the triacylglycerol of chylomicrons and in the loss of the apo-C (but not apo-E) polypeptides that return to HDL. The resulting lipoprotein or **remnant** is about half the diameter of the parent chylomicron and in terms of the percentage composition becomes relatively enriched in cholesterol and cholesteryl esters because of the loss of triacylglycerol.

B. Role of the Liver: Chylomicron remnants are taken up by the liver in vivo and by the perfused liver, in which system it has been shown that the cholesteryl esters and triacylglycerols of remnants are hydrolyzed and metabolized (Gardner and Mayes, 1978). Uptake into liver appears to be mediated by a receptor specific for apo-E.

When ^{125}I-VLDL were injected into humans, labeled apoprotein C was found in HDL as it became distributed between VLDL and HDL. On the other hand, labeled apoprotein B disappeared from VLDL and appeared in a lipoprotein of intermediate density (1.006–1.0l9, IDL). Finally, the radioactivity was found in apoprotein B of LDL, showing that the B apoprotein of VLDL is the precursor of apoprotein B of LDL. The role of the liver in this process is uncertain.

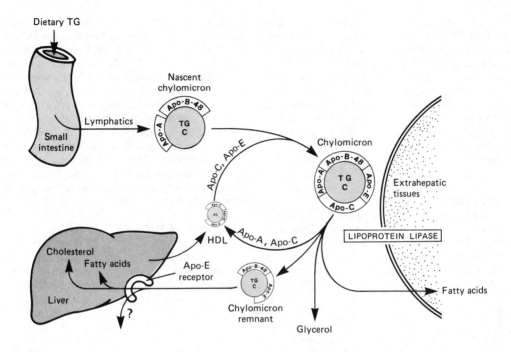

Figure 18–6. Metabolic fate of chylomicrons. (Apo-A, apolipoprotein A; Apo-B, apolipoprotein B; Apo-C, apolipoprotein C; Apo-E, apolipoprotein E; HDL, high-density lipoprotein; TG, triacylglycerol; C, cholesterol and cholesteryl ester; P, phospholipid.) Only the predominant lipids are shown.

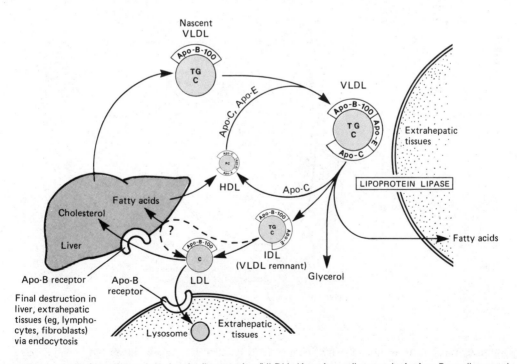

Figure 18–7. Metabolic fate of very low density lipoproteins (VLDL). (Apo-A; apolipoprotein A; Apo-B, apolipoprotein B; Apo-C, apolipoprotein C; Apo-E, apolipoprotein E; HDL, high-density lipoprotein; TG, triacylglycerol; IDL, intermediate-density lipoprotein; LDL, low-density lipoprotein; C, cholesterol and cholesteryl ester; P, phospholipid.) Only the predominant lipids are shown.

However, the IDL may represent the end of the degradation of VLDL by lipoprotein lipase and may correspond to chylomicron remnants. Only one IDL particle is formed from each VLDL particle (Fig 18–7). In humans, virtually all of the VLDL is converted to LDL, but in the rat most of the apo-B from VLDL appears in the liver and only a small percentage in LDL. This may be due to the fact that VLDL in the rat contains apo-B-48 as well as B-100. If the hepatic receptor is specific for B-48 as well as apo-E, this would account for much of the hepatic removal of IDL in the rat and for the low production of LDL.

Metabolism of LDL

Most LDL appears to be formed from VLDL and possibly chylomicrons, as described above, but there is evidence for some production directly by the liver. The half-time of disappearance from the circulation of apoprotein B in LDL is approximately 2½ days.

Studies on cultured human fibroblasts, lymphocytes, and arterial smooth muscle cells have shown the existence of specific binding sites for LDL, which are defective in familial hypercholesterolemia (Goldstein and Brown, 1977). In normal cells, the LDL is internalized, cholesteryl ester is hydrolyzed, the apoprotein is broken down in lysosomes, cholesterol is translocated in the cell and reesterified, and the activity of HMG-CoA reductase (see p 250) is repressed, thus inhibiting cholesterol synthesis within the cell. It appears that the number of LDL binding sites on the cell surface is regulated by the cellular need for cholesterol for membrane and steroid hormone synthesis. Approximately 50% of LDL is degraded in extrahepatic tissues and 50% in the liver.

Metabolism of HDL

HDL is synthesized and secreted from both liver and intestine. However, nascent HDL from intestine does not contain apoprotein C but only apoprotein A. Thus, apoprotein C seems to be synthesized in the liver

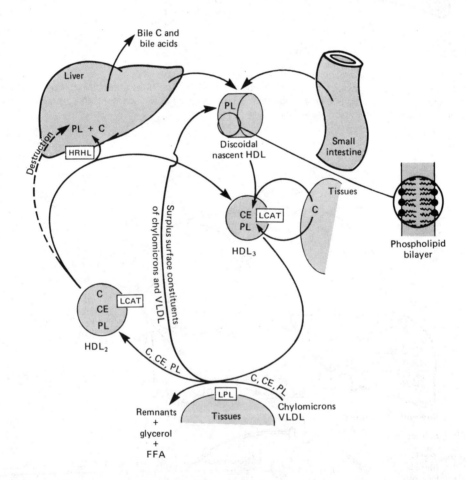

Figure 18–8. Metabolism of high-density lipoprotein (HDL). (HRHL, heparin-releasable hepatic lipase; LCAT, lecithin:cholesterol acyltransferase; LPL, lipoprotein lipase; C, cholesterol; CE, cholesteryl ester; PL, phospholipid; FFA, free fatty acids.) The figure illustrates the role of the 3 enzymes HRHL, LCAT, and LPL in the postulated HDL cycle for the transport of cholesterol from the tissues to the liver. HDL_2, HDL_3—see Table 16–4. HRHL hydrolyzes phospholipid on the surface of HDL_2, releasing cholesterol for uptake into the liver.

only and is transferred to intestinal HDL when the latter enters the plasma. Nascent HDL consists of discoid phospholipid bilayers containing apoprotein and free cholesterol. These lipoproteins are similar to the particles found in the plasma of patients with a deficiency of the plasma enzyme **lecithin:cholesterol acyltransferase (LCAT)** and in the plasma of patients with obstructive jaundice (see p 253). Hamilton et al proposed that LCAT—and possibly the LCAT activator apoprotein A-I—bind to the disk. Catalysis by LCAT converts surface phospholipid and free cholesterol into cholesteryl esters and lysolecithin. The nonpolar cholesteryl esters move into the hydrophobic interior of the bilayer, whereas lysolecithin is transferred to plasma albumin. The reaction continues generating a nonpolar core that pushes the bilayer apart until a spherical, pseudomicellar HDL is formed, covered by a surface film of polar lipids and apoproteins. The esterified cholesterol can be transferred from HDL to the lower density lipoproteins, eg, chylomicrons, VLDL, and LDL, by means of the **cholesteryl ester transfer protein,** which is probably another protein component of HDL (apoprotein D). Thus, the cholesteryl ester transfer protein allows cholesteryl ester of HDL to be transported to the liver via the remnants of chylomicrons and VLDL or via hepatic uptake of LDL. The LCAT system may be involved more with the removal of excess unesterified cholesterol from lipoproteins and from the tissues. The liver and possibly the intestines seem to be the final sites of degradation of HDL apoproteins.

An HDL cycle has been proposed (Nikkilä et al) to account for the transport of cholesterol from the tissues to the liver (Fig 18–8). This explains why HDL$_2$ (Table 16–4) concentrations in the plasma vary reciprocally with the chylomicron and VLDL concentration and directly with the activity of lipoprotein lipase. HDL (HDL$_2$) concentrations are inversely related to the incidence of coronary atherosclerosis, possibly because they reflect the efficiency of cholesterol-scavenging from the tissues. HDL$_C$ is found in the blood of diet-induced hypercholesterolemic animals. It is rich in cholesterol, and its sole apoprotein is apo-E. It is taken up by the liver via the apo-E remnant receptor but also by apo-B receptors. As a consequence, the latter are sometimes designated apo-B,E receptors. Atherosclerotic plaques contain scavenger cells that have taken up so much cholesterol that they are converted into cholesteryl ester–laden foam cells. Most of the cells arise from macrophages that ingest the more abnormal cholesterol-rich lipoproteins such as chemically modified LDL or β-VLDL (see p 255). Recent work (Brown and Goldstein, 1983) has shown that macrophages secrete both cholesterol (to a suitable receptor such as HDL) and apo-E. This apo-E, after suitable processing in the presence of LCAT, may be the source of cholesterol-rich HDL$_C$. Thus, HDL$_C$ could be an important component in the movement of cholesterol from the tissues to the liver (''reverse cholesterol transport''). It would therefore appear that all plasma lipoproteins are interrelated

components of one or more metabolic cycles that together are responsible for the complex process of plasma lipid transport.

ROLE OF THE LIVER IN LIPID METABOLISM

Much of the lipid metabolism of the body was formerly thought to be the prerogative of the liver. The discovery that most tissues have the ability to oxidize fatty acids completely and the knowledge which has accumulated showing that adipose tissue is extremely active metabolically have tended to modify the former emphasis on the role of the liver. Nonetheless, the concept of a central and unique role for the liver in lipid metabolism is still an important one. Apart from its role in facilitating the digestion and absorption of lipids by the production of bile, which contains cholesterol and bile salts synthesized within the liver, the liver has active enzyme systems for synthesizing and oxidizing fatty acids, for synthesizing triacylglycerols, phospholipids, cholesterol, and plasma lipoproteins, and for converting fatty acids to ketone bodies (ketogenesis). Some of these processes have already been described.

Triacylglycerol Synthesis & the Formation of VLDL

Experiments involving a comparison between hepatectomized and intact animals have shown that the liver is the main source of plasma lipoproteins derived from endogenous sources. Hepatic triacylglycerols are the immediate precursors of triacylglycerols contained in plasma VLDL. The fatty acids used in the synthesis of hepatic triacylglycerols are derived from 2 possible sources: (1) synthesis within the liver from acetyl-CoA derived in the main from carbohydrate and (2) uptake of free fatty acids from the circulation. The first source would appear to be predominant in the well-fed condition, when fatty acid synthesis is high and the level of circulating free fatty acids is low. As triacylglycerol does not normally accumulate in the liver under this condition, it must be inferred that it is transported from the liver as rapidly as it is synthesized. On the other hand, during fasting, during the feeding of high-fat diets, or in diabetes mellitus, the level of circulating free fatty acids is raised and more is abstracted into the liver. Under these conditions, free fatty acids are the main source of triacylglycerol fatty acids in the liver and in plasma lipoproteins because lipogenesis from acetyl-CoA is depressed. The enzyme mechanism responsible for the synthesis of triacylglycerols and phospholipids has been described on pp 222 and 224. Factors that enhance both the synthesis of triacylglycerol and the secretion of VLDL by the liver include the feeding of diets high in carbohydrate (particularly if they contain sucrose or fructose), high levels of circulating free fatty acids, ingestion of ethanol, and the presence of high concentrations of insulin and low concentrations of glucagon.

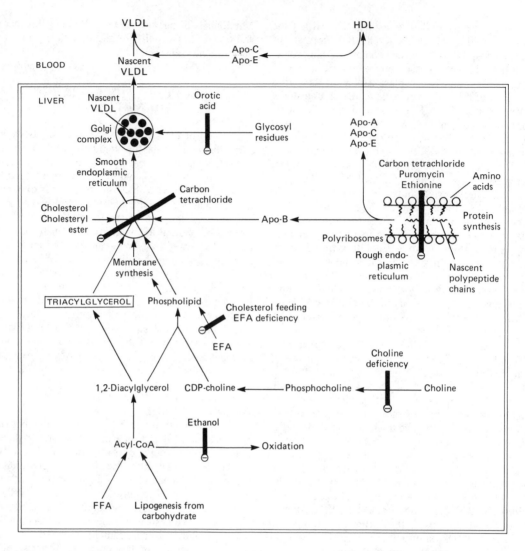

Figure 18–9. The synthesis of very low density lipoprotein (VLDL) and the possible loci of action of factors causing accumulation of triacylglycerol and a fatty liver. (EFA, essential fatty acids; FFA, free fatty acids; HDL, high-density lipoproteins; Apo-A, apolipoprotein A; Apo-B, apolipoprotein B; Apo-C, apolipoprotein C; Apo-E, apolipoprotein E.) The pathways indicated form a basis for events depicted in Fig 18–5B.

Fatty Livers & Lipotropic Factors (Fig 18–9)

For a variety of reasons, lipid—mainly as triacylglycerol—can accumulate in the liver. Extensive accumulation is regarded as a pathologic condition. When accumulation of lipid in the liver becomes chronic, fibrotic changes occur in the cells that progress to cirrhosis and impaired liver function.

Fatty livers fall into 2 main categories. The first type is associated with **raised levels of plasma free fatty acids** resulting from mobilization of fat from adipose tissue or from the hydrolysis of lipoprotein or chylomicron triacylglycerol by lipoprotein lipase in extrahepatic tissues. Increasing amounts of free fatty acids are taken up by the liver and esterified. The production of plasma lipoprotein does not keep pace with the influx of free fatty acids, allowing triacylglyc-

erol to accumulate, causing a fatty liver. The quantity of triacylglycerol present in the liver is significantly increased during starvation and the feeding of high-fat diets. In many instances (eg, in starvation), the ability to secrete VLDL is also impaired. In uncontrolled diabetes mellitus, eclampsia of ewes, and ketosis in cattle, fatty infiltration is sufficiently severe to cause visible pallor or fatty appearance and enlargement of the liver.

The second type of fatty liver is usually due to a **metabolic block in the production of plasma lipoproteins.** Theoretically, the lesion may be due to a block in lipoprotein apoprotein synthesis, a block in the synthesis of the lipoprotein from lipid and apoprotein, a failure in provision of phospholipids that are found in lipoproteins, or a failure in the secretory mechanism itself. It is often associated with deficiency of a substance known as a **lipotropic factor.** The deficiency causes triacylglycerol to accumulate even though only a normal rate of fatty acid synthesis and uptake of free fatty acids may be occurring. One type of fatty liver that has been studied extensively is due to a deficiency of choline. As choline may be synthesized using labile methyl groups donated by methionine in the process of **transmethylation** (see Chapters 22 and 23), the deficiency is basically due to a shortage of the type of methyl group donated by methionine. Thus, choline, methionine, and betaine can all act as lipotropic agents in curing fatty livers due to choline deficiency, and, conversely, processes that utilize methyl groups excessively or diets poor in protein (containing methionine) or lecithin (containing choline) will all tend to favor the production of fatty livers.

Several mechanisms have been suggested to explain the role of choline as a lipotropic agent. The VLDL are virtually absent from the blood of choline-deficient rats, indicating that the defect lies in the formation of VLDL from triacylglycerol. In the perfused rat liver, the uptake of labeled free fatty acids is not decreased in choline-deficient livers; however, more of the label is incorporated into liver triacylglycerol and non-choline-containing phospholipids, and significantly less is incorporated into the choline-containing phospholipids. Mookerjea has suggested that, in addition to causing an impairment in synthesis of lipoprotein phospholipids containing choline, a choline deficiency may impair availability of phosphocholine, which stimulates incorporation of glucosamine into glycolipoproteins. Deficiency of phospholipids containing choline may impair synthesis of intracellular membranes concerned in lipoprotein synthesis. It has been suggested that depression of long-chain fatty acid oxidation, which may occur in choline deficiency, may be due to depressed levels of carnitine (carnitine synthesis also being dependent on the provision of methyl groups). Decreased oxidation of fatty acids causes the diversion of acyl-CoA into triacylglycerol formation.

It is to be noted that the antibiotic puromycin, which inhibits protein synthesis, causes a fatty liver and a marked reduction in concentration of VLDL in rats. Other substances that cause fatty livers include ethionine (α-amino-γ-ethyl-mercaptobutyric acid), carbon tetrachloride, chloroform, phosphorus, lead, and arsenic. Choline will not protect the organism against these agents but appears to aid in recovery. The action of most of these substances is associated with inhibition of hepatic protein synthesis. The rapidity of action of carbon tetrachloride (within minutes), compared with the several hours required to elicit an effect with ethionine, indicates some difference in mode of action. It is very likely that carbon tetrachloride also affects the secretory mechanism itself or the conjugation of the lipid with lipoprotein apoprotein. Its effect is not direct but depends rather on further transformation of the molecule. This probably involves formation of free radicals that may disrupt lipid membranes in the endoplasmic reticulum, with formation of lipid peroxides. Some protection against carbon tetrachloride-induced lipid peroxidation is provided by vitamin E-supplemented diets. The action of ethionine is thought to be due to a reduction in availability of ATP. This results when ethionine, replacing methionine in S-adenosylmethionine, traps available adenine and prevents synthesis of ATP. This hypothesis is supported by the fact that the effect of ethionine may be reversed by administration of ATP or adenine. Administration of orotic acid also causes fatty livers. As VLDL accumulate in the Golgi complex, it is considered that orotic acid interferes with glycosylation of the lipoprotein, thus inhibiting its release and accounting for the marked decrease in plasma lipoproteins containing apo-B.

A deficiency of vitamin E enhances the hepatic necrosis of the choline deficiency type of fatty liver. Added vitamin E or a source of selenium (see Chapter 10) has a protective effect. In addition to protein deficiency, essential fatty acid and vitamin deficiencies (eg, pyridoxine and pantothenic acid) can cause fatty infiltration of the liver. A deficiency of essential fatty acids is thought to depress the synthesis of phospholipids; therefore, other substances such as cholesterol that compete for available essential fatty acids for esterification can also cause fatty livers.

Ethanol Metabolism

Alcoholism also leads to fat accumulation in the liver, hyperlipidemia, and ultimately cirrhosis. The exact mechanism of action of alcohol in this respect is still uncertain. Whether or not extra free fatty acid mobilization plays some part in causing the accumulation of fat is not clear, but several studies have demonstrated elevated levels of free fatty acids in the rat after administration of a single intoxicating dose of ethanol. However, alcohol consumption over a long period leads to the accumulation of fatty acids in the liver that are derived from endogenous synthesis rather than from adipose tissue. There is no impairment of hepatic synthesis of protein after ethanol ingestion. There is good evidence of increased hepatic triacylglycerol synthesis, decreased fatty acid oxidation, and decreased citric acid cycle activity, caused by oxidation of ethanol by **alcohol dehydrogenase.**

$$CH_3-CH_2-OH + NAD^+ \xrightarrow{\boxed{\text{ALCOHOL DEHYDROGENASE}}} CH_3-CHO + NADH + H^+$$

The NADH generated competes with reducing equivalents from other substrates for the respiratory chain, inhibiting their oxidation. The increased $[NADH]/[NAD^+]$ ratio causes a shift to the left in the equilibrium malate $\rightleftharpoons$ oxaloacetate, which may reduce activity of the citric acid cycle. The net effect of inhibiting fatty acid oxidation is to cause increased esterification of fatty acids in triacylglycerol, which appears to be the cause of the fatty liver. Oxidation of ethanol leads to the formation of acetaldehyde, which is oxidized by **aldehyde dehydrogenase** in mitochondria, acetate being the end product. Other effects of alcohol may include increased lipogenesis and cholesterol synthesis from acetyl-CoA. The increased [NADH]/[NAD$^+$] ratio also causes an increased [lactate]/[pyruvate] ratio that results in hyperlactacidemia, which in turn decreases the capacity of the kidney to excrete uric acid. The latter is probably the cause of aggravation of gout by drinking alcohol. Although the major route for ethanol metabolism is via the alcohol dehydrogenase pathway, some metabolism takes place via a microsomal ethanol oxidizing system involving NADPH and O_2.

$$CH_2-CH_2-OH + NADPH + H^+ + O_2 \longrightarrow CH_3-CHO + NADP^+ + 2H_2O$$

KETOSIS

Under certain metabolic conditions associated with a high rate of fatty acid oxidation, the liver produces considerable quantities of acetoacetate and D($-$)-3-hydroxybutyrate (β-hydroxybutyrate) that pass by diffusion into the blood. Acetoacetate continually undergoes spontaneous decarboxylation to yield acetone. These 3 substances are collectively known as the **ketone bodies** (also called acetone bodies or [incorrectly] "ketones") (Fig 18–10). Acetoacetate and 3-hydroxybutyrate are in equilibrium with each other, the equilibrium being controlled by the mitochondrial ratio of [NAD$^+$] to [NADH], ie, the **redox state.** The ratio [3-hydroxybutyrate]/[acetoacetate] in blood varies between 1:1 and 10:1.

The concentration of total ketone bodies in the blood of well-fed mammals does not normally exceed 1 mg/dL (as acetone equivalents). It is somewhat higher than this in ruminants. Loss via the urine is usually less than 1 mg/24 h in humans. Higher than normal quantities present in the blood or urine constitute **ketonemia** (hyperketonemia) or **ketonuria,** respectively. The overall condition is called **ketosis.** Acetoacetic and 3-hydroxybutyric acids are both moderately strong acids and are buffered when present in blood or the tissues. However, their continual excretion in quantity entails some loss of buffer cation (in spite of ammonia production by the kidney) that progressively depletes the alkali reserve, causing **ketoacidosis.** This may be fatal in uncontrolled diabetes mellitus.

The simplest form of ketosis occurs in starvation and involves depletion of available carbohydrate coupled with mobilization of free fatty acids. No other condition in which ketosis occurs seems to differ qualitatively from this general pattern of metabolism, but quantitatively it may be exaggerated to produce the pathologic states found in diabetes mellitus, eclampsia in sheep, and ketosis in lactating cattle. Nonpathologic forms of ketosis are found under conditions of high-fat feeding and after severe exercise in the postabsorptive state.

In vivo, the liver appears to be the only organ in nonruminants to add significant quantities of ketone bodies to the blood. Extrahepatic tissues utilize them as respiratory substrates. In ruminants, the rumen wall converts butyric acid, formed as a result of ruminal fermentation, to 3-hydroxybutyrate, which enters the bloodstream. The ruminant lactating mammary gland is also reported to produce ketone bodies. These extrahepatic sources of ketone bodies do not contribute significantly to the occurrence of ketosis in these species.

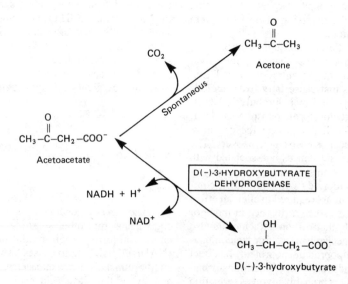

Figure 18–10. Interrelationships of the ketone bodies. D($-$)-3-Hydroxybutyrate dehydrogenase is a mitochondrial enzyme.

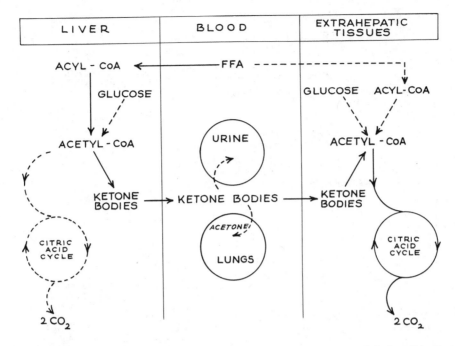

Figure 18–11. Formation, utilization, and excretion of ketone bodies. (The main pathway is indicated by the solid arrows.)

Enzymatic Mechanism for Ketogenesis in the Liver & for the Utilization of Ketone Bodies in Extrahepatic Tissues

The net flow of ketone bodies from the liver to the extrahepatic tissues results from an active enzymatic mechanism in the liver for the production of ketone bodies coupled with very low activity of enzymes responsible for their utilization. The reverse situation occurs in extrahepatic tissues (Fig 18–11).

Ketogenesis

Enzymes responsible for ketone body formation are associated mainly with the mitochondria. Originally it was thought that only one molecule of acetoacetate was formed from the terminal 4 carbons of a fatty acid upon oxidation. Later, to explain both the production of more than one equivalent of acetoacetate from a long-chain fatty acid and the formation of ketone bodies from acetic acid, it was proposed that C_2 units formed in β-oxidation condensed with one another to form acetoacetate. This may occur by a reversal of the **thiolase** reaction whereby 2 molecules of acetyl-CoA condense to form acetoacetyl-CoA. Thus, acetoacetyl-CoA, which is the starting material for ketogenesis, arises either directly during the course of β-oxidation or as a result of the condensation of acetyl-CoA (Fig 18–12). Two pathways for the formation of acetoacetate from acetoacetyl-CoA have been proposed. The first is by simple deacylation catalyzed by the enzyme **acetoacetyl-CoA deacylase.** The second pathway (Fig 18–13) involves the condensation of acetoacetyl-CoA with another molecule of acetyl-CoA to form 3-hydroxy-3-methylglutaryl-CoA (HMG-CoA), catalyzed by **3-hydroxy-3-methylglutaryl-CoA synthase.** The presence of another enzyme in the mitochondria, **3-hydroxy-3-methylglutaryl-CoA lyase,** causes acetyl-CoA to split off from the HMG-CoA, leaving free acetoacetate. The carbon atoms split off in the acetyl-CoA molecule are derived from the original acetoacetyl-CoA molecule (Fig 18–13). Both of these enzymes must be present in mitochondria for ketogenesis to take place. This occurs solely in liver and rumen epithelium.

Present opinion favors the HMG-CoA pathway as the major route of ketone body formation. Although there is a marked increase in activity of HMG-CoA lyase in fasting, evidence does not suggest that this enzyme is rate-limiting in ketogenesis.

Acetoacetate may be converted to D(–)-3-hydroxybutyrate by D(–)-**3-hydroxybutyrate dehydrogenase,** which is present in many tissues, including the liver. D(–)-3-Hydroxybutyrate is quantitatively the predominant ketone body present in the blood and urine in ketosis.

Utilization of Ketone Bodies

While the liver is equipped with an active enzymatic mechanism for the production of acetoacetate from acetoacetyl-CoA, acetoacetate once formed cannot be reactivated directly in the liver. This accounts for the net production of ketone bodies by the liver.

Two reactions shown below take place in extrahepatic tissues. These will activate acetoacetate to acetoacetyl-CoA. The enzymes responsible are absent from liver. One mechanism involves succinyl-CoA

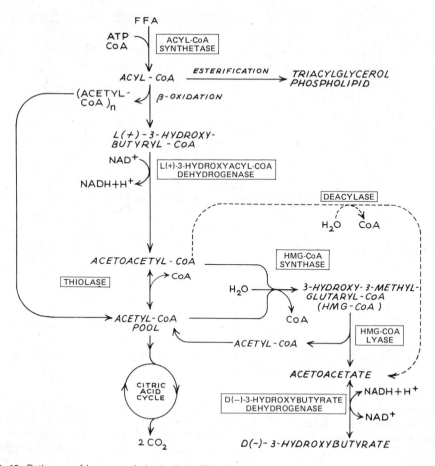

Figure 18–12. Pathways of ketogenesis in the liver. (FFA, free fatty acids; HMG, 3-hydroxy-3-methylglutaryl.)

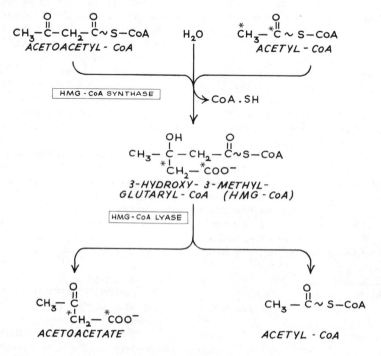

Figure 18–13. Formation of acetoacetate through intermediate production of HMG-CoA.

and the enzyme **succinyl-CoA-acetoacetate-CoA transferase** (thiophorase). Acetoacetate reacts with succinyl-CoA, the CoA being transferred to form acetoacetyl-CoA and succinate.

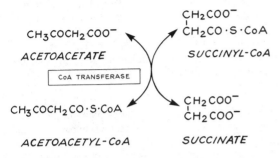

The other reaction involves the activation of acetoacetate with ATP in the presence of CoA catalyzed by acetoacetyl-CoA synthetase.

$$CH_3COCH_2COO^- + ATP + CoA \cdot SH \xrightarrow{\boxed{\begin{array}{c}\text{ACETOACETYL-CoA}\\\text{SYNTHETASE}\end{array}}}$$

Acetoacetate

$$CH_3COCH_2CO \cdot S \cdot CoA + AMP + PP_i$$

Acetoacetyl-CoA

D(−)-3-Hydroxybutyrate may be activated directly in extrahepatic tissues by a synthetase; however, conversion to acetoacetate with D(−)-3-hydroxybutyrate dehydrogenase and NAD$^+$, followed by activation to acetoacetyl-CoA, is the more important route leading to its further metabolism. The acetoacetyl-CoA formed by these reactions is split to acetyl-CoA by thiolase and oxidized in the citric acid cycle as shown in Fig 18–12.

Ketone bodies are oxidized in extrahepatic tissues proportionately to their concentration in the blood. They are also oxidized in preference to glucose and to FFA. If the blood level is raised, oxidation of ketone bodies increases until, at a concentration of approximately 70 mg/dL, they saturate the oxidative machinery; any further increase in the rate of ketogenesis serves merely to raise the blood concentration and the rate of urinary excretion precipitously. When this occurs, a large proportion of the oxygen consumption of the animal may be accounted for by the oxidation of ketone bodies.

Most of the evidence suggests that ketonemia is due to increased production of ketone bodies by the liver rather than to a deficiency in their utilization by extrahepatic tissues. However, the results of experiments on depancreatized rats support the possibility that ketosis in the severe diabetic may be enhanced by a reduced ability to catabolize ketone bodies.

In moderate ketonemia, the loss of ketone bodies via the urine is only a few percent of the total ketone body production and utilization. As there are renal threshold-like effects (there is not a true threshold) that vary between species and individuals, measurement of

the ketonemia, not the ketonuria, is the preferred method of assessing the severity of ketosis.

While acetoacetate and D(−)-3-hydroxybutyrate are readily oxidized by extrahepatic tissues, acetone is difficult to oxidize in vivo. When acetone is injected into human subjects, its concentration in the blood rises sharply and is maintained at a high level for several hours, indicating a very slow rate of utilization.

CHOLESTEROL METABOLISM

The greater part of the cholesterol of the body arises by **synthesis** (about 1 g/d), whereas only about 0.3 g/d is provided by the average diet. Cholesterol is eliminated via 2 main pathways: conversion to bile acids and excretion of neutral sterols in the feces. The synthesis of steroid hormones from cholesterol and the elimination of their products of degradation in the urine are of minor quantitative significance. **Cholesterol is typically a product of animal metabolism** and occurs therefore in foods of animal origin such as meat, liver, brain, and egg yolk (a particularly rich source).

Synthesis of Cholesterol & Other Isoprenoids

Virtually all tissues containing nucleated cells are capable of synthesizing cholesterol, particularly the liver, adrenal cortex, skin, intestines, testis, and aorta. The microsomal and cytosol fraction of the cell is responsible for cholesterol synthesis.

Acetyl-CoA is the source of all the carbon atoms in cholesterol. The manner of synthesis of this complex molecule has been the subject of investigation by many workers, with the result that it is possible at the present time to chart the origin of all parts of the cholesterol molecule (Figs 18–14, 18–15, and 18–16). Synthesis takes place in several stages. The first is the synthesis of mevalonate, a 6-carbon compound, from acetyl-CoA (Fig 18–14). The next major stage is the formation of isoprenoid units from mevalonate by loss of CO_2 (Fig 18–15). The isoprenoid units may be regarded as the building blocks not only of the steroid skeleton but also of other isoprenoid derivatives such as **dolichol** (pp 202 and 469) and **ubiquinone** (Fig 12–14). Six isoprenoid units condense to form the intermediate, squalene, which in turn gives rise to the parent steroid, lanosterol. Cholesterol is formed from lanosterol after several further steps, including the loss of 3 methyl groups (Fig 18–16).

Two separate pathways have been described for the formation of mevalonate. One involves the intermediate 3-hydroxy-3-methylglutaryl-CoA (HMG-CoA), and the other is through a 3-hydroxy-3-methylglutaryl-S-enzyme complex. The pathway through HMG-CoA is considered to be quantitatively the more significant and follows the same sequence of reactions described previously for the synthesis in mitochondria of ketone bodies. However, since cholesterol synthesis is extramitochondrial, the 2 pathways are distinct.

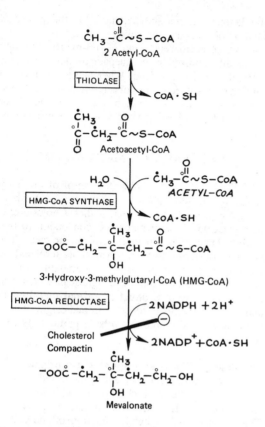

Figure 18–14. Biosynthesis of mevalonate. (HMG, 3-hydroxy-3-methylglutaryl.) HMG-CoA reductase is inhibited by cholesterol and the fungal metabolite compactin, which is competitive with HMG-CoA.

HMG-CoA is converted to mevalonate in a 2-stage reduction by NADPH catalyzed by **3-hydroxy-3-methylglutaryl-CoA reductase** (Fig 18–14).

In the second stage, mevalonate is phosphorylated by ATP to form several active phosphorylated intermediates (Fig 18–15). By means of a decarboxylation, the active isoprenoid unit, isopentenyl-pyrophosphate, is formed. The next stage involves the condensation of 3 molecules of isopentenylpyrophosphate to form farnesyl pyrophosphate. This occurs via an isomerization of isopentenylpyrophosphate involving a shift of the double bond to form dimethylallyl pyrophosphate, followed by condensation with another molecule of isopentenylpyrophosphate to form the 10-carbon intermediate, geranyl pyrophosphate (Fig 18–15). A further condensation with isopentenyl-pyrophosphate forms farnesyl pyrophosphate. Two molecules of farnesyl pyrophosphate condense at the pyrophosphate end in a reaction involving a reduction with NADPH with elimination of the pyrophosphate radicals. The resulting compound is squalene. Recently, evidence has been provided that an alternative pathway known as the "*trans*-methylglutaconate shunt" may be present. This pathway removes a significant proportion (20%) of the dimethylallyl pyro-

phosphate and returns it, via *trans*-3-methylglutaconate-CoA, to HMG-CoA. This pathway may have regulatory potential with respect to the overall rate of cholesterol synthesis.

Squalene has a structure that closely resembles the steroid nucleus (Fig 18–16). Before ring closure occurs, the methyl group on C_{14} is transferred to C_{13} and that on C_8 to C_{14}, and C_3 is hydroxylated. The latter reaction involves molecular oxygen, and the reaction is catalyzed by a microsomal hydroxylase system.

The last stage (Fig 18–16), the formation of cholesterol from lanosterol, takes place in the membranes of the endoplasmic reticulum (microsomes) and involves changes to the steroid nucleus and side chain. The methyl group on C_{14} is oxidized to CO_2 to form 14-desmethyl lanosterol. Likewise, 2 more methyl groups on C_4 are removed to produce zymosterol. $\Delta^{7,24}$-Cholestadienol is formed from zymosterol by the double bond between C_8 and C_9, moving to a position between C_8 and C_7. Desmosterol is formed at this point by a further shift in the double bond in ring B to take up a position between C_5 and C_6, as in cholesterol. Finally, cholesterol is produced when the double bond of the side chain is reduced, although this can occur at any stage of the overall conversion to cholesterol. The exact order in which the steps described actually take place is not known with certainty.

Farnesyl pyrophosphate is the branch point for the synthesis of the other polyisoprenoids, **dolichol** and **ubiquinone**. The polyisoprenyl alcohol dolichol is formed by the further addition of up to 16 isopentenyl pyrophosphate residues, whereas the side chain of ubiquinone is formed by the addition of a further 3–7 isoprenoid units.

It is probable that the intermediates from squalene to cholesterol are attached to a special carrier protein known as the **squalene and sterol carrier protein.** This protein binds sterols and other insoluble lipids, allowing them to react in the aqueous phase of the cell. In addition, it seems likely that it is in the form of cholesterol-sterol carrier protein that cholesterol is converted to steroid hormones and bile acids and participates in the formation of membranes and of lipoproteins. It is also as cholesterol-sterol carrier protein that cholesterol might affect the activity of HMG-CoA reductase (see below).

Control of cholesterol synthesis is exerted near the beginning of the pathway. There is a marked decrease in the activity of HMG-CoA reductase in fasting rats, which explains the reduced synthesis of cholesterol during fasting. On the other hand, the activity of this enzyme was not reduced in the livers of diabetic rats, which correlates well with the continued synthesis of cholesterol observed in the diabetic state. Siperstein has proposed a feedback mechanism whereby HMG-CoA reductase in liver is inhibited by cholesterol. Since a direct inhibition of the enzyme by cholesterol cannot be demonstrated, cholesterol (or a metabolite, eg, oxygenated sterol) may act either by repression of the synthesis of new reductase or by inducing

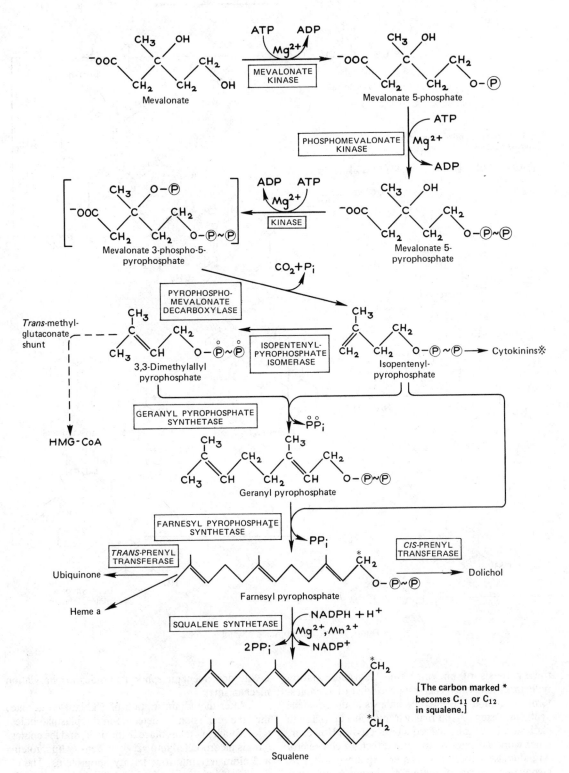

Figure 18–15. Biosynthesis of squalene, ubiquinone, and dolichol. (HMG, 3-hydroxy-3-methylglutaryl; ✳; isopentenyladenine, a component of tRNA.) A farnesyl residue is present in heme a of cytochrome oxidase.

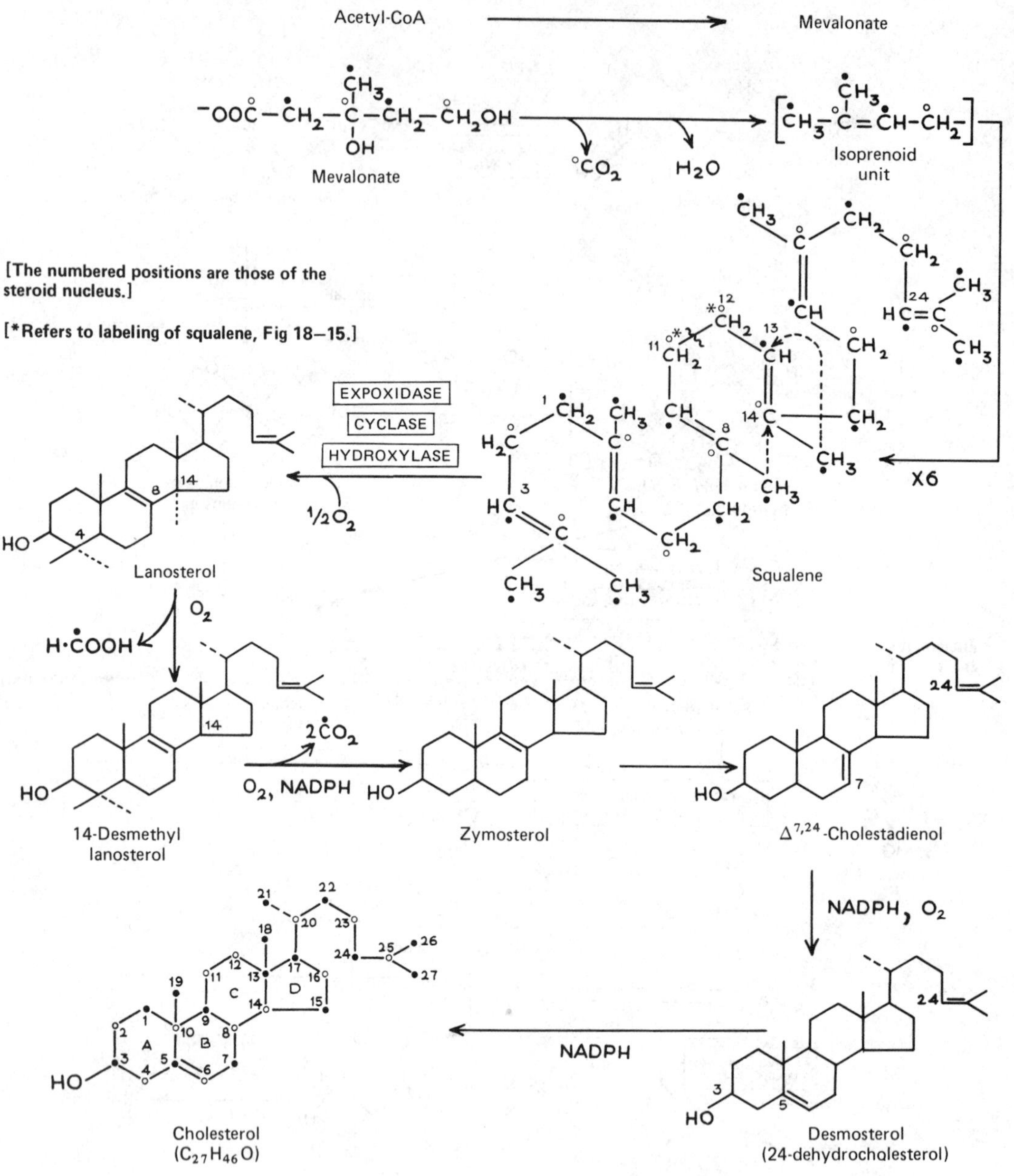

Figure 18–16. Biosynthesis of cholesterol.

the synthesis of enzymes that degrade existing reductase. It has also been proposed that LDL cholesterol can inhibit cholesterol synthesis at the squalene synthetase step. A diurnal variation occurs in both cholesterol synthesis and reductase activity. However, other work indicates more rapid effects of cholesterol on reductase activity than can be explained solely by changes in the rate of protein synthesis. Administration of insulin or thyroid hormone increases HMG-CoA reductase activity, whereas glucagon or glucocorticoids decrease it. The enzyme exists in both active and inactive forms that may be reversibly modified by cAMP-dependent phosphorylation-dephosphorylation mechanisms.

After the administration of ^{14}C-labeled acetate, the label can soon be detected in the plasma cholesterol. Synthesis takes place in the liver, and the cholesterol is incorporated into very low density lipoproteins and ultimately into low-density lipoproteins. The effect of variations in the amount of cholesterol in the diet on the endogenous production of cholesterol in rats has been studied. When there was only 0.05% cholesterol in the diet, 70–80% of the cholesterol of the liver, small intestine, and adrenal gland was synthesized within the body, whereas on a diet containing 2% cholesterol the endogenous production fell to 10–30%. However, endogenous production could not be completely suppressed by raising the dietary intake. It appears that it is only hepatic synthesis which is inhibited. Experiments with the perfused liver have demonstrated that cholesterol-rich chylomicron remnants (see p 240) inhibit sterol synthesis.

There is a species variation in the relative importance of the liver as a source of endogenous cholesterol. In humans, extrahepatic synthesis, mainly in the intestine, is more important, whereas in dogs and rats the liver is responsible for most cholesterol synthesis. Bile acids, rather than cholesterol, inhibit cholesterol synthesis in the intestine. A similar feedback control system at the HMG-CoA reductase step seems also to operate.

Attempts to lower plasma cholesterol in humans by reducing the amount of cholesterol in the diet are effective. An increase of 100 mg in dietary cholesterol causes a rise of 5 mg cholesterol per 100 mL serum.

Transport

Cholesterol in the diet is absorbed from the intestine and, in company with other lipids, including cholesterol synthesized in the intestines, incorporated into chylomicrons and VLDL. Of the cholesterol absorbed, 80–90% in the lymph is esterified with long-chain fatty acids. Esterification may occur in the intestinal mucosa. The plant sterols (sitosterols) are poorly absorbed. When chylomicron remnants react with the liver, much of their cholesteryl esters are hydrolyzed and the cholesterol taken up by the liver. VLDL formed in the liver transport cholesterol into the plasma.

In humans, the total plasma cholesterol is about 200 mg/dL, rising with age, although there are wide variations between individuals. The greater part is found in the esterified form. It is transported as lipoprotein in the plasma, the highest proportion of cholesterol being found in the LDL (β-lipoproteins), which are formed from VLDL. However, under conditions where the VLDL are quantitatively predominant, an increased proportion of the plasma cholesterol will continue to reside in this fraction. Ultimately, LDL are broken down, in extrahepatic tissues and the liver, and the cholesterol is taken up by the receptor-mediated process described previously (p 242).

Dietary cholesterol takes several days to equilibrate with cholesterol in the plasma and several weeks to equilibrate with cholesterol of the tissues. The turnover of cholesterol in the liver is relatively fast compared with the half-life of the total body cholesterol, which is several weeks. Free cholesterol in plasma and liver equilibrates in a matter of hours.

Equilibration of cholesteryl ester with free cholesterol in plasma takes several days in humans. In general, free cholesterol exchanges readily between tissues and lipoproteins, whereas cholesteryl ester exchanges between the major lipoproteins only in those species (eg, humans) possessing the cholesteryl ester

transfer protein. Most plasma cholesteryl ester is formed in HDL as a result of the transesterification reaction between cholesterol and the fatty acid in position 2 of phosphatidylcholine, catalyzed by **lecithin:cholesterol acyltransferase (LCAT)** (see pp 227 and 243). A familial deficiency of this enzyme has been described. In affected subjects, the plasma concentration of cholesteryl esters and lysolecithin is low, whereas the concentration of cholesterol and lecithin is raised. The plasma tends to be turbid. Abnormalities are also found in the lipoproteins. One HDL fraction contains disk-shaped structures in stacks or rouleaux, which are clearly nascent HDL unable to take up cholesterol owing to the absence of LCAT. LDL contains a larger particle having a lipid composition somewhat similar to VLDL (β-VLDL). Also present as an abnormal LDL subfraction is lipoprotein-X, otherwise found only in patients with cholestasis. VLDL are also abnormal, migrating as β-lipoproteins upon electrophoresis. Patients with parenchymal liver disease also show a decrease of LCAT activity and abnormalities in the serum lipids and lipoproteins. It would appear that LCAT is necessary for the normal metabolism of the plasma lipoproteins.

Thus, HDL is the probable vehicle, in combination with LCAT, for transporting cholesterol, as ester, from extrahepatic tissues back to the liver (Fig 18–8). Some of the cholesterol of HDL may be transferred to VLDL and chylomicrons and be recycled. Ultimately, all cholesterol destined for excretion from the body must enter the liver and be excreted in the bile, either as cholesterol or as cholic acid in the bile salts.

Excretion of Cholesterol

Approximately half of the cholesterol eliminated from the body is excreted in the feces after conversion to bile salts. The remainder is excreted as neutral steroids. Much of the cholesterol secreted in the bile is reabsorbed, and it is believed that the cholesterol that serves as precursor for the fecal sterols is derived from the intestinal mucosa. Coprostanol is the principal sterol in the feces; it is formed from cholesterol in the lower intestine by the bacterial flora therein. A large proportion of the biliary excretion of bile salts is reabsorbed into the portal circulation, taken up by the liver, and reexcreted in the bile. This is known as the **enterohepatic circulation** (see p 623). The bile salts not reabsorbed, or their derivatives, are excreted in the feces. Bile salts undergo changes brought about by intestinal bacteria. The rate of production of bile acids from cholesterol in the liver is reduced by infusion of bile salts, indicating the existence of another feedback control mechanism initiated by the product of the reaction.

Cholesterol, Coronary Heart Disease, & Atherosclerosis

Many investigators have demonstrated a correlation between raised serum lipid levels and the incidence of coronary heart disease and atherosclerosis in humans. Of the serum lipids, cholesterol has been the

Table 18–2. Typical fatty acid analyses of some fats of animal and plant origin.*
(All values in weight percentages of component fatty acids.)

	Saturated			Unsaturated		
	Palmitic	Stearic	Other	Oleic	Linoleic	Other
Animal fats						
Lard	29.8	12.7	1.0	47.8	3.1	5.6
Chicken	25.6	7.0	0.3	39.4	21.8	5.9
Butterfat	25.2	9.2	25.6	29.5	3.6	7.2
Beef fat	29.2	21.0	3.4	41.1	1.8	3.5
Vegetable oils						
Corn	8.1	2.5	0.1	30.1	56.3	2.9
Peanut	6.3	4.9	5.9	61.1	21.8	. . .
Cottonseed	23.4	1.1	2.7	22.9	47.8	2.1
Soybean	9.8	2.4	1.2	28.9	50.7	7.0†
Olive	10.0	3.3	0.6	77.5	8.6	. . .
Coconut	10.5	2.3	78.4	7.5	trace	1.3

*Reproduced from NRC Publication No. 575: *The Role of Dietary Fat in Human Health: A Report.* Food and Nutrition Board, National Academy of Sciences.
†Mostly linolenic acid.

one most often singled out as being chiefly concerned in the relationship. However, other parameters—such as the cholesterol:phospholipid ratio, Sf 12–400 lipoprotein concentration, serum triacylglycerol concentration, etc—show similar correlations. Patients with arterial disease can have any one of the following abnormalities: (1) elevated concentrations of VLDL (mainly triacylglycerols) with normal concentrations of LDL (D = 1.019–1.063) containing chiefly cholesterol; (2) elevated LDL (cholesterol) with normal VLDL (triacylglycerols); (3) elevation of both lipoprotein fractions (cholesterol plus triacylglycerols). There is also an inverse relationship between HDL (HDL$_2$) concentrations and coronary heart disease, and some consider that the most predictive relationship is the LDL/HDL cholesterol ratio. This relationship is explainable in terms of the proposed roles of LDL in transporting cholesterol to the tissues and of HDL acting as the scavenger of cholesterol.

Atherosclerosis is characterized by the deposition of cholesteryl ester and other lipids in the connective tissue of the arterial walls. Diseases in which prolonged elevated levels of low-density and very low density lipoproteins occur in the blood (eg, diabetes mellitus, lipid nephrosis, hypothyroidism, and other conditions of hyperlipidemia) are often accompanied by premature or more severe atherosclerosis.

Experiments on the induction of atherosclerosis in animals indicate a wide species variation in susceptibility. The rabbit, pig, monkey, and humans are species in which atherosclerosis can be induced by feeding cholesterol. The rat, dog, and cat are resistant. Thyroidectomy or treatment with thiouracil drugs will allow induction of atherosclerosis in the dog and rat. Low blood cholesterol is a characteristic of hyperthyroidism. However, hyperthyroidism is associated with an increased rate of cholesterol synthesis. The fall in level of plasma cholesterol may be due to an increased rate of turnover and excretion.

Of the factors that lower blood cholesterol, the substitution in the diet of polyunsaturated fatty acids for some of the saturated fatty acids has been the most intensely studied. Naturally occurring oils that are beneficial in lowering plasma cholesterol include peanut, cottonseed, corn, and soybean oil, whereas butterfat and coconut oil raise the level. Table 18–2 shows the high proportion of linoleic acid in the first group of oils and its relative deficiency or absence in butterfat or coconut oil, respectively. Sucrose and fructose have a greater effect in raising blood lipids than do other carbohydrates. A correlation between the increased consumption of sucrose and atherosclerosis has been claimed.

The reason for the cholesterol-lowering effect of polyunsaturated fatty acids is still not clear. However, several hypotheses have been advanced to explain the effect, including the stimulation of cholesterol excretion into the intestine and the stimulation of the oxidation of cholesterol to bile acids. It is possible that cholesteryl esters of polyunsaturated fatty acids are more rapidly metabolized by the liver and other tissues, which might enhance their rate of turnover and excretion. There is other evidence that the effect is largely due to a shift in distribution of cholesterol from the plasma into the tissues due to increased catabolic rate of LDL. Saturated fatty acids cause the formation of smaller VLDL particles that contain relatively more cholesterol, and they are utilized by extrahepatic tissues at a slower rate than are larger particles. All of these tendencies may be regarded as atherogenic.

Additional factors considered to play a part in atherosclerosis include high blood pressure, smoking, obesity, lack of exercise, and drinking soft as opposed to hard water. Elevation of plasma free fatty acids will also lead to increased VLDL secretion by the liver, involving extra triacylglycerol and cholesterol output into the circulation. Factors leading to higher or fluctuating levels of free fatty acids include emotional stress, nicotine from cigarette smoking, coffee drinking, and partaking of a few large meals rather than more continuous feeding. Premenopausal women appear to be protected against many of these deleterious factors, possibly because they have higher concentrations of HDL than men.

Hypolipidemic Drugs

When dietary measures fail to achieve reduced serum lipid levels, the use of hypolipidemic drugs may be resorted to. Several drugs are known to block the formation of cholesterol at various stages in the biosynthetic pathway. Many of these drugs have harmful effects, and it is now considered that direct interference with cholesterol synthesis is to be avoided. **Sitosterol** is a hypocholesterolemic agent that acts by blocking the absorption of cholesterol in the gastrointestinal tract. Drugs that are considered to increase the fecal excretion of cholesterol and bile acids include **dextrothyroxine** (Choloxin), **neomycin, probucol,** and possibly **clofibrate** (Atromid-S). On the other hand, **cholestyramine** (Questran) prevents the reabsorption of bile salts by combining with them, thereby increasing their fecal loss. Clofibrate exerts at least part of its hypolipidemic effect by diverting the hepatic inflow of free fatty acids from the pathways of esterification into those of oxidation, thus decreasing the secretion of triacylglycerol and cholesterol containing VLDL by the liver (Laker and Mayes, 1979). The clofibrate-induced increase in β-oxidation of free fatty acids by the peroxisomal pathway, which is partly uncoupled from ATP production (see p 210), may be important in disposing of the excess fatty acid. Other hypocholesterolemic drugs include **nicotinic acid** and **estrogens.**

Disorders of the Plasma Lipoproteins

A few individuals in the population exhibit inherited defects in their lipoproteins, leading to the primary condition of either hypo- or hyperlipoproteinemia. Many others having defects such as diabetes mellitus, hypothyroidism, and atherosclerosis show abnormal lipoprotein patterns that are very similar to one or the other of the primary inherited conditions. Virtually all of these diseases are due to a defect at one or another stage in the course of lipoprotein formation, transport, or destruction (Figs 18–6, 18–7, and 18–8).

A. Hypolipoproteinemia:

1. Abetalipoproteinemia–This is a rare inherited disease characterized by absence of β-lipoprotein (LDL) in plasma. Most of the blood lipids are present in low concentrations—especially acylglycerols, which are virtually absent since no chylomicrons or VLDL are formed. Both the intestine and the liver accumulate acylglycerols. It is due to a defect in apoprotein B synthesis.

2. Familial hypobetalipoproteinemia–In hypobetalipoproteinemia, LDL concentration is between 10 and 50% of normal, but chylomicron formation occurs. It must be concluded that apo-B is essential for triacylglycerol transport. Most individuals are healthy and long-lived.

3. Familial alpha-lipoprotein deficiency (Tangier disease)–In the homozygous individual, there is near absence of plasma HDL and accumulation of cholesteryl esters in the tissues. There is no impairment of chylomicron formation or secretion of VLDL by the liver. However, on electrophoresis, there is no pre-β-lipoprotein, but a broad β-band is found containing the endogenous triacylglycerol. This finding provides evidence that the normal pre-β-band contains other apoproteins normally provided by HDL. Although α-lipoprotein does not appear to be essential for acylglycerol transport, clearance from the plasma is slow when it is absent, the patients tending to develop hypertriacylglycerolemia, presumably as a result of the absence of apo-C-II, which activates lipoprotein lipase.

B. Hyperlipoproteinemia:

1. Familial lipoprotein lipase deficiency (type I)–Characterized by very slow clearing of chylomicrons from the circulation, leading to abnormally raised levels of chylomicrons. VLDL may be raised, but there is a decrease in LDL and HDL. Thus, the condition is fat-induced. It may be corrected by reducing the quantity of fat and increasing the proportion of complex carbohydrate in the diet. A variation of this disease is caused by a deficiency in apo-C-II, required as a cofactor for lipoprotein lipase.

2. Familial hypercholesterolemia (type II)–Characterized by hyperbetalipoproteinemia (LDL), which is associated with increased plasma total cholesterol. There may also be a tendency for the VLDL to be elevated in type IIb. Therefore, the patient may have somewhat elevated triacylglycerol levels but the plasma—as is not true in the other types of hyperlipoproteinemia—remains clear. Lipid deposition in the tissue (eg, xanthomas, atheromas) is common. A type II pattern may also arise as a secondary result of hypothyroidism. The disease appears to be associated with reduced rates of clearance of LDL from the circulation due to defective LDL receptors and is associated with an increased incidence of atherosclerosis. Reduction of dietary cholesterol and saturated fats may be of use in treatment. A disease producing hypercholesterolemia but due to a different cause is **Wolman's disease** (cholesteryl ester storage disease). This is due to a deficiency of cholesteryl ester hydrolase in lysosomes of cells such as fibroblasts that normally metabolize LDL.

3. Familial type III hyperlipoproteinemia (broad beta disease, remnant removal disease), familial dysbetalipoproteinemia–Characterized by an increase in both chylomicron and VLDL remnants; these are lipoproteins of density < 1.006 but appear as a broad β-band on electrophoresis (β-VLDL). They cause hypercholesterolemia and hypertriacylglycerolemia. Xanthomas and atherosclerosis of both peripheral and coronary arteries are present. Treatment by weight reduction and diets containing complex carbohydrates, unsaturated fats, and little cholesterol is recommended. The disease is due to a deficiency in remnant metabolism by the liver caused by an abnormality in apo-E, which is normally present in 3 isoforms, E2, E3, and E4. Patients with type III hyperlipoproteinemia possess only E2, which does not react with the E receptor.

4. Familial hypertriacylglycerolemia (type IV)–Characterized by high levels of endogenously produced triacylglycerol (VLDL). Cholesterol levels rise in proportion to the hypertriacylglycerolemia, and glucose intolerance is frequently present. Both LDL and HDL are subnormal in quantity. This lipoprotein pattern is also commonly associated with coronary heart disease, type II non–insulin-dependent diabetes mellitus, obesity, and many other conditions, including alcoholism and the taking of progestational hormones. Treatment of primary type IV hyperlipoproteinemia is by weight reduction; replacement of soluble diet carbohydrate with complex carbohydrate, unsaturated fat, low-cholesterol diets; and also hypolipidemic agents.

5. Familial type V hyperlipoproteinemia–The lipoprotein pattern is complex, since both chylomicrons and VLDL are elevated, causing both triacylglycerolemia and cholesterolemia. Concentrations of LDL and HDL are low. Xanthomas are frequently present, but the incidence of atherosclerosis is apparently not striking. Glucose tolerance is abnormal and frequently associated with obesity and diabetes. The reason for the condition, which is familial, is not clear. Treatment has consisted of weight reduction followed by a diet not too high in either carbohydrate or fat.

It has been suggested that a further cause of hyperlipoproteinemia is overproduction of apo-B, which can influence plasma concentrations of VLDL and LDL. An account of the dietary treatment of hyperlipidemia has been given by Connor and Connor (1982).

• • •

References

Bisgaier CL, Glickman RM: Intestinal synthesis, secretion, and transport of lipoproteins. *Annu Rev Physiol* 1983;**45**:625.

Björntorp P, Sjöström L: Carbohydrate storage in man: Speculations and some quantitative considerations. *Metabolism* 1978;**27**:1853.

Boyer PD (editor): *The Enzymes*, 3rd ed. Vol 16: *Lipid Enzymology*. Academic Press, 1983.

Brown MS, Goldstein JL: Lipoprotein metabolism in the macrophage: Implications for cholesterol deposition in atherosclerosis. *Annu Rev Biochem* 1983;**52**:223.

Brown MS, Goldstein JL: Multivalent feedback regulation of HMG-CoA reductase, a control mechanism coordinating isoprenoid synthesis and cell growth. *J Lipid Res* 1980;**21**:505.

Carlson LA, Pernow B (editors): *Metabolic Risk Factors in Ischemic Cardiovascular Disease*. Raven Press, 1982.

Connor WE, Connor SL: The dietary treatment of hyperlipidemia. *Med Clin North Am* 1982;**66**:485.

Crepaldi G, Lefebvre PJ, Alberti KGMM (editors): *Diabetes, Obesity and Hyperlipidemias*. Academic Press, 1978.

Cryer A: Tissue lipoprotein lipase activity and its action in lipoprotein metabolism. *Int J Biochem* 1981;**13**:525.

Dietschy JM, Gotto AM, Ontko JA (editors): *Disturbances in Lipid and Lipoprotein Metabolism*. American Physiological Society, 1978.

Eisenberg S: Lipoproteins and lipoprotein metabolism. *Klin Wochenschr* 1983;**61**:119.

Eisenberg S, Levy RI: Lipoprotein metabolism. *Adv Lipid Res* 1975;**13**:1.

Fain JN: Hormonal regulation of lipid mobilization from adipose tissue. Page 119 in: *Biochemical Actions of Hormones*. Vol 7. Litwack G (editor). Academic Press, 1980.

Frohlich J, McLeod R, Hon K: Lecithin:cholesterol acyltransferase (LCAT). *Clin Biochem* 1982;**15**:269.

Gardner RS, Mayes PA: Comparison of the metabolism of chylomicrons and chylomicron remnants by the perfused liver. *Biochem J* 1978;**170**:47.

Goldstein JL, Brown MS: The low-density lipoprotein pathway and its relation to atherosclerosis. *Annu Rev Biochem* 1977;**46**:897.

Hamilton RL et al: Discoidal bilayer structure of nascent high density lipoproteins from perfused rat liver. *J Clin Invest* 1976;**58**:667.

Kane JP: Apolipoprotein B: Structural and metabolic heterogeneity. *Annu Rev Physiol* 1983;**45**:637.

Krauss RM: Regulation of high density lipoprotein levels. *Med Clin North Am* 1982;**66**:403.

Kuksis A, Mookerjea S: Choline. *Nutr Rev* 1978;**36**:201.

Laker ME, Mayes PA: The immediate and long term effects of clofibrate on the metabolism of the perfused rat liver. *Biochem Pharmacol* 1979;**28**:2813.

Levy RI: The effect of hypolipidemic drugs on plasma lipoproteins. *Annu Rev Pharmacol* 1977;**17**:499.

Lewis B: *The Hyperlipidaemias*. Blackwell, 1976.

Lieber CS et al: Differences in hepatic and metabolic changes after acute and chronic alcohol consumption. *Fed Proc* 1975;**34**:2060.

Mahley RW, Innerarity TL: Lipoprotein receptors and cholesterol homeostasis. *Biochim Biophys Acta* 1983;**737**:197.

Miller NE, Lewis B (editors): *Lipoproteins, Atherosclerosis and Coronary Heart Disease*. Elsevier, 1981.

Morrisett JD, Jackson RL, Gotto AM: Lipoproteins: Structure and function. *Annu Rev Biochem* 1975;**44**:183.

Nordstrom JL, Rodwell VW, Mitschelen JJ: Interconversion of active and inactive forms of rat liver HMG-CoA reductase. *J Biol Chem* 1977;**252**:8924.

Pohl SL: Cyclic nucleotides and lipolysis. *Int J Obesity* 1981;**5**:627.

Scallen TJ et al: Sterol carrier protein hypothesis. *Fed Proc* 1974;**33**:1733.

Schroepfer GJ: Sterol biosynthesis. (2 parts.) *Annu Rev Biochem* 1981;**50**:585 and 1982;**51**:555.

Smith LC, Pownall HJ, Gotto AM: The plasma lipoproteins: Structure and metabolism. *Annu Rev Biochem* 1978;**47**:751.

Starr P: Atherosclerosis, hypothyroidism, and thyroid hormone therapy. *Adv Lipid Res* 1978;**16**:345.

Steinberg D: Interconvertible enzymes in adipose tissue regulated by cyclic AMP–dependent protein kinase. *Adv Cyclic Nucleotide Res* 1976;**7**:157.

Various authors: Disorders characterized by evidence of abnormal lipid metabolism. In: *The Metabolic Basis of Inherited Disease*, 5th ed. Stanbury JB et al (editors). McGraw-Hill, 1983.

Regulation of Carbohydrate & Lipid Metabolism | 19

Peter A. Mayes, PhD, DSc

The concept of respiratory control of the rate of oxidation of substrate provides a mechanism for the orderly burning of fuel molecules by each individual cell (see p 137). It explains, in terms of availability of ADP, why the metabolic fuel is not burned in an uncontrolled or explosive fashion but rather at just that precise rate necessary to provide the immediate energy requirements of the cell in the form of high-energy phosphate. For such a mechanism to function efficiently, a continuous supply of substrate or respiratory fuel molecules must always be available. Regulation of the metabolic pathways that provide these fuel molecules is essential if the supply is to be maintained under the variety of nutritional, metabolic, and pathologic conditions encountered in vivo. The term **caloric homeostasis** has been given to this type of metabolic regulation. It involves provision of the special fuel needs of each tissue, including the making available of alternative fuels. It also involves transport of various fuels about the body together with mechanisms to control their concentration in the blood.

GENERAL PRINCIPLES OF REGULATION OF METABOLIC PATHWAYS

Regulation of the overall flux along a metabolic pathway is often concerned with the control of only one or perhaps 2 key reactions in the pathway, catalyzed by "regulatory enzymes." The physicochemical factors that control the rate of an enzyme-catalyzed reaction, eg, substrate concentration (see Chapter 8), are of primary importance in the control of the overall rate of a metabolic pathway. However, temperature and pH, factors that can influence enzyme activity, are held constant in warm-blooded vertebrates and have little regulatory significance. (Note, however, the variation in pH in the gastrointestinal tract and its effect on digestion [see Chapter 44].)

Equilibrium & Nonequilibrium Reactions

In a reaction at equilibrium, the forward and reverse reactions take place at equal rates, and there is therefore no net flux in either direction. Many reactions in metabolic pathways are of this type, ie, "equilibrium reactions":

$$A \longleftrightarrow B \longleftrightarrow C \longleftrightarrow D$$

In vivo, under "steady-state" conditions, there would probably be a net flux from left to right due to continuous supply of A and continuous removal of D. Such a pathway could function, but there would be little scope for control of the flux via regulation of enzyme activity, since an increase in activity would only serve to speed up attainment of the equilibrium.

In practice, there are invariably one or more "nonequilibrium" type reactions in a metabolic pathway, where the reactants are present in concentrations that are far from equilibrium. In attempting to reach equilibrium, large losses of free energy occur as heat, making this type of reaction essentially nonreversible, eg,

$$A \longleftrightarrow B \xrightarrow{\text{Heat}} C \longleftrightarrow D$$

Nonequilibrium reaction

Such a pathway has both flow and direction but would exhaust itself if control were not exerted. The enzymes catalyzing nonequilibrium reactions are usually low in concentration and are subject to other controlling mechanisms. This is similar to the opening and shutting of a "one-way" valve, making it possible to control the net flow.

METABOLIC CONTROL OF AN ENZYME-CATALYZED REACTION

A hypothetical metabolic pathway, A,B,C,D, is shown in Fig 19–1, in which reactions A $\longleftrightarrow$ B and C $\longleftrightarrow$ D are equilibrium reactions and B $\rightarrow$ C is a nonequilibrium reaction. The flux through such a pathway can be regulated by the availability of substrate A. This depends on its supply from the blood, which in turn depends on adequate food intake to the gut or on certain key reactions that maintain and release major substrates to the blood, eg, phosphorylase in liver, which provides blood glucose, and hormone-sensitive lipase in adipose tissue, which supplies free fatty acids. It also depends on the ability of substrate A to permeate the cell membrane. The flux will also be determined by the efficiency of removal of the end product D and on the availability of cosubstrate or cofactors represented by X and Y.

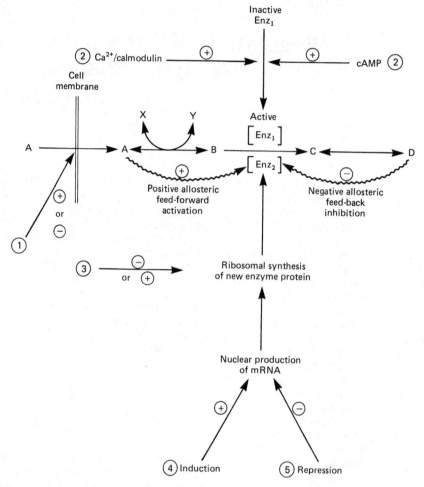

Figure 19–1. Mechanisms of control of an enzyme-catalyzed reaction. Circled numbers indicate possible sites of action of hormones. ① Alteration of membrane permeability, ② conversion of an inactive to an active enzyme, ③ alteration of the rate of translation of mRNA at the ribosomal level, ④ induction of new mRNA formation, and ⑤ repression of mRNA formation.

Enzymes catalyzing nonequilibrium reactions are often allosteric proteins subject to the action of "feed-back" or "feed-forward" control by allosteric modifiers (see Chapter 8). Other control mechanisms depend on the action of hormones. These act by several different mechanisms (see Chapter 35). One is **covalent modification** of the enzyme by phosphorylation and dephosphorylation. This is rapid and is often mediated through the formation of cAMP, which in turn causes the conversion of an inactive enzyme into an active enzyme. This change is brought about via the activity of a cAMP-dependent protein kinase that phosphorylates the enzyme. The active form of the enzyme can be either the phosphorylated enzyme (eg, phosphorylase a) or the dephosphorylated enzyme (eg, glycogen synthase a). Some regulatory enzymes can be phosphorylated without the mediation of cAMP and cAMP-dependent protein kinase. These enzymes respond to other metabolic signals such as the [ATP]/[ADP] ratio, eg, pyruvate dehydrogenase (Fig 19–2),

or Ca^{2+}/calmodulin–dependent protein kinase, eg, phosphorylase b kinase (Fig 15–10).

The synthesis of rate-controlling enzymes can be affected by hormones. Because this involves new protein synthesis, it is not a rapid change but is often a response to a change in nutritional state. Hormones can act as inducers or repressors of mRNA formation in the nucleus or as stimulators of the translation stage of protein synthesis at the ribosomal level (see Chapters 31 and 35).

REGULATION OF CARBOHYDRATE METABOLISM

It is convenient to divide the regulation of carbohydrate metabolism into 2 parts: (1) the regulation of carbohydrate metabolism at the cellular and enzymatic

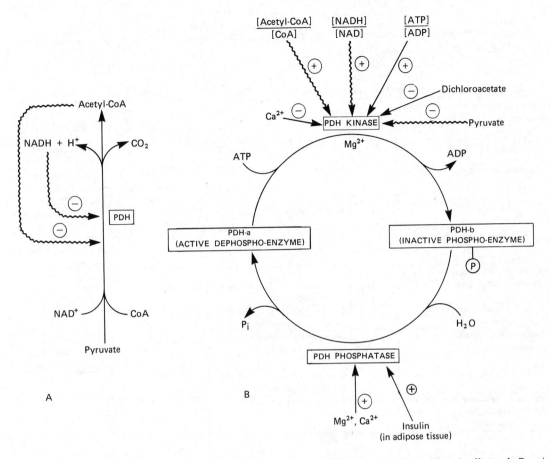

Figure 19–2. Regulation of pyruvate dehydrogenase (PDH). Arrows with wavy shafts indicate allosteric effects. *A:* Regulation by end product inhibition. *B:* Regulation by interconversion of active and inactive forms.

level, and (2) factors affecting the blood glucose. However, this is an arbitrary division, since the 2 parts are functionally related.

REGULATION OF CARBOHYDRATE METABOLISM AT THE CELLULAR & ENZYMATIC LEVEL

Gross effects on metabolism of changes in nutritional state or in the endocrine balance of an animal may be studied by observing changes in the concentration of blood metabolites. By such techniques as catheterization, it is also possible to study effects on individual organs by measuring arteriovenous differences, etc. However, the changes that occur in the metabolic balance of the intact animal are due to shifts in the pattern of metabolism in individual tissues which are usually associated with changes in availability of metabolites or changes in activity of key enzymes.

Changes in availability of substrates are either directly or indirectly responsible for most changes in metabolism. The concentration of glucose, fatty acids, and amino acids in blood influences their rate and pattern of metabolism in many tissues. Fluctuations in

their blood concentrations due to changes in dietary availability may alter the rate of secretion of hormones that influence, in turn, the pattern of metabolism in metabolic pathways—often by affecting the activity of key enzymes which attempt to compensate for the original change in substrate availability. Three types of mechanisms can be identified as responsible for regulating the activity of enzymes concerned in carbohydrate metabolism: (1) changes in the rate of enzyme synthesis, (2) conversion of an inactive to an active enzyme by covalent modification, and (3) allosteric effects.

Regulation of Glycolysis, Gluconeogenesis, & the Hexose Monophosphate Shunt
(Fig 19–3)

Some of the better-documented changes in enzyme activity that are considered to occur under various metabolic conditions are listed in Table 19–1. The information in this table applies mainly to the liver. The enzymes involved catalyze nonequilibrium reactions that may be regarded physiologically as "one-way" rather than balanced reactions. Often the effect is reinforced for the reason that the activity of the enzyme catalyzing the change in the opposite direction

Table 19–1. Regulatory and adaptive enzymes of the rat (mainly liver).

	Activity In		Inducer	Repressor	Activator	Inhibitor
	Carbo-hydrate Feeding	Starva-tion and Diabetes				
Enzymes of glycolysis and glycogenesis						
Hexokinase						*Glucose 6-phosphate
Glucokinase	↑	↓	Insulin			
Glycogen synthase system	↑	↓	Insulin		Insulin	Glucagon (cAMP), phosphorylase, glycogen
Phosphofructokinase-1	↑	↓	Insulin		*AMP, *fructose 6-P, *Pᵢ, *fructose 2,6-bisphosphate	*Citrate (fatty acids, ketone bodies), *ATP, glucagon (cAMP)
Pyruvate kinase	↑	↓	Insulin, fructose		*Fructose 1,6-bisphosphate	ATP, alanine, glucagon (cAMP), epinephrine
Pyruvate dehydrogenase	↑	↓			CoA, NAD, insulin‡, ADP, pyruvate	Acetyl-CoA, NADH, ATP (fatty acids, ketone bodies)
Enzymes of gluconeogenesis						
Pyruvate carboxylase	↓	↑	Glucocorticoids, glucagon, epinephrine	Insulin	*Acetyl-CoA	*ADP
Phosphoenolpyruvate carboxykinase	↓	↑	Glucocorticoids, glucagon, epinephrine	Insulin	Glucagon?	
Fructose 1,6-bisphosphatase	↓	↑	Glucocorticoids, glucagon, epinephrine	Insulin	Glucagon (cAMP)	*Fructose 1,6-bisphosphate, *AMP, fructose 2,6-bisphosphate
Glucose 6-phosphatase	↓	↑	Glucocorticoids, glucagon, epinephrine	Insulin		
Enzymes of the hexose monophosphate shunt, lipogenesis, and cholesterol synthesis						
Glucose 6-phosphate dehydrogenase	↑	↓	Insulin			
6-Phosphogluconate dehydrogenase	↑	↓	Insulin			
"Malic enzyme"	↑	↓	Insulin			
ATP-citrate lyase	↑	↓	Insulin			ADP
Acetyl-CoA carboxylase	↑	↓	Insulin?		*Citrate, insulin	Long-chain acyl-CoA, cAMP, glucagon
Fatty acid synthase	↑	↓	Insulin?			
HMG-CoA reductase		↓ ↑†			Insulin	Cholesterol

*Allosteric.
†Increased in diabetes.
‡In adipose tissue but not in liver.

varies reciprocally. Thus, glucokinase catalyzes the conversion of glucose to glucose 6-phosphate. In the same compartment of the cell (the extramitochondrial region) is found glucose 6-phosphatase, the enzyme catalyzing the same interconversion but in the reverse direction. Under conditions of a plentiful supply of carbohydrate, glucokinase activity is high whereas glucose 6-phosphatase activity is depressed. In starvation, glucokinase activity falls relative to glucose 6-phosphatase activity. In this way, a **substrate cycle** or "futile cycle" whose net result would be hydrolysis of ATP is minimized. However, it appears that some recycling does occur in the glucokinase/glucose 6-phosphatase cycle, which may have the physiologic advantage of allowing large changes in net flux of metabolites in either direction, controlled by substrate concentration only. It is also of importance that the key enzymes involved in a metabolic pathway are all activated or depressed in a coordinated manner. Table

19–1 shows that this is clearly the case. The enzymes involved in the utilization of glucose all become more active under the circumstance of a superfluity of glucose, and under these conditions the enzymes responsible for producing glucose by the pathway of gluconeogenesis are all low in activity. The secretion of insulin, which is responsive to the blood glucose concentration, controls the activity of the enzymes responsible for glycolysis and those responsible for gluconeogenesis. All of these effects, which can be explained on the basis of new enzyme synthesis, can be prevented by agents that block the synthesis of protein, such as puromycin and ethionine.

Both dehydrogenases of the hexose monophosphate pathway can be classified as adaptive enzymes, since they increase in activity in the well-fed animal and when insulin is given to a diabetic animal. Activity is low in diabetes or fasting. "Malic enzyme" and ATP-citrate lyase behave similarly, indicating that these 2 enzymes are probably involved in lipogenesis rather than gluconeogenesis.

Pyruvate dehydrogenase may also be regulated by phosphorylation involving an ATP-specific kinase that causes a decrease in activity, and by dephosphorylation by a phosphatase which causes an increase in activity of the dehydrogenase. The kinase is activated by increases in the [acetyl-CoA]/[CoA], [NADH]/[NAD$^+$], or [ATP]/[ADP] ratios. Thus, pyruvate dehydrogenase—and therefore glycolysis—is inhibited under conditions of fatty acid oxidation, which leads to increases in these ratios (Fig 19–2). In starvation, there is a decrease in the proportion of the enzyme in the active form, and an increase in activity occurs after administration of insulin but not in the liver. Glucagon inhibits glycolysis and stimulates gluconeogenesis in the liver by increasing the concentration of cAMP, which in turn activates cAMP-dependent protein kinase, leading to the phosphorylation and inactivation of pyruvate kinase. Glucagon also affects the concentration of fructose 2,6-bisphosphate and therefore glycolysis and gluconeogenesis, as explained below.

Several examples are available from carbohydrate metabolism to illustrate allosteric control of the activity of an enzyme. In gluconeogenesis, the synthesis of oxaloacetate from bicarbonate and pyruvate, catalyzed by the enzyme **pyruvate carboxylase**, requires the presence of acetyl-CoA as an allosteric activator. The addition of acetyl-CoA results in a change in the tertiary structure of the protein, lowering the K_m value for bicarbonate. This effect has important implications for the self-regulation of intermediary metabolism, for, as acetyl-CoA is formed from pyruvate, it automatically ensures the provision of oxaloacetate and its further oxidation in the citric acid cycle by activating pyruvate carboxylase. The activation of pyruvate carboxylase and the inhibition of pyruvate dehydrogenase by acetyl-CoA formed from the oxidation of fatty acids helps to explain the sparing action of fatty acid oxidation on the oxidation of pyruvate and the stimulation of gluconeogenesis in the liver (Fig 19–3). Probably the main role of fatty acid oxidation in promoting gluconeogenesis is to supply ATP required in the pyruvate carboxylase and phosphoenolpyruvate carboxykinase reactions.

Another enzyme that is subject to feedback control is **phosphofructokinase-1**. It occupies a key position in regulating glycolysis. Phosphofructokinase-1 is inhibited by citrate and by ATP and is activated by AMP. The presence of **adenylate kinase** in liver and many other tissues allows rapid equilibration of the reaction:

$$ATP + AMP \rightleftharpoons 2\,ADP$$

Thus, when ATP is used in energy-requiring processes resulting in formation of ADP, [AMP] rises. As [ATP] may be 50 times that of [AMP] at equilibrium, a small fractional decrease in [ATP] will cause a several-fold increase in [AMP]. Thus, a large change in [AMP] acts as a metabolic amplifier of a small change in [ATP].

This mechanism may allow the activity of phosphofructokinase-1 to be highly sensitive to even small changes in energy status of the cell and may control the quantity of carbohydrate undergoing glycolysis prior to its entry into the citric acid cycle. The increase in [AMP] can also explain why glycolysis is increased during anoxia when [ATP] decreases. Simultaneously, AMP activates phosphorylase, increasing glycogenolysis. The inhibition of phosphofructokinase-1 by citrate and ATP could be another explanation of the sparing action of fatty acid oxidation on glucose oxidation and also of the **Pasteur effect** whereby aerobic oxidation (via the citric acid cycle) inhibits the anaerobic degradation of glucose. A consequence of the inhibition of phosphofructokinase-1 is an accumulation of glucose 6-phosphate which, in turn, inhibits further uptake of glucose in extrahepatic tissues by allosteric inhibition of hexokinase. There appears to be a reciprocal relationship between the regulation of pyruvate dehydrogenase and pyruvate carboxylase in both liver and kidney that alters the metabolic fate of pyruvate as the tissue changes from carbohydrate oxidation, via glycolysis, to gluconeogenesis.

Role of Fructose 2,6-Bisphosphate

The most potent positive allosteric effector of phosphofructokinase-1 and inhibitor of fructose 1,6-bisphosphatase in liver is **fructose 2,6-bisphosphate.** It relieves inhibition of phosphofructokinase-1 by ATP and increases affinity for fructose 6-phosphate. It inhibits fructose 1,6-bisphosphatase by increasing the K_m for fructose 1,6-bisphosphate. Its concentration is under both substrate and hormonal controls (Fig 19–4). Fructose 2,6-bisphosphate is formed by phosphorylation of fructose 6-phosphate by **phosphofructokinase-2**. The same enzyme protein is also responsible for its breakdown, since it contains **fructose 2,6-bisphosphatase** activity. This bifunctional enzyme protein is under the allosteric control of fructose 6-phosphate, which when raised in concentration owing to an abundance of glucose, stimulates the kinase and inhibits the phosphatase. On the other hand, when glucose is short, glucagon stimulates the production of cAMP, activating cAMP-dependent protein kinase, which in turn inactivates phosphofructokinase-2 and activates fructose 2,6-bisphosphatase by phosphorylation. Thus, under a superfluity of glucose, fructose 2,6-bisphosphate increases in concentration, stimulating glycolysis by activating phosphofructokinase-1 and inhibiting fructose 1,6-bisphosphatase. Under conditions of glucose shortage, gluconeogenesis is stimulated by glucagon by decreasing the concentration of fructose 2,6-bisphosphate, which in turn inhibits phosphofructokinase-1 and activates fructose 1,6-bisphosphatase. This mechanism also ensures that glucagon stimulation of glycogenolysis in liver results in glucose release rather than glycolysis.

Regulation of Glycogen Metabolism

Regulation of glycogen metabolism is effected by a balance in activities between glycogen synthase and

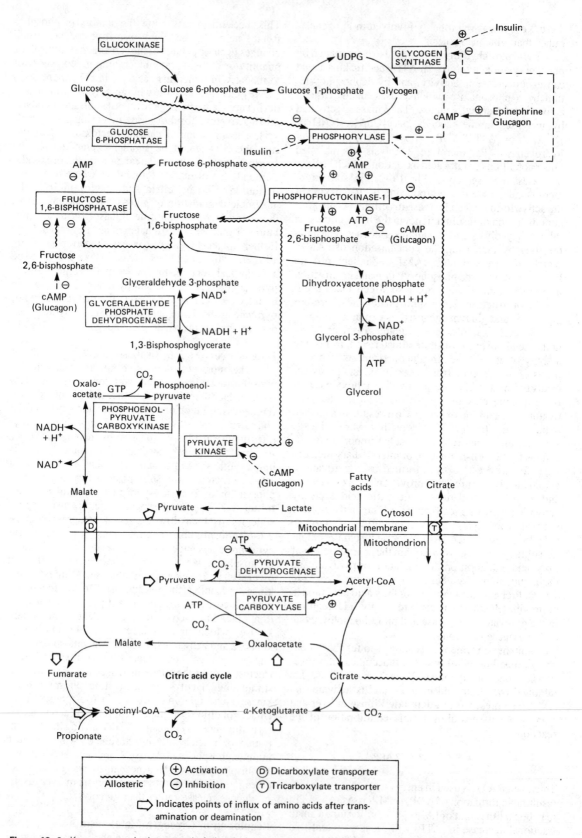

Figure 19–3. Key enzymes in the control of glycolysis, gluconeogenesis, and glycogen metabolism in liver. Indications of hormone action do not necessarily imply a direct action on the enzymes concerned.

phosphorylase, which are under substrate control (through allostery) as well as hormonal control. Not only is phosphorylase activated by a rise in concentration of cAMP, but glycogen synthase is at the same time converted to the inactive form (see Chapter 15). cAMP-dependent protein kinase both activates phosphorylase b kinase and inactivates glycogen synthase (Figs 15–10 and 15–11). Thus, inhibition of glycogenolysis enhances net glycogenesis, and inhibition of glycogenesis enhances net glycogenolysis. Of further significance in the regulation of glycogen metabolism in muscle is the finding that the dephosphorylation of phosphorylase a, phosphorylase kinase, and glycogen synthase b is accomplished by a single enzyme of wide specificity—protein phosphatase-1. In turn, protein phosphatase-1 is inhibited by cAMP-dependent protein kinase via inhibitor-1 (Fig 15–11). Thus, glycogenolysis can be terminated and glycogenesis can be stimulated synchronously. Both phosphorylase kinase and glycogen synthase may be reversibly phosphorylated in more than one site by separate kinases and phosphatases. These secondary phosphorylations modify the sensitivity of the primary sites to phosphorylation and dephosphorylation. Pyruvate dehydrogenase also shows evidence of **multisite phosphorylation.**

According to Hers, the major factor that controls glycogen metabolism in the liver is the concentration of phosphorylase a. Not only does this enzyme control the rate-limiting step in glycogenolysis, but it also inhibits the activity of synthase phosphatase (protein phosphatase-1) and thereby controls glycogen synthesis (Fig 19–3). Inactivation of phosphorylase is caused by glucose, and activation is caused by 5'-AMP. Catecholamines, including epinephrine, stimulate glycogenolysis by an additional mechanism not involving cAMP but via α-adrenergic receptors. These mechanisms involve direct stimulation of phosphorylase b kinase by Ca^{2+} and calmodulin. cAMP-independent glycogenolysis is also caused by vasopressin, oxytocin, and angiotensin II. Administration of insulin causes an immediate inactivation of phosphorylase followed by activation of glycogen synthase. The effects of insulin require the presence of glucose.

Regulation of the branching and debranching enzymes does not occur.

Regulation of the Citric Acid Cycle
(Fig 14–4)

The identification of regulatory enzymes of the citric acid cycle is difficult because of the many pathways with which the cycle interacts as well as its location within the mitochondrion wherein measurement of enzyme activity and substrate levels is relatively uncertain. In most tissues, where the primary function of the citric acid cycle is to provide energy,

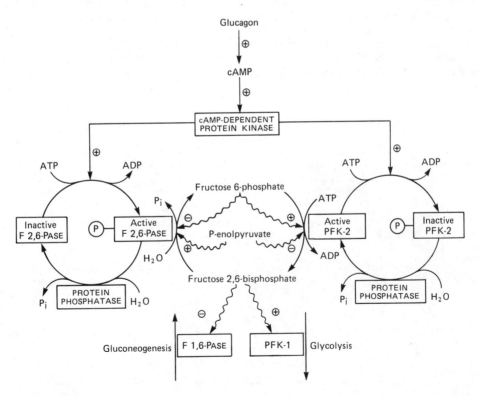

Figure 19–4. Control of glycolysis and gluconeogenesis in the liver by fructose 2,6-bisphosphate. (PFK-1, 6-phosphofructo-1-kinase; PFK-2, 6-phosphofructo-2-kinase; F 1,6-Pase, fructose 1,6-bisphosphatase; F 2,6-Pase, fructose 2,6-bisphosphatase.)

there is little doubt that respiratory control via the respiratory chain and oxidative phosphorylation is the overriding control on citric acid cycle activity. Thus, activity is immediately dependent on the supply of oxidized dehydrogenase cofactors (eg, NAD), which in turn is dependent on the availability of ADP and ultimately, therefore, on the rate of utilization of ATP. In addition to this overall or coarse control, the properties of some of the enzymes of the cycle indicate that control might also be exerted at the level of the cycle itself. In a tissue such as brain, which is largely dependent on carbohydrate to supply acetyl-CoA, control of the citric acid cycle may occur at the pyruvate dehydrogenase step. In the cycle proper, control may be exercised by allosteric inhibition of citrate synthase by ATP or long-chain fatty acyl-CoA. Allosteric activation of mitochondrial NAD-dependent isocitrate dehydrogenase by ADP is counteracted by ATP and NADH. The α-ketoglutarate dehydrogenase complex appears to be under control analogous to that of pyruvate dehydrogenase. Succinate dehydrogenase is inhibited by oxaloacetate, and the availability of oxaloacetate, as controlled by malate dehydrogenase, depends on the [NADH]/[NAD$^+$] ratio. Since the K_m for oxaloacetate of citrate synthase is of the same order of magnitude as the intramitochondrial concentration, it would appear that the concentration of oxaloacetate could play a part in controlling the rate of citrate formation. In the heart, the cycle is controlled by the [NADH]/[NAD$^+$] ratio via the availability of oxaloacetate and by the [ATP]/[ADP] ratio via inhibition of citrate synthase by succinyl-CoA in competition with acetyl-CoA. An increased [ATP]/[ADP] ratio is considered to raise the [GTP]/[GDP] ratio at the succinate thiokinase step, thereby increasing the con-

centration of succinyl-CoA. Which (if any) of these mechanisms operates in vivo has still to be resolved.

THE BLOOD GLUCOSE

Sources of Blood Glucose

    A. From Carbohydrates of the Diet: Most carbohydrates in the diet form glucose, galactose, or fructose upon digestion. These are transported to the liver via the portal vein. Galactose and fructose are readily converted to glucose in the liver (Figs 15–18 and 15–19).

    B. From Various Glucogenic Compounds That Undergo Gluconeogenesis: (Fig 19–3.) These compounds fall into 2 categories—those which involve a direct net conversion to glucose without significant recycling, such as some amino acids and propionate; and those which are the products of the partial metabolism of glucose in certain tissues and which are conveyed to the liver and kidney, where they are resynthesized to glucose. Thus, lactate, formed by the oxidation of glucose in skeletal muscle and by erythrocytes, is transported to the liver and kidney where it re-forms glucose, which again becomes available via the circulation for oxidation in the tissues. This process is known as the **Cori cycle** or lactic acid cycle (Fig 19–5). Glycerol for the triacylglycerols of adipose tissue is derived initially from the blood glucose, since free glycerol cannot be utilized readily for the synthesis of triacylglycerols in this tissue. Acylglycerols of adipose tissue are continually undergoing hydrolysis to form free glycerol, which diffuses out of the tissue into the blood. It is converted back to glucose by gluconeogenetic mechanisms in the liver and kidney. Thus, a

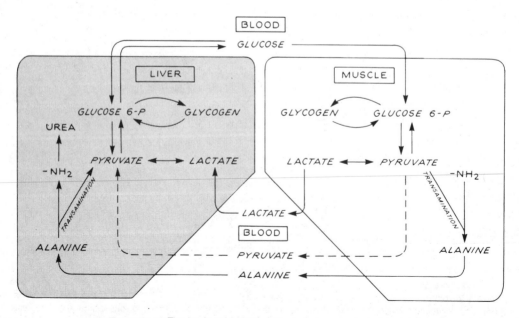

Figure 19–5. The lactic acid (Cori) cycle and glucose-alanine cycle.

continuous cycle exists in which glucose is transported from the liver and kidney to adipose tissue and whence glycerol is returned to be synthesized into glucose by the liver and kidney.

It has been noted that, of the amino acids transported from muscle to the liver during starvation, alanine predominates. This has led to the postulation of a **glucose-alanine cycle,** as shown in Fig 19–5, which has the effect of cycling glucose from liver to muscle and alanine from muscle to liver, effecting a net transfer of amino nitrogen from muscle to liver and of free energy from liver to muscle. The energy required for the hepatic synthesis of glucose from pyruvate is derived from the oxidation of fatty acids.

C. From liver glycogen by glycogenolysis.

The Concentration of the Blood Glucose

In the postabsorptive state, the blood glucose concentration in humans varies between 80 and 100 mg/dL. After the ingestion of a carbohydrate meal, it may rise to 120–130 mg/dL. During fasting, the level falls to around 60–70 mg/dL. Under normal circumstances, the level is controlled within these limits. The normal blood glucose level in ruminants is considerably lower, being approximately 40 mg/dL in sheep and 60 mg/dL in cattle. These lower normal levels appear to be associated with the fact that ruminants ferment virtually all dietary carbohydrate to lower (volatile) fatty acids, and these largely replace glucose as the main metabolic fuel of the tissues in the fed condition.

Regulation of the Blood Glucose

The maintenance of stable levels of glucose in the blood is one of the most finely regulated of all homeostatic mechanisms and one in which the liver, the extrahepatic tissues, and several hormones play a part. **Liver cells appear to be freely permeable to glucose,** whereas cells of **extrahepatic tissues are relatively impermeable.** As a result, the passage through the cell membrane is the rate-limiting step in the uptake of glucose in extrahepatic tissues, and it is rapidly phosphorylated by hexokinase on entry into the cells. On the other hand, it is probable that the activity of certain enzymes and the concentration of key intermediates exert a much more direct effect on the uptake or output of glucose from liver. Nevertheless, the concentration of glucose in the blood is an important factor controlling the rate of uptake of glucose in both liver and extrahepatic tissues. It is to be noted that hexokinase is inhibited by glucose 6-phosphate, so that some feedback control may be exerted on glucose uptake in extrahepatic tissues dependent on hexokinase for glucose phosphorylation. The liver is not subject to this constraint because glucokinase is not affected by glucose 6-phosphate. Glucokinase, which has a higher K_m (lower affinity) for glucose than does hexokinase, increases in activity over the physiologic range of glucose concentrations (Fig 19–6) and seems to be specifically concerned with glucose uptake into the liver at the higher concentrations found in the hepatic

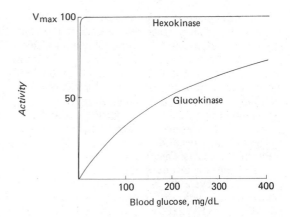

Figure 19–6. Variation in glucose phosphorylating activity of hexokinase and glucokinase with increase of blood glucose concentration. The K_m for glucose of hexokinase is 0.05 mmol/L (0.9 mg/dL) and of glucokinase is 10 mmol/L (180 mg/dL).

portal vein after a carbohydrate meal. Its absence in ruminants, which have low blood glucose concentrations, is compatible with this function.

At normal blood glucose concentrations (80–100 mg/dL), the liver appears to be a net producer of glucose. However, as the glucose level rises, the output of glucose ceases, so that at high levels there is a net uptake. In the rat, it has been estimated that the rate of uptake of glucose and the rate of output are equal at a hepatic portal vein blood glucose concentration of 150 mg/dL. In dogs, the blood glucose level at which there is net uptake by the liver varies with the type of diet. Thus, infusion of glucose into dogs maintained on a high-protein diet resulted in a rise in blood glucose, with a cessation of net hepatic glucose production only at hyperglycemic levels. In contrast, in carbohydrate-fed dogs, the blood glucose concentration increased very little upon glucose infusion, and there was an immediate net uptake of glucose by the liver. An explanation of these differences due to changes in diet is probably to be found in changes in activity of enzymes in the liver concerned with glycolysis and gluconeogenesis.

In addition to the direct effects of hyperglycemia in enhancing the uptake of glucose into both the liver and peripheral tissues, the hormone **insulin** plays a central role in the regulation of the blood glucose concentration. It is produced by the B cells of the islets of Langerhans in the pancreas and is secreted into the blood as a direct response to hyperglycemia. Its concentration in the blood parallels that of the blood glucose, and its administration results in prompt hypoglycemia. Substances causing release of insulin include also amino acids, free fatty acids, ketone bodies, glucagon, secretin, and tolbutamide. Epinephrine and norepinephrine block the release of insulin. In vitro (and probably in vivo), insulin has an immediate effect on tissues such as adipose tissue and muscle of increasing the rate of glucose uptake. It is considered that this action is due to an enhancement of glucose transport through the cell membrane by recruitment of insulin transporters from the interior of the cell to the plasma membrane. In contrast, there is no effect of insulin on glucose penetration of hepatic cells which agrees with the findings that glucose metabolism by liver cells is not rate-limited by their permeability to glucose. However, insulin does indirectly enhance uptake of glucose by the liver as a result of its actions on the enzymes controlling glycolysis and glycogenesis.

The **anterior pituitary gland** secretes hormones that tend to elevate the blood glucose and therefore antagonize the action of insulin. These are growth hormone, ACTH (corticotropin), and possibly other "diabetogenic" principles. Growth hormone secretion is stimulated by hypoglycemia. Growth hormone decreases glucose uptake in certain tissues, eg, muscle. Some of this effect may not be direct, since it mobilizes free fatty acids from adipose tissue which themselves inhibit glucose utilization. Chronic administration of growth hormone leads to diabetes. By producing hyperglycemia, it stimulates secretion of insulin, eventually causing B cell exhaustion. Although ACTH could have an indirect effect upon glucose utilization, since it enhances the release of free fatty acids from adipose tissue, its major effect on carbohydrate metabolism is due to its stimulation of the secretion of hormones of the adrenal cortex.

The **adrenal cortex** secretes a number of steroid hormones of which the glucocorticoids (11-oxysteroids) are important in carbohydrate metabolism. Upon administration, the glucocorticoids lead to gluconeogenesis. This is as a result of increased protein catabolism in the tissues, increased hepatic uptake of amino acids, and increased activity of transaminases and other enzymes concerned with gluconeogenesis in the liver. In addition, glucocorticoids inhibit the utilization of glucose in extrahepatic tissues. In all these actions, glucocorticoids act in a manner antagonistic to insulin.

Epinephrine, as secreted by the adrenal medulla, stimulates glycogen breakdown in muscle. However, administration of epinephrine leads to an outpouring of glucose from the liver (provided glycogen is present) owing to stimulation of phosphorylase. In muscle, as a result of the absence of glucose 6-phosphatase, glycogenolysis ensues with the formation of lactate. The lactate that diffuses into the blood is converted by the gluconeogenetic mechanisms back to glycogen in the liver (Cori cycle). Hypoglycemia causes a neural sympathetic discharge that increases epinephrine secretion, which in turn stimulates glycogenolysis and results in an increase in the blood glucose concentration.

Glucagon is the hormone produced by the A cells of the islets of Langerhans of the pancreas. Its secretion is stimulated by hypoglycemia, and, when it reaches the liver (via the portal vein), it causes glycogenolysis by activating phosphorylase in a manner similar to epinephrine. Most of the endogenous glucagon is cleared from the circulation by the liver. Unlike epinephrine, glucagon does not have an action on muscle phosphorylase. Glucagon also enhances gluconeogenesis from amino acids and lactate. Both hepatic glycogenolysis and gluconeogenesis contribute to the hyperglycemic effect of glucagon.

Thyroid hormone should also be considered as affecting the blood glucose. There is experimental evidence that thyroxine has a diabetogenic action and that thyroidectomy inhibits the development of diabetes. It has also been noted that there is a complete absence of glycogen from the livers of thyrotoxic animals. In humans, the fasting blood glucose is elevated in hyperthyroid patients and decreased in hypothyroid patients. However, hyperthyroid patients apparently utilize glucose at a normal or increased rate, whereas hypothyroid patients have a decreased ability to utilize glucose. In addition, hypothyroid patients are much less sensitive to insulin than are normal or hyperthyroid individuals. These effects of thyroid hormone on carbohydrate metabolism may be related to differences in end organ response, rates of destruction of insulin, or both.

The Renal Threshold for Glucose

When the blood glucose rises to relatively high levels, the kidney also exerts a regulatory effect. Glucose is continually filtered by the glomeruli but is ordinarily returned completely to the blood by the reabsorptive system of the renal tubules. The reabsorption of glucose is linked to oxidative phosphorylation and the provision of ATP in the tubular cells, a process similar to that responsible for the absorption of this sugar from the intestine. The capacity of the tubular system to reabsorb glucose is limited to a rate of about 350 mg/min. When the blood levels of glucose are elevated, the glomerular filtrate may contain more glucose than can be reabsorbed; the excess passes into the urine to produce **glycosuria.** In normal individuals, glycosuria occurs when the venous blood sugar exceeds 170–180 mg/dL. This level of the venous blood sugar is termed the **renal threshold** for glucose.

Glycosuria may be produced in experimental animals with phlorhizin, which inhibits the glucose reabsorptive system in the tubule. This is known as **renal glycosuria.** Glycosuria of renal origin may result from inherited defects in the kidney, or it may be acquired as a result of disease processes.

Carbohydrate Tolerance

The ability of the body to utilize carbohydrates may be ascertained by measuring its **carbohydrate tolerance.** It is indicated by the nature of the blood glucose curve following the administration of glucose. **Diabetes mellitus** ("sugar" diabetes) is characterized by decreased tolerance to carbohydrate due to decreased secretion of insulin. This is manifested by elevated blood glucose levels (hyperglycemia) and accompanying glycosuria and may be accompanied by changes in fat metabolism. Tolerance to carbohydrate declines not only in diabetes but also in conditions where the liver is damaged, in some infections, in obesity, and sometimes in atherosclerosis. It would also be expected to occur in the presence of hyperactivity of the pituitary or adrenal cortex, because of the antagonism of the hormones of these endocrine glands to the action of insulin.

Insulin, the hormone of the islets of Langerhans of the pancreas, increases tolerance to carbohydrate. Injection of insulin lowers the content of the glucose in the blood and increases its utilization and its storage in the liver and muscle as glycogen. An excess of insulin may lower the blood glucose level to such an extent that severe hypoglycemia occurs and results in convulsions and even in death unless glucose is administered promptly. In humans, hypoglycemic convulsions may occur when the blood glucose is lowered acutely to about 20 mg/dL or less. Increased tolerance to carbohydrate is also observed in pituitary or adrenocortical insufficiency; presumably this is attributable to a decrease in the normal antagonism to insulin which results in a relative excess of that hormone.

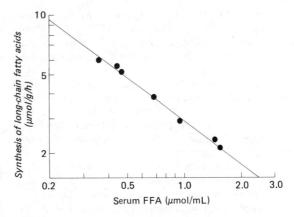

Figure 19–7. Direct inhibition of hepatic lipogenesis by free fatty acids. (Lipogenesis was determined from the incorporation of ^3H_2O into long-chain fatty acids in the perfused rat liver. FFA, free fatty acids.)

REGULATION OF LIPID METABOLISM

The regulation of the mobilization of free fatty acids from adipose tissue has been described previously (see pp 233–237).

REGULATION OF FATTY ACID SYNTHESIS
(Lipogenesis)

Many animals, including humans, take their food as spaced meals and must therefore store much of the energy of their diet for use between meals. The process of lipogenesis is concerned with the conversion of glucose and intermediates such as pyruvate, lactate, and acetyl-CoA to fat, which constitutes the anabolic phase of this cycle. The nutritional state of the organism and tissues is the main factor controlling the rate of lipogenesis. Thus, the rate is high in the well-fed animal whose diet contains a high proportion of carbohydrate. It is depressed under conditions of restricted caloric intake, on a high-fat diet, or when there is a deficiency of insulin, as in diabetes mellitus. All of these conditions are associated with increased concentrations of plasma free fatty acids. There is an **inverse relationship between hepatic lipogenesis and the concentration of serum free fatty acids** (Fig 19–7). The greatest inhibition of lipogenesis occurs over the range of free fatty acids (0.3–0.8 μmol/mL of plasma) through which the plasma free fatty acids increase during transition from the fed to the starved state. Fat in the diet causes depression of lipogenesis in the liver, and when there is more than 10% of fat in the diet, there is little conversion of dietary carbohydrate to fat. Lipogenesis is higher in livers from rats consum-

ing all their food in 2 hours. It is also higher when sucrose is fed instead of glucose. Because of the close association between the activities of the hexose monophosphate shunt on the one hand and of the lipogenic pathway on the other, it was considered that the block in lipogenesis in fasting was due to lack of NADPH generation from the shunt pathway. However, subsequent work in which an NADPH-generating system was added to a liver homogenate from fasting rats failed to promote fatty acid synthesis.

Long-chain fatty acid synthesis is controlled in the short term by allosteric and covalent modification of enzymes and in the long term by changes in rates of synthesis and degradation of enzymes. At present it is recognized that the rate-limiting reaction in the lipogenic pathway is at the **acetyl-CoA carboxylase step** (Fig 17–9). Long-chain acyl-CoA molecules inhibit acetyl-CoA carboxylase competitively with the activator citrate, an example of metabolic negative feedback inhibition by a product of a reaction sequence. Thus, if acyl-CoA accumulates because it is not esterified quickly enough, it will automatically reduce the synthesis of new fatty acid. Likewise, if acyl-CoA accumulates as a result of increased lipolysis or an influx of free fatty acids into the tissue, this will also inhibit synthesis of new fatty acid.

Acyl-CoA may also inhibit the mitochondrial tricarboxylate transporter, thus preventing egress of citrate from the mitochondria into the cytosol. There is also an inverse relationship between free fatty acids and the proportion of active to inactive pyruvate dehydrogenase, which would regulate the availability of acetyl-CoA for lipogenesis. Acyl-CoA may lead to an inhibition of pyruvate dehydrogenase by inhibiting the ATP-ADP exchange transporter of the inner mitochondrial membrane, which would lead to increased intramitochondrial [ATP]/[ADP] ratios and therefore to conversion of active to inactive pyruvate dehydrogenase (Fig 19–2). Also, oxidation of fatty acids due to increased levels of free fatty acids may increase the ratio of [acetyl-CoA]/[CoA] and [NADH]/[NAD$^+$] in mitochondria, inhibiting pyruvate dehydrogenase and thus blocking the supply of acetyl-CoA from carbohydrate via pyruvate.

Insulin stimulates lipogenesis by several possible mechanisms. It increases the transport of glucose into the cell (eg, in adipose tissue) and thereby increases the availability both of pyruvate for fatty acid synthesis and glycerol 3-phosphate for esterification of the fatty acids. Insulin converts the inactive form of pyruvate dehydrogenase to the active form in adipose tissue but not in liver (Laker and Mayes, 1984). In addition, insulin activates acetyl-CoA carboxylase, possibly by activation of a protein phosphatase. Also, insulin, by its ability to depress the level of intracellular cAMP, inhibits lipolysis and thereby reduces the concentration of long-chain acyl-CoA, an inhibitor of lipogenesis. Glucagon and epinephrine inhibit acetyl-CoA carboxylase, and therefore lipogenesis, by increasing cAMP, allowing cAMP-dependent protein kinase to inactivate the enzyme by phosphorylation. In addition, catecholamines inhibit the enzyme through α-adrenergic receptors and a Ca^{2+}-calmodulin-dependent protein kinase.

Flatt has suggested that lipogenesis from glucose in adipose tissue is an energy-releasing process and may be self-limiting because of respiratory control and availability of ADP. It is also clear that factors affecting the rate of glycolysis, which supplies acetyl-CoA for lipogenesis, must exert an overall control on the process. In ruminants, acetate—not glucose—is the starting material for lipogenesis. It follows that, in these species, many of the control mechanisms discussed above are bypassed and thus do not apply.

Various reports indicate that both the fatty acid synthase complex and acetyl-CoA carboxylase are adaptive enzymes, increasing in total amount in the fed state and decreasing in fasting, feeding of fat, and diabetes. Insulin is an important hormone causing induction of enzyme biosynthesis. These effects on lipogenesis take several days to become fully manifested and augment the direct and immediate effect of free fatty acids and hormones such as insulin and glucagon.

REGULATION OF KETOGENESIS
(See Fig 18–12.)

Ketosis does not occur in vivo unless there is a concomitant rise in the level of circulating free fatty acids, severe ketosis being accompanied invariably by very high concentrations of plasma free fatty acids that arise from lipolysis of triacylglycerol in adipose tissue. In addition, numerous experiments in vitro have demonstrated that fatty acids are the precursors of ketone bodies in the liver. The liver, both in fed and in fasting conditions, has the ability to extract about 30% or more of the free fatty acids passing through it, so that at high concentrations of free fatty acids the flux passing into

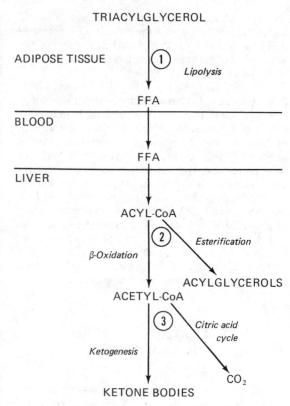

Figure 19–8. Regulation of ketogenesis. ①–③, three crucial steps in the pathway of metabolism of free fatty acids (FFA) that determine the magnitude of ketogenesis.

the liver is substantial. Therefore, the factors regulating mobilization of free fatty acids from adipose tissue are important in controlling ketogenesis (Fig 19–8). One of 2 fates awaits the free fatty acids upon uptake and after they are activated to acyl-CoA: They are **esterified** mainly to triacylglycerol and phospholipid, or they are **β-oxidized** to acetyl-CoA. In turn, acetyl-CoA is oxidized in the citric acid cycle or used to form ketone bodies (Fig 19–8). Experiments with fasting rats have demonstrated that the magnitude of ketonemia is more directly related to the quantity of triacylglycerol present in the depots than to the quantity present in the liver, indicating that plasma free fatty acids (derived from the fat depots) are a more significant source of ketone bodies than fatty acids derived from lipolysis of liver triacylglycerol.

Among several possible factors, the capacity for esterification as an antiketogenic factor depends on the availability of precursors in the liver to supply sufficient glycerol 3-phosphate. The concentration of glycerol 3-phosphate in the livers of fasted rats is depressed when compared to that in fed animals. However, the availability of glycerol 3-phosphate does not limit esterification in fasting perfused livers, where a constant fraction is esterified, irrespective of the mass of free fatty acids taken up. It has also been found in vivo that antiketogenic effects of glycerol and dihydroxyacetone are not correlated with the levels of glycerol 3-phosphate in the liver. Thus, whether the availability of glycerol 3-phosphate in the liver is ever rate-limiting on esterification is not clear; neither is there critical information on whether the in vivo activities of the enzymes involved in esterification are rate-limiting. It does not seem that they are, since neither free fatty acids nor any intermediates in their pathway of esterification to triacylglycerol (Fig 17–17) ever accumulate in the liver. Phosphatidate phosphohydrolase increases in activity in livers in which extra triacylglycerol synthesis is taking place. In the perfused liver, insulin increases the activity of glycerol phosphate acyltransferase, which catalyzes the first step in esterification. This may be due to the stimulation of a protein phosphatase.

Using the perfused liver, it has been shown that livers from fed rats esterify considerably more ^{14}C-free fatty acids than livers from fasted rats, the balance not esterified in the livers from fasted rats being oxidized to either $^{14}CO_2$ or ^{14}C-ketone bodies. These results may be explained by the fact that car-

nitine palmitoyltransferase I activity in the mitochondrial membrane regulates the entry of long-chain acyl groups into mitochondria prior to β-oxidation (Fig 17–2). Its activity is low in the fed state, when fatty acid oxidation is depressed, and high in fasting, when fatty acid oxidation increases. McGarry and Foster (1980) have shown that malonyl-CoA, the initial intermediate in fatty acid biosynthesis (Fig 17–7), which increases in concentration in the fed state, inhibits this enzyme, switching off β-oxidation. Thus, in the fed condition there is active lipogenesis and high [malonyl-CoA], which inhibits carnitine palmitoyltransferase I (Fig 19–9). Low concentrations of free fatty acids entering the liver cell are nearly all esterified to acylglycerols and transported out of the liver in VLDL. However, as the concentration of free fatty acids increases with the onset of starvation, acetyl-CoA carboxylase is inhibited and [malonyl-CoA] decreases, releasing the inhibition of carnitine palmitoyl transferase and allowing more acyl-CoA to be oxidized. These events are reinforced in starvation by the [insulin]/[glucagon] ratio, which decreases, caus-

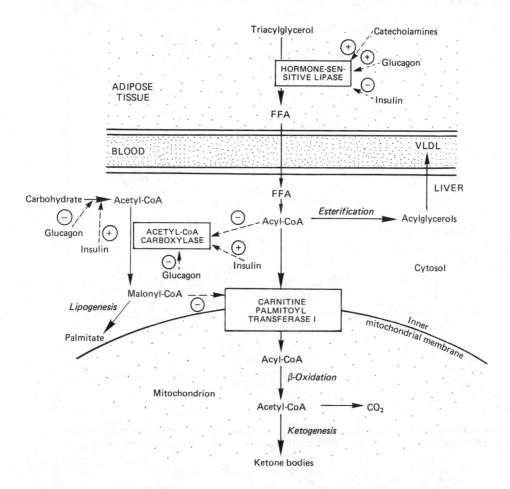

Figure 19–9. Regulation of long-chain fatty acid oxidation in the liver. (FFA, free fatty acids; VLDL, very low density lipoprotein.) Positive ((+)) and negative ((−)) regulatory effects are represented by broken lines and substrate flow by solid lines.

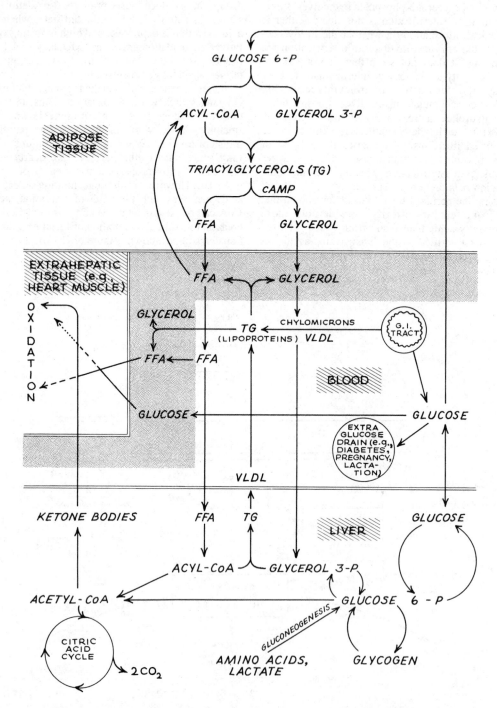

Figure 19–10. Metabolic interrelationships between adipose tissue, the liver, and extrahepatic tissues. (Stippled area, lipoprotein lipase region of capillary wall; FFA, free fatty acids; VLDL, very low density lipoproteins.)

ing increased lipolysis in adipose tissue, with release of free fatty acids, and inhibition of pyruvate kinase and acetyl-CoA carboxylase in the liver.

As the level of serum free fatty acids is raised, proportionately more free fatty acid is converted to ketone bodies and less is oxidized via the citric acid cycle to CO_2. The partition of acetyl-CoA between the ketogenic pathway and the pathway of oxidation to CO_2 is so regulated that the total free energy trapped in ATP which results from the oxidation of free fatty acids remains constant. It will be appreciated that **complete oxidation of 1 mol of palmitate involves a net production of 129 mol of ATP** via β-oxidation and CO_2 production in the citric acid cycle (see p 210), whereas **only 33 mol of ATP is produced when acetoacetate is the end product and only 21 mol when 3-hydroxybutyrate is the end product.** Thus, ketogenesis may be regarded as a mechanism that allows the liver to oxidize large quantities of fatty acids within an apparently tightly coupled system of oxidative phosphorylation, without increasing its total energy expenditure.

Several other hypotheses have been advanced to account for the diversion of fatty acid oxidation from CO_2 formation to ketogenesis. Theoretically, a fall in concentration of oxaloacetate, particularly within the mitochondria, could cause impairment of the citric acid cycle to metabolize acetyl-CoA. This has been considered to occur because of an increase in the [NADH]/[NAD$^+$] ratio. Krebs has suggested that since oxaloacetate is also on the main pathway of gluconeogenesis, enhanced gluconeogenesis leading to a fall in the level of oxaloacetate may be the cause of the severe forms of ketosis found in diabetes and the ketosis of cattle. Alternatively, it has been postulated that citrate synthase is inhibited, either by long-chain acyl-CoA or by increased concentrations of ATP. Utter and Keech have shown that pyruvate carboxylase, which catalyzes the conversion of pyruvate to oxaloacetate, is activated by acetyl-CoA. Consequently, when there are significant amounts of acetyl-CoA, there should be sufficient oxaloacetate to initiate the condensing reaction of the citric acid cycle. Recent work (Siess, Kientsch-Engel, and Wieland, 1984) suggests that 25–30% of the increase in ketone body production occurring at elevated fatty acid supply can be accounted for by the decrease in free oxaloacetate concentration in mitochondria.

In summary, ketosis arises as a result of a deficiency in available carbohydrate. This has the following actions in fostering ketogenesis (Figs 19–8 and 19–9): ① It causes an imbalance between esterification and lipolysis in adipose tissue, with consequent release of free fatty acids into the circulation. Free fatty acids are the principal substrates for ketone body formation in the liver, and therefore all factors, metabolic or endocrine, affecting the release of free fatty acids from adipose tissue influence ketogenesis. ② Upon entry of free fatty acids into the liver, the balance between their esterification and oxidation is governed by carnitine palmitoyltransferase I, whose activity is increased indirectly by the concentration of free fatty acids and the hormonal state of the liver. ③ As the amount of fatty acid oxidized increases, more forms ketone bodies and less forms CO_2, regulated in such a manner that the total ATP production remains constant. Ketone bodies are not oxidized significantly by the liver; they diffuse into the circulation whence they are extracted and oxidized by extrahepatic tissues preferentially to other fuels.

Ketosis in Vivo

The ketosis that occurs in starvation and fat feeding is relatively mild compared with the condition encountered in uncontrolled diabetes mellitus, eclampsia of ewes, ketosis of lactating cattle, or animals administered phlorhizin. The main reason appears to be that in the severe conditions carbohydrate is still less available to the tissues than in the mild conditions. Thus, in the milder forms of diabetes mellitus, in fat feeding, and in chronic starvation, glycogen is present in the liver in variable amounts, and free fatty acid levels are lower, which probably accounts for the less severe ketosis associated with these conditions.

In ketosis of ruminants or in phlorhizin poisoning, there is a severe drain of glucose from the blood owing to excessive fetal demands, the demands of heavy lactation, or impaired reabsorption by the kidney, respectively (Fig 19–10). Extreme hypoglycemia results, coupled with negligible amounts of glycogen in the liver. Ketosis in these conditions tends to be severe. As hypoglycemia develops, the secretion of insulin diminishes, allowing not only less glucose utilization but also enhancement of lipolysis in adipose tissue.

In diabetes mellitus, the lack (or relative lack) of insulin probably affects adipose tissue more than any other tissue, because of its extreme sensitivity to this hormone. As a result, free fatty acids are released in quantities that give rise to plasma free fatty acid levels more than twice those in fasting normal subjects. Many changes also occur in the activity of enzymes within the liver that enhance the rate of gluconeogenesis and transfer of glucose to the blood despite high levels of circulating glucose.

INTERCONVERSION OF MAJOR FOODSTUFFS
(See Fig 19–11.)

That animals may be fattened on a predominantly carbohydrate diet demonstrates the ease of conversion of carbohydrate into fat. A most significant reaction in this respect is the conversion of pyruvate to acetyl-CoA, as acetyl-CoA is the starting material for the synthesis of long-chain fatty acids. However, the pyruvate dehydrogenase reaction is essentially nonreversible, which prevents the direct conversion of acetyl-CoA, formed from the oxidation of fatty acids, to pyruvate. There cannot be a net conversion of acetyl-CoA to oxaloacetate via the citric acid cycle,

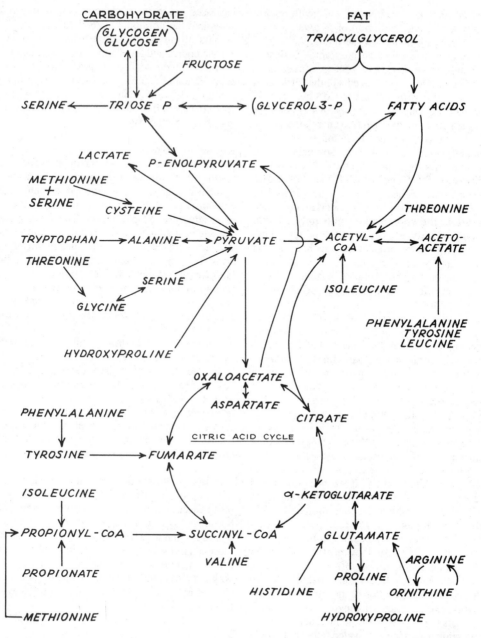

Figure 19–11. Interconversion of the major foodstuffs.

since one molecule of oxaloacetate is required to condense with acetyl-CoA and only one molecule of oxaloacetate is regenerated. For similar reasons, **there cannot be a net conversion of fatty acids having an even number of carbon atoms** (which form acetyl-CoA) **to glucose or glycogen.**

Only the terminal 3-carbon portion of a fatty acid having an odd number of carbon atoms is glycogenic, as this portion of the molecule will form propionate upon oxidation. Nevertheless, it is possible for labeled carbon atoms of fatty acids to be found ultimately in glycogen after traversing the citric acid cycle: This is because oxaloacetate is an intermediate both in the

citric acid cycle and in the pathway of gluconeogenesis. Many of the carbon skeletons of the nonessential amino acids can be produced from carbohydrate via the citric acid cycle and transamination. By reversal of these processes, glycogenic amino acids yield carbon skeletons that are either members or precursors of the citric acid cycle. They are therefore readily converted by gluconeogenic pathways to glucose and glycogen. The ketogenic amino acids give rise to acetoacetate, which will in turn be metabolized as ketone bodies, forming acetyl-CoA in extrahepatic tissues (see Chapter 18).

For the same reasons that it is not possible for a

net conversion of fatty acids to carbohydrate to occur, it is not possible for a net conversion of fatty acids to glucogenic amino acids to take place. Neither is it possible to reverse the pathways of breakdown of ketogenic amino acids, all of which fall into the category of "essential amino acids." Conversion of the carbon skeletons of glucogenic amino acids to fatty acids is possible, either by formation of pyruvate and acetyl-CoA or by reversal of nonmitochondrial reactions of the citric acid cycle from α-ketoglutarate to citrate followed by the action of ATP-citrate lyase to give acetyl-CoA (see Chapter 18). However, under most natural conditions, eg, starvation, a net breakdown of protein and amino acids is usually accompanied by a net breakdown of fat. The net conversion of amino acids to fat is therefore not a significant process except possibly in animals receiving a high-protein diet.

THE ECONOMICS OF CARBOHYDRATE & LIPID METABOLISM IN THE WHOLE BODY

Many of the details of the interplay between carbohydrate and lipid metabolism in various tissues have been described. The conversion of glucose to fat is a process that occurs readily under conditions of optimal nutritional intake. With the exception of the glycerol moiety, fat (triacylglycerol) cannot give rise to a net formation of glucose, because of the irreversible nature of the oxidative decarboxylation of pyruvate to acetyl-CoA (see p 271). Certain tissues, including the central nervous system and the erythrocytes, are much more dependent upon a continual supply of glucose than others. A minimal supply of glucose is probably necessary in extrahepatic tissues to maintain the integrity of the citric acid cycle. In addition, glucose appears to be the main source of glycerol 3-phosphate in tissues devoid of glycerokinase. There is a minimal and obligatory rate of glucose oxidation. Large quantities of glucose are also required for fetal nutrition and the synthesis of milk. Certain mechanisms, in addition to gluconeogenesis, safeguard essential supplies of glucose in times of shortage by allowing other substrates to spare its oxidation.

Randle et al have demonstrated that ketone bodies and free fatty acids spare the oxidation of glucose in muscle by impairing its entry into the cell, its phosphorylation to glucose 6-phosphate, the phosphofructokinase reaction, and the oxidative decarboxylation of pyruvate. Oxidation of free fatty acids and ketone bodies causes an increase in the concentration of intracellular citrate that in turn inhibits phosphofructokinase. These observations, taken with those of Olson, who demonstrated that acetoacetate was oxidized in the perfused heart preferentially to free fatty acids,

justify the conclusion that under conditions of carbohydrate shortage available **fuels are oxidized in the following order of preference:** (1) **ketone bodies** (and probably other short-chain fatty acids, eg, acetate), (2) **free fatty acids,** and (3) **glucose.** This does not imply that any particular fuel is oxidized to the total exclusion of any other (Fig 19–10). However, these mechanisms are more important in tissues having a high capacity for aerobic oxidation of fatty acids, eg, heart and slow-twitch muscle, than tissues with a low capacity, eg, fast-twitch muscle.

These facts help to explain the experiments of several investigators who have shown in vivo that under certain conditions fat mobilization can be reduced after the administration of noncarbohydrate calorigenic substrates, eg, oral administration of fat in rats or after the administration of acetate in sheep. Fat mobilization and ketogenesis in rats on all-fat diets can be reduced substantially, provided the quantity of fat ingested is increased to satisfy the caloric requirement of the animal. Thus, if substrates such as free fatty acids and ketone bodies spare the oxidation of glucose in muscle, more glucose will be available, causing a reduction in output of free fatty acids from adipose tissue (either directly or via stimulation of insulin secretion) and allowing the plasma level of free fatty acids to fall. As glucose is the fuel that is "burned last," it may be appreciated how adipose tissue is sensitive to a general deficiency in calorigenic substrates in the whole body through a mechanism based specifically on the availability of glucose. The combination of the effects of free fatty acids in sparing glucose utilization in muscle and heart and the effect of the spared glucose in inhibiting free fatty acid mobilization in adipose tissue has been called the "glucose-fatty acid cycle."

STARVATION

On high-carbohydrate diets, fatty acid oxidation is spared. As the animal passes from the fed to the fasting condition, glucose availability becomes less, liver glycogen being drawn upon in an attempt to maintain the blood glucose. The concentration of insulin in the blood decreases, and glucagon increases. As glucose utilization diminishes in adipose tissue and the inhibitory effect of insulin on lipolysis becomes less, fat is mobilized as free fatty acids and glycerol. The free fatty acids are transported to nonadipose tissues, where they are either oxidized or esterified. Glycerol joins the carbohydrate pool after activation to glycerol 3-phosphate, mainly in the liver and kidney. During this transition phase from the fully fed to the fully fasting state, endogenous glucose production (from amino acids and glycerol) does not keep pace with its utilization and oxidation, since the liver glycogen stores become depleted and blood glucose tends to fall. Thus, fat is mobilized at an ever-increasing rate, but in several hours the plasma free fatty acids and blood glucose stabilize at the fasting level (0.7–0.8 μmol/

mL and 60–70 mg/dL, respectively). At this point, it must be presumed that in the whole animal the supply of glucose balances the obligatory demands for glucose utilization and oxidation. This is achieved by the increased oxidation of free fatty acids and ketone bodies, sparing the nonobligatory oxidation of glucose. This fine balance is disturbed in conditions that demand more glucose or in which glucose utilization is impaired and which therefore lead to further mobilization of fat. The provision of carbohydrate by adipose tissue, in the form of **glycerol,** is an important function, for it is only this source of carbohydrate together with that provided by **gluconeogenesis from protein** that can supply the fasting organism with the glucose needed for those processes which must utilize glucose. In prolonged starvation in humans, gluconeogenesis from protein is diminished owing to reduced release of amino acids, particularly alanine, from muscle. This coincides with adaptation of the brain to replace approximately half of the glucose oxidized with ketone bodies.

A feedback mechanism for controlling free fatty acid output from adipose tissue in starvation may operate as a result of the action of ketone bodies and free fatty acids to directly stimulate the pancreas to produce insulin. Under most conditions, free fatty acids are mobilized in excess of oxidative requirements, since a large proportion are esterified, even during fasting. As the liver takes up and esterifies a considerable proportion of the free fatty acid output, it plays a regulatory role in removing excess free fatty acids from the circulation. When carbohydrate supplies are adequate, most of the influx is esterified and ultimately retransported from the liver as VLDL to be utilized by other tissues. However, in the face of an increased influx of free fatty acids, an alternative route, ketogenesis, is available that enables the liver to continue to retransport much of the influx of free fatty acids in a form which is readily utilized by extrahepatic tissues under all nutritional conditions.

Most of these principles are depicted in Fig 19–10. It will be noted that there is a carbohydrate cycle involving release of glycerol from adipose tissue and its conversion in the liver to glucose, followed by its transport back to adipose tissue to complete the cycle. The other cycle, a lipid cycle, involves release of free fatty acids by adipose tissue, its transport to and esterification in the liver, and retransport as VLDL back to adipose tissue. Disturbances in carbohydrate or lipid metabolism often involve these 2 interrelated cycles where they interact in adipose tissue and in the liver.

•   •   •

References

Cohen P: *Control of Enzyme Activity,* 2nd ed. Chapman & Hall, 1983.

Cohen P (editor): *Recently Discovered Systems of Enzyme Regulation by Reversible Phosphorylation.* Elsevier/North Holland, 1980.

Czech MP: Molecular basis of insulin action. *Annu Rev Biochem* 1977;**46:**359.

Davies DD (editor): *Rate Control of Biological Processes.* Cambridge Univ Press, 1973.

Denton RM, Hughes WA: Pyruvate dehydrogenase and the hormonal regulation of fat synthesis in mammalian tissues. *Int J Biochem* 1978;**9:**545.

Exton JH: Mechanisms involved in effects of catecholamines on liver carbohydrate metabolism. *Biochem Pharmacol* 1979; **28:**2237.

Hems DA: Hormonal control of glycogen-metabolizing enzymes in liver. *Biochem Soc Trans* 1978;**6:**33.

Hers HG: The control of glycogen metabolism in the liver. *Annu Rev Biochem* 1976;**45:**167.

Hers HG, Hue L: Gluconeogenesis and related aspects of glycolysis. *Annu Rev Biochem* 1983;**52:**617.

Hers HG, Van Schaftingen E: Fructose 2,6-bisphosphate two years after its discovery. *Biochem J* 1982;**206:**1.

Hue L, Van de Werve G (editors): *Short-term Regulation of Liver Metabolism.* Elsevier/North Holland, 1981.

Krebs EG, Beavo JA: Phosphorylation-dephosphorylation of enzymes. *Annu Rev Biochem* 1979;**48:**923.

Laker ME, Mayes PA: Investigations into the direct effects of insulin on hepatic ketogenesis, lipoprotein secretion and pyruvate dehydrogenase activity. *Biochim Biophys Acta* 1984; **795:**4.

Lin ECC: Glycerol utilization and its regulation in mammals. *Annu Rev Biochem* 1977;**46:**765.

Masoro EJ: Lipids and lipid metabolism. *Annu Rev Physiol* 1977;**39:**301.

Mayes PA, Laker ME: Regulation of ketogenesis in the liver. *Biochem Soc Trans* 1981;**9:**339.

McGarry JD, Foster DW: Regulation of hepatic fatty acid oxidation and ketone body production. *Annu Rev Biochem* 1980; **49:**395.

Newsholme EA, Start C: *Regulation in Metabolism.* Wiley, 1973.

Rennie MJ, Edwards RHT: Carbohydrate metabolism of skeletal muscle and its disorders. Page 1 in: *Carbohydrate Metabolism and Its Disorders.* Vol 3. Randle PJ, Steiner DF, Whelan WJ (editors). Academic Press, 1981.

Siess EA, Kientsch-Engel RI, Wieland OH: Concentration of free oxaloacetate in the mitochondrial compartment of isolated liver cells. *Biochem J* 1984;**218:**171.

Söling HD, Seufert CD (editors): *Biochemical and Clinical Aspects of Ketone Body Metabolism.* Thieme, 1978.

Söling HD, Willms B (editors): *Regulation of Gluconeogenesis.* Thieme, 1971.

Wakil SJ, Stoops JK, Joshi VC: Fatty acid synthesis and its regulation. *Annu Rev Biochem* 1983;**52:**537.

Biosynthesis of Amino Acids | 20

Victor W. Rodwell, PhD

AMINO ACID METABOLISM

Amino acid metabolism includes several major topics of medical interest—protein synthesis and degradation, conversion of the carbon skeletons of amino acids to amphibolic intermediates, urea synthesis, and formation of a variety of physiologically active compounds such as neurogenic amines (Fig 20–1).

We shall first consider the metabolic pathways and enzymic reactions by which amino acids are synthesized.

Viewed from a worldwide perspective, the supply of food for humans is limited more by the availability of reduced ("fixed") nitrogen in the form of ammonia or its derivatives than by the availability of any other nutrient. While in the Western world vast quantities of energy are consumed in the chemical reduction (in fertilizer factories) of N_2 to NH_3 (a quantity equivalent to 2 billion gallons of gasoline in the USA in 1970), the nitrogen economy of the planet as a whole depends on the ability of soil bacteria and plants to convert gaseous N_2 to a form utilizable by humans and other animals.

There are, for practical purposes, 20 amino acids present in mammalian proteins. If, during protein synthesis, a single one of these amino acids is missing, protein synthesis ceases. Since continual synthesis and degradation of proteins (protein turnover) is characteristic of all forms of life, the availability of α-amino acids in, for example, humans must reflect their distribution in human proteins. If not, protein synthesis becomes nutrient-restricted.

NUTRITIONALLY ESSENTIAL & NUTRITIONALLY NONESSENTIAL AMINO ACIDS

Some life forms (plants, many bacteria) can form all 20 amino acids from amphibolic intermediates. Others, including humans and other animals, can biosynthesize only about half of those required. The remainder, which must therefore be supplied by the diet, are termed **nutritionally essential** amino acids. Those that an organism can biosynthesize are termed **nutritionally nonessential.** A given amino acid may be nutritionally essential for one form of life but nutritionally nonessential for another.

Nutritional scientists frequently refer to nu-

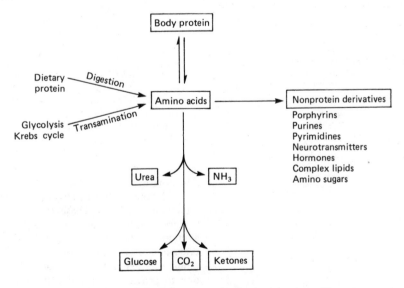

Figure 20–1. Overall sources and utilization of amino acids.

Table 20–1. Amino acid requirements of humans.

Nutritionally Essential	Nutritionally Nonessential
Arginine*	Alanine
Histidine*	Asparagine
Isoleucine	Aspartic acid
Leucine	Cysteine
Lysine	Glutamic acid
Methionine	Glutamine
Phenylalanine	Glycine
Threonine	Hydroxyproline†
Tryptophan	Proline
Valine	Serine
	Tyrosine

*"Nutritionally semiessential." Synthesized at rates inadequate to support growth of children.
†Not necessary for protein synthesis but formed during post-synthetic processing of collagen.

tritionally essential amino acids as "essential" or "indispensable" amino acids and to nutritionally nonessential amino acids as "nonessential" or "dispensable." While in a nutritional context these terms are correct, they obscure the biologically essential nature of all 20 amino acids. It might be argued that the nutritionally nonessential amino acids are more important to the cell than the nutritionally essential ones, since organisms (eg, humans) have evolved that lack the ability to manufacture the latter but not the former group.

The existence of nutritional requirements suggests that dependence on an external supply of a required intermediate can be of greater survival value than the ability to biosynthesize it. If a specific intermediate is present in the food, an organism that can synthesize it is reproducing and transferring to future generations genetic information of negative survival value. The survival value is negative rather than nil because ATP and nutrients are used to synthesize un-

Table 20–2. Enzymes required for the synthesis of amino acids from amphibolic intermediates.

Number of Enzymes Required to Synthesize:			
Nutritionally Essential		Nutritionally Nonessential	
Arg*	7	Ala	1
His	6	Asp	1
Thr	6	Asn†	1
Met	5 (4 shared)	Glu	1
Lys	8	Gln*	1
Ile	8 (6 shared)	Pro*	3
Val	1 (7 shared)	Ser	3
Leu	3 (7 shared)	Gly‡	1
Phe	10	Cys§	2
Trp	5 (8 shared)	Tyr‖	1
	59		15

*From Glu. †From Asp. ‡From Ser. §From Ser plus S²⁻ ‖From Phe.

necessary DNA. The number of enzymes required by prokaryotic cells to synthesize the nutritionally essential amino acids is large relative to the number of enzymes required to synthesize the nutritionally nonessential amino acids (Table 20–2). This suggests that there is a survival advantage in retaining the ability to manufacture "easy" amino acids while losing the ability to make "difficult" amino acids.

BIOSYNTHESIS OF NUTRITIONALLY NONESSENTIAL AMINO ACIDS

Nutritionally nonessential amino acids are formed either from amphibolic intermediates (eg, pyruvate, acetyl-CoA, citric acid cycle intermediates) or from other amino acids. In 3 instances (cysteine, tyrosine, and hydroxylysine), the precursor amino acids are themselves nutritionally essential. We shall consider first those amino acids formed from amphibolic intermediates and subsequently those formed from other amino acids.

NUTRITIONALLY NONESSENTIAL AMINO ACIDS FORMED FROM AMPHIBOLIC INTERMEDIATES

Alanine

Alanine is formed from pyruvate by transamination (Fig 20–2). For a detailed description of transamination, see Chapters 10 and 21.

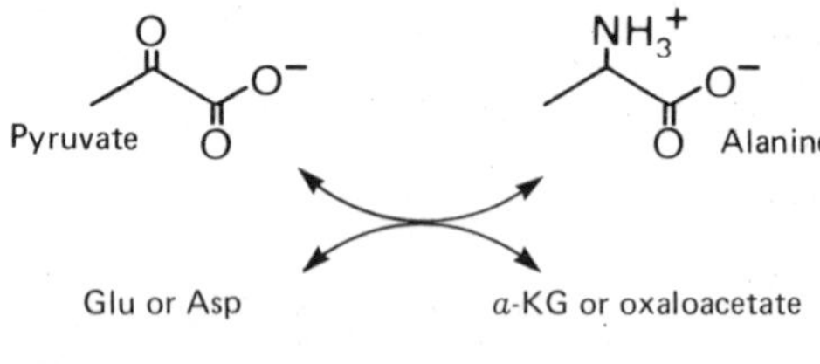

Figure 20–2. Formation of alanine by transamination of pyruvate. The amino donor may be glutamate or aspartate. The other product thus is α-ketoglutarate (α-KG) or oxaloacetate.

Glutamate

Glutamate is formed by the reaction catalyzed by L-glutamate dehydrogenase (Fig 20–3). Plants and bacteria synthesize amino acids from glucose plus ammonia. When cattle are fed diets rich in carbohydrate plus urea, rumen bacteria convert urea to ammonia and then utilize glutamate dehydrogenase reaction to provide the cattle with glutamate and other amino acids.

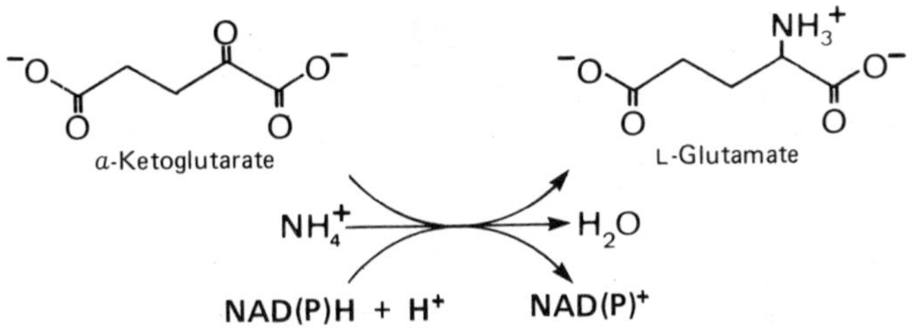

Figure 20-3. The glutamate dehydrogenase reaction. Reductive amination of α-ketoglutarate by NH_4^+ proceeds at the expense of NAD(P)H.

Aspartate

Aspartic acid is formed by transamination of oxaloacetate (Fig 20–2).

Glutamine

L-Glutamine and L-glutamate are of fundamental importance for amino acid biosynthesis in all forms of life. In plants, animals, and bacteria, synthesis of glutamine is catalyzed by glutamine synthase. In this reaction, NH_4^+ aminates glutamate in a reaction requiring ATP (Fig 20–4).

Asparagine

Biosynthesis of asparagine is catalyzed by asparagine synthase (Fig 20–5). The reaction resembles the glutamine synthase reaction (Fig 20–4). In both cases, synthesis of the amide bond requires the free acid (Asp or Glu), an amino donor, and MgATP. However, while ATP is converted to ADP + Pi in the glutamine synthase reaction, AMP + PPi are formed

in the reaction catalyzed by asparagine synthase. In mammalian systems, the amino donor probably is glutamine. In bacteria it is ammonia, and in plants the cyano group of β-cyanoalanine. Since pyrophosphatase catalyzes hydrolysis of PPi to 2 Pi (pyrophosphatases), the overall reaction

$$Asp + R-NH_3^+ + ATP \xrightarrow{Mg^{2+}} Asn + R + AMP + 2\ P_i$$

is more favored than that of glutamine synthesis by about 8 kcal/mol.

Serine

Two pathways for serine biosynthesis coexist in mammalian tissues. In both cases the carbon skeleton is provided by D-3-phosphoglycerate, an intermediate in glycolysis (see Chapter 14). One pathway uses nonphosphorylated intermediates and the other phosphorylated intermediates (Fig 20–6).

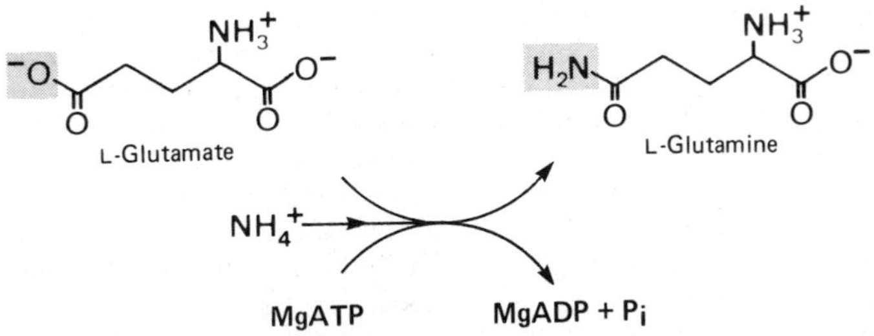

Figure 20-4. The glutamine synthase reaction.

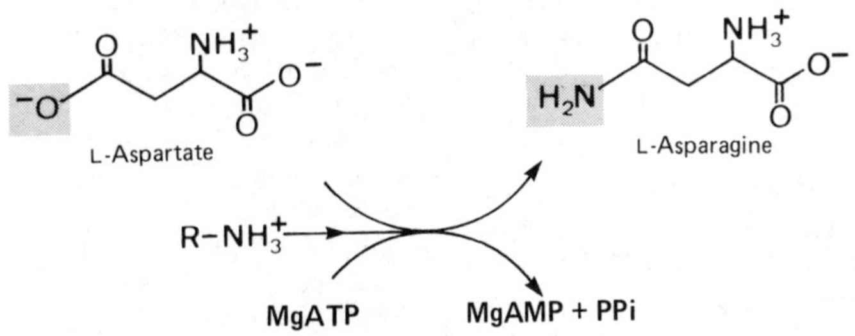

Figure 20-5. The asparagine synthase reaction. Note similarities to and differences from the glutamine synthase reaction (Fig 20–4). The nature of the amino donor (R—NH_3^+) differs depending on the life form considered.

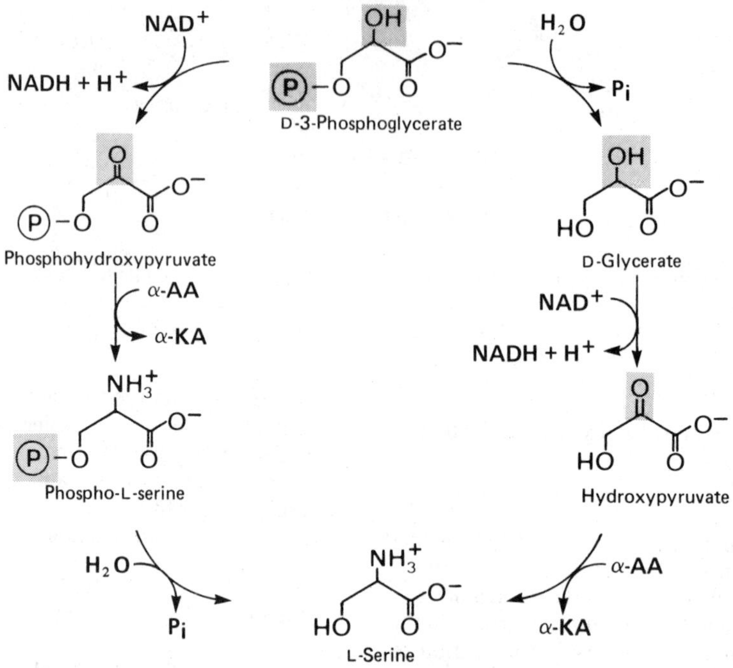

Figure 20–6. Serine biosynthesis via phosphorylated and nonphosphorylated intermediates. (α-AA, α-amino acids; α-KA, α-keto acids.)

Synthesis via phosphorylated intermediates involves oxidation of 3-phosphoglycerate to phosphohydroxypyruvate, transamination to phosphoserine, and hydrolytic removal of the phosphate catalyzed by a phosphatase. For synthesis via nonphosphorylated intermediates, phosphoglycerate is dephosphorylated to glycerate by a phosphatase, oxidized to hydroxypyruvate, and transaminated to L-serine. The pathway involving phosphorylated intermediates probably accounts for the majority of the serine synthesized by mammalian tissues, plants, and bacteria.

Glycine

Synthesis of glycine in mammalian tissues can occur in several ways. Liver cytosol contains glycine transaminases that catalyze the synthesis of glycine from glyoxylate and glutamate or alanine. Unlike most transaminase reactions, this strongly favors glycine synthesis. Two additional important mammalian routes for glycine formation are from choline (Fig 20–7) and from serine via the serine hydroxymethyltransferase reaction (Fig 20–8).

NUTRITIONALLY NONESSENTIAL AMINO ACIDS FORMED FROM OTHER NUTRITIONALLY NONESSENTIAL AMINO ACIDS

Proline

In mammals and some other life forms, proline is

formed from glutamate by reversal of the reactions of proline catabolism (Fig 20–9).

Hydroxyproline

Since proline serves as a precursor of hydroxyproline, proline and hydroxyproline belong to the glutamate family of amino acids. Although both 3- and 4-hydroxyprolines occur in mammalian tissues, little is known of the metabolic significance of 3-hydroxyproline (present in rat tail tendon and in the antibiotic telomycin). What follows refers solely to *trans*-4-hydroxyproline.

Hydroxyproline, like hydroxylysine, is almost exclusively associated with collagen, the most abundant protein of mammalian tissues. Collagen contains about one-third glycine and one-third proline and hydroxyproline. Hydroxyproline, which accounts for many of the amino acid residues of collagen, stabilizes the collagen triple helix to digestion by proteases. Unlike the hydroxyl groups of hydroxylysine, which serve as sites for attachment of galactosyl and glucosyl residues, the hydroxyl groups of collagen hydroxyproline are unsubstituted.

A unique feature of hydroxyproline and hydroxylysine metabolism is that the preformed amino acids, as they may occur in ingested food protein, are not incorporated into collagen. There is no tRNA capable of accepting hydroxyproline or hydroxylysine and inserting them into an elongating polypeptide chain. Dietary proline is, however, a precursor of collagen hydroxyproline, and dietary lysine a precursor of collagen hydroxylysine. Hydroxylation of proline or

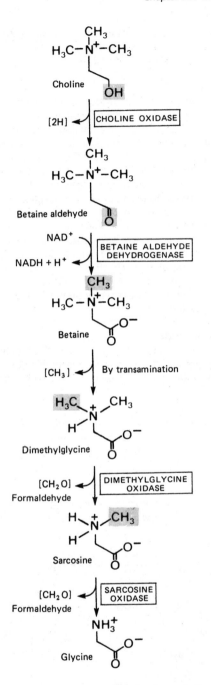

Figure 20–7. Formation of glycine from choline.

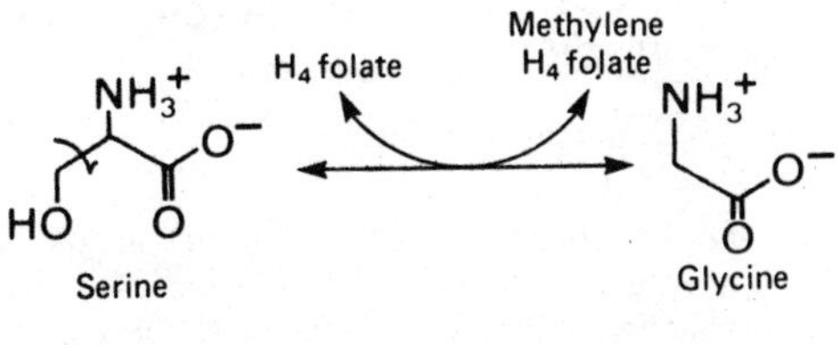

Figure 20–8. The serine hydroxymethyltransferase reaction. The reaction is freely reversible. (H_4folate, tetrahydrofolate.)

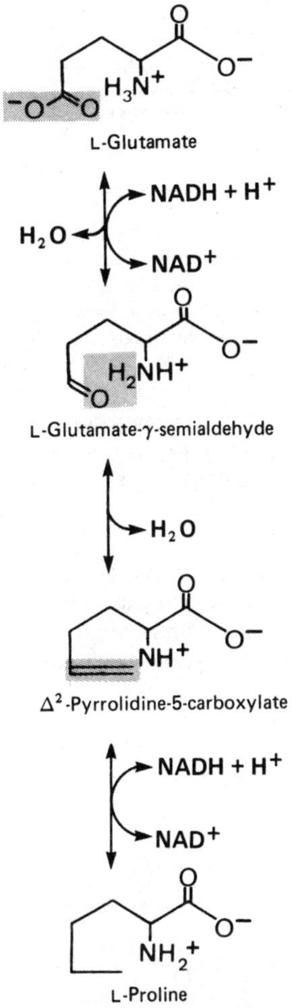

Figure 20–9. Biosynthesis of proline from glutamate by reversal of the reactions of proline catabolism.

lysine is catalyzed by prolyl hydroxylase or by lysyl hydroxylase, enzymes associated with the microsomal fraction of many tissues (skin, liver, lung, heart, skeletal muscle, and granulating wounds). These enzymes are peptidyl hydroxylases, since hydroxylation only occurs subsequent to incorporation of proline or lysine into polypeptide linkage (see Chapter 34).

Both hydroxylases are mixed function oxygenases that require, in addition to substrate, molecular O_2, ascorbate, Fe^{2+}, and α-ketoglutarate. Prolyl hydroxylase has been more extensively studied, but lysyl hydroxylase appears to be an entirely analogous enzyme. For every mole of proline hydroxylated, 1 mol of α-ketoglutarate is decarboxylated to succinate. During this process, one atom of molecular O_2 is incorporated into proline and one into succinate (Fig 20–10).

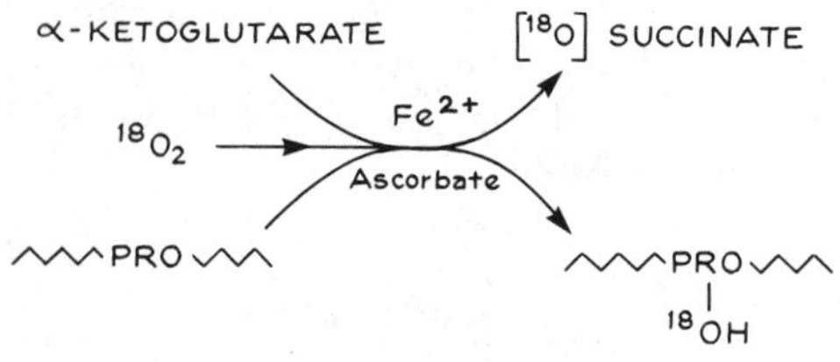

Figure 20–10. The proline hydroxylase reaction. The substrate is a proline-rich peptide. During the course of the reaction, molecular oxygen is incorporated into both succinate and proline (shown by the use of heavy oxygen, $^{18}O_2$).

NUTRITIONALLY NONESSENTIAL AMINO ACIDS FORMED FROM NUTRITIONALLY ESSENTIAL AMINO ACIDS

Cysteine

Cysteine, while not itself nutritionally essential, is formed from methionine (nutritionally essential) and serine (nutritionally nonessential). Methionine is first converted to homocysteine via S-adenosylmethionine

and S-adenosylhomocysteine (see Chapter 22). Conversion of homocysteine and serine to cysteine and homoserine is shown in Fig 20–11.

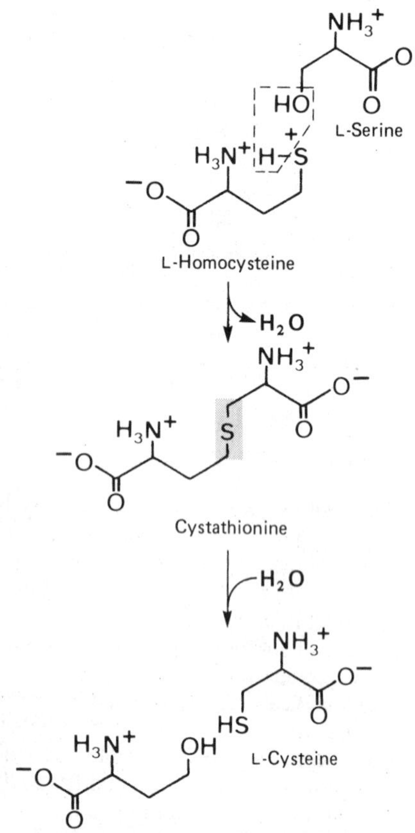

Tyrosine

Tyrosine is formed from phenylalanine by the reaction catalyzed by phenylalanine hydroxylase (Fig 20–12). Thus, whereas phenylalanine is a nutritionally essential amino acid, tyrosine is not—provided the diet contains adequate quantities of phenylalanine. The reaction is not reversible, so tyrosine cannot replace the nutritional requirement for phenylalanine. The **phenylalanine hydroxylase complex** is a mixed function oxygenase present in mammalian liver but absent from other tissues. The reaction involves incorporation of one atom of molecular oxygen into the para position of phenylalanine while the other atom is reduced, forming water (Fig 20–12). The reducing power, supplied ultimately by NADPH, is immediately provided as **tetrahydrobiopterin,** a pteridine resembling folic acid.

Hydroxylysine

5-Hydroxylysine (α,ϵ-diamino-δ-hydroxycaproate) is present in collagen but absent from most other mammalian proteins. Collagen hydroxylysine arises

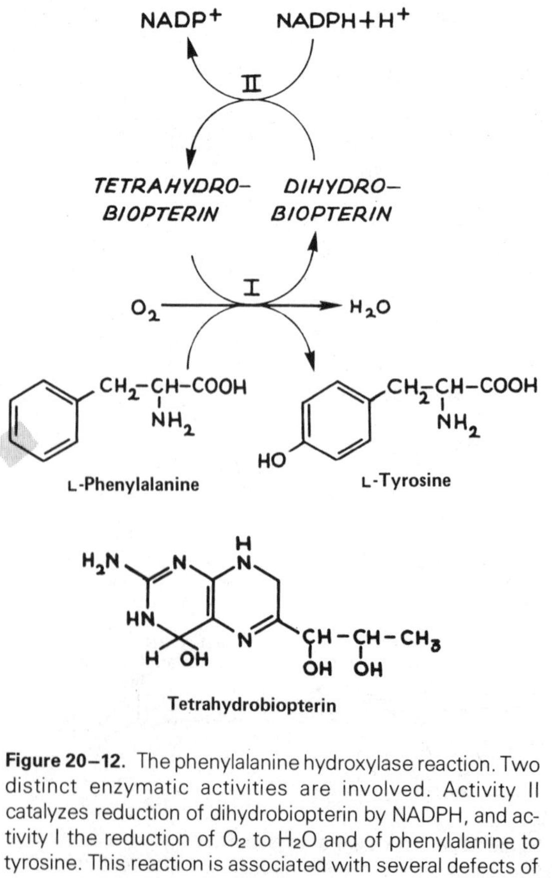

Figure 20–11. Conversion of homocysteine and serine to homoserine and cysteine. Note that while the sulfur of cysteine derives from methionine by transulfuration, the carbon skeleton is provided by serine.

Figure 20–12. The phenylalanine hydroxylase reaction. Two distinct enzymatic activities are involved. Activity II catalyzes reduction of dihydrobiopterin by NADPH, and activity I the reduction of O_2 to H_2O and of phenylalanine to tyrosine. This reaction is associated with several defects of phenylalanine metabolism discussed on p 306.

directly from dietary lysine, not dietary hydroxylysine. Before lysine is hydroxylated, it must first be incorporated into peptide linkage. Hydroxylation of the lysyl peptide is then catalyzed by lysyl hydroxylase, a mixed function oxidase analogous to prolyl hydroxylase (Fig 20–10).

BIOSYNTHESIS OF NUTRITIONALLY ESSENTIAL AMINO ACIDS

Biosynthesis of nutritionally essential amino acids by bacteria from glutamate, aspartate, or other amphibolic intermediates is outlined below. These reactions do not occur in mammalian tissues.

BIOSYNTHESIS OF NUTRITIONALLY ESSENTIAL AMINO ACIDS FROM GLUTAMATE

Arginine (Bacteria)

Arginine, a nutritionally essential amino acid for growing humans, can be synthesized by rats but not in quantities sufficient to permit normal growth. Microorganisms biosynthesize arginine from glutamate, via N-acetylated intermediates (Fig 20–13). One in-

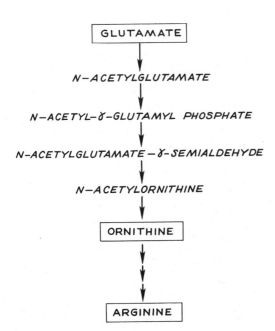

Figure 20–13. Biosynthesis of L-arginine from L-glutamate via acylated intermediates in bacteria. The reactions from glutamate to ornithine do not occur in mammalian tissues. The reactions leading from ornithine to arginine are those of the urea cycle (see Chapter 21) and are common to both bacteria and mammals.

termediate, N-acetylglutamate-γ-semialdehyde, is also a precursor of proline in bacteria. In humans and other animals, however, proline is formed from glutamate.

BIOSYNTHESIS OF NUTRITIONALLY ESSENTIAL AMINO ACIDS FROM ASPARTATE

Aspartate is the precursor of a family of amino acids that includes lysine, methionine, threonine, and isoleucine (Fig 9–6). The regulatory implications of this relationship in bacteria are discussed in Chapter 9.

Methionine & Threonine (Bacteria)

Following conversion of aspartate-β-semialdehyde to homoserine, the pathways for methionine and threonine biosynthesis diverge. The interconversion of homoserine and methionine is discussed in Chapter 22.

Lysine (Bacteria)

Bacteria form lysine from aspartate-β-semialdehyde via condensation with pyruvate. The dihydropicolinate formed serves, in addition, a role in spore formation in certain spore-forming bacteria, and the diaminopimelate performs a role in bacterial cell wall synthesis.

Isoleucine

Isoleucine is considered below with other branched-chain amino acids.

BIOSYNTHESIS OF NUTRITIONALLY ESSENTIAL AMINO ACIDS FROM AMPHIBOLIC INTERMEDIATES

Lysine (Bacteria & Yeast)

Lysine biosynthesis in yeast starts from α-ketoglutarate and acetyl-CoA and utilizes a series of reactions analogous to those of the citric acid cycle but catalyzed by a set of enzymes with slightly different substrate specificities.

Leucine, Valine, & Isoleucine

While leucine, valine, and isoleucine are all nutritionally essential amino acids for humans and other higher animals, mammalian tissues do contain transaminases that reversibly catalyze interconversion of all 3 amino acids with their corresponding α-keto acids (see Chapter 22). This explains the ability of the appropriate keto acids to replace their amino acids in the diet.

Histidine

Histidine, like arginine, is nutritionally semiessential. Adult humans and adult rats have been maintained in nitrogen balance for short periods in the absence of histidine. The growing animal does, however, require histidine in the diet. If studies were to be carried on for longer periods, it is probable that a requirement for histidine in adult human subjects would also be elicited.

Biosynthesis starts with 7-pyrophosphoribosyl-5-phosphate (PPriboseP), which condenses with ATP, forming N'-(5-phosphoribosyl)-ATP. This reaction thus closely resembles the initial reaction of purine biosynthesis.

• • •

References

Biosynthesis

Burnstein P: The biosynthesis of collagen. *Annu Rev Biochem* 1974;**43**:567.

Cardinale GJ, Udenfriend S: Prolyl hydroxylase. *Adv Enzymol* 1974;**41**:245.

Greenberg DM, Rodwell VW: Biosynthesis of amino acids and related compounds. Pages 237 and 317 in: *Metabolic Pathways*. Vol 3. Academic Press, 1969.

Meister A: *Biochemistry of the Amino Acids,* 2nd ed. Vol 2. Academic Press, 1965.

Truffa-Bachi P, Cohen GN: Some aspects of amino acid biosynthesis in microorganisms. *Annu Rev Biochem* 1968;**37**:79.

Regulation of Biosynthesis

Calvo JM, Fink GR: Regulation of biosynthetic pathways in bacteria. *Annu Rev Biochem* 1971;**40**:943.

Cohen GN: The aspartokinases and homoserine dehydrogenases of *Escherichia coli. Curr Top Cell Regul* 1969;**1**:183.

Feigelson P: Studies on the allosteric regulation of tryptophan oxygenase: Structure and function. *Adv Enzyme Regul* 1968;**7**:119.

Knox WE: The regulation of tryptophan pyrrolase activity by tryptophan. *Adv Enzyme Regul* 1966;**4**:287.

Knox WE, Greengard O: The regulation of some enzymes of nitrogen metabolism: An introduction to enzyme physiology. *Adv Enzyme Regul* 1965;**3**:247.

Schimke RT: On the roles of synthesis and degradation in regulation of enzyme levels in mammalian tissues. *Curr Top Cell Regul* 1969;**1**:77.

Schimke RT, Doyle D: Control of enzyme levels in animal tissues. *Annu Rev Biochem* 1970;**39**:929.

Tyler B: Regulation of the assimilation of nitrogen compounds. *Annu Rev Biochem* 1978;**47**:1127.

Umbarger HE: Amino acid biosynthesis and its regulation. *Annu Rev Biochem* 1978;**47**:533.

Wood WA: Allosteric L-threonine dehydrases of microorganisms. *Curr Top Cell Regul* 1969;**1**:161.

Catabolism of Amino Acid Nitrogen | 21

Victor W. Rodwell, PhD

We shall consider how nitrogen is removed from amino acids and converted to urea and the medical problems that arise when there are defects in these reactions.

OVERALL VIEW

In a healthy human adult, normal protein turnover amounts to 1–2% of total body protein per day. This protein turnover results predominantly from degradation of muscle protein to amino acids. However, approximately 75–80% of the released amino acids are reutilized for new protein synthesis. The remainder are metabolized to nitrogenous waste and glucose, ketones, and/or carbon dioxide (Figs 20–1 and 21–1). The net daily loss of protein amounts to 30–40 g. Since approximately 16% of the atomic mass of proteins is nitrogen, 5–7 g of nitrogen is lost per day. To maintain a healthy steady state, the average adult requires 30–60 g of protein or the equivalent in amino acids per day, but the **quality is important.** Protein quality here refers to the concentration of essential amino acids in a food relative to their concentrations in protein molecules being synthesized. Regardless of their source, amino acids that are not immediately incorporated into new protein are rapidly degraded; ie, **excess amino acids are not stored.** Consumption of excess amino acids thus is wasteful, since this surplus is catabolized to form energy, a function that carbohydrates and lipids can serve at a lower cost. This lower cost reflects the high energy requirement for fixing nitrogen.

A diet adequate in energy but limited in protein, either qualitatively or quantitatively, leads to the clinical condition known as **kwashiorkor.** The clinical deficiency of both energy and protein (protein-energy malnutrition) is called **marasmus.**

Amino Acid Catabolism

Amino acids in excess of needs for protein biosynthesis cannot be stored, nor are they excreted as such. Amino groups of surplus amino acids are removed by transamination or oxidative deamination, and the carbon skeletons are converted to amphibolic intermediates. Some organisms (fishes) excrete free ammonia as the end product of N catabolism and are referred to as **ammonotelic.** Some organisms (birds and amphibians) excrete uric acid instead and are referred to as **uricotelic,** and some organisms (mammals) excrete urea and are referred to as **ureotelic.**

Ammonia is toxic to the central nervous system by mechanisms that are not fully understood but likely involve the reversal of glutamate dehydrogenase (discussed below) and the consequent depletion of α-ketoglutarate, a necessary intermediate in the citric acid cycle. **Uric acid** and its salts are highly **insoluble** and precipitate in tissues and fluids when their concentrations exceed several milligrams per deciliter. Therefore, neither of these end products of nitrogen metabolism is well tolerated by higher organisms. Accordingly, humans and other mammals have evolved with the capacity to convert their nitrogenous waste to the **highly soluble, nontoxic compound urea.**

$$H_2N \overset{\overset{\textstyle O}{\|}}{-\!C\!-} NH_2$$

Urea

The biosynthesis of urea will be divided for discussion into 4 stages: (1) transamination, (2) oxidative deamination, (3) ammonia transport, and (4) reactions of the urea cycle. Figure 21–2 relates these areas to overall catabolism of amino acid nitrogen. Although each stage also plays a role in amino acid biosynthesis

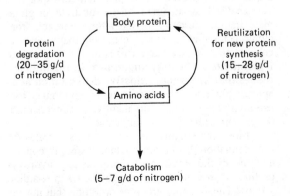

Figure 21–1. Quantitative relationships for protein and amino acid turnover.

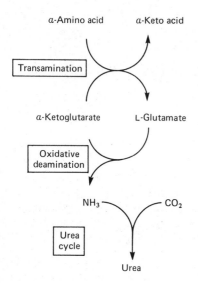

Figure 21–2. Overall flow of nitrogen in amino acid catabolism. Although the reactions shown are reversible, they are represented as being unidirectional to emphasize the direction of metabolic flow in mammalian amino acid catabolism.

(see Chapter 20), what follows is discussed from the viewpoint of amino acid catabolism. Vertebrates other than mammals share all features of this scheme except urea synthesis.

TRANSAMINATION

Transamination, catalyzed by enzymes termed **transaminases** or **aminotransferases,** interconverts a pair of amino acids and a pair of keto acids. These generally are α-amino and α-keto acids (Fig 21–3).

Pyridoxal phosphate forms an essential part of the active site of transaminases and of many other en-zymes with amino acid substrates. In all pyridoxal phosphate–dependent reactions of amino acids, the initial step is formation of an enzyme-bound Schiff base intermediate (Fig 10–16). This intermediate, stabilized by interaction with a cationic region of the active site, can be rearranged in ways that include release of a keto acid with formation of enzyme-bound pyridoxamine phosphate. The bound amino form of the coenzyme can then form an analogous Schiff base intermediate with a keto acid. During transamination, bound coenzyme thus serves as a carrier of amino groups (Figs 10–17 and 10–18). Since the equilibrium constant for most transaminase reactions is close to unity, transamination is a freely reversible process. This permits transaminases to function both in amino acid catabolism and biosynthesis.

Two transaminases, alanine-pyruvate trans-aminase (**alanine transaminase**) and glutamate-α-ketoglutarate transaminase (**glutamate transaminase),** present in most mammalian tissues, catalyze transfer of amino groups from most amino acids to form alanine (from pyruvate) or glutamate (from α-ketoglutarate) (Fig 21–4).

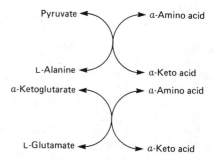

Figure 21–4. Alanine *(top)* and glutamate *(bottom)* transaminases.

Each transaminase is specific for the specified pair of amino and keto acids as one pair of substrates but nonspecific for the other pair, which may be any of a wide variety of amino acids and their corresponding keto acids. Since alanine is also a substrate for gluta-mate transaminase, all of the amino nitrogen from amino acids that can undergo transamination can be concentrated in glutamate. This is important, because **L-glutamate is the only amino acid in mammalian tissues that undergoes oxidative deamination** at an appreciable rate. The formation of ammonia from α-amino groups thus occurs mainly via conversion to the α-amino nitrogen of L-glutamate.

Most (but not all) amino acids are substrates for transamination. Exceptions include lysine, threonine, and the cyclic imino acids, proline and hydroxy-proline. Transamination is not restricted to α-amino groups. The δ-amino group of ornithine (but not the ε-amino group of lysine) is readily transaminated, forming glutamate γ-semialdehyde (Fig 22–3). Serum

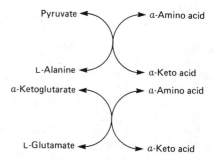

Figure 21–3. Transamination. The reaction is shown for 2 α-amino and 2 α-keto acids. Non–α-amino or carbonyl groups also participate in transamination, although this is relatively uncommon. The reaction is freely reversible with an equilibrium constant of about 1.

levels of transaminases are elevated in some disease states (see Chapter 8).

OXIDATIVE DEAMINATION

Oxidative conversion of many amino acids to their corresponding α-keto acids occurs in mammalian liver and kidney. Although most of the activity toward L-α-amino acids is due to the coupled action of transaminases plus L-**glutamate dehydrogenase**, both L- and D-amino acid oxidase activities occur in mammalian liver and kidney tissue and are widely distributed in other animals and microorganisms. It must be noted, however, that the physiologic function of L- and D-amino acid oxidase of mammalian tissue is not known.

Amino acid oxidases are **auto-oxidizable flavoproteins;** ie, the reduced FMN or FAD is reoxidized directly by molecular oxygen, forming hydrogen peroxide (H_2O_2) without participation of cytochromes or other electron carriers (Fig 21–5). The toxic product H_2O_2 is then split to O_2 and H_2O by **catalase,** which occurs widely in tissues, especially liver. Although the amino acid oxidase reactions are reversible, if catalase is absent the α-keto acid product is nonenzymically decarboxylated by H_2O_2, forming a carboxylic acid with one less carbon atom. It is doubtful, however, whether this decarboxylation occurs to any great extent in intact human tissues.

In the amino acid oxidase reactions (Fig 21–5), the amino acid is first dehydrogenated by the flavoprotein of the oxidase, forming an α-imino acid. This spontaneously adds water, then decomposes to the corresponding α-keto acid with loss of the α-imino nitrogen as ammonium ion.

Mammalian L-amino acid oxidase, an FMN-flavoprotein, is restricted to kidney and liver tissue. Its activity is quite low, and it is essentially without activity toward glycine or the L-isomers of dicarboxylic or β-hydroxy-α-amino acids. It thus is not likely that this enzyme fulfills a major role in mammalian amino acid catabolism.

Mammalian D-amino acid oxidase, an FAD-flavoprotein of broad substrate specificity, occurs in the liver and kidney tissue of most mammals. D-Asparagine and D-glutamine are not oxidized, and glycine and the D-isomers of the acidic and basic amino acids are poor substrates. The physiologic significance of this enzyme in mammals is not known.

L-Glutamate Dehydrogenase

The amino groups of most amino acids ultimately are transferred to α-ketoglutarate by transamination, forming L-glutamate (Fig 21–2). Release of this nitrogen as ammonia is catalyzed by L-**glutamate dehydrogenase,** an enzyme of high activity widely distributed in mammalian tissues (Fig 21–6). Liver glutamate dehydrogenase is a regulated enzyme whose activity is affected by allosteric modifiers such as ATP, GTP, and NADH, which inhibit the enzyme, and ADP, which activates the enzyme. Certain hormones appear also to influence glutamate dehydrogenase activity in vitro.

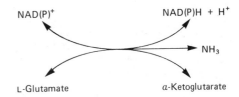

Figure 21–6. The L-glutamate dehydrogenase reaction. NAD(P)$^+$ means that either NAD$^+$ or NADP$^+$ can serve as cosubstrate. The reaction is reversible, but the equilibrium constant favors glutamate formation.

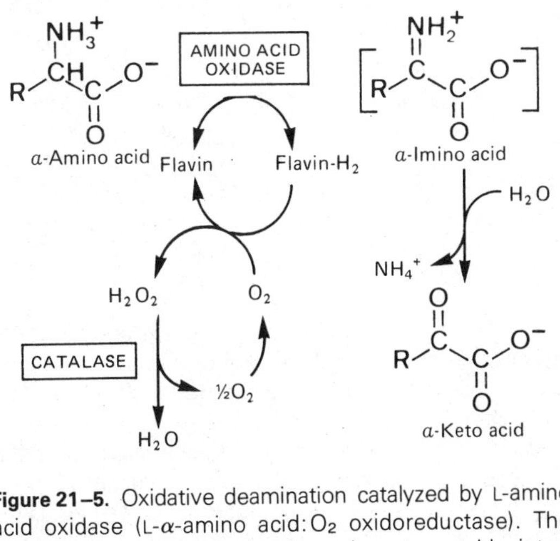

Glutamate dehydrogenase uses either NAD$^+$ or NADP$^+$ as cosubstrate. The reaction is reversible and functions both in amino acid catabolism and biosynthesis. It therefore functions not only to funnel nitrogen from glutamate to urea (catabolism) but also to catalyze **amination** of α-ketoglutarate by free ammonia (see Chapter 20).

FORMATION OF AMMONIA*

In addition to ammonia formed in the tissues, a considerable quantity is produced by intestinal bacteria from dietary protein and from urea present in fluids secreted into the gastrointestinal tract. This ammonia is absorbed from the intestine into the portal venous blood, which characteristically contains higher levels

Figure 21–5. Oxidative deamination catalyzed by L-amino acid oxidase (L-α-amino acid: O_2 oxidoreductase). The α-imino acid, shown in brackets, is not a stable intermediate.

*Present at physiologic pH almost exclusively as ammonium ion, NH_4^+.

of ammonia than does systemic blood. Under normal circumstances, the liver promptly removes the ammonia from the portal blood, so that blood leaving the liver (and indeed all of the peripheral blood) is virtually ammonia-free. This is essential, since even minute quantities of ammonia are toxic to the central nervous system. The symptoms of **ammonia intoxication** include a peculiar flapping tremor, slurring of speech, blurring of vision, and, in severe cases, coma and death. These symptoms resemble those of the syndrome of hepatic coma which occurs when blood and, presumably, brain ammonia levels are elevated. Ammonia intoxication is assumed to be a factor in the etiology of hepatic coma. Therefore, treatment includes measures designed to reduce blood ammonia levels.

With severely impaired hepatic function or development of collateral communications between the portal and systemic veins (as may occur in cirrhosis), portal blood may bypass the liver. Ammonia may thus rise to toxic levels in the systemic blood. Surgically produced shunting procedures (Eck fistula, or other forms of portacaval shunts) are also conducive to ammonia intoxication, particularly after ingestion of protein or after gastrointestinal hemorrhage, which provides blood proteins to colonic bacteria.

The ammonia content of the blood in renal veins exceeds that in renal arteries, indicating that the kidneys produce ammonia and add it to the blood. However, the excretion into the urine of the ammonia produced by renal tubular cells constitutes a far more significant aspect of renal ammonia metabolism. Ammonia production, an important renal tubular mechanism for regulation of acid-base balance and conservation of cations, is markedly increased in metabolic acidosis and depressed in alkalosis. This ammonia is derived, not from urea, but from intracellular amino acids, particularly glutamine. Ammonia release is catalyzed by renal **glutaminase** (Fig 21–7).

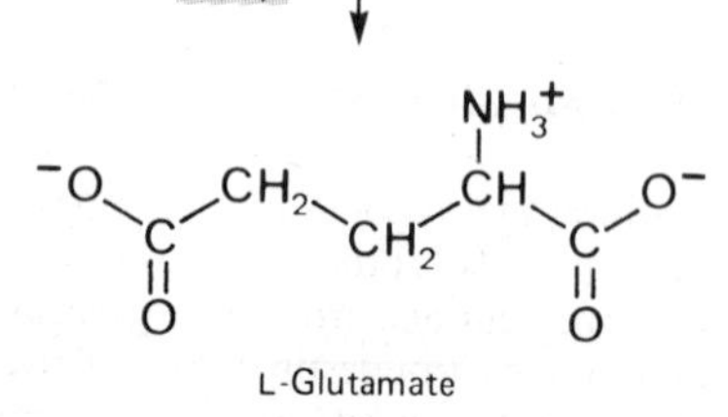

TRANSPORT OF AMMONIA

Although ammonia may be excreted as ammonium salts—particularly in metabolic acidosis—the vast majority is excreted as urea, the principal nitrogenous component of urine. Ammonia, constantly produced in the tissues but present only in traces in peripheral blood (10–20 μg/dL), is rapidly removed from the circulation by the liver and converted to glutamate, to glutamine, or to urea. The trace levels of ammonia in blood contrast sharply with the more considerable quantities of free amino acids, particularly glutamine (Table 21–1).

Table 21–1. Mean concentrations of free amino acids in blood plasma of newborn infants and adults (expressed as mg/dL).*

Amino Acid	Newborn	Adult
Alanine	2.9	3.1
a-Amino-n-butyric acid	0.15	0.17
Arginine	0.94	1.4
Asparagine	0.6	0.6
Aspartic acid	0.11	0.22
Citrulline	0.28	0.53
Cystine	1.5	1.8
Glutamic acid	0.76	0.86
Glutamine	11.2	8.3
Glycine	2.6	1.7
Histidine	1.2	1.2
Hydroxyproline	0.42	. . .
Isoleucine	0.52	0.71
Leucine	0.95	1.32
Lysine	2.9	2.5
Methionine	0.44	0.32
Ornithine	1.2	0.92
Phenylalanine	1.3	0.95
Proline	2.1	2.7
Serine	1.7	1.2
Taurine	1.8	0.83
Threonine	2.6	1.9
Tryptophan	0.65	0.98
Tyrosine	1.3	0.91
Valine	1.6	2.0

*Modified from Dickinson JC, Rosenblum H, Hamilton PB: Ion exchange chromatography of the free amino acids in the plasma of the newborn infant. *Pediatrics* 1965;**36**:2.

L-Glutamine

L-Glutamate

Figure 21–7. The glutaminase reaction proceeds essentially irreversibly in the direction of glutamate and NH$_4^+$ formation. Note that the amide nitrogen, not the α-amino nitrogen, is removed.

Removal of ammonia via **glutamate dehydrogenase** was mentioned above. Formation of glutamine is catalyzed by **glutamine synthase** (Fig 21–8), a mitochondrial enzyme present in highest quantities in renal tissue. Synthesis of the amide bond of glutamine is accomplished at the expense of hydrolysis of one equivalent of ATP to ADP and P$_i$. The reaction is thus strongly favored in the direction of glutamine synthesis (see also Chapter 20).

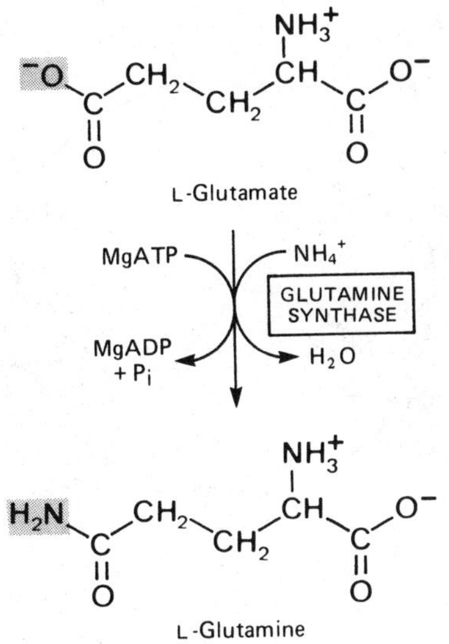

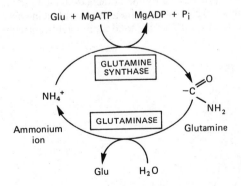

Figure 21–8. The glutamine synthase reaction. The reaction strongly favors glutamine synthesis.

glutaminase have both been investigated as antitumor agents, since certain tumors exhibit abnormally high requirements for glutamine and asparagine.

Whereas in brain the major mechanism for removal of ammonia is glutamine formation, in the liver the most important pathway is urea formation. Brain tissue can form urea, although this does not play a significant role in ammonia removal. Formation of glutamine in the brain must be preceded by synthesis of glutamate in the brain, because the supply of blood glutamate is inadequate in the presence of high levels of blood ammonia. The immediate precursor of glutamate is α-ketoglutarate. Thus, formation of glutamine from ammonia would rapidly deplete citric acid cycle intermediates unless they could be replaced by CO_2 fixation with conversion of pyruvate to oxaloacetate (see Chapter 14). A significant fixation of CO_2 into amino acids does indeed occur in the brain, presumably by way of the citric acid cycle, and after infusion of ammonia more oxaloacetate is diverted to the synthesis of glutamine (rather than to aspartate) via α-ketoglutarate.

Liberation of the amide nitrogen of glutamine as ammonia occurs, not by reversal of the glutamine synthase reaction, but by hydrolytic removal of ammonia catalyzed by **glutaminase** (Fig 21–7). The glutaminase reaction, unlike the glutamine synthase reaction, does not involve adenine nucleotides, strongly favors glutamate formation, and does not function in glutamine synthesis. Glutamine synthase and glutaminase thus catalyze interconversion of free ammonium ion and glutamine (Fig 21–9) in a manner reminiscent of the interconversion of glucose and glucose 6-phosphate by glucokinase and glucose 6-phosphatase (see Chapter 14).

A reaction analogous to that catalyzed by glutaminase is catalyzed by **L-asparaginase** of animal, plant, and microbial tissue. Asparaginase and

INTERORGAN AMINO ACID EXCHANGE IN THE POSTABSORPTIVE STATE

The maintenance of steady-state concentrations of circulating plasma amino acids between meals (eg, after fasting overnight following supper) depends upon the net balance between release from endogenous protein stores and utilization by various tissues. Muscle accounts for the generation of greater than 50% of the total body pool of free amino acids, while liver is the site of the urea cycle enzymes necessary for disposal of nitrogenous waste. Thus, muscle and liver play a major role in determining the circulating levels and the turnover of amino acids.

Muscle

Alanine and glutamine account for more than 50% of the total α-amino acid nitrogen **released** from muscle tissue. In contrast to the significant output of α-amino acids, muscle consistently takes up small quantities of serine, cysteine, and glutamate from the circulation.

Liver & Gut

The liver and gut (the splanchnic tissues) consistently **take up** from the plasma large quantities of alanine and glutamine, the predominant amino acids released by muscle. The liver is the primary site of uptake of alanine, and the gut is the site of utilization of glutamine. In the gut, the majority of the amino groups of glutamine are released from that tissue as alanine or free ammonia. Serine is extracted by these splanchnic tissues as well as by muscle.

Kidney

The kidney is the major source of release of

Figure 21–9. Interconversion of ammonia and of glutamine catalyzed by glutamine synthase and glutaminase. Both reactions are strongly favored in the directions indicated by the arrows. Glutaminase thus serves solely for glutamine deamidation and glutamine synthase solely for synthesis of glutamine from glutamate. (Glu, glutamate.)

serine; in addition, the kidney releases small but significant quantities of alanine. The kidney takes up glutamine, proline, and glycine from the circulation.

Thus, in general, there is a fairly close correspondence between the output of most amino acids from peripheral muscle and their uptake by the splanchnic tissues.

Brain

The uptake of valine by the brain exceeds that of all other amino acids, and the capacity of the rat brain to oxidize the branched-chain amino acids (leucine, isoleucine, and valine) is at least 4-fold greater than that of muscle and liver. Although in the postabsorptive state significant quantities of these branched-chain amino acids are released from muscle, they are not extracted by liver, and thus it is likely that the brain is the primary site of utilization of these amino acids.

Fig 21–10 summarizes the postabsorptive state. Free amino acids, particularly alanine and glutamine, are released from muscle into the circulation. Alanine, which appears to be the vehicle of nitrogen transport in the plasma, is extracted primarily by the liver. Glutamine is extracted by the gut and the kidney, both of which convert a significant portion to alanine. Glutamine also serves as a source of ammonia for excretion by the kidney. The kidney provides a major source of serine for uptake by peripheral tissues, including liver and muscle. Branched-chain amino acids, particularly valine, are released by muscle and taken up predominantly by brain.

Alanine serves as a key protein-derived glucose precursor, ie, a key **gluconeogenic amino acid** (Fig 21–11). In the liver, the rate of glucose synthesis from alanine and serine is far higher than that observed from all other amino acids. The capacity of the liver for gluconeogenesis from alanine is enormous; it does not reach saturation until the alanine concentration is 9 mmol/L, some 20–30 times its physiologic level. The predominance of alanine in the outflow of α-amino acids from muscle does not result from its high alanine content. Alanine makes up no more than 7–10% of muscle proteins but accounts for at least 30% of the net outflow of α-amino acid from muscle to the splanchnic

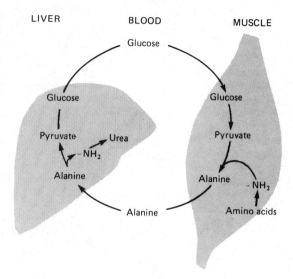

Figure 21–11. The glucose-alanine cycle. Alanine is synthesized in muscle by transamination of glucose-derived pyruvate, released into the bloodstream, and taken up by the liver. In the liver, the carbon skeleton of alanine is reconverted to glucose and released into the bloodstream, where it is available for uptake by muscle and resynthesis of alanine. (Reproduced, with permission, from Felig P: Amino acid metabolism in man. *Annu Rev Biochem* 1975;**44**:938. Copyright © 1975 by Annual Reviews, Inc.) .

tissues. Instead, alanine appears to be **synthesized in muscle** by transamination of pyruvate derived from glucose by glycolysis.

INTERORGAN AMINO ACID EXCHANGE IN THE FED STATE

Following the ingestion of a protein-rich meal, the splanchnic tissues release a large quantity of amino acids, predominantly the branched-chain amino acids (Fig 21–12). Valine, isoleucine, and leucine account for at least 60% of the total amino acids entering the

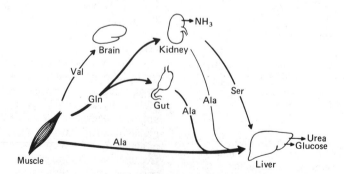

Figure 21–10. Interorgan amino acid exchange in normal postabsorptive humans. The key role of alanine in amino acid output from muscle and gut and uptake by the liver is shown. (Reproduced, with permission, from Felig P: Amino acid metabolism in man. *Annu Rev Biochem* 1975;**44**:937. Copyright © 1975 by Annual Reviews, Inc.)

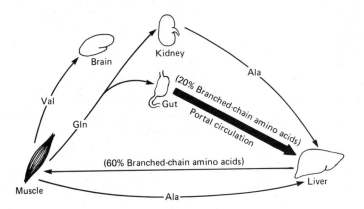

Figure 21–12. Summary of amino acid exchange between organs immediately after feeding.

systemic circulation (as opposed to the portal circulation), even though they make up only 20% of the total amino acids in a lean protein meal. Concomitant with the release of amino acids from the splanchnic tissues following a meal, the peripheral muscles extract amino acids, predominantly the branched-chain amino acids. Amino acid uptake by muscle tissue in the first hour following a meal consists of at least 50% branched-chain amino acids. Two to three hours after the meal, 90–100% of the amino acids taken up by peripheral tissues are the branched-chain amino acids. The branched-chain amino acids, which are also oxidized in muscle in response to feeding, probably serve as the major donors of amino groups for the transamination of pyruvate to alanine.

Thus, the branched-chain amino acids have a special role in nitrogen metabolism, both in the fasting state, when they provide the brain with an energy source, and after feeding, when they are extracted predominantly by muscles, having been spared by the liver. In muscle, they seem to provide an important source of energy as well as of nitrogen.

UREA SYNTHESIS

Overall View

A moderately active man consuming about 300 g of carbohydrate, 100 g of fat, and 100 g of protein daily must excrete about 16.5 g of nitrogen daily. Ninety-five percent is eliminated by the kidneys and the remaining 5% in the feces. The **major pathway of nitrogen excretion in humans is as urea** synthesized in the liver, released into the blood, and cleared by the kidney. In humans eating an occidental diet, urea constitutes 80–90% of the nitrogen excreted.

Reactions of the Urea Cycle

The reactions and intermediates in biosynthesis of 1 mol of urea from 1 mol each of ammonium ion, of carbon dioxide (activated with Mg^{2+} and ATP), and of the α-amino nitrogen of aspartate are shown in Fig

21–13. The overall process requires 3 mol of ATP (2 of which are converted to ADP + P_i and 1 to AMP + PP_i) and the successive participation of 5 enzymes catalyzing the numbered reactions of Fig 21–13. Of the 6 amino acids involved in urea synthesis, one (N-acetylglutamate) functions as an enzyme activator rather than as an intermediate. The remaining 5—aspartate, arginine, ornithine, citrulline, and argininosuccinate—all function as carriers of atoms which ultimately become urea. Two (aspartate and arginine) occur in proteins, while the remaining 3 (ornithine, citrulline, and argininosuccinate) do not. The major metabolic role of these latter 3 amino acids in mammals is urea synthesis. Note that urea formation is in part a **cyclical process.** The ornithine used in reaction 2 is regenerated in reaction 5. There is thus no net loss or gain of ornithine, citrulline, argininosuccinate, or arginine during urea synthesis; however, ammonium ion, CO_2, ATP, and aspartate are consumed.

Reaction 1: Synthesis of carbamoyl phosphate. Condensation of 1 mol each of ammonium ion, carbon dioxide, and phosphate (derived from ATP) to form carbamoyl phosphate is catalyzed by **carbamoyl phosphate synthase,** an enzyme present in liver **mitochondria** of all ureotelic organisms, including humans. The 2 mol of ATP hydrolyzed during this reaction provide the driving force for synthesis of 2 covalent bonds—the amide bond and the mixed carboxylic acid–phosphoric acid anhydride bond of carbamoyl phosphate. In addition to Mg^{2+}, a dicarboxylic acid, preferably N-acetylglutamate, is required. The exact role of N-acetylglutamate is not known with certainty. Its presence brings about a profound conformational change in the structure of carbamoyl phosphate synthase that exposes certain sulfhydryl groups, conceals others, and affects the affinity of the enzyme for ATP.

Reaction 2: Synthesis of citrulline. Transfer of a carbamoyl moiety from carbamoyl phosphate to ornithine, forming citrulline + P_i, is catalyzed by **L-ornithine transcarbamoylase** of liver mitochondria. The reaction is highly specific for ornithine, and the equilibrium strongly favors citrulline synthesis.

Reaction 3: Synthesis of argininosuccinate. In

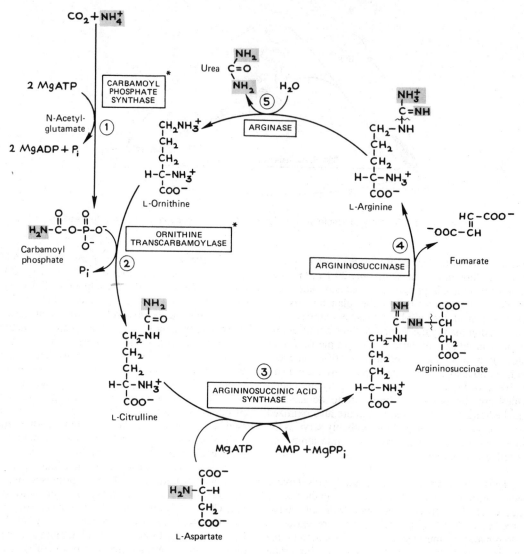

Figure 21–13. Reactions and intermediates of urea biosynthesis. The amines contributing to the formation of urea are shaded. (*Mitochondrial enzymes.)

the argininosuccinate synthase reaction, aspartate and citrulline are linked together via the amino group of aspartate. The reaction requires ATP, and the equilibrium strongly favors argininosuccinate synthesis.

Reaction 4: Cleavage of argininosuccinate to arginine and fumarate. Reversible cleavage of argininosuccinate to arginine plus fumarate is catalyzed by **argininosuccinase,** an enzyme of mammalian liver and kidney tissues. The reaction proceeds via a *trans* elimination mechanism. The fumarate formed may be converted to oxaloacetate via the fumarase and malate dehydrogenase reactions and then transaminated to regenerate aspartate.

Reaction 5: Cleavage of arginine to ornithine and urea. This reaction completes the urea cycle and regenerates ornithine, a substrate for reaction 2. Hydrolytic cleavage of the guanidino group of arginine is

catalyzed by **arginase,** present in the livers of all ureotelic organisms. Smaller quantities of arginase also occur in renal tissue, brain, mammary gland, testicular tissue, and skin. Mammalian liver arginase is activated by Co^{2+} or Mn^{2+}. Ornithine and lysine are potent inhibitors competitive with arginine.

REGULATION OF UREA SYNTHESIS

Functional Interaction Between Glutamate Dehydrogenase & Carbamoyl Phosphate Synthase

Carbamoyl phosphate synthase acts with mitochondrial glutamate dehydrogenase to channel nitrogen from glutamate (and hence from all amino acids; see Fig 21–2) into carbamoyl phosphate and thus into urea. While the equilibrium constant of the glutamate dehydrogenase reaction favors glutamate rather than ammonia formation, removal of ammonia by carbamoyl phosphate synthase and oxidation of α-ketoglutarate by citric acid cycle enzymes in the mitochondrion serve to favor glutamate catabolism. This effect is enhanced by ATP, which, in addition to being a substrate for carbamoyl phosphate synthesis, stimulates glutamate dehydrogenase activity unidirectionally, favoring ammonia formation.

METABOLIC DISORDERS OF THE UREA CYCLE

Metabolic disorders associated with a deficiency of each of the 5 enzymes of hepatic urea synthesis (Fig 21–13) are known. The rate-limiting reactions of urea synthesis appear to be catalyzed by carbamoyl phosphate synthase (reaction 1), ornithine transcarbamoylase (reaction 2), and arginase (reaction 5). Since the urea cycle converts ammonia to the nontoxic compound urea, all disorders of urea synthesis cause ammonia intoxication. This intoxication is more severe when the metabolic block occurs at reactions 1 or 2, since some covalent linking of ammonia to carbon has already occurred if citrulline can be synthesized. Clinical symptoms common to all urea cycle disorders include vomiting in infancy, avoidance of high-protein foods, intermittent ataxia, irritability, lethargy, and mental retardation.

The clinical features and the treatment of all 5 of the disorders discussed below are similar. Significant improvement is noted on a low-protein diet, and much of the brain damage may thus be prevented. Food intake should be in frequent small meals to avoid sudden increases in blood ammonia levels.

Hyperammonemia Type I

One case of **carbamoyl phosphate synthase** deficiency (reaction 1, Fig 21–13) has been reported. This probably is a familial disorder.

Hyperammonemia Type II

Numerous patients have been shown to suffer from a deficiency of **ornithine transcarbamoylase** (reaction 2, Fig 21–13). This disease is X chromosome-linked. The mothers also exhibited hyperammonemia and an aversion to high-protein foods. The only consistent clinical finding was an elevation of glutamine in blood, cerebrospinal fluid, and urine. This probably reflects enhanced synthesis of glutamine by glutamine synthase (Fig 21–8) consequent to elevated tissue levels of ammonia.

Citrullinemia

This rare disorder probably is recessively inherited. Large quantities (1–2 g/d) of citrulline are excreted in the urine, and both plasma and cerebrospinal fluid citrulline levels are markedly elevated. In one patient, complete absence of **argininosuccinate synthase** activity (reaction 3, Fig 21–13) was noted. In another, a less profound modification of this enzyme had occurred. The K_m for citrulline for the synthase from cultured fibroblasts from this patient was 25 times normal. This suggests a mutation causing a significant but not "lethal" modification of the catalytic site of the synthase.

Citrulline (and argininosuccinate [see below]) may serve as a carrier of waste nitrogen, since it contains nitrogen intended for urea synthesis. Feeding arginine enhances the excretion of citrulline in these patients. Similarly, feeding benzoate diverts ammonium nitrogen to hippurate via glycine (Fig 23–2).

Argininosuccinic Aciduria

This rare recessive inherited disease is characterized by elevated levels of argininosuccinic acid in the blood, cerebrospinal fluid, and urine. It frequently is associated with the occurrence of friable, tufted hair (trichorrhexis nodosa). While both early- and late-onset types are known, the disease is always manifest by age 2 and usually terminates fatally early in life.

Argininosuccinic aciduria reflects the absence of **argininosuccinase** (reaction 4, Fig 21–13). Cultured skin fibroblasts from normal subjects contain this enzyme, whereas those from patients with argininosuccinic acidemia do not. Argininosuccinase is also absent from brain, liver, kidney, and erythrocytes of patients with this disease. While the diagnosis is readily made by 2-dimensional paper chromatography of the urine, additional abnormal spots appear in urine on standing owing to the tendency of argininosuccinate to form cyclic anhydrides. Confirmatory diagnosis is by measurement of erythrocyte levels of argininosuccinase. This test can be performed on umbilical cord blood for early detection. Since argininosuccinase is present in amniotic fluid cells, diagnosis by amniocentesis is also possible. For reasons discussed relevant to citrullinemia, feeding arginine and benzoate promotes nitrogen waste excretion in these patients also.

Hyperargininemia

This defect in urea synthesis is characterized by elevated blood and cerebrospinal fluid arginine levels, low erythrocyte levels of **arginase** (reaction 5, Fig 21–13), and a urinary amino acid pattern resembling that of lysine-cystinuria. Possibly this pattern reflects competition by arginine with lysine and cystine for reabsorption in the renal tubule. In patients, a low-protein diet resulted in lowering of plasma ammonia levels and disappearance of the urinary lysine-cystinuria pattern.

● ● ●

References

Adams E, Frank L: Metabolism of proline and the hydroxypro-lines. *Annu Rev Biochem* 1980;**49:**1005.

Batshaw ML et al: Treatment of inborn errors of urea synthesis: Activation of alternative pathways of waste nitrogen synthesis and excretion. *N Engl J Med* 1982;**306:**1387.

Fasman GD (editor): Rapid short column chromatography of amino acids related to metabolic diseases. Page 128 in: *Handbook of Biochemistry and Molecular Biology.* Vol 2. CRC Press, 1976.

Felig P: Amino acid metabolism in man. *Annu Rev Biochem* 1975;**44:**933.

Goldberg AL, Dice JF: Intracellular protein degradation in mammalian and bacterial cells. *Annu Rev Biochem* 1974; **43:**835.

Morris DR, Fillingame H: Regulation of amino acid decarboxylation. *Annu Rev Biochem* 1974;**43:**303.

Msall M et al: Neurologic outcome in children with inborn errors of urea synthesis: Outcome of urea-cycle enzymopathies. *N Engl J Med* 1984;**310:**1500.

Nyhan WL: *Heritable Disorders of Amino Acid Metabolism: Patterns of Clinical Expression and Genetic Variation.* Wiley, 1974.

Ratner S: Enzymes of arginine and urea synthesis. *Adv Enzymol* 1973;**39:**1.

Ratner S: A long view of nitrogen metabolism. *Annu Rev Biochem* 1977;**46:**1.

Stanbury JB et al: *The Metabolic Basis of Inherited Disease,* 5th ed. McGraw-Hill, 1983.

Tyler B: Regulation of the assimilation of nitrogen compounds. *Annu Rev Biochem* 1978;**47:**1127.

Wellner D, Meister A: A survey of inborn errors of amino acid metabolism and transport in man. *Annu Rev Biochem* 1981; **50:**911.

Catabolism of the Carbon Skeletons of Amino Acids | 22

Victor W. Rodwell, PhD

CONVERSION OF CARBON SKELETONS OF COMMON L-α-AMINO ACIDS TO AMPHIBOLIC INTERMEDIATES

This section deals with conversion of the carbon skeletons of common L-amino acids to amphibolic intermediates and with the metabolic diseases or "inborn errors of metabolism" associated with these catabolic pathways. Chapter 23 considers conversion of these carbon skeletons or of the amino acids themselves to certain specialized products.

That the carbon skeletons of the common amino acids are converted to amphibolic intermediates was evident from nutritional studies carried out in the period 1920–1940. These data, reinforced and confirmed by studies using isotopically labeled amino acids conducted from 1940 to 1950, supported the concept of the interconvertibility of fat, carbohydrate, and protein carbons and established that each amino

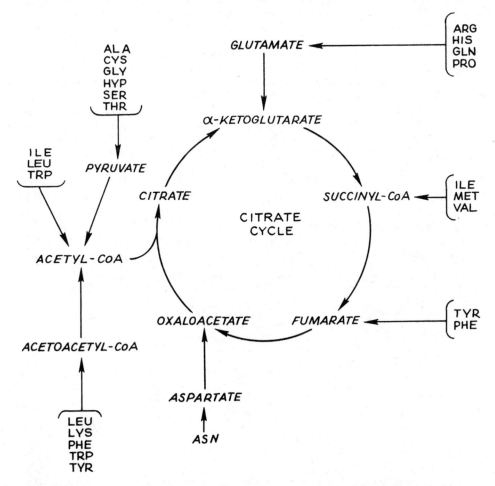

Figure 22–1. Amphibolic intermediates formed from the carbon skeleton of amino acids.

Table 22–1. Fates of the carbon skeletons of the common L-α-amino acids.

Converted to amphibolic intermediates forming:		
Glycogen ("Glycogenic")	Fat ("Ketogenic")	Glycogen and Fat ("Glycogenic" and "Ketogenic")
Ala	Hyp	Leu	Ile
Arg	Met		Lys
Asp	Pro		Phe
Cys	Ser		Trp
Glu	Thr		Tyr
Gly	Val		
His			

acid is convertible either to carbohydrate (13 amino acids), fat (one amino acid), or both (5 amino acids) (Table 22–1). Although at the time a detailed explanation of these interconversions was not possible, it was established that they indeed occur. How they occur is outlined in Fig 22–1.

In what follows, individual amino acids are grouped for discussion on the basis of the first amphibolic intermediates formed as end products of their catabolism. Note that an early step in amino acid catabolism—frequently the first reaction—involves removal of the α nitrogen. This usually (but not always, eg, proline, hydroxyproline, lysine) involves transamination. Once removed, the nitrogen enters the general metabolic pool. Depending upon demand, it may then be reutilized for anabolic processes (eg, protein synthesis) or, if in excess, converted to urea and excreted (see Chapter 21). The nitrogen-free carbon skeleton that remains is, in most instances, merely an oxidized hydrocarbon and can no longer be specifically identified as an amino acid derivative. As such, it is degraded to amphibolic intermediates by reactions similar to those by which other oxidized hydrocarbons

are catabolized (eg, linear and branched fatty acids). Analogies to other areas of metabolism, particularly of fatty acids (see Chapter 17), are particularly striking. For example, the carbon skeletons derived from the branched-chain amino acids leucine, isoleucine, and valine are degraded by reactions analogous to those for catabolism of branched-chain lipids.

Metabolic Defects of Amino Acid Metabolism

Historically, certain metabolic disorders of amino acid metabolism in humans played key roles in elucidation of the pathways by which amino acids are metabolized in normal human subjects. Most of these diseases are rare, and in some cases they have been reported in fewer than 6 individuals. As such, they are unlikely to be encountered by most practicing physicians. Their apparently low incidence in part reflects the absence, until recently, of automated techniques for identification and quantitation of individual amino acids in blood, urine, and spinal fluid. Recently developed techniques for screening the blood and urine of large populations for abnormal amino acids or for abnormal levels of common amino acids may lead to more frequent recognition of these disorders. Techniques have also been developed to assay enzymes in the blood cells or in cultures of skin fibroblasts of patients. Techniques yet to be developed will expand the horizons still further. Consequently, it seems safe to predict an increase both in the number and in the apparent incidence of human metabolic disorders of amino acid metabolism.

Even though uncommon, these disorders present a formidable challenge to the psychiatrist, pediatrician, genetic counselor, or biochemist. They are detected most frequently at infancy, often are fatal at an early age, and often result in irreversible brain damage if untreated. Early detection and rapid initiation of appropriate treatment, if available, is essential. Since

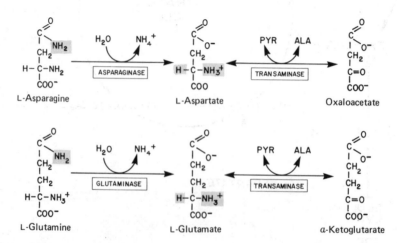

Figure 22–2. Catabolism of L-asparagine *(top)* and of L-glutamine *(bottom)* to amphibolic intermediates. (PYR, pyruvic acid; ALA, L-alanine.) In this and subsequent figures, shading on functional groups highlights portions of the molecules undergoing chemical change.

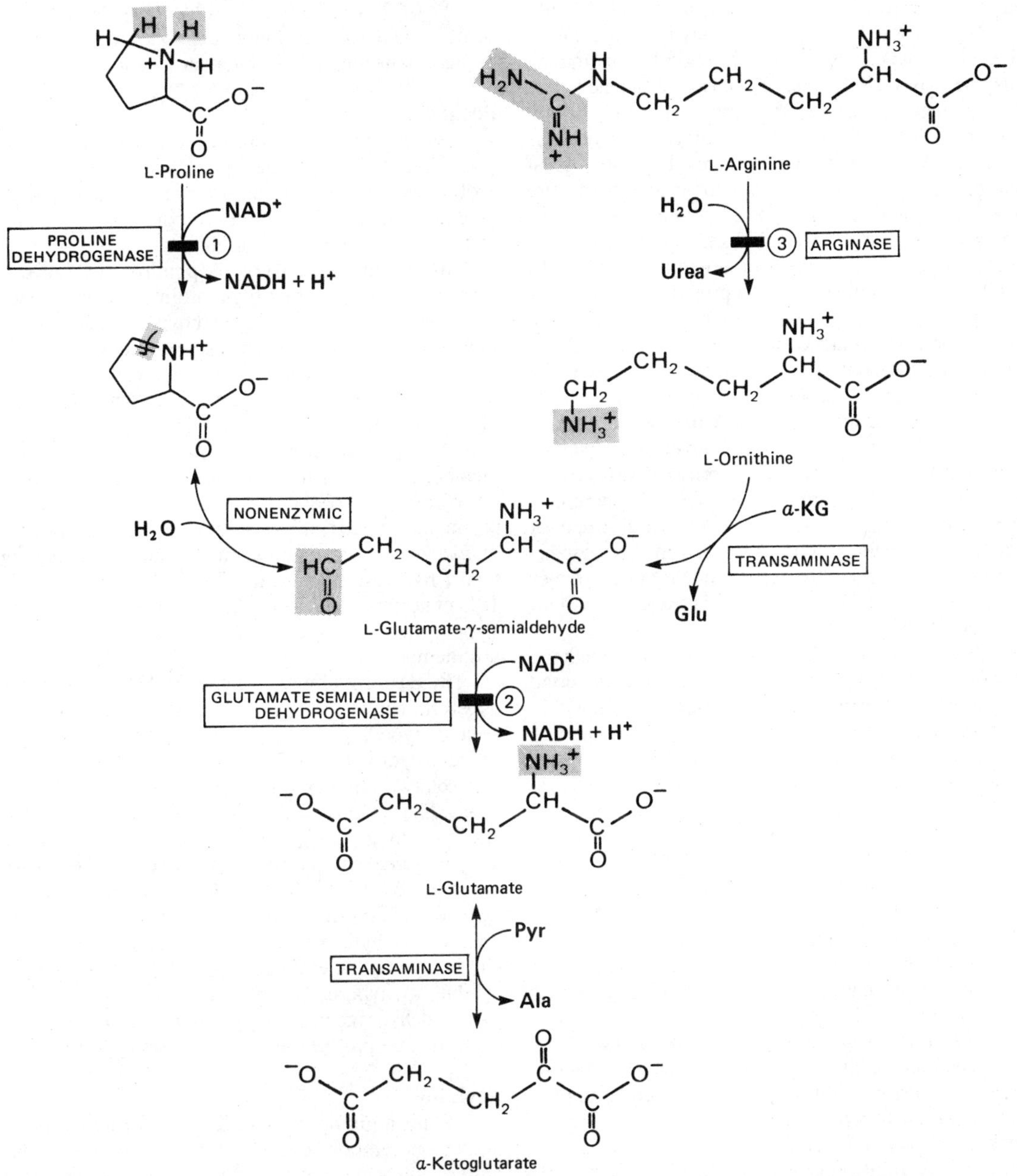

Figure 22-3. Catabolism of L-proline *(left)* and of L-arginine *(right)* to α-ketoglutarate. The circled numerals represent the sites of the metabolic defects in ① type II hyperprolinemia, ② type I hyperprolinemia, and ③ hyperargininemia (see Chapter 21).

several of the enzymes concerned are detectable in cultures of amniotic fluid cells, prenatal diagnosis of these disorders by amniocentesis is a distinct possibility. While current treatment consists primarily of feeding diets low in the amino acids whose catabolism is impaired, more effective treatment may some day be available. For example, circulating the patient's blood through a column containing the missing enzyme in an immobilized state may "replace" the deficient or de-

fective enzyme in question. Recombinant DNA technology may eventually provide a means of correcting genetic defects by "gene therapy."

These metabolic disorders, which result from genetic mutations, cause production of proteins with modified primary structures (see Chapters 4, 6, and 30). Depending on the nature of the primary change, other orders of protein structure may also be affected. While some changes in the primary structures of enzymes may have little or no effect, others may profoundly modify the 3-dimensional structure of catalytic or regulatory sites (see Chapters 5 and 6). The modified or mutant enzyme may possess altered catalytic efficiency (low V_{max} or high K_m) or altered ability to bind an allosteric regulator of its catalytic activity. Since most proteins contain over 100 amino acid residues, there are a great number of possible alterations in the primary structure of even a single enzyme, and many enzymes are involved in amino acid catabolism. Predictably, the number of discrete disorders of amino acid catabolism is potentially extremely high. In principle, a wide variety of mutations may cause the same clinical disease. For example, any mutation that causes a substantial loss of the catalytic activity of argininosuccinase (see Fig 21-13) will cause the metabolic disorder known as argininosuccinicacidemia. It is extremely unlikely, however, that all cases of argininosuccinicacidemia represent the same alteration in primary structure of argininosuccinase. In this sense they are, therefore, distinct molecular diseases. Some known disorders of amino acid metabolism are discussed in this chapter. For further examples, the reader should consult major reference works that specialize in this subject, eg, Stanbury et al, 1983.

We shall first consider the pathways by which the carbon skeletons of the L-α-amino acids are converted to amphibolic intermediates. Subsequently, and within each section, we will discuss certain representative metabolic defects of these pathways that arise as a consequence of genetic defects in human subjects.

AMINO ACIDS FORMING OXALOACETATE

Asparagine & Aspartate

All 4 carbons of asparagine and of aspartate are converted to oxaloacetate via asparaginase and a transaminase (Fig 22-2, top).

No known metabolic defect is associated with this short catabolic pathway, possibly because a defect in the transaminase might have grave consequences incompatible with life. Transaminases fulfill central anabolic as well as catabolic functions in the metabolism of several different amino acids (see Chapter 20 and below).

AMINO ACIDS FORMING α-KETOGLUTARATE

Glutamine & Glutamate

Catabolism of glutamine and of glutamate proceeds like that of asparagine and aspartate but with formation of α-ketoglutarate, the methylene homolog of oxaloacetate (Fig 22-2, bottom). While both glutamate and aspartate are substrates for the same transaminase, deamidation of asparagine and glutamine is catalyzed by distinct enzymes. A dual specificity glutaminase-asparaginase exists in some bacteria.

Possibly for the reasons alluded to above for asparagine and aspartate, there are no known metabolic defects of the glutamine-glutamate catabolic pathway.

Proline

All 5 carbons of L-proline form α-ketoglutarate (Fig 22-3, left). Proline is oxidized to a dehydroproline which, on addition of water, forms glutamate γ-semialdehyde. This is then oxidized to glutamate and transaminated to α-ketoglutarate.

Metabolic disorders of proline catabolism. Two genetically distinct hyperprolinemias have been described. Both type I and type II hyperprolinemias are inherited, apparently as autosomal recessive traits. Despite the occurrence of mental retardation in half of the known cases, both type I and type II hyperprolinemia are believed to be harmless.

A. Hyperprolinemia Type I: The site of the metabolic block in hyperprolinemia type I is proline dehydrogenase (Fig 22-3). In contrast to hyperprolinemia type II, there is no associated impairment of *hydroxy*proline catabolism. An animal model for type I hyperprolinemia, the Pro/Re mouse, has only 10% of normal hepatic proline dehydrogenase activity. Type I heterozygotes exhibit only a mild hyperprolinemia.

B. Hyperprolinemia Type II: The extent of the hyperprolinemia in the type II condition exceeds that seen in type I patients. The urine contains Δ^1-pyrroline-3-hydroxy-5-carboxylate. The site of the metabolic block in hyperprolinemia type II is the dehydrogenase that catalyzes the oxidation of glutamate γ-semialdehyde to glutamate (Fig 22-3). Since the same dehydrogenase functions in hydroxyproline catabolism to oxidize 4-hydroxyglutamate-γ-semialdehyde to erythro-4-hydroxyglutamate (Fig 22-12), both proline and hydroxyproline catabolism are affected. Unlike type I heterozygotes, type II heterozygotes exhibit no hyperprolinemia. This suggests that the shared dehydrogenase plays different roles in regulation of free proline and hydroxyproline pools.

Arginine

While arginine and histidine also form α-ketoglutarate, one carbon and either 2 (histidine) or 3 (arginine) nitrogens must first be removed from these 6-carbon amino acids. With arginine, this requires but a single step: hydrolytic removal of the guanidino group catalyzed by arginase. The product, ornithine, then undergoes transamination of the δ-amino group, forming glutamate γ-semialdehyde, which is converted to α-ketoglutarate as described above for proline (Fig 22-3).

Hyperargininemia, a metabolic disorder of arginine catabolism in which the affected enzyme is liver arginase, is discussed in Chapter 21 in conjunction with metabolic disorders of enzymes of the urea cycle.

Histidine

For histidine, removal of the extra carbon and nitrogens requires 4 reactions (Fig 22-4). Deamina-

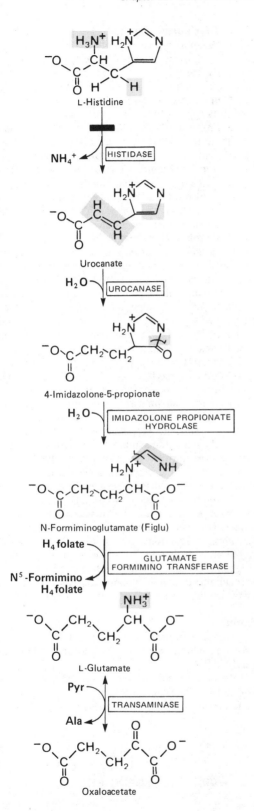

Figure 22–4. Catabolism of L-histidine to α-ketoglutarate. (H$_4$folate, tetrahydrofolate.) The reaction catalyzed by histidase represents the site of the probable metabolic defect in histidinemia.

tion of histidine produces urocanate. Conversion of urocanate to 4-imidazolone-5-propionate, catalyzed by urocanase, involves both addition of H$_2$O and an internal oxidation-reduction. Although 4-imidazolone-5-propionate may undergo additional fates, conversion to α-ketoglutarate involves hydrolysis to N-formiminoglutamate followed by transfer of the formimino group on the α carbon to tetrahydrofolate, forming N^5-formiminotetrahydrofolate. In patients with folic acid deficiency, this last reaction is partially or totally blocked and N-formiminoglutamate (Figlu) is excreted in the urine. This forms the basis for a test for folic acid deficiency in which N-formiminoglutamate is detected in the urine following a large dose of histidine.

Metabolic disorders of histidine catabolism. Histidinemia, a metabolic disorder of histidine catabolism in which the affected enzyme is histidase (Fig 22–4), is inherited as an autosomal recessive trait. Over half of patients with histidinemia are mentally retarded and exhibit a characteristic speech defect.

In addition to increased levels of histidine in blood and urine, there is also increased excretion of imidazolepyruvate (which in a color test with ferric chloride may be mistaken for phenylpyruvate, so that a mistaken diagnosis of phenylketonuria could be made). The metabolic defect in histidinemia is inadequate activity of liver histidase, which impairs conversion of histidine to urocanate (Fig 22–4). An alternative route of histidine metabolism, transamination to imidazolepyruvate, is then favored, and the excess imidazolepyruvate is excreted in the urine. Imidazoleacetate and imidazolelactate, the reduction products of imidazolepyruvate, have also been detected in the urine of histidinemic patients.

The quantity of histidine in normal urine is relatively large. For this reason it can be more readily detected than most amino acids. A conspicuous increase in histidine excretion is a characteristic finding in normal pregnancy but does not occur in gestational hypertensive disorders. The normally increased excretion of histidine during pregnancy apparently does not result from a metabolic defect in histidine metabolism. The phenomenon may be explained largely on the basis of the changes in renal function characteristic of normal pregnancy as well as gestational hypertensive disorders. Furthermore, the alterations in amino acid excretion during pregnancy are not confined to histidine.

AMINO ACIDS FORMING PYRUVATE

Conversion of the carbon skeletons of alanine, cysteine, cystine, glycine, threonine, and serine to pyruvate is summarized diagrammatically below. Both carbons of glycine and all 3 carbons of alanine, cysteine, and serine—but only 2 of the carbons of

Figure 22–5. The freely reversible serine hydroxymethyl-transferase reaction. (H$_4$folate, tetrahydrofolate.)

threonine—form pyruvate. Pyruvate may then be converted to acetyl-CoA.

$$\text{L-Threonine} \rightarrow \text{Glycine} \rightarrow \text{L-Serine} \quad \text{L-Cystine}$$

L-Alanine → Pyruvate ← L-Cysteine → Acetyl-CoA

Glycine

Amphibolic intermediates formed from glycine include pyruvate, CO_2, and 5,10-methylene tetrahydrofolate. Formation of pyruvate from glycine can occur by conversion to serine, catalyzed by serine hydroxymethyltransferase (Fig 22–5), followed by the serine dehydratase reaction (Fig 22–7; see also Serine, below).

The major pathway for glycine catabolism in vertebrates involves conversion to CO_2, NH_4^+, and 5,10-methylenetetrahydrofolate catalyzed by the glycine synthase complex. This reversible reaction (Fig 22–6) resembles conversion of pyruvate to acetyl-CoA by enzymes of the pyruvate dehydrogenase complex. Both complexes comprise macromolecular aggregates in liver mitochondria. The reactions of glycine cleavage occur in liver tissue of most vertebrates, including humans, other mammals, birds, and reptiles.

The reactions of the glycine cleavage system probably constitute the major route, not only for glycine but also for serine catabolism in humans and many other vertebrates (see also Serine, below).

Metabolic disorders of glycine catabolism. Discussed below are 2 disorders of glycine metabolism.

A. Glycinuria: Glycinuria, a rare disorder of glycine metabolism, has so far been described in only one family. It is characterized by excess urinary excretion of glycine (glycinuria) in association with a tendency to formation of oxalate renal stones, although the amount of oxalate excreted in the urine is normal. Glycinuria appears to be inherited as a dominant, possibly X-linked, trait. The plasma content of glycine is normal in the glycinuric patients that have been studied, while the urinary excretion of glycine ranges from 600 to 1000 mg/d. Consequently, glycinuria is attributed to a defect in renal tubular transport of glycine whereby decreased reabsorption of glycine by the renal tubule permits the amino acid to escape into the urine in greatly increased amounts.

B. Primary Hyperoxaluria: Primary hyperoxaluria is a metabolic disease characterized biochemically by continuous high urinary excretion of oxalate unrelated to dietary intake of oxalate. The history of the disease is that of progressive bilateral calcium oxalate urolithiasis, nephrocalcinosis, and recurrent infection of the urinary tract. Death occurs in childhood or early adult life from renal failure or hypertension. The excess oxalate is apparently of endogenous origin, possibly from glycine, which may be deaminated to form glyoxylate, a precursor of oxalate. The metabolic defect is considered to be a disorder of glyoxylate metabolism associated with failure to convert glyoxylate to formate or to glycine by transamination. As a result, the excess glyoxylate is oxidized to oxalate. Glycine transaminase deficiency, together with some impairment of oxidation of glyoxylate to formate, may be the biochemical explanation for the inherited metabolic disease primary hyperoxaluria.

As might be expected, vitamin B$_6$-deficient animals (rats) excrete markedly increased quantities of oxalate, because the glutamic- or alanine-glyoxylic transaminase reactions are vitamin B$_6$-dependent. Excretion of oxalate in B$_6$-deficient rats is enhanced by feeding glycine or vitamin B$_6$ antagonists. However, administration of vitamin B$_6$ has not been of benefit in clinical cases of endogenous hyperoxaluria.

Alanine

Transamination of L-alanine (Fig 22–7) forms pyruvate, which may then be decarboxylated to acetyl-CoA.

Possibly for the reasons advanced under glutamate and aspartate catabolism, there is no known metabolic defect of α-alanine catabolism.

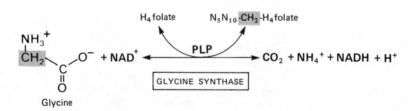

Figure 22–6. The reversible cleavage of glycine by the mitochondrial glycine synthase complex. PLP, pyridoxal phosphate.

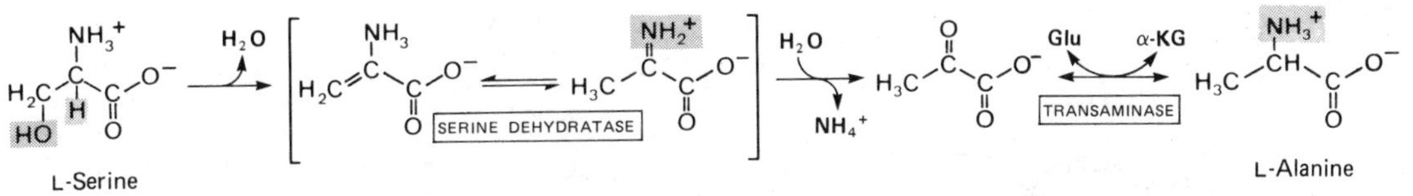

Figure 22–7. Conversion of alanine and serine to pyruvate. Both the alanine transaminase and serine dehydratase reactions require pyridoxal phosphate as coenzyme. The serine dehydratase reaction proceeds via elimination of H_2O from serine, forming an unsaturated amino acid. This rearranges to an α-imino acid that is spontaneously hydrolyzed to pyruvate plus ammonia. There is thus no net gain or loss of water during the serine dehydratase reaction. (Glu, glutamate; α-KG, α-ketoglutarate.)

Serine

Conversion of serine to pyruvate by serine dehydratase, a pyridoxal phosphate protein, involves both elimination of water and hydrolytic loss of ammonia from an imino acid intermediate (Fig 22–7). Rat and guinea pig liver is rich in serine dehydratase. Whereas in these species conversion of serine to pyruvate by serine dehydratase is of considerable physiologic significance, in humans and many other vertebrates, serine is degraded primarily to glycine and 5,10-methylenetetrahydrofolate. The initial reaction is catalyzed by serine hydroxymethyltransferase (Fig 22–5). Further catabolism of serine then merges with glycine catabolism (Fig 22–6).

Cystine

Like carbon and nitrogen, sulfur is continuously recycled through the biosphere through the combined metabolic activities of prokaryotic and eukaryotic organisms. Mammals, which play no role in sulfur assimilation, participate in this cycle by catabolism of organic sulfur compounds to inorganic sulfur compounds. For example, human subjects excrete approximately 20–30 mmol of sulfur per day, at least 80% of which is inorganic sulfate.

The major catabolic fate of cystine in mammals is conversion to cysteine, principally by the reaction catalyzed by cystine reductase (Fig 22–8). From this point, catabolism of cystine merges with that of cysteine (discussed below).

Cysteine

Cysteine is catabolized in mammals via 2 principal catabolic pathways: the direct oxidative (cysteine sulfinate) pathway and the transamination (3-mercaptopyruvate) pathway (Fig 22–9). A third pathway involving cysteine desulfhydrase, present in bacteria, was formerly thought also to be functional in mammals. However, since cysteine desulfhydrase activity has never been detected in mammalian tissues, catabolism of cysteine by this route is unlikely.

A. The Direct Oxidative Pathway of Cysteine Catabolism: Conversion of cysteine to cysteine sulfinate (Fig 22–9) is catalyzed by cysteine dioxygenase, an enzyme that requires Fe^{2+} and NAD(P)H. Further catabolism of cysteine sulfinate probably involves its transamination to β-sulfinylpyruvate. However, while transaminases present in mammalian tissues accept cysteine sulfinate as the amino donor, it is not clear whether these are distinct from classic glutamate-aspartate transaminase. In addition, the presumed product, β-sulfinylpyruvate, has yet to be isolated as a catabolite of cysteine sulfinate. Conversion of the putative intermediate β-sulfinylpyruvate to pyruvate and sulfite may not be enzyme-catalyzed. Desulfination is extremely rapid even in the absence of enzymic catalysis, for transamination of cysteine sulfinate forms stoichiometric quantities of sulfite.

B. The Transaminase (3-Mercaptopyruvate) Pathway of Cysteine Catabolism: Despite considerable evidence supportive of its importance in mamma-

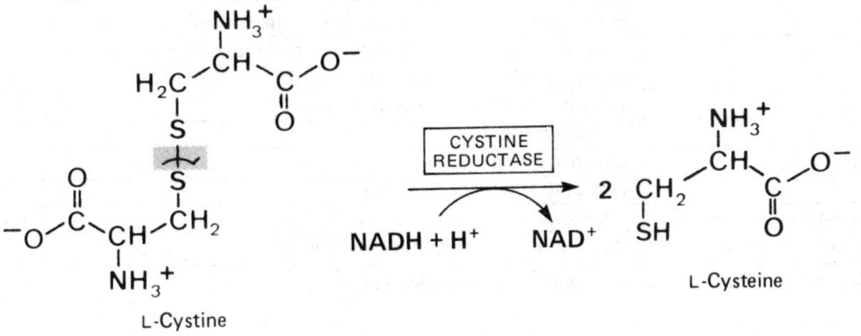

Figure 22–8. The cystine reductase reaction.

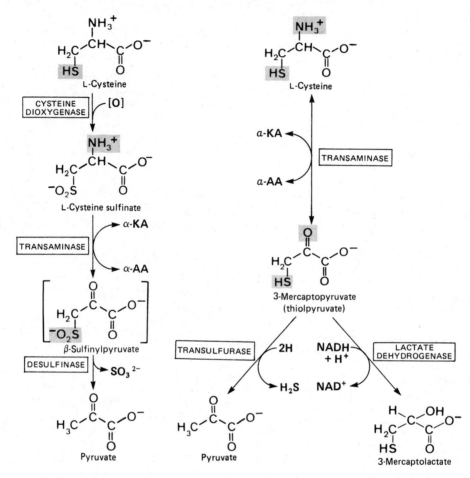

Figure 22–9. Catabolism of L-cysteine via the direct oxidative (cysteine sulfinate) pathway *(left)* and by the transamination (3-mercaptopyruvate) pathway *(right)*. β-Sulfinylpyruvate is bracketed, since it is a putative intermediate. Oxidation of the sulfite produced in the last reaction of the direct oxidative pathway is catalyzed by sulfite oxidase.

Table 22–2. Inborn errors of sulfur-containing amino acid metabolism.

Name	Defect	Reference
Homocystinuria I	Cystathione β-synthase	Fig 20–11, reaction 1
Homocystinuria II	N^5, N^{10}-methylenetetrahydrofolate reductase	
Homocystinuria III	Low N^5-methyltetrahydrofolate-homocysteine transmethylase owing to inability to synthesize methylcobalamin	
Homocystinuria IV	Low N^5-methyltetrahydrofolate-homocysteine transmethylase owing to defective intestinal absorption of cobalamin	
Hypermethioninemia	Liver methionine adenosyltransferase*	Fig 22–22
Cystathioninuria	Cystathionase	Fig 20–11, reaction 2
Sulfituria (sulfocysteinuria)	Sulfite oxidase	Fig 20–9, legend
Cystinosis	Defect in lysosomal function	
3-Mercaptopyruvate-cysteine disulfiduria	3-Mercaptopyruvate sulfurtransferase	Fig 22–9
Methionine malabsorption syndrome	Inability to absorb methionine from gut	

*May also occur in cystathioninuria, tyrosinemia, and fructose intolerance.

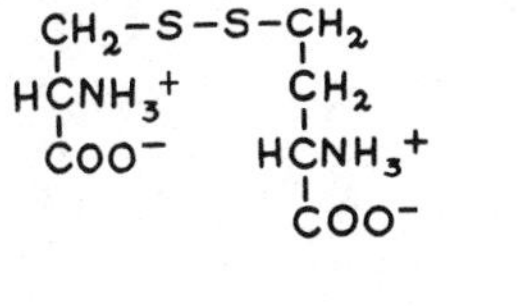

Figure 22–10. Mixed disulfide of cysteine and homocysteine.

lian tissues, less attention has been devoted to the 3-mercaptopyruvate catabolic pathway for cysteine catabolism. Reversible transamination of cysteine to 3-mercaptopyruvate (thiolpyruvate) is catalyzed by specific cysteine transaminases or by glutamate or asparagine transaminases of mammalian liver and kidney (Fig 22–9). 3-Mercaptopyruvate may then be reduced in a reaction catalyzed by L-lactate dehydrogenase. The product, 3-mercaptolactate, is a normal constituent of human urine in the form of its mixed

disulfide with cysteine and is excreted in increased amounts in the urine of patients with mercaptolactate-cysteine disulfiduria. Alternatively, 3-mercaptopyruvate undergoes desulfuration, forming pyruvate and H_2S (Fig 22–9).

Table 22–2 summarizes known defects of sulfur-containing amino acid catabolism.

Metabolic disorders of sulfur-containing amino acids. Several disorders of the catabolism of S-containing amino acids are discussed below.

A. Cystinuria (Cystine-Lysinuria): In this inherited metabolic disease, urinary excretion of cystine is 20–30 times normal. Excretion of lysine, arginine, and ornithine is also markedly increased. Cystinuria is considered to be due to a renal transport defect. The greatly increased excretion of lysine, arginine, and ornithine as well as cystine in urine of cystinuric patients suggests a defect in the renal reabsorptive mechanisms for these 4 amino acids. It is possible that a single reabsorptive site is involved. Thus, as far as renal mechanisms are concerned, cystinuria is not an uncomplicated defect affecting only cystine; the term

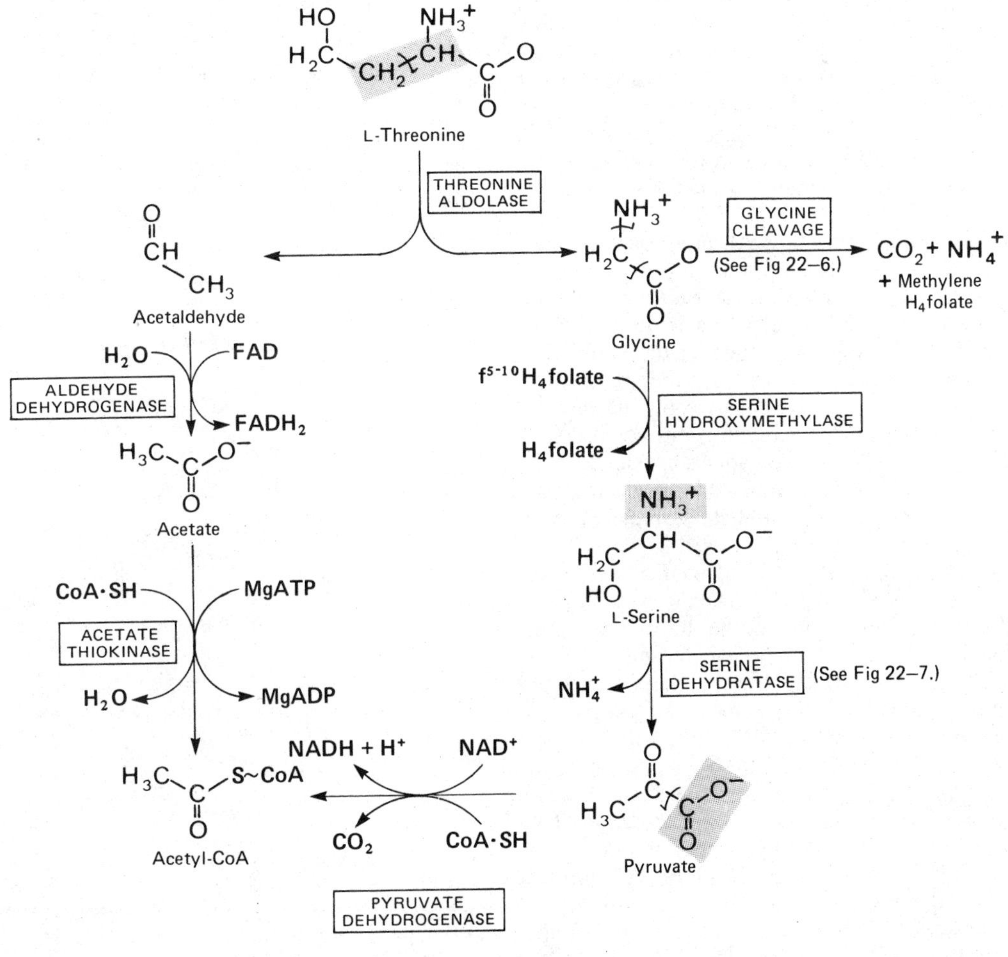

Figure 22–11. Conversion of threonine and glycine to serine, pyruvate, and acetyl-CoA. ($f^{5-10} \cdot H_4$folate, formyl [5–10] tetrahydrofolic acid.)

"cystinuria" is therefore actually a misnomer. Cystine-lysinuria may now be the preferred descriptive term for this disease.

Because cystine is relatively insoluble, in cystinuric patients it may precipitate in the kidney tubules and form cystine calculi. This may be a major complication of the disease. Were it not for this possibility, cystinuria would be an entirely benign anomaly and probably would escape recognition in many cases.

Although cystine is the principal sulfur-containing amino acid in the urine of cystinuric patients, another sulfur-containing amino acid has also been detected in significant quantities. This is a mixed disulfide of L-cysteine and L-homocysteine (Fig 22–10). This compound is somewhat more soluble than cystine. To the extent that it may be formed at the expense of cystine, it reduces the tendency to formation of cystine crystals and calculi in the urine.

There may also be an intestinal transport defect for these amino acids. A failure in concentration of cystine and lysine in cells of the jejunal mucosa obtained by biopsy of the jejunal area of the intestine of cystinuric patients has been detected. In an investigation of the transport of the affected amino acids in cystinuria into kidney slices obtained by biopsy from normal and cystinuric patients, lysine and arginine transport was defective in the cystinuric tissue but cystine transport was normal. The above experiments suggest that some revision of the present concepts of the etiology of cystinuria may be required.

B. Cystinosis (Cystine Storage Disease): Cystinosis is different from cystinuria. In cystinosis, which is also inherited, cystine crystals are deposited in many tissues and organs (particularly the reticuloendothelial system) throughout the body. It is usually accompanied by a generalized aminoaciduria in which all amino acids are considerably increased in the urine. Various other renal functions are also seriously impaired, and affected patients usually die at an early age with all of the manifestations of acute renal failure. Recent evidence implicates impaired lysosomal function as the primary defect.

C. Homocystinurias: The incidence of these heritable defects of methionine catabolism is estimated at 1:160,000 births. Homocystine (up to 300 mg/d), together with S-adenosylmethionine in some cases, is excreted in the urine, and plasma methionine levels are elevated. At least 4 known metabolic defects give rise to homocystinuria (Table 22–2). In homocystinuria type I, associated clinical findings include the occurrence of thromboses, osteoporosis, dislocated lenses in the eyes, and frequently mental retardation. Two forms of this disease are known: a vitamin B_6–responsive form and a vitamin B_6–unresponsive form. Feeding a diet low in methionine and high in cystine effectively prevents pathologic changes if initiated early in life.

Other types of homocystinuria reflect defects in the remethylation cycle (Table 22–2).

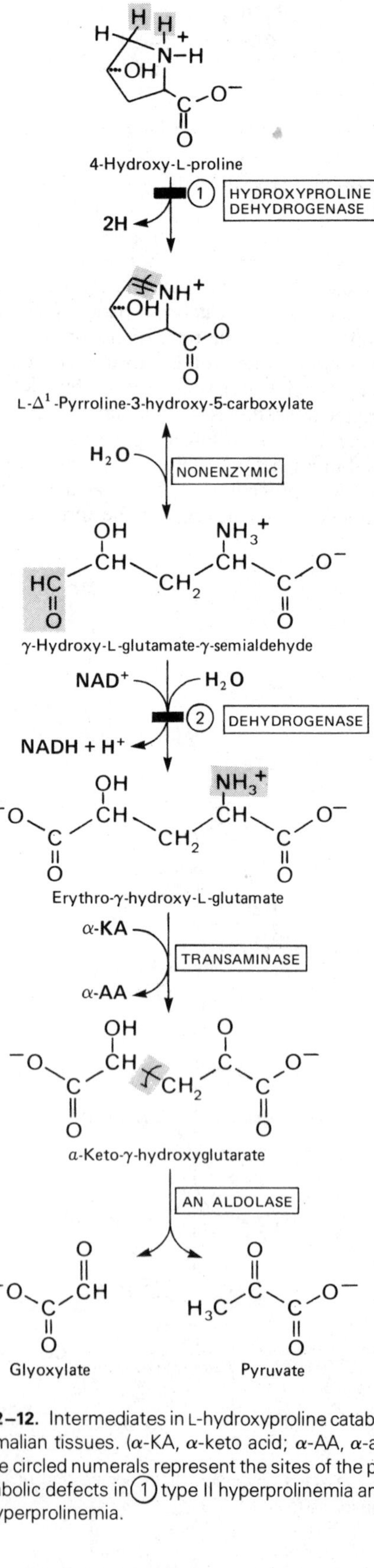

Figure 22–12. Intermediates in L-hydroxyproline catabolism in mammalian tissues. (α-KA, α-keto acid; α-AA, α-amino acid.) The circled numerals represent the sites of the probable metabolic defects in ① type II hyperprolinemia and ② type I hyperprolinemia.

Threonine

Threonine is cleaved to acetaldehyde and glycine by **threonine aldolase.** Acetaldehyde then forms acetyl-CoA (Fig 22–11). Catabolism of glycine is discussed above.

Hydroxyproline

Three of the 5 carbons of 4-hydroxy-L-proline are converted to pyruvate (Fig 22–12). The remaining 2 form glyoxylate. A mitochondrial dehydrogenase catalyzes conversion of hydroxyproline to L-Δ^1-pyrroline-3-hydroxy-5-carboxylate. This is in nonenzymic equilibrium with γ-hydroxy-L-glutamate-γ-semialdehyde, formed by addition of water. The semialdehyde is oxidized to the corresponding carboxylic acid, erythro-γ-hydroxyglutamate, and transaminated to α-keto-γ-hydroxyglutarate. An aldol type cleavage then forms glyoxylate plus pyruvate.

Metabolic disorders of hydroxyproline catabolism. Hyperhydroxyprolinemia is a metabolic disorder characterized by high plasma levels of 4-hydroxyproline, which normally is present in plasma at low levels (< 0.01 mmol/L). The site of the metabolic defect in this autosomal recessive trait is 4-hydroxyproline dehydrogenase (Fig 22–12). In contrast to type II hyperprolinemia, there is no accompanying impairment of proline catabolism, since the affected enzyme functions solely in hydroxyproline catabolism. The condition has no effect on collagen metabolism and, like the hyperprolinemias, appears to be harmless.

AMINO ACIDS FORMING ACETYL–COENZYME A

All amino acids forming pyruvate (alanine, cysteine, cystine, glycine, hydroxyproline, serine, and threonine) are convertible to acetyl-CoA. In addition, 5 amino acids form acetyl-CoA without first forming pyruvate. These include the aromatic amino acids phenylalanine, tyrosine, and tryptophan, the basic amino acid lysine, and the neutral branched-chain amino acid leucine.

Tyrosine

A. Overall Reaction Sequence: Five sequential enzymatic reactions convert tyrosine to fumarate and to acetoacetate (Fig 22–13): (1) transamination to p-hydroxyphenylpyruvate; (2) simultaneous oxidation and migration of the 3-carbon side chain and decarboxylation, forming homogentisate; (3) oxidation of homogentisate to maleylacetoacetate; (4) isomerization of maleylacetoacetate to fumarylacetoacetate; and (5) hydrolysis of fumarylacetoacetate to fumarate and acetoacetate. Acetoacetate may then undergo thiolytic cleavage to acetate plus acetyl-CoA.

Several intermediates of tyrosine metabolism were discovered during studies of the human genetic disease alkaptonuria. Patients with alkaptonuria excrete homogentisate in the urine, and much useful information was obtained by feeding suspected precursors of homogentisate to these patients. Early difficulties arising from the instability of several of the intermediates were resolved by the discovery that α-ketoglutarate and ascorbate are required for tyrosine oxidation by liver extracts. Subsequently, each individual enzymic reaction was studied in detail.

B. Transamination of Tyrosine: Transamination of tyrosine to p-hydroxyphenylpyruvate is catalyzed by **tyrosine-α-ketoglutarate transaminase,** an inducible enzyme of mammalian liver.

C. Oxidation of p-Hydroxyphenylpyruvate to Homogentisate: Although the reaction (Fig 22–13) appears to involve hydroxylation of p-hydroxyphenylpyruvate in the ortho position accompanied by oxidative loss of the carboxyl carbon, it actually involves migration of the side chain. Ring hydroxylation and side chain migration occur in a concerted manner. **p-Hydroxyphenylpyruvate hydroxylase** is a copper metalloprotein similar to **tyrosinase.** Although other reducing agents can replace ascorbate as a cofactor for this reaction in vitro, scorbutic patients excrete incompletely oxidized products of tyrosine metabolism.

D. Conversion of Homogentisate to Fumarate and Acetoacetate: The benzene ring of homogentisate is ruptured, forming maleylacetoacetate in an oxidative reaction catalyzed by **homogentisate oxidase,** an iron metalloprotein of mammalian liver. Since the reaction is inhibited by α,α'-dipyridyl, a chelating agent that binds iron, treatment with α,α'-dipyridyl induces alkaptonuria in experimental animals.

Conversion of maleylacetoacetate to fumarylacetoacetate, a *cis* to *trans* isomerization about the double bond, is catalyzed by **maleylacetoacetate *cis, trans* isomerase,** an –SH enzyme of mammalian liver. Hydrolysis of fumarylacetoacetate by **fumarylacetoacetate hydrolase** forms fumarate and acetoacetate. Acetoacetate can then be converted to acetyl-CoA plus acetate by the β-ketothiolase reaction (see Chapter 17).

Metabolic disorders of tyrosine catabolism. Several metabolic disorders are characterized by tyrosinemia, tyrosinuria, and phenolaciduria.

A. Tyrosinemia Type I (Tyrosinosis): Tyrosinosis is characterized by accumulation of metabolites that adversely affect the activities of several enzymes and transport systems. The pathophysiology of this disorder thus is complex. The proposed metabolic defect is in fumarylacetoacetate hydrolase (Fig 22–13) and possibly in maleylacetoacetate hydrolase as well.

Both acute and chronic forms of tyrosinosis are known. In acute tyrosinosis, infants exhibit diarrhea, vomiting, a "cabbagelike" odor, and failure to thrive. Death from liver failure in untreated acute tyrosinosis ensues within 6–8 months. In chronic tyrosinemia, similar but milder symptoms lead to death by the age of 10 years. Plasma tyrosine levels are elevated (6–12 mg/dL), as are those of additional amino acids, notably methionine. Treatment involves a diet low in tyrosine and phenylalanine and, on occasion, low in methionine also.

B. Tyrosinemia Type II (Richner-Hanhart

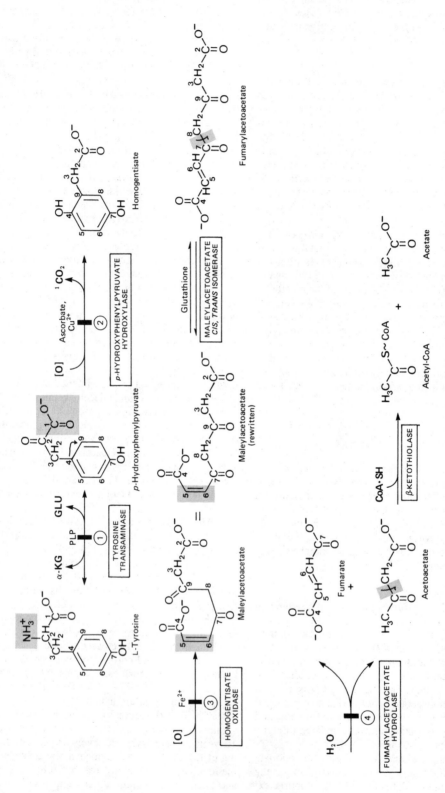

Figure 22–13. Intermediates in tyrosine catabolism. With the exception of β-ketothiolase, reactions are discussed in the text. Carbon atoms of intermediates are numbered to assist readers in determining the ultimate fate of each carbon (see also Fig 22–15). (α-KG, α-ketoglutarate; Glu, glutamate; PLP, pyridoxal phosphate.) The circled numerals represent the probable sites of the metabolic defects in ① type II tyrosinemia, ② neonatal tyrosinemia, ③ alkaptonuria, and ④ type I tyrosinemia, or tyrosinosis.

Syndrome): The probable site of the metabolic defect in tyrosinemia type II is hepatic tyrosine transaminase (Fig 22–13). Clinical findings include elevated plasma tyrosine levels (4–5 mg/dL), characteristic eye and skin lesions, and moderate mental retardation. Self-mutilation and disturbances of fine coordination have also been reported. Tyrosine is the only amino acid whose urinary concentration is elevated. However, renal clearance and reabsorption of tyrosine fall within normal limits. Metabolites excreted in the urine include p-hydroxyphenylpyruvate, p-hydroxyphenyl-lactate, p-hydroxyphenylacetate, N-acetyltyrosine, and tyramine (Fig 22–14).

C. Neonatal Tyrosinemia: Although the precise site of the metabolic defect in neonatal tyrosinemia remains to be identified with certainty, the disorder is thought to result from a relative deficiency of p-hydroxyphenylpyruvate hydroxylase (Fig 22–13). Blood levels of tyrosine and phenylalanine are elevated, as are urinary levels of tyrosine, p-hydroxyphenylace-tate, N-acetyltyrosine, and tyramine. Therapy involves feeding a diet low in protein.

D. Alkaptonuria: This inherited metabolic disorder, noted in medical literature as early as the 16th century, was characterized in 1859. The disease is of considerable historic interest, because it formed the basis for Garrod's ideas concerning heritable metabolic disorders. Its most striking clinical manifestation is the occurrence of dark urine on standing in air. Late in the disease, there occur generalized pigmentation of connective tissues (ochronosis) and a form of arthritis. The metabolic defect is attributable to lack of **homogentisate oxidase** (Fig 22–13). The substrate, homogentisate, is excreted in the urine, where it is oxidized in air to a brownish-black pigment. Over 600 cases have been reported; the estimated incidence of alkaptonuria is 2–5 per million live births.

Alkaptonuria is inherited as an autosomal recessive trait. At present, no diagnostic procedure for the detection of heterozygotes is available. While the precise mechanism of the ochronosis is not known, it is believed to involve oxidation of homogentisate by polyphenol oxidase (see p 130), forming benzoqui-

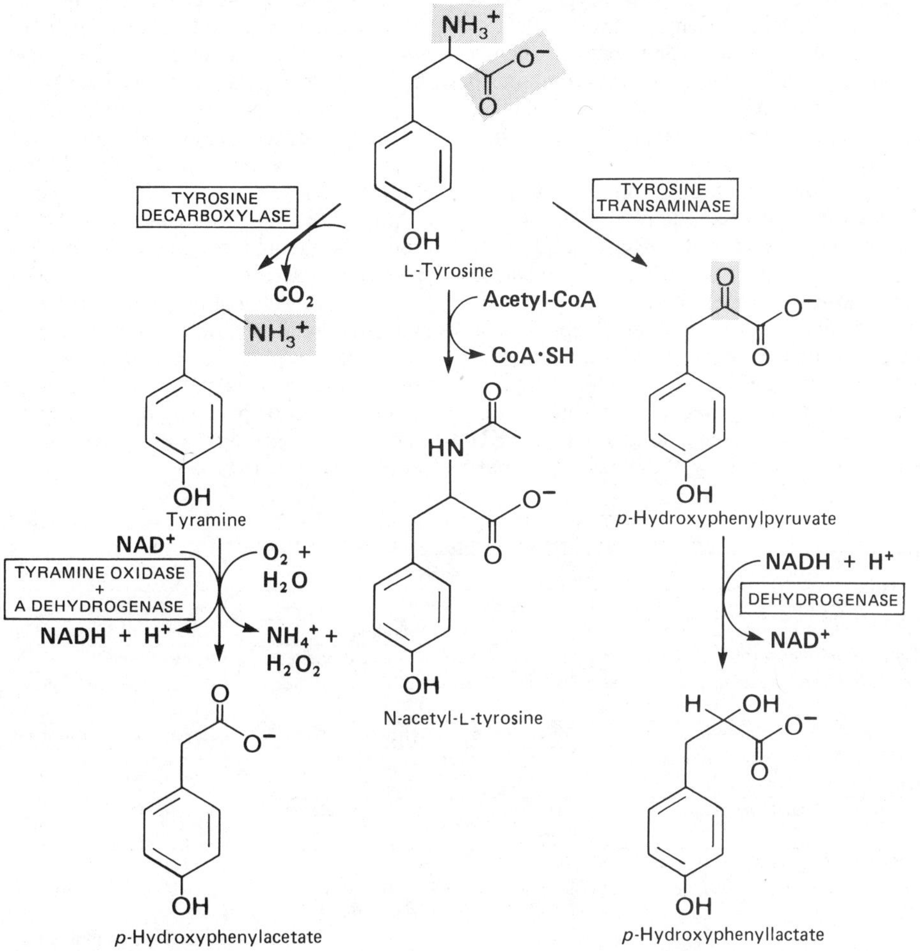

Figure 22–14. Alternative catabolites of tyrosine. p-Hydroxyphenylacetaldehyde is formed as an intermediate during oxidation of tyramine to p-hydroxyphenylacetate.

noneacetate, which polymerizes and binds to connective tissue macromolecules.

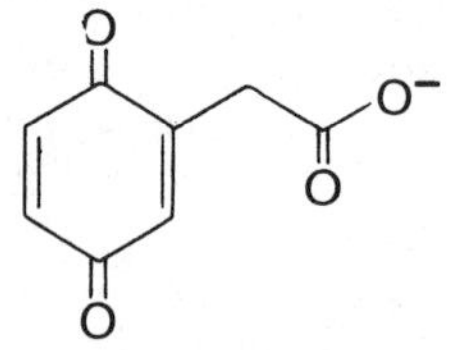

Benzoquinoneacetate

L-Phenylalanine

Fumarate   Acetoacetate   Carbon dioxide

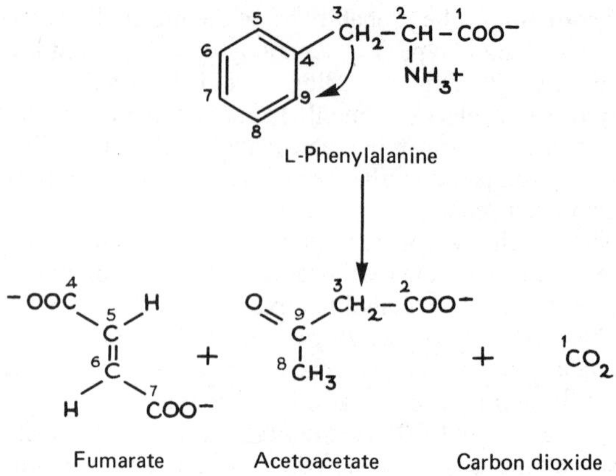

Figure 22-15. Ultimate catabolic fate of each carbon atom of phenylalanine. Pattern of isotopic labeling in the ultimate catabolites of phenylalanine (and tyrosine).

Phenylalanine

Phenylalanine is first converted to tyrosine by phenylalanine hydroxylase (Fig 20–12). The labeling pattern in the amphibolic products fumarate and acetoacetate (Fig 22–15) thus is identical to that for tyrosine (Fig 22–13).

Metabolic disorders of phenylalanine catabolism. Major metabolic disorders associated with impaired ability to convert phenylalanine to tyrosine (see Fig 20–12) may be classified into 3 broad groups: defects in phenylalanine hydroxylase (hyperphenylalaninemia type I, or classic phenylketonuria), defects in dihydrobiopterin reductase (hyperphenylalaninemia types II and III), and defects in dihydrobiopterin biosynthesis (hyperphenylalaninemia types IV and V). Additional types have, however, been identified (Table 22–3).

The major consequence of untreated **hyperphenylalaninemia type I (classic phenylketonuria; PKU)** is the mental retardation that results in IQ below 70 in late childhood. Additional clinical signs include seizures, psychoses, eczema, and a "mousy" odor. However, if diagnosis and initiation of appropriate treatment are prompt, these symptoms may be avoided. Because of the availability of animal models and because prompt dietary intervention can ameliorate the otherwise inevitable mental retardation, PKU has served as a model for study of the mental retardation associated with metabolic diseases. In classic PKU, a heritable disorder with a frequency of about 1:10,000 live births, levels of component I of liver phenylalanine hydroxylase (Fig 20–12) average approximately 25% of normal, and the hydroxylase is insensitive to regulation by phenylalanine.

The patient is unable to convert phenylalanine to tyrosine, and, as a result, alternative catabolites of phenylalanine are produced (Fig 22–16). These include phenylpyruvic acid, the product of deamination of phenylalanine; phenyllactic acid, the reduction product of phenylpyruvic acid; and phenylacetic acid, produced by decarboxylation and oxidation of phenylpyruvic acid. Much of the phenylacetate is conjugated in the liver with glutamine and excreted in the urine as the conjugate, phenylacetylglutamine. Table 22–4 illustrates the chemical pattern in the blood and urine of a phenylketonuric patient. The presence in urine of the keto acid phenylpyruvate gives the disease its name—phenylketonuria.

Table 22–3. Hyperphenylalaninemias.*

Type	Condition	Defect	Treatment
I	Phenylketonuria	Phe hydroxylase absent	Low Phe diet
II	Persistent hyperphenylalaninemia	Decreased Phe hydroxylase	None, or temporary dietary therapy
III	Transient mild hyperphenylalaninemia	Maturational delay of hydroxylase	Same as type II
IV	Dihydropteridine reductase deficiency	Deficient or absent dihydropteridine reductase	Dopa, 5-OH-tryptophan, carbidopa
V	Abnormal dihydrobiopterin function	Dihydrobiopterin synthesis defect	Dopa, 5-OH-tryptophan, carbidopa
VI	Persistent hyperphenylalaninemia and tyrosinemia	? Catabolism tyrosine	Reduced Phe intake
VII	Transient neonatal tyrosinemia	p-Hydroxyphenyl pyruvic oxidase inhibition	Vitamin C
VIII	Hereditary tyrosinemia	Deficiency: 1. p-OH phenylpyruvate deoxygenase 2. Cytoplasmic tyrosine aminotransferase 3. Fumarylacetoacetate	Low Tyr diet Low Tyr diet plus glutathione injections

*Modified and reproduced, with permission, from Tourian A, Sidbury JB: Phenylketonuria and hyperphenylalaninemia. Page 273 in: Stanbury JB et al (editors): *The Metabolic Basis of Inherited Disease,* 5th ed. McGraw-Hill, 1983.

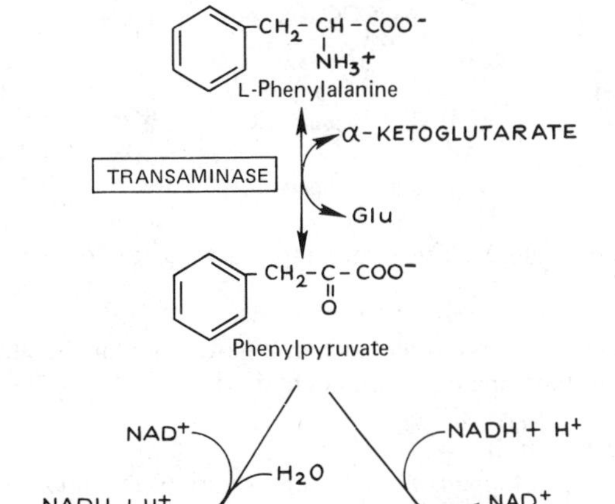

Figure 22–16. Alternative pathways of phenylalanine catabolism of particular importance in phenylketonuria. The reactions shown also occur in the liver tissue of normal individuals but are of minor significance if a functional phenylalanine hydroxylase is present. (Glu, glutamate; Gln, glutamine.)

In the absence of a normal catabolic pathway for phenylalanine, several reactions of otherwise minor quantitative importance in normal liver assume a major catabolic role. In phenylketonurics, phenylpyruvate, phenyllactate, phenylacetate, and its glutamine conjugate phenacetylglutamine are formed and occur in the blood and urine (Fig 22–16). Although phenylpyruvate, present in the urine of most phenylketonuric

patients, can be detected by a simple biochemical spot test, definitive diagnosis requires determination of elevated plasma phenylalanine levels.

Further deterioration of mental performance of phenylketonuric children can be prevented if they are maintained on a diet containing very low levels of phenylalanine. This is accompanied by a return to the normal range of blood phenylalanine levels and a reduced excretion of "alternative catabolites." Detection of the disease as early in infancy as possible is important if dietary treatment is to yield favorable results in mental development. The diet can be terminated at 6 years of age, when high concentrations of phenylalanine and its derivatives no longer are injurious to the brain.

Plasma phenylalanine may be measured by an automated micro method that requires as little as 20 μL of blood. It is important to note, however, that abnormally high blood phenylalanine levels may not occur in phenylketonuric infants until the third or fourth day of life, because of their initially low intake of dietary protein. Furthermore, false-positive results may occur in premature infants owing to delayed maturation of the enzymes required for phenylalanine catabolism. A useful but less reliable screening test depends on detecting elevated urinary levels of phenylpyruvate with ferric chloride.

Administration of phenylalanine to a phenylketonuric subject should result in prolonged elevation of the level of this amino acid in the blood, indicating diminished tolerance to phenylalanine. However, abnormally low tolerance to injected phenylalanine and a high fasting level of phenylalanine are also characteristic of the parents of phenylketonurics. Evidently, the defective gene responsible for phenylketonuria can be detected biochemically in the phenotypically normal, heterozygous parents.

Lysine

Lysine provides an exception to the rule that the first step in catabolism of an amino acid is removal of its α-amino group by transamination. In mammalian tissues, neither the α- nor ϵ-nitrogen atoms of L-lysine undergo transamination. Mammals convert the intact carbon skeleton of L-lysine to α-aminoadipate and α-ketoadipate (Fig 22–17). L-Lysine was formerly thought to be degraded via pipecolic acid, a cyclic imino acid. However, while liver degrades D-lysine via

Table 22–4. Metabolites of phenylalanine accumulating in the plasma and urine of phenylketonuric patients.

Metabolite	Plasma (mg/dL)		Urine (mg/dL)	
	Normal	Phenylketonuric	Normal	Phenylketonuric
Phenylalanine	1–2	15–63	30	300–1000
Phenylpyruvate		0.3–1.8		300–2000
Phenyllactate				290–550
Phenylacetate				Increased
Phenylacetylglutamine			200–300	2400

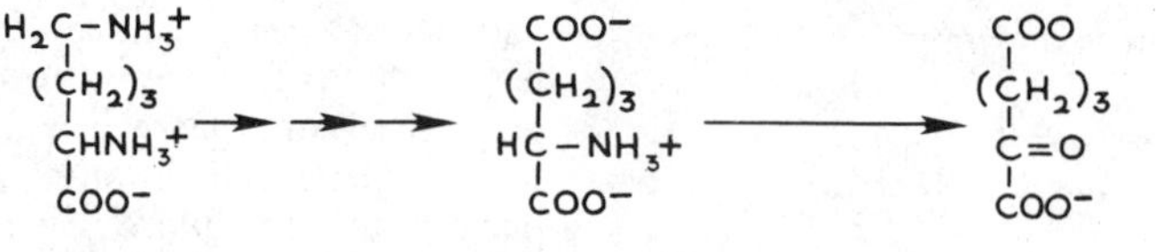

Figure 22–17. Conversion of L-lysine to α-aminoadipate and α-ketoadipate. Multiple arrows represent multiple reactions.

pipecolate, L-lysine is degraded via saccharopine (Fig 22–18), an intermediate in lysine biosynthesis by fungi.

L-Lysine first condenses with α-ketoglutarate, splitting out water and forming a Schiff base. This is reduced to saccharopine by a dehydrogenase and then oxidized by a second dehydrogenase. Addition of water forms L-glutamate and L-α-aminoadipate-δ-semialdehyde. The net effect of this reaction sequence is equivalent to removal of the ε nitrogen of lysine by transamination. One mole each of L-lysine and of α-ketoglutarate are converted to α-aminoadipate-δ-semialdehyde and glutamate. However, NAD$^+$ and NADH are specifically required as cofactors, even though no net oxidation or reduction occurs.

Further catabolism of α-aminoadipate involves transamination to α-ketoadipate, probably followed by oxidative decarboxylation to glutaryl-CoA. While lysine is both glycogenic and ketogenic, the nature of the subsequent catabolites of glutaryl-CoA in mammalian systems is not known.

Metabolic disorders of lysine catabolism. Two rare metabolic abnormalities of lysine catabolism have been described. Both result from defects in enzymes that catabolize lysine to acetoacetyl-CoA, and in both instances the primary defect appears to involve impaired conversion of L-lysine and α-ketoglutarate to saccharopine (Fig 22–18).

A. Periodic Hyperlysinemia With Associated Hyperammonemia: In periodic hyperlysinemia, ingestion of normal levels of protein triggers hyperlysinemia. Secondary to the hyperlysinemia, hyperammonemia results from competitive inhibition of liver arginase activity (Fig 21–13) by elevated levels of tissue lysine. Fluid therapy and restriction of dietary lysine intake relieve both the hyperammonemia and its clinical manifestations. Conversely, administration of a lysine load precipitates severe crises and coma. No information is available concerning the genetic basis of this disorder.

B. Persistent Hyperlysinemia Without Hyperammonemia: Clinical and biochemical findings have varied widely in the 12 reported cases of persistent hyperlysinemia. Some but not all patients are mentally retarded. There is no associated hyperammonemia, even in response to a lysine load. Lysine catabolites may or may not accumulate in biologic fluids. Persistent hyperlysinemia is believed to be inherited as an autosomal recessive trait. In addition to impaired conversion of lysine and α-ketoglutarate to saccharopine, some patients appear to have an additional deficiency

in the conversion of saccharopine to L-glutamate and α-aminoadipate-δ-semialdehyde (Fig 22–18).

Tryptophan

Tryptophan, notable for its variety of important metabolic reactions and products, was among the first amino acids shown to be nutritionally essential. *Neurospora* mutants, the bacterium *Pseudomonas,* and isolation of tryptophan metabolites from urine have proved invaluable aids in unraveling the details of tryptophan metabolism.

Although a large portion of the isotope of administered ^{14}C-L-tryptophan is incorporated into proteins, a considerable fraction appears in the urine as various catabolites. The carbon atoms both of the side chain and of the aromatic ring may be completely degraded to amphibolic intermediates via the **kynurenine-anthranilate pathway** (Fig 22–19), important both for tryptophan degradation and for conversion of tryptophan to **nicotinamide** (see Fig 10–11).

Tryptophan oxygenase (tryptophan pyrrolase) catalyzes cleavage of the indole ring with incorporation of 2 atoms of molecular oxygen, forming N-formylkynurenine. The oxygenase is an iron porphyrin metalloprotein present in the liver of mammals, amphibians, birds, and insects. Tryptophan oxygenase is inducible in liver by adrenal corticosteroids and tryptophan itself. A considerable portion of newly synthesized enzyme is in a latent form that requires activation. Tryptophan also stabilizes the oxygenase toward proteolytic degradation. Tryptophan oxygenase is feedback-inhibited by nicotinic acid derivatives, including NADPH.

Hydrolytic removal of the formyl group of N-formylkynurenine is catalyzed by **kynurenine formylase** of mammalian liver. Hydrolysis in H$_2$^{18}O$_2$ incorporates one equivalent of ^{18}O into the formate formed. The enzyme catalyzes similar reactions with various arylformylamines.

The reaction catalyzed by kynurenine formylase produces **kynurenine** (Fig 22–19). This may be deaminated by transamination of the amino group of the side chain to ketoglutarate. The resulting keto derivative, 2-amino-3-hydroxybenzoyl pyruvate, loses water, and spontaneous ring closure forms **kynurenic acid.** This compound, a by-product of kynurenine, is not formed in the main pathway of tryptophan breakdown (Fig 22–19).

Further metabolism of kynurenine involves conversion to **3-hydroxykynurenine,** which is converted to **3-hydroxyanthranilate.** Hydroxylation requires

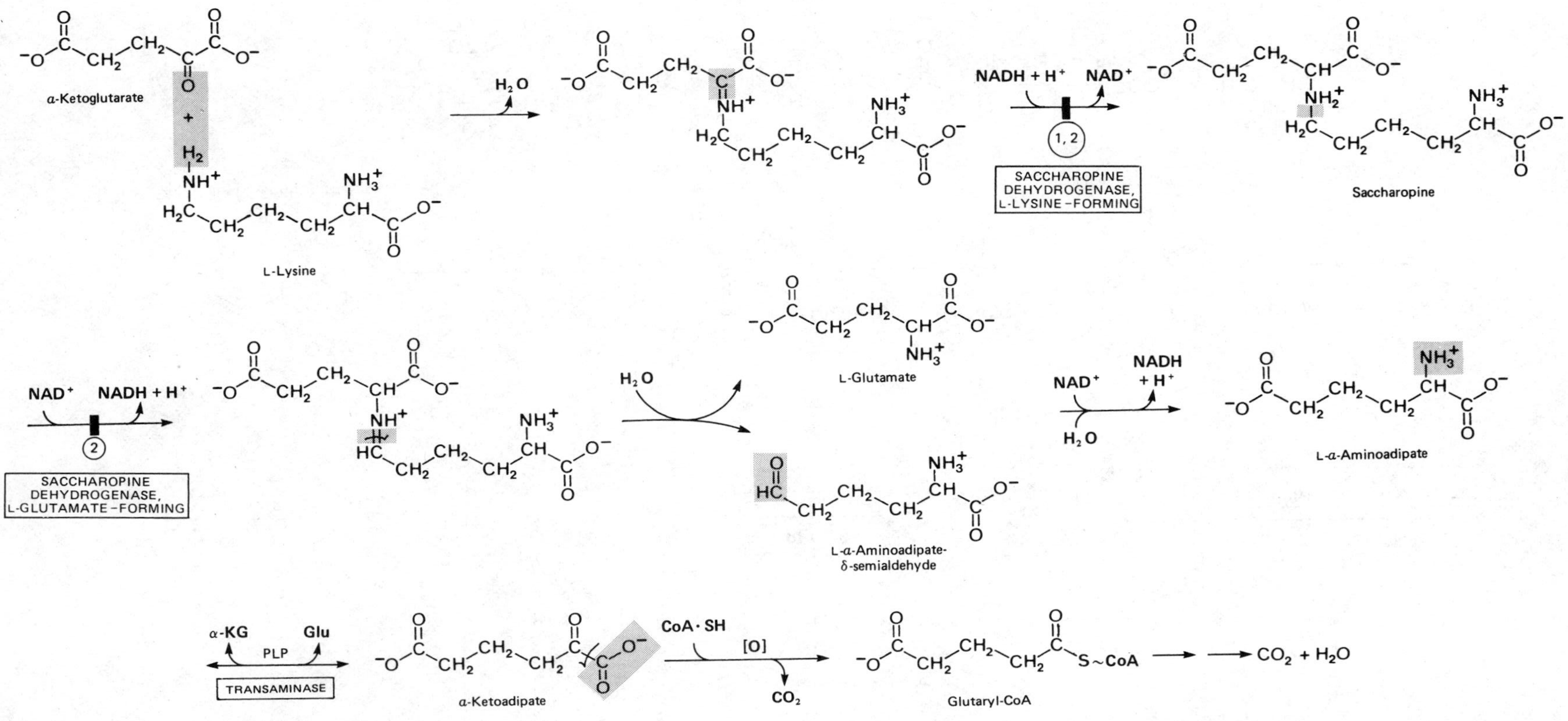

Figure 22–18. Catabolism of L-lysine. (α-KG, α-ketoglutarate; Glu, glutamate; PLP, pyridoxal phosphate.) The circled numerals indicate the probable sites of the metabolic defects in ① periodic hyperlysinemia with associated hyperammonemia, and ② persistent hyperlysinemia without associated hyperammonemia.

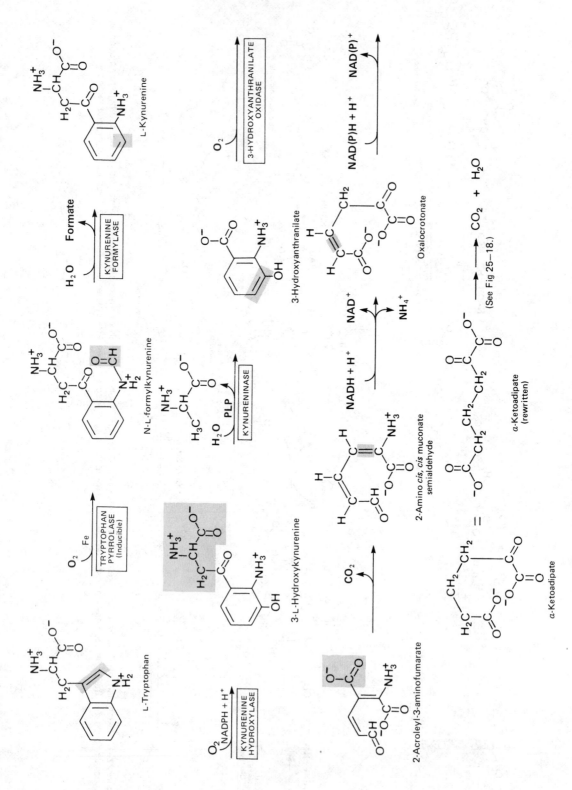

Figure 22–19. Catabolism of L-tryptophan. (PLP, pyridoxal phosphate.)

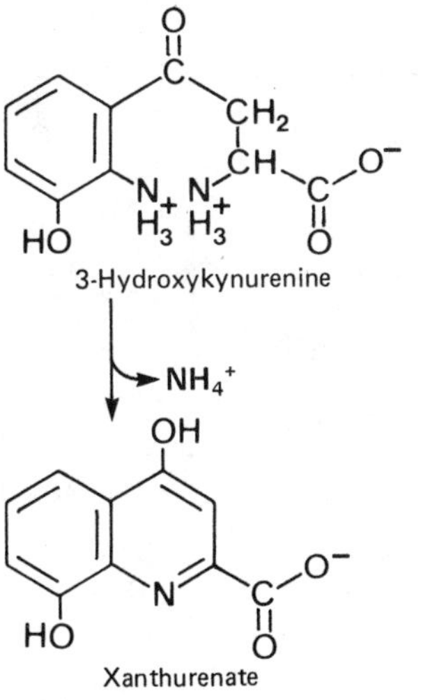

Figure 22–20. Formation of xanthurenate in vitamin B_6 deficiency. Conversion of the tryptophan metabolite 3-hydroxykynurenine to 3-hydroxyanthranilate is impaired (see Fig 22–19). A large portion is therefore converted to xanthurenate.

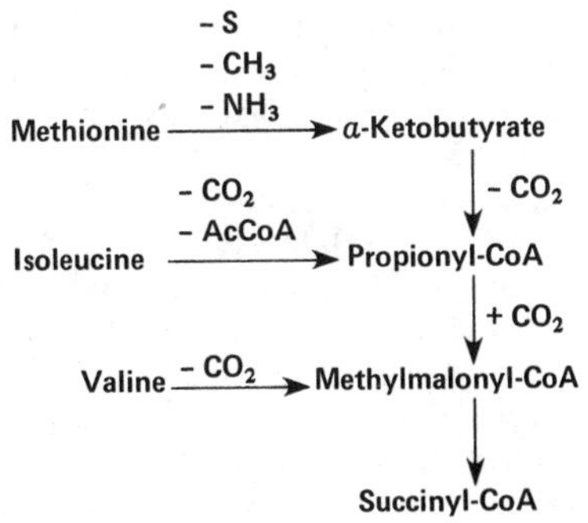

Figure 22–21. Overall catabolism of methionine, isoleucine, and valine to succinyl-CoA. AcCoA, acetyl-CoA.

molecular oxygen in an NADPH-dependent reaction similar to that for hydroxylation of phenylalanine (see Chapter 20).

Kynurenine and hydroxykynurenine are converted to hydroxyanthranilate by **kynureninase,** a pyridoxal phosphate enzyme. A deficiency of vitamin B_6 results in partial failure to catabolize these kynurenine derivatives, which thus reach extrahepatic tissues where they are converted to **xanthurenate** (Fig 22–20). This abnormal metabolite occurs in the urine of humans, monkeys, and rats when dietary vitamin B_6 is inadequate. Feeding excess tryptophan induces excretion of xanthurenate in vitamin B_6 deficiency.

In many animals, conversion of tryptophan to nicotinic acid makes a supply of the vitamin in the diet unnecessary (see Chapter 10). In the rat, rabbit, dog, and pig, tryptophan can completely replace the vitamin

in the diet; in humans and other animals, tryptophan increases the urinary excretion of nicotinic acid derivatives (eg, N-methylnicotinamide). In vitamin B_6 deficiency, synthesis of NAD^+ and $NADP^+$ may be impaired, a result of inadequate conversion of tryptophan to nicotinic acid for pyridine nucleotide synthesis. If an adequate supplement of nicotinic acid is supplied, pyridine nucleotide synthesis proceeds normally even in the absence of vitamin B_6.

Metabolic disorders of tryptophan catabolism. Hartnup disease, a hereditary abnormality in metabolism of tryptophan, is characterized by a pellagralike skin rash, intermittent cerebellar ataxia, and mental deterioration. The urine of patients with Hartnup disease contains greatly increased amounts of indoleacetate (α-N[indole-3-acetyl]glutamine) and tryptophan.

AMINO ACIDS FORMING SUCCINYL–COENZYME A

Overall Reactions

While succinyl-CoA is the amphibolic end product for catabolism of methionine, isoleucine, and valine, only portions of the skeletons are converted (Fig 22–21). Four-fifths of the carbons of valine, three-

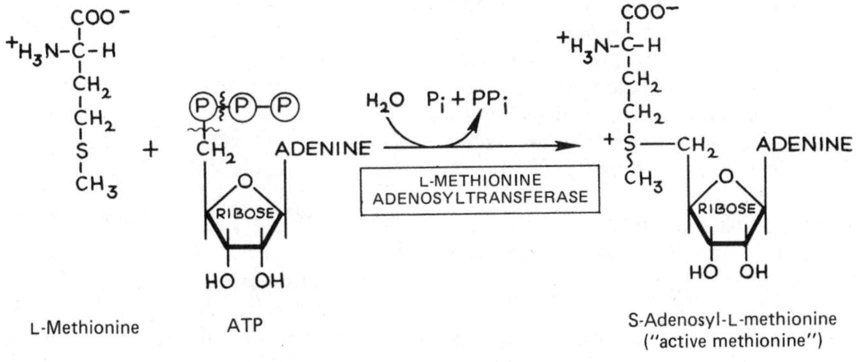

Figure 22–22. Formation of S-adenosylmethionine. The $\sim CH_3$ represents the high transfer potential of the CH_3 of "active methionine."

fifths of those of methionine, and half of those of isoleucine form succinyl-CoA. The carboxyl carbons of all 3 form CO_2. The terminal 2 carbons of isoleucine form acetyl-CoA, and the S-methyl group of methionine is removed as such.

What follows relates only to conversion of methionine and isoleucine to propionyl-CoA and of valine to methylmalonyl-CoA. The reactions leading from propionyl-CoA through methylmalonyl-CoA to succinyl-CoA are discussed in Chapters 10 and 17 in connection with catabolism of propionate and of fatty acids containing an odd number of carbon atoms.

Methionine

L-Methionine condenses with ATP, forming S-adenosylmethionine, or "active methionine" (Fig 22–22). The activated S-methyl group may transfer to various acceptor compounds.* Removal of the methyl group forms S-adenosylhomocysteine. Hydrolysis of the S–C bond yields L-homocysteine plus adenosine. Homocysteine then condenses with serine, forming cystathionine. Hydrolytic cleavage of cystathionine forms L-homoserine plus cysteine, so that the net effect is conversion of homocysteine to homoserine and of serine to cysteine. These 2 reactions are therefore also involved in biosynthesis of cysteine from serine (see Chapter 20). Homoserine is converted to α-ketobutyrate by homoserine deaminase (Fig 22–24). Conversion of α-ketobutyrate to propionyl-CoA then occurs in the usual manner for oxidative decarboxylation of α-keto acids (eg, pyruvate, α-ketoglutarate) to form acyl-CoA derivatives.

Metabolic disorders of methionine catabolism. See Table 22–2.

Leucine, Valine, & Isoleucine

As might be suspected from their structural similarities, catabolism of L-leucine, L-valine, and L-isoleucine initially involves the same reactions. This common pathway then diverges, and each amino acid skeleton follows a unique pathway to amphibolic intermediates (Figs 22–25 and 22–26). The nature of these amphibolic end products (β-hydroxy-β-methylglutaryl-CoA, succinyl-CoA, and acetyl-CoA) determines whether an amino acid is glycogenic (valine), ketogenic (leucine), or both (isoleucine). **Many of the reactions involved are analogous to reactions of straight- and branched-chain fatty acid catabolism.** Because of the similarities noted in Fig 22–26, it is convenient to discuss initial reactions in catabolism of all 3 amino acids together. In what follows, reaction numbers refer to reactions of Figs 22–26 through 22–29.

A. Transamination: Reversible transamination (reaction 1) of all 3 branched L-α-amino acids in mammalian tissues probably involves a single trans-

*Compounds whose methyl groups derive from S-adenosylmethionine include betaines, choline, creatine, epinephrine, melatonin, sarcosine, N-methylated amino acids, nucleotides, and many plant alkaloids.

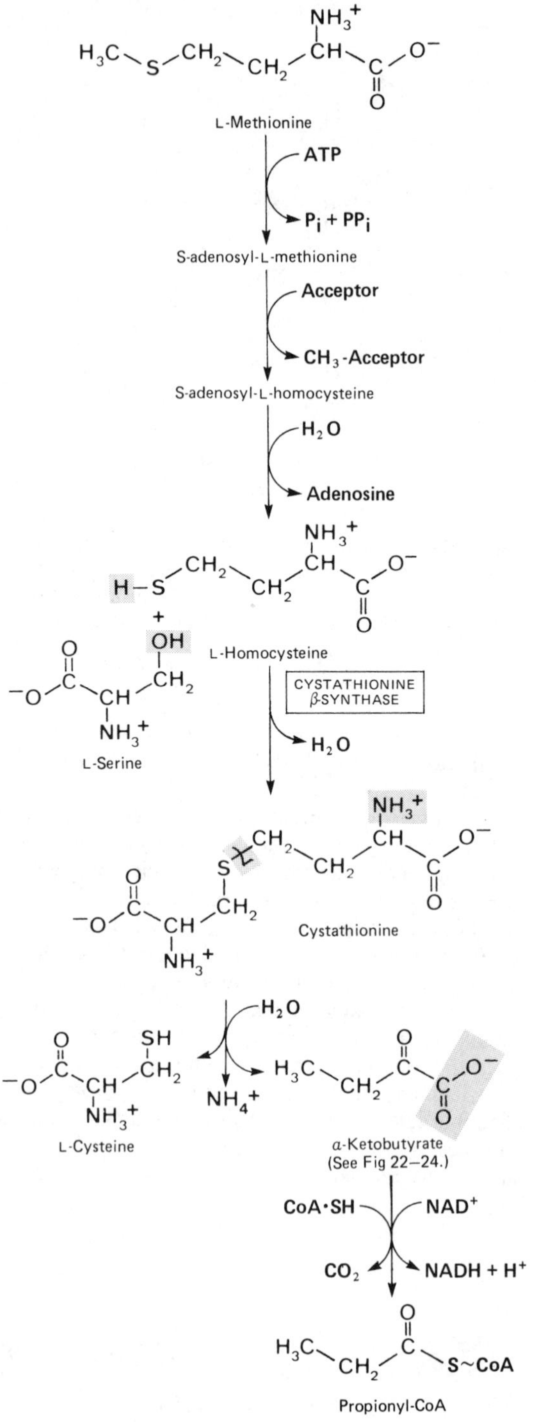

Figure 22–23. Conversion of methionine to propionyl-CoA.

aminase. Reversibility of this reaction accounts for the ability of the corresponding α-keto acids to replace the L-α-amino acids in the diet if other adequate sources of N are available.

B. Oxidative Decarboxylation to Acyl-CoA Thioesters: This reaction (reaction 2) is analogous to

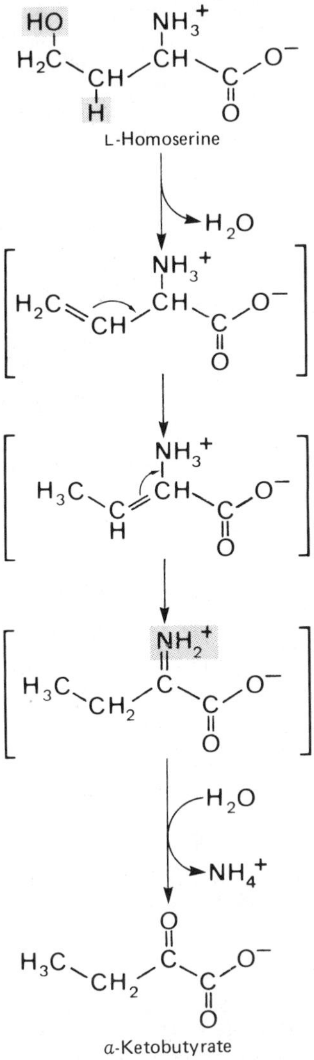

HO   NH₃⁺
H₂C—CH—CH—C—O⁻
      | ||
      H   O
L-Homoserine

↓ ⟶ H₂O

$$\left[\begin{array}{c} NH_3^+ \\ H_2C=CH-CH-C-O^- \\ \qquad \qquad \quad || \\ \qquad \qquad \quad O \end{array}\right]$$

↓

$$\left[\begin{array}{c} NH_3^+ \\ H_3C-C=CH-C-O^- \\ \qquad \quad H \qquad || \\ \qquad \qquad \quad O \end{array}\right]$$

↓

$$\left[\begin{array}{c} NH_2^+ \\ || \\ H_3C-CH_2-C-C-O^- \\ \qquad \qquad \quad || \\ \qquad \qquad \quad O \end{array}\right]$$

↓ ⟶ H₂O

↓ ⟶ NH₄⁺

O
||
H₃C—CH₂—C—C—O⁻
              ||
              O
α-Ketobutyrate

Figure 22–24. Conversion of L-homoserine to α-ketobutyrate, by homoserine deaminase.

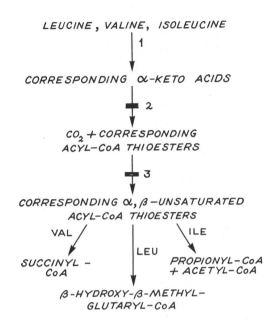

Figure 22–25. Catabolism of the branched-chain amino acids in mammals. Reactions *1–3* are common to all 3 amino acids; thereafter, the pathways diverge. Double lines intersecting arrows mark sites of metabolic blocks in 2 rare human diseases: at *2*, maple syrup urine disease, a defect in catabolism of all 3 amino acids; and at *3*, isovaleric acidemia, a defect of leucine catabolism.

oxidation of pyruvate to acetyl-CoA and CO_2 by pyruvate dehydrogenase and of α-ketoglutarate to CO_2 and succinyl-CoA by α-ketoglutarate dehydrogenase (see Chapter 15). The mammalian branched-chain α-keto acid dehydrogenase is an intramitochondrial multienzyme complex of molecular weight greater than 2 million. The complex catalyzes oxidative decarboxylation of α-ketoisocaproate (from leucine), α-keto-β-methylvalerate (from isoleucine), and α-ketoisovalerate (from valine).

The branched-chain α-keto acid dehydrogenase complex is composed of subunits analogous to those of pyruvate dehydrogenase. The catalytic activities associated with these subunits are an α-keto acid decarboxylase, a transacylase, and a dihydrolipoyl dehydrogenase. As is also true for pyruvate dehydrogenase, the complex is inactivated when phosphorylated by

ATP in a reaction catalyzed by a protein kinase. A Ca^{2+}-independent phosphoprotein phosphatase catalyzes its dephosphorylation and accompanying reactivation. The phosphorylation state thus can regulate the catabolism of the branched-chain amino acids. The protein kinase is inhibited by ADP, the branched-chain α-keto acid products, the hypolipidemic agents clofibrate and dichloroacetate, and coenzyme A thioesters (eg, acetoacetyl-CoA). Of the branched-chain α-keto acids, α-ketoisocaproate (α-ketoleucine) is the most potent inhibitor. This may be related to the differential abilities of leucine (as opposed to valine or isoleucine) to affect amino acid metabolism, protein synthesis and degradation, and insulin release.

C. Dehydrogenation to α,β-Unsaturated Acyl-CoA Thioesters: This reaction (reaction 3) is analogous to dehydrogenation of straight-chain acyl-CoA thioesters in fatty acid catabolism. It is not known whether a single enzyme catalyzes dehydrogenation of all 3 branched acyl-CoA thioesters. Indirect evidence suggesting that at least 2 enzymes are required derives from **isovaleric acidemia** wherein, following ingestion of protein-rich foods, isovalerate accumulates in the blood. An increase in other branched α-keto acids does not occur. Isovalerate is formed by deacylation of isovaleryl-CoA, the substrate for the above dehydrogenase. Its formation suggests accumulation of isovaleryl-CoA, possibly due to a defective isovaleryl-CoA dehydrogenase. If a single dehy-

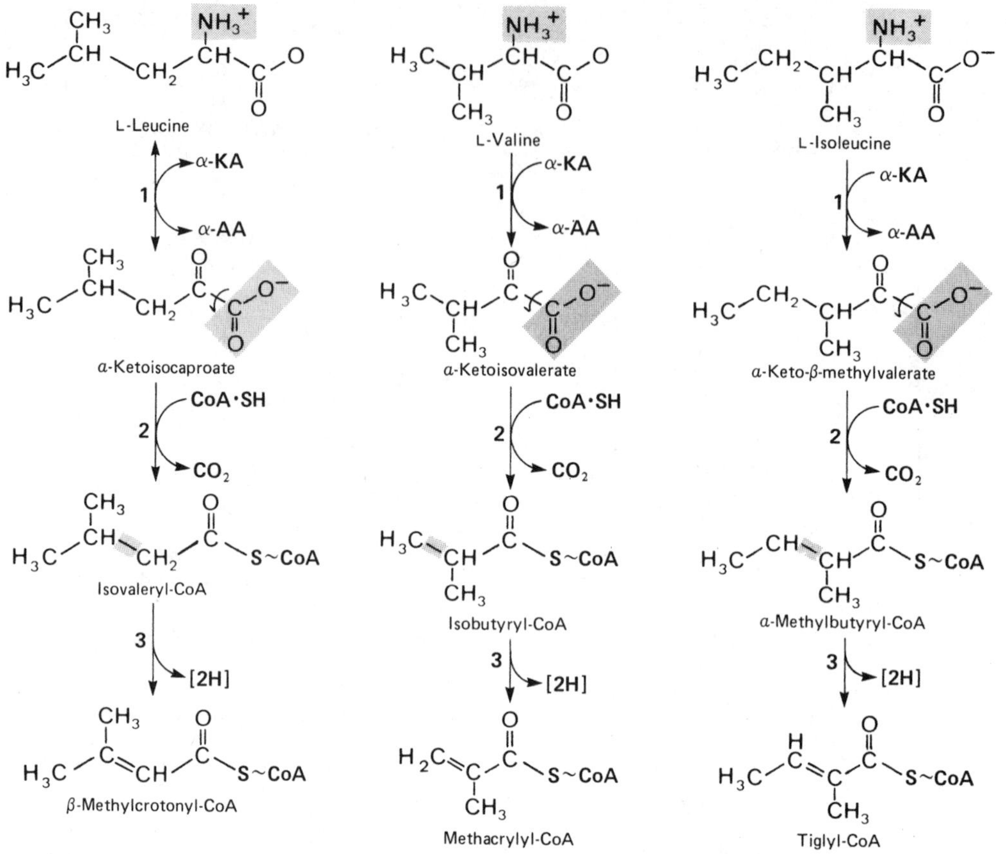

Figure 22–26. The analogous first 3 reactions in the catabolism of leucine, valine, and isoleucine. Note also the analogy in reactions 2 and 3 to the catabolism of fatty acids. This latter analogy continues, as shown in subsequent figures.

drogenase served to dehydrogenate all 3 branched acyl-CoA thioesters, accumulation of isobutyrate (from valine) and α-methylbutyrate (from isoleucine) would be anticipated following a protein-rich meal.

Reactions Specific to Leucine Catabolism
(Fig 22–27.)

Reaction 4L: Carboxylation of β-methylcro-tonyl-CoA. A key observation leading to explanation of the ketogenic action of leucine was the discovery that 1 mol of CO_2 was "fixed" (ie, covalently bound) per mole of isopropyl groups (from the terminal isopropyl group of leucine) converted to acetoacetate. This CO_2 fixation (reaction 4L, Fig 22–27) requires biotinyl-CO_2, formed from enzyme-bound biotin and CO_2 at the expense of ATP. Both in bacteria and in mammalian liver, this reaction forms β-methylglutaconyl-CoA as an intermediate.

Reaction 5L: Hydration of β-methylgluta-conyl-CoA. The reaction product, β-hydroxy-β-methylglutaryl-CoA, is a precursor not only of ketone bodies (reaction 6L, Fig 22–27) but also of mevalonate, and hence of cholesterol and other polyisoprenoids (see Chapter 15).

Reaction 6L: Cleavage of β-hydroxy-β-methyl-glutaryl-CoA. Cleavage of β-hydroxy-β-methylglutaryl-CoA to acetyl-CoA and acetoacetate occurs in mammalian liver, kidney, and heart mitochondria. It explains the strongly ketogenic effect of leucine, since not only is 1 mol of acetoacetate formed per mole of leucine catabolized but another ½ mole of ketone bodies may be formed indirectly from the remaining product, acetyl-CoA (see Chapter 15).

Reactions Specific to Valine Catabolism
(Fig 22–28.)

Reaction 4V: Hydration of methylacrylyl-CoA. This reaction, which occurs nonenzymatically at a relatively rapid rate, is catalyzed by crotonase, a hydrolase of broad specificity for L-β-hydroxyacyl-CoA thioesters having 4–9 carbon atoms.

Reaction 5V: Deacylation of β-hydroxyisobu-tyryl-CoA. Since the CoA thioester is not a substrate for the subsequent reaction (reaction 6V, Fig 22–28), it must first be deacylated to β-hydroxyisobutyrate (reaction 5V, Fig 22–28). This is catalyzed by a deacylase, present in many animal tissues, whose only other substrate is β-hydroxypropionyl-CoA.

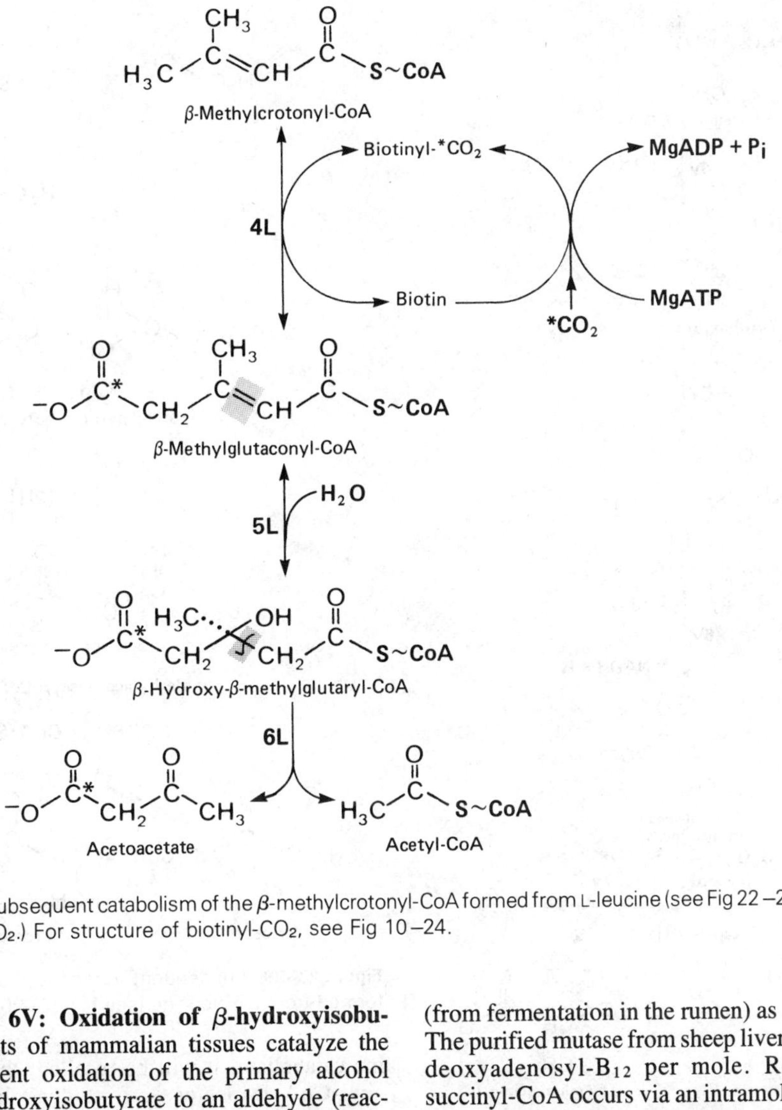

Figure 22–27. Subsequent catabolism of the β-methylcrotonyl-CoA formed from L-leucine (see Fig 22–26). (*Carbon atoms derived from CO_2.) For structure of biotinyl-CO_2, see Fig 10–24.

Reaction 6V: Oxidation of β-hydroxyisobutyrate. Extracts of mammalian tissues catalyze the NAD^+-dependent oxidation of the primary alcohol group of β-hydroxyisobutyrate to an aldehyde (reaction 6V, Fig 25–25), forming methylmalonate semialdehyde. The reaction is readily reversible.

Reaction 7V: Fate of methylmalonate semialdehyde. Two fates are possible for methylmalonate semialdehyde in mammalian tissues: transamination to β-aminoisobutyrate (reaction 7V, Fig 22–28) and conversion to succinyl-CoA (reactions 8V through 10V, Fig 22–28). Transamination to α-aminoisobutyrate, a normal urinary amino acid, is catalyzed by various mammalian tissues including kidney. The second major fate involves oxidation to methylmalonate, acylation to methylmalonyl-CoA, and isomerization to succinyl-CoA (reactions 8V through 10V, Fig 22–28). Isomerization (reaction 10V, Fig 22–28) requires adenosylcobalamin coenzyme and is catalyzed by methylmalonyl-CoA mutase. This reaction is important not only for valine catabolism but also for that of propionyl-CoA, a catabolite of isoleucine (Fig 22–29). In cobalamin (vitamin B_{12}) deficiency, mutase activity is impaired. This produces a "dietary metabolic defect" in ruminants that utilize propionate

(from fermentation in the rumen) as an energy source. The purified mutase from sheep liver contains 2 mol of deoxyadenosyl-B_{12} per mole. Rearrangement to succinyl-CoA occurs via an intramolecular shift of the CoA-carboxyl group. Although the overall reaction resembles isomerization of threo-β-methylaspartate to glutamate, the reaction mechanisms appear to differ.

Reactions Specific to Isoleucine Catabolism (Fig 22–29.)

As with valine and leucine, the first data concerning isoleucine catabolism came from dietary studies in intact animals that identified isoleucine as glycogenic and weakly ketogenic. Glycogen synthesis from isoleucine was confirmed using D_2O. Use of ^{14}C-labeled intermediates and liver slice preparations revealed that the isoleucine skeleton was cleaved, forming acetyl-CoA and propionyl-CoA (Fig 22–29).

Reaction 4I: Hydration of tiglyl-CoA. This reaction, like the analogous reaction in valine catabolism (reaction 4V, Fig 22–28), is catalyzed by mammalian crotonase.

Reaction 5I: Dehydrogenation of α-methyl-β-hydroxybutyryl-CoA. This reaction is analogous to reaction 5V of valine catabolism (Fig 22–28). In val-

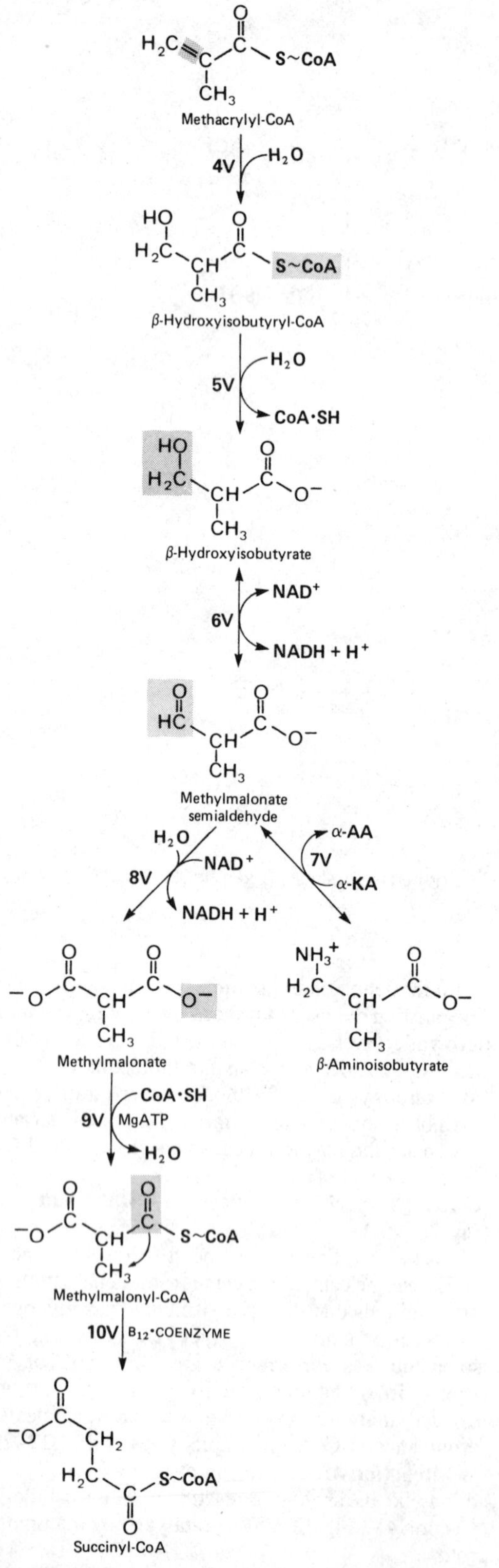

Figure 22–28. Subsequent catabolism of the methacrylyl-CoA formed from L-valine (see Fig 22–26). (α-KA, α-keto acid; α-AA, α-amino acid.)

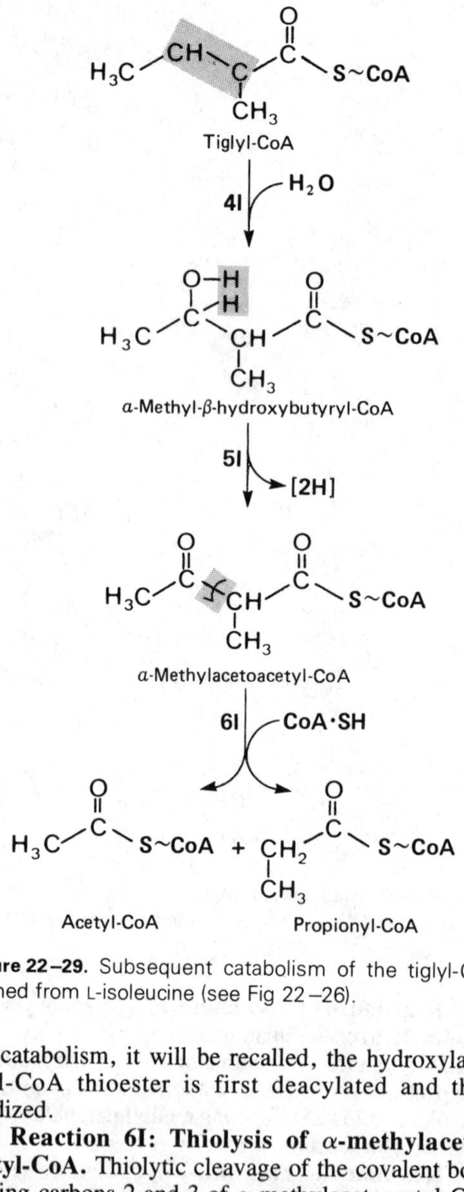

Figure 22–29. Subsequent catabolism of the tiglyl-CoA formed from L-isoleucine (see Fig 22–26).

ine catabolism, it will be recalled, the hydroxylated acyl-CoA thioester is first deacylated and then oxidized.

Reaction 6I: Thiolysis of α-methylaceto-acetyl-CoA. Thiolytic cleavage of the covalent bond linking carbons 2 and 3 of α-methylacetoacetyl-CoA resembles thiolysis of acetoacetyl-CoA to 2 mol of acetyl-CoA catalyzed by β-ketothiolase. The products, acetyl-CoA (ketogenic) and propionyl-CoA (glycogenic), account for the ketogenic and glycogenic properties of isoleucine.

Metabolic Defects of Branched-Chain Amino Acid Catabolism (Leucine, Valine, Isoleucine)

Four defects in branched-chain amino acid catabolism are known. Of these, maple syrup urine disease has been most extensively studied. Over 50 cases have been reported. The incidence of the disease has been estimated as 5–10 per million live births. Hypervalinemia, intermittent branched-chain ketonuria, and isovaleric acidemia have been reported in fewer than 5 children.

Table 22–5. Ability of leukocytes from a patient with hypervalinemia and of leukocytes from 2 normal individuals to catalyze transamination of branched-chain amino acids.*

Amino Acid	Relative Rate of Transamination	
	Hypervalinemia	Control (Range)
Valine	0	70–135
Isoleucine	346	220–270
Leucine	387	140–185

*From Dancis J et al: Hypervalinemia: A defect in valine transamination. *Pediatrics* 1967;**39**:813.

A. Hypervalinemia: This metabolic disease, characterized by elevated plasma levels of valine (but not of leucine or isoleucine), reflects the inability to transaminate valine to α-ketoisovalerate (reaction 1, Fig 22–26). However, transamination of leucine and isoleucine (reaction 1, Fig 22–26) is unimpaired. (See Table 22–5.) In the one known instance of hypervalinemia, feeding a diet low in valine prevented vomiting, improved weight gain, and reduced hyperkinesia.

B. Maple Syrup Urine Disease: As the name implies, the most striking feature of this hereditary disease is the characteristic odor of the urine, which resembles that of maple syrup or burnt sugar. In afflicted individuals, plasma and urinary levels of the branched-chain amino acids leucine, isoleucine, and valine and their corresponding α-keto acids are greatly elevated (Table 22–6). For this reason, the disease has also been termed **branched-chain ketonuria.** Smaller quantities of branched-chain α-hydroxy acids, formed by reduction of the α-keto acids, also are present in the urine.

Although the afflicted newborn infant initially appears normal, characteristic signs of the disease are evident by the end of the first week of extrauterine life. In addition to the biochemical abnormalities described above, the infant is difficult to feed and may vomit. The patient may also exhibit lethargy. Diagnosis prior to 1 week of age is possible only by enzymic analysis. Extensive brain damage occurs in surviving children. Without treatment, death usually occurs by the end of the first year of life.

The biochemical defect is the absence or greatly reduced activity of the α-**keto acid decarboxylase** that catalyzes conversion of all 3 branched-chain α-keto acids to CO_2 plus acyl-CoA thioesters (reaction 2, Fig 22–26). This was established by enzymic analysis of leukocytes and of cultured skin fibroblasts from afflicted children. The mechanism of toxicity, which is

Table 22–6. Plasma levels of branched-chain amino acids in normal individuals and in 3 patients with maple syrup urine disease.

Amino Acid	Concentration (mg/dL)			
	Normal (Range)	Maple Syrup Urine Disease, Patient		
		A	B	C
Leucine	1.5–3.0	52	14	21
Valine	2.0–3.0	24	13	14
Isoleucine	0.8–1.5	18	2.2	8.5

probably complex, is unknown. Possible factors in toxicity include the ability of large excesses of the branched-chain amino acids to impair transport of other amino acids, to alter amino acid pool sizes, and thus, possibly, to impair protein synthesis. All 3 branched-chain α-keto acids also are competitive inhibitors of L-glutamate dehydrogenase activity (see Fig 21–6).

Early diagnosis is very important, so that the patient can be placed on a diet in which protein is replaced by a mixture of purified amino acids from which leucine, isoleucine, and valine are omitted. When plasma levels of these amino acids fall within the normal range, they are restored to the diet in the form of milk and other foods in amounts adequate to supply—but not to exceed—the requirements for branched-chain amino acids. There is no indication when, if ever, dietary restrictions may be eased. One fatality occurred as late as age 8. In those cases where treatment was initiated in the first week of life, considerable success was achieved in mitigating the dire consequences of the disease.

C. Intermittent Branched-Chain Ketonuria: This disease, a variant of maple syrup urine disease, probably reflects a less severe structural modification of the α-**keto acid decarboxylase.** The decarboxylase activity of leukocytes and of fibroblasts, while distinctly lower than that of normal individuals, is well above those characteristic of classic maple syrup urine disease. Since affected individuals appear to possess an impaired but nevertheless distinct capability for catabolism of leucine, valine, and isoleucine, it is perhaps understandable that the typical symptoms of maple syrup urine disease occur later in life and only intermittently. The prognosis for successful use of dietary therapy would appear to be far more favorable in these individuals.

Taken together, maple syrup urine disease and intermittent branched-chain ketonuria appear to illustrate the situation described in the introduction to this section—mutations causing different changes in the primary structure of the same enzyme. It is probable that a spectrum of activities ranging from frank disease through intermittent manifestations to normal values in fact occurs in individual subjects.

D. Isovaleric Acidemia: Relevant findings include a persistent "cheesy" odor of the breath and body fluids, vomiting, acidosis, and coma precipitated by excessive ingestion of protein or by an episode of infectious disease. Mild mental retardation was associated with the 3 known cases. The impaired enzyme is **isovaleryl-CoA dehydrogenase** (reaction 3, Fig 22–26). Isovaleryl-CoA thus accumulates, is hydrolyzed to isovalerate, and is excreted in the urine and sweat.

Additional Metabolic Defects Related to Amino Acid Catabolism (Propionate, Methylmalonate, & Vitamin B_{12})

Propionyl-CoA (Fig 22–21) is formed from isoleucine (Fig 22–26) and methionine (Fig 22–23), as well as from the side chain of cholesterol and from fatty acids with odd numbers of carbon atoms. The conversion of propionyl-CoA to amphibolic intermediates involves biotin-dependent carboxylation to methylmalonyl-CoA. Methylmalonyl-CoA also is formed directly (ie, without prior formation of propionyl-CoA) from valine (Figs 22–21 and 22–28, reaction 9V). A vitamin B_{12} coenzyme–dependent isomerization converts methylmalonyl-CoA to succinyl-CoA, a citric acid cycle intermediate, which is oxidized to CO_2 and water.

Shortly after the discovery that 5'-deoxyadenosylcobalamin is a cofactor for the isomerization of methylmalonyl-CoA to succinyl-CoA, patients with acquired vitamin B_{12} deficiency were observed to excrete large quantities of methylmalonate in their urine. This methylmalonic aciduria disappeared when sufficient vitamin B_{12} was administered.

A. Propionic Acidemia: Propionyl-CoA carboxylase deficiency is characterized by high serum propionate levels and by defective catabolism of propionate by leukocytes. Treatment involves feeding a low-protein diet and measures to counteract metabolic acidosis.

B. Methylmalonic Aciduria: Two forms of methylmalonic aciduria are known. One responds to parenteral administration of physiologic doses of vitamin B_{12}; the other does not. A patient with this latter condition responded favorably to massive (pharmacologic) doses (1 g/d) of vitamin B_{12}. When fibroblasts from this patient were cultured in a medium containing vitamin B_{12} (25 pg/mL) and were oxidized with ^{14}C-propionate, they were found to oxidize poorly. The cultured cells contained only about 10% as much 5'-deoxyadenosylcobalamin as did control cells. When the concentration of vitamin B_{12} in the medium was increased 10,000-fold, the rate of propionate oxidation and the intracellular concentration of 5'-deoxyadenosylcobalamin both approached normal. No defect in binding the coenzyme to the mutase apoenzyme was observed. The defect in the latter form of methylmalonic aciduria thus appears to be the inability to form 5'-deoxyadenosylcobalamin from normal levels of the vitamin.

The above selection of inherited diseases of amino acid catabolism is generally confined to the better studied diseases now known. For a more extensive recent review of this subject, see Wellner and Meister, 1981.

● ● ●

References

Conversion of the Carbon Skeletons of the Common Amino Acids to Amphibolic Intermediates

Cooper AJL: Biochemistry of the sulfur-containing amino acids. *Annu Rev Biochem* 1983;**52:**187.

Felig P: Amino acid metabolism in man. *Annu Rev Biochem* 1975;**44:**933.

Greenberg DM, Rodwell VW: Carbon catabolism of amino acids. Pages 95 and 191 in: *Metabolic Pathways.* Vol 3. Greenberg DM (editor). Academic Press, 1969.

Meister A: *Biochemistry of the Amino Acids,* 2nd ed. Vol 2. Academic Press, 1965.

Paxton R, Harris RA: Isolation of rabbit liver branched chain α-ketoacid dehydrogenase and regulation by phosphorylation. *J Biol Chem* 1982;**257:**14433.

Paxton R, Harris RA: Regulation of branched-chain α-ketoacid dehydrogenase kinase. *Arch Biochem Biophys* 1984;**231:**48.

Metabolic Defects in Amino Acid Metabolism

Bremer HJ et al: *Amino Acid Metabolism: Clinical Chemistry and Diagnosis.* Urban & Schwarzenberg, 1981.

Frimter GW: Aminoacidurias due to disorders of metabolism. (2 parts.) *N Engl J Med* 1973;**289:**835, 895.

Morris DR, Fillingame RH: Regulation of amino acid decarboxylation. *Annu Rev Biochem* 1974;**43:**303.

Motulsky AG: Brave new world? *Science* 1974;**185:**653.

Nyhan WL (Editor): *Heritable Disorders of Amino Acid Metabolism: Patterns of Clinical Expression and Genetic Variation.* Wiley, 1974.

Schwarz V: *A Clinical Companion to Biochemical Studies.* Freeman, 1978.

Shih VE: *Laboratory Techniques for the Detection of Hereditary Metabolic Disorders.* CRC Press, 1973.

Stanbury JB et al (editors): *The Metabolic Basis of Inherited Disease,* 5th ed. McGraw-Hill, 1983.

Wellner D, Meister A: A survey of inborn errors of amino acid metabolism and transport in man. *Annu Rev Biochem* 1981;**50:**911.

Conversion of Amino Acids to Specialized Products | 23

Victor W. Rodwell, PhD

Amino acids, the primary source of nitrogen for animals, serve as precursors for other nitrogenous compounds. These include heme, purines, pyrimidines, hormones, and neurotransmitters including biologically active peptides. In addition, many proteins contain amino acids that have been modified for a specific function, eg, calcium binding or crosslinking, and thus the amino acid residues in those proteins serve as precursors for these modified residues. Finally, there are small peptides or peptidelike molecules not synthesized on ribosomes that carry out

specific functions in cells. Since most of these products are not amino acids per se, the discussion merges with metabolic pathways discussed elsewhere in this book.

GLYCINE

Synthesis of Heme

The α-carbon and nitrogen atoms of glycine are used for synthesis of the porphyrin moiety of hemo-

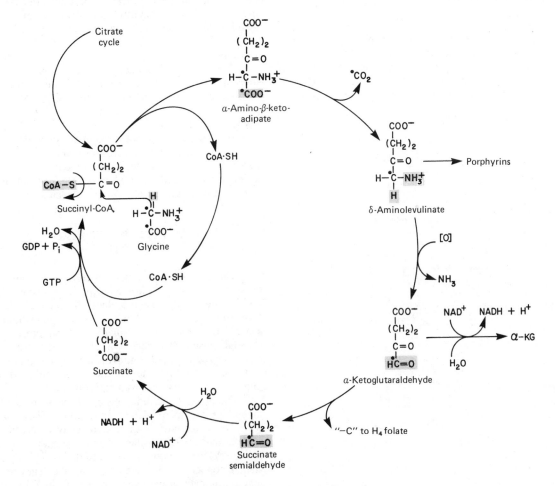

Figure 23–1. The succinate-glycine cycle.

globin (see Chapter 24). The pyrrole nitrogen is derived from glycine nitrogen and an adjoining carbon from the α carbon of glycine. The α carbon is also the source of the methylene bridge atoms linking the pyrrole rings.

In the "**succinate-glycine cycle**" (Fig 23–1), succinyl-CoA condenses on the α-carbon atom of glycine to form α-amino-β-ketoadipate. This links glycine metabolism to the citric acid cycle, which provides succinyl-CoA. α-Amino-β-ketoadipate is decarboxylated to δ-aminolevulinate, a precursor for porphyrin synthesis. Succinate and α-ketoglutarate (α-KG), which may return to the citric acid cycle, are also formed.

Metabolic disorders of heme metabolism are discussed in Chapter 24.

Synthesis of Purines

The entire glycine molecule is utilized to form positions 4, 5, and 7 of the purine skeleton. (See Chapter 26.)

Synthesis of Glutathione

Glycine is a precursor of the glycine tripeptide glutathione (Fig 3–12).

Conjugation

Glycine conjugates with cholic acid, forming glycocholic acid (see Chapter 44). With benzoate, it forms hippurate (Fig 23–2). The quantitative ability of liver to convert a measured dose of benzoate to hippurate formerly was used as a test of liver function.

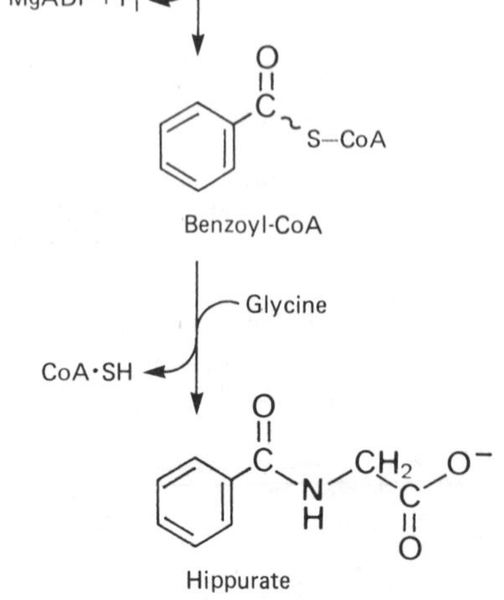

Figure 23–2. Hippurate biosynthesis.

Synthesis of Creatine

The sarcosine (N-methylglycine) component of creatine is derived from glycine and S-adenosylmethionine.

α-ALANINE

Alanine, together with glycine, makes up a considerable fraction of the amino nitrogen in human plasma. Both D- and L-alanine are utilized by tissues, but at differing rates. Alanine is a major component of bacterial cell walls, partly as the D-isomer: 39–50% in *Streptococcus faecalis*; 67% in *Staphylococcus aureus*.

β-ALANINE

Little free β-alanine is present in tissues. Considerably more is present as β-alanyl dipeptides (see below) and as coenzyme A (see Fig 10–22).

Biosynthesis

While microorganisms form β-alanine by α-decarboxylation of aspartate, mammalian tissue β-alanine arises principally from catabolism of uracil (see Fig 26–17), carnosine, and anserine (Fig 23–3).

Catabolism

Catabolism of β-alanine in mammals involves transamination to malonate semialdehyde, which is then oxidized to acetate and thence to CO_2.

Hyper-β-alaninemia

In this rare metabolic disorder (one reported case), free β-alanine levels are elevated in body fluids (plasma, cerebrospinal fluid, urine) and tissues (brain, kidney, liver, and skeletal muscle). Taurine and β-aminoisobutyrate levels also are elevated.

β-ALANYL & RELATED DIPEPTIDES

The major fraction of β-alanine in humans is present in the skeletal muscle dipeptide carnosine (Fig 23–3). The closely related β-alanyl dipeptide anserine (N-methylcarnosine or β-alanyl-1-methyl-L-histidine; Fig 23–3) is absent from human muscle but present in skeletal muscle of species whose skeletal muscle is characterized by rapid contractile activity (rabbit limb and bird pectoral muscle). It thus may fulfill physiologic functions distinct from carnosine.

The physiologic functions of β-alanyl-imidazole dipeptides are incompletely understood. They may serve to buffer the pH of anaerobically contracting skeletal muscle. Carnosine and anserine both activate myosin ATPase activity in vitro. Both dipeptides also chelate copper and enhance copper uptake. They thus may participate in pathologic processes in Wilson's disease (see Chapter 6).

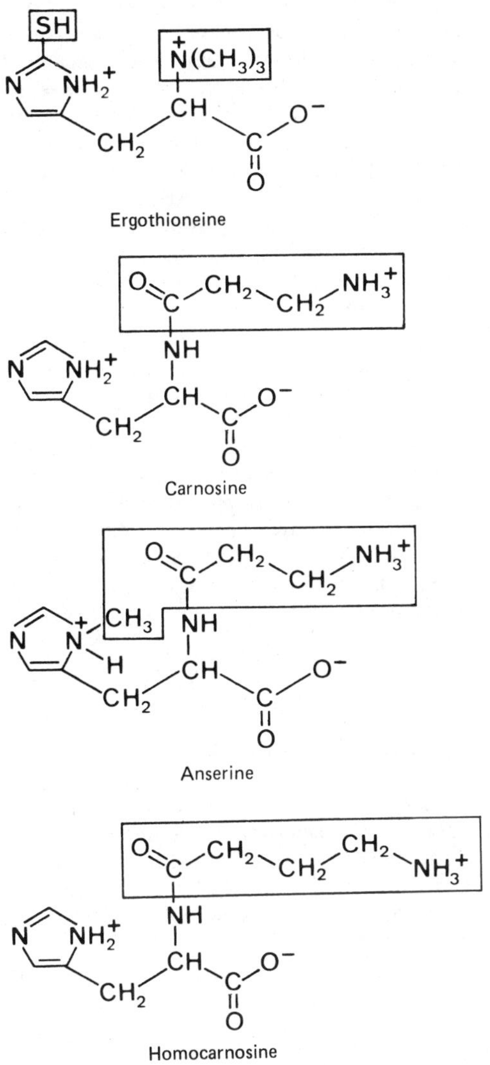

Ergothioneine

Carnosine

Anserine

Homocarnosine

Figure 23–3. Compounds related to histidine. The boxes surround the components not derived from histidine.

Biosynthesis

Carnosine is formed from β-alanine and L-histidine in an ATP-requiring reaction catalyzed by carnosine synthetase:

ATP + L-Histidine + β-Alanine → AMP + PP$_i$ + Carnosine

Anserine is formed from carnosine (the methyl group donor is S-adenosylmethionine) in a reaction catalyzed by carnosine N-methyltransferase:

S-adenosylmethionine + Carnosine →

S-adenosylhomocysteine + Anserine

The overall reaction involves enzyme-bound β-alanyl-adenylate (see Chapter 6).

Uptake of β-Alanyl Dipeptides

Kidney tissue and intestinal enterocytes take up carnosine and β-alanine by membrane carriers that discriminate one substrate from the other and both from other dipeptides. This ability to differentiate β-alanine from carnosine uptake has been applied to the definition of Hartnup disease, a heritable disorder in the transport of certain neutral α-amino acids (see Chapter 22). In patients with Hartnup disease, the blood histidine response is normal if carnosine is fed but is attenuated following administration of L-histidine.

Catabolism

Carnosine is hydrolyzed to β-alanine and L-histidine by the serum zinc metalloenzyme carnosinase (carnosine hydrolase). Two forms of carnosinase are present in serum.

Homocarnosine

The physiologic function of homocarnosine (γ-aminobutyryl-L-histidine; Fig 23–3), a central nervous system dipeptide closely related structurally and metabolically to carnosine, is not known. This dipeptide of γ-aminobutyrate and L-histidine is present in human brain tissue, where its concentration varies with the region examined. Biosynthesis of homocarnosine in human brain appears to be catalyzed by carnosine synthetase. However, serum carnosinase does not hydrolyze homocarnosine.

Serum Carnosinase Deficiency

This presumably autosomal recessive, heritable disorder is characterized by persistent carnosinuria and occasionally also by carnosinemia. Carnosinuria persists even if carnosine is excluded from the diet.

Homocarnosinosis

Levels of homocarnosine are elevated in cerebrospinal fluid and in brain but not in plasma or urine. A single case has been reported.

SERINE

Much of the serine in phosphoproteins is present as O-phosphoserine.

Serine is involved in synthesis of sphingosine. (See Chapter 17.)

Serine participates in purine and pyrimidine synthesis. The β carbon is a source of the methyl groups of thymine (and of choline) and of the carbon in positions 2 and 8 of the purine nucleus. (See Chapters 10 and 26.)

THREONINE

Since threonine does not participate in transamination, the D-isomer and the α-keto acid are not utilized by mammals. Threonine is present in certain proteins as O-phosphothreonine.

METHIONINE

Methionine as a methyl group donor is discussed in Chapter 22. In the form of S-adenosylmethionine, it is the principal source of methyl groups in the body. In addition to direct utilization, the methyl group is also oxidized. The methyl carbon may be used to produce the one-carbon moiety that conjugates with glycine in synthesis of serine. As S-adenosylmethionine, methionine serves as precursor to the 1,3-diaminopropane portions of the polyamines spermine and spermidine (see ornithine, below, and Fig 23–6).

CYSTEINE

Urinary sulfate arises almost entirely from oxidation of L-cysteine. The sulfur of methionine (as homocysteine) is transferred to serine (see Fig 20–11) and thus contributes to the urinary sulfate indirectly (ie, via cysteine). L-Cysteine serves as a precursor of the thioethanolamine portion of coenzyme A (see Chapter 10). Cysteine is also a precursor of the taurine that conjugates with bile acids, forming taurocholic acid and other products (see Chapter 44).

HISTIDINE

Histamine is derived from histidine by decarboxylation, a reaction catalyzed in mammalian tissues by an **aromatic L-amino acid decarboxylase.** This enzyme also catalyzes decarboxylation of dopa, 5-hydroxytryptophan, phenylalanine, tyrosine, and tryptophan (see below). The decarboxylase is inhibited by α-methyl amino acids in vitro and in vivo that thus have clinical application as antihypertensive agents. In addition to the aromatic amino acid decarboxylase, a different enzyme, **histidine decarboxylase,** present in most cells, catalyzes decarboxylation of histidine.

Histidine compounds present in the body include **ergothioneine,** in red blood cells and liver; carnosine; and anserine (Fig 23–3). 1-Methylhistidine in human urine probably is derived from anserine. 3-Methylhistidine, identified in human urine in amounts of about 50 mg/dL, is unusually low in the urine of patients with Wilson's disease.

ARGININE

Arginine serves as a formamidine donor for creatine synthesis in primates (Fig 23–11) and for streptomycin synthesis in *Streptomyces*. Other fates include conversion, via ornithine, to putrescine, spermine, and spermidine (Fig 23–4) and synthesis of arginine phosphate (functionally analogous to creatine phosphate) in invertebrate muscle.

ORNITHINE

In addition to its role in urea biosynthesis (see Chapter 21), ornithine (in conjunction with methionine) serves as a precursor of the ubiquitous mammalian (and bacterial) polyamines spermidine and spermine (Fig 23–5). Normal humans biosynthesize approximately 0.5 mmol of spermine per day. Pharmacologic doses of polyamines are hypothermic and hypotensive.

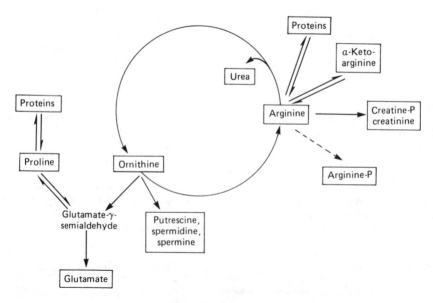

Figure 23–4. Arginine, ornithine, and proline metabolism. Reactions with solid arrows all occur in mammalian tissues. Putrescine and spermine synthesis occurs in both mammals and bacteria. Arginine phosphate occurs in invertebrate muscle, where it functions as a phosphagen analogous to creatine phosphate in mammalian tissues.

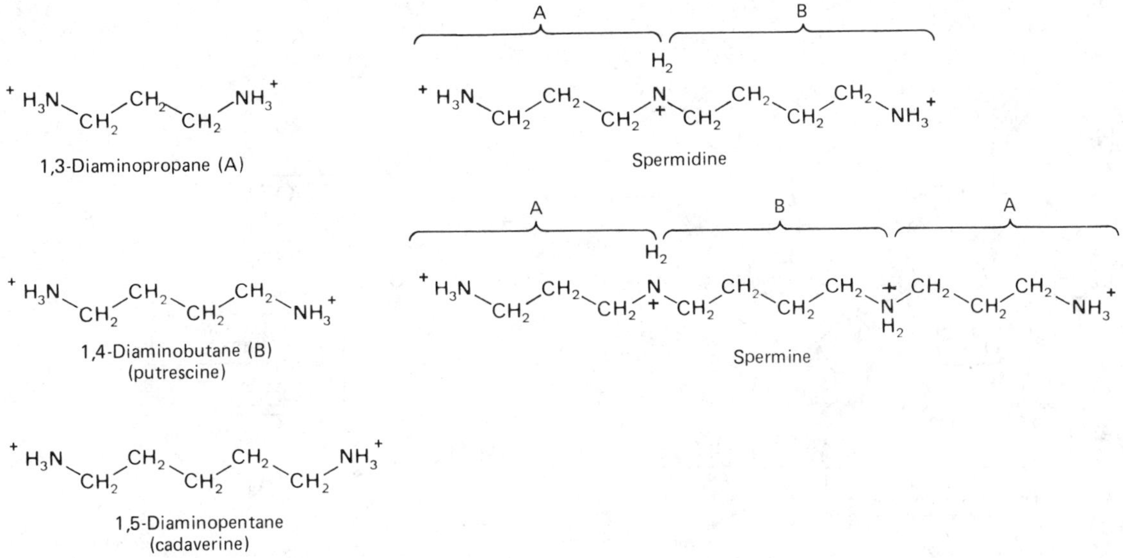

Figure 23–5. Structures of the natural polyamines. Note that spermidine and spermine are polymers of diaminopropane (A) and diaminobutane (B). Diaminopentane (cadaverine) also occurs in mammalian tissues.

Spermidine and spermine are implicated in diverse physiologic processes that share as a common thread a close relationship to cell proliferation and growth. They are growth factors for cultured mammalian and bacterial cells and have been implicated in the stabilization of intact cells, subcellular organelles, and membranes. As a consequence of their multiple positive charges, polyamines associate readily with polyanions such as DNA and RNAs and have been implicated in such fundamental processes as stimulation of DNA and RNA biosynthesis, DNA stabilization, and packaging of DNA in bacteriophages. Polyamines also exert diverse effects on protein synthesis and act as inhibitors of enzymes that include protein kinases.

While it is not presently possible to explain (in precise mechanistic terms) the mode of action of polyamines on any specific metabolic process, the essential nature of polyamines in mammalian metabolism is convincingly documented by experiments of the following type. The initial reaction in polyamine biosynthesis is catalyzed by ornithine decarboxylase (Fig 23–6). Addition to cultured mammalian cells of inhibitors of ornithine decarboxylase activity (eg, α-methylornithine or difluoromethylornithine) triggers overproduction of ornithine decarboxylase. This suggests an essential physiologic role for this enzyme, whose only known function is polyamine biosynthesis.

Biosynthesis of Polyamines

Fig 23–6 summarizes the pathway of polyamine biosynthesis in mammalian tissues. Note that the putrescine portion of spermidine and spermine derives from L-ornithine (a urea cycle intermediate; see Chapter 21) and the diaminopropane portion from L-methionine via intermediate formation of S-adenosylmethionine. Ornithine decarboxylase and S-adenosylmethi-

onine decarboxylase both are inducible enzymes with short half-lives. Spermine and spermidine synthases are, by contrast, neither inducible nor unusually labile enzymes.

Of the enzymes of mammalian polyamine biosynthesis, 2 (ornithine decarboxylase and S-adenosylmethionine decarboxylase) are of interest with respect to both their regulation and their potential for enzyme-directed chemotherapy. The half-life of ornithine decarboxylase (approximately 10 minutes) is shorter than that of any other known mammalian enzyme, and its activity responds rapidly and dramatically to many stimuli. Increases in ornithine decarboxylase activity of 10- to 200-fold rapidly follow administration to cultured mammalian cells of growth hormone, corticosteroids, testosterone, or epidermal growth factor. Polyamines added to cultured cells induce synthesis of a protein antizyme that binds to ornithine decarboxylase and inhibits its activity. The activity of ornithine decarboxylase thus appears also to be controlled by a protein-protein interaction reminiscent of the regulation of trypsin activity by protein trypsin inhibitors. Difluoromethylornithine, a "suicide inhibitor" of ornithine decarboxylase, has been used both to isolate mutant cell lines that overproduce ornithine decarboxylase and to inhibit cell replication by enzyme-directed chemotherapy.

S-adenosylmethionine decarboxylase is the only known eukaryotic enzyme that contains bound pyruvate as an essential cofactor (decarboxylases normally contain pyridoxal phosphate, which is absent from S-adenosylmethionine decarboxylase). It has been highly purified from several mammalian tissues, has a short half-life (1–2 hours), and responds to promoters of cell growth in a manner qualitatively similar to ornithine decarboxylase. Both the rapidity and the

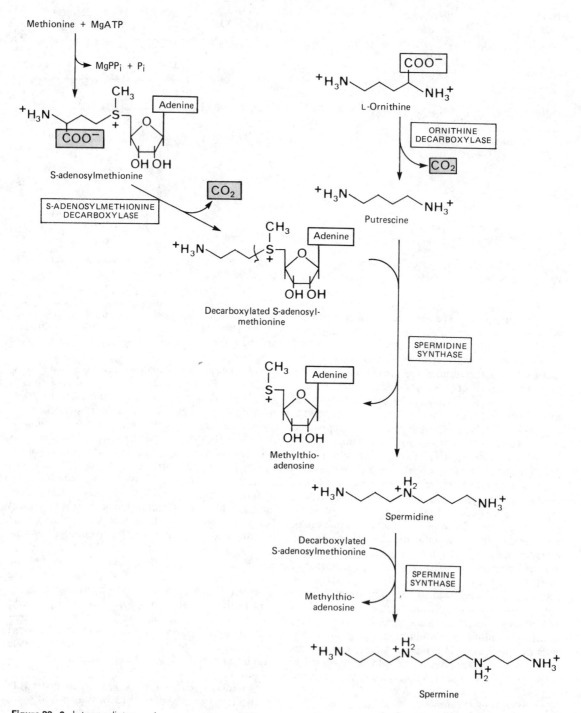

Figure 23–6. Intermediates and enzymes that participate in the biosynthesis of spermidine and spermine. Methylene groups are abbreviated to facilitate visualization of the overall process.

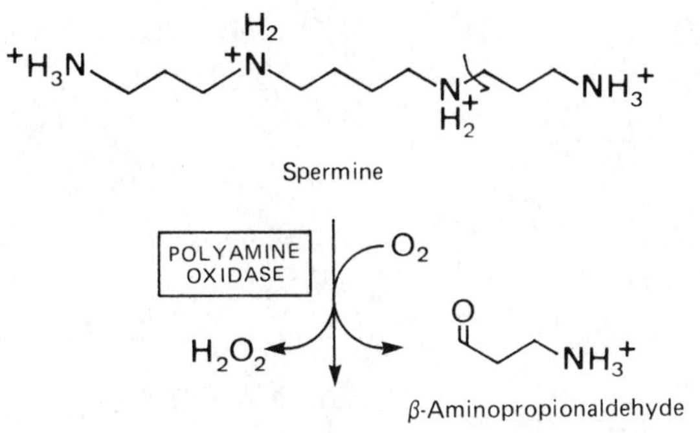

Figure 23–7. Catabolism of polyamines. Structures are abbreviated to facilitate presentation.

extent of the response are, however, less dramatic than for ornithine decarboxylase. The activity of S-adenosylmethionine decarboxylase (Fig 23–6) is inhibited by decarboxylated S-adenosylmethionine and activated by putrescine.

Catabolism of Polyamines

Fig 23–7 summarizes the catabolism of polyamines in mammalian tissues. The enzyme polyamine oxidase, present in liver peroxisomes, oxidizes spermine to spermidine and subsequently oxidizes spermidine to putrescine. Both diaminopropane moieties are converted to β-aminopropionaldehyde. Subsequently, putrescine is partially oxidized to NH_4^+ and CO_2 by mechanisms that remain to be elucidated but which may involve intermediate formation of acetylputrescine and subsequent oxidation by monoamine oxidase. However, major portions of putrescine and spermidine are excreted in urine as conjugates, principally as acetyl derivatives.

TRYPTOPHAN

Serotonin

A secondary pathway for the metabolism of tryptophan involves hydroxylation to 5-hydroxytryptophan. Oxidation of tryptophan to the hydroxy derivative is analogous to conversion of phenylalanine to tyrosine (Fig 20–12), and liver phenylalanine hydroxylase also catalyzes hydroxylation of tryptophan. Decarboxylation of 5-hydroxytryptophan forms **5-hydroxytryptamine (serotonin)** (reaction ①, Fig 23–8), a potent vasoconstrictor and stimulator of smooth muscle contraction.

The 5-hydroxytryptophan decarboxylase that forms serotonin from hydroxytryptophan is present in the kidney (hog and guinea pig), liver, and stomach. However, the widely distributed aromatic L-amino acid decarboxylase will also catalyze decarboxylation of 5-hydroxytryptophan.

Most serotonin is metabolized by oxidative deamination to 5-hydroxyindoleacetate. The enzyme that catalyzes this reaction is **monoamine oxidase** (reaction ②, Fig 23–8). Inhibitors of this enzyme include iproniazid. It is hypothesized that the psychic stimulation that follows the administration of this drug is attributable to its ability to prolong the stimulating action of serotonin through inhibition of monoamine oxidase. In normal human urine, 2–8 mg of 5-hydroxyindoleacetate is excreted per day.

Greatly increased production of serotonin occurs in malignant **carcinoid** (argentaffinoma), a disease characterized by widespread serotonin-producing tumor cells in the argentaffin tissue of the abdominal cavity. Carcinoid has been considered an abnormality in tryptophan metabolism in which a much greater proportion of tryptophan than normal is metabolized by way of hydroxyindole. One percent of tryptophan is normally converted to serotonin, but in the carcinoid patient as much as 60% may follow this pathway. This metabolic diversion markedly reduces production of nicotinic acid from tryptophan; consequently, symptoms of pellagra as well as negative nitrogen balance may occur. Other metabolites of serotonin identified in the urine of patients with carcinoid include 5-hydroxyindoleaceturate (the glycine conjugate of 5-hydroxyindoleacetate) and N-acetylserotonin conjugated with glucuronic acid.

Melatonin

Melatonin is derived from serotonin by N-acetylation (reaction ③, Fig 23–8) followed by methylation of the 5-hydroxy group (reaction ④, Fig 23–8). Methylation is localized in pineal body tissue. In addition to methylation of N-acetylserotonin, direct methylation of serotonin (reaction ⑤, Fig 23–8) and of 5-hydroxyindoleacetate (reaction ⑥, Fig 23–8), the serotonin metabolite, also occurs.

Serotonin and 5-methoxytryptamine are metabolized to the corresponding acids by monoamine oxidase. Circulating melatonin is taken up by all tissues, including brain, but is rapidly metabolized by hy-

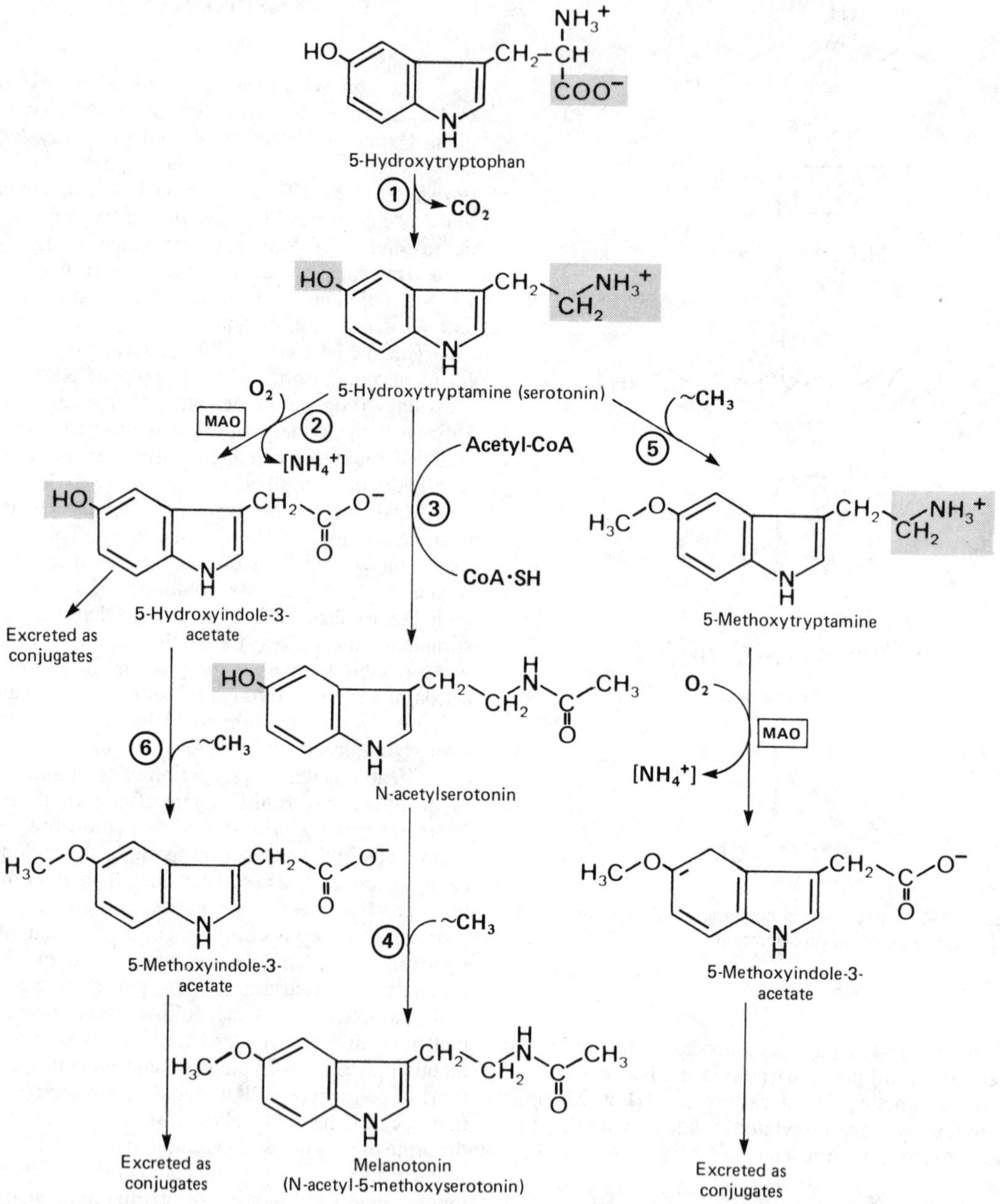

Figure 23–8. Biosynthesis and metabolism of melatonin. ([NH$_4^+$], by transamination; MAO, monoamine oxidase.) The numbered reactions are referred to in the text.

droxylation at position 6 followed by conjugation with sulfate (70%) and with glucuronic acid (6%). A portion is also converted to nonindolic reacting compounds.

Indole Derivatives in Urine

Tryptophan may be converted to several indole derivatives (Fig 23–8). The end products of these conversions that appear in the urine are principally 5-hydroxyindoleacetate, the major end product of the hydroxy tryptophan-to-serotonin pathway, and indole-3-acetate, from decarboxylation and oxidation of indolepyruvate, the keto acid of tryptophan.

Mammalian kidney and liver and bacteria from human feces decarboxylate tryptophan to tryptamine, which can then be oxidized to indole-3-acetate. Patients with phenylketonuria excrete increased quantities of indoleacetate (and indolelactate, formed by reduction of indolepyruvate).

MELANINS

Eumelanins are insoluble, heterogeneous, high-molecular-weight, black to brown heteropolymers of 5,6-dihydroxyindole and several of its biosynthetic precursors. **Pheomelanins** are yellow to reddish-brown polymers but, while also of high molecular weight, are soluble in dilute alkali. The low-molecular-weight **trichochromes** are related to pheomelanins (both are derived from cysteine and dopaquinone). Pheomelanins and trichochromes are present primarily in hair and feathers.

Melanin Biosynthesis

Discussion of melanin biosynthesis is complicated by the protracted, branched, and incomplete biosynthetic pathway, the complex chemical structures of melanin heteropolymers, and the insolubility of these polymers, all of which hinder their structural determination. Melanins are synthesized in **melanosomes**—membrane-bound particles within melanocytes, which are cells of neural crest origin. The developing eumelanin polymer is thought to entrap free radicals and to undergo partial degradation by H_2O_2 generated during the auto-oxidative process. Pheomelanins and eumelanins then complex with proteins of the melanosomal matrix, forming **melanoprotein.**

Fig 23–9 summarizes the known intermediates and reactions of eumelanin and pheomelanin biosynthesis. The initial reaction is catalyzed by tyrosinase, a copper-dependent enzyme. **The tyrosinase reaction is defective in tyrosinase-negative oculocutaneous albinism** (see below).

Metabolic Defects of Melanin Biosynthesis

As might be anticipated from the number of reactions involved in melanin biosynthesis, mutations in many genes can give rise to metabolic defects in melanin biosynthesis.

The term "albinism" encompasses a spectrum of clinical syndromes characterized by **hypomelanosis** arising from heritable defects in the pigment cells (melanocytes) of the eye and skin. Several useful rodent models of albinism are known.

Clinical signs common to all 10 human forms of **oculocutaneous albinism** include decreased pigmentation of the skin and eye. All 10 forms can be differentiated on the basis of their clinical, biochemical, ultrastructural, and genetic characteristics. All but the dominant form are inherited as autosomal recessive traits.

Tyrosinase-negative albinos completely lack visual pigment. Hair bulbs from these patients fail to convert added tyrosine to pigment in vitro, and their melanocytes contain unpigmented melanosomes. **Tyrosinase-positive albinos** have some visible pigment, although this may not be evident in white infants. Hair color ranges from white-yellow to light tan, and lightly pigmented nevi may be present. Hair bulb

melanocytes may contain lightly pigmented melanosomes, which convert tyrosine to black eumelanin in vitro.

Ocular albinism occurs both as an autosomal recessive and as an X-linked trait. The melanocytes of X-linked and heterozygous (but not autosomal recessive) ocular albinos contain macromelanosomes. The retinas of females heterozygous for X-linked ocular albinism (Nettleship variety) exhibit a mosaic pattern of pigment distribution due to random X-chromosome inactivation. The precise metabolic defects leading to hypomelanosis in ocular albinism are unknown.

Oculocutaneous albinoidism is inherited as an autosomal recessive trait. With rare exceptions, patients lack associated nystagmus, photophobia, and decreased visual acuity.

TYROSINE

Tyrosine is a precursor of **epinephrine** and **norepinephrine,** which are formed in cells of neural origin. Although dopa is an intermediate in the formation of both melanin in melanocytes and norepinephrine in neuronal cells, different enzymes carry out the tyrosine hydroxylation reactions in the different cell types. **Tyrosine hydroxylase,** an enzyme that is not copper-dependent but utilizes tetrahydrobiopterin as much as does phenylalanine hydroxylase, forms dopa in the neuronal and adrenal cells on the pathway to norepinephrine and epinephrine production (Fig 23–10). **Dopa decarboxylase,** a pyridoxal phosphate–dependent enzyme, forms dopamine. The latter is subjected to further hydroxylation by dopamine β-oxidase, a copper-dependent enzyme that seems to utilize vitamin C to generate norepinephrine. In the **adrenal medulla,** the enzyme phenylethanolamine N-methyltransferase utilizes S-adenosylmethionine to methylate the primary amine of norepinephrine to form **epinephrine** (Fig 23–10).

Tyrosine is also a precursor of the thyroid hormones triiodothyronine and thyroxine (see Chapter 38).

Tyrosine is excreted in urine both free and as a sulfate, but most phenolic compounds are conjugated with sulfate when present in the urine.

CREATINE & CREATININE

Creatine is present in muscle, brain, and blood, both as phosphocreatine and in the free state. Traces of creatine are also normally present in urine. Creatinine, the anhydride of creatine, is formed largely in muscle by irreversible nonenzymic dehydration of creatine phosphate (Fig 23–11).

The 24-hour excretion of creatinine in the urine of a given subject is remarkably constant from day to day and proportionate to muscle mass.

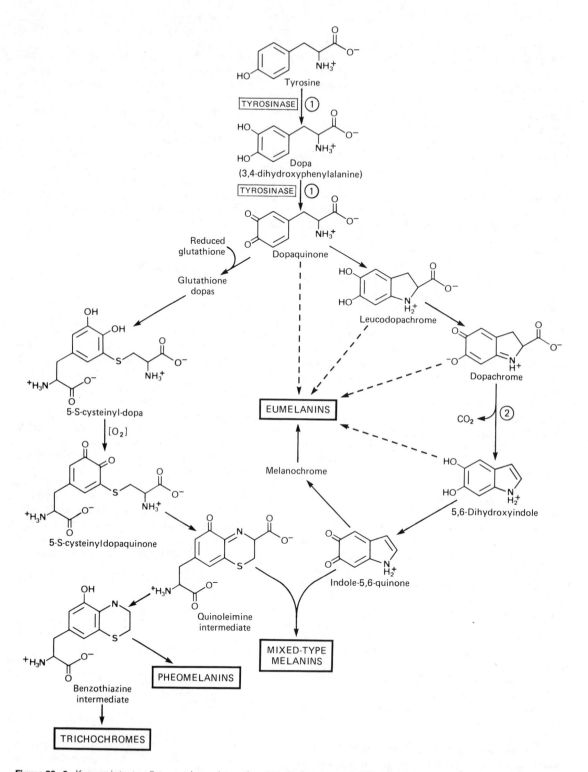

Figure 23–9. Known intermediates and reactions of eumelanin and pheomelanin biosynthesis. Melanin polymers contain both eumelanin and pheomelanin in varying proportions. Dotted arrows indicate that intermediates contribute toward synthesis of eumelanins in varying proportions. Circled numerals indicate probable regulated reactions of the biosynthetic pathway. Reaction ①, that catalyzed by tyrosinase, is defective in tyrosinase-negative oculocutaneous albinism.

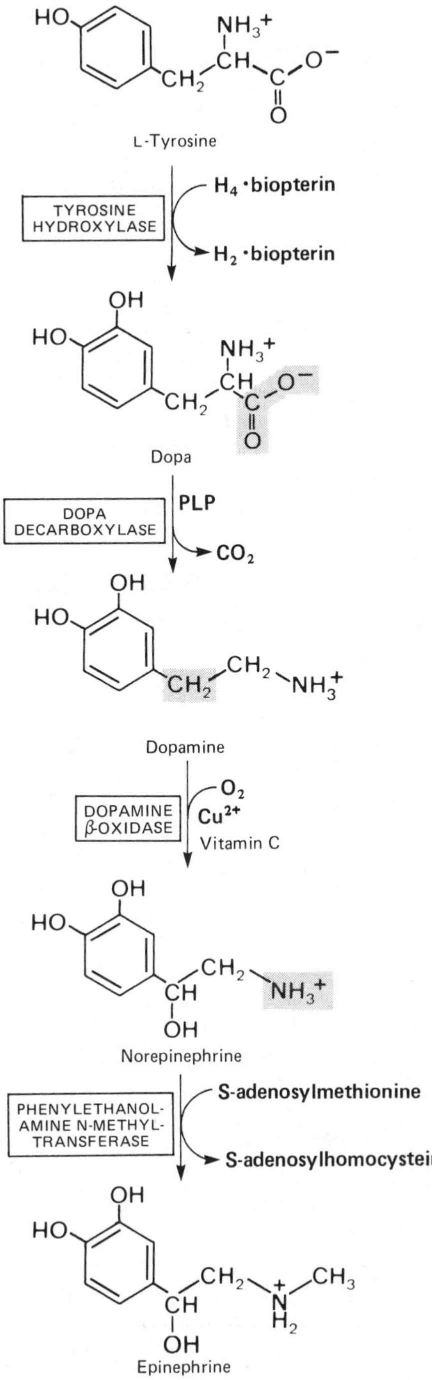

Figure 23-10. Conversion of tyrosine to epinephrine and norepinephrine in neuronal and adrenal cells. PLP, pyridoxal phosphate.

For synthesis of creatine, 3 amino acids—**glycine, arginine,** and **methionine**—are directly involved. The first reaction is transamidination from arginine to glycine to form guanidoacetate (glycocyamine). This occurs in the kidney but not in the liver or in heart muscle. Synthesis of creatine is completed by methylation of glycocyamine by "active methionine" in the liver.

γ-AMINOBUTYRATE

Biosynthesis

γ-Aminobutyrate (GABA) is formed by decarboxylation of L-glutamate, a reaction catalyzed by the pyridoxal phosphate–dependent enzyme L-glutamate decarboxylase (Fig 23–12). This decarboxylase is present in the tissues of the central nervous system, principally in the gray matter. While decarboxylation of L-glutamate represents the major route of γ-aminobutyrate biosynthesis, 2 reaction sequences convert putrescine (Fig 23–5) to γ-aminobutyrate. One involves deamination by diamine oxidase; the other utilizes N-acetylated intermediates. The relative importance of these 3 routes of γ-aminobutyrate biosynthesis varies among tissues and with developmental stage. For example, the polyamine precursor ornithine (Fig 23–6) is efficiently converted to γ-aminobutyrate in embryonic chick retinal tissue and in adult brain nerve terminals.

Catabolism

Catabolism of γ-aminobutyrate (Fig 23–12) involves transamination, catalyzed by γ-aminobutyrate transaminase, to succinate semialdehyde. Succinate semialdehyde may undergo reduction to γ-hydroxybutyrate, a reaction catalyzed by L-lactate dehydrogenase, or oxidation to the critic acid cycle intermediate succinate and thence to CO_2 and H_2O.

Aminobutyric Acidemia

γ-Aminobutyrate, in common with the anions of other ω-amino acids, is poorly transported across plasma cell membranes. The urinary levels of γ-aminobutyrate vary directly with the serum levels of this compound. While the precise biochemical defect is not known, it may result from impaired transamination of γ-aminobutyrate to succinate semialdehyde.

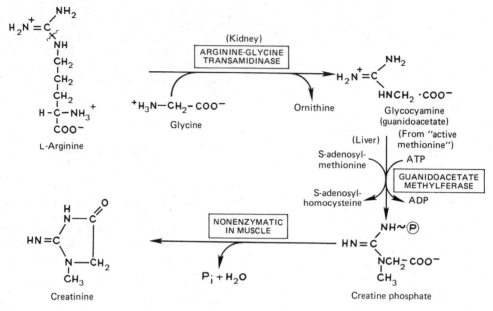

Figure 23–11. Biosynthesis of creatine and creatinine.

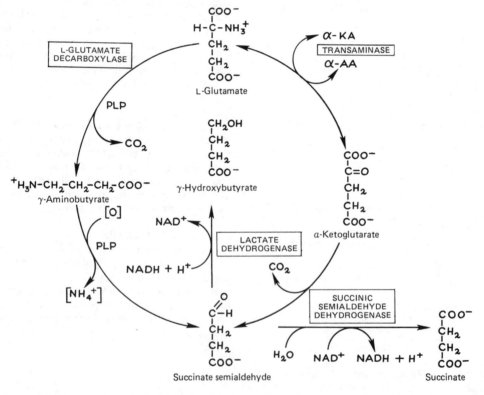

Figure 23–12. Metabolism of γ-aminobutyrate. (α-KA, α-keto acids; α-AA, α-amino acids; PLP, pyridoxal phosphate.)

●   ●   ●

Reference

Tabor CW, Tabor H: Polyamines. *Annu Rev Biochem* 1984;
  53:749.

Porphyrins & Bile Pigments | 24

David W. Martin, Jr., MD

PORPHYRINS

Porphyrins are cyclic compounds formed by the linkage of 4 pyrrole rings through methenyl bridges (Fig 24–1). A characteristic property of the porphyrins is the formation of complexes with metal ions bound to the nitrogen atom of the pyrrole rings. Examples are the iron porphyrins such as **heme** of hemoglobin and the magnesium-containing porphyrin **chlorophyll,** the photosynthetic pigment of plants.

In nature, the metalloporphyrins are conjugated to proteins to form many compounds important in biologic processes. These include the following:

A. Hemoglobins: Iron porphyrins attached to the protein, globin. These conjugated proteins possess the ability to combine reversibly with oxygen. They serve as the transport mechanism for oxygen within the blood (see Chapter 5).

B. Erythrocruorins: Iron porphyrinoproteins that occur in the blood and in the tissue fluids of some invertebrates. They correspond in function to hemoglobin.

C. Myoglobins: Respiratory pigments that occur in the muscle cells of vertebrates and invertebrates. An example is the myoglobin obtained from the heart muscle of the horse and crystallized by Theorell in 1934. A myoglobin molecule is similar to a subunit of hemoglobin.

D. Cytochromes: Compounds that act as electron transfer agents in oxidation-reduction reactions. An important example is **cytochrome c,** which has a molecular weight of about 13,000 and contains 1 gram-atom of iron per mole.

E. Catalases: Iron porphyrin enzymes, several of which have been obtained in crystalline form. They are assumed to have a molecular weight of about 225,000 and to contain 4 gram-atoms of iron per mole. In plants, catalase activity is minimal, but the iron porphyrin enzyme peroxidase performs similar functions. A peroxidase from horseradish has been crystallized; it has a molecular weight of 44,000 and contains 1 gram-atom of iron per mole.

F. The Enzyme Tryptophan Pyrrolase: This enzyme catalyzes the oxidation of tryptophan to formyl kynurenine. It is an iron porphyrin protein.

Structure of Porphyrins

The porphyrins found in nature are compounds in which various side chains are substituted for the 8 hydrogen atoms numbered in the porphin nucleus shown in Fig 24–1. As a simple means of showing these substitutions, Fischer proposed a shorthand formula in which the methenyl bridges are omitted and each pyrrole ring is shown as a bracket with the 8 substituent positions numbered as shown (Fig 24–2).

Pyrrole

Porphin
$(C_{20}H_{14}N_4)$

Figure 24–1. The porphin molecule. Rings are labeled I, II, III, IV. Substituent positions on rings are labeled 1, 2, 3, 4, 5, 6, 7, 8. Methenyl bridges are labeled α, β, γ, δ.

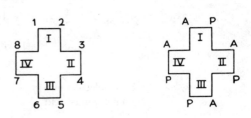

Figure 24–2. Uroporphyrin III.

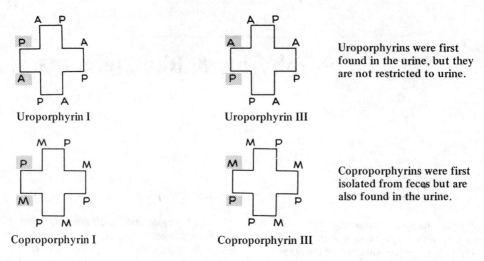

Uroporphyrins were first found in the urine, but they are not restricted to urine.

Coproporphyrins were first isolated from feces but are also found in the urine.

Figure 24–3. Uroporphyrins and coproporphyrins.

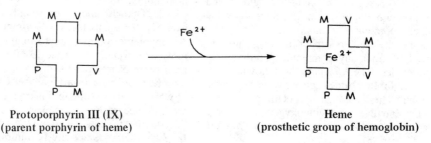

Figure 24–4. Addition of iron to protoporphyrin to form heme.

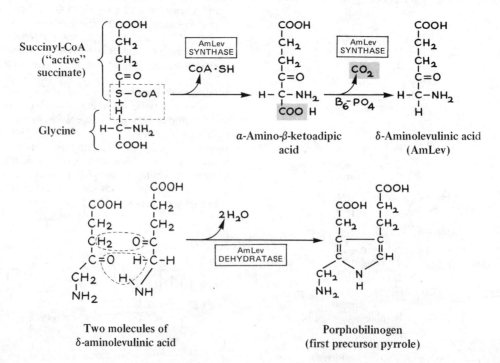

Figure 24–5. Biosynthesis of porphobilinogen. AmLev synthase occurs in the mitochondria, whereas AmLev dehydratase is present in the cytosol.

Uroporphyrin, whose detailed structure is shown in Fig 24–7, would be represented as shown in Fig 24–2. (A = –CH_2COOH; P = –CH_2CH_2COOH; M = –CH_3.)

The arrangement of the A and P substituents in the uroporphyrin shown in Fig 24–2 is asymmetric (in ring IV, the expected order of the acetate and propionate substituents is reversed). A porphyrin with this type of **asymmetric substitution** is classified as a type III porphyrin. A porphyrin with a completely symmetric arrangement of the substituents is classified as a type I porphyrin. Only types I and III are found in nature, and the **type III series** is by far the more abundant (Fig 24–3).

The compounds shown in Fig 24–4 are both type III porphyrins (ie, the methyl groups are asymmetrically distributed, as in type III coproporphyrin). However, they are sometimes identified as belonging to series IX, because they were designated ninth in a series of isomers postulated by Hans Fischer, the pioneer worker in the field of porphyrin chemistry.

Biosynthesis of Porphyrins

Both chlorophyll, the photosynthetic pigment of plants, and heme, the iron protoporphyrin of hemoglobin in animals, are synthesized in living cells by a common pathway. The 2 starting materials are "active succinate," the **coenzyme A derivative of succinic acid,** derived from the citric acid cycle in mitochondria, and the amino acid **glycine.** Pyridoxal phosphate is also necessary in this reaction to "activate" glycine. It is probable that pyridoxal reacts with glycine to form a Schiff base, whereby the alpha carbon of glycine can be combined with the carbonyl carbon of succinate. The product of the condensation reaction between succinyl-CoA and glycine is α-amino-β-ketoadipic acid, which is rapidly decarboxylated to form δ-aminolevulinic acid (AmLev) (Fig 24–5). This step is catalyzed by the enzyme **AmLev synthase.** This appears to be the **rate-controlling** enzyme in porphyrin biosynthesis in mammalian liver. Synthesis of aminolevulinic acid occurs in the **mitochondria.** In the cytosol, 2 molecules of AmLev are condensed by the enzyme **AmLev dehydratase** to form 2 molecules of water and one of **porphobilinogen** (Fig 24–5). AmLev dehydratase is a Zn-containing enzyme and is sensitive to inhibition by lead.

The formation of a tetrapyrrole, ie, a porphyrin, occurs by condensation of 4 monopyrroles derived from porphobilinogen (Fig 24–6). In each instance, the amino carbon (originally derived from the alpha carbon of glycine) serves as the source of the methylene (alpha, beta, gamma, delta) carbons that connect each pyrrole in the tetrapyrrole structure. Although the conversion of porphobilinogen to a porphyrin can be accomplished simply by heating under acid conditions, such as in an acid urine, this conversion is catalyzed in the tissues by specific enzymes.

It has been pointed out that only types I and III porphyrins occur in nature, and it may be assumed that the type III isomers are the more abundant, since the biologically important porphyrins such as heme and the cytochromes are type III isomers.

At present, the detailed steps leading to the formation of the uroporphyrinogens from condensation of porphobilinogens remain obscure. The formation from porphobilinogen of uroporphyrinogen III, the obligatory intermediate in heme biosynthesis, is catalyzed by a complex interaction of 2 enzymes. **Uroporphyrinogen I synthase** (also called porphobilinogen deaminase) condenses porphobilinogen to uroporphyrinogen I in vitro (Fig 24–6). However, when a second enzyme, **uroporphyrinogen III cosynthase,** is present, interaction between these 2 enzymes results in the formation of uroporphyrinogen III rather than the symmetric isomer uroporphyrinogen I (Fig 24–6). Under normal conditions, the uroporphyrinogen formed is almost exclusively the III isomer, but in certain of the porphyrias (discussed below) the type I isomers of porphyrinogens are also formed in excess.

Note that both of these uroporphyrinogens have the pyrrole rings connected by **methylene** bridges, which do not form a conjugated ring system. Thus, these compounds (as are all porphyrinogens) are **colorless.** However, the porphyrinogens are readily autooxidized to their respective porphyrins, as shown in Fig 24–7 for uroporphyrinogen III. These oxidations are catalyzed by light and by the porphyrins that are formed.

Uroporphyrinogen III is converted to coproporphyrinogen III by decarboxylation of all of the acetate (A) groups, which changes them to methyl (M) substituents. The reaction is catalyzed by **uroporphyrinogen decarboxylase,** which is also capable of converting uroporphyrinogen I to coproporphyrinogen I (Fig 24–8). Coproporphyrinogen III then enters the mitochondria, where it is converted to **protoporphyrinogen III** and then to **protoporphyrin III.** Several steps seem to be involved in this conversion (Fig 24–9). The mitochondrial enzyme **coproporphyrinogen oxidase** catalyzes the decarboxylation and oxidation of 2 propionic side chains to form protoporphyrinogen. This enzyme is able to act only on type III coproporphyrinogen, which would explain why a type I protoporphyrin has not been identified in natural materials. The oxidation of protoporphyrinogen to protoporphyrin is catalyzed by another mitochondrial enzyme, **protoporphyrinogen oxidase.** In mammalian liver, the conversion of coproporphyrinogen to protoporphyrin requires molecular oxygen.

Formation of Heme

The final step in heme synthesis involves the incorporation of ferrous iron into protoporphyrin in a reaction catalyzed by **heme synthase** or **ferrochelatase,** another mitochondrial enzyme (Fig 24–4). This reaction occurs readily in the absence of enzymes, but it is noted to be much more rapid in the presence of tissue preparations, presumably because of the tissue contribution of enzymes active in catalyzing this iron chelation.

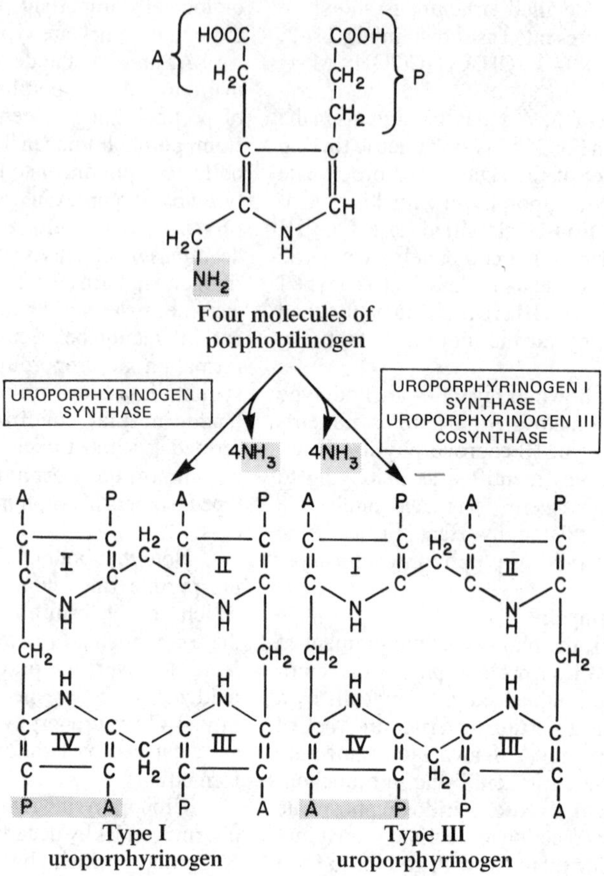

Figure 24–6. Conversion of porphobilinogen to uroporphyrinogens.

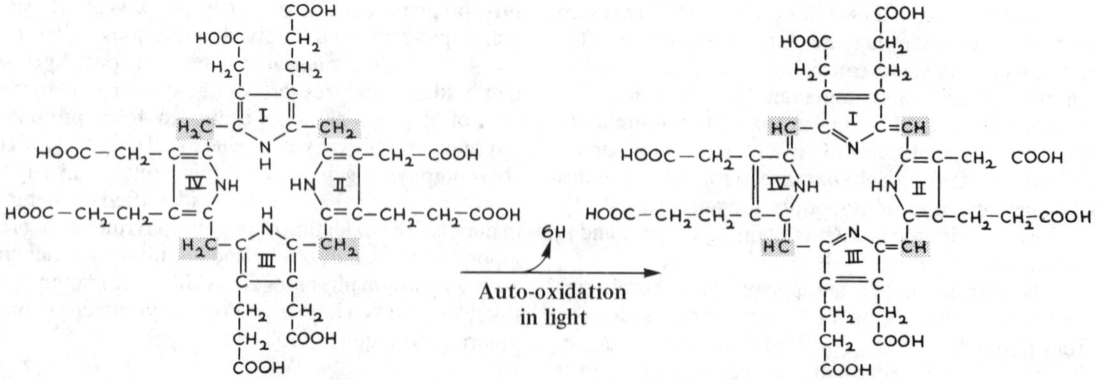

Figure 24–7. Oxidation of uroporphyrinogen to uroporphyrin. The methylene bridges between the pyrrole rings are oxidized (dehydrogenated) to methenyl bridges, generating a conjugated ring (colored) system.

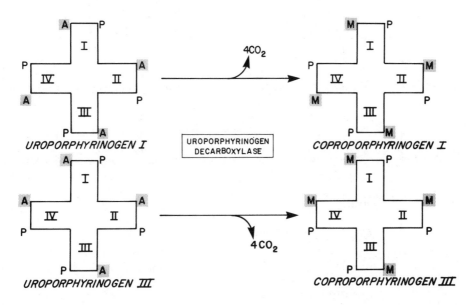

Figure 24–8. Decarboxylation of uroporphyrinogens to coproporphyrinogens in cytosol. (A, acetyl; M, methyl; P, propyl.)

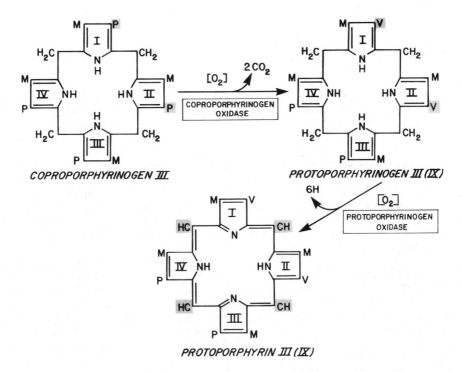

Figure 24–9. Conversion of coproporphyrinogen to protoporphyrin in mitochondria. (M, methyl; P, propyl; V, vinyl.)

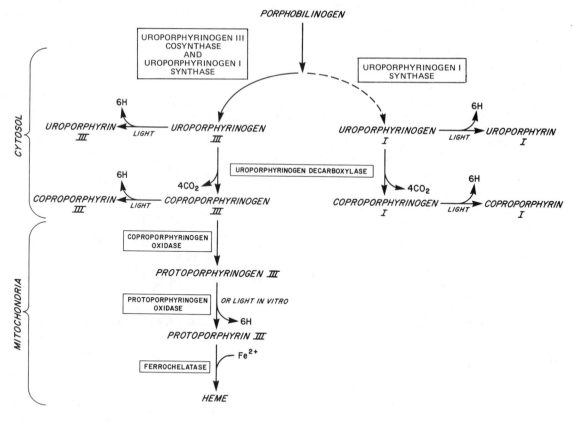

Figure 24–10. Steps in the biosynthesis of the porphyrin derivatives from porphobilinogen.

A summary of the steps in the biosynthesis of the porphyrin derivatives from porphobilinogen is given in Fig 24–10. Heme biosynthesis occurs in most mammalian tissues with the exception of mature erythrocytes, which do not contain mitochondria.

The porphyrinogens that have been described above are colorless, containing 6 extra hydrogen atoms as compared to the corresponding **colored porphyrins.** It is now apparent that these reduced porphyrins (the porphyrinogens) and not the corresponding porphyrins are the actual intermediates in the biosynthesis of protoporphyrin and of heme.

Regulation of Heme Biosynthesis

The rate-limiting reaction for the synthesis of heme occurs at the condensation of succinyl-CoA and glycine to form δ-aminolevulinic acid (AmLev) (Fig 24–5), a reaction catalyzed by the enzyme aminolevulinic acid synthase (AmLev synthase). The levels of AmLev synthase activity in normal tissues capable of synthesizing heme are significantly lower than those of the other enzymes of the heme synthetic pathway. However, AmLev synthase is a regulated enzyme. It appears that heme, probably acting through an aporepressor molecule, acts as a negative regulator of the accumulation of AmLev synthase. This repression and derepression mechanism is depicted diagrammatically in Fig 24–11. It is possible that there is

also significant feedback inhibition at this step, but the major regulatory effect of heme appears to be one in which the rate of accumulation of AmLev synthase increases greatly in the absence of heme and is diminished in its presence. The rate of AmLev synthase turnover is normally rapid (half-life is about 1 hour) in mammalian liver, not a surprising property for an enzyme catalyzing a rate-limiting reaction.

Many compounds of diverse structures, including presently used insecticides, carcinogens, and pharmaceuticals, when administered to humans, can result in a marked increase in hepatic AmLev synthase. Most of these drugs are metabolized by a system in the liver that utilizes a specific hemoprotein, cytochrome P-450. During the process of metabolizing these drugs, the consumption of heme by cytochrome P-450 is greatly increased, which in turn diminishes the intracellular heme concentration. This latter event effects a derepression of AmLev synthase with a corresponding increased rate of heme synthesis to meet the needs of the cells.

Several other factors affect the induction of AmLev synthase in the liver. Glucose can prevent the induction of AmLev synthase; iron in chelated form exerts a synergistic effect on the induction of hepatic AmLev synthase; and steroids play at least a permissive role in the drug-mediated derepression of AmLev synthase in vivo. The administration of hematin in

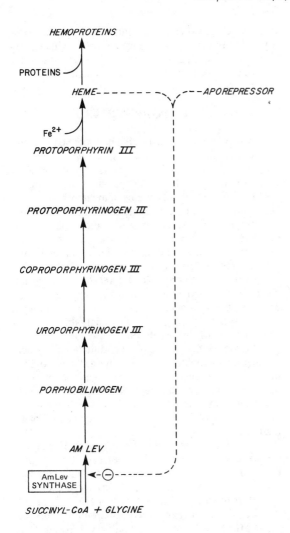

Figure 24–11. Regulation of heme synthesis at the level of AmLev synthase by a repression-derepression mechanism mediated by heme and its hypothetical aporepressor. The dotted lines indicate the negative (⊖) regulation by repression.

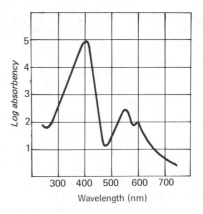

Figure 24–12. Absorption spectrum of hematoporphyrin (0.01% solution in 5% HCl).

vivo can prevent the drug-mediated derepression of AmLev synthase, as well as that of other hemoproteins in liver. In erythropoietic tissues, hypoxia increases AmLev synthase activity without having a demonstrable effect on AmLev synthase activity in liver.

The importance of these regulatory mechanisms is discussed below along with the diseases classified among the porphyrias.

Chemistry of Porphyrins

Because of the presence of tertiary nitrogens in the 2 pyrrolene rings contained in each porphyrin, these compounds act as weak bases. Those which possess a carboxyl group on one or more side chains act also as acids. Their isoelectric points range from pH 3.0 to 4.5, and within this pH range the porphyrins may easily be precipitated from an aqueous solution.

The various porphyrinogens are colorless, whereas the various **porphyrins are all colored.** In the study of porphyrins or porphyrin derivatives, the characteristic absorption spectrum that each exhibits, both in the visible and the ultraviolet regions of the spectrum, is of great value. An example is the absorption curve for a solution of porphyrin in 5% hydrochloric acid (Fig 24–12). Note the sharp absorption band near 400 nm. This is a distinguishing feature of the porphin ring and is characteristic of all porphyrins regardless of the side chains present. This band is termed the **Soret band,** after its discoverer. Hematoporphyrin in acid solution, in addition to the Soret band, has 2 weaker absorption bands with maxima at 550 and 592 nm.

When porphyrins dissolved in strong mineral acids or in organic solvents are illuminated by ultraviolet light, they emit a strong red fluorescence. This **fluorescence** is so characteristic that it is frequently used to detect small amounts of free porphyrins. The double bonds in the porphyrins are responsible for the characteristic absorption and fluorescence of these compounds, and, as previously noted, the reduction (by addition of hydrogen) of the methenyl (–HC=) bridges to methylene (–CH$_2$–) leads to the formation of colorless compounds termed **porphyrinogens.**

When a porphyrin combines with a metal, its absorption in the visible spectrum becomes changed. This is exemplified by protoporphyrin, the iron-free precursor of heme. In alkaline solution, protoporphyrin shows several sharp absorption bands (at 645, 591, and 540 nm), whereas heme has a broad band with a plateau extending from 540 to 580 nm.

Tests for Porphyrins

The presence of coproporphyrins or of uroporphyrins is of clinical interest, since these 2 types of compounds are excreted in increased amounts in the porphyrias. Coproporphyrins I and III are soluble in glacial acetic acid-ether mixtures, from which they may then be extracted by hydrochloric acid. Uropor-

Table 24–1. Upper limits of normal excretory values and concentrations of porphyrins and porphyrin precursors.*

	Urine (μg/24 h)	Feces (μg/g dry wt)	Erythrocytes (μg/dL cells)
AmLev	4000	–	–
Porphobilinogen	1500	–	–
Uroporphyrin	50	5	trace
Coproporphyrin	300	50	3
Protoporphyrin	–	120	80

*Modified and reproduced, with permission, from Meyer UA, Schmid R: The porphyrias. In: *The Metabolic Basis of Inherited Disease,* 4th ed. Stanbury JB, Wyngaarden JB, Fredrickson DS (editors). McGraw-Hill, 1978.

phyrins, on the other hand, are not soluble in acetic acid–ether mixtures but are partially soluble in ethyl acetate, from which they may be extracted by hydrochloric acid. In the HCl solution, ultraviolet illumination gives a characteristic red fluorescence. A spectrophotometer may then be used to demonstrate the characteristic absorption bands.

The upper limits of normal excretory values of porphyrins and porphyrin precursors are given in Table 24–1. In healthy subjects, the total urinary coproporphyrin averages about 67 μg/24 h; the type I isomer comprises on the average 14 μg/24 h and type III 53 μg/24 h. An alteration in the normal ratio of the excretion of types I and III coproporphyrins may be of value in detection of certain types of diseases of the liver.

During the synthesis of heme from AmLev, there is an increase in the hydrophobic qualities of the various intermediate compounds. The acetyl carboxyl groups on uroporphyrinogen are removed when it is converted to coproporphyrinogen, and 2 of the propyl groups are decarboxylated in the course of the conversion of coproporphyrinogen to protoporphyrinogen. The relative distributions in the urine and feces of the intermediates of heme biosynthesis reflect this increasing hydrophobic quality. Thus, the more polar uroporphyrinogen will be excreted to a greater extent in urine

than in feces, whereas the more hydrophobic coproporphyrinogen and protoporphyrinogen will increasingly distribute themselves in the bile and ultimately the feces rather than in the aqueous urine.

THE PORPHYRIAS

The porphyrias constitute a heterogeneous group of diseases, all of which exhibit increased excretion of porphyrins or porphyrin precursors. Some forms of porphyria are inherited, whereas others are acquired. Several different classifications of the porphyrias have been proposed. It is convenient to divide the inherited porphyrias into 3 general groups—the erythropoietic porphyrias, the hepatic porphyrias, and those with both erythropoietic and hepatic abnormalities (Table 24–2). In most types of inherited porphyria, the defect is present in all tissues, but for reasons that are not clear, the metabolic abnormalities are expressed preferentially in one or another tissue type. There follows a brief description of the biochemical abnormalities characteristic of the porphyrias.

Studies of the biochemical and metabolic abnormalities characteristic of the porphyrias have provided much information about the pathogenesis of these diseases and their management. These studies have also been responsible for increased knowledge of the normal pathway for the synthesis of heme and of its regulation.

The pattern of excretion of porphyrin and porphyrin precursors is characteristic for each type of porphyria. In Fig 24–13, these patterns and their relationships to the heme synthetic pathway are depicted.

Intermittent acute porphyria (IAP) is an autosomal, dominantly inherited disease in humans that usually is not expressed before puberty. It results from an inherited partial deficiency of **uroporphyrinogen I synthase.** Individuals with this disease are heterozygous for a defective structural gene for uroporphyrinogen I synthase, with the result that only 50% of the normal specific catalytic activity of that enzyme is present within their cells. Patients with IAP excrete

Table 24–2. Classification of human porphyrias.*

Condition	Mode of Inheritance	Demonstrated or Suspected Enzyme Defect	Predominant Site(s) of Metabolic Expression
Congenital erythropoietic porphyria	Autosomal recessive	Uroporphyrinogen I synthase and/or uroporphyrinogen III cosynthase	Erythroid cells
Hepatic porphyrias			
Intermittent acute porphyria	Autosomal dominant	Uroporphyrinogen I synthase	Liver
Hereditary coproporphyria	Autosomal dominant	Coproporphyrinogen oxidase	Liver
Variegate porphyria	Autosomal dominant	Protoporphyrinogen oxidase	Liver
Porphyria cutanea tarda	Autosomal dominant (?)	Uroporphyrinogen decarboxylase	Liver
Toxic porphyria	Acquired	Variable	Liver
Protoporphyria	Autosomal dominant	Ferrochelatase	Erythroid cells and liver (?)

*Reproduced, with permission, from Meyer UA, Schmid R: The porphyrias. In: *The Metabolic Basis of Inherited Disease,* 4th ed. Stanbury JB, Wyngaarden JB, Fredrickson DS (editors). McGraw-Hill, 1978.

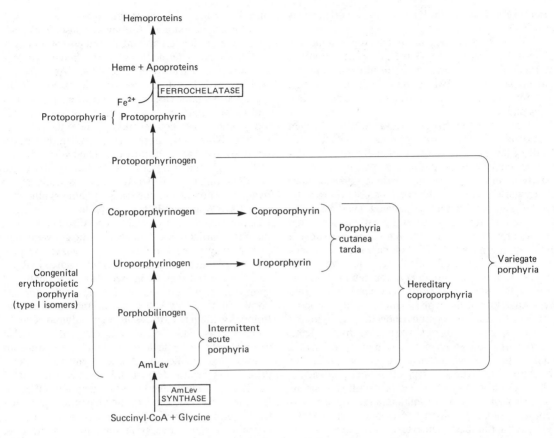

Figure 24–13. Patterns of urinary porphyrin and porphyrin precursor excretion in the porphyrias in relation to the pathway of heme biosynthesis. Intermediates of the pathway excessively excreted during the acute phase of each of the porphyrias are within the respective brackets. AmLev, δ-aminolevulinic acid. (Modified from Kaufman L, Marver HS: Biochemical defects in two types of human hepatic porphyria. *N Engl J Med* 1970;**283**:954.)

massive quantities of **porphobilinogen** and **AmLev** in the urine. Both of these compounds are **colorless,** but porphobilinogen upon exposure to light and air polymerizes spontaneously but slowly to form 2 colored compounds: porphobilin and porphyrin. These cause a **darkening of the urine upon standing** in light and air.

Both porphobilinogen and AmLev are present in the plasma and spinal fluid of these patients, particularly during acute exacerbations. Drugs and steroid hormones that require metabolism by heme-containing proteins such as cytochrome P-450 can precipitate acute exacerbations. Apparently, because of the increased consumption of heme proteins necessitated by the metabolism of these porphyria-inducing compounds, there is a derepression of AmLev synthase activity brought about by diminished intracellular heme concentration. The increased AmLev synthase activity combined with the partial block in the uroporphyrinogen I synthase results in a massive accumulation of AmLev and porphobilinogen. The acute attacks of abdominal pain, vomiting, constipation, cardiovascular abnormalities, and neuropsychiatric signs and symptoms correlate with the increased production of

AmLev and porphobilinogen in these patients. However, experimental data suggest that depletion of heme diminishes the activity of tryptophan pyrrolase and thereby leads to the accumulation of the neuroactive substances tryptophan and 5-hydroxytryptamine.

Patients with IAP do not have abnormal sensitivity to light, as do patients with other types of hepatic porphyrias. This is understandable when it is considered that these patients do not accumulate porphyrins or porphyrinogens, because the inherited metabolic defect occurs in the heme synthetic pathway *prior to* the formation of the first porphyrinogen (uroporphyrinogen).

As mentioned above, the metabolic defect in IAP occurs in other cells, including erythrocytes, cultured fibroblasts, and cultured amniotic fluid cells. Thus, although the enzymatic deficiency is ubiquitous, the increased AmLev synthase activity responsible for the overproduction of AmLev and porphobilinogen is predominantly a hepatic phenomenon. This probably is because the liver is the organ in which the inducing agents are metabolized. IAP is one of the rare examples of a disease phenotype being expressed in a heterozygote in whom the known enzyme deficiency is only 50%.

As might be predicted from the proposed mechanism of regulation of AmLev synthase by a repression-derepression system, the infusion of hematin into patients with IAP can ameliorate the induction of AmLev synthase and thereby ameliorate the clinical signs and symptoms.

Congenital erythropoietic porphyria is an even rarer congenital disease having an autosomal recessive mode of inheritance. The molecular nature of the defect in congenital erythropoietic porphyria is not clearly defined, but there is a definite imbalance between the relative activities of uroporphyrinogen III cosynthase and uroporphyrinogen I synthase. The formation of uroporphyrinogen I greatly exceeds that of uroporphyrinogen III, the normal isomer on the pathway to heme synthesis. Although the genetic defect is present in all cells, it is for an unknown reason expressed predominantly in erythropoietic tissue. Patients with congenital erythropoietic porphyria excrete large quantities of the **type I isomers** of both uroporphyrinogen and coproporphyrinogen, which in the urine are spontaneously oxidized to uroporphyrin I and coprophyrin I, both fluorescent, red pigments. There is reported to be a small increase in uroporphyrin III, but the ratio of the type I to type III isomer approaches 100:1. Circulating erythrocytes contain high concentrations of uroporphyrin I, although the highest concentration of this porphyrin is present in bone marrow cells and not in the hepatocytes.

Apparently because of the decreased formation of the true precursor of heme, uroporphyrinogen III, and thus a relative deficiency of heme, AmLev synthase is induced in the erythropoietic tissues of patients with congenital erythropoietic porphyria. This induction of AmLev synthase promotes the massive overproduction of the type I porphyrinogens. Concomitant with the increase in AmLev synthase and overproduction of the type I porphyrinogens is an increased production and excretion of porphobilinogen and AmLev. Thus, from the biochemical abnormalities one can predict the existence of clinical symptoms comparable to those of IAP but with the addition of cutaneous photosensitivity, because of the absorption spectrum of the porphyrin compounds that are formed in abnormal quantities in this disorder. These patients also exhibit a prominent increased cutaneous fragility and hemolysis.

Hereditary coproporphyria is an autosomal dominant disorder due to partial deficiency of **coproporphyrinogen oxidase,** the mitochondrial enzyme responsible for the conversion of coproporphyrinogen III to protoporphyrinogen IX (Fig 24–9). Coproporphyrinogen III is excreted in excessive quantities in feces, but, because of its solubility in water, it is excreted also in large quantities in urine. As is true also of uroporphyrinogen, in the presence of air and light, coproporphyrinogen is rapidly oxidized to coproporphyrin, a red pigment.

The limited capacity to produce heme in this disease—particularly under conditions of stress—will result in derepression of AmLev synthase. This leads to the overproduction of AmLev and porphobilinogen and the other intermediates in the heme synthetic pathway proximal to the inherited block. Accordingly, patients with hereditary coproporphyria exhibit the signs and symptoms associated with the excess AmLev and porphobilinogen, such as those present in IAP, along with some photosensitivity due to the presence of excessive coproporphyrinogens and uroporphyrinogens. Again, the infusion of hematin can effect at least a partial repression of AmLev synthase and amelioration of the signs and symptoms secondary to overproduction of intermediates in heme synthesis.

Variegate porphyria, or protocoproporphyria hereditaria, is an autosomal dominant disorder in which there is a partial block in the enzymatic conversion of protoporphyrinogen to heme. Two enzymes, protoporphyrinogen oxidase and ferrochelatase, both located in the **mitochondria,** seem to be normally responsible for this conversion. Patients with variegate porphyria have only half of the normal level of **protoporphyrinogen oxidase** in their cultured skin fibroblast cells. Patients with variegate porphyria also exhibit a relative heme deficiency under stressful conditions, and the hepatic AmLev synthase is derepressed. As discussed above, this increased activity of AmLev synthase leads to overproduction of all of the intermediates in the heme synthetic pathway proximal to the block. Accordingly, patients with variegate porphyria excrete excessive quantities of AmLev, porphobilinogen, uroporphyrin, and coproporphyrin in their urines, and uroporphyrin, coproporphyrin, and protoporphyrin in their feces. Thus, their urines are pigmented and fluoresce, and they exhibit cutaneous photosensitivity—the latter indistinguishable from that observed in porphyria cutanea tarda, discussed below.

As with the other porphyria syndromes, the increased excretion of the accumulated intermediates of the heme pathway may be normal or only slightly elevated under nonstressful conditions but increase greatly when the demand for heme is increased—particularly in the liver, for reasons explained above. The plasma of patients frequently exhibits a remarkable red fluorescence which seems to correlate with the high concentration of coproporphyrinogen in that fluid. Erythrocyte porphyrin levels remain normal in this disease.

Porphyria cutanea tarda is probably the most common form of porphyria. It is usually associated with some form of hepatic injury, particularly alcohol or iron overload. The nature of the metabolic defect has not been well defined, but it is perhaps attributable to a partial deficiency of **uroporphyrinogen decarboxylase.** The defect appears to be transmitted as an autosomal dominant disorder, but the penetrance of the disease is variable, in most cases being dependent upon the existence of some form of hepatic injury. Predictably, the urine contains increased quantities of uroporphyrins of both type I and type III, but elevated urinary excretion of AmLev and porphobilinogen occurs only rarely. Although the urine may occasionally contain sufficient porphyrins to produce a pinkish color, upon acidification it frequently exhibits a pink fluorescence under ultraviolet light.

The liver contains large quantities of porphyrins, so that it fluoresces intensely, whereas the erythrocytes and cells of the bone marrow do not. In porphyria cutanea tarda, the major clinical manifestation is **cutaneous photosensitivity.** The lack of increased AmLev synthase activity and corresponding lack of excess porphobilinogen and AmLev in the urines of these patients correlate positively with the lack of the acute manifestations typical of IAP.

Protoporphyria, or erythropoietic protoporphyria, appears to result from a dominantly inherited partial deficiency of **ferrochelatase** activity in the mitochondria of all tissues, and it is associated clinically with acute urticaria on exposure to sunlight. The erythrocytes, plasma, and feces contain increased quantities of protoporphyrin IX, and the reticulocytes (young erythrocytes) and skin obtained by biopsy frequently exhibit red fluorescence.

The liver probably also contributes to the overproduction of protoporphyrin IX, but there is no increased urinary excretion of porphyrin precursors or porphyrins.

Acquired (toxic) porphyria can result from exposure to toxic compounds such as hexachlorobenzene, lead, and other salts of heavy metals, as well as drugs such as griseofulvin and apronalide (Sedormid). Heavy metals inhibit several enzymes in the heme synthetic pathway, including AmLev dehydratase, uroporphyrinogen synthase, and ferrochelatase.

CATABOLISM OF HEME; FORMATION OF BILE PIGMENTS

Under physiologic conditions in the human adult, $1-2 \times 10^8$ erythrocytes are destroyed per hour. Thus, in 1 day, a 70-kg human turns over approximately 6 g of hemoglobin. When hemoglobin is destroyed in the body, the protein portion, globin, may be reutilized either as such or in the form of its constituent amino acids, and the iron of heme enters the iron pool, also for reuse. However, the iron-free porphyrin portion of heme is degraded, mainly in the reticuloendothelial cells of the liver, spleen, and bone marrow.

The catabolism of heme from all of the heme proteins appears to be carried out in the microsomal fractions of the reticuloendothelial cells by a complex enzyme system called **heme oxygenase.** By the time the heme of heme proteins reaches the heme oxygenase system, the iron has usually been oxidized to the ferric form, constituting **hemin,** and may be loosely bound to albumin as methemalbumin. The heme oxygenase system is substrate-inducible. It is located in close proximity to the microsomal electron transport system. As depicted in Fig 24–14, the hemin is reduced with NADPH, and, with the aid of more NADPH, oxygen is added to the α-methenyl bridge between pyrroles I and II of the porphyrin. The ferrous iron is again oxidized to the ferric form. With the further addition of oxygen, **ferric ion** is released, **carbon monoxide** is produced, and an equimolar quantity of **biliverdin IX-α** results from the splitting of the tetrapyrrole ring. The heme itself participates in this reaction as a catalyst.

In birds and amphibia, the green biliverdin IX-α is excreted; in mammals, a soluble enzyme called **biliverdin reductase** reduces the methenyl bridge between pyrrole III and pyrrole IV to a methylene group to produce **bilirubin IX-α,** a yellow pigment (Fig 24–14).

It is estimated that 1 g of hemoglobin yields 35 mg of bilirubin. The daily bilirubin formation in human adults is approximately 250–350 mg.

The chemical conversion of heme to bilirubin by the reticuloendothelial cells can be observed in vivo as the purple color of the heme in a hematoma is slowly converted to the yellow pigment of bilirubin.

The further metabolism of bilirubin occurs primarily in the liver. It can be divided into 3 processes: (1) uptake of bilirubin by liver parenchymal cells, (2) conjugation of bilirubin in the smooth endoplasmic reticulum, and (3) secretion of conjugated bilirubin into the bile. Each of these processes will be considered separately.

Uptake of Bilirubin by the Liver

Bilirubin is only sparingly soluble in plasma and water, but in the plasma it is protein-bound, specifically to albumin. Each molecule of albumin appears to have one high-affinity site and one low-affinity site for bilirubin. In 100 mL of plasma, approximately 25 mg of bilirubin can be **tightly bound to albumin** at its high-affinity site. Bilirubin in excess of this quantity can be bound only loosely and thus can easily be detached and diffused into tissues. A number of compounds such as antibiotics and other drugs compete with bilirubin for the high-affinity binding site on albumin. Thus, these compounds can displace bilirubin from albumin and have significant clinical effects.

In the liver, the bilirubin seems to be removed from the albumin and taken up at the sinusoidal surface of the hepatocytes by a carrier-mediated saturable system. This facilitated transport system has a very large capacity, so that even under pathologic conditions the system does not appear to be rate-limiting in the metabolism of bilirubin.

Since this facilitated transport system allows the equilibration of bilirubin across the sinusoidal membrane of the hepatocyte, the net uptake of bilirubin will be dependent upon the removal of bilirubin by subsequent metabolic pathways.

Conjugation of Bilirubin

By adding polar groups to bilirubin, the liver converts bilirubin to a water-soluble form that can subsequently be secreted into the bile. This process of **increasing the water solubility** or polarity of bilirubin is achieved by conjugation. It is a process carried out,

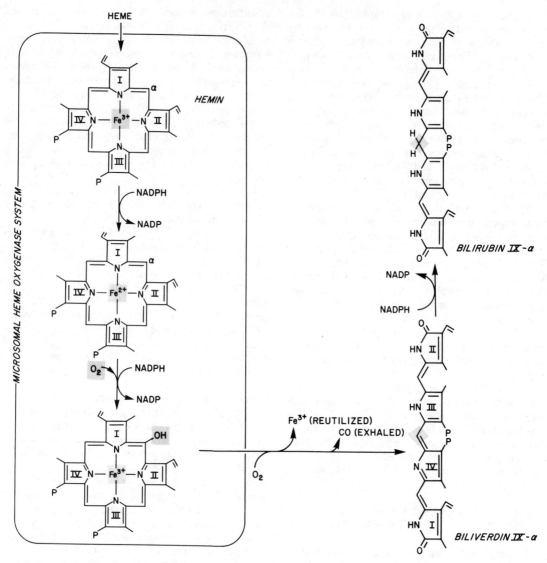

Figure 24–14. Schematic representation of the microsomal heme oxygenase system. (Modified from Schmid R, McDonough AF in: *The Porphyrins.* Dolphin D [editor]. Academic Press, 1978.)

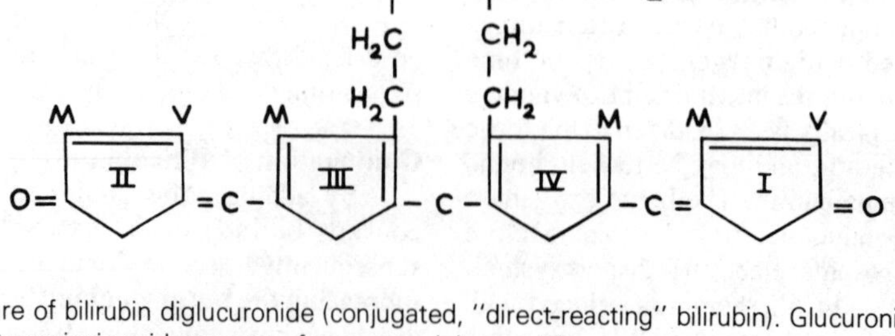

Figure 24–15. Structure of bilirubin diglucuronide (conjugated, "direct-reacting" bilirubin). Glucuronic acid is attached via ester linkage to the 2 propionic acid groups to form an acylglucuronide.

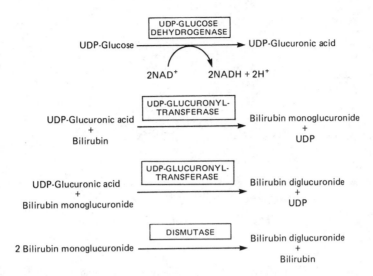

Figure 24–16. Conjugation of bilirubin with glucuronic acid. The glucuronate donor, UDP-glucuronic acid, is formed from UDP-glucose as depicted.

at least initially, in the smooth endoplasmic reticulum with the aid of a specific set of enzymes. Most of the bilirubin excreted in the bile of mammals is in the form of a **bilirubin diglucuronide** (Fig 24–15). The formation of the intermediate monoglucuronide of bilirubin is catalyzed by uridine diphosphate glucuronate glucuronyltransferase **(UDP-glucuronyltransferase)**, an enzyme that exists in the smooth endoplasmic reticulum and is probably composed of more than a single entity. The reaction is depicted in Fig 24–16. It occurs chiefly in the liver but also in the kidney and the intestinal mucosa. When bilirubin conjugates exist abnormally in human serum, they are predominantly monoglucuronides.

The formation of the diglucuronide of bilirubin may occur in the bile canalicular region of the hepatocyte membrane by a similar UDP-glucuronyltransferase (Fig 24–16) or by an enzyme-catalyzed dismutation of 2 mol of bilirubin monoglucuronide to 1 mol of bilirubin diglucuronide and 1 mol of unconjugated bilirubin (Fig 24–16). More will be said about this conjugation system in the discussion of the inherited disorders of bilirubin conjugation.

UDP-glucuronyltransferase activity can be **induced** by a number of clinically useful drugs, including phenobarbital.

Secretion of Bilirubin into Bile

Secretion of conjugated bilirubin into the bile occurs against a large concentration gradient and must be carried out by an active transport mechanism. The **active transport** is probably **rate-limiting** for the entire process of hepatic bilirubin metabolism. The hepatic transport of conjugated bilirubin into the bile is inducible by those same drugs that are capable of inducing the conjugation of bilirubin. Thus, the conjugation and excretion systems for bilirubin behave as a coordinated functional unit.

Under physiologic conditions, essentially all (>97%) of the bilirubin secreted into the bile is conjugated. Only after phototherapy can significant quantities of unconjugated bilirubin be found in bile.

In the liver, there are multiple systems for secreting naturally occurring and pharmaceutical compounds into the bile after their metabolism. Some of these secreting systems are shared by the bilirubin diglucuronides, but others seem to operate independently.

METABOLISM OF BILIRUBIN IN THE INTESTINE

As the conjugated bilirubin reaches the terminal ileum and the large intestine, the glucuronides are removed by specific bacterial enzymes (β-glucuronidases), and the pigment is subsequently reduced by the fecal flora to a group of colorless tetrapyrrolic compounds called **urobilinogens** (Fig 24–17). In the terminal ileum and large intestine, a small fraction of the urobilinogens is reabsorbed and reexcreted through the liver to constitute the **intrahepatic urobilinogen cycle**. Under abnormal conditions, particularly when excessive bile pigment is formed or liver disease interferes with this intrahepatic cycle, urobilinogen may also be excreted in the urine.

Normally, most of the **colorless urobilinogens** formed in the colon by the fecal flora are oxidized there to urobilins (colored compounds) and are excreted in the feces (Fig 24–17). Darkening of feces upon standing in air is due to the oxidation of residual urobilinogens to urobilins.

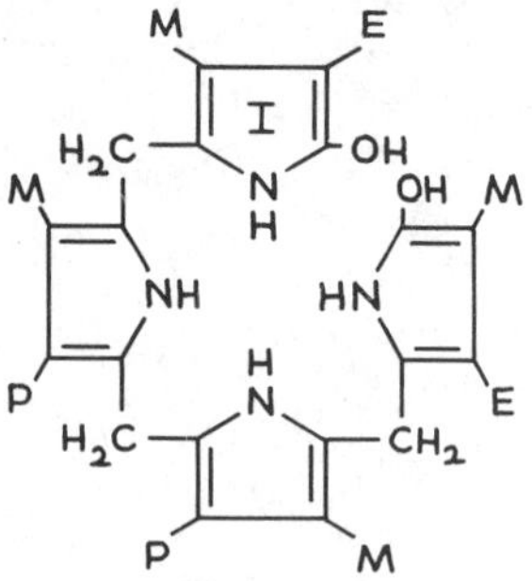

Mesobilirubinogen
($C_{33}H_{44}O_6N_4$)

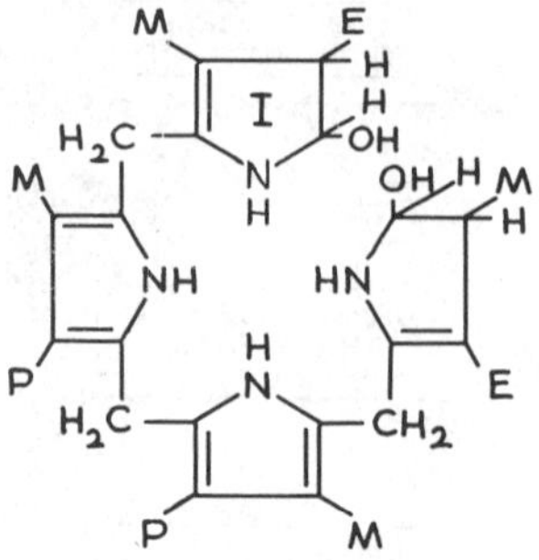

Stercobilinogen
(L-urobilinogen)

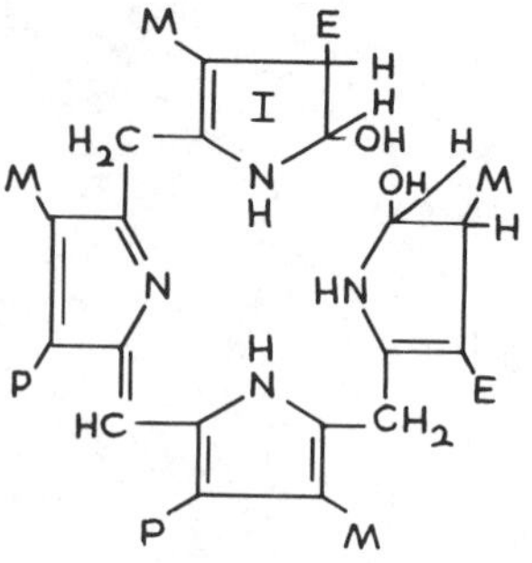

Stercobilin
(L-urobilin)

Figure 24-17. Structure of some bile pigments.

HYPERBILIRUBINEMIA

When bilirubin in the blood exceeds 1 mg/dL (17.1 μmol/L), hyperbilirubinemia exists. Hyperbilirubinemia may be due to the production of more bilirubin than the normal liver can excrete, or it may result from the failure of a damaged liver to excrete bilirubin produced in normal amounts. In the absence of hepatic damage, obstruction to the excretory ducts of the liver—by preventing the excretion of bilirubin—will also cause hyperbilirubinemia. In all of these situations, bilirubin accumulates in the blood, and when it reaches a certain concentration, it diffuses into the tissues, which then become yellow. The condition is called **jaundice** or **icterus.**

In clinical studies of jaundice, measurement of bilirubin in the serum is of great value. A method for quantitatively assaying the bilirubin content of the serum was first devised by Van den Bergh by application of Ehrlich's test for bilirubin in urine. The Ehrlich reaction is based on the coupling of diazotized sulfanilic acid (Ehrlich's diazo reagent) and bilirubin to produce a reddish-purple azo compound. In the original procedure as described by Ehrlich, methanol was used to provide a solution in which both bilirubin and the diazo reagent were soluble. Van den Bergh inadvertently omitted the methanol on an occasion when assay of bile pigment in human bile was being attempted. To his surprise, normal development of the color occurred "directly." This form of bilirubin that would react without the addition of methanol was thus termed "direct-reacting." It was then found that this same direct reaction would also occur in serum from cases of jaundice due to biliary obstruction. However, it was still necessary to add methanol to detect bilirubin in normal serum or that which was present in excess in serum from cases of hemolytic jaundice where no evidence of obstruction was to be found. To that form of bilirubin which could be measured only after the addition of methanol, the term "indirect-reacting" was applied.

It has now been demonstrated that the indirect bilirubin is "free" (unconjugated) bilirubin en route to the liver from the reticuloendothelial tissues where the bilirubin was originally produced by the breakdown of heme porphyrins. Since this bilirubin is not water-soluble, it requires methanol to initiate coupling with the diazo reagent. In the liver, the free bilirubin becomes conjugated with glucuronic acid, and the conjugate, bilirubin glucuronide, can then be excreted into the bile. Furthermore, conjugated bilirubin, being water-soluble, can react directly with the diazo reagent, so that the "direct bilirubin" of Van den Bergh is actually a bilirubin conjugate (bilirubin glucuronide).

Depending on the type of bilirubin present in plasma, ie, unconjugated bilirubin or conjugated bilirubin, the hyperbilirubinemia may be classified as **retention** hyperbilirubinemia or **regurgitation** hyperbilirubinemia, respectively.

Only unconjugated bilirubin can cross the blood-brain barrier into the central nervous system; thus, encephalopathy due to hyperbilirubinemia (kernicterus) can occur only in connection with retention bilirubin or unconjugated hyperbilirubinemia. On the other hand, only conjugated bilirubin can appear in urine. Accordingly, **choluric jaundice** occurs only in regurgitation hyperbilirubinemia, and **acholuric jaundice** occurs only in the presence of an excess of unconjugated bilirubin.

Unconjugated Hyperbilirubinemia

Even in the event of extensive hemolysis, unconjugated hyperbilirubinemia is usually only slight (< 4 mg/dL; < 68.4 μmol/L), because of the liver's large capacity for handling bilirubin. However, if the handling of bilirubin is defective owing to either an acquired defect or an inherited abnormality, unconjugated hyperbilirubinemia may occur.

The most common cause of unconjugated hyperbilirubinemia is the transient neonatal "physiologic jaundice." This hyperbilirubinemia results from an accelerated hemolysis and an immature hepatic system for the uptake, conjugation, and secretion of bilirubin. Not only is the **UDP-glucuronyltransferase** activity reduced, but there probably is reduced synthesis of the substrate for that enzyme, UDP-glucuronic acid. Since the increased bilirubin is unconjugated, it is capable of penetrating the blood-brain barrier when its concentration in plasma exceeds that which can be tightly bound by albumin (20–25 mg/dL). This can result in a hyperbilirubinemic toxic encephalopathy, or **kernicterus.** Because of the recognized inducibility of this bilirubin metabolizing system, phenobarbital has been administered to jaundiced neonates and is effective in this disorder. In addition, exposure to visible light (by a mechanism that is not understood) can promote the hepatic excretion of unconjugated bilirubin by converting some of the bilirubin to other derivatives such as maleimide fragments and geometric isomers that are excreted in the bile.

A. Crigler-Najjar Syndrome, Type I; Congenital Nonhemolytic Jaundice: Type I Crigler-Najjar syndrome, a rare autosomal recessive disorder of humans, is due to a primary metabolic defect in the conjugation of bilirubin. It is characterized by severe congenital jaundice due to the inherited absence of bilirubin UDP-glucuronyltransferase activity in hepatic tissues. The disease is usually fatal within the first 15 months of life, but a few teenagers have been reported who did not develop difficulties until puberty. These children have been treated with phototherapy with some reduction in plasma bilirubin levels. Phenobarbital and other drugs that induce the bilirubin metabolizing systems in normal liver have no effect on the formation of bilirubin glucuronides in patients with type I Crigler-Najjar syndrome. Serum bilirubin usually exceeds 20 mg/dL when untreated.

B. Crigler-Najjar Syndrome, Type II: This rare inherited disorder seems to result from a milder defect in the bilirubin conjugating system and has a more benign course. The serum bilirubin concentrations usually do not exceed 20 mg/dL, but all of the bilirubin accumulated is of the unconjugated type. Surprisingly, the bile in these patients does contain bilirubin monoglucuronide, and it has been proposed that the genetic defect may involve the hepatic UDP-glucuronyltransferase that adds the second glucuronyl group to bilirubin monoglucuronide.

It has been demonstrated that patients with this syndrome can respond to treatment with large doses of phenobarbital. In these patients, the drug-mediated reduction of hyperbilirubinemia seems to result from induction of the entire bilirubin metabolizing system and not simply a stimulation of bilirubin conjugation.

In several instances, presumed heterozygotes for this disorder exhibited a mild unconjugated hyperbilirubinemia indistinguishable from that seen in Gilbert's disease (see below). Thus, it is possible that the autosomal recessive type II Crigler-Najjar syndrome is the homozygous state of the defect present in heterozygous form in the mild chronic hyperbilirubinemia of Gilbert.

C. Gilbert's Disease: Gilbert's disease is a heterogeneous group of disorders, many of which are now recognized to be due to a compensated hemolysis associated with unconjugated hyperbilirubinemia. There also appears to be a defect in the hepatic clearance of bilirubin, possibly due to a defect in the uptake of bilirubin by the liver parenchymal cells. However, bilirubin UDP-glucuronyltransferase activities in the livers of those patients studied with this disease were found to be reduced.

In general, the benign disorders collectively termed Gilbert's disease seem to be transmitted in an autosomal dominant manner.

D. Toxic Hyperbilirubinemia: Unconjugated hyperbilirubinemia can result from toxin-induced liver dysfunction such as that caused by chloroform, arsphenamines, carbon tetrachloride, acetaminophen, hepatitis virus, cirrhosis, and *Amanita* mushroom poisoning. Although most of these acquired disorders are due to hepatic parenchymal cell damage, there is frequently a component of obstruction of the biliary tree within the liver that results in the presence of some conjugated hyperbilirubinemia.

Conjugated Hyperbilirubinemia

Because conjugated bilirubin is water-soluble, it is detectable in the urine of most patients with conjugated hyperbilirubinemia; thus, they are frequently said to have choluric jaundice.

A. Chronic Idiopathic Jaundice (Dubin-Johnson Syndrome): This autosomal recessive disorder consists of conjugated hyperbilirubinemia in childhood or during adult life. The hyperbilirubinemia is apparently caused by a defect in the hepatic secretion of conjugated bilirubin into the bile. However, this secretory defect of conjugated compounds is not restricted to bilirubin but also involves secretion of conjugated estrogens and test compounds such as the dye sulfobromophthalein. In fact, the secretory defect of conjugated sulfobromophthalein results in its reflux into the plasma, leading to a secondary rise in the plasma concentration of this test dye, a phenomenon that is pathognomonic for Dubin-Johnson syndrome. When test compounds such as indocyanine green and rose bengal, which do not require conjugation for excretion, are used, such secondary rises in plasma concentration do not appear in these patients. Thus, the defect appears to be in the secretory process that normally deals only with conjugated compounds including conjugated bilirubins.

Another interesting but unexplained phenomenon associated with Dubin-Johnson syndrome is the abnormal distribution of coproporphyrin I and III in the urine. In patients with Dubin-Johnson syndrome, 80–90% of the coproporphyrins are of the type I isomer, in contrast to the normal situation. This abnormality includes an absolute increase in coproporphyrin I and an absolute decrease in coproporphyrin III excretion. However, there do not seem to be any abnormalities of porphyrin synthesis in Dubin-Johnson syndrome. Characteristically, in patients with Dubin-Johnson syndrome, the hepatocytes in the centrolobular area contain an abnormal pigment that has not been identified.

B. Biliary Tree Obstruction: Conjugated hyperbilirubinemia also results from blockage of the

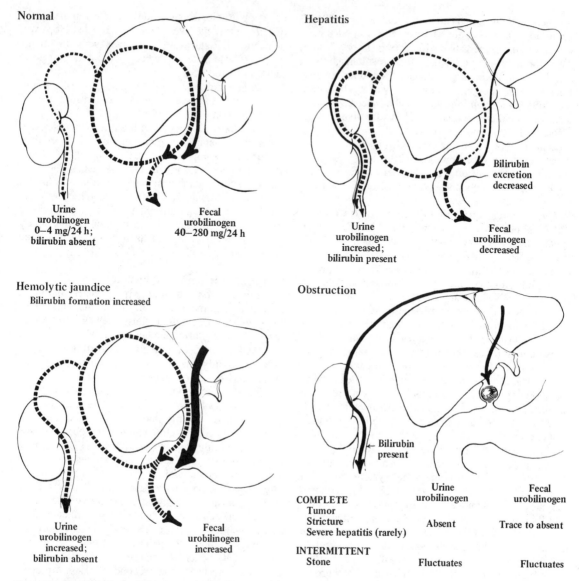

Normal

Urine
urobilinogen
0–4 mg/24 h;
bilirubin absent

Fecal
urobilinogen
40–280 mg/24 h

Hepatitis

Bilirubin
excretion
decreased

Urine
urobilinogen
increased;
bilirubin present

Fecal
urobilinogen
decreased

Hemolytic jaundice
Bilirubin formation increased

Urine
urobilinogen
increased;
bilirubin absent

Fecal
urobilinogen
increased

Obstruction

Bilirubin
present

	Urine urobilinogen	Fecal urobilinogen
COMPLETE Tumor Stricture Severe hepatitis (rarely)	Absent	Trace to absent
INTERMITTENT Stone	Fluctuates	Fluctuates

Figure 24–18. Bilirubin-urobilinogen cycle. (Solid arrows = bilirubin glucuronide; dotted arrows = urobilinogen.) (Reproduced, with permission, from Krupp MA et al: *Physician's Handbook,* 21st ed. Lange, 1985.)

hepatic or common bile ducts. The bile pigment is believed to pass from the blood into the liver cells as usual but fails to be excreted. As a consequence of this, the conjugated bilirubin is absorbed into the hepatic veins and lymphatics.

The term **cholestatic jaundice** may be used to include all forms of extrahepatic obstructive jaundice in addition to some forms of parenchymal jaundice characterized by conjugated hyperbilirubinemia.

Urine Urobilinogen

Normally, there are mere traces of urobilinogen in the urine (average, 0.64 mg; maximum normal, 4 mg [in 24 hours]). In complete obstruction of the bile duct, no urobilinogen is found in the urine, since

bilirubin has no access to the intestine where it can be converted to urobilinogen. In this case, the presence of bilirubin in the urine without urobilinogen suggests **obstructive jaundice,** either intrahepatic or posthepatic.

In **hemolytic jaundice,** the increased production of bilirubin leads to increased production of urobilinogen, which appears in the urine in large amounts. Bilirubin is not usually found in the urine in hemolytic jaundice, so that the combination of increased urobilinogen and absence of bilirubin is suggestive of hemolytic jaundice. Increased blood destruction from any cause (eg, pernicious anemia) will, of course, also bring about an increase in urine urobilinogen. Furthermore, infection of the biliary passages may increase the urobilinogen in the absence of any reduction in liver function, because of the reducing activity of the infecting bacteria.

The diagrams in Fig 24–18 summarize the events characterizing the handling of bilirubin and urobilino-gen by the liver, intestine, and kidney under normal circumstances and in the presence of hemolytic jaundice, hepatitis, or jaundice associated with obstruction of the bile duct.

• • •

References

Battersby AR et al: Biosynthesis of the pigments of life: Formation of the macrocycle. *Nature* 1980;**285:**17.

Eales L, Grosser Y, Sears WG: The clinical biochemistry of the human hepatocutaneous porphyrias in the light of recent studies of newly identified intermediates and porphyrin derivatives. *Ann NY Acad Sci* 1975;**244:**441.

Goldberg A, Rimington C: *Diseases of Porphyrin Metabolism.* Thomas, 1962.

Kappas A, Sassa S, Anderson KE: The porphyrias. In: *The Metabolic Basis of Inherited Disease,* 5th ed. Stanbury JB et al (editors). McGraw-Hill, 1983.

Lemberg R, Legge JW: *Hematin Compounds and Bile Pigments.* Interscience, 1949.

Meyer UA et al: Intermittent acute porphyria: Demonstration of a genetic defect in porphobilinogen metabolism. *N Engl J Med* 1972;**286:**1277.

Rimington C: Haem pigments and porphyrins. *Annu Rev Biochem* 1957;**26:**561.

Schmid R: Cutaneous porphyria in Turkey. *N Engl J Med* 1960;**263:**397.

Schmid R, McDonough AF: Formation and metabolism of bile pigments in vivo. In: *The Porphyrins.* Dolphin D (editor). Academic Press, 1978.

Symposium: Porphyrin Biosynthesis and Metabolism. Ciba Foundation. Little, Brown, 1954.

Watson CJ: Gold from dross: The first century of the urobilinoids. *Ann Intern Med* 1969;**70:**839.

25 | Nucleotides

David W. Martin, Jr., MD

The nucleotides are important intracellular molecules of low molecular weight that participate in a wide variety of biochemical processes. Perhaps the best known role of the purine and pyrimidine nucleotides is to serve as the monomeric precursors of RNA and DNA. However, the **purine** ribonucleotides serve also in biologic systems as the ubiquitous high-energy source, ATP; as regulatory signals (cyclic AMP [cAMP] and cyclic GMP) in a wide variety of tissues and organisms; and as components of the widely used coenzymes FAD, NAD, and NADP and of an important methyl donor, S-adenosylmethionine.

The **pyrimidine** nucleotides, in addition to providing monomeric precursors for nucleic acids, serve as high-energy intermediates, such as UDP-glucose and UDP-galactose in carbohydrate metabolism and CDP-acylglycerol in lipid synthesis.

The various purine and pyrimidine bases that occur in the nucleotides are derived by appropriate substitution on the ring structures of the parent substances, purine or pyrimidine. Structures of these parent nitrogenous bases are shown in Fig 25–1. The positions on the rings are numbered according to the international system. Note that the direction of the numbering of the purine ring is different from that of the pyrimidine ring but that the number 5 carbon is the same in both heterocyclic compounds. Because of their π electron clouds, both the purine and pyrimidine bases are planar molecules, the significance of which is discussed in Chapter 27.

The 3 major **pyrimidine bases** found in the nucleotides of both prokaryotes and eukaryotes are **cytosine, thymine,** and **uracil** (Fig 25–2). The **purine**

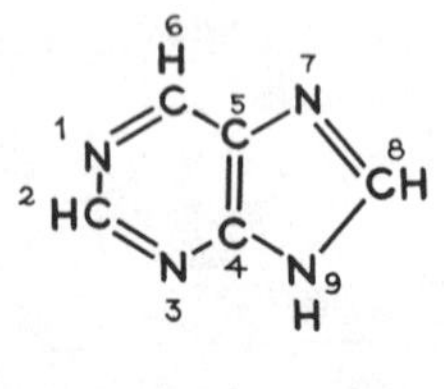

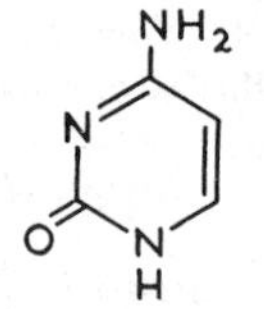

Cytosine
(2-oxy-4-aminopyrimidine)

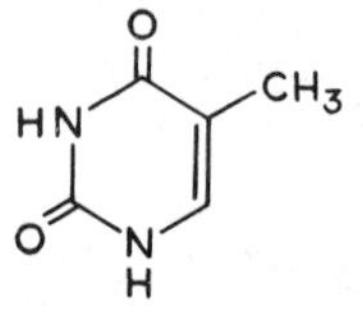

Thymine
(2,4-dioxy-5-methylpyrimidine)

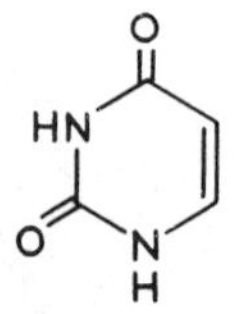

Uracil
(2,4-dioxypyrimidine)

Figure 25–2. The 3 major pyrimidine bases found in nucleotides.

bases, adenine and **guanine,** are the 2 major purines found in living organisms. Two other purine bases, **hypoxanthine** and **xanthine,** also occur as intermediates in the metabolism of adenine and guanine (Fig 25–3). In humans, a completely oxidized purine base, **uric acid,** is formed as the end product of purine catabolism. This compound is discussed in greater detail in Chapter 26.

Because of keto-enol tautomerism, these aromatic molecules can exist in a lactim or lactam form (Fig 25–4); the latter is by far the predominant tautomer of guanine or thymine under physiologic conditions. (The importance of the lactim versus the lactam form becomes apparent in the discussions on base pairing and mutagenesis in Chapters 28 and 30.)

In plants, a series of purine bases containing methyl substituents occurs (Fig 25–5). Many have pharmacologic properties. Examples are coffee, which contains caffeine (1,3,7-trimethylxanthine); tea, which contains theophylline (1,3-dimethylxanthine); and cocoa, which contains theobromine (3,7-dimethylxanthine). The biologic properties of these

Purine

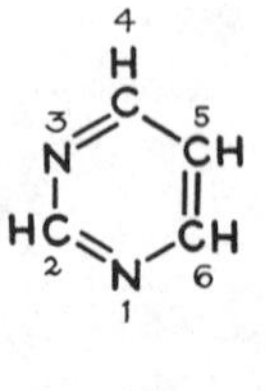

Pyrimidine

Figure 25–1. Structures of purine and pyrimidine with the positions of the elements numbered according to the international system.

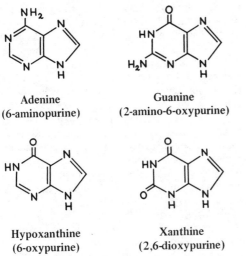

Adenine
(6-aminopurine)

Guanine
(2-amino-6-oxypurine)

Hypoxanthine
(6-oxypurine)

Xanthine
(2,6-dioxypurine)

Figure 25–3. The major purine bases present in nucleotides.

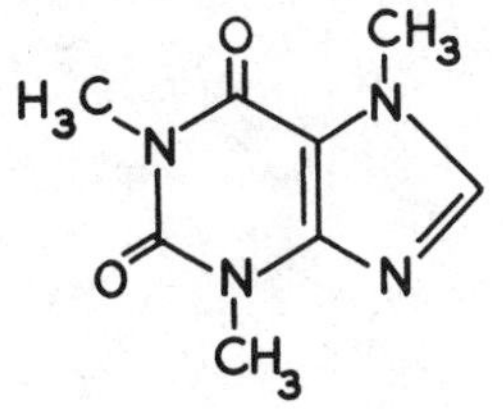

Caffeine
(1,3,7-trimethyl-
xanthine)

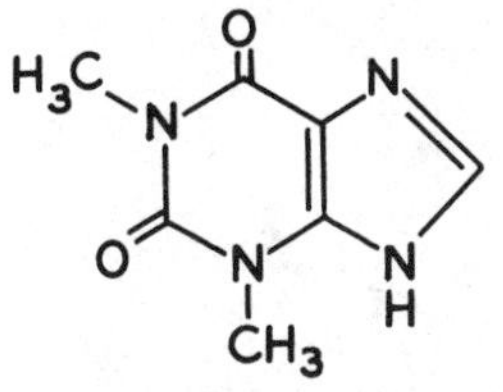

Theophylline
(1,3-dimethyl-
xanthine)

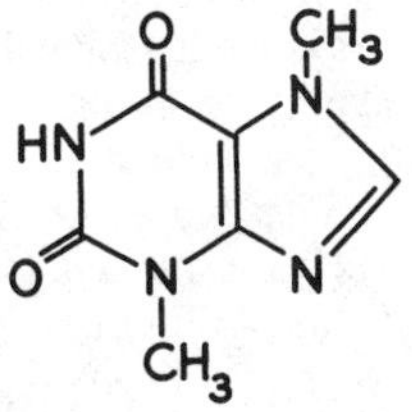

Theobromine
(3,7-dimethyl-
xanthine)

Figure 25–5. The structures of some methyl xanthines commonly occurring in foodstuffs.

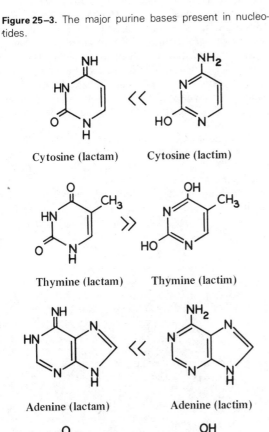

Cytosine (lactam)   Cytosine (lactim)

Thymine (lactam)   Thymine (lactim)

Adenine (lactam)   Adenine (lactim)

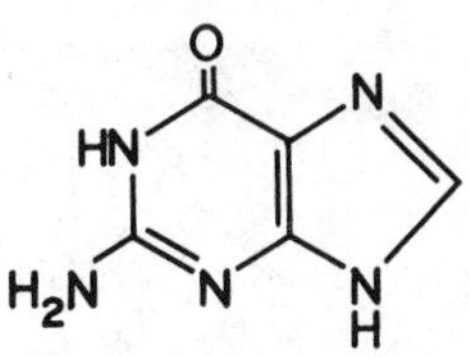

Guanine (lactam) 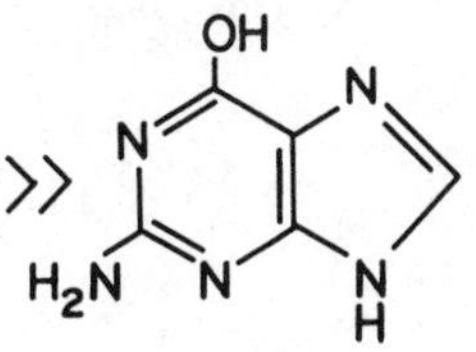   Guanine (lactim)

Figure 25–4. The structures of the tautomers of cystosine, thymine, adenine, and guanine with the predominant forms indicated.

compounds are described in Chapter 26 in the discussion of the metabolism of cyclic nucleotides.

In natural materials, numerous minor (ie, unusual) bases occur in addition to the 5 major bases— adenine, guanine, cytosine, thymine, and uracil— described above. Some of these unusual substituted bases are found only in the nucleic acids of bacteria and viruses, but many are also found in the DNA and transfer RNAs of both prokaryotes and eukaryotes. Both bacterial and human DNA contain, for example, significant quantities of 5-methylcytosine; bacteriophages contain 5-hydroxymethylcytosine (Fig 25–6). More recently, several unusual bases have been discovered in the messenger RNA molecules of mammalian cells. N^6-methyladenine, N^6,N^6-dimethyladenine, and N^7-methylguanine are found in the nucleic acids of mammalian cells (Fig 25–7). A uracil modified at the N_3 position by the attachment of an (α-amino,

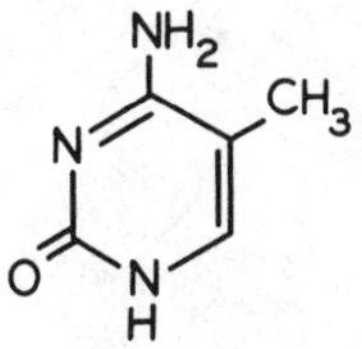

5-Methylcytosine 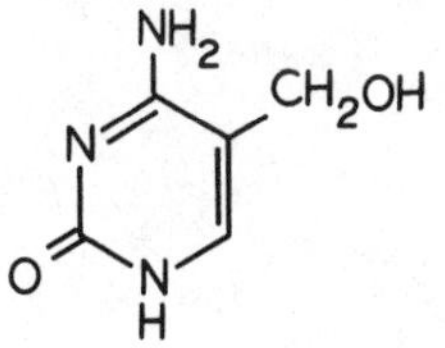   5-Hydroxymethylcytosine

Figure 25–6. The structures of 2 uncommon naturally occurring pyrimidine bases.

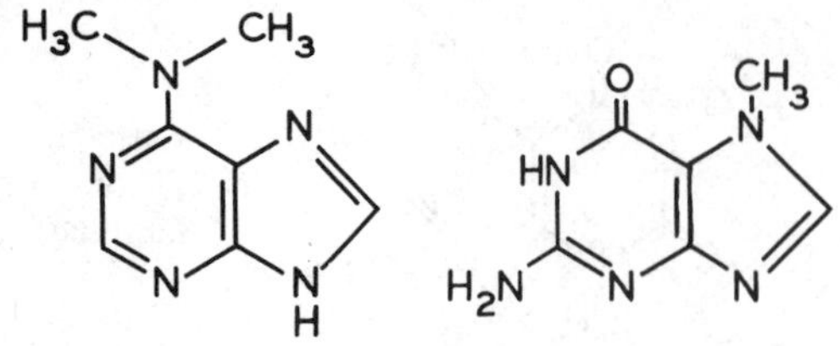

N⁶,N⁶-Dimethyladenine   N⁷-Methylguanine

Figure 25–7. The structures of 2 uncommon naturally occurring purine bases.

α-carboxyl)-propyl group has also been detected in bacteria. The functions of these substituted purine and pyrimidine nucleotide bases are not fully understood.

At neutral pH, guanine is the least soluble of the bases, followed in this respect by xanthine. Although uric acid as urate is relatively soluble at a neutral pH, its pK is 5.75, so that it becomes highly insoluble in a solution with a lower pH, such as urine. Guanine is not a normal constituent of human urine, but xanthine and uric acid do occur in human urine. In view of their low solubility, it is not surprising that these latter 2 purines are most likely to be found as constituents of stones formed within the urinary tract.

NUCLEOSIDES & NUCLEOTIDES

The **free** bases occurring in nature are much less abundant forms of purines and pyrimidines than are their nucleosides and nucleotides. A **nucleoside** (Fig 25–8) is composed of a purine or a pyrimidine base to

which a sugar (usually either D-ribose or 2-deoxyribose) is attached in β-linkage at the N_9 or N_1, respectively. Thus, the adenine ribonucleoside **adenosine** consists of adenine with D-ribose attached at the 9 position. **Guanosine** consists of guanine with D-ribose attached at the 9 position. Cytidine is cytosine with ribose attached at its N_1 position. Uridine consists of ribose attached at the N_1 position of uracil.

The 2′-deoxyribonucleosides consist of 2-deoxyribose attached to the purine or pyrimidine bases at the same positions described above. The attachment of the ribose or 2-deoxyribose to the ring structures of the purine or pyrimidine bases is through an N-glycosidic bond, which is relatively acid-labile. Although, theoretically, free rotation occurs about this N-glycosidic bond of the sugar moiety and the purine or pyrimidine ring structure, steric hindrance between these 2 moieties in fact hinders free rotation. In the naturally occurring nucleosides, the **anti** conformation is strongly favored over the **syn** form (Fig 25–9). As is discussed in Chapter 27, the anti form is necessary for the proper positioning of the complementary purine and pyrimidine bases in the double-stranded B form of deoxyribonucleic acid. (Because of the conventional representation of the D-ribose, in most figures of this and other chapters, the purine and pyrimidine nucleosides and nucleotides are shown in the less favored syn conformation.)

Nucleotides are nucleosides phosphorylated on one or more of the hydroxyl groups of the sugar (ribose or deoxyribose) (Fig 25–10). Thus, adenosine monophosphate (AMP or adenylate) is adenine + ribose + phosphate. 2′-Deoxyadenosine monophosphate (dAMP or deoxyadenylate) consists of adenine + 2-deoxyribose + phosphate. The only sugar com-

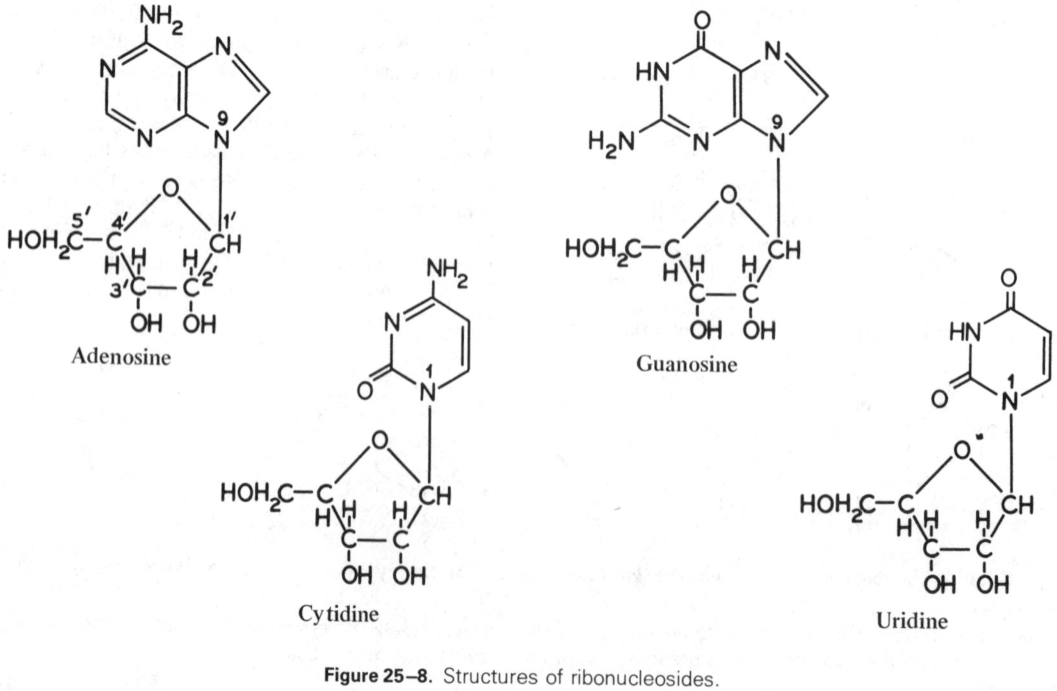

Adenosine

Guanosine

Cytidine

Uridine

Figure 25–8. Structures of ribonucleosides.

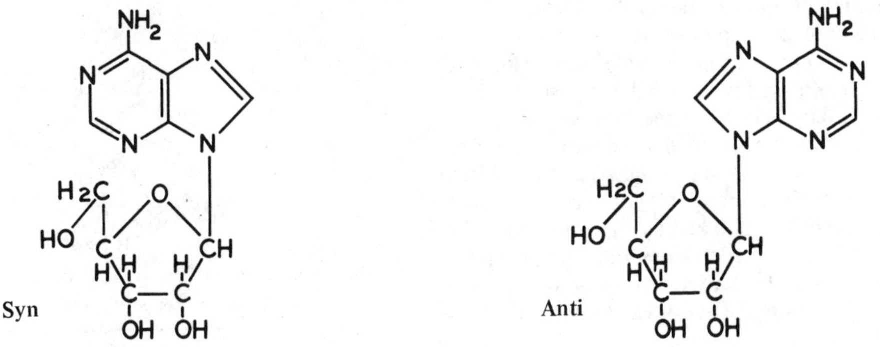

Figure 25–9. The structures of the **syn** and **anti** configurations of adenosine.

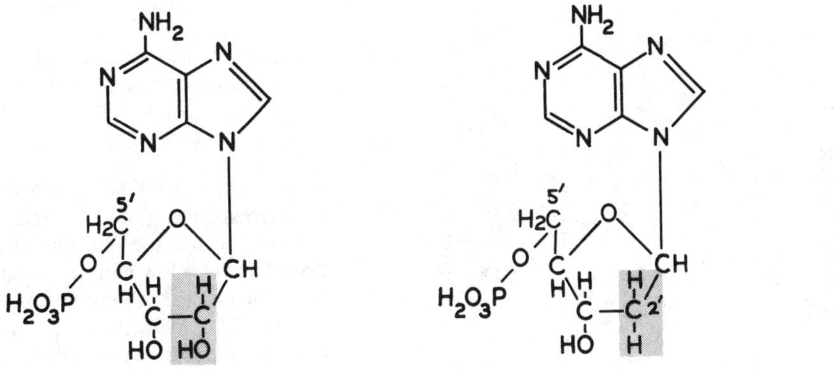

Figure 25–10. The structures of adenylic acid (AMP) *(left)* and 2′-deoxyadenylic acid (dAMP) *(right).*

monly found attached to uracil is ribose, and that commonly found attached to thymine is 2-deoxyribose. Therefore, thymidylic acid (TMP) is thymine + 2-deoxyribose + phosphate, and uridylic acid (UMP) is uracil + ribose + phosphate (Fig 25–11). DNA is a polymer of thymidylic acid, 2′-deoxycytidylic acid, 2′-deoxyadenylic acid, and 2′deoxyguanylic acid. RNA is a polymer containing uridylate, cytidylate, adenylate, and guanylate.

There are exceptions to the above structures of nucleotides. For example, in tRNA the ribose moiety is occasionally attached to uracil at the 5 position, thus establishing a carbon-to-carbon linkage instead of the usual nitrogen-to-carbon linkage. This unusual compound is called pseudouridine (Ψ). The tRNA molecules contain another unusual nucleotide structure, ie, thymine attached to ribose monophosphate. This compound is formed subsequent to the synthesis of the tRNA by methylation of the UMP residue by S-adenosylmethionine (see below). Pseudouridylic acid (ΨMP) is similarly rearranged from uridylic acid after the tRNA molecule has been synthesized.

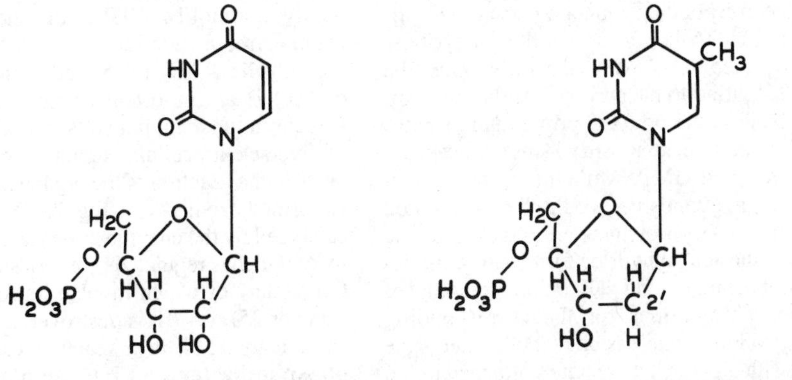

Figure 25–11. The structures of uridylic acid (UMP) *(left)* and thymidylic acid (TMP) *(right).*

Nomenclature of Nucleosides & Nucleotides

The position of the phosphate in the nucleotide is indicated by a numeral. For example, adenosine with the phosphate attached to carbon 3 of the sugar ribose would be designated adenosine 3'-phosphate. The prime mark after the numeral is required to differentiate the numbered position on the sugar moiety from the numbered position on a purine or pyrimidine base, which would not be followed by the prime mark. A nucleotide of 2'-deoxyadenosine with the phosphate moiety attached to the carbon 5 position of the sugar would be designated 2'-deoxyadenosine-5'-phosphate. (Fig 25–12.)

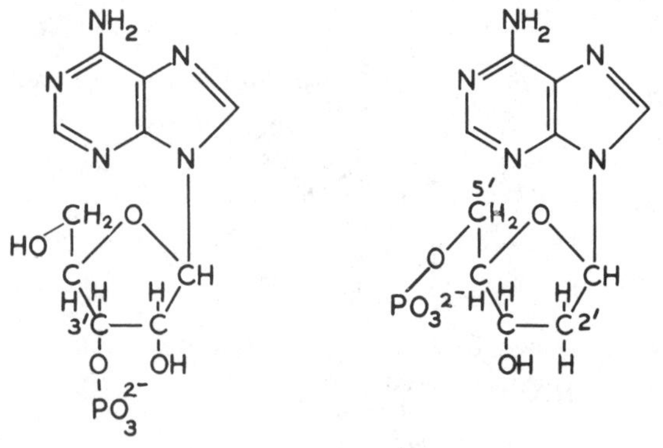

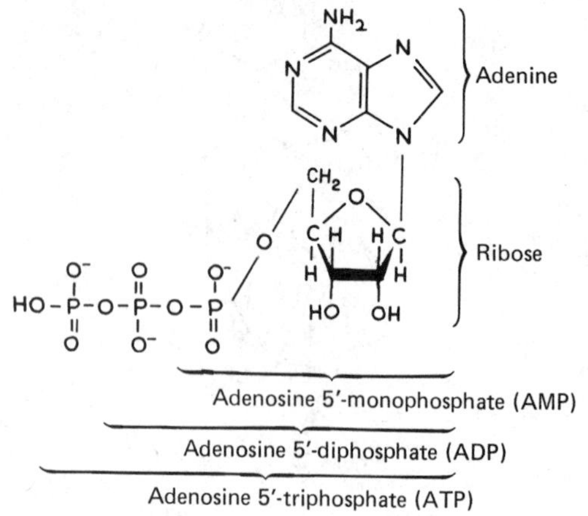

Figure 25–13. The structure of ATP and the structures of the corresponding diphosphate and monophosphate forms.

Figure 25–12. The structures of adenosine 3'-monophosphate *(left)* and 2'-deoxyadenosine-5'-monophosphate *(right)*.

The abbreviations A, G, C, T, and U may be used to designate a nucleoside in accordance with the purine or pyrimidine base it contains: adenine, guanine, cytosine, thymine, or uracil, respectively. The prefix d is added if the sugar of the nucleoside is 2'-deoxyribose. When the nucleoside occurs in the free form as a mononucleotide (ie, not a component of nucleic acid polynucleotide), the abbreviation MP (monophosphate) may be added to the abbreviation designating the nucleoside. For example, guanosine containing 2'-deoxyribose would be designated dG (deoxyguanosine) and the corresponding monophosphate with the phosphate esterified to the carbon 3 of the deoxyribose moiety is designated dG-3'-MP. Generally, when the phosphate is esterified to the carbon 5 of the ribose or deoxyribose moiety, the prefixed primed number (5') is omitted. For example, guanosine 5'-monophosphate would be abbreviated GMP, while the 5'-monophosphate of 2'-deoxyguanosine would be designated dGMP. When 2 or 3 phosphates are attached to the sugar moiety in the acid anhydride form, the abbreviations DP (diphosphate) and TP (triphosphate) are added to the abbreviations for the corresponding purine or pyrimidine nucleoside. Thus, adenosine triphosphate with 3 phosphate residues attached to the 5' carbon of the adenosine would be abbreviated ATP.

The structure of ATP is shown in Fig 25–13 along with its corresponding diphosphate and monophosphate forms. Because the phosphates are in the acid anhydride form—a low entropy situation—the phosphates are said to be high-energy ones, ie, high potential energy. The hydrolysis of 1 mol of ATP to ADP releases about 7 kcal of potential energy.

NATURALLY OCCURRING NUCLEOTIDES

Free nucleotides that are not an integral part of nucleic acids are also found in tissues. Many have important functions. Some of these compounds are briefly described.

Adenosine Derivatives

Adenosine diphosphate and adenosine triphosphate are important compounds in view of their participation in oxidative phosphorylation and, in the case of ATP, as the source of high-energy phosphate for nearly every energy-requiring reaction in the cell. The ATP concentration in most living mammalian cells is nearly 1 mmol/L. ATP is the most abundant intracellular free nucleotide.

Cyclic AMP (3',5'-adenosine monophosphate; cAMP) is an important adenosine derivative that is present in most animal cells. cAMP mediates a series of diverse extracellular signals of considerable importance to the function of the organism as a whole. cAMP is formed from ATP (Fig 25–14). The reaction is catalyzed by the enzyme **adenylate cyclase,** the activity of which is regulated by a series of complex interactions many of which involve hormone receptors (see Chapter 35). cAMP is destroyed in tissues by its conversion to AMP in a reaction catalyzed by **cAMP phosphodiesterase.** Intracellular cAMP concentrations are usually near 1 μmol/L.

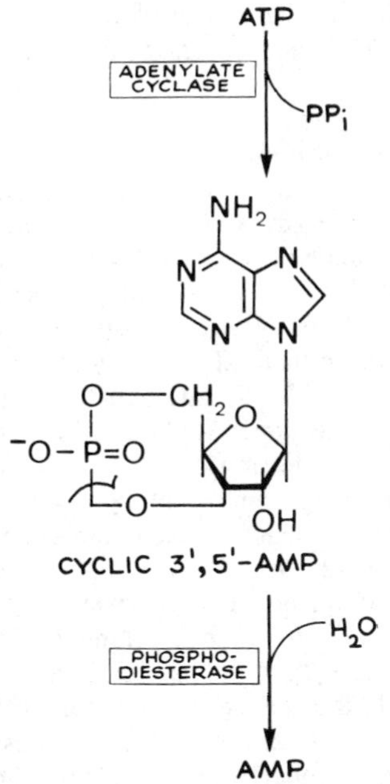

Figure 25–14. Formation of cAMP from ATP and destruction of cAMP by phosphodiesterase.

The incorporation of sulfate into ester linkages in compounds such as sulfated proteoglycans (see Chapter 32) requires the preliminary "activation" of the sulfate molecule. Sulfate is "activated" by reacting with ATP to form adenosine 3'-phosphate-5'-phosphosulfate (PAPS) in the reaction shown in Fig 25–15. The active sulfate moiety is also required as the substrate for sulfate conjugation reactions.

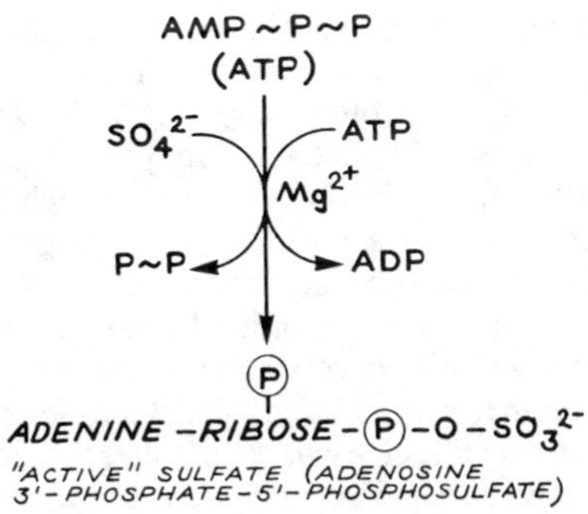

Figure 25–15. The formation of adenosine 3'-phosphate-5'-phosphosulfate.

Another important naturally occurring adenosine derivative, **S-adenosylmethionine** (Fig 25–16), serves as a form of "active" methionine. S-Adenosylmethionine serves widely as a methyl donor in many diverse methylation reactions and as a source of propylamine for the synthesis of polyamines.

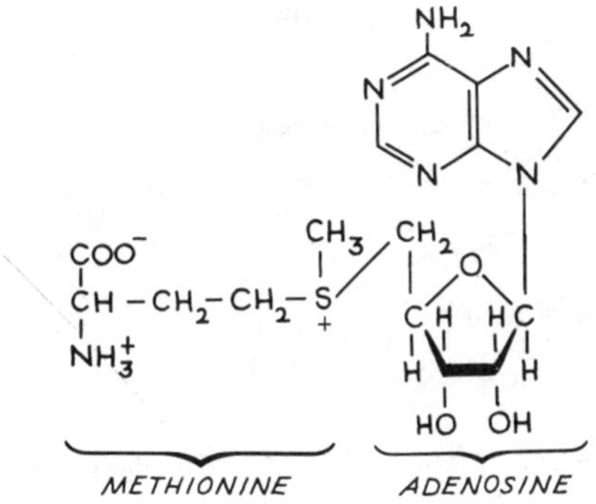

Figure 25–16. The structure of S-adenosylmethionine.

Guanosine Derivatives

Guanosine nucleotides, particularly guanosine diphosphate and guanosine triphosphate, serve in several energy-requiring systems. These are analogs of ADP and ATP, respectively. For example, the oxidation of α-ketoglutaric acid to succinyl-CoA in the tricarboxylic acid cycle involves oxidative phosphorylation with transfer of phosphate to GDP to form GTP. This phosphorylation reaction is quite similar to those involving the phosphorylation of ADP to ATP. GTP is required for the activation of adenylate cyclase by some hormones and serves both as an allosteric regulator and as an energy source for protein synthesis on polyribosomes. It therefore has an important role in the maintenance of the internal milieu.

Cyclic GMP (3',5'-guanosine monophosphate; cGMP [Fig 25–17]) appears also to be an important intracellular signal of extracellular events. In at least some cases, cGMP acts antagonistically to cAMP. cGMP is formed from GTP by an enzyme called **guanylate cyclase,** which is similar in many ways to adenylate cyclase. Guanylate cyclase, like adenylate cyclase, appears to be regulated by a variety of effectors, including hormones. cGMP is also catabolized by a phosphodiesterase to produce its respective 5'-monophosphate.

Hypoxanthine Derivatives

Hypoxanthine ribonucleotide, usually called inosinic acid (IMP, or inosinate in the salt form), is a

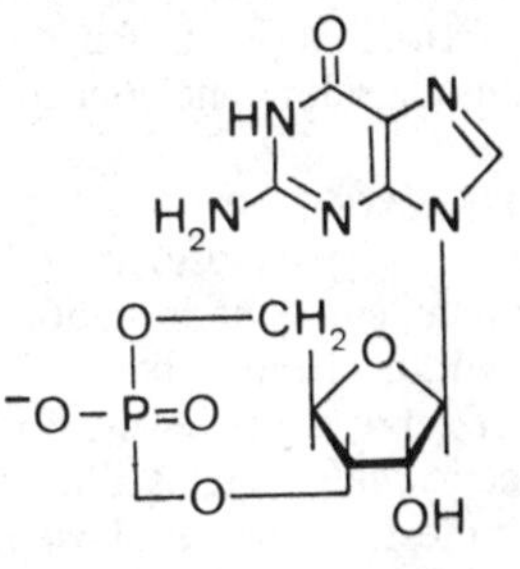

Figure 25–17. The structure of cyclic 3',5'-guanosine monophosphate (cyclic GMP; cGMP).

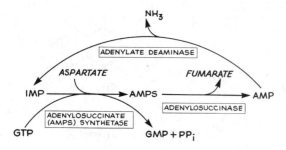

Figure 25–18. The purine nucleotide cycle.

precursor of all purine ribonucleotides synthesized de novo. Inosinate can also be formed by the deamination of AMP, a reaction which occurs particularly in muscle as part of the purine nucleotide cycle (Fig 25–18). Inosinate, derived from AMP, when reconverted to AMP results in the net production of ammonia from aspartate. Removal of the phosphate group from IMP forms the nucleoside inosine (hypoxanthine riboside), an intermediate in another cycle referred to as the purine salvage cycle (see Chapter 26).

Analogs of ADP and ATP in which the purine nucleoside derivative is inosine rather than adenosine have been found occasionally to participate in phosphorylation reactions. These compounds are inosine diphosphate (IDP) and inosine triphosphate (ITP).

Uracil Derivatives

Uridine nucleotide derivatives are important coenzymes in reactions involving the metabolism of hexoses and the polymerization of sugars to form starch and the oligosaccharide moieties of glycoproteins and proteoglycans. (See Chapter 33.) In these reactions, the substrates are uridine diphospho- sugars. For example, uridine diphosphoglucose (UDPGlc) is the precursor of glycogen. Another uridine nucleotide coenzyme, uridine diphosphoglucuronic acid (UDPGlcUA), serves as the "active" glucuronide for conjugation reactions such as the formation of bilirubin glucuronide (see Chapter 24).

Uracil also participates in the formation of high-energy phosphate compounds analogous to ATP, GTP, or ITP. Uridine triphosphate (UTP) is utilized, for example, in the reactions involving conversion of galactose to glucose in which the UDPGlc and UDP-Gal also are formed. UTP is the precursor for the polymerization of uridine nucleotides into RNA.

Cytosine Derivatives

Cytidine (cytosine-ribose) may form the high-energy phosphate compounds cytidine diphosphate (CDP) and cytidine triphosphate (CTP); the latter serves also as the precursor for the polymerization of CMP into nucleic acids. CTP is a nucleotide required for the biosynthesis of some phosphoglycerides in animal tissue. Reactions involving ceramide and CDP-choline are responsible for the formation of sphingomyelin and other substituted sphingosines.

Cyclic nucleotide derivatives of cytidine, analogous to those of adenosine and guanosine, have been described.

Vitamin Nucleotides

The functional moieties of many vitamins are nucleotides with structures analogous to purine and pyrimidine nucleotides. Riboflavin (vitamin B_2; see Chapter 10) functions as a ribitol 5'-phosphate derivative linked to AMP by a pyrophosphate bridge (FAD). Niacin is a constituent of 2 coenzymes, nicotinamide adenine dinucleotide (NAD) and nicotinamide adenine dinucleotide phosphate (NADP). In both of these cases, nicotinamide ribose phosphate is joined to an adenosine monophosphate through a pyrophosphate linkage. Coenzyme A is pantetheine linked to adenosine 3'-phosphate through a pyrophosphate moiety. One of the biologically active derivatives of cobalamin (vitamin B_{12}) requires the attachment of a 5'-deoxyadenosyl moiety through the 5' carbon to the cobalt.

It should thus be clear that beyond providing the monomers of the structures of nucleic acids, the purine and pyrimidine nucleosides and nucleotides serve many diverse functions in living organisms.

SYNTHETIC DERIVATIVES

Synthetic analogs of nucleobases, nucleosides, and nucleotides are widely used in the medical sciences and clinical medicine. In the past, most of these uses have depended upon the role of nucleotides as components of nucleic acids for cellular growth and division. For a cell to divide, its nucleic acids must be replicated, requiring that the precursors of nucleic acids—the normal purine and pyrimidine deoxyribonucleotides—be readily available. One of the most important components of the oncologist's pharmacopeia is the group of synthetic analogs of purine and pyrimidine nucleobases and nucleosides.

The pharmacologic approach has been to use an analog in which either the heterocyclic ring structure or the sugar moiety has been altered in such a way as to induce toxic effects when the analog becomes incorporated into various cellular constituents. Many of these effects result from inhibition by the drug of specific enzyme activities necessary for nucleic acid synthesis or from the incorporation of metabolites of the drug into the nucleic acids where they alter the required base pairing essential to accurate transmission of information.

The most commonly used analogs of the purine or pyrimidine rings have substituents which do not occur naturally and which alter the base pairing or the interaction of the nucleotides with specific enzymes (Fig 25–19). Examples of these would be the 5-fluoro or 5-iodo derivatives of uracil or deoxyuridine, all of which serve as thymine or thymidine analogs, respectively. Both 6-thioguanine and 6-mercaptopurine, in which naturally occurring hydroxyl groups are replaced with thiol groups at the 6 position, are widely

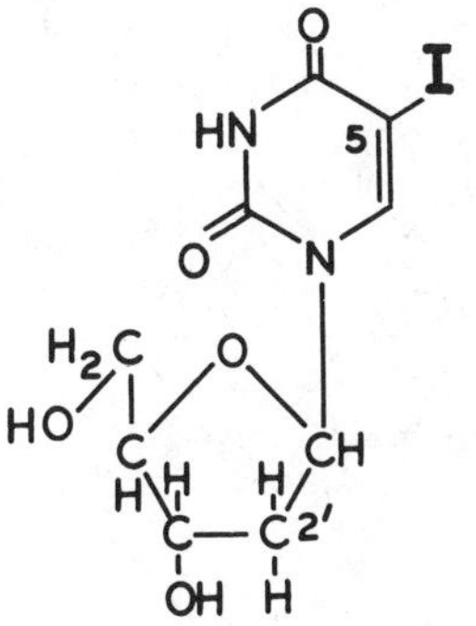

5-Iodo-2′-deoxyuridine

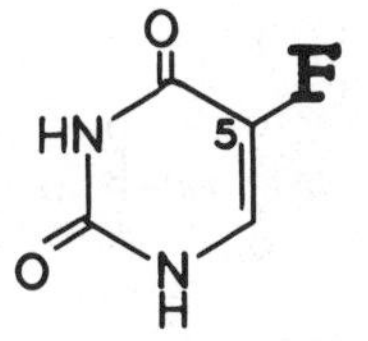

5-Fluorouracil

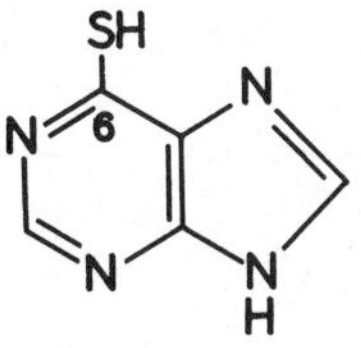

6-Mercaptopurine

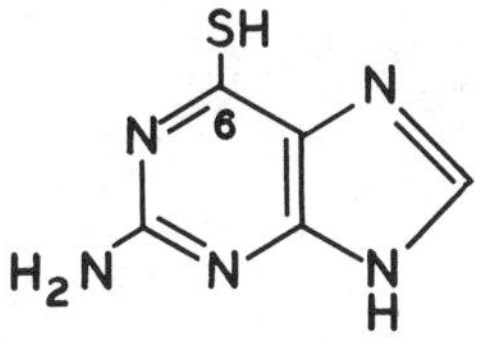

6-Thioguanine

Figure 25–19. The structures of 2 synthetic pyrimidine analogs *(above)* and 2 synthetic purine analogs *(below).*

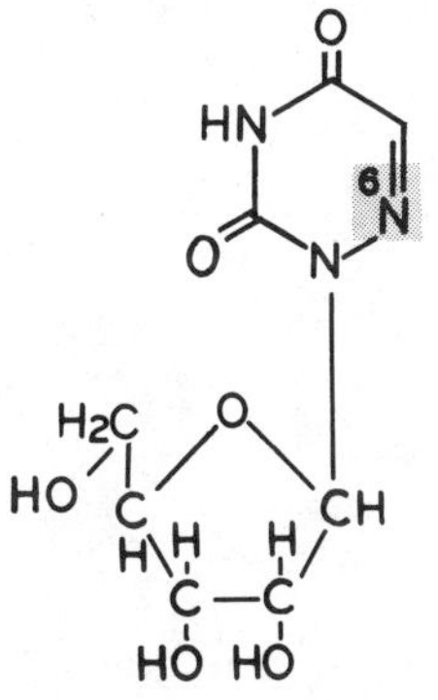

6-Azauridine

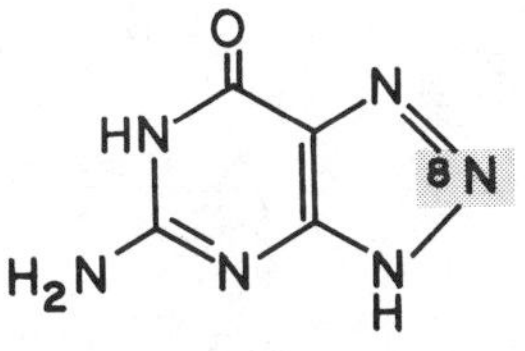

8-Azaguanine

Figure 25–20. The structures of 6-azauridine *(left)* and 8-azaguanine *(right).*

used clinically. The analogs in which the purine or pyrimidine ring contains extra nitrogen atoms, such as 5- or 6-azauridine or azacytidine and 8-azaguanine (Fig 25–20), also have been tested clinically.

The purine analog 4-hydroxypyrazolopyrimidine (allopurinol) is widely marketed as an inhibitor of de novo purine biosynthesis and of xanthine oxidase. It is used for the treatment of hyperuricemia and gout. Nucleosides containing arabinose rather than ribose as the sugar moieties, notably cytarabine (arabinosyl cytosine, Ara-C) and vidarabine (arabinosyl adenine, Ara-A), are used in the chemotherapy of cancer and viral infections. (See Fig 25–21 for structures of these substances.)

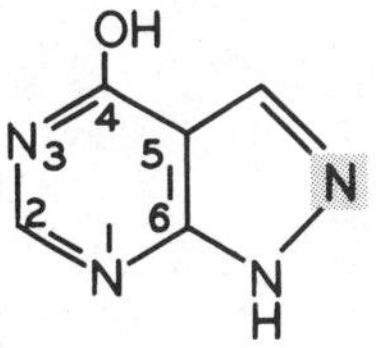

Allopurinol (lactim)

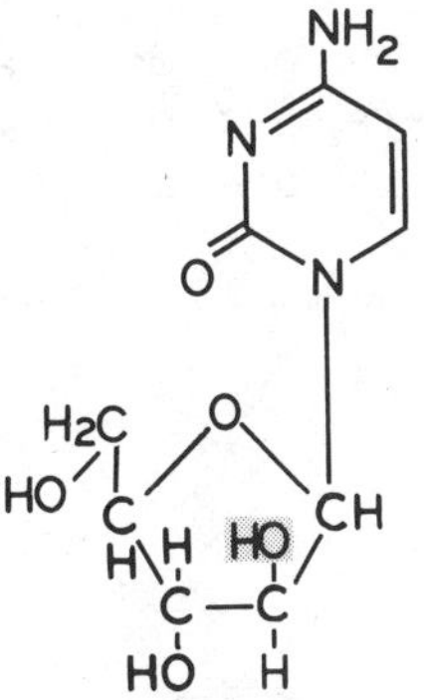

Arabinosyl cytosine

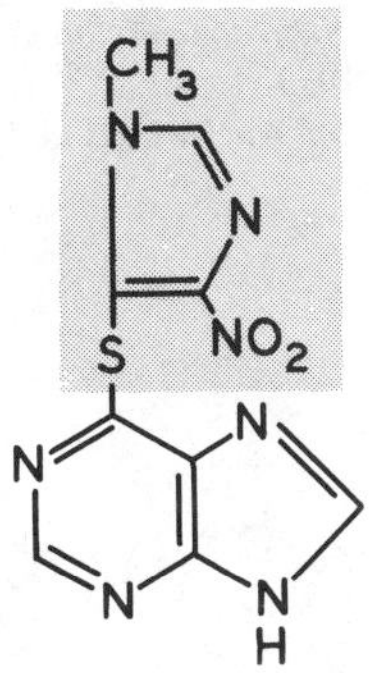

Azathioprine

Figure 25–21. The structures of 4-hydroxypyrazolopyrimidine (allopurinol), arabinosyl cytosine (cytarabine), and azathioprine.

Azathioprine, which is catabolized to 6-mercaptopurine, is useful in organ transplantation as a suppressor of events involved in immunologic rejection. A series of nucleoside analogs with antiviral activities has been studied for several years; one, 5-iododeoxyuridine (see above), has been demonstrated to be effective in the local treatment of herpetic keratitis, an infection of the cornea by herpesvirus.

Numerous analogs of purine and pyrimidine ribonucleotides have been synthesized so as to generate nonhydrolyzable di- or triphosphates for use in vitro. These analogs allow the investigator to determine whether given biochemical effects of nucleoside di- or triphosphates require hydrolysis or whether their effects are mediated by occupying specific nucleotide binding sites on enzymes or regulatory proteins. Fig 25–22 depicts 2 such analogs of guanosine triphosphate.

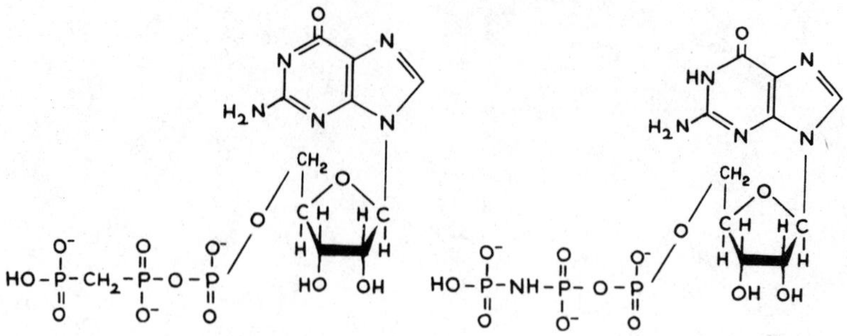

Figure 25–22. β-γ Methylene and β-γ imino derivatives of GTP, which cannot be hydrolyzed between the β and γ phosphates.

●   ●   ●

References

Henderson JF, Paterson ARP: *Nucleotide Metabolism: An Intro-duction.* Academic Press, 1973.

Michelson AM: *The Chemistry of Nucleosides and Nucleotides.* Academic Press, 1963.

Prusoff WH, Ward DC: Nucleoside analogs with antiviral activity. *Biochem Pharmacol* 1976;**25:**1233.

Metabolism of Purine & Pyrimidine Nucleotides | 26

David W. Martin, Jr., MD

The chemistry and, to some extent, the general biologic roles of the purine and pyrimidine compounds have been discussed in Chapter 25. The chemistry of the nucleic acids will be described in Chapter 27. In this chapter, the metabolism of the purines and pyrimidines and their nucleosides and nucleotides will be discussed. A summary of these purine and pyrimidine derivatives is given in Table 26–1.

DIGESTION

Mammals and most lower vertebrates are said to be "prototrophic" for purines and pyrimidines, ie, capable of synthesizing purine and pyrimidine nucleotides de novo and thus not dependent upon exogenous sources of these important compounds. As a result, although mammals consume significant quantities of nucleic acids and nucleotides in their food, their survival is not dependent upon the absorption of these compounds or their breakdown products. Most dietary nucleic acids are ingested in the form of nucleoproteins from which the nucleic acids are liberated in the intestinal tract by the action of proteolytic enzymes. The pancreatic juice contains enzymes (nucleases) that degrade nucleic acids into nucleotides. These nucleases may be specific for the 2 major types of nucleic acids, RNA and DNA, and are appropriately termed ribonucleases and deoxyribonucleases. Intestinal enzymes—polynucleotidases or phosphoesterases—supplement the action of the pancreatic nucleases in producing mononucleotides from the nucleic acids. The mononucleotides are subsequently hydrolyzed to nucleosides by various nucleotidases and phosphatases, and the various nucleosides so produced can be either absorbed directly or further degraded by intestinal phosphorylase to the free purine or pyrimidine bases. The bases themselves may be oxidized; eg, guanine may be converted to xanthine and then to uric acid, or adenosine may be converted to inosine, to hypoxanthine, and then to uric acid (Fig 26–1). Uric acid can be absorbed across the intestinal mucosa and excreted in the urine as uric acid per se. In humans, it appears that the majority of purines in ingested nucleic acids are **directly converted to uric acid** without having previously been incorporated into the nucleic acids of the ingesting organism. Free pyrimidine orally administered to rats is mostly catabolized and excreted without having entered the nucleic acids of the ingesting organism. It would thus appear that practically none of the free purines or pyrimidines of the diet serve as a direct precursor of tissue nucleic acids.

Table 26–1. The naturally occurring purine and pyrimidine bases and their related nucleosides and nucleotides.

Base	Nucleoside (Base + Sugar)	Nucleotide (Base + Sugar + Phosphoric Acid)
Purines		
Adenine (6-aminopurine)	Adenosine	Adenylic acid
	Deoxyadenosine	Deoxyadenylic acid
Guanine (2-amino-6-oxypurine)	Guanosine	Guanylic acid
	Deoxyguanosine	Deoxyguanylic acid
Hypoxanthine (6-oxypurine)	Inosine (hypoxanthine riboside)	Inosinic acid (hypoxanthine ribotide)
	Deoxyinosine (hypoxanthine deoxyriboside)	Deoxyinosinic acid (hypoxanthine deoxyribotide)
Xanthine (2,6-dioxypurine)	Xanthosine	Xanthinylic acid
Pyrimidines		
Cytosine (2-oxy-4-aminopyrimidine)	Cytidine	Cytidylic acid
	Deoxycytidine	Deoxycytidylic acid
Thymine (2,4-dioxy-5-methylpyrimidine)	Thymidine (thymine deoxyriboside)	Thymidylic acid (thymine deoxyribotide)
Uracil (2,4-dioxypyrimidine)	Uridine	Uridylic acid
	Pseudouridine (5-ribosyl linkage)	Pseudouridylic acid

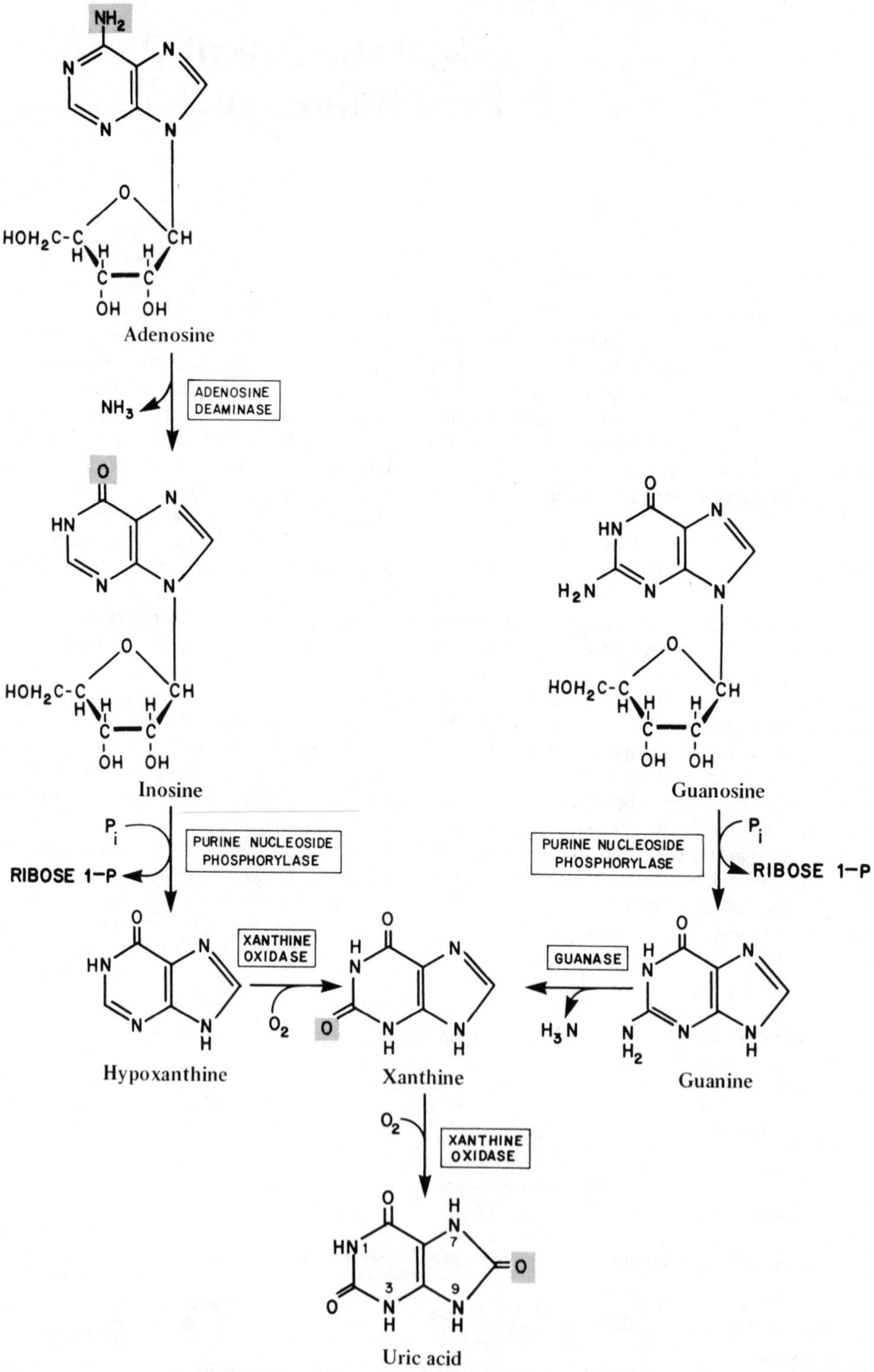

Figure 26–1. Generation of uric acid from purine nucleosides by way of the purine bases hypoxanthine, xanthine, and guanine. Purine deoxyribonucleosides are degraded by the same pathway and enzymes, all of which exist in the mucosa of the mammalian gastrointestinal tract.

Somewhat different results are obtained when purines or pyrimidines are administered parenterally as nucleosides or nucleotides. Injected thymidine may be incorporated into DNA unaltered. This is the basis of a valuable technique for labeling newly produced DNA in a great variety of biologic materials both in vivo and in vitro. For these purposes, ^{3}H-thymidine—ie, thymidine containing tritium (^{3}H), the radioactive isotope of hydrogen—is used.

PURINES

Biosynthesis of Purine Nucleotides

In humans and other mammals, purine nucleotides are synthesized to meet the needs of the organism for the monomeric precursors of nucleic acids and for those other functions described in Chapter 25. In some organisms (birds, amphibians, and reptiles), the synthesis of purine nucleotides has an additional function, which is to serve as the chemical vehicle to excrete nitrogen waste products as uric acid. Such organisms are referred to as **uricotelic,** whereas those organisms which dispose of nitrogenous waste products in the form of urea, as humans do, are referred to as **ureotelic.** Because the uricotelic organisms must dispose of their nitrogenous wastes in the form of uric acid, they synthesize purine nucleotides at a relatively greater rate than do ureotelic organisms. However, the steps involved in de novo purine nucleotide synthesis in mammals (ureotelic) are analogous to those in birds (uricotelic).

Information on the sources of the various atoms of the purine base obtained by tracer studies in birds, rats, and humans is presented in Fig 26–2.

The biosynthetic pathway for the synthesis of purine nucleotides is shown in Fig 26–3. In order to understand the regulation of de novo purine nucleotide synthesis, the first step (reaction 1, Fig 26–3) in the synthesis of purine nucleotides must be regarded as the

formation of 1-pyrophosphorylribosyl-5-phosphate (PPriboseP). Although the conversion of ribose 5-phosphate of ATP to AMP + PPriboseP (Fig 26–3) is not uniquely committed to the synthesis of purine nucleotides, it appears from a regulatory aspect to be a most important process. As discussed in the latter part of this chapter, PPriboseP also serves as a precursor of the pyrimidine nucleotides and is required for the synthesis of NAD and NADP, 2 cofactors derived from niacin (see Chapter 10).

PPriboseP then reacts (reaction 2, Fig 26–3) with glutamine in a reaction catalyzed by the enzyme **phosphoribosylpyrophosphate amidotransferase** to form 5-phosphoribosylamine accompanied by the displacement of pyrophosphate and the formation of glutamic acid. Although other mechanisms have been proposed for the synthesis of 5-phosphoribosylamine in mammalian tissues, genetic experiments confirm that the physiologically important reaction is that catalyzed by the amidotransferase. The 5-phosphoribosylamine so formed then reacts (reaction 3, Fig 26–3) with glycine to produce glycinamide ribosylphosphate (glycinamide ribotide [GAR]). The amido group from glutamine contributes the 9 N of the eventual purine ring while the glycine contributes carbons 4 and 5 and the 7 N. The enzyme catalyzing reaction 3 is designated **glycinamide kinosynthetase,** since it requires ATP and generates ADP and phosphate in that reaction.

The N_7 of glycinamide ribosylphosphate is then formylated (reaction 4, Fig 26–3), which requires N^5,N^{10}-methenyltetrahydrofolate (see Chapter 10) and the enzyme **glycinamide ribosylphosphate formyltransferase** to transfer the C_1 moiety which becomes the C_8 of the purine base. In reaction 5, again with glutamine as the amide donor, amidation occurs at the C_4 of the formylglycinamide ribosylphosphate, catalyzed by **formylglycinamidine ribosylphosphate synthetase,** which requires ATP in addition to glutamine. The amide N becomes position 3 in the purine.

The closure of the imidazole ring is catalyzed by the enzyme **aminoimidazole ribosylphosphate synthetase,** which also requires ATP and which forms aminoimidazole ribosylphosphate. The synthesis progresses (reaction 7) to aminoimidazole carboxylate ribosylphosphate by addition to the precursor compound of a carbonyl group, the source of which is respiratory CO_2. The source of the nitrogen in the 1 position is the α-amino group of aspartate (reaction 8), the remaining portion of which is indicated as the succinyl moiety of aminoimidazole succinyl carboxamide ribosylphosphate, abbreviated as SAICAR. In reaction 9, the succinyl group of SAICAR is split off as fumaric acid. Aminoimidazole carboxamide ribosylphosphate, which remains, is then formylated (reaction 10) by N^{10}-formyltetrahydrofolate ($f^{10}\cdot H_4$folate) to form amidoimidazole carboxamide ribosylphosphate in a reaction catalyzed by the appropriate **formyltransferase.** The newly added carbon, which, like the C_8 of the purine base, is derived from

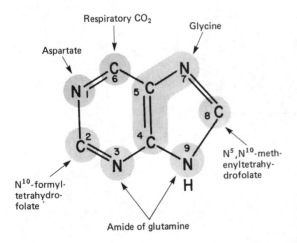

Figure 26–2. The sources of the nitrogen and carbon atoms of the purine ring.

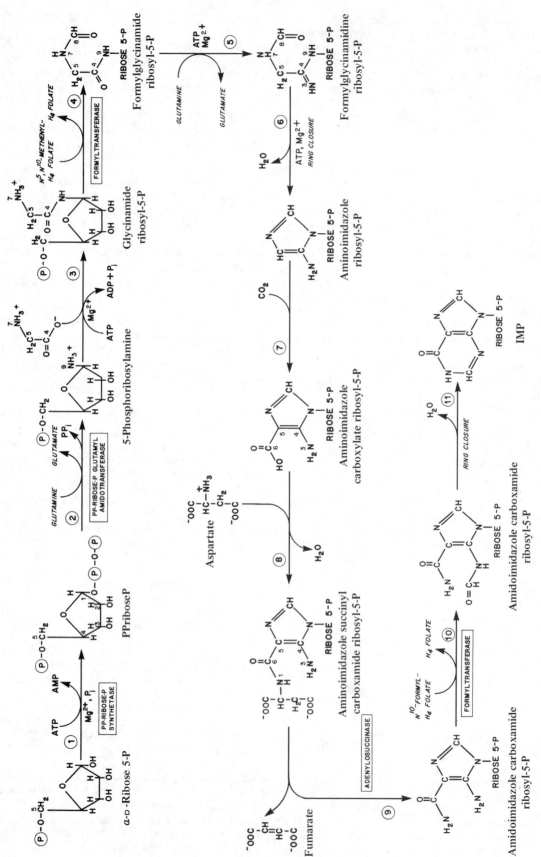

Figure 26–3. The pathway of de novo purine biosynthesis from ribose 5-phosphate and ATP. (See text for explanation.)

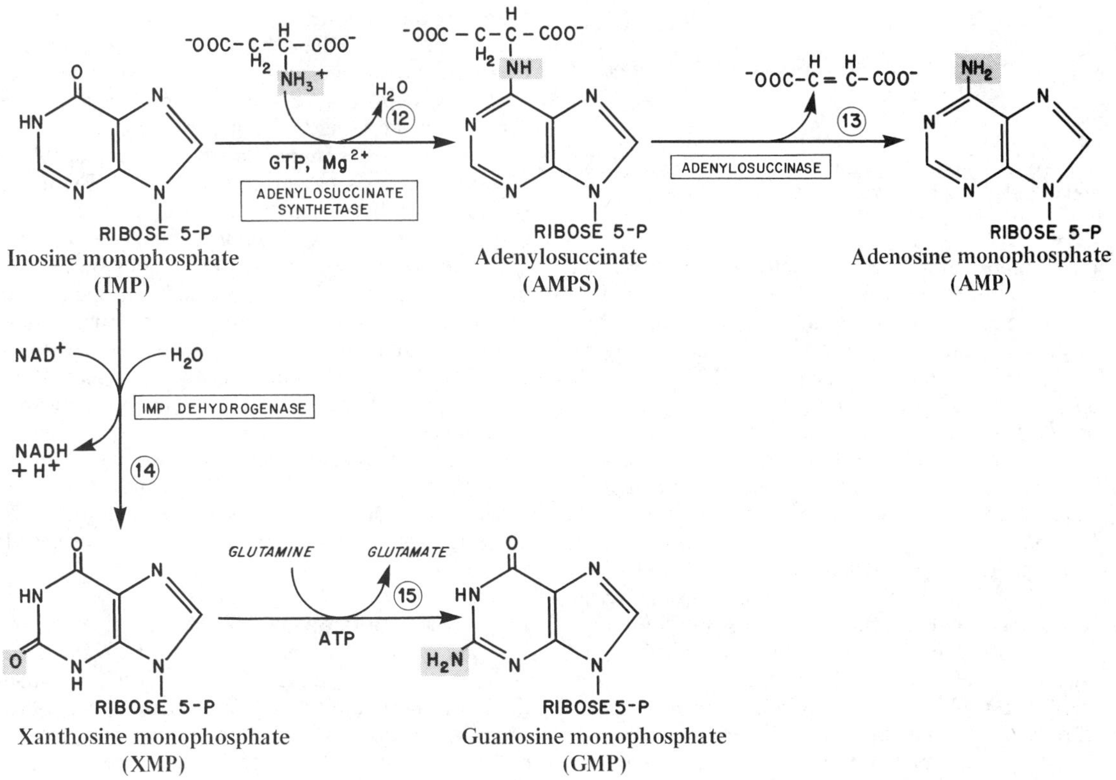

Figure 26–4. The conversions of IMP to AMP and GMP. (See text for explanation.)

the C_1 pool via the tetrahydrofolate carrier, will be C_2 of the purine nucleus. Ring closure now occurs (reaction 11) via **IMP cyclohydrolase,** and the first purine nucleotide, **inosinic acid (inosine monophosphate, IMP),** is thus formed.

The importance of folate metabolism (see Chapter 10) in the de novo synthesis of purine nucleotides should be evident. Two one-carbon moieties are added to the purine ring at positions 8 and 2 by N^5,N^{10}-methenyltetrahydrofolate and N^{10}-formyltetrahydrofolate, respectively. The latter is derived from the former. The N^5,N^{10}-methenyltetrahydrofolate is derived from the NADP-dependent dehydrogenation of N^5,N^{10}-methylenetetrahydrofolate. The N^5,N^{10}-methylenetetrahydrofolate can donate a one-carbon moiety to numerous acceptors, but once N^5,N^{10}-methenyltetrahydrofolate is formed, the one-carbon group is committed to transfer only into purines, whence it is donated either directly or after conversion to N^{10}-formyltetrahydrofolate. Thus, any inhibition of the formation of these tetrahydrofolate compounds will have a detrimental effect upon the de novo synthesis of purines.

As is clear from the scheme in Fig 26–4, adenine nucleotides (reactions 12 and 13) and guanine nucleotides (reactions 14 and 15) are derived from **inosine monophosphate** (IMP) by amination and by oxidation and amination, respectively. The amination of IMP is accomplished through the formation of an intermediate

compound in which aspartic acid is attached to inosinic acid to form adenylosuccinate. This reaction is similar to that of a preceding reaction (reaction 9) in which the nitrogen at position 1 of the purine nucleus was added by way of α nitrogen of aspartic acid. The formation of adenylosuccinate is catalyzed by **adenylosuccinate synthetase,** and it requires GTP, which provides a potential regulatory mechanism. The splitting off, as fumaric acid, of the remaining portion of aspartic acid from adenylosuccinate produces the final product, adenylic acid (adenosine monophosphate, AMP). Cleavage of fumaric acid from adenylosuccinate is catalyzed by the enzyme **adenylosuccinase,** which is also responsible for the cleavage of fumarate from the succinyl of aminoimidazole succinyl carboxamide ribosylphosphate (reaction 9).

Also in 2 steps, IMP is converted to guanosine monophosphate (GMP). The first reaction in this sequence (reaction 14) is an oxidation utilizing NAD as cofactor and water to form xanthosine monophosphate (XMP). XMP is aminated by the amido group of glutamine in a reaction that requires ATP, somewhat analogous to the requirement of GTP for the conversion of IMP to AMP.

Several antimetabolites that are glutamine analogs are effective inhibitors of various steps in purine biosynthesis. **Azaserine** (O-diazoacetyl-L-serine) is an antagonist to glutamine, particularly at reaction 5. **Diazonorleucine** ([6-diazo-5-oxo]-L-norleu-

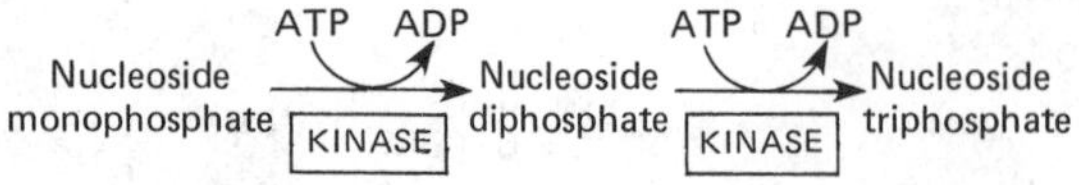

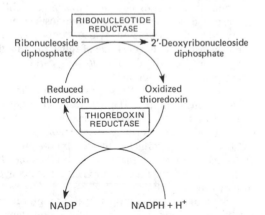

Figure 26–5. The reactions responsible for the conversion of nucleoside monophosphates to nucleoside diphosphates and nucleoside triphosphates.

cine) blocks reaction 2 in purine synthesis, and **6-mercaptopurine,** among its other actions, inhibits reactions 13 and 14 in the synthesis of AMP and GMP, respectively. Mycophenolic acid inhibits reaction 14.

The conversions of AMP and GMP to their respective nucleoside diphosphates and nucleoside triphosphates occur in 2 successive steps (Fig 26–5). The successive transfers of the high-energy phosphate groups from ATP are catalyzed by **nucleoside monophosphate kinase** and **nucleoside diphosphate kinase,** respectively. The enzyme that phosphorylates adenylate is also called **myokinase** (see Chapter 34).

The synthesis of the purine and pyrimidine deoxyribonucleotides occurs by **direct reduction at the 2′ carbon** in the ribose moiety of the corresponding nucleotide (see below) rather than by the synthesis of the entire nucleotide utilizing a 2′-deoxy analog of PPriboseP. The reduction at the 2′ carbon occurs only after the purine and pyrimidine nucleotides have been converted to their respective nucleoside diphosphates. In some bacteria, cobalamin (vitamin B_{12}) is required for this reductive process, although it is not required for the same reaction in mammals. The reduction of ribonucleoside diphosphates to deoxyribonucleoside diphosphates is a complex reaction in mammals. The reaction (Fig 26–6) is catalyzed by **ribonucleotide reductase** and requires **thioredoxin** (a protein cofactor), **thioredoxin reductase** (a flavoprotein), and NADPH as a cofactor. The immediate electron donor to the nucleotide is the reduced form of thioredoxin that has accepted electrons from NADPH. The reversible oxidation-reduction of thioredoxin is catalyzed by

thioredoxin reductase. The reduction of the ribonucleoside diphosphate by reduced thioredoxin is catalyzed by ribonucleotide reductase. This complex enzyme system is present in cells only when they are actively synthesizing DNA and dividing.

Not all tissues in the human body are capable of de novo synthesis of purine nucleotides. The erythrocytes and polymorphonuclear leukocytes are incapable of synthesizing 5-phosphoribosylamine and therefore are dependent upon exogenous purines for the formation of purine nucleotides. Peripheral lymphocytes do possess some ability to synthesize purines de novo. Mammalian brain appears to have a reduced content of PPriboseP amidotransferase; indeed, it has been suggested that the human brain is dependent upon exogenous purines for the formation of purine nucleotides. The mammalian liver is a major site of purine nucleotide synthesis and provides purines in the form of bases or nucleosides to be salvaged and utilized by those tissues incapable of synthesizing purines de novo.

Purine Salvage Pathways

The salvage of these preformed purine compounds can occur by 2 general mechanisms. The quantitatively more important mechanism is the **phosphoribosylation of the free purine bases** by specific enzymes requiring PPriboseP as the ribose phosphate donor. The second general mechanism is the **phosphorylation of purine nucleosides** on their 5′-hydroxyl groups.

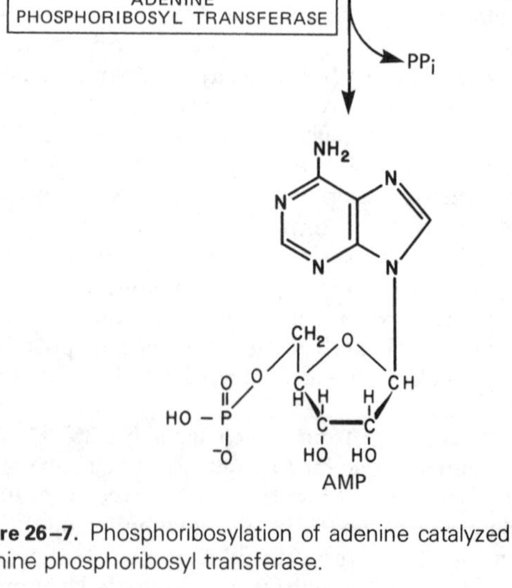

Figure 26–6. The reactions involved in the reduction of ribonucleoside diphosphates to 2′-deoxyribonucleoside diphosphates.

Figure 26–7. Phosphoribosylation of adenine catalyzed by adenine phosphoribosyl transferase.

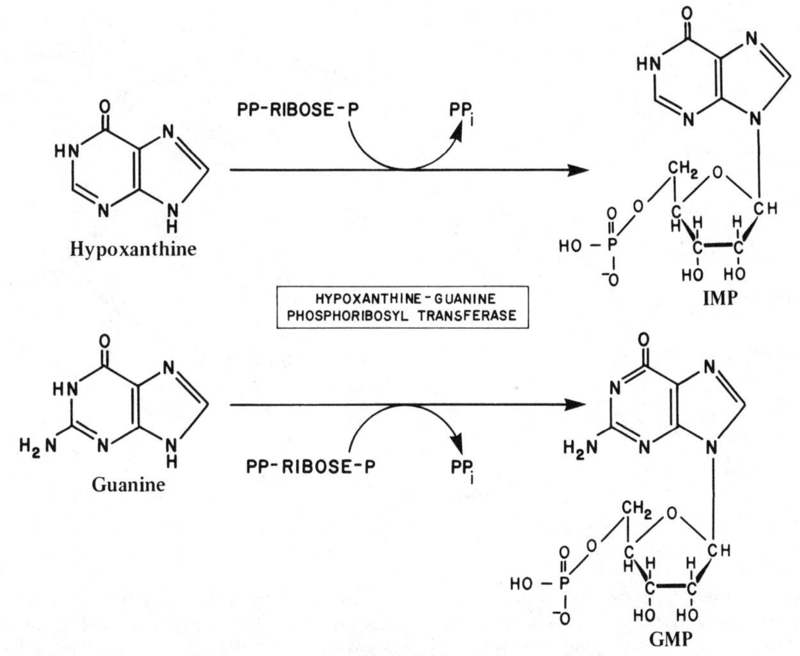

Figure 26–8. Phosphoribosylation of hypoxanthine and guanine to form IMP and GMP, respectively. The reactions are catalyzed by the enzyme hypoxanthine-guanine phosphoribosyl transferase.

There are 2 enzymes in human tissues that can phosphoribosylate purine bases. One enzyme (Fig 26–7) is capable of phosphoribosylating adenine with PPriboseP to generate AMP: **adenine phosphoribosyl transferase.** The second, **hypoxanthine-guanine phosphoribosyl transferase** (Fig 26–8), is capable of phosphoribosylating hypoxanthine and guanine with PPriboseP to yield IMP and GMP, respectively. As will be discussed below, the latter pathway (the salvage of hypoxanthine and guanine to IMP and GMP) is more active than the formation of AMP from adenine.

The salvage of purine ribonucleosides to purine ribonucleotides is carried out in humans by **adenosine kinase** only (Fig 26–9). Adenosine kinase also phosphorylates 2′-deoxyadenosine but demonstrates minimal ability to phosphorylate guanosine, inosine, or their 2′-deoxy derivatives to their respective ribonu-cleotides. Deoxycytidine kinase, in addition to phosphorylating deoxycytidine, can phosphorylate 2′-deoxyadenosine and 2′-deoxyguanosine to deoxy AMP and deoxy GMP, respectively.

However, there is more to the purine salvage pathways. In humans, there is a cycle (Fig 26–10) in which IMP and GMP as well as their respective deoxyribonucleotides are converted to their respective nucleosides (inosine, deoxyinosine, guanosine, and deoxyguanosine) by a **purine 5′-nucleotidase.** These purine ribonucleosides and 2′-deoxynucleosides are converted to hypoxanthine or guanine by **purine nucleoside phosphorylase,** producing ribose 1-phosphate or 2′-deoxyribose 1-phosphate as phosphorolysis products. The hypoxanthine and guanine can then again be phosphoribosylated by PPriboseP to IMP and GMP to complete the cycle. The functions of this purine salvage cycle are unknown, but it is clear

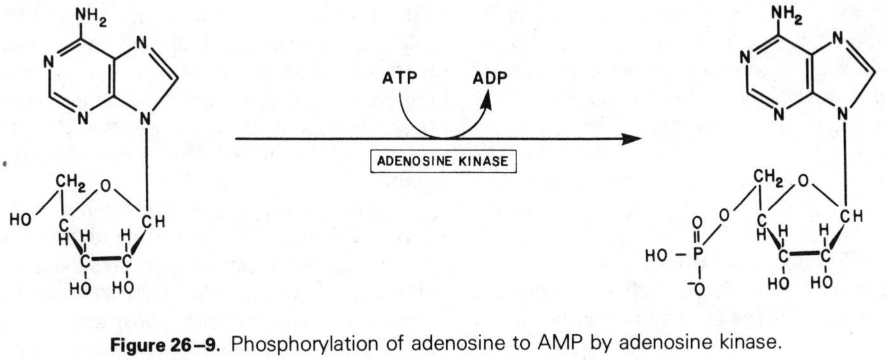

Figure 26–9. Phosphorylation of adenosine to AMP by adenosine kinase.

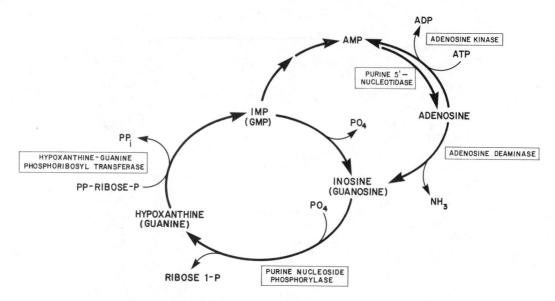

Figure 26–10. The purine salvage cycles involving the interconversion of AMP, IMP, and—to a lesser extent—GMP to their respective ribonucleosides and their eventual reconversion to purine ribonucleotides. Deoxyadenosine, deoxyinosine, and deoxyguanosine share the same pathways except that deoxyadenosine and deoxyguanosine can be directly phosphorylated to deoxy AMP and deoxy GMP, respectively.

that, in the human organism as a whole, the consumption of PPriboseP by this salvage cycle is greater than the consumption of PPriboseP for the synthesis of purine nucleotides de novo.

There is a lateral pathway of this cycle that involves the conversion of IMP to AMP (reactions 12 and 13, Fig 26–4), with the subsequent conversion of AMP to adenosine. The latter is probably catalyzed by the same purine 5′-nucleotidase that hydrolyzes IMP to inosine. The adenosine so produced is then either salvaged directly back to AMP via **adenosine kinase** or is converted to inosine by the enzyme **adenosine deaminase.** Quantitatively, the function of this inosine loop is less important than the previously described cycle. Qualitatively, the action of adenosine deaminase is an important process, particularly for the immune system, as described in the discussion of inherited disorders of purine metabolism.

The salvage of the free purine adenine by adenine phosphoribosyl transferase seems to prevent the xanthine oxidase–mediated oxidation of adenine to 2,8-dihydroxyadenine. Dihydroxyadenine is a highly insoluble product that appears as kidney stones in patients devoid of adenine phosphoribosyl transferase activity. The source of free adenine for such a salvage process is not known with certainty, although it probably derives from the hydrolysis of 5′-methylthioadenosine, a by-product of the synthesis of polyamines from S-adenosylmethionine.

Regulation of Purine Biosynthesis

The de novo synthesis of IMP consumes the equivalent of 6 high-energy phosphodiester bonds (by ATP hydrolysis) along with the other required precursors, glycine, glutamine, methenyltetrahydrofolate, and aspartate. Thus, it is important for the conservation of energy and nutrients that the cell economically regulate its rate of de novo purine biosynthesis. The single most important regulator of de novo purine biosynthesis is the intracellular concentration of PPriboseP. As with so many other intracellular compounds, the regulation of PPriboseP concentration is dependent upon its rate of synthesis versus its rate of utilization or degradation. The rate of synthesis of PPriboseP is dependent upon (1) the availability of its substrates, particularly ribose 5-phosphate, which is more likely to be limiting than is ATP; and (2) the catalytic activity of PPriboseP synthetase, which is dependent upon the intracellular phosphate concentration as well as the concentrations of the purine and pyrimidine ribonucleotides acting as allosteric regulators (Fig 26–11). The rate of utilization of PPriboseP is dependent to a large extent on its consumption by the salvage pathway that phosphoribosylates hypoxanthine and guanine to their respective ribonucleotides. To a lesser extent, utilization is dependent upon the rate of de novo purine synthesis. This conclusion stems from the observation that, in males with inherited deficiencies of hypoxanthine-guanine phosphoribosyl transferase, the levels of PPriboseP in their erythrocytes and cultured fibroblasts are elevated severalfold.

The first enzyme uniquely committed to de novo purine synthesis, PPriboseP amidotransferase, demonstrates in vitro a sensitivity to feedback inhibition by purine nucleotides, particularly adenosine monophosphate and guanosine monophosphate. These feedback inhibitors of the amidotransferase are competitive with

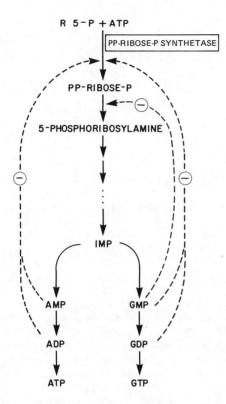

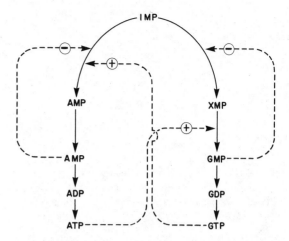

Figure 26–11. A regulatory scheme for the control of the rate of de novo purine synthesis. Solid lines represent chemical flow, and dotted lines represent feedback inhibition by end products of the pathway.

Figure 26–12. The regulation of the interconversion of IMP to adenosine nucleotides and guanosine nucleotides. Solid lines represent chemical flow, and dotted lines represent both positive ($\oplus$) and negative ($\ominus$) feedback regulation.

proper balancing of deoxyribonucleotides for the synthesis of DNA.

Catabolism of Purines

In humans, the ultimate catabolite (end product) of purines is uric acid. Reasoning from observations made in humans with inherited enzyme deficiencies, it appears that over 99% of the uric acid is derived from substrates of purine nucleoside phosphorylase, a com-

the substrate PPriboseP, and thus, again, PPriboseP plays a major role in the regulation of de novo purine synthesis. Numerous indirect experiments suggest that the regulation of de novo purine synthesis by amidotransferase is physiologically less important than that by PPriboseP synthetase.

The conversion of IMP to GMP or to AMP is regulated by 2 mechanisms (Fig 26–12). AMP feedback regulates its own synthesis at the level of adenylosuccinate synthetase; GMP regulates its own synthesis by feedback inhibition of IMP dehydrogenase. Furthermore, the conversion of IMP to adenylosuccinate en route to AMP requires the presence of GTP. The conversion of xanthinylate to GMP requires the presence of ATP. Thus, there is significant cross-regulation between the divergent pathways in the metabolism of IMP. This regulation prevents the synthesis of one purine nucleotide when there is a deficiency of the other. Hypoxanthine-guanine phosphoribosyl transferase, which converts hypoxanthine and guanine to IMP and GMP, respectively, is quite sensitive to product inhibition by these same nucleotides.

The reduction of ribonucleoside diphosphates to deoxyribonucleoside diphosphates is subject to complex regulation (Fig 26–13). This process of regulation, which is depicted in Fig 26–13, provides for the

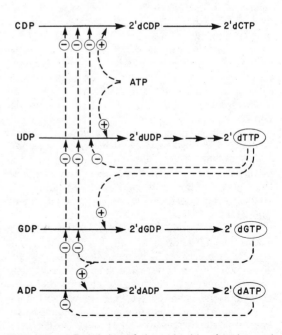

Figure 26–13. Regulation of the reduction of purine and pyrimidine ribonucleotides to their respective 2′-deoxyribonucleotides. Solid lines represent chemical flow, and dotted lines represent negative ($\ominus$) or positive ($\oplus$) feedback regulation.

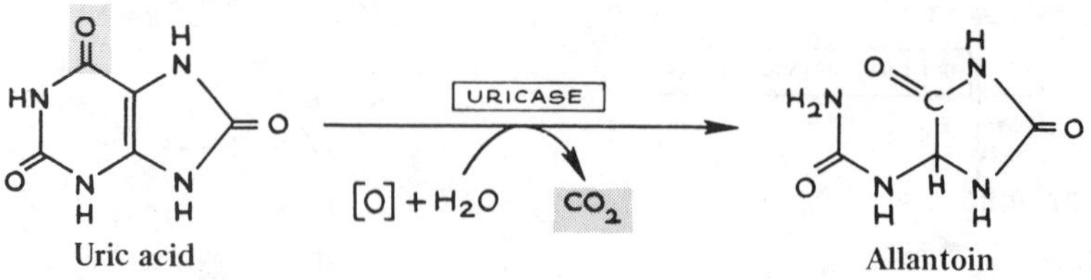

Figure 26–14. Conversion of uric acid to allantoin.

ponent of the purine salvage pathway described above. The purine products of purine nucleoside phosphorylase, guanine and hypoxanthine, are converted to uric acid by way of xanthine in reactions catalyzed by the enzymes **guanase** and **xanthine oxidase,** respectively (Fig 26–1). Xanthine oxidase is very active in liver, small intestine, and kidney, and in its absence no uric acid is formed. As described above, some uric acid may be produced from ingested nucleic acids by the bacterial flora of the intestinal tract, whence it is absorbed and directly excreted. This pathway seems to be a minor contributor to the urinary uric acid of persons on a normal diet.

As discussed below under the disorders of purine metabolism, the activity of xanthine oxidase is an important site for pharmacologic intervention in patients with hyperuricemia and gout. In lower primates and other mammals, the enzyme **uricase** is responsible for the hydrolysis of uric acid to allantoin (Fig 26–14), a highly water-soluble end product of purine catabolism in those animals. Amphibians, birds, and reptiles do not possess uricase activity. These animals excrete uric acid and guanine as the end products of both purine metabolism and nitrogen (protein) metabolism. (In fact, the word guanine is derived from guano [*huanu,* dung], a white crystalline material deposited, for example, on many coastal rocks by marine birds.)

Organisms that form uric acid as the major nitrogenous waste product are said to be **uricotelic.** Birds, amphibians, and reptiles seem to have evolved a uricotelic system to regain water of hydration from uric acid after it precipitates out, as it will at rather low concentrations. If they were to use urea as the end product of nitrogen metabolism, the water of hydration could not be regained, since urea is water-soluble up to 10 mol/L, a concentration far higher than any kidney can attain.

The metabolism of uric acid in humans has been studied by the use of isotopically labeled uric acid as well as its precursors, glycine and formate. Single doses of N^{15} uric acid were injected intravenously into normal human subjects and patients suffering from gout, a disease characterized by increased accumulation of uric acid and sodium urate. The dilution of the injected labeled isotope was used to calculate the quantity of total uric acid equilibrating with body water, a quantity referred to as the **miscible urate pool.** The mass of the rapidly miscible pool of uric acid in 25 normal male adult subjects averaged 1200 mg with a range of 866–1578 mg. In 3 normal female subjects

the pool ranged from 541 to 687 mg. In gouty subjects the miscible urate pool was much larger, generally ranging from 2000 to 4000 mg in patients without tophi, ie, deposits of sodium urate in soft tissues. However, in severe tophaceous gout the pool was as high as 31,000 mg. The turnover of the miscible pool of total uric acid in normal persons is approximately 600 mg/24 h. Isotope studies have demonstrated that 18–20% of the lost uric acid is not excreted in the urine but is degraded to CO_2 and ammonia and excreted in the feces, where it can be further metabolized by intestinal flora. It is known that some uric acid is excreted in the bile and thus is subject to degradation by intestinal flora. However, in humans, the breakdown of uric acid to CO_2 and NH_3 is independent of intestinal bacteria.

In humans, urate appears to play a role beyond that of an end product of purine metabolism. Urate by itself can serve as an antioxidant, undergoing nonenzymatic conversion to allantoin. It has been proposed that this naturally occurring antioxidant, urate, has in primates replaced ascorbate, which primates have lost the ability to synthesize. Thus, it may well be that during evolution the loss of uricase provided selective advantage to those organisms which had previously lost the ability to reduce gulonolactone to ascorbic acid (see Fig 10–32).

The handling of sodium urate, a salt of uric acid, by the mammalian kidney has been the subject of many studies. It appears from recent studies that sodium urate is freely filtered by the mammalian glomerulus, is extensively reabsorbed and partially secreted in the proximal tubule, is further secreted in the loop of Henle, and perhaps is again partially reabsorbed in the distal convoluted tubule. The net excretion of total uric acid in normal men is 400–600 mg/24 h. Many pharmacologic and naturally occurring compounds influence the renal absorption and secretion of sodium urate. Aspirin in high doses competitively inhibits urate excretion as well as reabsorption.

PYRIMIDINES

Biosynthesis of Pyrimidines

The pyrimidine nucleotides possess a heterocyclic ring structure that occurs also in purine molecules. These nucleotides have chemical and physiologic properties similar to those of purine nucleotides. Although the pyrimidine nucleus is simpler and its synthetic pathway briefer than that of the purine structure, the 2 share several common precursors. **PPriboseP, glutamine, CO₂,** and **aspartate** are required for the synthesis of all pyrimidine and purine nucleotides. For the thymidine nucleotides and for all purine nucleotides, **tetrahydrofolate** derivatives are also necessary. There is one striking difference between the synthesis of pyrimidine nucleotides and that of purine nucleotides, namely, that the synthesis of the purine nucleotides commences with ribose phosphate as an integral part of the earliest precursor molecule, whereas the

pyrimidine base is formed and **attachment of the ribose phosphate moiety delayed until the later steps** of the pathway.

The synthesis of the pyrimidine ring commences with the formation of **carbamoyl phosphate** from glutamine, ATP, and CO_2 in a reaction catalyzed by the carbamoyl phosphate synthase located in the **cytosol** of the cell (Fig 26–15). In contrast, the carbamoyl phosphate synthase enzyme responsible for the early steps in urea synthesis resides in the mitochon-

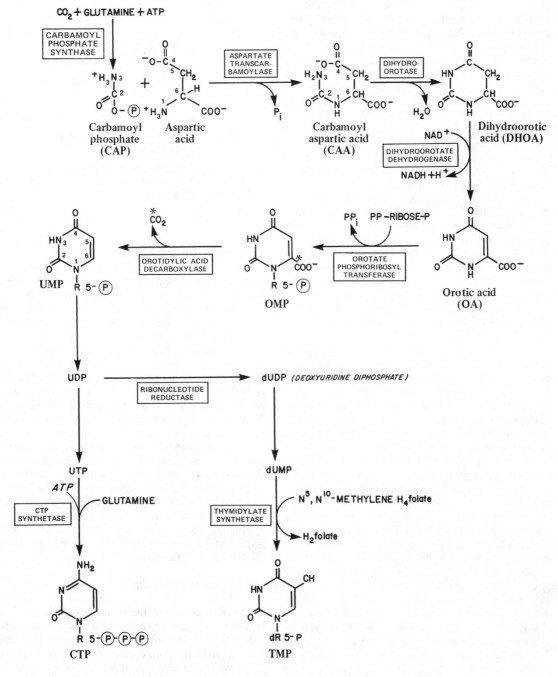

Figure 26–15. The biosynthetic pathway for pyrimidine nucleotides.

dria. The first step uniquely committed to the biosynthesis of pyrimidines is the formation of carbamoyl aspartate by the condensation of carbamoyl phosphate and aspartate, a reaction catalyzed by the enzyme **aspartate transcarbamoylase.** A ring structure can then be formed from carbamoyl aspartate by loss of H_2O catalyzed by the enzyme **dihydroorotase.** In a subsequent dehydrogenation step catalyzed by **dihydroorotate dehydrogenase** and utilizing NAD as a cofactor, **orotic acid** is formed. The next step is that in which a ribose phosphate moiety is added to orotic acid to form **orotidylate (orotidine monophosphate, OMP).** This reaction is catalyzed by **orotate phosphoribosyl transferase,** an enzyme analogous to the hypoxanthine-guanine phosphoribosyl transferase and the adenine phosphoribosyl transferase involved in the phosphoribosylation of preformed purine rings. The first true pyrimidine ribonucleotide is formed by the decarboxylation of orotidylate to form **uridylate (uridine monophosphate, UMP).** Thus, only at the penultimate step in the formation of UMP is the heterocyclic ring phosphoribosylated.

Dihydroorotate dehydrogenase is **mitochondrial;** all the other enzymes in the de novo pyrimidine nucleotide pathway are in the **cytosol.**

By mechanisms analogous to those described for the further phosphorylation of the purine nucleoside monophosphates, the pyrimidine nucleoside monophosphates are converted to their diphosphate and triphosphate derivatives. UTP is aminated to CTP, a reaction in which glutamine provides the amino group and which requires ATP. The reduction of the pyrimidine nucleoside diphosphates to the respective 2'-deoxynucleoside diphosphates occurs by a mechanism also analogous to that described for the purine nucleotides (Figs 26–6 and 26–13).

The formation of **thymidylate (thymidine monophosphate, TMP)** is the one reaction in pyrimidine nucleotide biosynthesis that requires a **tetrahydrofolate** donor of a single carbon compound. The 2'-deoxy UMP is methylated by **thymidylate synthetase,** which utilizes as a methyl donor N^5,N^{10}-methylenetetrahydrofolate. The methylene group of N^5,N^{10}-methylenetetrahydrofolate, which is added as a methyl group to the C_5 of deoxy UMP, must be reduced in the process of its donation. While the methylene is reduced to a methyl group, the tetrahydrofolate carrier is oxidized to dihydrofolate, and the net redox state of the reaction is thus unchanged. The methylation of deoxy UMP to TMP results in an overall reduction of the hydroxymethyl group from serine to a methyl group with the simultaneous oxidation of tetrahydrofolate to dihydrofolate. In order to continue to use the folate carrier, the cell must reduce dihydrofolate to tetrahydrofolate, a reaction carried out by the enzyme dihydrofolate reductase. Thus, dividing cells that by necessity are generating TMP and dihydrofolate are especially sensitive to inhibitors of dihydrofolate reductase. An example of such an inhibitor is methotrexate (amethopterin), a widely used anticancer drug.

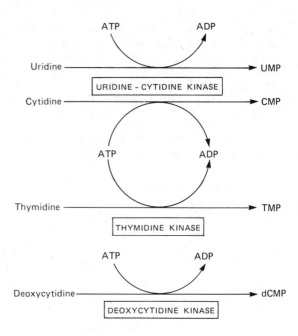

Figure 26–16. The pyrimidine nucleoside kinase reactions responsible for formation of the respective pyrimidine nucleoside monophosphates.

Pyrimidine Salvage Pathways

Mammalian cells do not appear to possess efficient means of salvaging **free** pyrimidine bases to their respective pyrimidine nucleotides. However, they do have active salvage pathways for converting the pyrimidine **ribonucleosides** uridine and cytidine and the 2'-deoxyribonucleosides thymidine and deoxycytidine to their respective nucleotides (Fig 26–16). 2'-Deoxycytidine is phosphorylated by a distinct enzyme called deoxycytidine kinase that can also phosphorylate deoxyguanosine and deoxyadenosine. The enzyme required for de novo pyrimidine biosynthesis, **orotate phosphoribosyl transferase,** is capable of salvaging orotic acid to OMP, but in a strict sense orotic acid is not considered a complete pyrimidine base. The orotate phosphoribosyl transferase cannot use normal pyrimidine bases as substrates, although it is capable of converting allopurinol (4-hydroxypyrazolopyrimidine) to a nucleotide in which the ribosyl phosphate is attached to the N_1 of the pyrimidine ring of that drug. The anticancer drug 5-fluorouracil is also phosphoribosylated by orotate phosphoribosyl transferase.

Catabolism of Pyrimidines

The catabolism of pyrimidines occurs mainly in the liver. It results in the production of a series of highly soluble end products. This contrasts with the production of the sparingly soluble uric acid and sodium urate by purine catabolism. The proposed pathways for the degradation of pyrimidines, based on fragmentary evidence, are shown in Fig 26–17. The

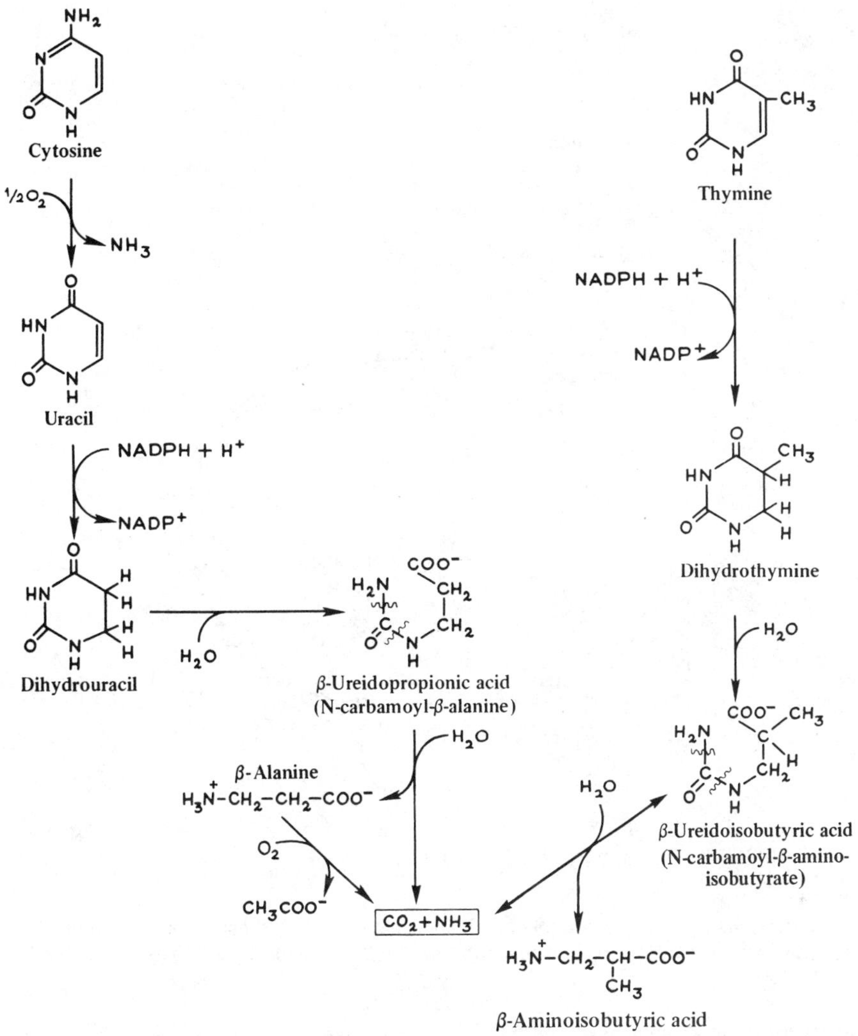

Figure 26-17. Catabolism of pyrimidines.

release of respiratory CO_2 from the ureido carbon (C_2) of the pyrimidine nucleus represents a major pathway for the catabolism of uracil, cytosine, and thymine. β-Alanine and β-aminoisobutyric acid are the major end products of cytosine, uracil, and thymine catabolism, respectively.

Thymine is the precursor of β-aminoisobutyric acid, both in laboratory animals and in humans. The excretion of β-aminoisobutyric acid is increased in leukemia as well as after the body has been subjected to x-irradiation. This is undoubtedly a reflection of increased destruction of cells and their DNA. A familial occurrence of an abnormally high excretion of β-aminoisobutyric acid has also been observed in otherwise normal individuals. This genetic trait is traceable to a recessively expressed gene. High excretors result only when the trait is homozygous. It is of interest that approximately 25% of tested persons of Chinese or Japanese ancestry consistently excreted

large amounts of β-aminoisobutyric acid. Although little is known about the mechanisms whereby β-aminoisobutyric acid is degraded in humans, an enzyme that catalyzes the reversible transamination reaction has been identified in pig kidney. The β-aminoisobutyric acid is converted to methylmalonic semialdehyde and thence to propionic acid, which in turn proceeds to succinate.

It should be noted that the initial steps in the degradation of pyrimidine nucleotides, including the removal of the sugar phosphate moiety by hydrolysis of the N-glycosidic bond, are similar to reversing the latter part of the synthetic pathway. For pseudouridine, which is formed in situ in tRNA by a rearrangement reaction, there is no mechanism to catalyze the hydrolysis or phosphorolysis of this unusual nucleoside to its respective pyrimidine base, uracil. Consequently, pseudouridine is excreted unchanged in the urine of normal persons.

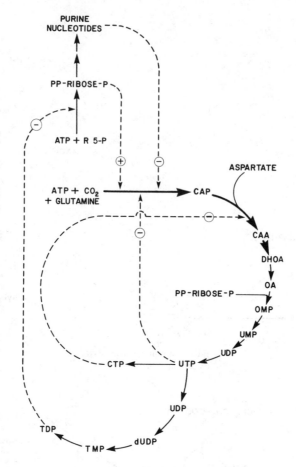

Figure 26–18. Regulatory scheme for the control of pyrimidine nucleotide synthesis. Solid lines represent chemical flow, and broken lines represent positive and negative feedback regulation. The abbreviations used are defined in Figure 26–15.

Regulation of Pyrimidine Biosynthesis

The pathway of pyrimidine nucleotide biosynthesis is regulated by 2 general mechanisms. The first 2 enzymes in the pathway are sensitive to **allosteric regulation,** while the first 3 enzymes are regulated by an apparently coordinate **repression and derepression,** as are the last 2 enzymes of the pathway. **Carbamoyl phosphate synthase** is inhibited by UTP and purine nucleotides but activated by PPriboseP (Fig 26–18). **Aspartate transcarbamoylase** is particularly sensitive to inhibition by CTP. The allosteric properties of the aspartate transcarbamoylase in microorganisms have been the subject of extensive and now classic studies in allostery.

It has been estimated from isotope incorporation studies that on a molar basis the rate of pyrimidine biosynthesis parallels that of purine biosynthesis, demonstrating a coordinate control of purine and pyrimidine nucleotide synthesis. It should be noted that PPriboseP synthetase, an enzyme that forms a necessary precursor for both purine nucleotide and pyrimidine nucleotide biosynthesis, is subject to feedback inhibition by both purine and pyrimidine nucleotides. Furthermore, carbamoyl phosphate synthase is sensitive to feedback inhibition by both purine and pyrimidine nucleotides and activation by PPriboseP. Thus, there are several sites at which there is significant cross-regulation between purine and pyrimidine nucleotide synthesis.

CLINICAL DISORDERS OF PURINE METABOLISM
(See Table 26–2.)

Hyperuricemia & Gout

The predominant form of uric acid is determined by the pH of its milieu (eg, blood, urine, cerebrospinal fluid). The **pK of the N^9 proton is 5.75,** and the pK of the N^1 proton is 10.3. Thus, under physiologic conditions—ie, at the usual pH of physiologic fluids—only uric acid and its monosodium salt, sodium urate, are found. In a fluid where the pH is less than 5.75, the predominant molecular species will be uric acid. In a fluid at pH 5.75, the concentration of sodium urate will equal that of uric acid. At a pH greater than 5.75, sodium urate will predominate in the solution.

The miscible urate pool in the body is reflected by

Table 26–2. Inherited disorders of purine metabolism and their associated enzyme abnormalities.

Clinical Disorder	Defective Enzyme	Nature of the Defect	Characteristics of Clinical Disorder	Inheritance Pattern
Gout	PPriboseP synthetase	Superactive (increased V_{max})	Purine overproduction and overexcretion	X-linked recessive
Gout	PPriboseP synthetase	Resistance to feedback inhibition	Purine overproduction and overexcretion	X-linked recessive
Gout	PPriboseP synthetase	Low K_m for ribose 5-phosphate	Purine overproduction and overexcretion	Probably X-linked recessive
Gout	HGPRTase*	Partial deficiency	Purine overproduction and overexcretion	X-linked recessive
Lesch-Nyhan syndrome	HGPRTase*	Complete deficiency	Purine overproduction and overexcretion; cerebral palsy and self-mutilation.	X-linked recessive
Immune deficiency	Adenosine deaminase	Severe deficiency	Combined (T cell and B cell) immunodeficiency, deoxyadenosinuria	Autosomal recessive
Immune deficiency	Purine nucleoside phosphorylase	Severe deficiency	T cell deficiency, inosinuria, deoxyinosinuria, guanosinuria, deoxyguanosinuria, hypouricemia	Autosomal recessive
Renal lithiasis	Adenine phosphoribosyl transferase	Complete deficiency	2,8-Dihydroxyadenine renal lithiasis	Autosomal recessive
Xanthinuria	Xanthine oxidase	Complete deficiency	Xanthine renal lithiasis, hypouricemia	Autosomal recessive

*HGPRTase = hypoxanthine-guanine phosphoribosyl transferase.

the sodium urate concentration in the serum. When this level exceeds the solubility of sodium urate in serum, a circumstance referred to as **hyperuricemia,** the serum becomes supersaturated and crystals of sodium urate may precipitate. The solubility of sodium urate in serum at 37 °C is 7 mg/dL. There is currently no convincing evidence that under physiologic conditions sodium urate is bound by serum proteins. Crystals of sodium urate that precipitate out of solution can collect and deposit in soft tissues, particularly in or about joints. These urate deposits are referred to as **tophi.** Accumulation of sodium urate crystals in the tissues, including phagocytosis of the crystals by polymorphonuclear leukocytes in joint spaces, can lead to an acute inflammatory reaction called **acute gouty arthritis.** The chronic inflammatory changes induced by the deposition of sodium urate tophi can generate **chronic gouty arthritis,** resulting in joint destruction.

In aqueous solutions, uric acid—the protonated form of urate—is only one-seventeenth as soluble as sodium urate. Urine at pH 5 becomes saturated with urates at 15 mg/dL. Because the pH of urine of normal persons generally is below the pK of uric acid (ie, 5.75), the predominant form of urate in urine is as uric acid, the highly insoluble form. Accordingly, if the urine is alkalinized to pH 7, it will accommodate 150–200 mg of urates per deciliter.

Uric acid becomes the predominant form once the urine is acidified to a pH of less than 5.75, a process that occurs in the distal tubule and collecting ducts of the kidney. If crystals of this end product of purine catabolism are formed in the urinary system, they will be sodium urate at any site proximal to the site of acidification of urine; at any site distal to the acidification, uric acid crystals will be formed. Therefore, most stones of the urinary collecting system are uric acid. As

noted above, the precipitation of uric acid stones can be prevented to a considerable extent by alkalinization of the urine to ensure that sodium urate, the more soluble form, will predominate.

The needle-shaped sodium urate crystals are intensely **negatively birefringent** (optically anisotropic); thus, when viewed through a polarizing microscope, they can be distinguished from other types of crystals. If the synovial or joint fluid of a patient shows polymorphonuclear leukocytes containing crystals whose color is yellow when viewed with their long axis parallel to the plane of polarized light and blue when perpendicular to the plane of light, then sodium urate crystals are present. The diagnosis is gout. It should be noted, however, that calcium pyrophosphate crystals, which are found in synovial fluid, are positively birefringent and can be responsible for a syndrome referred to as "pseudogout."

The classification of the disorders of purine metabolism includes those exhibiting **hyperuricemia,** those exhibiting **hypouricemia,** and the immunodeficiency diseases. As shown in Table 26–3, individuals with hyperuricemia can be divided into 2 groups: those

Table 26–3. Classification of patients with hyperuricemia.

I. Normal excretion of urate; renal disorder responsible for elevated serum urate.

II. Excessive excretion of urate because of overproduction.
   A. Secondary to other diseases, eg, cancer, psoriasis.
   B. Known enzyme defects responsible for overproduction.
      1. PPriboseP synthetase abnormalities.
      2. Hypoxanthine-guanine phosphoribosyl transferase deficiencies.
      3. Glucose 6-phosphatase deficiencies.
   C. Unrecognized defects.

with normal urate excretion rates and those excreting excessive quantities of total urates.

Among those individuals with hyperuricemia and no other associated disease, the majority excrete urates at a normal rate; a renal disorder is responsible for the hyperuricemia. This renal disorder is somewhat analogous to an elevated threshold wherein excretion of the normal amount of urate formed daily requires that the level of serum urate be elevated to "flow over the dam," so to speak.

Lesch-Nyhan Syndrome & Von Gierke's Disease

Some individuals with urate overexcretion (greater than 600 mg of uric acid per 24 hours) can be categorized as having secondary hyperuricemia. They have other disease processes such as cancer or psoriasis that lead to enhanced tissue turnover.

Finally, there are persons with identifiable enzyme defects, including abnormalities of PPriboseP synthetase (feedback-resistant and enhanced enzyme activities), the HGPRTase (hypoxanthine-guanine phosphoribosyl transferase) deficiencies (both the complete [Lesch-Nyhan syndrome] and incomplete deficiencies), and **glucose 6-phosphatase deficiency** (von Gierke's disease). There exists also a group of patients exhibiting idiopathic overproduction hyperuricemia, which will certainly be regarded as a heterogeneous group of diseases once the molecular bases for their metabolic defects are recognized.

The **Lesch-Nyhan syndrome** (complete HGPRTase deficiency) is an inherited X-linked recessive disorder characterized by cerebral palsy with choreoathetosis and spasticity, a bizarre syndrome of self-mutilation, and severe overproduction hyperuricemia. There is usually an associated uric acid lithiasis. The mothers of affected children are heterozygous and mosaic for the HGPRTase deficiency and frequently exhibit overproduction hyperuricemia but without any neurologic manifestations. There also exist male patients with partial deficiencies of HGPRTase attributable to a different mutation of the same gene. These males have severe overproduction hyperuricemia but usually are without significant neurologic signs and symptoms.

Purine overproduction by patients deficient in hypoxanthine-guanine phosphoribosyl transferase is related to the increased intracellular concentrations of PPriboseP. Increased PPriboseP levels seem to result from the sparing of PPriboseP by the deficient salvage pathway. The biochemical basis for the neurologic disorder in Lesch-Nyhan syndrome is unknown.

The basis of purine overproduction and hyperuricemia in von Gierke's disease is purportedly secondary to the enhanced activity of the hexose monophosphate shunt and thus enhanced generation of ribose 5-phosphate, from which PPriboseP is synthesized. However, patients with glucose 6-phosphatase deficiency also have chronic lactic acidosis and thus have elevated renal thresholds for secretion of urate contributing to the accumulation of total body urates.

All of the known enzyme defects (except the glucose 6-phosphatase deficiency, which has not been tested) are associated with increased intracellular concentrations of PPriboseP, and the theoretic basis for purine overproduction in the glucose 6-phosphatase deficiency is probably similar. Thus, it seems likely that many more disorders of overproduction hyperuricemia will eventually be found to be associated with increased accumulation of intracellular PPriboseP.

Other Purine Disorders

Hypouricemia is due either to enhanced excretion or to decreased production of urate and uric acid. Dalmatian dogs, although possessing uricase activity, as do all dogs, are not capable of reabsorbing completely the filtered uric acid in their kidneys. They excrete urate and uric acid in amounts that are excessive in respect to their serum urate levels. Similar defects have been discovered in humans with hypouricemia.

Deficiency of the enzyme xanthine oxidase, due either to an inherited genetic defect or to severe liver damage, results in hypouricemia and increased excretion of the oxypurines, hypoxanthine and xanthine. In severe xanthine oxidase deficiencies, patients frequently exhibit **xanthinuria** and xanthine lithiasis.

A deficiency of the enzyme purine nucleoside phosphorylase is associated with hypouricemia because individuals lacking this enzyme are not capable of producing hypoxanthine and guanine from inosine and guanosine, respectively. As a result, excessive quantities of purine nucleosides are excreted in their urine. Two of the purine nucleosides excreted in significant quantities, guanosine and deoxyguanosine, have limited solubility and can therefore result in renal lithiasis.

Two immunodeficiency diseases associated with deficiencies of purine metabolizing enzymes have been described in recent years. **Adenosine deaminase deficiency** is associated with a severe combined immunodeficiency disease in which both thymus-derived lymphocytes (T cells) and bone marrow–derived lymphocytes (B cells) are sparse and dysfunctional. **Purine nucleoside phosphorylase deficiency** is associated with a severe thymus-derived lymphocyte deficiency with apparently normal B cell function, a milder form of immunodeficiency. Both of these immunodeficiency diseases are inherited as autosomal recessive disorders. The metabolic bases for the immune dysfunctions seem to involve the intracellular accumulation of the triphosphates of the deoxyribonucleoside substrates of purine nucleoside phosphorylase and adenosine deaminase, respectively. These toxic deoxynucleoside triphosphates, deoxy GTP and deoxy ATP, are capable of allosterically inhibiting ribonucleotide reductase and thereby depleting cells, such as T cells, of the precursors of DNA synthesis, particularly deoxy CTP.

Purine deficiency states are rare in humans. These

are limited to circumstances attributable primarily to deficiencies of folic acid and perhaps of vitamin B_{12} when the latter results in a secondary deficiency of folate derivatives (see Chapter 10).

CLINICAL DISORDERS OF PYRIMIDINE METABOLISM
(See Table 26–4.)

As described above, the end products of pyrimidine metabolism, unlike those of purine metabolism, are **highly water-soluble compounds** such as CO_2, ammonia, β-alanine, and propionate. Thus, in circumstances where pyrimidine overproduction occurs, clinically detectable abnormalities are rarely evident. In cases of hyperuricemia associated with severe PPriboseP overproduction, there is concomitant overproduction of pyrimidine nucleotides with increased excretion of compounds such as β-alanine. Because of the requirement for N^5,N^{10}-methylenetetrahydrofolate for thymidylate synthesis, disorders of folate and vitamin B_{12} metabolism result in deficiencies of TMP (in the case of vitamin B_{12} deficiency, by an indirect mechanism).

β-Aminoisobutyric aciduria is an autosomal, recessively inherited disorder prevalent among Orientals. It is not associated with any pathologic state. It has been discussed above in connection with pyrimidine catabolism.

As described earlier, pseudouridine appears in normal urine. When increased nucleic acid turnover occurs in patients with leukemia or lymphoma, there is a markedly increased urinary excretion of pseudouridine. This compound is highly soluble and by itself produces no disease.

Two types of primary **hereditary orotic aciduria** have been reported. The more common type (type I), although still rare, is that in which both orotate phosphoribosyl transferase and orotidylate (OMP) decarboxylase are missing in all cell types tested (Fig 26–19). The patients are pyrimidine auxotrophs. They are readily treated with uridine. As infants, these patients exhibit failure to thrive and megaloblastic anemias and orange crystalluria (orotic acid). Unless treated with a source of pyrimidine nucleosides, they succumb to infections. The second type of hereditary orotic aciduria (type II) is due to a deficiency only of OMP decarboxylase (Fig 26–19). In patients with type I orotic aciduria, orotic acid is the major abnormal excretory product. In the one patient with type II, orotidine is the major excretory product, although some orotic acid is also excreted. In the erythrocytes of patients with type I orotic aciduria, the specific catalytic activities of aspartate transcarbamoylase and dihydroorotase were found to be greatly increased but returned to normal upon treatment of the patient with oral uridine. These observations suggest that one or more end products of the pathway are normally re-

sponsible for the maintenance of these enzyme activities at a regulated level. In a deficient state when the cells are deprived of the end products of this pathway, there is a derepression, probably a coordinate one, of at least those 2 enzymes.

The enzymology of the de novo pyrimidine pathway has suggested that there is a common protein molecule providing the carbamoyl phosphate synthase, aspartate transcarbamoylase, and dihydroorotase catalytic activities, and another accounting for both orotate phosphoribosyl transferase and OMP decarboxylase activities.

Increased excretion of orotic acid, uracil, and uridine has been described in patients deficient in ornithine transcarbamoylase, a liver mitochondrial enzyme responsible for an early step in urea and arginine biosynthesis. In these patients there is apparently mitochondrial carbamoyl phosphate accumulation in response to the enzyme deficiency. The mitochondrial carbamoyl phosphate diffuses into the cytosol to be utilized as a substrate for de novo pyrimidine nucleotide synthesis. The excess production of orotic acid is then manifested as orotic aciduria, which usually occurs in a mild degree and appears without crystal formation but increases upon the ingestion of foodstuffs such as meat that contain large amounts of nitrogen.

At least 2 drugs, one of which is widely used clinically, can result in orotic aciduria. Allopurinol, 4-hydroxypyrazolopyrimidine, a purine analog that directly inhibits xanthine oxidase, can be phosphoribosylated by orotate phosphoribosyl transferase, thereby competitively inhibiting the phosphoribosylation of orotic acid. Furthermore, the unusual nucleotide formed inhibits orotidylate decarboxylase, producing orotic aciduria and orotidinuria. In humans, at least, the pyrimidine pathway appears to readjust itself to this inhibition so that the organism is only transiently starved for pyrimidine nucleotides during the early stages of treatment.

6-Azauridine, after conversion to 6-azauridylate, is a competitive inhibitor of OMP decarboxylase, inducing high rates of excretion of orotic acid and orotidine as a result.

In specific liver mitochondrial failure, such as in Reye's syndrome, there is a secondary orotic aciduria. It is probably secondary to the inability of the mitochondria to utilize carbamoyl phosphate, which then, as in the inherited deficiency of ornithine transcarbamoylase, causes overproduction of orotic acid and a resultant orotic aciduria.

Table 26—4. Inherited disorders of pyrimidine metabolism and their associated enzyme abnormalities.

Clinical Disorder	Defective Enzyme	Nature of the Defect	Characteristics of Clinical Disorder	Inheritance Pattern
β-Aminoisobutyric aciduria	Transaminase	Deficiency	No symptoms; frequent in Orientals.	Autosomal recessive
Orotic aciduria, type I	Orotate phosphoribosyl-transferase and orotidylate decarboxylase	Deficiencies	Orotic acid crystalluria, failure to thrive, and megaloblastic anemia. (?) Immune deficiency. Remission with oral uridine.	Autosomal recessive
Orotic aciduria, type II	Orotidylate decarboxylase	Deficiency	Orotidinuria and orotic aciduria, megaloblastic anemia. Remission with oral uridine.	Autosomal recessive
Ornithine transcarbamoylase deficiency	Ornithine transcarbamoylase	Deficiency	Protein intolerance, hepatic encephalopathy, and mild orotic aciduria.	X-linked recessive

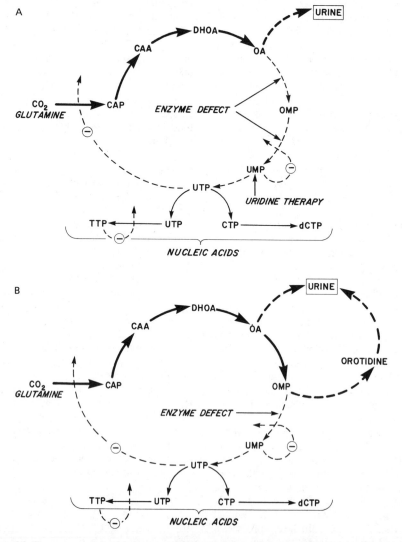

Figure 26–19. *Panel A:* The enzyme defect and consequences of orotic aciduria type I, in which both orotate phosphoribosyl transferase and orotidylic decarboxylase are deficient. *Panel B:* The defect and consequences of orotic aciduria type II, in which orotidylic decarboxylase is deficient. The dotted lines in which a negative sign is inserted represent feedback inhibition that exists under normal conditions. In type I orotic aciduria, orotic acid is spilled in the urine, whereas in type II both orotic acid and orotidine appear in the urine. The abbreviations used are defined in Fig 26–15. (Redrawn and reproduced, with permission, from Smith LH Jr: Pyrimidine metabolism in man. *N Engl J Med* 1973;**288**:764.)

● ● ●

References

Ames BN et al: Uric acid provides an antioxidant defense in humans against oxidant- and radical-caused aging and cancer: A hypothesis. *Proc Natl Acad Sci USA* 1981;**78:**6858.

Henderson JF: *Regulation of Purine Biosynthesis.* Monograph No. 170. American Chemical Society, 1972.

Henderson JF, Paterson ARP: *Nucleotide Metabolism: An Introduction.* Academic Press, 1973.

Jones M: Pyrimidine nucleotide biosynthesis in animal cells. *Annu Rev Biochem* 1980;**49:**253.

Kempe TD et al: Stable mutants of mammalian cells that overproduce the first three enzymes of pyrimidine nucleotide biosynthesis. *Cell* 1976;**9:**541.

Martin DW Jr, Gelfand EW: Biochemistry of diseases of immunodevelopment. *Annu Rev Biochem* 1981;**50:**845.

Smith LH Jr: Pyrimidine metabolism in man. *N Engl J Med* 1973;**288:**764.

Stanbury JB et al (editors): *The Metabolic Basis of Inherited Disease,* 5th ed. McGraw-Hill, 1983.

Thelander L, Reichard P: Reduction of ribonucleotides. *Annu Rev Biochem* 1979;**48:**133.

Wyngaarden JB, Kelley WN: *Gout and Hyperuricemia.* Grune & Stratton, 1976.

27 | Nucleic Acid Structure & Function

David W. Martin, Jr., MD

DNA

By any assessment of the major discoveries in science by the fourth quarter of the 20th century, it appears certain that the discovery that genetic information is coded along the length of a polymeric molecule composed of only 4 types of monomeric units will be regarded as a major scientific achievement of this century. This polymeric molecule, **DNA, is the chemical basis of heredity.** The demonstration that DNA contained the genetic information was first made in 1944 in a series of experiments by Avery, MacLeod, and McCarty, who showed that the genetic determination of the character (type) of the capsule of a specific pneumococcus could be transmitted to another of a distinctly different capsular type by introducing purified DNA from the former coccus into the latter. These authors referred to the agent (DNA) accomplishing the change as "transforming factor." Sub-

sequently, this type of genetic manipulation has become commonplace in bacteriologic and genetic laboratories. Similar experiments have recently been performed utilizing cultured mammalian cells and insect and rodent embryos as recipients and cloned DNA as the donor of genetic information.

Chemical Nature of DNA

The chemical nature of the monomeric units of DNA—**deoxyadenylate, deoxyguanylate, deoxycytidylate,** and **thymidylate**—is described in Chapter 25. These monomeric units of DNA are held in polymeric form by 3′,5′-phosphodiester bridges constituting a single strand, as depicted in Fig 27–1. The informational content of DNA resides in the sequence in which these monomers—purine and pyrimidine deoxyribonucleotides—are ordered. The polymer as depicted possesses a polarity; one end has a 5′-hydroxyl or phosphate terminus while the other has a 3′-phos-

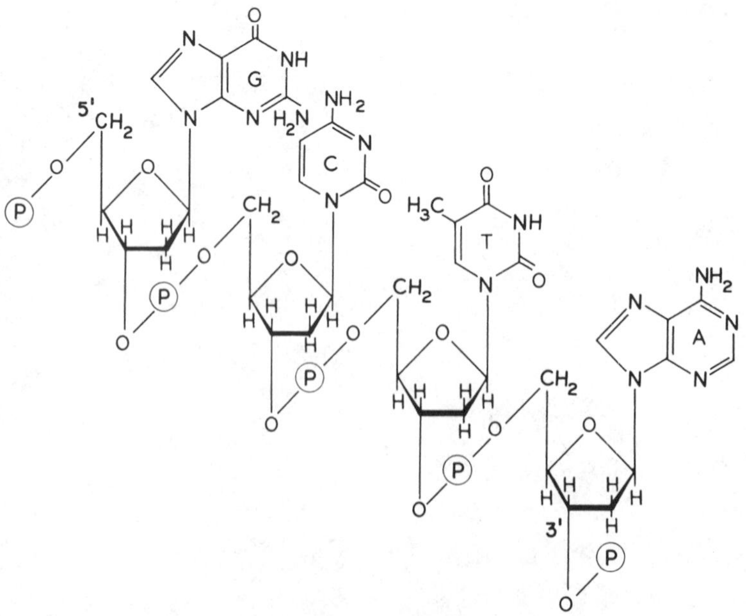

Figure 27–1. A segment of a structure of DNA molecule in which the purine and pyrimidine bases adenine (A), thymine (T), cytosine (C), and guanine (G) are held together by a phosphodiester backbone between 2′-deoxyribosyl moieties attached to the nucleobases by an N-glycosidic bond. Note that the backbone has a polarity (ie, a direction).

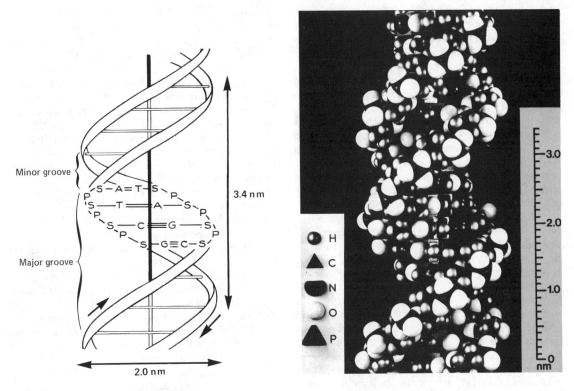

Figure 27–2. The Watson and Crick model of the double helical structure of DNA. *Left:* Diagrammatic representation of structure (modified). (A, adenine; C, cytosine; G, guanine; T, thymine; P, phosphate; S, sugar [deoxyribose].) *Right:* Space-filling model of DNA structure. (Photograph from James D. Watson, *Molecular Biology of the Gene,* 3rd ed. Copyright © 1976, 1970, 1965, by W.A. Benjamin, Inc., Menlo Park, Calif.)

phate or hydroxyl moiety. The importance of this polarity will become evident. Since the genetic information resides in the order of the monomeric units within the polymers, there must exist a mechanism of reproducing or replicating this specific information with a high degree of fidelity. That requirement, together with x-ray diffraction data from the DNA molecule and the observation of Chargaff that in DNA molecules the concentration of deoxyadenosine (A) nucleotides equals that of thymidine (T) nucleotides (A = T), while the concentration of deoxyguanosine (G) nucleotides equals that of deoxycytidine (C) nucleotides (G = C), led Watson, Crick, and Wilkins to propose in the early 1950s a model of a double-stranded DNA molecule. A model of the B form of DNA is depicted in Fig 27–2. The 2 strands of this right-handed, double-stranded molecule are held together by **hydrogen bonds** between the purine and pyrimidine bases of the respective linear molecules. The pairings between the purine and pyrimidine nucleotides on the opposite strands are very specific and are dependent upon hydrogen bonding of **A with T,** and **G with C** (Fig 27–3).

In the double-stranded molecule, restrictions imposed by the rotation about the phosphodiester bond, the favored **anti** configuration of the glycosidic bond (Fig 25–9), and the predominant tautomers (Fig 25–4)

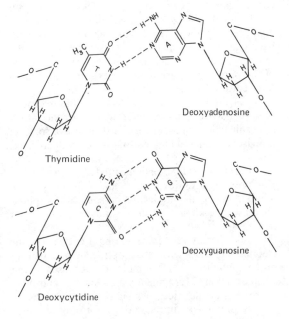

Figure 27–3. Base pairing between deoxyadenosine and thymidine and between deoxycytidine and deoxyguanosine, as proposed by Watson and Crick. The broken lines represent hydrogen bonds. (The phosphodiester bridges are not shown.)

of the 4 bases (A, G, T, and C) allow A to pair only with T, and G only with C, as depicted in Fig 27–3. This base-pairing restriction explains the earlier observation that in a double-stranded DNA molecule the content of A equals that of T and the content of G equals that of C. The 2 strands of the double helical molecule, each of which possesses a polarity, are **antiparallel;** ie, one strand runs in the 5′ to 3′ direction and the other in the 3′ to 5′ direction. This is analogous to 2 parallel streets, each running one way but carrying traffic in opposite directions. In the double-stranded DNA molecules, since the information resides in the sequence of nucleotides on one strand, the opposite strand might be considered "antitemplate," ie, the complement of the "template" strand.

As depicted in Fig 27–3, three hydrogen bonds hold the deoxyguanosine nucleotide to the deoxycytidine nucleotide whereas the other pair, the A-T pair, is held together by 2 hydrogen bonds. Thus, the G-C bond is stronger by approximately 50%.

Structure of DNA

The B form, the overwhelmingly dominant form of DNA under physiologic conditions, has a pitch of 3.4 nm per turn (Fig 27–2). Within a single turn 10 base pairs exist, each planar base being stacked to resemble 2 winding stacks of coins side by side. The 2 stacks are held together by hydrogen bonding at each level between the 2 coins on opposite stacks and by 2 ribbons wound in a right-hand turn about the 2 stacks and representing the phosphodiester backbone.

This double-stranded structure in solution can be melted by increasing temperature or decreasing salt concentration. Not only do the 2 stacks of bases pull apart, but the bases themselves unstack while still connected in the polymer by the phosphodiester backbone. Concomitant with this **denaturation** of the DNA molecule is an increase in the optical absorbency of the purine and pyrimidine bases—a phenomenon referred to as **hyperchromicity** of denaturation. Because of the stacking of the bases and the hydrogen bonding between the stacks, the double-stranded DNA molecule exhibits properties of a fiber and in solution is a viscous material that loses its viscosity upon denaturation.

Careful examination of the model depicted in Fig 27–2 reveals a **major groove** and a **minor groove** winding along the molecule parallel to the phosphodiester backbones. In these grooves, proteins can interact specifically with exposed atoms of the nucleotides and thereby recognize and bind to specific nucleotide sequences without disrupting the base pairing of the double helical DNA molecule. As discussed in Chapters 29 and 31, regulatory proteins can control the expression of specific genes via such interactions.

A previously unrecognized form of double-stranded DNA was discovered in 1980 by the x-ray crystallographic study of a 6-base-pair synthetic DNA molecule consisting of alternating C and G deoxyribonucleotides. This new form of DNA forms a **left-handed double helix** in which the phosphodiester

backbone zigzags along the molecule (Fig 27–4); hence, it has been named **Z-DNA** by its discoverers, Alexander Rich and colleagues. Z-DNA is the least twisted (12 base pairs per turn) and skinniest DNA helix known to exist. The existence of Z-DNA is not only restricted to sequences of alternating purine and pyrimidine nucleotides but also requires one or more stabilizing influences. These stabilizing influences include (1) the presence of high-salt or specific cations such as spermine or spermidine, (2) a high degree of negative supercoiling of the DNA (see Chapter 28), (3) the binding of Z-DNA–specific proteins, and (4) the methylation of the 5-carbon of some of the deoxycytidine nucleotides in the alternating sequence. The latter is of particular interest because of its implied involvement in the regulation of gene expression (see below and Chapter 31).

While human DNA does contain potential Z-DNA–forming regions dispersed throughout the genome, the actual existence of Z-DNA in *Drosophila* (fruit fly) chromosomes has been demonstrated utilizing antibodies that recognize and bind specifically to Z-DNA. In addition, it has been demonstrated in vitro that Z-DNA can exist as short stretches within longer B-form DNA, the transition region extending over a length of about 5 base pairs.

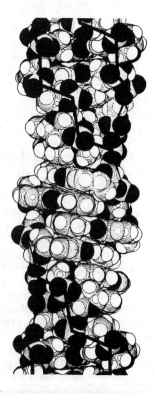

Figure 27–4. Computer representation of Z-DNA. The black zigzag line connects the phosphate groups of the polynucleotide chain. Compare with Fig 27–2. (Reproduced, with permission, from: Wang AHJ et al: Left-handed double helical DNA: Variations in the backbone conformation. *Science* 1981;**211**:171. Copyright © 1981 by the American Association for the Advancement of Science.)

The function of Z-DNA is unknown, but it has been suggested that it could exert regulatory effects both proximal and distal to the site of its existence. For instance, some proteins that bind in the minor or major groove of B-form DNA could probably not bind to the Z form. In addition, the reversion of Z form to a B form of DNA, an event that might occur as a consequence of loss of methyl groups from 5-methyldeoxycytidine, would likely result in tortional differences of DNA distal to the actual site of Z-DNA. As discussed below, tortional winding and unwinding are thought to affect gene activity.

In some organisms such as bacteria, bacteriophages, and many DNA-containing animal viruses, the 2 ends of the DNA molecules are joined to create a closed circle with no terminus. This of course does not destroy the polarity of the molecules, but it eliminates all free 3' and 5' hydroxyl and phosphoryl groups.

Function of DNA

The genetic information stored in the nucleotide sequence of DNA serves 2 purposes. It is the source of information for the synthesis of all protein molecules of the cell and organism, and it provides the information inherited by daughter cells or offspring. Both of these functions require that the DNA molecule serve as a template—in the first case for the transcription of the information into RNA and in the second case for the replication of the information into daughter DNA molecules.

The complementarity of the Watson and Crick double-stranded model of DNA strongly suggests that replication of the DNA molecule occurs in a semiconservative manner. Thus, when each strand of the double-stranded DNA molecule separates from its complement during replication, **each can then serve as a template** on which a new complementary strand can be synthesized (Fig 27–5). The 2 newly formed double-stranded DNA molecules, each containing one strand (but complementary rather than identical) from the parent double-stranded DNA molecule, can then be sorted between the 2 daughter cells (Fig 27–6). Each daughter cell will contain DNA molecules with information identical to that which the parent possessed; yet in each daughter cell the DNA molecule of the parent cell has been only semiconserved.

The **semiconservative** nature of DNA replication in the bacterium *Escherichia coli* was unequivocally demonstrated by Meselson and Stahl in a classic experiment using the heavy isotope of nitrogen and centrifugal equilibrium techniques. This experiment is depicted in Fig 27–7. The DNA of *E coli* is chemically identical to that of humans, although the sequences of nucleotides are, of course, different, and the human cell contains about 1000 times more DNA per cell than does the bacterium. Furthermore, the chemistry of replication of DNA in prokaryotes such as *E coli* appears to be identical to that in eukaryotes, including humans, even though the enzymes carrying out the reactions of DNA synthesis and replication are different. Thus, any observations on the chemical nature or

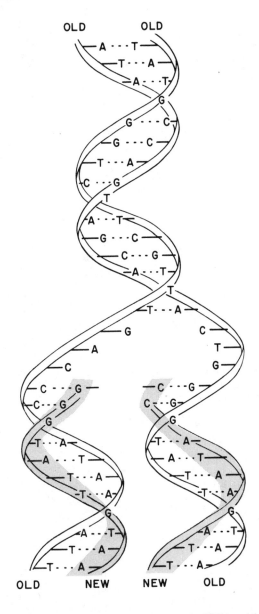

Figure 27–5. The double-stranded structure of DNA and the template function of each old strand on which a new complementary strand (shaded) is synthesized. (From James D. Watson, *Molecular Biology of the Gene,* 3rd ed. Copyright © 1976, 1970, 1965, by W.A. Benjamin, Inc., Menlo Park, Calif.)

chemical reactions of nucleic acids of prokaryotes are very likely applicable to eukaryotic organisms. Indeed the Meselson and Stahl type of experiment has now been performed in mammalian cells and has yielded results comparable to those obtained with *E coli*.

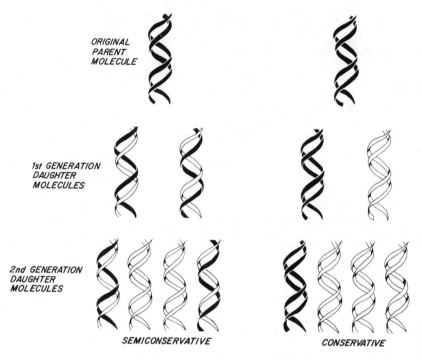

Figure 27–6. The expected distributions of parental DNA strands during semiconservative and conservative replication. The parental strands are solid, and the newly synthesized strands are open. (Redrawn and reproduced, with permission, from Lehninger AL: *Biochemistry,* 2nd ed. Worth, 1975.)

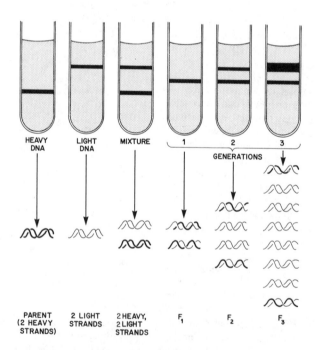

Figure 27–7. Schematic representation of the results of the Meselson-Stahl experiment demonstrating semiconservative replication of bacterial DNA. The tubes in which the equilibrium centrifugation conditions have been established are represented at the top and contain the bands of DNA with the indicated densities. In the lower part of the figure are represented the parent DNA strands containing the heavy isotope of nitrogen (^{15}N) and the strands isolated from daughter cells grown in the presence of the naturally occurring light isotope of nitrogen (^{14}N). The appearance of a band of DNA with an intermediate density and its persistence through 3 generations with the subsequent appearance of totally light DNA confirms the semiconservative nature of DNA replication. (Redrawn and reproduced, with permission, from Lehninger AL: *Biochemistry,* 2nd ed. Worth, 1975.)

RNA

Chemical Nature of RNA

Ribonucleic acid (RNA) is a polymer of purine and pyrimidine ribonucleotides linked together by 3',5'-phosphodiester bridges analogous to those in DNA (Fig 27–8). Although sharing many features with DNA, RNA possesses several specific differences:

(1) As indicated by its name, the sugar moiety in RNA to which the phosphates and purine and pyrimidine bases are attached is **ribose** rather than the 2'-deoxyribose of DNA.

(2) Although RNA contains the ribonucleotides of adenine, guanine, and cytosine, it does not possess thymine except in the rare case mentioned below. Instead of thymine, RNA contains the ribonucleotide of **uracil.** Thus, the pyrimidine components of RNA differ from those of DNA.

(3) RNA exists as a **single strand,** whereas DNA exists as a double-stranded helical molecule. However, given the proper complementary base sequence with opposite polarity, the single strand of RNA, as demonstrated in Fig 27–9, is capable of folding back on itself like a hairpin and thus acquiring double-stranded characteristics.

(4) Since the RNA molecule is a single strand complementary to only one of the 2 strands of a gene, its guanine content does *not* necessarily equal its cytosine content, nor does its adenine content necessarily equal its uracil content.

(5) RNA can be **hydrolyzed by alkali** to 2',3' cyclic diesters of the mononucleotides. A necessary intermediate in this hydrolysis is the 2',3',5'-triester, an intermediate that cannot be formed in alkali-treated

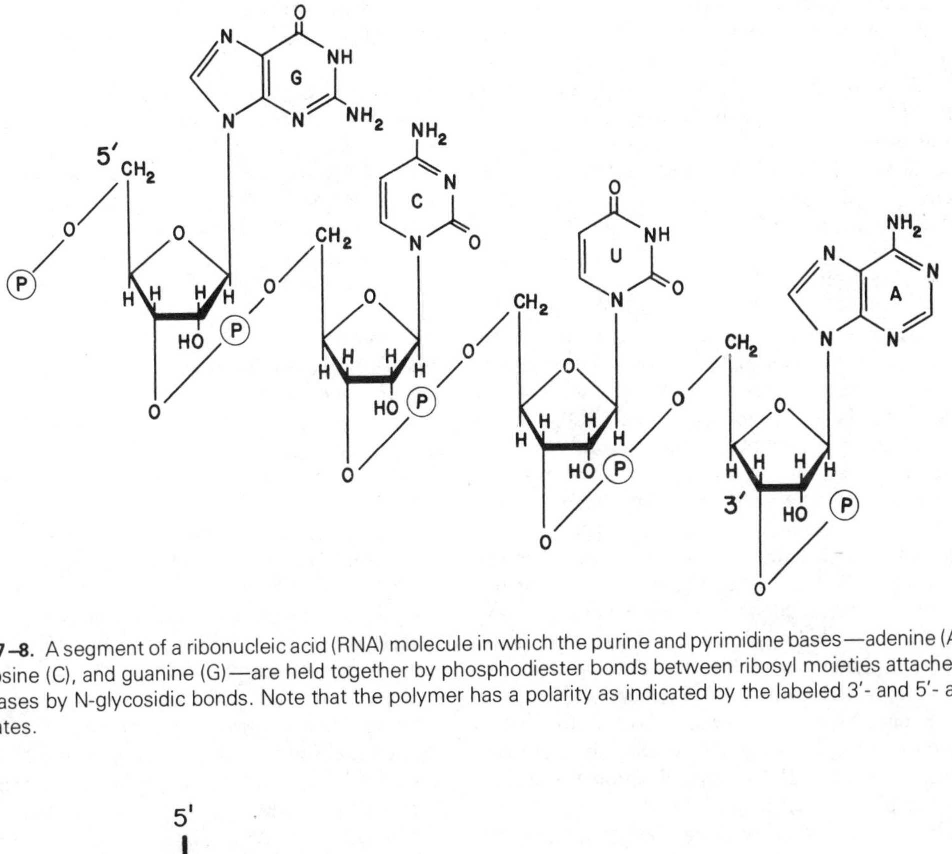

Figure 27–8. A segment of a ribonucleic acid (RNA) molecule in which the purine and pyrimidine bases—adenine (A), uracil (U), cytosine (C), and guanine (G)—are held together by phosphodiester bonds between ribosyl moieties attached to the nucleobases by N-glycosidic bonds. Note that the polymer has a polarity as indicated by the labeled 3'- and 5'- attached phosphates.

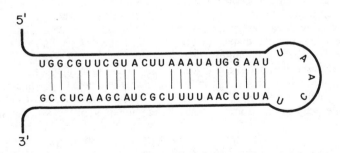

Figure 27–9. Diagrammatic representation of the secondary structure of an RNA molecule in which a "hairpin" has been formed and is dependent upon the intramolecular base pairing.

DNA strands:

Antitemplate → 5'-T G G A A T T G T G A G C G G A T A A C A A T T T C A C A C A G G A A A C A G C T A T G A C C A T G- 3'
Template ⟶ 3'-A C C T T A A C A C T C G C C T A T T G T T A A A G T G T G T C C T T T G T C G A T A C T G G T A C- 5'

RNA
transcript   5'   pA U U G U G A G C G G A U A A C A A U U U C A C A C A G G A A A C A G C U A U G A C C A U G   3'

Figure 27–10. The relationship between the sequences of an RNA transcript and its gene, in which the template and antitemplate strands are shown with their polarities. The RNA transcript with a 5' to 3' polarity is complementary to the template strand with its 3' to 5' polarity. Note that the sequence in the RNA transcript and its polarity is the same as that in the antitemplate strand, except that the U of the transcript replaces the T of the gene.

DNA because of the absence of a 2'-hydroxyl group. The alkali lability of RNA is useful both diagnostically and analytically.

Information within the single strand of RNA is contained in its sequence ("primary structure") of purine and pyrimidine nucleotides within the polymer. The sequence is complementary to the "template" strand of the gene from which it was transcribed. Because of this complementarity, an RNA molecule will bind specifically via the base-pairing rules to its template DNA strand; it will not bind ("hybridize") with the other or "antitemplate" strand of its gene. The sequence of the RNA molecule (except for U replacing T) is the same as that of the "antitemplate" strand of the gene (Fig 27–10).

Biologic Function of RNA

Although all naturally occurring RNA molecules contain information in their sequences, some of these molecules never have any of their informational content translated into the specific amino acid sequence of a protein molecule. Those cytoplasmic RNA molecules that serve as templates for protein synthesis are designated as mRNA. Many other cytoplasmic RNA molecules have structural roles wherein they contribute to the formation of ribosomes (the organellar machinery for protein synthesis) or serve as adapter molecules (tRNA) for the translation of RNA information into specific sequences of polymerized amino acids. Most of the RNA synthesized from DNA templates in eukaryotic cells, including mammalian cells, is **degraded within the nucleus,** and it never serves as either a structural or an informational entity within the cellular cytoplasm. As discussed in Chapter 29, these portions of RNA molecules nonetheless are thought to play some regulatory roles.

Most RNA molecules transcribed in the cell nucleus appear to have at least portions that are involved in protein synthesis, but there are in cultured human cells nuclear small RNA species not directly involved in protein synthesis but which may have roles in RNA processing and the cellular architecture. These relatively small molecules vary in size from 90 to about 300 nucleotides.

The genetic material for some animal and plant viruses is RNA rather than DNA. Although some RNA viruses do not ever have their information transcribed into a DNA molecule, many animal RNA viruses—

specifically the retroviruses—are transcribed by an **RNA-dependent DNA polymerase** to produce a double-stranded DNA copy of their RNA genome. In many cases, the resulting double-stranded DNA transcript is integrated into the host genome and subsequently serves as a template for gene expression and from which new viral RNA genomes can be transcribed.

Structural Organization of RNA

In all prokaryotic and eukaryotic organisms, 3 main classes of RNA molecules exist: **messenger RNA (mRNA), transfer RNA (tRNA),** and **ribosomal RNA (rRNA).** Each class differs from the others by size, function, and general stability.

The **messenger RNA (mRNA)** class is the most heterogeneous in size and stability. All of the members of the class function as messengers conveying the information in a gene to the protein-synthesizing machinery, where each serves as a template on which a specific sequence of amino acids is polymerized to form a specific protein molecule, the ultimate gene product (Fig 27–11).

Messenger RNAs are single strands complementary to the template strand of their respective structural genes. The RNA molecules, particularly in eukaryotes, have some unique chemical characteristics. The 5' terminus of mRNA is "capped" by a 7-methylguanosine triphosphate that is linked to an adjacent 2'-O-methyl ribonucleoside at its 5'-hydroxyl through the 3 phosphates (Fig 27–12). The mRNA molecules frequently contain internal 6-methyladenylates and other 2'-O-ribose methylated nucleotides. Although the function of this capping of mRNAs is not completely understood, the cap is probably involved in the recognition of mRNA by the translating machinery. The protein-synthesizing machinery begins translating the mRNA into proteins at the 5' or capped terminus. The other end of most mRNA molecules, the 3'-hydroxyl terminus, has attached a polymer of adenylate residues 20–250 nucleotides in length. The specific function of the **poly(A) "tail"** at the 3'-hydroxyl terminus of mRNAs is not fully understood, but it seems that it maintains the intracellular stability of the specific mRNA. Some mRNAs, including those for the histones, do not contain poly(A).

In **mammalian cells,** including cells of humans, the mRNA molecules present in the cytoplasm are not

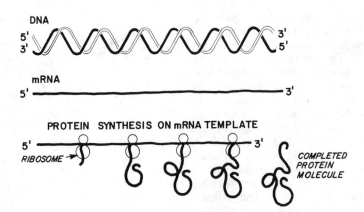

Figure 27–11. The expression of genetic information in DNA into the form of an mRNA transcript. This is subsequently translated by ribosomes into a specific protein molecule.

the RNA products immediately synthesized from the DNA template but must be formed by processing from a precursor molecule before entering the cytoplasm. Thus, in mammalian nuclei, the immediate products of gene transcription constitute a fourth class of RNA molecules. These nuclear RNA molecules are very heterogeneous in size and are quite large. The **heterogeneous nuclear RNA (hnRNA)** molecules may exceed 10^7 daltons, whereas the mRNA molecules are generally smaller than 2×10^6 daltons. As is discussed in Chapter 29, the hnRNA molecules are processed to generate the mRNA molecules which then enter the

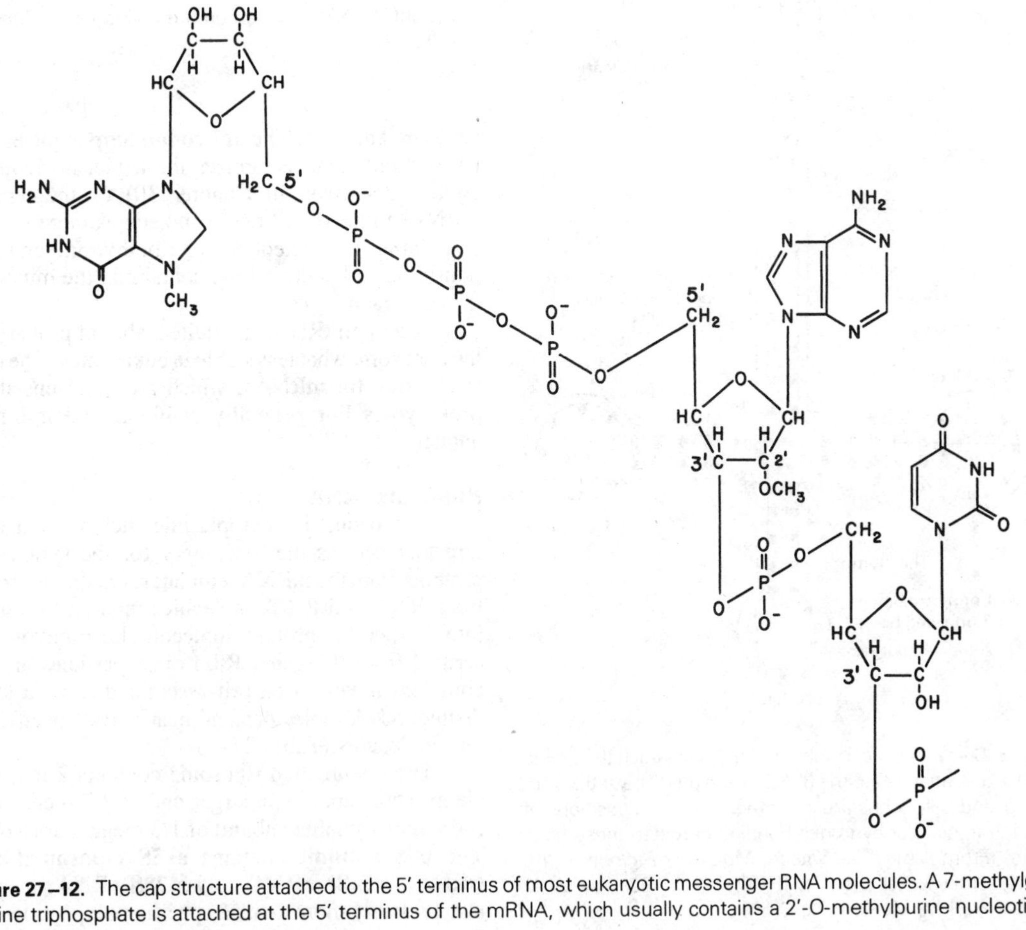

Figure 27–12. The cap structure attached to the 5′ terminus of most eukaryotic messenger RNA molecules. A 7-methylguanosine triphosphate is attached at the 5′ terminus of the mRNA, which usually contains a 2′-O-methylpurine nucleotide.

cytoplasm to serve as templates for protein synthesis.

The **transfer RNA (tRNA)** molecules consist of approximately 75 nucleotides and thus have a molecular weight of 25,000. They also are generated by nuclear processing of a precursor molecule (see Chapter 29). The tRNA molecules serve as adaptors for the translation of the information in the sequence of nucleotides of the mRNA into specific amino acids. There are at least 20 species of tRNA molecules in every cell, at least one corresponding to each of the 20 amino acids required for protein synthesis. Although each specific tRNA differs from the others in its sequence of nucleotides, the tRNA molecules as a class have many features in common. The primary structure—ie, the nucleotide sequence—of all tRNA molecules allows extensive folding and intrastrand complementarity to generate a secondary structure that appears like a cloverleaf (Fig 27–13). X-ray diffraction studies have allowed the formulation of a schematic diagram illustrating the folding of the phenylalanine-accepting tRNA from yeast (Fig 27–14).

The features that all tRNA molecules have in common include an **ACC sequence** at the 3′ termini. It is through an ester bond to the 3′-hydroxyl group of the adenosyl moiety that the carboxyl groups of amino

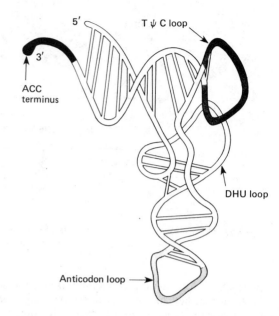

Figure 27–14. The 3-dimensional structure of a tRNA molecule as determined by x-ray crystallography. The specified amino acid is attached at the ACC 3′ terminus. The T ψ C loop, the dihydrouracil (DHU) loop, and the anticodon loop are indicated. (Redrawn and reproduced, with permission, from Stryer L: *Biochemistry.* Freeman, 1975. Copyright © 1975. [Based on a drawing by Dr Sung-Han Kim.])

acids are attached. The **anticodon loop** at the end of a base-paired stem recognizes the triplet nucleotide or codon (discussed in Chapter 30) of the template mRNA. In nearly all tRNA molecules there is a loop containing the nucleotides of ribothymine and pseudouridine and another loop containing the minor base dihydrouracil.

Although tRNAs are quite stable in prokaryotes, they are somewhat less stable in eukaryotes. The opposite is true for mRNAs, which are quite unstable in prokaryotes but generally stable in eukaryotic organisms.

Ribosomal RNA

A ribosome is a cytoplasmic nucleoprotein structure that acts as the machinery for the synthesis of proteins from the mRNA templates. On the ribosomes, the mRNA and tRNA molecules interact to translate into a specific protein molecule information transcribed from the gene. Ribosomal particles are very complex, having been self-assembled from at least 4 distinct RNA molecules and nearly 100 specific protein molecules (Table 27–1).

The mammalian ribosome contains 2 major nucleoprotein subunits, a larger one of 2.7 megadaltons (60S) and a smaller subunit of 1.3 megadaltons (40S). The **60S subunit** contains a **5S ribosomal RNA (rRNA)**, a **5.8S rRNA**, and a **28S rRNA**; there are also probably more than 50 specific polypeptides. The

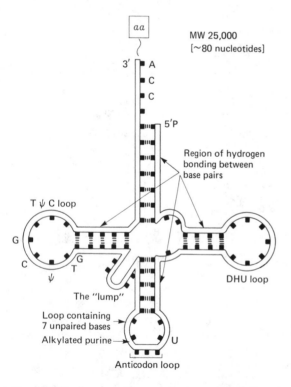

Figure 27–13. A typical aminoacyl tRNA in which the amino acid (αα) is attached to the 3′ ACC terminus. The anticodon, T ψ C, and DHU loops are indicated, as are the positions of the intramolecular hydrogen bonding between these base pairs. (From James D. Watson, *Molecular Biology of the Gene,* 3rd ed. Copyright © 1976, 1970, 1965, by W.A. Benjamin, Inc., Menlo Park, Calif.)

Table 27–1. RNA components of mammalian ribosomes.

Subunit Size (Svedberg Units)	Subunit MW	RNA Size (Svedberg Units)	RNA MW
60S (>50 polypeptides)	2.7 × 10⁶	5S	35,000
		5.8S	45,000
		28S	1.5 × 10⁶
40S (>30 polypeptides)	1.3 × 10⁶	18S	750,000

toplasm, or in both. They range in size from 90 to 300 nucleotides and are present in 100,000–1,000,000 copies per cell. Although the functions of these small nuclear RNAs (snRNA) and small cytoplasmic RNAs (scRNA) are not fully understood, at least some appear to be involved in the processing of heterogeneous nuclear RNA (hnRNA) to mature mRNA (see Chapter 29). Table 27–2 summarizes some characteristics of these small stable RNAs.

smaller or **40S subunit** contains a single **18S rRNA** and approximately 30 polypeptide chains. All of the ribosomal RNA molecules except the 5S rRNA are processed from a single 45S precursor RNA molecule in the nucleolus (see Chapter 30). The 5S rRNA apparently has its own precursor that is independently transcribed. The highly methylated ribosomal RNA molecules are packaged in the nucleolus with the specific ribosomal proteins. In the cytoplasm, the ribosomes remain quite stable and capable of many translations. The functions of the ribosomal RNA molecules in the ribosomal particle are not fully understood, but they are necessary for ribosomal assembly and seem to play key roles in the binding of mRNA to ribosomes and its translation.

Small Stable RNA

A large number of discrete, highly conserved, and stable small RNA species are found in eukaryotic cells. The majority of these molecules exist as ribonucleoproteins and are distributed in the nucleus, in the cy-

Table 27–2. Abundant species of small stable RNAs in mammalian cells.*

Species	Nucleotides	Abundancy	Localization	snRNA	Class III
7-3	300	2 × 10⁵	Nucleus		X
7-2, 1	290	1 × 10⁵	Nucleus and cytoplasm		X
7S	280	5 × 10⁵	Nucleus and cytoplasm		X
U3	216	3 × 10⁵	Nucleolus	X	
U2	188/189	5 × 10⁵	Nucleoplasm	X	
U1	165	1 × 10⁶	Nucleoplasm/ hnRNA	X	
U4	139	1 × 10⁵	Nucleoplasm	X	
U5	118	2 × 10⁵	Nucleoplasm	X	
U6	106	3 × 10⁵	Perichromatin granules	X	
4.5S	91–95	3 × 10⁵	Nucleus and cytoplasm		X

*Reproduced, with permission, from Zieve GW: Two groups of small stable RNAs. *Cell* 1981;**25**:295. Copyright © 1981 by the Massachusetts Institute of Technology.

• • •

References

Brawerman G: Eukaryotic messenger RNA. *Annu Rev Biochem* 1974;**43**:621.

Nordheim A et al: Antibodies to left-handed Z-DNA bind to interband regions of *Drosophila* polytene chromosomes. *Nature* 1981;**294**:417.

Rich A et al: The chemistry and biology of left-handed Z-DNA. *Annu Rev Biochem* 1984;**53**:847.

Watson JD: *The Double Helix*. Atheneum, 1968.

Watson JD, Crick FHC: Molecular structure of nucleic acids. *Nature* 1953;**171**:737.

Zieve GW: Two groups of small stable RNAs. *Cell* 1981;**25**:296.

28 | DNA Organization & Replication

David W. Martin, Jr., MD

CHROMATIN

Chromatin is the chromosomal material extracted from nuclei of cells of eukaryotic organisms.* Chromatin consists of very long double-stranded **DNA molecules** and a nearly equal mass of rather small basic proteins termed **histones** as well as a smaller amount of **nonhistone proteins** (most of which are acidic and larger than histones) and a small quantity of **RNA.** Electron microscopic studies of chromatin have demonstrated dense spherical particles called **nucleosomes,** which are approximately 10 nm in diameter and connected by DNA filaments (Fig 28–1). When one (H1) of the histone components is removed from chromatin, the nucleosomes are not so closely packed, suggesting that histone H1 is involved in the super-packing of nucleosomes in nuclei.

Histones & Nucleosomes

The H1 histones are somewhat heterogeneous, consisting of a series of closely related **basic proteins.** Among the histones, H1 histones are the least tightly bound to chromatin and are, therefore, easily removed with a salt solution, after which chromatin becomes soluble. The isolated core nucleosomes contain 4 classes of histones: **H2A, H2B, H3,** and **H4.** The structures of slightly lysine-rich histones—H2A and H2B—appear to have been significantly conserved between species, while the structures of arginine-rich histones—H3 and H4—have been highly conserved between species. This severe conservation implies that the function of histones is identical in all eukaryotes and that the entire molecule is involved quite specifically in carrying out this function. The C-terminal two-thirds of the molecules have a usual amino acid composition, while their N-terminal thirds contain

most of the basic amino acids. These 4 core histones are subject to 5 types of **covalent modifications:** acetylation, methylation, phosphorylation, ADP-ribosylation, and covalent linkage (H2A only) to ubiquitin, the nuclear protein. These histone modifications likely play some role in chromatin structure and function, but little is currently understood.

When removed from chromatin, the histones interact with each other in very specific ways. **H3 and H4 aggregate to form a tetramer** containing 2 molecules of each ($H3_2$-$H4_2$), while **H2A and H2B form dimers** (H2A-H2B) and higher oligomeric complexes ([H2A-H2B]$_n$). The tetrameric H3-H4 does not associate with the H2A-H2B dimer or oligomer, and H1 does not associate directly with any of the other histones in solution.

However, when the $H3_2$-$H4_2$ tetramer and H2A-H2B dimers are mixed with purified, double-stranded DNA, the same x-ray diffraction pattern is formed as that observed in freshly isolated chromatin. Electron microscopic studies confirm the existence of reconstituted **nucleosomes.** Furthermore, the reconstitution of nucleosomes from DNA and histones H2A, H2B, H3, and H4 is independent of the organismal or cellular origin of the various components. The histone H1 and the nonhistone proteins are *not* necessary for the reconstitution of the nucleosome core.

In the nucleosome, the DNA is supercoiled in a left-handed helix over the surface of the disk-shaped histone octamer consisting of one H3-H4 tetramer ($H3_2$-$H4_2$) and two H2A-H2B dimers (Fig 28–2). The DNA is not bent uniformly into the supercoil but exhibits several regions of tight bending that may resemble kinking. The histones interact with the DNA on the inside of the supercoil without protruding.

The $H3_2$-$H4_2$ itself can confer nucleosomelike properties on DNA and thus has a central role in the formation of the nucleosome. The $H3_2$-$H4_2$ can protect approximately 80 base pairs of DNA in the central turn of the nucleosome from attack by nucleases. The addition of two H2A-H2B dimers stabilizes the primary particle and binds firmly 2 additional half-turns of DNA previously bound only loosely to the $H3_2$-$H4_2$. Thus, **1.75 superhelical turns of DNA** are wrapped around the surface of the histone octamer, **protecting 146 base pairs of DNA** and forming the **nucleosome core** (Fig 28–2). As the DNA wraps around the surface

*So far as possible, the discussion of this chapter and of Chapters 29, 30, and 31 will pertain to mammalian organisms, which are, of course, among the higher eukaryotes. At times it will be necessary to refer to observations made in prokaryotic organisms such as bacteria and viruses, but when such occurs it will be acknowledged as being information that must be extrapolated to mammalian organisms. The division of the material presented in Chapters 27–31 is somewhat arbitrary and should not be taken to mean that the processes described are not fully integrated and interdependent.

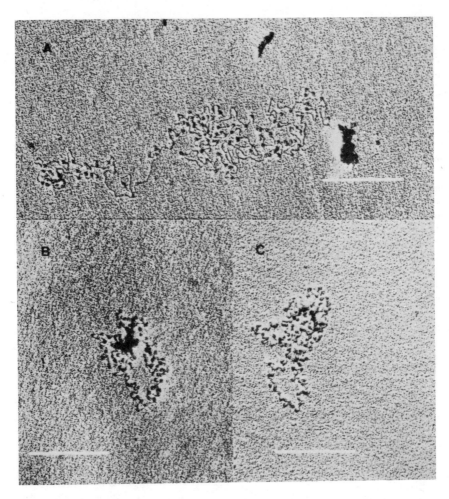

Figure 28–1. Electron micrograph of nucleosomes attached by strands of nucleic acid. (White bar represents 2.5 μm.) (Reproduced, with permission, from Oudet P, Gross-Bellard M, Chambon P: Electron microscopic and biochemical evidence that chromatin structure is a repeating unit. *Cell* 1975;**4**:281.)

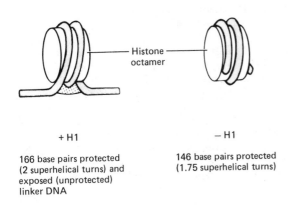

166 base pairs protected
(2 superhelical turns) and
exposed (unprotected)
linker DNA

146 base pairs protected
(1.75 superhelical turns)

Figure 28–2. Model for the structure of the nucleosome *(left)* and nucleosome core *(right)*, in which DNA is wrapped around the surface of a flat protein cylinder consisting of 2 each of histones H2A, H2B, H3, and H4. (Reproduced, with permission, from Laskey RA, Earnshaw WC: Nucleosome assembly. *Nature* 1980;**286**:763.)

of the histone octamer to form the nucleosome, it comes in contact with the histones in the order

$$H2A-H2B-H4-H3-H3-H4-H2B-H2A$$

Histone H1 binds to the DNA, where it enters and leaves the nucleosome core to seal a **2-turn, 166-base-pair DNA superhelix** generating the **nucleosome.**

The assembly of nucleosomes is probably mediated by the anionic nuclear protein **nucleoplasmin.** Histones, which are strongly cationic, can bind nonspecifically to the strongly anionic DNA by forming salt bridges. Clearly, such a nonspecific interaction of histones and DNA would be detrimental to nucleosome formation and chromatin function. Nucleoplasmin is an anionic pentameric protein that binds neither to DNA nor to chromatin, but it can interact reversibly and stoichiometrically with one histone octamer in such a way that the histones no longer adhere nonspecifically to negatively charged surfaces such as DNA.

It seems that nucleoplasmin thereby maintains in the nucleus an ionic environment conducive to the specific interaction of histones and DNA and assembly nucleosomes. As the nucleosome is assembled, nucleoplasmin must be released from the histones. DNA topoisomerase I, a nicking-closing enzyme discussed below, may also be involved in nucleosome assembly. Nucleosomes appear to exhibit preference for certain regions on specific DNA molecules, but the basis for this nonrandom distribution, termed **phasing,** is unknown, although it is probably related to the relative physical flexibility of certain nucleotide sequences that are able to accommodate the regions of kinking within the supercoil.

The super-packing of nucleosomes in nuclei is seemingly dependent upon the interaction of the H1 histones with the double-stranded DNA connecting the nucleosomes. The topology of the interaction of the double-stranded DNA with the H1 histones to form the internucleosome spacer regions is not well delineated but probably has an effect on transcriptional activity.

Electron microscopy of chromatin reveals 2 higher orders of structure—the 10-nm fibril and the 25- to 30-nm chromatin fiber—beyond that of the nucleosome itself. The disklike nucleosome structure has a 10-nm diameter and a height of 5 nm. The **10-nm fibril** seems to consist of nucleosomes arranged with their edges touching and their flat faces parallel with the fibril axis (Fig 28–3). The 10-nm fibril is probably further supercoiled with 6–7 nucleosomes per turn to form the **30-nm chromatin fiber** (Fig 28–4). Each

Figure 28–3. Proposed structure of the 10-nm fibril of chromatin made up of disk-shaped nucleosomes. The positions of the H1 histone-spacer regions are undefined.

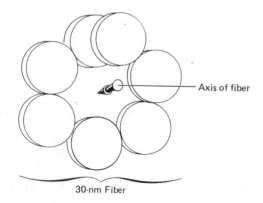

Figure 28–4. Proposed structure of the 30-nm chromatin fiber consisting of superhelixes of 10-nm fibrils of nucleosomes. The axis of the 30-nm fiber is perpendicular to the plane of the page.

turn of the supercoil would be relatively flat, and the faces of the nucleosomes of successive turns would be nearly parallel to each other. H1 histones appear to stabilize the 30-nm fiber, but their position and that of the variable length spacer DNA are not clear. It is probable that nucleosomes can form a variety of packed structures. In order to form a mitotic chromosome, the 30-nm fiber must be compacted in length another 100-fold (see below).

In **interphase chromosomes,** chromatin fibers appear to be organized into 30–100 thousand base-pair **loops or domains** anchored in a scaffolding (or supporting matrix) within the nucleus. Within these domains, the DNA sequences are located nonrandomly; repetitive DNA (see below) is enriched near the proximal or anchored regions of the loops. Each looped domain of chromatin may correspond to a separate genetic function, containing both coding and noncoding regions of the gene.

Active Chromatin

Generally, every cell of an individual metazoan organism contains the same genetic information in the form of the same DNA sequences. Thus, the differences between different cell types within an organism must be explained by differential expression of the common genetic information. Chromatin containing active genes (ie, transcriptionally active chromatin) has been shown to differ in several ways from that of nonactive regions. The nucleosome structure of active chromatin appears to be altered or even absent in highly active regions. DNA in active chromatin contains large regions (about 100,000 bases long) that are **sensitive to digestion by a nuclease** such as DNase I. The sensitivity to DNase I of chromatin regions being actively transcribed reflects only a potential for transcription rather than transcription itself and in several systems can be correlated with a relative lack of 5-methyldeoxycytidine in the DNA. To a great extent, the altered structure appears to result from the local presence of the nonhistone proteins HMG (high-mobility group) 14 and 17, which may replace the H1 histone in the internucleosomal regions. The presence of **HMG 14 and 17** can reversibly sensitize genes to DNase I. HMG 14 and 17 are highly conserved proteins found throughout vertebrate organisms, where they appear in active chromatin.

Within the large regions of active chromatin there exist shorter stretches of 100–300 nucleotides that exhibit an even greater (another 10-fold) sensitivity to DNase I. These **hypersensitive sites** probably result from the existence of regions of single-stranded DNA immediately upstream from the active gene, regions that may be effected by the presence of so-called enhancer elements (see Chapters 29 and 31). In many cases, it seems that if a gene is capable of being transcribed, it must have a DNase hypersensitive site in the chromatin immediately upstream. Perhaps the hypersensitive sites provide proteins involved in gene transcription with the necessary **access to the template strand.**

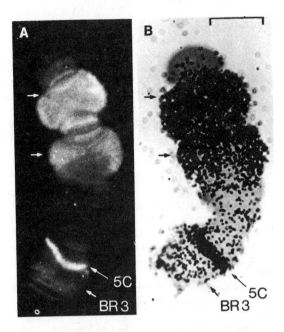

Figure 28–5. *A:* Distribution of RNA polymerase detected by immunofluorescence in isolated chromosome IV from a salivary gland from a *Chironomus tentans* larva exposed to a heat shock (39 °C, 30 minutes). The 5C and BR3 are specific bands of chromosome IV. *B:* Autoradiogram of a chromosome IV that was labeled with ³H-uridine for 5 minutes immediately after the heat shock (39 °C, 30 minutes). Exposure time, 14 days. Bar = 7 μm. (Reproduced, with permission, from Sass H: RNA polymerase B in polytene chromosomes. *Cell* 1982;28:274. Copyright © 1982 by the Massachusetts Institute of Technology.)

Transcriptionally inactive chromatin is more densely packed during interphase as observed by electron microscopic studies and is referred to as **heterochromatin;** transcriptionally active chromatin stains less densely and is referred to as **euchromatin.** Generally, euchromatin is replicated earlier in the mammalian cell cycle (see below) than is heterochromatin.

There are 2 types of heterochromatin, constitutive heterochromatin and facultative heterochromatin. **Constitutive heterochromatin** is always condensed and, thus, inactive. Constitutive heterochromatin is found in the regions near the chromosomal centromere and at chromosomal ends (telomeres). **Facultative heterochromatin** is at times condensed, but at other times it is actively transcribed and, thus, uncondensed and appearing as euchromatin. Of the 2 members of the X chromosome pair in mammalian females, one X chromosome is almost completely inactive transcriptionally and is heterochromatic. However, during gametogenesis the heterochromatic X chromosome decondenses and becomes transcriptionally active during early embryogenesis; thus, it is facultative heterochromatin.

Certain cells of insects, eg, *Chironomus,* contain giant chromosomes that have been replicated for 10 cycles without separation of daughter chromatids.

These copies of DNA line up side by side in precise register and produce a banded chromosome containing regions of condensed chromatin and lighter bands of more extended chromatin. Transcriptionally active regions of these **polytene chromosomes** are especially decondensed into **"puffs,"** which can be shown to contain the enzymes responsible for transcription and to be the sites of RNA synthesis (Fig 28–5).

Chromosomes

At metaphase, mammalian **chromosomes** possess a 2-fold symmetry, with identical **sister chromatids** connected at a **centromere,** the relative position of which is characteristic for a given chromosome (Fig 28–6). Each sister chromatid probably contains one double-stranded DNA molecule. During interphase, the packing of the DNA molecule is less dense than it is in the condensed chromosome during the metaphase. Metaphase chromosomes are transcriptionally **inactive.**

The human haploid genome consists of 3.5×10^9 base pairs or pairs of nucleotides extending over 1.7×10^7 nucleosomes. Thus, each of the 23 chromatids in the human haploid genome would contain on the average 1.5×10^8 nucleotides in one double-stranded DNA molecule. The length of each DNA molecule must be **compressed about 8000-fold** to generate the structure of a condensed metaphase chromosome. In metaphase chromosomes, the 25- to 30-nm chromatin

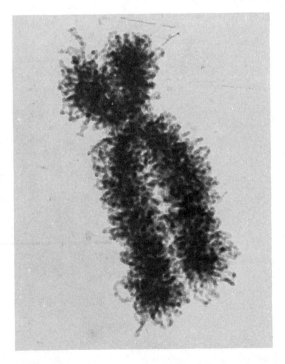

Figure 28–6. The 2 sister chromatids of human chromosome 12. × 27,850. (Reproduced, with permission, from DuPraw EJ: *DNA and Chromosomes.* Holt, Rinehart, & Winston, 1970.)

Table 28–1. The packing ratios of each of the orders of DNA structure.

Chromatin Form	Packing Ratio
Bare double-helix DNA	≡ 1.0
~ 2 turns of DNA on nucleosome	2.5
10-nm fibril of nucleosomes	5
25- to 30-nm chromatin fiber of superhelical nucleosomes	30
Condensed metaphase chromosome of loops	8000

fibers are also folded into a series of **looped domains,** the proximal portions of which are anchored to a nonhistone proteinaceous scaffolding. The packing ratios of each of the orders of DNA structure are summarized in Table 28–1.

The packaging of nucleoproteins within chromatids is not random, as evidenced by the characteristic patterns observed when chromosomes are stained with specific dyes such as quinacrine or Giemsa's stain (Fig 28–7).

From individual to individual within a single species, the pattern of staining (banding) of the entire chromosome complement is highly reproducible; nonetheless, it differs significantly from other species, even those closely related. Thus, the packaging of the nucleoproteins in chromosomes of higher eukaryotes must in some way be dependent upon species-specific characteristics of the DNA molecules.

GENETIC ORGANIZATION OF THE MAMMALIAN GENOME

The **diploid** genome of each human cell consists of 7×10^9 base pairs of DNA, subdivided into 23 pairs of chromosomes. The entire diploid genome contains sufficient DNA to code for nearly 3 million pairs of genes. However, studies of mutation rates and of the complexities of the genomes of higher organisms strongly suggest that humans have only about 30–100 thousand essential proteins. This implies that most of the DNA is noncoding; ie, its information is never translated into an amino acid sequence of a protein molecule. Certainly, some of the excess DNA sequences serve to regulate the expression of genes during development, differentiation, and adaptation to the environment. Some excess clearly makes up the intervening sequences that split the coding regions of genes, but most of the excess appears to be composed of many families of repeated sequences for which no functions have been clearly defined.

Intervening Sequences in Coding Regions

The coding regions of DNA, the transcripts of which ultimately appear in the cytoplasm as single mRNA molecules, **are interrupted in the genome by large intervening sequences of noncoding DNA.** Accordingly, the primary transcripts of DNA—hnRNA—contain noncoding intervening sequences of RNA that must be removed in a process which also joins together the appropriate coding segments to form

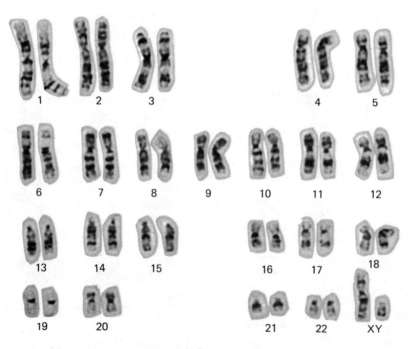

Figure 28–7. A human karyotype (of a man with a normal 46 XY constitution), in which the chromosomes have been stained by the Giemsa method and aligned according to the Paris Convention. (Courtesy of Helen Lawce and Dr Felix Conte, Department of Pediatrics, University of California School of Medicine, San Francisco.)

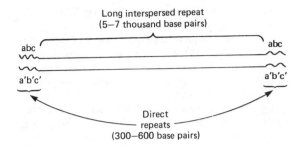

Figure 28–8. Representation of a long interspersed repeated sequence with its short direct repeat sequences (abc) and complements (a'b'c') indicated at the termini.

the mature mRNA. Most coding sequences for a single mRNA are interrupted in the genome (and thus in the primary transcript) by at least one—and as many as 50 in some cases—noncoding intervening sequences (**introns**). In most cases the **introns** are much longer than the continuous coding regions (**exons**).

The function of the intervening sequences or introns is not clear. They may serve to separate functional domains (exons) of coding information in a form that permits genetic rearrangement by recombination to occur more rapidly than if all coding regions for a given genetic function were contiguous. Such an enhanced rate of genetic rearrangement of functional domains might allow more rapid evolution of biologic function.

Repetitive Sequences in DNA

Eukaryotic DNA contains different "sequence classes" whose members can be broadly classified as (1) unique, (2) moderately repetitive, or (3) highly repetitive. Most DNA sequences coding for proteins fall within the **unique sequence** category. In human DNA, approximately 20–30% of the genome consists of repetitive sequences.

The **highly repetitive sequences** consist of 5–500 base-pair lengths usually **clustered** in centromeres and telomeres of the chromosome and are present in about 1–10 million copies per haploid genome. These sequences are transcriptionally inactive and may play a structural role in the chromosome.

The **moderately repetitive sequences,** which are defined as being present at less than 10^6 copies per haploid genome, are not clustered but are interspersed with unique sequences and can be categorized as being long or short in length. The **long interspersed repeats** are 5–7 thousand base pairs in length and are present at 1–100 thousand copies per haploid genome. These long interspersed repeats are flanked on either side by 300–600 base-pair **direct repeats** that closely resemble the **long terminal repeats** (LTR) at the ends of integrated retrovirus DNAs (Fig 28–8). In many cases, these long interspersed repeats are transcribed by **RNA polymerase II** and contain caps indistinguishable from those on mRNA.

The **short interspersed repeats** are families of related but individually distinct members that consist of a few to several hundred nucleotide pairs. The short interspersed repeats are actively transcribed either as integral components of introns or by DNA-dependent RNA polymerase III (see Chapter 29) as discrete elements. Of the short interspersed repeats in the human genome, one family, the **Alu family,** is present in about 500 thousand copies per haploid genome and accounts for at least 3–6% of the human genome. Members of the human Alu family and their closely related analogs in other animals are transcribed as integral components of hnRNA or as discrete RNA molecules, including the well-studied 4.5S RNA and 7S RNA. These particular family members are highly conserved within a species as well as between mammalian species (Fig 28–9). The structures of the short interspersed repeats, including the members of the Alu family, resemble the retroviral long terminal repeat (LTR) itself and are likely to be mobile elements, capable of jumping into and out of various sites within the genome (see below).

ALTERATION & REARRANGEMENT OF GENETIC MATERIAL

An alteration in the sequence of purine and pyrimidine bases in a gene due to a change, a removal, or an insertion of one or more bases may result in an altered gene product that in most instances ultimately is a protein. Such alteration in the genetic material

5′ <u>AAAAGGAAACTTGGAAAGGA</u>GCTGGAGAGATGGCTCGAGGTTAAGAGCACCAACTGCTGTTCCAGAGGTCCTGAGTTC

AATTCCCAGCAACCACATGGTGGCTCATAACAATCTATAATGAGATCTGGTGCCCTCTTCTGGTGTGCAGATATATATGG

AAGCAGAATGTTGTATACA↓TAATAAATAAATAAAATCTTAAAAAAA<u>AAAAGGAAACTTGGAAAGGA</u> 3′

Figure 28–9. A composite sequence of a short interspersed repetitive DNA element containing a part of the Chinese hamster Alu equivalent sequence. On the 3′ side of residue 107 is another sequence of 96 residues unrelated to the Alu sequence. To the 3′ side of the arrow is an A-rich region of the structure $TA_2TA_3TA_3TA_4TCTTA_7$. The entire structure is flanked on either side by 20-residue direct repeats, indicated by continuous underlining. (Reproduced, with permission, from Haynes SR et al: The Chinese hamster Alu-equivalent sequence: A conserved, highly repetitious, interspersed deoxyribonucleic acid sequence in mammals has a structure suggestive of a transposable element. *Mol Cell Biol* 1981;**1**:573.)

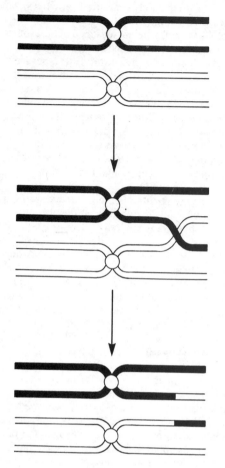

Figure 28–10. The process of crossing-over between homologous chromosomes to generate recombinant chromosomes.

results in a **mutation,** the consequences of which are discussed in detail in Chapter 30.

Prokaryotic and eukaryotic organisms are capable of exchanging genetic information between similar or homologous chromosomes. The exchange or **recombination** event occurs primarily during meiosis in mammalian cells and requires alignment of homologous chromosomes, an alignment that almost always occurs with great exactness. A process of crossing-over occurs as shown in Fig 28–10. This usually results in an equal and reciprocal exchange of genetic information between homologous chromosomes. If the homologous chromosomes possess different alleles of the same genes, the crossover may produce noticeable and heritable genetic linkage differences. In the rare case where the alignment of homologous chromosomes is not exact, the crossing-over or recombination event may result in an unequal exchange of information. One chromosome may receive less genetic material and thus a deletion, while the other partner of the chromosome pair receives more genetic material and thus an insertion or duplication (Fig 28–10). Unequal crossing-over does occur in humans, as evidenced by the existence of hemoglobins designated Lepore and anti-Lepore. **Unequal crossover** affects tandem arrays of repeated DNAs whether they are related globin genes, as in Fig 28–11, or more abundant repetitive DNA. The unequal crossover through slippage in the pairing can result in expansion or contraction in the copy number of the repeat family and may contribute to the expansion and fixation of variant members throughout the array.

Some bacterial viruses (bacteriophages) are capable of recombining with the DNA of a bacterial host in such a way that the genetic information of the bacteriophage is incorporated in a linear fashion into the genetic information of the host. This integration or

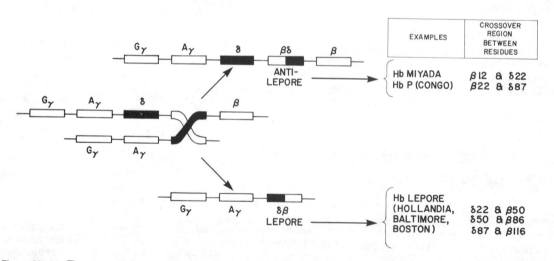

Figure 28–11. The process of unequal crossover in the region of the mammalian genome that harbors the structural genes for hemoglobin and the generation of the unequal recombinant products hemoglobin delta-beta Lepore and beta-delta anti-Lepore. The examples given show the locations of the crossover regions between amino acid residues. (Redrawn and reproduced, with permission, from Clegg JB, Weatherall DJ: β° Thalassemia: Time for a reappraisal? *Lancet* 1974;2:133.)

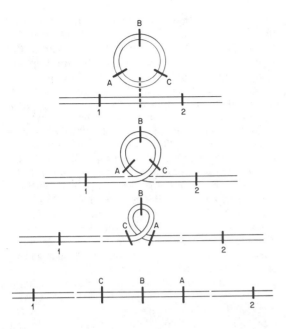

Figure 28–12. The integration of a circular genome (with genes A, B, and C) into the DNA molecule of a host (with genes 1 and 2) and the consequent ordering of the genes.

transposition, which is a form of recombination, occurs by the mechanism simplified in Fig 28–12. The backbone of the circular bacteriophage genome is broken, as is that of the DNA molecule of the host; the appropriate ends are resealed with the proper polarity. The bacteriophage DNA is figuratively straightened out ("linearized") as it is integrated into the bacterial DNA molecule—frequently a closed circle as well. The site at which the bacteriophage genome integrates or recombines with the bacterial genome is chosen by one of 2 mechanisms. If the bacteriophage contains a DNA sequence **homologous** to a sequence in the host DNA molecule, then a recombination event analogous to that occurring between homologous chromosomes can occur. However, some bacteriophages synthesize proteins that bind specific sites on bacterial chromosomes with a nonhomologous site specifically of the bacteriophage DNA molecule. Integration occurs at the site and is said to be **"site-specific."**

Many animal viruses, particularly the oncogenic viruses—either directly or, in the case of RNA viruses, their DNA transcripts—can be integrated into chromosomes of the mammalian cell. The integration of the animal virus into the animal genome is not "site-specific." In eukaryotic cells, small DNA elements that clearly are not viruses are capable of transposing themselves in and out of the host genome in ways that affect the function of neighboring DNA sequences. These mobile elements can carry flanking regions of DNA and, therefore, profoundly affect evolution. As mentioned above, the Alu family of moderately repeated DNA sequences has structural characteristics similar to the termini of retroviruses

that account for the ability of the latter to move into and out of the mammalian genome.

Direct evidence for the transposition of small DNA elements into the human genome has been provided by the discovery of "processed genes" for immunoglobulin molecules and α-globin molecules. These **processed genes** consist of deoxynucleotide sequences identical or nearly identical to those of the messenger RNA for the appropriate gene product. That is, the 5′ nontranscribed region, the coding region without intron representation, and the 3′ poly(A) tail are all present contiguously. This particular DNA sequence arrangement must have resulted from the reverse transcription of an appropriately processed messenger RNA molecule from which the intron regions had been removed and the poly(A) tail added. The only recognized mechanism that this reverse transcript could have used to integrate into the genome would have been a transposition event. In fact, these "processed genes" have short terminal repeats at each end, as do known transposed sequences in lower organisms. Some of the processed genes have been randomly altered through evolution so that they now contain nonsense codons that preclude their expression (see Chapter 30). Thus, they are referred to as **"pseudogenes."**

Besides unequal crossover and transposition, a third mechanism can effect rapid changes in the genetic material. Similar sequences on homologous or nonhomologous chromosomes may occasionally pair up and eliminate any mismatched sequences between them. This may lead to the accidental fixation of one variant or another throughout a family of repeated sequences and thereby homogenize the sequences of the members of repetitive DNA families. This latter process is referred to as **gene conversion.**

In diploid eukaryotic organisms such as humans, after cells progress through the S phase they contain a tetraploid content of DNA. This is in the form of sister chromatids of chromosome pairs. Each of these sister chromatids contains identical genetic information, since each is a product of the semiconservative replication of the original parent DNA molecule of that chromosome. Crossing-over occurs between these genetically identical sister chromatids. Of course, these **sister chromatid exchanges** (Fig 28–13) have no genetic consequence so long as the exchange is the result of an equal crossover.

In mammalian cells, some interesting gene rearrangements occur normally during development and differentiation. For example, in mice the V_L and C_L genes for a single immunoglobulin molecule (see Chapters 31 and 45) are widely separated in the germ line DNA. In the DNA of a differentiated immunoglobulin-producing (plasma) cell, the same V_L and C_L genes have been moved physically closer together in the genome. However, even then, this rearrangement of DNA during differentiation does not bring the V_L and C_L genes into contiguity in the DNA. Instead, the DNA contains an interspersed or interruption sequence of about 1200 base pairs at or near the junction of the V

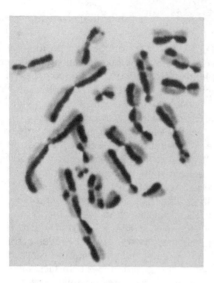

Figure 28–13. Sister chromatid exchanges between human chromosomes. These are detectable by Giemsa staining of the chromosomes of cells replicated for 2 cycles in the presence of bromodeoxyuridine. (Courtesy of Dr Sheldon Wolff and Judy Bodycote, Laboratory of Radiobiology and Department of Anatomy, University of California School of Medicine, San Francisco.)

and C regions. The interspersed sequence is transcribed into RNA along with the V_L and C_L genes, and the interspersed information is removed from the RNA during its nuclear processing (see Chapters 29 and 31).

DNA SYNTHESIS & REPLICATION

The primary function of DNA replication is understood to be the provision of progeny with the genetic information possessed by the parent. Thus, the replication of DNA must be complete and carried out with **high fidelity to maintain genetic stability** within the organism and the species. The process of DNA replication is complex and involves many cellular functions and several verification procedures to ensure fidelity in replication. The first enzymologic observations on DNA replication were made in *Escherichia coli* by Arthur Kornberg, who described in that organism the existence of an enzyme now called DNA polymerase I. This enzyme has multiple catalytic activities, a complex structure, and a requirement for the triphosphates of the 4 deoxyribonucleosides of adenine, guanine, cytosine, and thymine. The polymerization reaction catalyzed by DNA polymerase I of *E coli* has served as a prototype for all DNA polymerases of both prokaryotes and eukaryotes, even though it is now recognized that the major role of this polymerase is to ensure fidelity and to repair rather than to replicate DNA.

The initiation of DNA synthesis (Fig 28–14) is surprisingly complex, requiring priming by a **short link of RNA,** about 10 nucleotides in length. This priming process involves the **nucleophilic attack by the 3′-hydroxyl group of the RNA primer to the alpha phosphate of the deoxynucleoside triphosphate** with the splitting off of pyrophosphate. The 3′-hydroxyl group of the recently attached deoxyribonucleoside monophosphate is then free to carry out a nucleophilic attack on the next entering deoxyribonucleoside triphosphate, again at its alpha phosphate moiety, with the splitting off of pyrophosphate. Of course, the selection of the proper deoxyribonucleotide whose terminal 3′-hydroxyl group is to be attacked is dependent upon **proper pairing with the other (template) strand** of the DNA molecule according to the rules proposed originally by Watson and Crick (Fig 28–15). When an adenine deoxyribonucleoside monophosphoryl moiety is in the template position, a thymidine triphosphate will enter and its alpha phosphate will be attacked by the 3′-hydroxyl group of the deoxyribonucleoside monophosphoryl most recently added to the polymer. By this stepwise process, the template dictates which deoxyribonucleoside triphosphate is complementary and by hydrogen bonding holds it in place while the 3′-hydroxyl group of the growing strand attacks and incorporates the new nucleotide into the polymer. These fragments of DNA attached to an RNA initiator component, discovered by Okazaki, are referred to as **Okazaki pieces** (Fig 28–16). In mammals, after many Okazaki pieces are generated, the replication complex begins to remove the RNA primers, to fill in the gaps left by their removal with the proper base-paired deoxynucleotide, and then to seal the fragments of newly synthesized DNA by enzymes referred to as **DNA ligases.**

As has already been noted, DNA molecules are double-stranded and the 2 strands are antiparallel, ie, running in opposite directions. The replication of DNA in prokaryotes and eukaryotes occurs on **both strands simultaneously.** However, an enzyme capable of polymerizing DNA in the 3′ to 5′ direction does not exist in any organism, so that both of the newly replicated DNA strands cannot grow in the same direction simultaneously. Nevertheless, the same enzyme appears to replicate both strands at the same time. The single enzyme replicates **one strand ("leading strand") in a continuous manner in the 5′ to 3′ direction,** with the same overall forward direction. It replicates the **other strand ("lagging strand") discontinuously** by "turning its back," as it were, in the overall direction of replication, while polymerizing the nucleotides in short spurts of 150–250 nucleotides again in the 5′ to 3′ direction, but at the same time it faces toward the back end of the preceding RNA primer rather than toward the unreplicated portion. This process of semidiscontinuous DNA synthesis is shown diagrammatically in Fig 28–17.

In the mammalian nuclear genome, all of the RNA primers are eventually removed as part of the replication process, whereas after replication of the mitochondrial genome the small piece of RNA remains as an integral part of the closed circular DNA structure.

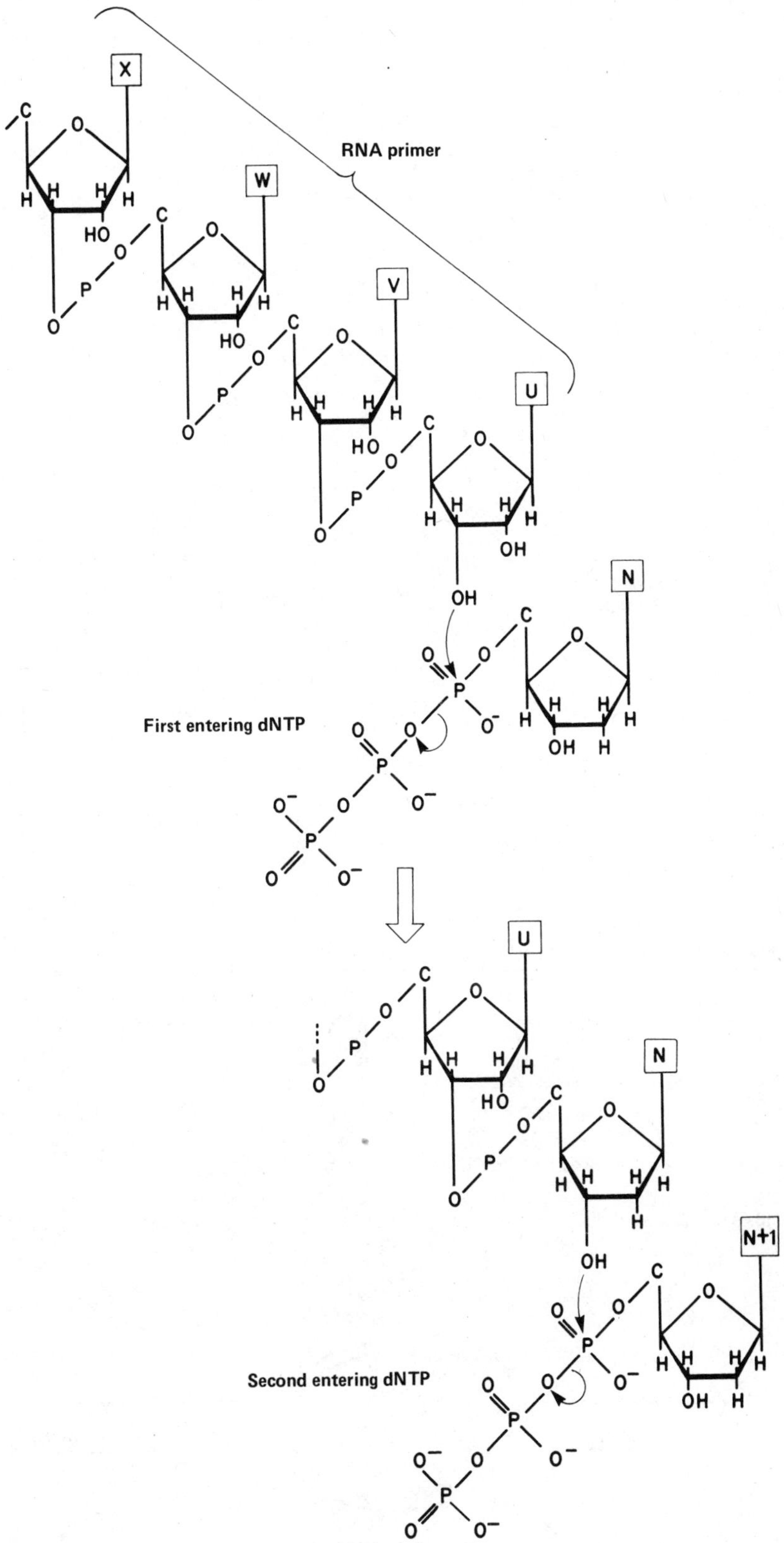

Figure 28–14. The initiation of DNA synthesis upon a primer of RNA and the subsequent attachment of the second deoxyribonucleoside triphosphate.

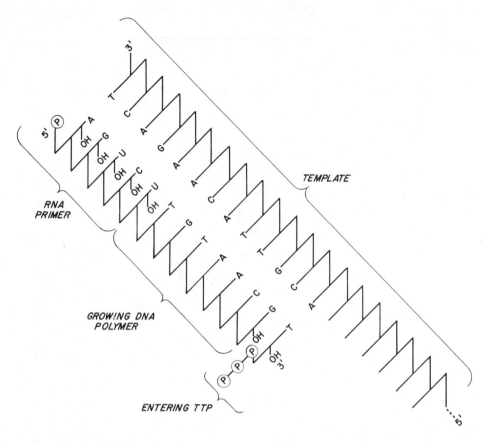

Figure 28-15. The synthesis of DNA on an RNA primer demonstrating the template function of the complementary strand of parental DNA.

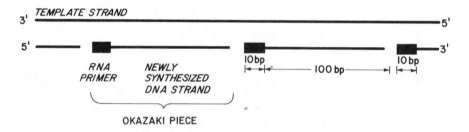

Figure 28-16. The discontinuous polymerization of deoxyribonucleotides and formation of Okazaki pieces.

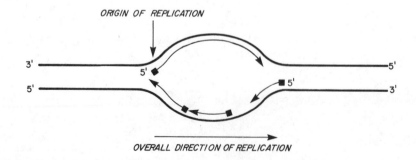

Figure 28-17. The process of semidiscontinuous, simultaneous replication of both strands of double-stranded DNA.

In mammalian cells, there is one class of DNA polymerase enzymes, called maxi (large) polymerase or **polymerase alpha,** which is present in the nucleus and responsible for chromosome replication. One polymerase alpha molecule is capable of polymerizing about 100 nucleotides per second, a rate 10-fold less than the rate of polymerization of deoxynucleotides by the bacterial DNA polymerase. This reduced rate almost certainly results from the interference by nucleosomes that do remain attached to DNA during its replication, perhaps all remaining attached to the leading strand. Newly synthesized core histones in the octameric form would then attach to the other strand as the replication fork progresses.

A lower-molecular-weight polymerase, mini polymerase or **polymerase beta,** is also present in mammalian nuclei but is not responsible for the usual DNA replication. It may function in DNA repair (see below). Mitochondrial DNA polymerase, **polymerase gamma,** is responsible for replication of the mitochondrial genome, another DNA molecule that exists in circular form.

To replicate the entire mammalian genome in 9 hours, the average period required for formation of a tetraploid genome from a diploid genome in a replicating cell, there are on the chromosomes **multiple origins** of DNA replication that occur in clusters of up to 100 of these replication units. Replication occurs in **both directions** up and down the chromosome and on both strands simultaneously. This replication process generates ''replication bubbles'' (Fig 28–18).

The multiple sites that serve as origins for DNA replication in eukaryotes are poorly defined except in a few animal viruses. However, it is clear that initiation is regulated both spacially and temporally, since clusters of adjacent sites initiate synchronously. There are suggestions that functional domains of chromatin replicate as intact units, implying that the origins of replication are specifically located with respect to transcription units. This suggests that replication may occur at the bases of the loops where chromatin fibers attach to the matrix of interphase nuclei.

During the replication of the double-stranded helix of DNA, there must be a separation of the 2

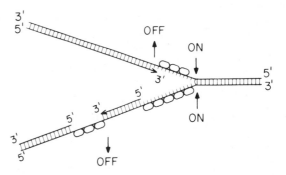

Figure 28–19. Hypothetical scheme for single-strand binding protein action at a replicating fork. The protein is recycled after binding single-stranded regions of the template and facilitating replication. (Courtesy of Professor B Alberts, Department of Biochemistry, University of California School of Medicine, San Francisco.)

strands to allow each to serve as a template by hydrogen bonding its nucleotide bases to the incoming deoxynucleoside triphosphate. The separation of the DNA double helix is promoted by specific protein molecules that **stabilize the single-stranded structure** as the replication fork progresses. These stabilizing proteins bind stoichiometrically to the single strands without interfering with the abilities of the nucleobases to serve as templates (Fig 28–19). In addition to separating the 2 strands of the double helix, there must be an **unwinding** of the molecule (once every 10 nucleotide pairs) to allow the rewinding of the newly formed semiconserved DNA replicas. Given the time during which DNA replication must occur in prokaryotes, it can be calculated that the molecule must unwind at approximately 400,000 turns per second, which is clearly an impossible feat. Thus, there must be multiple ''swivels'' interspersed in the DNA molecules of all organisms. The swivel function is provided by specific enzymes that introduce **''nicks'' in one strand of the unwinding double helix,** thereby allowing the unwinding process to proceed. The nicks are quickly resealed without requiring

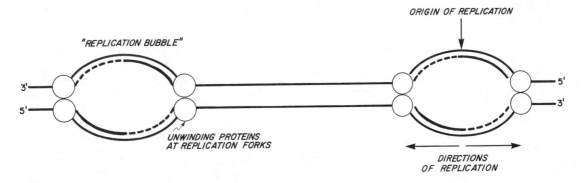

Figure 28–18. The generation of ''replication bubbles'' during the process of DNA synthesis. The bidirectional replication and the proposed positions of unwinding proteins at the replication forks are depicted.

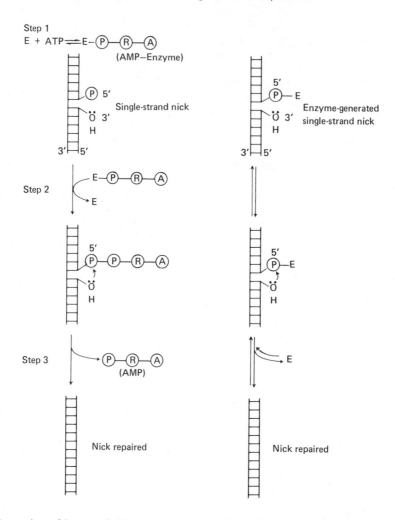

Figure 28–20. Comparison of 2 types of nick-sealing reactions on DNA. The series of reactions at left is catalyzed by DNA ligase; that at right by DNA topoisomerase I. (Slightly modified and reproduced, with permission, from Lehninger AL: *Biochemistry,* 2nd ed. Worth, 1975.)

energy input, because of the formation of a high-energy covalent bond between the nicked phosphodiester backbone and the nicking-sealing enzyme. This process is depicted diagrammatically in Fig 28–20 and there compared to the ATP-dependent resealing carried out by the DNA ligases. The nicking-resealing enzymes are called DNA **topoisomerases** and are also capable of unwinding supercoiled DNA. Supercoiled DNA is a higher-ordered structure occurring in circular (or extraordinarily long) DNA molecules wrapped around a core, as depicted in Fig 28–21.

It has been discovered that there exists in one species of animal viruses (retroviruses) a class of enzymes capable of synthesizing a single-stranded and then a double-stranded DNA molecule from a single-stranded RNA template. This polymerase, RNA-dependent DNA polymerase or **"reverse transcriptase"** first synthesizes a DNA-RNA hybrid molecule utilizing the RNA genome as a template. A specific enzyme, RNase H, degrades the RNA strand, and the remaining DNA strand in turn serves as a template to form a double-stranded DNA molecule containing the information originally present in the RNA genome of the animal virus.

Regulation of DNA Synthesis

In animal cells, including human cells, the replication of the DNA genome occurs only at specified times during the life span of the cell. These periods are referred to as synthetic or S phases. They are usually temporally separated from the mitotic phase by non-synthetic periods referred to as gap 1 (G_1) and gap 2 (G_2), occurring before and after the S phase, respectively (Fig 28–22). The cell regulates its DNA synthesis grossly by allowing it to occur only at specific times and mostly in cells preparing to divide by a mitotic process. The regulation of the entry of a cell into an S phase involves cyclic purine nucleotides and perhaps the substrates for DNA synthesis, but the mechanisms

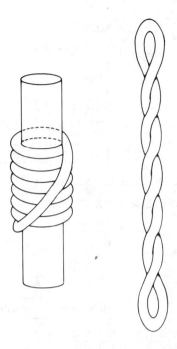

Figure 28–21. Supercoiling of DNA. A left-handed toroidal (selenoidal) supercoil, at left, will convert to a right-handed interwound supercoil, at right, when the cylindric core is removed. Such a transition is analogous to that which occurs when nucleosomes are disrupted by the high salt extraction of histones from chromatin.

are unknown. Many of the cancer-causing viruses (oncoviruses) are capable of alleviating or disrupting the apparent restriction that normally controls the entry of mammalian cells from G_1 into the S phase. Again, this mechanism is currently unknown but probably involves the phosphorylation of specific host protein molecules.

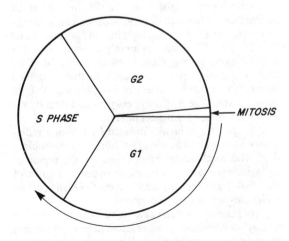

Figure 28–22. Mammalian cell cycle. The DNA synthetic phase (S phase) is separated from mitosis by gap 1 (G_1) and gap 2 (G_2). (Arrow indicates direction of cell progression.)

During the S phase, mammalian cells contain greater quantities of polymerase alpha than during the nonsynthetic phases of the cell cycle. Furthermore, those enzymes responsible for the formation of the substrates for DNA synthesis, ie, deoxyribonucleoside triphosphates, are also increased in activity, and their activity will diminish following the synthetic phase until the reappearance of the signal for renewed DNA synthesis. During S phase, the nuclear DNA is **completely replicated once and only once.** It seems that once chromatin has been replicated, it is marked so as to prevent its further replication until it again passes through mitosis. It has been suggested that DNA methylation may serve as such a covalent marker.

In general, a given pair of chromosomes will replicate simultaneously and within a fixed portion of the S phase upon every replication. On a chromosome, clusters of replication units replicate coordinately. The nature of the signals that regulate DNA synthesis at these levels is unknown, but the regulation does appear to be an intrinsic property of each individual chromosome.

Degradation & Repair of DNA

The maintenance of the integrity of the information in DNA molecules is of utmost importance to the survival of a particular organism as well as to survival of the species. Thus, it might be concluded that surviving species must have evolved mechanisms for repairing DNA damage incurred as a result of either replication errors or environmental insults. It has been estimated that DNA replication and environmentally induced DNA damage result in an average of about 6 nucleotide changes per year in the human germ line. Presumably, at least that number of nucleotide changes or mutations must occur per year in the somatic cells as well.

As described in Chapter 27, the major responsibility for the fidelity of replication resides in the specific pairing of nucleotide bases. Proper pairing is dependent upon the presence of the favored tautomers of the purine and pyrimidine nucleotides (see Fig 25–4), but the equilibrium wherein one tautomer is more stable than another is only about 10^4 or 10^5 in favor of that with the greater stability. Although this is not sufficiently favorable to ensure the high fidelity that is necessary, the favoring of the preferred tautomers, and thus of the proper base pairing, could be assured by monitoring the base pairing twice. Such double monitoring does appear to occur in both bacterial and mammalian systems: once at the time of insertion of the deoxyribonucleoside triphosphates, and later by a follow-up, energy-requiring mechanism which removes all improper bases that may occur in the newly formed strand. This double monitoring does not permit errors of mispairing due to the presence of the unfavored tautomers to occur more frequently than once every 10^8–10^{10} base pairs. The molecule responsible for this monitoring mechanism in *E coli* is the built-in $3' \rightarrow 5'$ exonuclease activity of DNA polymerase, but mammalian DNA polymerases do not clearly possess such a nuclease "editing" function. It is interesting to note that an enzyme which can self-prime or start a chain de novo cannot effectively self-correct the first nucleotide base-pairing event by such an exonuclease editing function. Thus, it does not seem unreasonable that ribonucleotides rather than deoxyribonucleotides serve as a primer for DNA synthesis, since the former automatically mark those sequences as a "bad" or "risky" copy that is to be subsequently removed.

Damage to DNA by environmental, physical, and chemical agents may be classified into 4 types (Table 28–2). The damaged regions of DNA may be **repaired, replaced** by recombination, or **retained.** Retention leads to mutations and, potentially, cell death. Repair and replacement exploit the redundancy of information inherent in the double helical DNA structure. The defective region in one strand can be returned to its original form by relying on the complementary information stored in the unaffected strand.

The key to all of the repair or recombinational processes is the initial **recognition of the defect** and either repairing it during the recognition step or marking it for future attention. The **depurination** of DNA, which happens spontaneously owing to the thermal lability of the purine N-glycosidic bond, occurs at a rate of 5–10 thousand/cell/d at 37 °C. Specific enzymes recognize a depurinated site and replace the appropriate purine directly, without interruption of the phosphodiester backbone.

Both cytosine and adenine bases in DNA spontaneously **deaminate** to form uracil and hypoxanthine, respectively. Since neither uracil nor hypoxanthine normally exists in DNA, it is not surprising that specific N-glycosylases can recognize these abnormal bases and remove the base itself from the DNA. This removal marks the site of the defect and allows an apurinic or apyrimidinic endonuclease to incise the appropriate backbone near the defect. Subsequently, the sequential actions of an exonuclease, a repair DNA polymerase, and a ligase return the DNA to its original state (Fig 28–23). This series of events is called

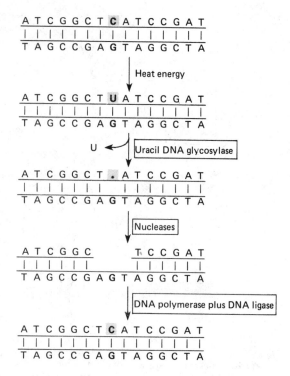

Figure 28–23. The enzyme uracil DNA glycosylase removes the uracil created by spontaneous deamination of cytosine in the DNA. (Courtesy of Professor B Alberts, Department of Biochemistry, University of California School of Medicine, San Francisco.)

Table 28–2. Types of damage to DNA.

I.   **Single-base alteration**
   A. Depurination
   B. Deamination of cytosine to uracil
   C. Deamination of adenine to hypoxanthine
   D. Alkylation of base
   E. Insertion or deletion of nucleotide
   F. Base-analog incorporation
II. **Two-base alteration**
   A. UV light–induced thymine-thymine dimer
   B. Bifunctional alkylating agent cross-linkage
III. **Chain breaks**
   A. Ionizing radiation
   B. Radioactive disintegration of backbone element
IV. **Cross-linkage**
   A. Between bases in same or opposite strands
   B. Between DNA and protein molecules (eg, histones)

excision-repair. By a similar series of steps involving initially the recognition of the defect, alkylated bases and base analogs can be removed from DNA and the DNA returned to its original informational content.

The repair of insertions or deletions of nucleotides normally occurs by recombinational mechanisms either with or without replication.

Ultraviolet light induces the formation of pyrimidine-pyrimidine dimers, predominantly the dimerization of 2 juxtaposed thymines in the same strand (Fig 28–24). There are apparently 2 mechanisms for removing or repairing these thymine-thymine dimers. One is excision-repair analogous to that described above. The second mechanism involves visible light photoactivation of a specific enzyme that directly reverses the dimer formation in situ.

Single-strand breaks induced by ionizing radiation can be repaired by direct ligation or by recombination. The mechanisms responsible for the repair of cross-linkages between bases on opposite strands of the DNA double helix or between the DNA and protein molecules are poorly understood.

In general, damage caused by ionizing radiation and by alkylation of bases is repaired in short patches of excision and resynthesis. Ultraviolet light damage and strand cross-linkages are repaired by long patches of excision and resynthesis. In mammalian cells, repair replication can be observed as **unscheduled DNA**

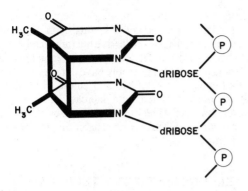

Figure 28–24. A thymine-thymine dimer formed via a cyclobutane moiety between juxtaposed thymine residues of DNA.

synthesis, ie, incorporation of DNA precursors (radioactive thymidine) into DNA when a cell is not in S phase.

Associated with the increased excision-repair activity in response to DNA damaging agents, mammalian cells exhibit increased activity of the enzyme **poly(ADP-ribose) polymerase.** This enzyme uses the coenzyme NAD^+ to ADP-ribosylate chromatin proteins. It adds mostly mono(ADP-ribose), but to some extent homopolymeric chains of ADP-ribose are

added. It is not evident what function poly(ADP-ribose) polymerase or its product, $(ADP\text{-}ribose)_n$, has in the excision-repair process. There is a temporal relationship between the increased repair activity and the increased specific enzyme. Furthermore, inhibition of the enzyme by specific inhibitors prevents the rejoining of broken DNA strands. The increased activity of poly(ADP-ribose) polymerase appears to be a response to DNA fragmentation in the nucleus. This fragmentation might be induced primarily by physical agents such as x-ray, or secondarily by the incision mechanism responding to other chemical or physical agents such as ultraviolet light or alkylating agents. The activity of the polymerase is sufficiently great to cause a depletion of intracellular NAD^+ following environmentally induced DNA damage.

Xeroderma pigmentosum is an autosomal recessive genetic disease. The clinical syndrome includes marked sensitivity to sunlight (ultraviolet) with subsequent formation of multiple skin cancers and premature death. The inherited defect seems to involve the repair of damaged DNA. Cells cultured from patients with xeroderma pigmentosum exhibit low activity for the photoactivated thymine dimer cleavage process. However, the involved DNA repair processes in this disease are quite complex; there are at least 7 genetic complementation groups.

Table 28–3. Substrate specificities of some type II restriction endonucleases.[*]

Enzyme	Sequence	Number of Cleavage Sites			Microorganism
		λ	Ad2	SV40	
Hap II	CCGG	>50	>50	1	*Haemophilus aphrophilus*
Bsu I	GGCC	>50	>50	18	*Bacillus subtilis* strain X5
Alu I	AGCT	>50	>50	32	*Arthrobacter luteus*
Eco RII	CCTGG	>35	>35	16	*Escherichia coli* R245
Eco RII	CCAGG	>35	>35	16	*Escherichia coli* R245
Hind III	AAGCTT	6	11	6	*Haemophilus influenzae* R$_d$
Hinc II	GTPyPuAC	34	>20	7	*Haemophilus influenzae* R$_c$
Hpa I	GTTAAC	11	6	5	*Haemophilus parainfluenzae*
Eco RI	GAATTC	5	5	1	*Escherichia coli* RY13
Bam HI	GGATTC	5	3	1	*Bacillus amyloliquefaciens* H
Bal I	CGGCCG	15	17	0	*Brevibacterium albidum*
Hae II	PuGCGCPy	>30	>30	1	*Haemophilus aegyptius*
Hha I	GCGC	>50	>50	2	*Haemophilus haemolyticus*
Mbo I	GATC	>50	>50	6	*Moraxella bovis*
Sma I	CCCGGG	3	12	0	*Serratia marcescens* Sb$_b$
Bgl II	AGATCT	5	10	0	*Bacillus globigii*
Hinf I	GANTC	>50	>50	10	*Haemophilus influenzae* R$_f$
Taq I	TCGA	?	?	?	*Thermus aquaticus* YTI

[*]Arrows indicate the site of cleavage and sequence specificity of the endonucleases. The number of cleavage sites refers to the genomes of lambda bacteriophage (λ), adenovirus 2 (Ad2), and simian virus 40 (SV40).

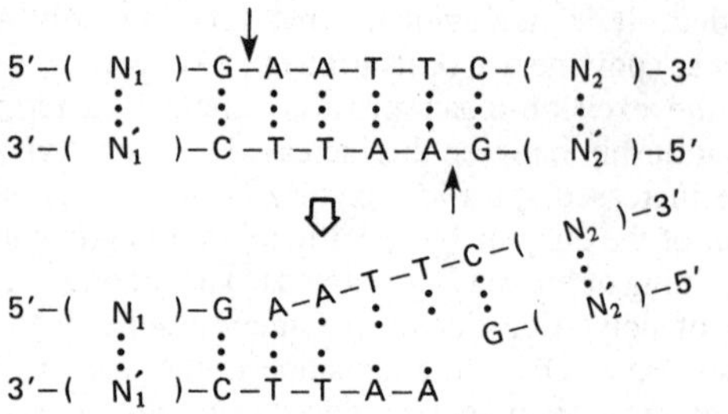

$$5'-(\ N_1\ )-G\overset{\downarrow}{-}A-A-T-T-C-(\ N_2\ )-3'$$
$$3'-(\ N_1'\ )-C-T-T-A-A-\underset{\uparrow}{G}-(\ N_2'\ )-5'$$

$$\Downarrow$$

$$5'-(\ N_1\ )-G\quad A-\overset{A-T}{}-T-C-(\ N_2\ )-3'$$
$$3'-(\ N_1'\ )-C-T-T-A-\underset{}{A}\quad G-(\ N_2'\ )-5'$$

Figure 28–25. The sequence-specific symmetric cleavage of a double-stranded DNA molecule by EcoRI restriction endonuclease. The interstrand H bonds are depicted by the dots and other nucleotides by N and N'. Cohesive ("sticky") ends are generated by the symmetric staggered cleavage.

In cells from most if not all complementation groups of xeroderma pigmentosum, there is an abnormal temporal or quantitative response of the poly(ADP-ribose) polymerase to ultraviolet light exposure. It seems that the abnormal response in at least one complementation group is due to the inability to incise the DNA strand at the site of damage, since the addition of deoxyribonuclease to permeabilized defective cells is followed by a normal or nearly normal increase in poly(ADP-ribose) polymerase activity.

In patients with **ataxia-telangiectasia,** an autosomal recessive disease in humans resulting in the development of cerebellar ataxia and lymphoreticular

neoplasms, there appears to exist an increased sensitivity to damage by x-ray. Patients with **Fanconi's anemia,** an autosomal recessive anemia characterized also by an increased frequency of cancer and by chromosomal instability, probably have defective repair of cross-linking damage. All 3 of these clinical syndromes are associated with increased frequency of cancer. It is likely that other human diseases resulting from disordered DNA repair capabilities will be found in the future.

RECOMBINANT DNA TECHNOLOGY

With the advancement of DNA chemistry and enzymology in recent years, it has been possible to synthesize specific genes in vitro. Some of these synthetic genes can express their genetic information in vivo in the form of an ultimate gene product—a specific protein molecule which itself has normal function. Some of the genes have been synthesized, utilizing a purified naturally occurring specific mRNA and an RNA-dependent DNA polymerase (reverse transcriptase) that generates a double-stranded DNA (cDNA) gene complementary to the mRNA molecule. Other synthetic genes have been synthesized chemically using the information contained within the nucleotide sequence of the naturally occurring gene.

Great interest has been shown in a series of enzymes capable of recognizing specific sequences of

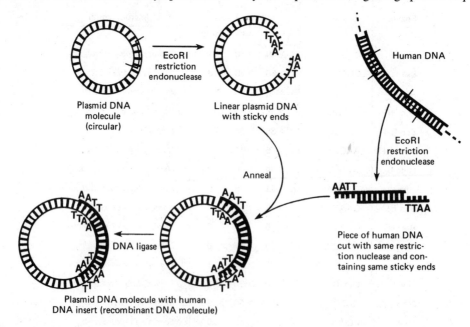

Figure 28–26. Use of restriction nucleases to make new recombinant DNA molecules. When inserted back into a bacterial cell, the **plasmid DNA replicates not only itself but also the new DNA insert.** Since recombining the sticky ends, as indicated, regenerates the same DNA sequence recognized by the original restriction enzyme (Fig 28–25), the cloned DNA insert **can be cleanly cut back out of the recombinant plasmid circle with this nuclease.** If a mixture of all of the DNA pieces created by treatment of total human DNA with a single restriction nuclease is used as the source of the human DNA, a million or so different types of recombinant DNA molecules can be obtained, each pure in its own bacterial clone. (Modified and reproduced, with permission, from Cohen SN: The manipulation of genes. *Sci Am* [July] 1975;**233**:24.)

Step 1

Isolate the population (~10^{12}) of identical DNA molecules. (Identical molecules will, of course, have identical termini, nucleotide sequence, and length.) DNA molecular cloning and restriction endonuclease digestion clearly provide the most effective means for obtaining the molecules.

5' ⌐——————————————————⌐ 3'
3' ⌐——————————————————⌐ 5'

Step 2

Label 5'- (or 3'-) ends of each strand with radioactivity (∗).

∗ ⌐——————————————————⌐ 3'
3' ⌐——————————————————⌐ ∗

Step 3

Physically separate strands and isolate the population of one.

∗ ⌐——————————————————— 3'

Step 4

Divide into 4 tubes. To each tube is added a different specific chemical reagent that will destroy specifically one or 2 of the 4 nucleobases (A, T, C, G) at the sites where they occur in the DNA strand and thereby break the strand at that site. The destruction must be controlled so that it is incomplete and only some of the strands are broken at each of the sites where a given base exists.

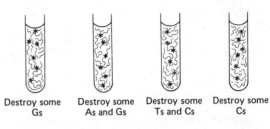

Destroy some   Destroy some   Destroy some   Destroy some
     Gs   As and Gs   Ts and Cs   Cs

This will generate in each tube a mixture of radioactively labeled strand-fragments (and many unlabeled fragments) of different lengths. The lengths of the labeled fragments will reflect the number of nucleotides between the labeled (∗) end and the specific nucleobases (which were destroyed) where they appear in the single-stranded molecule.

Step 5

The components of each mixture of strand-fragments are then separated by size (length) using polyacrylamide gel slab electrophoresis. The shorter fragments move more rapidly than the longer fragments. The slab gel is autoradiographed, and the bands of the labeled strand-fragment components of each mixture produce an image on the x-ray film.

Sequence of original strand:
∗ – A – G – T – C – T – T – G – G – A – G – C – T – 3'

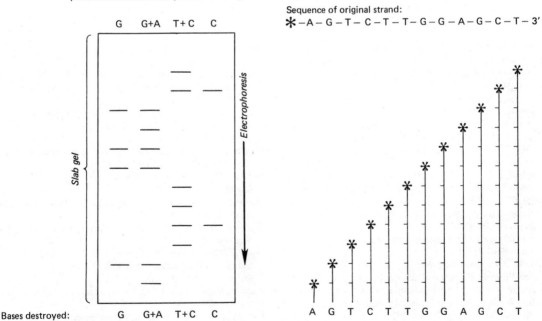

The ladderlike arrays represent from bottom to top all of the successively longer fragments of the original DNA strand. Knowing which specific one or 2 nucleobases were chemically destroyed to produce each mixture of fragments, one can determine the sequence of nucleotides from the labeled end toward the unlabeled end by reading up the gel. The base-pairing rules of Watson and Crick (A–T, G–C) dictate the sequence of the other (complementary) strand.

Figure 28–27. Sequencing of DNA by the method devised by Maxam and Gilbert.

nucleotides in a DNA molecule and subsequently catalyzing the cleavage of phosphodiester backbone at specific symmetric sites within the specific sequences (Fig 28–25). These enzymes, termed **restriction endonucleases,** are isolated from bacteria, in which they play a defensive role to destroy DNA from foreign organisms. The type II restriction endonucleases (Table 28–3) have provided scientists with the means of physically isolating, purifying, and mapping DNA molecules and recombining DNA molecules from different sources to create new genetic sequences. These latter exercises are referred to as **recombinant DNA experiments.** They have received much attention both in the lay press and in the scientific literature.

Some bacteria harbor circular DNA molecules that replicate autonomously in the bacterial protoplasm. Such an autonomous DNA molecule is called a **plasmid.** Plasmids may carry genetic information to confer **resistance to antibiotics** on the host bacterium. When **recombinant DNA technology** is used, a specific segment of DNA can be integrated in vitro into a plasmid (Fig 28–26). In this manner, a bacterial culture can be utilized for the autonomous replication of the recombinant plasmid including the new segment of DNA. With similar approaches, it is possible to use recombinant plasmids to introduce specific nonbacterial genes into bacteria that can then act as factories for the production of the specific protein molecules coded for by the introduced gene. By such techniques, some protein hormones have been produced in pharmaceutic quantities. Restriction endonucleases can also be used to clip out specifically the sequence originally inserted into the plasmid and thus to obtain milligram quantities of specific DNA sequences. Such technology provides great potential medical and agricultural benefits to society and is responsible for the unprecedented rapid rate at which new biologic information is being acquired in this decade.

DNA Sequencing

The segments of specific DNA molecules obtained by recombinant DNA technology can be analyzed for their nucleotide sequence (Fig 28–27). The method depends upon having a large number of identical DNA molecules. This requirement can be satisfied by recombinant DNA technology and the stringent sequence specificity of the restriction endonucleases. The method shown is that of Maxam and Gilbert and employs chemical methods to cleave the DNA molecules where they contain the specific nucleobases. A second method (Sanger's) employs specific nucleotide analogs that terminate DNA strand synthesis at specific nucleobases as the strand is synthesized on purified template nucleic acid.

●   ●   ●

References

Bauer WR et al: Supercoiled DNA. *Sci Am* (July) 1980;**243:**118.

Breathnach R, Chambon P: Organization and expression of eukaryotic split genes coding for proteins. *Annu Rev Biochem* 1981;**50:**349.

Busch H et al: SnRNAs, SnRNPs, and RNA processing. *Annu Rev Biochem* 1982;**51:**617.

Cantor CR: DNA choreography. *Cell* 1981;**25:**293.

Cartwright IL et al: Chromatin structure and gene activity: The role of nonhistone chromosomal proteins. *CRC Crit Rev Biochem* 1982;**13:**1.

Challberg MD, Kelly TJ: Eukaryotic DNA replication: Viral and plasmid model systems. *Annu Rev Biochem* 1982;**51:**901.

DePamphilis ML, Wassarman PM: Replication of eukaryotic chromosomes: A close-up of the replication fork. *Annu Rev Biochem* 1980;**49:**627.

Efstratiadis A et al: Enzymatic in vitro synthesis of globin genes. *Cell* 1976;**7:**279.

Flint SJ: RNA processing. *Fed Proc* 1982;**41:**2781.

Fritsch EF et al: Molecular cloning and characterization of the human beta-like globin gene cluster. *Cell* 1980;**19:**959.

Gilbert W, Villa-Komaroff L: Useful proteins from recombinant bacteria. *Sci Am* (April) 1980;**242:**74.

Igo-Kemenes T, Hörz W, Zachau HG: Chromatin. *Annu Rev Biochem* 1982;**51:**89.

Jelinek WR, Schmid CW: Repetitive sequences in eukaryotic DNA and their expression. *Annu Rev Biochem* 1982;**51:**813.

Jongstra J et al: Induction of altered chromatin structures by simian virus 40 enhancer and promoter elements. *Nature* 1984;**307:**708.

Kornberg A: *DNA Replication.* Freeman, 1980.

Laskey RA, Earnshaw WC: Nucleosome assembly. *Nature* 1980;**286:**763.

Lindahl T: DNA repair enzymes. *Annu Rev Biochem* 1982;**51:**61.

Loeb LA, Kunkel TA: Fidelity of DNA synthesis. *Annu Rev Biochem* 1982;**51:**429.

Mathog D et al: Characteristic folding pattern of polytene chromosomes in *Drosophila* salivary gland nuclei. *Nature* 1984;**308:**414.

Maxam AM: Sequencing the DNA of recombinant chromosomes. *Fed Proc* 1980;**39:**2830.

McGhee JD, Felsenfeld G: Nucleosome structure. *Annu Rev Biochem* 1980;**49:**1115.

Nossal NG: Prokaryotic DNA replication systems. *Annu Rev Biochem* 1983;**52:**581.

Ogawa T, Okazaki T: Discontinuous DNA replication. *Annu Rev Biochem* 1980;**49:**421.

Oudet P, Gross-Bellard M, Chambon P: Electron microscopic and biochemical evidence that chromatin structure is a repeating unit. *Cell* 1975;**4:**281.

Razin A, Riggs AD: DNA methylation and gene function. *Science* 1980;**210:**604.

Richmond TJ et al: Structure of the nucleosome core particle at 7Å resolution. *Nature* 1984;**311:**532.

Sass H: RNA polymerase B in polytene chromosomes. *Cell* 1982;**28:**269.

Singer MF: SINEs and LINEs: Highly repeated short and long interspersed sequences in mammalian genomes. *Cell* 1982;**28:**433.

Weisbrod S: Active chromatin. *Nature* 1982;**297:**289.

Yuan R: Structure and mechanism of multifunctional restriction endonucleases. *Annu Rev Biochem* 1981;**50:**285.

RNA Synthesis & Processing | 29

David W. Martin, Jr., MD

RNA SYNTHESIS

The process of synthesizing RNA from a DNA template has been characterized best in prokaryotes. Although in mammalian cells the regulation of RNA synthesis and the processing of the RNA transcripts are different from that in prokaryotes, the process of RNA synthesis per se is quite similar in these 2 classes of organisms. Therefore, the description of RNA synthesis in prokaryotes will be applicable to eukaryotes even though the enzymes involved and the regulatory signals are different.

The sequence of ribonucleotides in an RNA molecule is complementary to the sequence of deoxyribonucleotides in one strand of the double-stranded DNA molecule (see Fig 27–10). The strand that is transcribed into an RNA molecule is referred to as the **template strand** of the DNA. The other DNA strand is frequently referred to as the **antitemplate strand** of that gene. In the case of a double-stranded DNA molecule containing many genes, the template strand for each gene will not necessarily be the same strand of the DNA double helix (Fig 29–1). Thus, a given strand of a double-stranded DNA molecule will serve as the template strand for some genes and the antitemplate strand of other genes. Note that the nucleotide sequence of an RNA transcript will be the same (except for U replacing T) as that of the antitemplate strand.

DNA-dependent RNA polymerase is responsible for the polymerization of ribonucleotides into a sequence complementary to the template strand of the gene (Fig 29–2). The enzyme attaches at a specific site, the **promoter,** toward the 3′ pole of the template strand of the gene to be transcribed. The DNA-dependent RNA polymerase of the bacterium *Esche-*

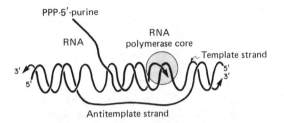

Figure 29–2. The RNA polymerase–catalyzed polymerization of ribonucleotides into an RNA sequence complementary to the template strand of the gene. (From James D. Watson, *Molecular Biology of the Gene,* 3rd ed. Copyright © 1976, 1970, 1965, by W.A. Benjamin, Inc., Menlo Park, Calif.)

richia coli exists as a core molecule composed of 4 subunits; 2 of these are identical to each other (the α subunits), and 2 are similar to each other but not identical (the β subunit and the β′ subunit). The core RNA polymerase utilizes a specific protein factor (the sigma [σ] factor) that assists the core enzyme to attach more tightly to the specific deoxynucleotide sequence of the promoter region (Fig 29–3). Bacteria contain multiple σ factors, each of which acts as a regulatory protein that modifies the **promoter recognition specificity** of the RNA polymerase. The appearance of different σ factors can be correlated temporally with the programs of bacteriophage and endospore development.

The process of RNA synthesis, depicted in Fig 29–4, involves first the binding of the RNA holopolymerase molecule to the template at the promoter site. Initiation of formation of the RNA molecule at its 5′ end then follows with the release of the σ factor, while the elongation of the RNA molecule from the 5′ to its 3′ end continues **antiparallel** to its template. The enzyme polymerizes the ribonucleotides in a specific sequence that is dictated by the template strand and interpreted by the base-pairing rules. Pyrophosphate is released in the polymerization reaction. In both prokaryotes and eukaryotes, a purine ribonucleotide is the first to be polymerized into the RNA molecule.

As the elongation complex containing the core RNA polymerase progresses along the DNA molecule, **DNA unwinding** must occur in order to provide access

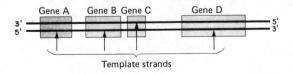

Figure 29–1. Template strands of the linked genes. These are not necessarily the same strand of the DNA double helix.

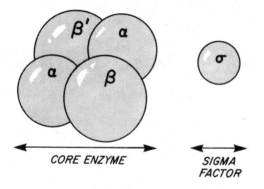

for the appropriate base pairing to the nucleotides of the template strand. The extent of DNA unwinding is constant throughout the transcription and has been deduced to be about 17 base pairs per polymerase molecule. Thus, it appears that the size of the unwound DNA region is tightly controlled by the polymerase and is independent of the DNA sequence in the complex. This suggests that RNA polymerase has associated a leading "unwindase" activity that opens the

DNA helix and a lagging "rewindase" which subsequently re-forms the DNA helix. The latter would also promote displacement of the RNA transcript from the template DNA strand as this elongation complex moves along the gene. The fact that the DNA double helix must unwind and the strands part at least transiently for transcription implies some disruption of the nucleosome structure of eukaryotic cells.

Termination of the synthesis of the RNA molecule is signaled by a sequence in the template strand of the DNA molecule, a signal that is recognized by a termination protein, the rho (ρ) factor. Following termination of synthesis of the RNA molecule, the core enzyme separates from the DNA template. With the assistance of another σ factor, the core enzyme then recognizes a promoter at which the synthesis of a new RNA molecule commences. More than one RNA polymerase molecule may transcribe the same template strand of a gene simultaneously, but the process is phased and spaced in such a way that at any one moment each is transcribing a different portion of the DNA sequence. RNA synthesis is shown electronmicrographically in Fig 29–5.

Mammalian cells possess several DNA-dependent RNA polymerases, the properties of which are described in Table 29–1. Each of these DNA-dependent RNA polymerases seems to be responsible for the transcription of different sets of genes. The subunit structures of mammalian polymerases have been de-

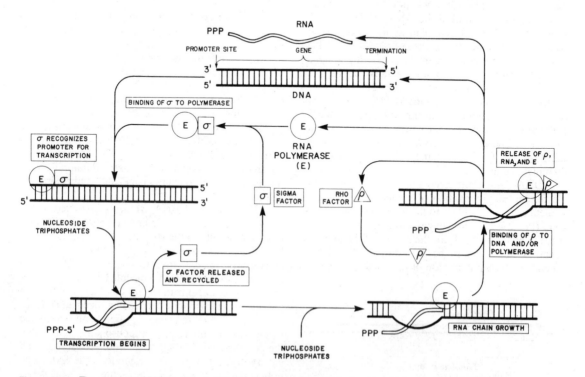

Figure 29–4. The process of RNA synthesis. It begins at the upper left-hand portion of the figure with the binding of sigma to polymerase to form a complex that recognizes the promoter for transcription. The process is completed as the RNA transcriptase is released from the gene, and all of the catalytic components are free to recycle. (From James D. Watson, *Molecular Biology of the Gene,* 3rd ed. Copyright © 1976, 1970, 1965, by W.A. Benjamin, Inc., Menlo Park, Calif.)

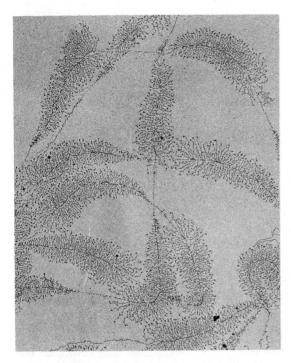

Figure 29–5. Electron photomicrograph of multiple copies of ribosomal RNA genes being transcribed in an amphibian cell. × 6000. Note that the length of the transcripts increases as the RNA polymerase molecules have progressed along the individual ribosomal RNA genes. Thus, the proximal end of the transcribed gene has short transcripts attached to it, while much longer transcripts are attached to the distal end of the gene. (Reproduced, with permission, from Miller OL Jr, Beatty BR: Portrait of a gene. *J Cell Physiol* 1969; **74**[Suppl 1]:225.)

Table 29–1. Nomenclature and localization of animal DNA-dependent RNA polymerases.

Class of Enzyme	Sensitivity to α-Amanitin	Products	Principal Localization
I (A)	Insensitive	rRNA	Nucleolar
II (B)	Sensitive to low concentration (10^{-8} to 10^{-9} mol/L)	hnRNA (mRNA)	Nucleoplasmic
III (C)	Sensitive to high concentration	tRNA and 5S RNA	Nucleoplasmic

karyotic nucleoplasmic DNA-dependent RNA polymerase (RNA polymerase II) and as such has proved to be a powerful research tool.

Transcriptional Signals

The DNA sequence analysis of specific genes obtained by recombinant DNA technology has allowed the recognition of a number of signal sequences important in gene transcription. From the large number of bacterial genes studied it is possible to construct consensus models of transcription promoter and termination signals. Bacterial **promoters** are approximately 40 nucleotide pairs (4 turns of the DNA double helix) in length, a region sufficiently small to be covered by an *E coli* RNA holopolymerase molecule. In this consensus promoter region are 2 short, conserved sequences. Approximately 35 base pairs upstream of the transcription start site there is a consensus sequence of 8 nucleotide pairs, shown in Fig 29–6. More proximal to the transcription start site, centered 7 nucleotides upstream, is a 6-nucleotide-pair AT-rich sequence. The latter sequence will have a low melting temperature because of its deficiency of GC nucleotide pairs. Thus, the TATA or **Pribnow box** is thought to ease the dissociation between the template and antitemplate strand so that RNA polymerase bound to the promoter region can have access to the nucleotide sequence of its immediately downstream template strand.

The **termination signals** in the bacteria *E coli* also appear to have a distinct consensus sequence, as shown in Fig 29–7. The conserved consensus se-

scribed, but the functions of each of the subunits are not yet understood. Certainly, many must have regulatory functions, such as serving to assist the core polymerase in the recognition of specific sequences like promoters and termination signals.

One toxin from the mushroom *Amanita phalloides*, α-amanitin, is a specific inhibitor of the eu-

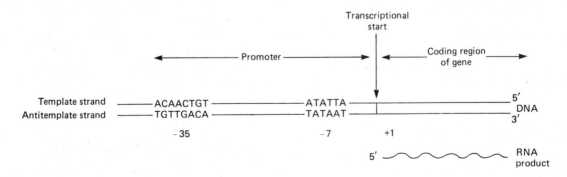

Figure 29–6. Bacterial promoters share 2 regions of highly conserved nucleotide sequence centered 35 and 7 base pairs proximal to the start site of transcription, indicated as +1.

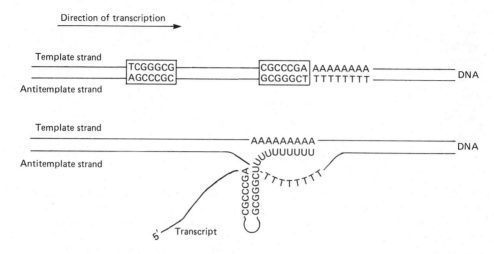

Figure 29–7. The bacterial transcriptional termination signal in the gene contains an inverted, hyphenated repeat followed by a stretch of T:A base pairs (above) that upon being transcribed can generate the secondary structure in the RNA transcript shown below.

quence, which also extends about 40 nucleotide pairs in length, can be seen to contain a hyphenated or interrupted inverted repeat, followed by a series of AT base pairs. As transcription proceeds through the hyphenated, inverted repeat, the generated transcript can form the intramolecular hairpin structure, also depicted in Fig 29–7. Transcription continues into the AT region, and with the aid of a termination protein factor called rho (ρ) the RNA polymerase stops and dissociates, releasing the primary transcript.

The transcription signals in mammalian cells are, not unexpectedly, more complex. An extensive analysis of eukaryotic transcription signals has been conducted utilizing recombinant DNA technology and the structural gene that codes for the thymidine kinase enzyme of herpes simplex virus. The herpesvirus utilizes its mammalian host transcriptional system for gene expression, and the studies have been conducted by McKnight and his colleagues using a cloned herpes thymidine kinase gene so as to be certain that only host components are utilized for transcription. It is clear

that the signals in DNA which control transcription are of 2 types. One defines **where** transcription is to commence along the DNA, and the other determines **how frequently** this event is to occur. In the thymidine kinase gene, there is a unique transcription start site, and accurate transcription from this start site depends upon a nucleotide sequence 32–16 nucleotides upstream from the start site. This region, frequently referred to as the **Goldberg-Hogness box,** has the consensus sequence of **TATAAAAG** and bears remarkable homology to the functionally related **Pribnow box** (TATAAT) centered about 7 base pairs upstream from prokaryotic mRNA start points. It is clear that the RNA polymerase II binds to DNA in the region of the TATA box and then commences transcription of the template strand about 32 nucleotides downstream at a T, which is surrounded by purines (Fig 29–8). Therefore, the Goldberg-Hogness (or TATA) box seems to provide the "where" signal.

Two segments of nucleotides farther upstream from the start site are responsible for determining how

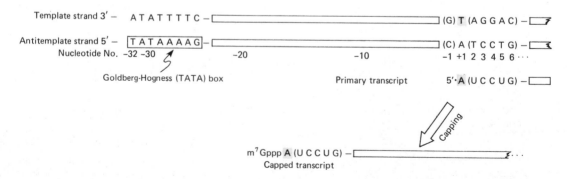

Figure 29–8. The DNA-dependent RNA polymerase II binds to the complement of the TATA box and commences transcription of the **template strand** about 32 nucleotides downstream at a T that is surrounded by purines. The primary transcript is rapidly capped at the first nucleotide (5'-purine).

CCCGGAAGAAATATATTTGCATGTCTTTAGTTCTATGATGACACAAACCCCGCCCAGCGTCTTGTCATTGG**CGAATT**CGAACACGCAGATGCAGT CGGGGCGGCGGCGGT CCGAGGTCCACTTCGCATAT**TAAGGT**GACGCGTGTGGCCTCGAACACCGAGCGACCCTGCAGCGACCCGCTTAAC

$\bullet\!\!-\!\!\bullet\longrightarrow$ tk mRNA $\longrightarrow$

Figure 29–9. Schematic diagram showing the boundaries of transcriptional control regions adjacent to the HSV thymidine kinase gene. The nucleotide sequence of the antitemplate strand of the tk gene is shown. Underlining delineates the evolutionarily conserved segments. Double-hatched box indicates the extent of quantitative control ("how frequently") region and single-hatched boxes the regions required for accurate ("where") transcriptional expression. (Modified and reproduced, with permission, from McKnight SL et al: Analysis of transcriptional regulatory signals of the HSV thymidine kinase gene: Identification of an upstream control region. *Cell* 1981;**25**:385.)

frequently this transcription event occurs. One guanine-rich segment between 61 and 47 nucleotides upstream from the start site (ie, between nucleotides number –61 and –47) and a cytosine-rich segment between bases –105 and –80 profoundly affect the efficiency of transcription. Mutations in either of these regions reduce the frequency of transcriptional starts 10- to 20-fold (Fig 29–9). The 5' termini of the primary RNA transcript and the mature cytoplasmic mRNA are identical. Thus, the **start point of transcription corresponds to the 5' nucleotide of the mRNA.** The primary transcripts generated by RNA polymerase II are promptly capped by 7-methylguanosinetriphosphate (Fig 27–10)—caps that persist and eventually appear on the mature cytoplasmic mRNA. These caps are necessary for the subsequent processing of the primary transcript to mRNA, as described below.

The signals for the termination of transcription by eukaryotic RNA polymerase II probably have some

resemblance to the signal utilized by *E coli* DNA-dependent RNA polymerase. However, it appears that the termination signal, which is probably an imperfect inverted repeat (Fig 29–7), exists far downstream of the coding sequence of eukaryotic genes. For example, the transcription termination signal for mouse β-globin occurs at a defined position 1400 bases beyond the site at which the poly(A) tail will eventually be added. Little is known about the termination factors required by RNA polymerase II in eukaryotic cells except that they appear to include specific proteins and a small nuclear RNA, perhaps "U4." The formation of the mRNA 3' terminus appears to involve 3 steps. The RNA polymerase terminates in a region 3' to a signal, probably an inverted repeat of about 20 bases. Next, an RNA endonuclease hydrolyzes the primary transcript, trimming the tail down to about 15 bases 3' to a consensus sequence of **AAUAAA** that seems to serve in eukaryotic transcripts as a cleavage signal. Finally, the newly formed 3' terminus is polyad-

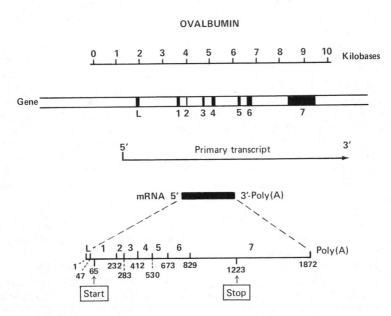

Figure 29–10. The arrangement of noncoding intervening sequences within the gene for chicken ovalbumin. Those informational segments eventually appearing in the mature mRNA are numbered and shown solid. The primary transcript commences upstream of the untranslated L exon and extends beyond the untranslated region of exon 7. The expanded depiction of the mature mRNA includes the corresponding numbers of the exons along the top and the numbers of nucleotides along the bottom. The positions of the start and stop codons are indicated.

enylated in the nucleoplasm, as described below.

DNA-dependent RNA polymerase III, which transcribes the tRNA genes and the small stable RNA genes (ssRNA; see Chapter 27), recognizes a promoter that is **internal to the gene** to be expressed, rather than upstream of the transcription starting point. In the case of eukaryotic tRNA genes, 2 separated blocks (A and B) of sequences exist that act as an intragenic promoter. The sequences within the A and B blocks exist in the mature tRNA molecule in regions that are highly conserved and participate in the formation of the DHU loop and the T ψ C loop, respectively (Fig 27–13). By manipulating the structure of tRNA genes, it has been shown that for promoter function the optimal distance between the A and B blocks is 30–40 base pairs and that the transcription start point occurs between 10 and 16 base pairs proximal to the A block. For the 5S RNA gene, which is also transcribed by RNA polymerase III, there appears to be a specific transcription protein factor which, once bound to the intragenic promoter for that gene, probably interacts with an RNA polymerase III molecule to position its catalytic sites on the transcription start point of the DNA.

PROCESSING OF RNA MOLECULES

In prokaryotic organisms, most RNA molecules transcribed from the template strand of a gene begin to serve as translation templates even before their transcription has been completed. Thus, they are subjected to little modification and processing prior to carrying out their intended function in protein synthesis. The exception is the tRNA molecules, which are transcribed in units considerably longer than the ultimate tRNA molecule. In fact, many of the transcription units contain more than one tRNA molecule. Thus, in prokaryotes the processing of these tRNA precursor molecules is required for the generation of the ultimate functional molecules, the specific tRNAs.

Nearly all eukaryotic RNA primary transcripts undergo extensive processing between the time they are synthesized and the time at which they serve their ultimate function, whether it be as mRNA or as a structural molecule such as a tRNA. The processing occurs primarily within the nucleus. The processing includes **capping, nucleolytic and ligation reactions, terminal additions** of nucleotides, and **nucleoside modifications.** However, it is clear that, for mammalian cells, 50–75% of the nuclear RNA, including those with capped 5′ termini, do not contribute to the cytoplasmic mRNA. This nuclear RNA loss is significantly greater than can be reasonably accounted for by the loss of intervening sequences alone (see below). Thus, the function of the seemingly excessive transcripts in the nucleus of a mammalian cell is unknown.

As a result of advances in techniques for mapping DNA molecules by restriction endonucleases and DNA sequencing, it is now apparent that interspersed within the amino acid–coding portions, **exons,** of many genes are long sequences of deoxynucleotides that do not contribute to the genetic information ultimately translated into the amino sequence of a protein molecule (see Chapter 28). These **intervening sequences, introns,** exist within most but not all genes of higher eukaryotes (Fig 29–10). The primary RNA transcripts of the structural genes contain the transcripts of the interspersed sequences. However, the intron RNA sequences are cleaved out of the transcript, and the exons of the transcript are appropriately spliced together in the nucleus before the resulting mRNA molecule appears in the cytoplasm for translation (Fig 29–10).

The precise mechanisms whereby the introns are removed from the primary transcript in the nucleus, the exons are ligated to form the mRNA molecule, and the mRNA molecule is transported to the cytoplasm are not known. However, again based on recombinant DNA technology, it has been possible at least to propose mechanisms consistent with the observations. Although the sequences of nucleotides in the introns of the various eukaryotic transcripts, and even those within a single transcript, are very heterogeneous, there is a consensus sequence at each of the 2 exon-intron (splice) junctions (Fig 29–11). This **consensus sequence at the splice junction** is not sufficiently unique to allow a specific nuclease to cleave only at exon-intron junctions. The very **abundant small nuclear RNA, U1 RNA,** possesses a ribonucleotide sequence with **complementarity to the consensus sequence across the potential splice sites** (Fig 29–12). The U1 RNA molecules are also found associated with specific protein molecules in eukaryotic nuclei. These RNA-protein complexes preferentially bind to the 5′ and 3′ splice junction sequences in RNA, and antibodies to the U1-protein complexes inhibit intron excision in vitro.

Interestingly, patients with lupus erythematosus, an autoimmune disease, have antibodies to some of these specific nuclear U1-protein molecules. The relationship to the autoimmune disease per se is unknown.

Recently, it has been discovered that during the process of removing the intron sequence from pre-mRNA, there is formed an unusual RNA molecule resembling a lariat. It appears that the 5′ end of the intervening sequence is joined via a 2′–5′ phosphodiester linkage to an adenylate residue 28–37 nucleotides upstream from the 3′ end of the intervening sequence. This process and structure are diagrammed in Fig 29–13.

It seems that the mystery of the relationship between hnRNA and the corresponding mature mRNA in eukaryotic cells is solved. The hnRNA molecules are the primary transcripts plus their early processed products, which, after the addition of caps and poly(A) tails and removal of the portion corresponding to the introns, are transported to the cytoplasm as mature mRNA molecules.

The processing of hnRNA molecules is a potential site for regulation of gene expression. In fact, it has been demonstrated that alternative patterns of RNA splicing are subject to developmental control. For example, the cytoplasmic mRNAs for α-amylase in rat salivary gland and in rat liver differ in their 5′ nucleotide sequence, while the remainder of the mRNA genes containing the coding region and poly(A) addition sites are identical. Further analysis has revealed that although the primary transcripts are huge and overlapping, different splice sites are used to join 2 different cap and leader sequences to the same mRNA "body."

In addition, alternative patterns of RNA splicing are used to generate 2 different immunoglobulin heavy-chain mRNAs—one that codes for a membrane-bound heavy chain and another that codes for a secreted heavy chain (see Chapter 31). Thus, not only is RNA splicing necessary for the generation of messenger RNA molecules, but the splicing function also provides a site for differential regulation of gene expression.

Gene	5′ Exon ⟶ Intron ⟶ Exon 3′	
Rat insulin	CAGGUAUGU	. . .	CUAUCUUCCAGG
Rat insulin	AAGGUAAGC	. . .	CUCCCUGGCAGU
Rat insulin	CAGGUAUGU	. . .	CUAUCUUCCAGG
γ1 Chain (newborn mouse)		. . .	UUUUCUUGUAGC
	UUGGUGAGA		UCUCUCCACAGU
γ1 Chain (newborn mouse)	CAGGUAAGU	. . .	UUCAUCCUUAGU
γ1 Chain (newborn mouse)	AAGGUGAGA	. . .	CCCACCCACAGG
			UUUUCUUGUAGC
γ1 Chain (mouse myeloma)	UUGAGAGGA	. . .	UCUCUCCACAGU
	CAGGUAAGU		UUCAUCCUUAGU
γ2 Chain (mouse myeloma)	AAGGUGAGA	. . .	CUCACUCACAGG
γ1 Chain (mouse myeloma)	CAGGUCAGC	. . .	CCUGUUUGCAGG
	CAGGUCAGC		UCUGUUUGCAGG
γ1 Chain (mouse myeloma)	UAGGUGAGU	. . .	UCAUCCUGCGGC
	AACGUAAGU		UCCUUCCUCAGG
γ2 Chain	AACGUAAGU	. . .	UCCUUCCUCAGG
λ1 Chain	AACCUAAGU	. . .	UCCUUCCUCAGG
κ Chain	AACGUAAGU	. . .	UCCUUCCUCAGG
κ Chain	AACGUAAGU	. . .	UCCUUCCUCAGG
κ Chain	AAGGUUAAA	. . .	UCCACUCCUAGG
κ Chain	CAGGUUGGU	. . .	UCCCUUUUUAGG
κ Chain	AGGGUGAGU	. . .	UAUUCCCACAGC
κ Chain	CAGGUUGGU	. . .	CAUUUUCUCAGG
Mouse β-globin	AGGGUGAGU	. . .	UUUUCCUACAGC
Rabbit β-globin		. . .	UCCUCCCACAGC
Rabbit β-globin		. . .	CUUCUCCGCAGC
Human β-globin	AAGGUAGGC	. . .	GUUUGCUCUAGA
Human δ-globin	AAGGUGAGC	. . .	UUCAAUUACAGG
Chicken ovalbumin	CAGGUACAG	. . .	UUUCUAUUCAGU
Chicken ovalbumin	CCAGUAAGU	. . .	UUGCUUUACAGG
Chicken ovalbumin	AUGGUAAGG	. . .	CAUUCUUAAAGG
Chicken ovalbumin	GAGGUAUAU	. . .	UGGUUCUCCAGC
Chicken ovalbumin	CAGGUAUGG	. . .	UUUCCUUGCAGC
Chicken ovalbumin	AAGGUACCU	. . .	UUUUAUUUCAGG
SV40 late mRNAs	AAGGUUCGU	. . .	UUUUAUUUCAGG
SV40 late mRNAs	CUGGUAAGU	. . .	UUUUAUUUCAGG
SV40 late mRNAs	CUGGUAAGU	. . .	UUUACUUCUAGG
SV40 early mRNAs	AAGGUAAAU	. . .	GUGUAUUUAGA
SV40 early mRNAs	GAGGUAUUU	. . .	GUGUAUUUUAGA
Polyoma late mRNAs	CAAGUAAGU	. . .	UAUUUCCCUAGG
Polyoma late mRNAs	CAAGUAAGU	. . .	UUUAAUUCUAGG
Polyoma late mRNAs	CAAGUAAGU	. . .	UCUAUUUUAAGA
Silk fibroin	CAGGUGAGU	. . .	UUUUGUUUCAGU
Consensus	^A_CAGGUAAGU		UYUYYYU CAGG

5′ Exon ⟶ Intron ⟶ Exon 3′

Figure 29–11. Sequences at splice junctions. The 36 "donor" (5′ end) sequences and 37 "acceptor" (3′ end) sequences represent 43 possible splicing events (each event is depicted on a separate line). Underlined sequences are redundant (either because they are identical to a homologous region or because they represent an alternative splice involving the same region) and were not included in the tabulation. (Slightly modified and reproduced, with permission, from Lerner MR et al: Are snRNPs involved in splicing? *Nature* 1980;**283**:220.)

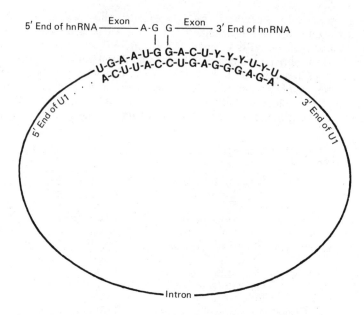

Figure 29–12. Proposed mechanism for establishing the splice site for intron removal from the hnRNA. The U1 RNA molecule is complementary to the portion of the intron across the splice site.

At least one form of β-thalassemia, a disease in which the beta-globin gene of hemoglobin is severely underexpressed, appears to result from a nucleotide change at an exon-intron junction, precluding removal of the intron and therefore leading to diminished or absent synthesis of the β chain. It is also evident from other studies that primary transcripts of genes lacking introns are likely not ever to appear in the cytosol as mature mRNA molecules.

In yeast, the mitochondrial gene for cytochrome b contains introns which in themselves code for a portion of a protein molecule, referred to as a maturase. The maturase is responsible for removing one intron region from the primary transcript to generate message for the cytochrome b. Thus, the primary transcript is translated by reading through the exon-intron junction and into the intron region to form the maturase, which subsequently processes its own template to provide a spliced template for cytochrome b and eliminate the synthesis of itself. This unusual mechanism provides for a rather surprising autoregulatory mechanism.

Messenger RNA (mRNA)

As mentioned above, mammalian mRNA molecules contain a capped structure at their 5′-phosphate terminus and a poly(A) tail at the 3′ terminus. The cap structures are added in the nucleus prior to transport of the mRNA molecule to the cytoplasm. The poly(A) tails (when present) appear to be added either in the nucleus or in the cytoplasm. The secondary methylations of mRNA molecules, those on the 2′-hydroxy groups and the N_6 of adenylate residues, occur after the mRNA molecule has appeared in the cytoplasm. They also occur in the nucleus and may play a positive role in RNA splicing. The 5′ cap of the RNA transcript appears to be required for the formation of the ribonucleoprotein complex necessary for the splicing reactions and may be involved in mRNA translation initiation.

The function of the poly(A) tail is unknown. In any event, the presence or absence of the poly(A) tail does not determine whether a precursor molecule in the nucleus appears in the cytoplasm, because all

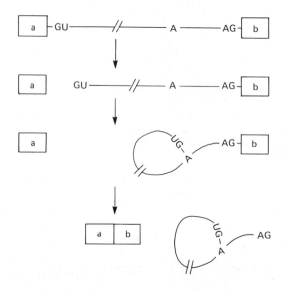

Figure 29–13. Proposed pathway for pre-mRNA splicing. Cleavage at the 5′ site is followed by lariat formation and subsequent release of the lariat by cleavage from exon b. The intron is represented by the line and exons a and b by boxes.

poly(A)-tailed hnRNA molecules do not contribute to cytoplasmic mRNA, nor do all cytoplasmic mRNA molecules contain poly(A) tails. Cytoplasmic processes in mammalian cells can both add and remove adenylate residues from the poly(A) tails.

The turnover of poly(A)-containing mRNA in cultured mammalian cells is a first-order process with a half-time approximately equal to the doubling time of the cell culture. The kinetics of the degradation of histone mRNA that does not contain a poly(A) tail appears to be a zero-order process in which there is an age-dependent decay with a lifetime of approximately 6 hours. It is not clear whether this difference is related to the presence or absence of poly(A) or to some intrinsic property of these mRNA molecules.

The size of the cytoplasmic mRNA molecules even after the poly(A) tail is removed is still considerably greater than the size required to code for the specific protein for which it is template. A summary of the required sizes and actual sizes of different mRNAs is given in Table 29–2. The extra nucleotides occur in untranslated regions both 5' and 3' to the coding region.

Transfer RNA (tRNA)

The tRNA molecules, as described in Chapters 27 and 30, serve as adapter molecules for the translation of mRNA into protein sequences. The tRNAs contain many peculiar bases; some are simply methylated derivatives and some possess rearranged glycosidic bonds. The tRNA molecules are transcribed in both prokaryotes and eukaryotes as large precursors, frequently containing the sequence for more than one tRNA, which are then subjected to **nucleolytic processing** and reduced in size by a specific class of ribonucleases. In addition, the genes of some tRNA molecules contain—very near the portion corresponding to the anticodon loop—an intron of about 18 nucleotides. As expected, these introns in the tRNA genes are transcribed. Thus, the processing of the precursor transcripts of many tRNA molecules must include removal of the 18-ribonucleotide intron and proper splicing of the anticodon region to generate an active adapter molecule for protein synthesis. The nucleolytic processing of tRNA precursors is not determined directly by nucleotide sequence but recognizes 3-dimensional structure and thereby processes only molecules capable of folding into functionally competent products.

The further modification of the tRNA molecules includes nucleotide **alkylations** and the **attachment of the characteristic C·C·A terminus** at the 3' end of the

Table 29–2. Lengths of isolated messenger RNAs.*†

Cell	Protein	Coding Length	mRNA Length	Poly(A) Length
Rabbit red blood cell	Globin	430	550 610 650	40
Mouse red blood cell	Globin			40, 60, 100
Duck red blood cell	Globin			100
Mouse myeloma	Light Ig	660	1200 1250 1300	200
Mouse myeloma	Heavy Ig	1350	1800	150–200
Chick oviduct	Ovalbumin	1164	1670 2640	Not known
Calf lens	α A2-Crystallin	520	1460	200
Calf lens	δ-Crystallin	1260	2000	Not known
Bombyx mori silk gland	Fibroin	14,000	16,000	100
Lytechinus pictus (sea urchin)	Histone f2al	310	370–400	None
HeLa‡	Molecules: 50% total 25% total 25% total	 < 1000 1000–2000 > 2000	 < 1400 1400–3000 > 3000	 150–200 150–200 150–200
	Mass: 50% total 50% total	 < 2100 > 2100	 < 2200 > 2200	 150–200 150–200

*Reproduced, with permission, from Lewin B: Units of transcription and translation: Sequence components of heterogeneous nuclear RNA and messenger RNA. *Cell* 1975;4:480.

†Coding lengths are the number of nucleotides required to specify each protein, estimated from its number of amino acids or molecular weight. The lengths of the mRNAs are those determined experimentally; where more than one value is shown, each represents an independent determination. The length of poly(A) on a messenger is not constant but declines with age; thus, the apparent length depends on whether it is determined by steady state or by pulse labeling, which explains the variation in measured globin mRNA poly(A) lengths. "Not known" indicates that poly(A) is present but that its length has not been determined.

‡The distribution of HeLa protein and messenger sizes is only approximate; an estimate of the number of molecules in each size class suggests a median coding length in mRNA of about 1200 nucleotides (1400 less the poly[A] content), and an estimate of the mass of protein or mRNA in each size class suggests a number-average molecular weight for the coding length of 2000 (ie, 2200 less the poly[A] content).

molecule. This C·C·A terminus is the point of attachment for the specific amino acid that is to enter into the polymerization reaction of protein synthesis. The methylation of mammalian tRNA precursors probably occurs in the nucleus, whereas the cleavage and attachment of C·C·A are cytoplasmic functions, since the termini turn over more rapidly than do the tRNA molecules themselves. Enzymes within the cytoplasm of mammalian cells are required for the attachment of amino acids to the C·C·A residues. The tRNA molecules are more stable in growing eukaryotic cells than in resting cells. In the growing cells, the half-time is approximately 60 hours.

Ribosomal RNA (rRNA)

In mammalian cells, the 2 major rRNA molecules and one minor rRNA molecule are transcribed from a single large precursor molecule (Fig 29–14). The precursor is subsequently processed in the **nucleolus** to provide the ribosome subunits for the cytoplasm. The rRNA genes are located in the nucleoli of mammalian cells. Thousands of copies of these genes are present in every cell. The rRNA genes are transcribed as units,

each of which contains, from 5' to 3', an 18S, a 5.8S, and a 28S ribosomal RNA. The primary transcript is a 45S molecule that is highly methylated in the nucleolus. In the **45S precursor,** the eventual 28S segment contains 65 ribose-methyl groups and 5 base-methyl groups. Only those portions of the precursor that eventually become rRNA molecules are methylated. The 45S precursor is nucleolytically processed, but the processing signals are clearly distinct from those in hnRNA. Therefore, the nucleolytic processing likely is mediated by a mechanism distinct from that responsible for processing hnRNA to mRNA.

Nearly half of the original transcript is discarded as ''degradation products,'' as shown in Fig 29–14. During the processing of rRNA, further methylation occurs, and eventually in the nucleoli the 28S chains self-assemble with ribosomal proteins newly synthesized in the cytoplasm to form the larger 60S subunit. The smaller (40S) ribosomal subunits may not be formed in the nucleoli from the 18S rRNA molecule. The 5.8S rRNA molecule also formed from the 45S precursor RNA in the nucleolus becomes an integral part of the smaller ribosomal subunit.

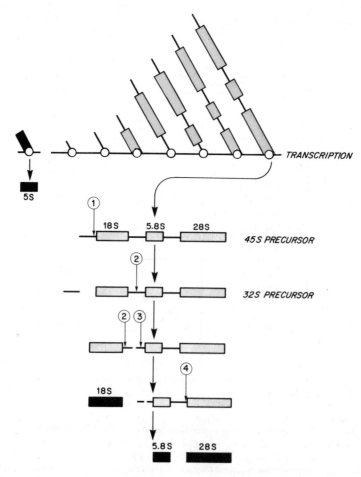

Figure 29–14. Diagrammatic representation of the processing of ribosomal RNA from precursor RNA molecules. The final products are solid. (Reproduced, with permission, from Perry RP: Processing of RNA. *Annu Rev Biochem* 1976;**45**:605.)

Both of the 2 major rRNA species present in the cytoplasm are stable in growing cells but unstable in resting cells. In resting cells, the 28S rRNA exhibits even greater instability than does the 18S tRNA.

NUCLEASES

Enzymes capable of degrading nucleic acids have been recognized for many years. These can be classified in several ways. Those which exhibit specificity for deoxyribonucleic acid are referred to as **deoxyribonucleases.** Those which specifically hydrolyze ribonucleic acids are **ribonucleases.** Within both of these classes are enzymes capable of cleaving internal phosphodiester bonds to produce either 3′-hydroxyl and 5′-phosphoryl termini or 5′-hydroxyl and 3′-phosphoryl termini. These are referred to as **endonucleases.** Some are capable of hydrolyzing both strands of a **double-stranded** molecule, whereas others can only cleave **single strands** of nucleic acids. Some nucleases can hydrolyze only unpaired single strands, while others are capable of hydrolyzing single strands participating in the formation of a double-stranded molecule. There exist classes of endonucleases that recognize specific sequences in DNA; the majority of these are the **restriction endonucleases,** which have in recent years become an important tool in molecular genetics and medical sciences.

A list of some currently recognized restriction endonucleases is presented in Table 28–3.

Some nucleases are capable of hydrolyzing a nucleotide only when it is present at a terminus of a molecule; these are referred to as **exonucleases.** Exonucleases may act in one direction (3′ → 5′ or 5′ → 3′) only. In bacteria, a 3′ → 5′ exonuclease is an integral part of the DNA replication machinery and there serves to edit the most recently added deoxynucleotide for base-pairing errors.

• • •

References

Abelson HT et al: Changes in RNA in relation to growth of the fibroblast: The lifetime of mRNA, rRNA, and tRNA in resting and growing cells. *Cell* 1974;**1**:161.

Breathnach R, Chambon P: Organization and expression of eucaryotic split genes coding for proteins. *Annu Rev Biochem* 1981;**50**:349.

Busch H et al: SnRNAs, SnRNPs, and RNA processing. *Annu Rev Biochem* 1982;**51**:617.

Chambon P: Eukaryotic nuclear RNA polymerases. *Annu Rev Biochem* 1975;**44**:613.

Cordin J et al: Promoter sequences of eukaryotic protein-coding genes. *Science* 1980;**209**:1406.

Crick F: Split genes and RNA splicing. *Science* 1979;**204**:264.

Flint SJ: RNA processing. *Fed Proc* 1982;**41**:2781.

Galli G: Biochemical complementation with RNA in the *Xenopus* oocyte: A small RNA is required for the generation of the 3′ histone mRNA termini. *Cell* 1983;**34**:823.

Hamkalo B, Miller OL Jr: Electron microscopy of genetic activity. *Annu Rev Biochem* 1973;**42**:379.

Kantor JA et al: Beta thalassemia: Mutations which affect pro-cessing of the beta-globin mRNA precursor. *Cell* 1980;**21**:149.

Konarska MM et al: Recognition of cap structure in splicing in vitro of mRNA precursors. *Cell* 1984;**38**:731.

Lerner MR et al: Are snRNPs involved in splicing? *Nature* 1980;**283**:220.

Nevins JR: The pathway of eukaryotic mRNA formation. *Annu Rev Biochem* 1983;**52**:441.

Perry RP: Processing of RNA. *Annu Rev Biochem* 1976;**45**:605.

Rich A, RajBhandary UL: Transfer RNA: Molecular structure, sequence, and properties. *Annu Rev Biochem* 1976;**45**:805.

Rogers J, Wall R: A mechanism for RNA splicing. *Proc Natl Acad Sci USA* 1980;**77**:1877.

Ruskin B et al: Excision of an intact intron as a novel lariat structure during pre-mRNA splicing in vitro. *Cell* 1984;**38**:317.

Yuan R: Structure and mechanism of multifunctional restriction endonucleases. *Annu Rev Biochem* 1981;**50**:285.

Ziff EB: Transcription and RNA processing by the DNA tumour viruses. *Nature* 1980;**287**:491.

30 | Protein Synthesis & the Genetic Code

David W. Martin, Jr., MD

As previously described, the genetic information within the nucleotide sequence of DNA is transcribed in the nucleus into the specific nucleotide sequence of an RNA molecule. The sequence of nucleotides in the RNA transcript is complementary to the nucleotide sequence of the template strand of its gene in accordance with the base-pairing rules. In higher eukaryotic cells, this transcript, heterogeneous nuclear RNA (hnRNA), is processed in the nucleus, and the appropriately spliced portion appears subsequently in the cytoplasm as messenger RNA (mRNA).

In a series of elegant experiments by Charles Yanofsky, it has been shown that in prokaryotes there is a linear correspondence between the gene and its polypeptide product or protein. Using the techniques of genetic mapping and protein sequencing, Yanofsky demonstrated that the order of mutants on the genetic map of tryptophan synthase in *Escherichia coli* was the same as the order of the corresponding changes in the amino acid sequence of the tryptophan synthase enzyme molecule (Fig 30–1).

The cell must possess the machinery necessary to translate information from the nucleotide sequence of an mRNA into the sequence of amino acids of the corresponding specific protein. This process, termed **translation,** was not understood for many years, until the relatively recent clarification of our understanding of the process of translation and the deciphering of the genetic code, which is undoubtedly a major accomplishment of modern biology. It was realized early that mRNA molecules in themselves have no affinity for amino acids and, therefore, that the translation of the information in the mRNA nucleotide sequence into the amino acid sequence of a protein requires an intermediate, adapter molecule. This **adapter molecule** must recognize a specific nucleotide sequence on the one hand as well as a specific amino acid on the other. With such an adapter molecule, the cell can direct a specific amino acid into the proper sequential position of a protein as dictated by the nucleotide sequence of the specific mRNA. In fact, the functional groups of the amino acids do not themselves actually come into contact with the mRNA template.

In the nucleotide sequence of the mRNA molecule, code words exist for each amino acid. This is referred to as the **genetic code.** The adapter molecules that translate the code words into the amino acid sequence of a protein are the **transfer RNA (tRNA)** molecules. The **ribosome** is the cellular component on which these various functional entities interact to assemble the protein molecule. Many of these subcellular units (ribosomes) can aggregate to translate

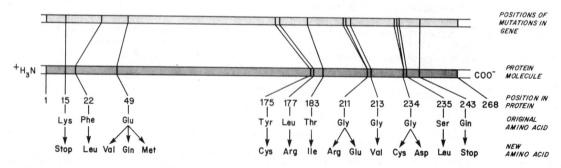

Figure 30–1. A diagram of the colinearity of the gene (TrpA) for the tryptophan synthase A protein with the protein molecule itself. The positions of the mutations in the TrpA gene are indicated in the top bar, and the position of the corresponding altered amino acid determined by sequence analyses of the mutant protein molecule is shown in the lower bar. The numbers represent the number of the altered amino acid starting at the amino terminus of the protein molecule. Shown below the numbers of the altered amino acid residues are the original amino acids at those positions in the normal protein molecule. Below the normal amino acids are those occurring in the protein as the result of a mutation in the gene at the corresponding positions. (From Stryer L: *Biochemistry.* Freeman, 1975. Copyright © 1975. Redrawn, with permission, from Yanofsky C: Gene structure and protein structure. *Sci Am* [May] 1967;**216**:89.)

simultaneously a single mRNA molecule and, in so doing, form a **polyribosome.** The **rough endoplasmic reticulum** is a compartment of membrane-attached polyribosomes that provides for the synthesis of integral membrane proteins and proteins to be exported. Polyribosomal structures also exist free in the cytoplasm, where they synthesize proteins that remain within the cell.

Twenty different amino acids are required for the synthesis of proteins, and thus there must be at least 20 distinct code words that comprise the genetic code. Since there are only 4 different nucleotides in mRNA, each code word must consist of more than a single purine or pyrimidine nucleotide. Code words consisting of 2 nucleotides each could provide for only 16 (4 × 4) specific code words, whereas code words of 3 nucleotides could provide 64 (4 × 4 × 4) specific code words.

As a result of the initial observations of Matthaei and Nirenberg, it is now known that each code word, termed a **codon,** consists of a sequence of 3 nucleotides; ie, it is a triplet code. The deciphering of the genetic code (Table 30–1) was carried out largely in the laboratory of Marshall Nirenberg. It depended heavily on the chemical synthesis of nucleotide polymers, particularly triplets, by Khorana.

Three codons do not code for specific amino acids; these have been termed **nonsense codons.** At least 2 of these so-called nonsense codons are utilized in the cell as signals to terminate the polymerization of amino acids where a protein molecule is to end. The

remaining 61 codons code for 20 amino acids. Thus, there must be "degeneracy" in the genetic code. An examination of the genetic code in Table 30–1 reveals that the 64 possible codons may be arranged in **16 families,** a family of codons being those which have the **same first 2 bases.** In Table 30–1, each family occupies a single column between the horizontal lines. For example, the codons CCN, where N can be U, C, A, or G, define a family located in Table 30–1 in the second column of the second box from the top. In some families, all 4 codons code for the same amino acid, as do the members of the CC family described immediately above. These are referred to as **unmixed** families. Eight of the 16 families of codons are unmixed (Table 30–1). Those families of codons which code for more than one amino acid are said to be **mixed** families. In 6 of the mixed families, codons with pyrimidines (U or C) at the third position code for one amino acid, while members with purines (A or G) at the third position code for another amino acid or chain termination signal (Table 30–1). The 2 remaining families—the UG family and the AU family—do not exhibit either pattern and are unique. Thus, in general, the third nucleotide in a codon is less important than the other 2 in determining the specific amino acid to be incorporated, and this accounts for most of the **degeneracy** of the code. However, for any specific codon only a single amino acid is indicated; the genetic code is **unambiguous**—ie, given a specific codon, only a single amino acid is indicated. The distinction between ambiguity and degeneracy is an important concept to be emphasized.

The unambiguous but degenerate code can be described in molecular terms. The recognition of specific codons in the mRNA by the tRNA adapter molecules is dependent upon their **anticodon region** and the base-pairing rules. Each tRNA molecule contains a specific sequence, complementary to a codon, which is termed its anticodon. For a given codon in the mRNA, only a single species of tRNA molecule possesses the proper anticodon. Since each tRNA molecule can be charged with only one specific amino acid, each codon therefore specifies only one amino acid. However, some tRNA molecules can utilize the anticodon to recognize more than one codon. As can be seen from the example of unmixed families, the nucleotide in the anticodon that recognizes the third (3'-) base of the codon could be less discriminating (mixed families) or nondiscriminating (unmixed families) and still manage to insert the proper amino acid when called for. This reduced stringency between the third base of the codon and the complementary nucleotide in the anticodon is referred to as **wobble.** Therefore, given a specific codon, only a specific amino acid will be incorporated—although, given a specific amino acid, more than one codon may call for it.

As discussed below, the reading of the genetic code during the process of protein synthesis does not involve any overlap of codons. Furthermore, once the reading is commenced at a specific codon, there is **no punctuation** between codons, and the message is read

Table 30–1. The genetic code (codon assignments in messenger RNA).*

First Nucleotide	Second Nucleotide				Third Nucleotide
	U	C	A	G	
U	Phe	Ser	Tyr	Cys	U
	Phe	Ser	Tyr	Cys	C
	Leu	Ser	CT	CT†	A
	Leu	Ser	CT	Trp	G
C	Leu	Pro	His	Arg	U
	Leu	Pro	His	Arg	C
	Leu	Pro	Gln	Arg	A
	Leu	Pro	Gln	Arg	G
A	Ile	Thr	Asn	Ser	U
	Ile	Thr	Asn	Ser	C
	Ile†	Thr	Lys	Arg†	A
	Met (CI)	Thr	Lys	Arg†	G
G	Val	Ala	Asp	Gly	U
	Val	Ala	Asp	Gly	C
	Val	Ala	Glu	Gly	A
	Val	Ala	Glu	Gly	G

*The terms first, second, and third nucleotide refer to the individual nucleotides of a triplet codon. U = uridine nucleotide; C = cytosine nucleotide; A = adenine nucleotide; G = guanine nucleotide; CI = chain initiator codon; CT = chain terminator codon. (Abbreviations of amino acids are explained in Chapter 3.)

†In mammalian mitochondria, AUA codes for Met, UGA for Trp, and AGA and AGG serve as chain terminators.

Table 30–2. Codon usage in α- and β-globin, immunoglobulin, and insulin mRNAs.*

2 \ 1		U	α	β	Im	Ins		C	α	β	Im	Ins		A	α	β	Im	Ins		G	α	β	Im	Ins	2 / 3
U	Phe	UUU	0	3	1	1	Ser	UCU	3	3	1	0	Tyr	UAU	2	1	2	0	Cys	UGU	0	1	1	2	U
	Phe	UUC	8	5	7	2		UCC	4	3	6	2		UAC	1	2	5	3		UGC	1	0	1	4	C
	Leu	UUA	0	0	0	0		UCA	0	0	4	0	Term	UAA	1	0	0	0	Term	UGA	0	1	0	1	A
	Leu	UUG	1	0	2	1		UCG	0	0	0	0		UAG	0	0	0	0	Trp	UGG	1	2	1	1	G
C	Leu	CUU	0	0	0	2	Pro	CCU	1	3	1	2	His	CAU	1	4	1	0	Arg	CGU	1	0	0	4	U
	Leu	CUC	2	2	1	3		CCC	5	0	4	2		CAC	10	5	2	2		CGC	0	0	0	0	C
	Leu	CUA	0	0	1	0		CCA	0	1	5	1	Gln	CAA	0	0	2	3		CGA	0	0	1	0	A
	Leu	CUG	14	16	0	8		CCG	1	0	0	2		CAG	1	4	2	5		CGG	1	0	2	1	G
A	Ile	AUU	0	1	2	1	Thr	ACU	2	2	5	0	Asn	AAU	1	4	3	0	Ser	AGU	1	4	1	0	U
	Ile	AUC	3	0	2	1		ACC	10	2	10	2		AAC	3	4	8	3		AGC	3	0	5	1	C
	Ile	AUA	0	0	1	0		ACA	0	0	3	1	Lys	AAA	2	3	6	1	Arg	AGA	0	0	0	0	A
	Met	AUG	1	1	1	0		ACG	0	0	2	0		AAG	10	9	10	2		AGG	1	3	1	0	G
G	Val	GUU	0	4	0	1	Ala	GCU	1	7	2	3	Asp	GAU	0	1	3	2	Gly	GGU	1	4	1	3	U
	Val	GUC	0	2	3	2		GCC	10	6	3	3		GAC	7	3	2	1		GGC	8	6	2	2	C
	Val	GUA	0	0	2	0		GCA	0	1	2	1	Glu	GAA	3	4	1	2		GGA	0	0	1	1	A
	Val	GUG	10	12	2	5		GCG	2	1	0	0		GAG	4	6	1	7		GGG	0	1	0	2	G

*Reproduced, with permission, from Heindell HC et al: The primary sequence of rabbit α-globin mRNA. *Cell* 1978;**15**:43.

in a continuing sequence of nucleotide triplets until a nonsense codon is reached.

Until recently, the genetic code (Table 30–1) was thought to be universal. It has now been shown that the set of tRNA molecules in mitochondria from lower and higher eukaryotes, including humans, reads 4 codons differently from the tRNA molecules in the cytoplasm of even the same cells. As noted in Table 30–1, the codon AUA is read as Met, and UGA codes for Trp in mammalian mitochondria. These 2 codons reside in the 2 codon families noted to be unique: the UG family and the AU family. Apparently, in order to minimize the number of tRNA molecules necessary to translate the genetic code, mitochondria have managed to convert the UG family and the AU family to simple mixed types. In addition, the codons AGA and AGG are read as stop or chain terminator codons rather than as Arg. As a result, mitochondria require only 22 tRNA molecules to read their genetic code, whereas the cytoplasmic translation system possesses a full complement of 31 tRNA species. These exceptions noted, **the genetic code is universal.** The frequency of use of each amino acid codon in 4 different mammalian proteins is given in Table 30–2.

TRANSFER RNA FUNCTION

There exists at least one species of transfer RNA (tRNA) for each of the 20 amino acids. All of the tRNA molecules have extraordinarily similar functions and extraordinarily similar 3-dimensional structures. The adapter function of the tRNA molecules requires the charging of each specific tRNA with its specific amino acid. Since there is no affinity of nucleic acids for specific functional groups of amino acids, this recognition must be carried out by a protein molecule capable of recognizing both a specific tRNA molecule and a specific amino acid. At least 20 specific enzymes are required for these specific recognition functions and for the proper attachment of the 20 amino acids to specific tRNA molecules. The process of recognition and attachment (charging) is carried out in 2 steps by one enzyme for each of the 20 amino acids. These enzymes are termed **aminoacyl-tRNA synthetases.** They form an activated intermediate of aminoacyl-AMP-enzyme complex as depicted in Fig 30–2. The specific aminoacyl-AMP-enzyme complex then recognizes a specific tRNA to which it attaches the aminoacyl moiety at the 3′-hydroxyl adenosine terminus (Fig 30–3). The amino acid remains attached to its specific tRNA in an ester linkage until it is polymerized at a specific position in the fabrication of a polypeptide precursor of a protein molecule.

The common features of tRNA molecules are diagrammatically represented in Fig 27–13. The 3′-hydroxyl terminus possesses an A•C•C sequence which, as described in Chapter 29, is continually turning over in the cell cytoplasm. **At the 3′-hydroxyl adenosyl terminus, the specific amino acid is at-**

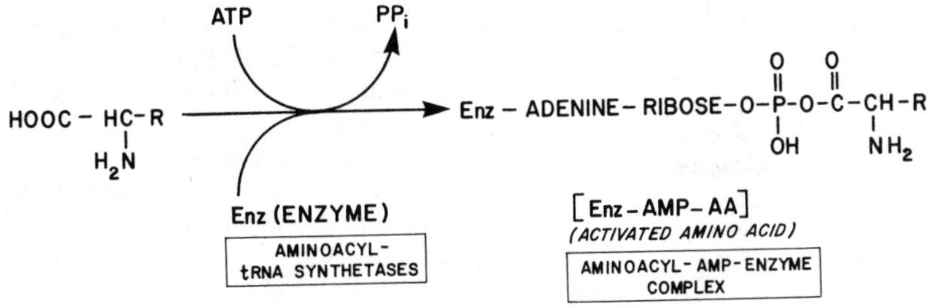

$$\text{HOOC}-\underset{\underset{\text{H}_2\text{N}}{|}}{\text{HC}}-\text{R} \xrightarrow[\text{Enz (ENZYME)}]{\text{ATP} \quad \text{PP}_i} \text{Enz}-\text{ADENINE}-\text{RIBOSE}-\text{O}-\underset{\underset{\text{OH}}{|}}{\overset{\overset{\text{O}}{\|}}{\text{P}}}-\text{O}-\underset{\underset{\text{NH}_2}{|}}{\overset{\overset{\text{O}}{\|}}{\text{C}}}-\text{CH}-\text{R}$$

Enz (ENZYME)

AMINOACYL-
tRNA SYNTHETASES

$\left[\text{Enz}-\text{AMP}-\text{AA}\right]$
(ACTIVATED AMINO ACID)

AMINOACYL-AMP-ENZYME
COMPLEX

Figure 30–2. Activation of amino acids by the formation of an enzyme-AMP–amino acid complex. The formation of the complex is catalyzed by the specific aminoacyl-tRNA synthetase itself.

tached through an ester bond. The thymidine-pseu-douridine-cytidine (T•ψ•C) loop is involved in the binding of the aminoacyl-tRNA to the ribosomal surface at the site of protein synthesis. There exists an extra arm (the lump) that is variable among the different species of tRNA molecules. The loop containing dihydrouracil (DHU loop) is one of the sites important for the proper recognition of a given tRNA species by its proper charging enzyme or aminoacyl-tRNA synthetase.

The anticodon loop exists at a pole of the tRNA molecule quite distant from the pole to which the aminoacyl moiety is attached. The **anticodon loop** of tRNA molecules consists of 7 nucleotides. The sequence read from the 3' to 5' direction in that anticodon loop consists of a variable base•modified purine•X•Y•Z•pyrimidine•pyrimidine-5'. Note that this direction of reading the anticodon is 3' to 5', whereas the genetic code in Table 30–1 is read 5' to 3', since the codon and the anticodon loop of the mRNA and tRNA molecules, respectively, are **antiparallel** in their complementarity.

Fig 27–12 is a schematic diagram of the 3-dimensional structure of yeast phenylalanine tRNA as deduced from x-ray crystallographic studies.

The degeneracy of the genetic code resides mostly in the last nucleotide of the codon triplet, suggesting that the base pairing between this last nucleotide and the corresponding nucleotide of the anticodon is not strict. As referred to above, this is called **wobble;** the pairing of the codon and anticodon can

"wobble" at this specific nucleotide-to-nucleotide pairing site. For example, the 2 anticodons for arginine, A•G•A and A•G•G, can bind to the same codon having a uracil at its 5' end. Similarly, 3 codons for glycine, G•G•U, G•G•C, and G•G•A, can base-pair with one anticodon, C•C•I. I is an inosine nucleotide, another of the peculiar bases appearing in tRNA molecules.

The codon recognition by a tRNA molecule does not depend upon the amino acid that is attached at its 3'-hydroxyl terminus. This has been ingeniously demonstrated by charging a tRNA specific for cysteine (tRNAcys) with radioactively labeled cysteine. By chemical means, the cysteinyl residue was then altered to generate a tRNA molecule specific for cysteine but charged instead with alanine. The chemical transformation of the cysteinyl to the alanyl moiety did not alter the anticodon portion of the cysteine-specific tRNA molecule. When this alanyl-tRNAcys was used in the translation of a hemoglobin mRNA, a radioactive alanine was incorporated at what was normally a cysteine site in the hemoglobin protein molecule. The experiment demonstrated that the aminoacyl derivative of an aminoacyl-tRNA molecule does not play a role in the codon recognition. As already noted, the aminoacyl moiety never comes in contact with the template mRNA containing the codons.

MUTATIONS

A mutation is a change in the nucleotide sequence of a gene. Although the initial change may not occur in the template strand of the double-stranded DNA molecule for that gene, after replication, daughter DNA molecules with mutations in the template strand will segregate and appear in the population of organisms. Single base changes may be **transitions** or **transversions.** In the former, a given pyrimidine is changed to the other pyrimidine or a given purine is changed to the other purine. Transversions are changes from a purine to either of the 2 pyrimidines or the change of a pyrimidine into either of the 2 purines, as shown in Fig 30–4.

If the nucleotide sequence of the gene containing the mutation is transcribed into an RNA molecule, then

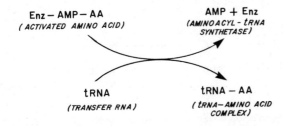

Enz – AMP – AA
(ACTIVATED AMINO ACID)

AMP + Enz
(AMINOACYL-tRNA SYNTHETASE)

tRNA
(TRANSFER RNA)

tRNA – AA
(tRNA–AMINO ACID COMPLEX)

Figure 30–3. Formation of the aminoacyl-tRNA from the activated amino acid and the appropriate tRNA. During the formation of the aminoacyl-tRNA complex, AMP and the aminoacyl-tRNA synthetase enzyme are released.

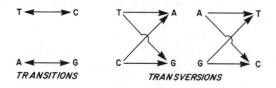

Figure 30–4. Diagrammatic representation of transition mutations and transversion mutations.

the RNA molecule will possess a complementary base change at this corresponding locus.

Single base changes in the mRNA molecules may have one of several effects when translated into protein:

(1) There may be **no detectable effect** because of the degeneracy of the code. This would be more likely if the changed base in the mRNA molecule were to fall on the third nucleotide of a codon. The translation of a codon is least sensitive to a change at the third position.

(2) A **missense** effect will occur when a different amino acid is incorporated at the corresponding site in the protein molecule. This mistaken amino acid, or missense, depending upon its location in the specific protein, might be **acceptable, partially acceptable,** or **unacceptable** to the function of that protein molecule. From a careful examination of the genetic code, one can conclude that most single base changes would result in the replacement of one amino acid by another with rather similar functional groups. This is an effective mechanism to avoid drastic change in the physical properties of a protein molecule. If an acceptable missense effect occurs, the resulting protein molecule may not be distinguishable from the normal one. A partially acceptable missense will result in a

protein molecule with partial but abnormal function. If an unacceptable missense effect occurs, then the protein molecule will not be capable of functioning in its assigned role.

(3) A **nonsense** codon may appear that would then result in the **premature termination** of amino acid incorporation into a peptide chain and the production of only a fragment of the intended protein molecule. The probability is high that a prematurely terminated protein molecule would not function in its assigned role.

Much information is available on the amino acid sequences of the normal and abnormal human hemoglobins (see Chapter 5). The hemoglobin molecule can be used to demonstrate the effects of single base changes in the hemoglobin structural gene. The **lack of effect** of a single base change would be demonstrable only by sequencing the nucleotides in the messenger RNA molecules or structural genes for hemoglobin from a large number of humans with normal hemoglobin molecules. However, it can be deduced that the codon for valine at position 67 of the β chain of hemoglobin is not identical in all persons possessing the normal β chain of hemoglobin. Hemoglobin Milwaukee has at position 67 a glutamic acid; hemoglobin Bristol contains aspartic acid at position 67. In order to account for the amino acid change by the change of a single nucleotide residue in the codon for amino acid 67, one must infer that the precursor of hemoglobin Bristol possessed a G·U·U or G·U·C codon prior to a later change to G·A·U or G·A·C, both codons for aspartic acid (Fig 30–5). However, the precursor of hemoglobin Milwaukee would have to possess at position 67 a codon G·U·A or G·U·G in order that a single nucleotide change could provide for the appearance of the glutamic acid codons G·A·A or G·A·G. Hemo-

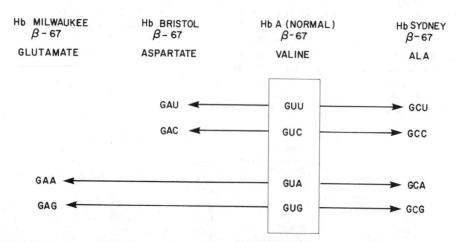

Figure 30–5. The normal valine at position 67 of the β chain of hemoglobin A can be coded for by one of the 4 codons shown in the box. In abnormal hemoglobin Milwaukee, the amino acid at position 67 of the β chain contains glutamate, coded for by G·A·A or G·A·G, either one of which could have resulted from a single-step transversion from the valine codons G·U·A or G·U·G. Similarly, the alanine present at position 67 of the β chain of hemoglobin Sydney could have resulted from a single-step transition from any one of the 4 valine codons. However, the aspartate residue at position 67 of hemoglobin Bristol could have resulted from a single-step transversion only from the G·U·U or G·U·C valine codons.

globin Sydney, which contains an alanine at position 67, could have arisen by the change of a single nucleotide in any of the 4 codons for valine (G•U•U, G•U•C, G•U•A, or G•U•G) to the alanine codons (G•C•U, G•C•C, G•C•A, or G•C•G, respectively).

An example of an **acceptable missense** mutation (Fig 30–6, top) in the structural gene for the β chain of hemoglobin could be detected by the presence of an electrophoretically altered hemoglobin in the red cells of an apparently healthy individual. Hemoglobin Hikari has been found in at least 2 families of Japanese people. This hemoglobin has asparagine substituted for lysine at the 61 position in the β chain. The corresponding transversion might be either A•A•A or A•A•G changed to either A•A•U or A•A•C. The replacement of the specific lysine with asparagine apparently does not alter the normal function of the β chain in these individuals.

A **partially acceptable missense** mutation (Fig 30–6, center) is best exemplified by **hemoglobin S,** sickle hemoglobin, in which the normal amino acid in position 6 of the β chain, glutamic acid, has been replaced by valine. The corresponding single nucleotide change within the codon would be G•A•A or G•A•G of glutamic acid to G•U•A or G•U•G of valine. Clearly, this missense mutation hinders normal function and results in sickle cell anemia when the mutant gene is present in the homozygous state. The glutamate-to-valine change may be considered to be partially acceptable because hemoglobin S does bind

and release oxygen, although abnormally.

An **unacceptable missense** mutation (Fig 30–6, bottom) in a hemoglobin gene generates a nonfunctioning hemoglobin molecule. For example, the hemoglobin M mutations generate molecules that allow the Fe^{2+} of the heme moiety to be oxidized to Fe^{3+} producing methemoglobin. Methemoglobin cannot transport oxygen. (See Chapter 5.)

Frame shift mutations, as a result of the deletion or insertion of nucleotides in the gene, generate altered nucleotide sequences of mRNA molecules. The deletion of a single nucleotide from the template strand of a gene would result in an altered reading frame in the mRNA. The machinery translating the mRNA would not recognize that a base was missing, since there is no punctuation in the reading of codons. A severe alteration in the sequence of polymerized amino acids, as depicted in Fig 30–7, would result. Altering the reading frame would result in a garbled translation of the mRNA distal to the single nucleotide deletion. Not only would the sequence of amino acids distal to this deletion be garbled, but the reading of the message might also result in the appearance of a nonsense codon and thus the production of a polypeptide prematurely terminated and garbled near its carboxyl terminus.

If 3 nucleotides or a multiple of 3 were deleted from a gene, the corresponding messenger when translated would provide a protein from which was missing the corresponding number of amino acids. Because the reading frame is a triplet, the reading phase would not

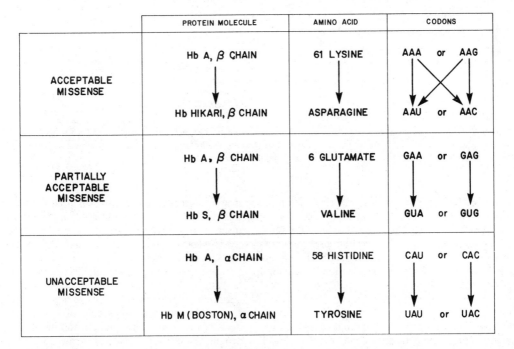

Figure 30–6. Examples of 3 types of missense mutations resulting in abnormal hemoglobin chains. The amino acid alterations and possible alterations in the respective codons are indicated. The hemoglobin Hikari β chain mutation has apparently normal physiologic properties but is electrophoretically altered. Hemoglobin S has a β chain mutation and partial function; hemoglobin S combines oxygen but precipitates when deoxygenated. Hemoglobin M Boston, an α chain mutation, permits the oxidation of the heme ferrous iron to the ferric state and thus will not bind oxygen at all.

Chapter 30. Protein Synthesis & the Genetic Code

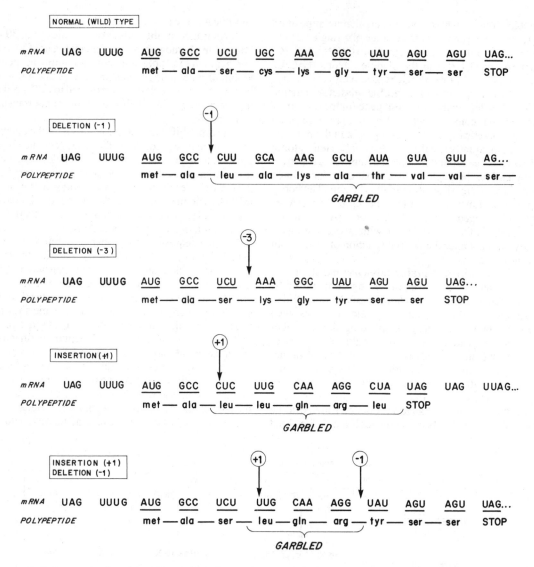

Figure 30–7. Demonstration of the effects of deletions and insertions in a gene on the sequence of the mRNA transcript and of the polypeptide chain translated therefrom. The arrows indicate the sites of deletions or insertions, and the numbers in the circles indicate the number of nucleotide residues deleted or inserted.

be disturbed for those codons distal to the deletion. If, however, deletion of one or 2 nucleotides occurs just prior to or within the normal termination codon (nonsense codon), the reading of the normal termination signal would then be disturbed. Such a deletion might result in reading through a termination signal until another nonsense codon was encountered. Excellent examples of this phenomenon are described in discussions of hemoglobinopathies.

Insertions of one or 2 or nonmultiples of 3 nucleotides into a gene will result in an mRNA in which the reading frame will be distorted upon translation, and the same effects that occur with deletions would be reflected in the mRNA translation. This may be **garbled amino acid sequences** distal to the insertion, and the generation of a **nonsense codon** at or distal to the

insertion, or perhaps **reading through** the normal termination codon. Following a deletion in a gene, an insertion (or vice versa) can reestablish the proper reading frame. The corresponding mRNA, when translated, would contain a garbled amino acid sequence between the insertion and deletion. Beyond the reestablishment of the reading frame, the amino acid sequence would be correct. One can imagine that different combinations of deletions, of insertions, or of deletions and insertions would result in formation of a protein wherein a portion is abnormal, but this portion is surrounded by the normal amino acid sequences. Such phenomena have been demonstrated convincingly in the bacteriophage T4, a finding which contributed significantly to evidence that the reading frame is a triplet.

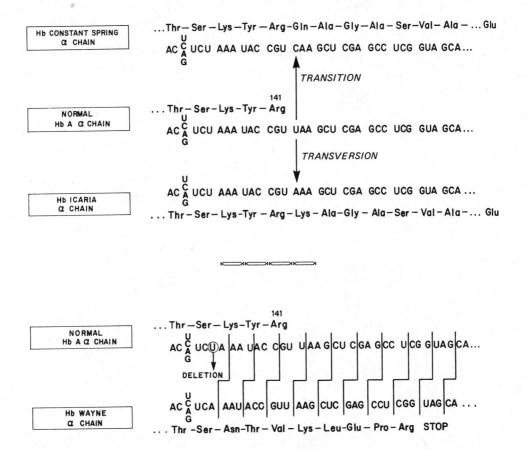

Figure 30–8. The demonstration of the effects of transitions or a deletion in the end of the hemoglobin α chain gene. Three abnormal hemoglobin molecules can result. The vertical lines in the lower portion represent the reading frame in the mRNA for hemoglobin Wayne and its origin.

The hemoglobinopathies again provide excellent examples of the effects of frame shift mutations. Generally speaking, fragments of normal proteins resulting from premature termination or proteins containing significant portions that are garbled are rapidly degraded in the cell by normal protein monitoring processes of the organism. Unfortunately, there are no currently available examples of hemoglobins demonstrating significant fractions that are garbled distal to deletions or insertions. However, 2 forms of β°-thalassemia are due to the mutational generation of nonsense codons within the coding regions of the β chain.

Hemoglobin Wayne results from a frame shift mutation at position 138 of the structural gene for the hemoglobin α chain. As shown in Fig 30–8, an adenosine nucleotide has been deleted so that the codon for amino acid 139 has been changed from A•A•A to A•A•U. The distal reading frame has been altered so that the normal termination signal, U•A•A, is read through but is out of phase. This results in the addition of 5 amino acids to the terminally garbled 3 amino acids of the protein. The reading is terminated when the new termination signal, U•A•G, appears in the out-of-phase reading.

Also shown in Fig 30–8 are 2 other mutants in the

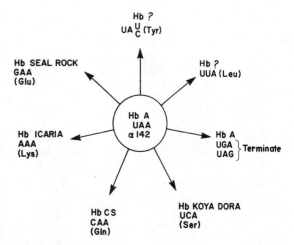

Figure 30–9. The results of all possible alterations of the normal termination signal (U•A•A) at position 142 of the mRNA for the α chain of hemoglobin A. Hemoglobin CS represents hemoglobin Constant Spring, and the hemoglobins with tyrosine or leucine at position 142 have yet to be discovered. (Redrawn and reproduced, with permission, from Weatherall DJ: Molecular pathology of the thalassemia disorders. *West J Med* 1976; **124**:388.)

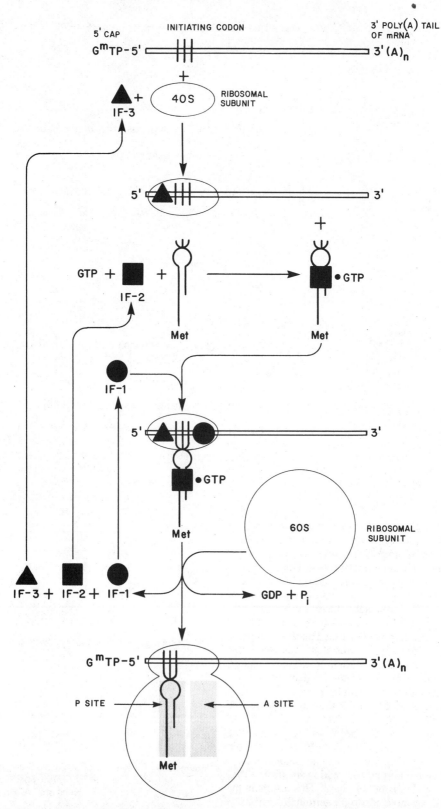

Figure 30–10. Diagrammatic representation of the initiation of protein synthesis on the mRNA template containing a 5′ cap and 3′ poly(A) terminus. IF-1, IF-2, and IF-3 represent initiation factor 1, initiation factor 2, and initiation factor 3, respectively; and the hairpinlike structure with Met at one end represents the methionyl-tRNA. The P site and the A site represent the peptidyl-tRNA and aminoacyl-tRNA binding sites of the ribosome, respectively.

gene for the α chain of hemoglobin that result in an **altered termination signal.** In hemoglobin Icaria the normal termination signal U•A•A has been altered by a single base change to A•A•A in the mRNA, allowing the peptide-synthesizing machinery to read through this normal termination signal. Similarly, the first nucleotide of the normal termination signal U•A•A has been changed to a C in the message for hemoglobin Constant Spring. This mutation results in the addition of a similar abnormal peptide at the carboxyl terminus of the α chain of the hemoglobin molecule.

Fig 30–9 summarizes the **chain termination mutants** that affect the codon U•A•A at position 142 of the α chain of the hemoglobin molecule. Note that all but 2 of the predicted mutations have been observed. Note also that, because of the degeneracy of the termination signal, 2 of the nucleotide changes (to U•G•A or to U•A•G) would not be detectable by examination of the hemoglobin molecule.

The above discussion of the altered protein products of gene mutations is based on the presence of normally functioning tRNA molecules. However, in prokaryotic and lower eukaryotic organisms, **abnormally functioning tRNA molecules** have been discovered that are themselves the results of mutations. Some of these abnormal tRNA molecules are capable of suppressing the effects of mutations in distant structural genes. These **suppressor tRNA molecules,** usually as the result of alterations in their anticodon regions, are capable of suppressing missense mutations, nonsense mutations, and frame shift mutations. However, since the suppressor tRNA molecules are not capable of distinguishing between a normal codon and one resulting from a gene mutation, their presence in a cell usually results in decreased viability. For instance, the nonsense suppressor tRNA molecules can suppress the normal termination signals to allow a read-through when it is not desirable. Frame shift suppressor tRNA molecules may read a normal codon plus a component of a juxtaposed codon to provide a frame shift, also when it is not desirable. Suppressor tRNA molecules have not been found in mammalian cells.

PROTEIN SYNTHESIS

The general structural characteristics of ribosomes and their self-assembly process have been discussed in Chapter 29. These particulate entities serve as the machinery on which the mRNA nucleotide sequence is translated into the sequence of amino acids of the specified protein. The translation of the mRNA commences near its 5′ terminus with the formation of the corresponding amino terminus of the protein molecule. The message is read toward its 3′ terminus, concluding with the formation of the carboxyl terminus of the protein. As described in Chapter 29, the transcription of a gene into the corresponding mRNA or its precursor first forms the 5′ terminus of the RNA

molecule. In prokaryotes, this allows for the beginning of mRNA translation before the transcription of the gene is completed. In eukaryotic organisms, the process of transcription is a nuclear one; mRNA translation occurs in the cytoplasm. This precludes simultaneous transcription and translation in eukaryotic organisms and makes possible the processing necessary to generate mature mRNA from the primary transcript—hnRNA.

The process of protein synthesis, like that of gene transcription, can be described in 3 phases: initiation, elongation, and termination.

Initiation of Protein Synthesis
(See Fig 30–10.)

The 5′ termini of most mRNA molecules in eukaryotes are "capped" as described in Chapter 29. This methyl-guanosyl triphosphate cap may be involved in the binding of many mRNA molecules to the 40S ribosomal subunit. The first codon to be translated, usually A•U•G, is indented from the capped 5′ terminus. The 18S ribosomal RNA (rRNA) of the 40S ribosomal subunit binds to a region of the mRNA that precedes the first translated codon. This binding of the mRNA to the 40S ribosomal subunit requires the presence of a protein factor, initiation factor 3 (IF-3).

The aminoacyl-tRNA called for by the first codon then interacts with GTP and initiation factor 2 (IF-2) to form a complex. This complex in the presence of initiation factor 1 (IF-1) attaches the anticodon of the tRNA to the first codon of the message to form an initiation complex with the 40S ribosomal subunit. Upon release of the initiation factors (IF-1, IF-2, and IF-3), the 60S ribosomal subunit attaches and the GTP is hydrolyzed. The formation of the 80S ribosome is thus complete.

The complete ribosome contains 2 sites for tRNA molecules. The peptidyl or **P site** contains the peptidyl-tRNA attached to its codon on the mRNA. The aminoacyl or **A site** contains the aminoacyl-tRNA attached to its respective codon on the mRNA. With the formation of the initiation complex for the first codon, the aminoacyl-tRNA molecule enters at what will become the P site, leaving the A site free. Thus, the reading frame is defined by attachment of the tRNA to the first codon to be translated in the mRNA. The recognition of this specific initiating codon is apparently dependent upon the secondary structure of the mRNA molecule and in addition involves in prokaryotes, and perhaps in eukaryotes, a specific sequence of nucleotides complementary to a segment of the 16S (18S) ribosomal RNA.

In prokaryotes, a specific aminoacyl-tRNA is involved in the initiation of synthesis of most, if not all, protein molecules. N-Formylmethionyl-tRNA initiates most proteins in prokaryotes. Although methionine is the N-terminal amino acid in many eukaryotic proteins, the methionyl-tRNA is not formylated in eukaryotes. In prokaryotes, the N-formylation of the methionyl on the tRNA seems to deceive the

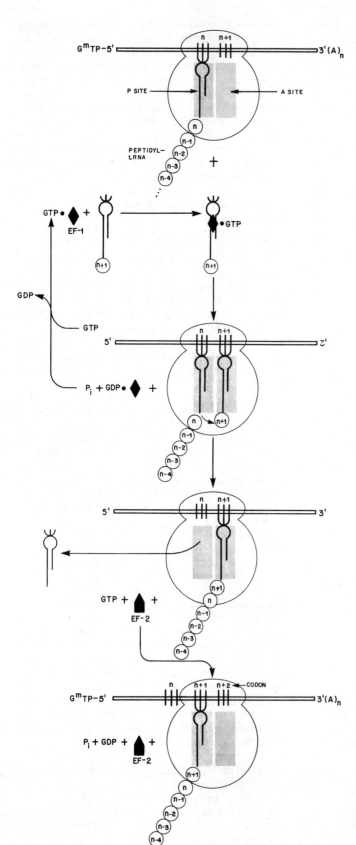

Figure 30–11. Diagrammatic representation of the peptide elongation process of protein synthesis. The small circles labeled n−1, n, n+1, etc, represent the amino acid residues of the newly formed protein molecule. EF-1 and EF-2 represent elongation factors 1 and 2, respectively. The peptidyl-tRNA and aminoacyl-tRNA sites on the ribosome are represented by P site and A site, respectively.

P site of the ribosome by appearing to be a peptide bond. There exists also in prokaryotes an enzyme capable of removing the N-terminal formyl moiety or N-terminal methionyl residue (or both) from proteins, in many cases even before the complete protein molecule has been formed.

Elongation

In the complete 80S ribosome formed during the process of initiation, the A site is free. The binding of the proper aminoacyl-tRNA in the A site requires proper codon recognition. Elongation factor 1 (EF-1) forms a complex with GTP and the entering aminoacyl-tRNA (Fig 30–11). This complex then allows the aminoacyl-tRNA to enter the A site with the release of EF-1·GDP and phosphate. As shown in Fig 30–11, EF-1·GDP then recycles to EF-1·GTP with the aid of other soluble protein factors and GTP.

The α amino group of the new aminoacyl-tRNA in the A site carries out a nucleophilic attack on the esterified carboxyl group of the peptidyl-tRNA occupying the P site. This reaction is catalyzed by a protein component, **peptidyl transferase,** of the 60S ribosomal subunit. Because the amino acid on the aminoacyl-tRNA is already "activated," no further energy source is required for this reaction. The reaction results in attachment of the growing peptide chain to the tRNA in the A site.

Upon removal of the peptidyl moiety from the tRNA in the P site, the discharged tRNA quickly vacates the P site. Elongation factor 2 (EF-2) and GTP are responsible for the **translocation** of the newly formed peptidyl-tRNA at the A site into the vacated P site. The GTP required for EF-2 is hydrolyzed to GDP and phosphate during the translocation process. The translocation of the newly formed peptidyl-tRNA and its corresponding codon into the P site then frees the A site for another cycle of aminoacyl-tRNA codon recognition and elongation.

The charging of the tRNA molecule with the aminoacyl moiety requires the hydrolysis of an ATP to an AMP, equivalent to the hydrolysis of 2 ATPs to 2 ADPs and phosphates. The entry of the aminoacyl-tRNA into the A site results in the hydrolysis of one GTP to GDP. The translocation of the newly formed peptidyl-tRNA in the A site into the P site by EF-2 similarly results in the hydrolysis of GTP to GDP and phosphate. Thus, the energy requirements for the formation of one peptide bond include the equivalent of the hydrolysis of 2 ATP molecules to ADP and 2 GTP molecules to GDP.

Termination

After multiple cycles of elongation culminating in polymerization of the specific amino acids into a protein molecule, the nonsense or terminating codon of mRNA appears in the A site. There is no tRNA with an anticodon to recognize such a termination signal. **Releasing factors** are capable of recognizing that a termination signal resides in the A site (Fig 30–12). The releasing factor, in conjunction with GTP and the

peptidyl transferase, promotes the hydrolysis of the bond between the peptide and the tRNA occupying the P site. This hydrolysis releases the protein and the tRNA from the P site. Upon hydrolysis and release, the **80S ribosome dissociates** into its 40S and 60S subunits, which are then recycled.

The releasing factors are proteins that hydrolyze the peptidyl-tRNA bond when a nonsense codon occupies the A site.

Many ribosomes can translate the same mRNA molecule simultaneously. Because of their relatively large size, the ribosome particles cannot attach to an mRNA any closer than 80 nucleotides apart. Multiple ribosomes on the same mRNA molecule form a **polyribosome,** or "polysome." In an unrestricted system, the number of ribosomes attached to an mRNA (and thus the size of polyribosomes) correlates positively with the length of the mRNA molecule. The mass of the mRNA molecule is, of course, quite small compared to the mass of even a single ribosome.

A single mammalian ribosome is capable of translating in 2 minutes about 200 codons into a protein with a molecular weight of approximately 20,000.

Polyribosomes actively synthesizing proteins can exist as free particles in the cellular cytoplasm or may be attached to sheets of membranous cytoplasmic material referred to as endoplasmic reticulum. The attachment of the particulate polyribosomes to the endoplasmic reticulum is responsible for its "rough" appearance as seen by electron microscopy. The proteins synthesized by the attached polyribosomes are extruded into the cisternal space between the sheets of rough endoplasmic reticulum and are exported from there. Some of the protein products of the rough endoplasmic reticulum are packaged by the Golgi apparatus into zymogen particles for eventual exportation. (See Chapter 32.) The polyribosomal particles free in the cytosol are responsible for the synthesis of proteins required for intracellular functions.

Protein Processing

Some animal viruses, notably poliovirus (an RNA virus), synthesize long polycistronic proteins from one long mRNA molecule. These protein molecules are subsequently cleaved at specific sites to provide the several specific proteins required for viral function. In animal cells, many proteins are modified following their synthesis from the mRNA template. Insulin, a low-molecular-weight protein having 2 polypeptide chains with interchain and intrachain disulfide bridges, is synthesized as a preproinsulin molecule. The single polypeptide proinsulin folds to allow the disulfide bridges to form, and then a specific protease clips out a segment at the head of the hairpin. These posttranslational modifications are responsible for generation of the functional insulin molecule.

Many other peptide hormones are synthesized as **prohormones** that require modification before attaining biologic activity. Many of the posttranslational modifications involve the removal of N-terminal amino acid residues by specific aminopeptidases. Col-

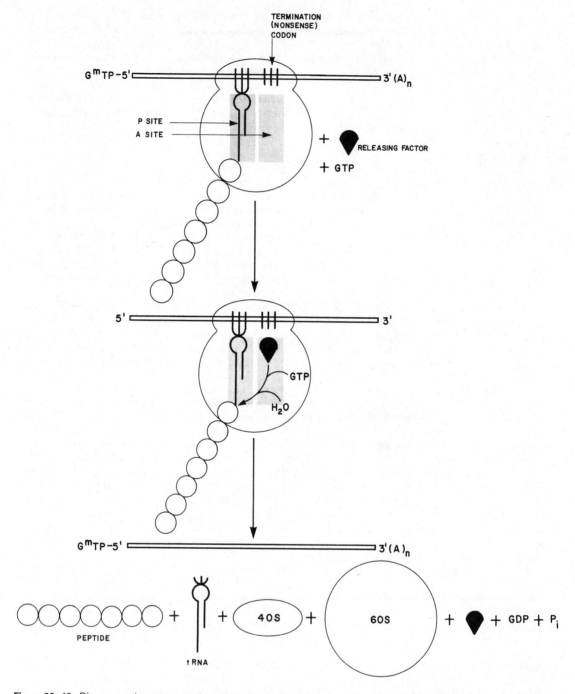

Figure 30–12. Diagrammatic representation of the termination process of protein synthesis. The peptidyl-tRNA and aminoacyl-tRNA sites are indicated as P site and A site, respectively. The hydrolysis of the peptidyl-tRNA complex is shown by the entry of H_2O.

lagen, an abundant protein in the extracellular spaces of higher eukaryotes, is synthesized as procollagen. Three procollagen polypeptide molecules, frequently not identical in sequence, align themselves in a way dependent upon the existence of specific amino-terminal peptides. Specific enzymes then carry out hydrox-

ylations and oxidations of specific amino acid residues within the procollagen molecules to provide cross-links for greater stability. Amino-terminal peptides are cleaved off the molecule to form the final product, a strong, insoluble collagen molecule. (See Chapter 34.)

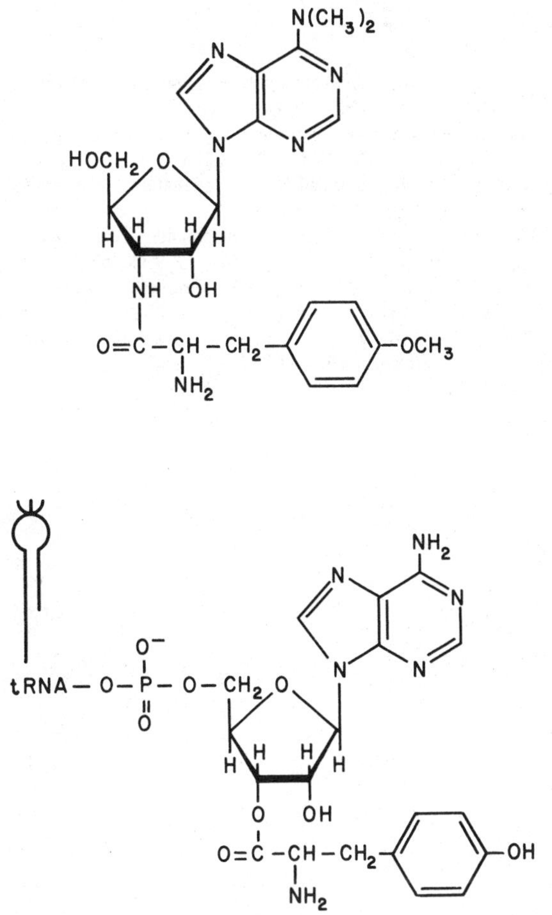

Figure 30-13. The comparative structures of the antibiotic puromycin and the 3' terminal portion of tyrosinyl-tRNA.

Inhibitors of Protein Synthesis

Many clinically effective antibiotics act by specifically inhibiting protein synthesis in prokaryotic organisms. Most of these inhibitors interact specifically with the proteins of prokaryotic ribosomes. A number of the effective antibiotics do not interact with the specific proteins of eukaryotic ribosomal particles and are thus not toxic to eukaryotes.

Puromycin, the structure of which is shown in Fig 30-13, is a structural analog of tyrosinyl-tRNA. Puromycin is incorporated via the A site on the ribosome into the carboxy-terminal position of a peptide but causes the premature release of the polypeptide. Puromycin, as a tyrosinyl-tRNA analog, effectively inhibits protein synthesis in both prokaryotes and eukaryotes.

Diphtheria toxin, an exotoxin of *Corynebacterium diphtheriae* infected with a specific lysogenic phage, catalyzes the ADP ribosylation of EF-2 in mammalian cells. This modification inactivates EF-2 and thereby specifically inhibits mammalian protein synthesis. Many organisms such as mice are resistant to diphtheria toxin. This resistance is due to inability of diphtheria toxin to cross the cell membrane rather than to insensitivity of mouse EF-2 to diphtheria toxin-catalyzed ADP ribosylation by NAD.

Table 30-3 summarizes the effects of some antibiotics on the 3 phases of protein synthesis.

Table 30-3. Antibiotic inhibitors of translation.

	Eukaryotes (Cytoplasm)	Eukaryotes (Mitochondria)	Prokaryotes
Initiation			
Aurintricarboxylic acid	−	−	+
Elongation			
Amicetin	?	?	+
Anisomycin	−	?	+
Chloramphenicol	−	+	+
Cycloheximide	+	−	−
Fusidic acid	?	?	+
Lincocin	−	?	+
Puromycin	+	+	+
Sparsomycin	+	+	+
Tetracyclines	−	+	+
Termination			
Anisomycin	?	?	*
Amicetin	?	?	+
Chloramphenicol	−	+	+
Erythromycin	−	+	+
Lincocin	?	?	+
Sparsomycin	+	+	+
Streptomycin	+	±	+

+ = inhibition; − = no inhibition; * = stimulation; ? = unknown.

• • •

References

Barrell BG et al: Different pattern of codon recognition by mammalian mitochondrial tRNAs. *Proc Natl Acad Sci USA* 1980;**77**:3164.

Caskey CT: Peptide chain termination. *Trends Biochem Sci* 1980;**5**:234.

Drake JW, Baltz RH: The biochemistry of mutagenesis. *Annu Rev Biochem* 1976;**45**:11.

Forget BG: Molecular genetics of human hemoglobin synthesis. *Ann Intern Med* 1979;**91**:605.

Haselkorn R, Rothman-Denes LB: Protein synthesis. *Annu Rev Biochem* 1973;**42**:397.

Roth JR: Frameshift mutations. *Annu Rev Genet* 1974;**8**:319.

Schafritz DA et al: Evidence for the role of $M^7G^{5'}$-phosphate group in recognition of eukaryotic mRNA by inhibition factor IF-M_3. *Nature* 1976;**261**:291.

Schlessinger D: Genetic and antibiotic modification of protein synthesis. *Annu Rev Genet* 1974;**8**:135.

Weatherall D: Molecular pathology of the thalassemia disorders. *West J Med* 1976;**124**:388.

Weatherall D, Clegg J: Recent developments in the molecular genetics of human hemoglobin. *Cell* 1979;**16**:487.

Weissbach G, Ochoa S: Soluble factors required for eukaryotic protein synthesis. *Annu Rev Biochem* 1976;**45**:191.

Wool I: The structure and function of eukaryotic ribosomes. *Annu Rev Biochem* 1979;**48**:719.

Regulation of Gene Expression | 31

David W. Martin, Jr., MD

The genetic information present in each somatic cell of a metazoan organism is practically identical. The exceptions are found in those few cells that have amplified or rearranged genes in order to carry out specialized cellular functions. The expression of the genetic information must be regulated during ontogeny and differentiation of the organism and its cellular components. Furthermore, in order for the organism to adapt to its environment and to conserve energy and nutrients, the expression of genetic information must be responsive to extrinsic signals. As organisms have evolved, more sophisticated regulatory mechanisms have appeared to provide the organism and its cells with the responsiveness necessary for survival in its complex environment. Mammalian cells possess only about 1000 times more genetic information than does the bacterium *Escherichia coli;* however, much of this additional genetic information is probably involved in the regulation of gene expression.

In simple terms, there are only 2 types of gene regulation: **positive regulation** and **negative regulation** (Table 31–1). When the expression of genetic information is quantitatively **increased** by the presence of a specific regulatory element, regulation is said to be **positive;** whereas when the expression of genetic information is **diminished** by the presence of a specific regulatory element, regulation is said to be **negative.** The element or molecule mediating the negative regulation is said to be a negative regulator; that mediating positive regulation is a positive regulator. However, a **double negative** has the effect of acting as a **positive.** Thus, an effector that inhibits the function of a negative regulator will appear to bring about a positive regulation. In many regulated systems that appear to be induced, they are, in fact, derepressed at the molecular level. (See Chapter 9 for a description of these terms.)

In biologic organisms, there are 3 types of temporal responses to a regulatory signal. These 3 responses are depicted diagrammatically in Fig 31–1 as rate of gene expression in temporal response to an inducing signal.

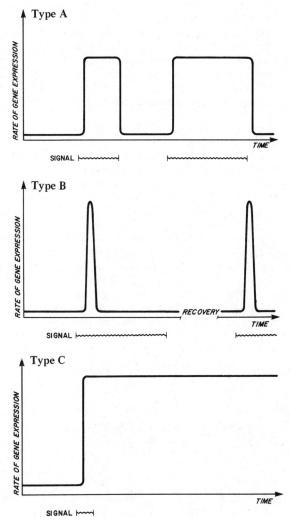

Figure 31–1. Diagrammatic representations of the responses of the rate of expression of a gene to specific regulatory signals such as a hormone.

Table 31–1. Effects of positive and negative regulation on gene expression.

	Rate of Gene Expression	
	Negative Regulation	**Positive Regulation**
Regulator present	Decreased	Increased
Regulator absent	Increased	Decreased

A **type A response** is characterized by an increased rate of gene expression that is **dependent** upon the continued presence of the inducing signal. When the inducing signal is removed, the rate of gene expression diminishes to its basal level, but the rate repeatedly increases in response to the reappearance of the specific signal. This type of response is commonly observed in many higher organisms after exposures to inducers such as steroid hormones (see Chapter 35).

A **type B response** exhibits an increased rate of gene expression that is **transient** even in the continued presence of the regulatory signal. After the regulatory signal has terminated and the cell has been allowed to recover, a second transient response to a subsequent regulatory signal may be observed. This type of response may commonly occur during development of an organism when only the transient appearance of a specific gene product is required although the signal persists.

The **type C response** pattern exhibits, in response to the regulatory signal, an increased rate of gene expression that persists **indefinitely** even after the termination of the signal. The signal acts as a trigger in this pattern. The response is typical of a differentiative process. Once the gene expression is initiated in the cell, it cannot be terminated even in the daughter cells; it is therefore an irreversible and inherited alteration.

Models for the Study of the Regulation of Gene Expression

In the last 20 years, with the understanding of how information flows from the gene through a messenger RNA to a specific protein molecule, there has developed sophisticated knowledge of the regulation of gene expression in prokaryotic cells. Most of the detailed knowledge about molecular mechanisms has been limited until recent years to prokaryotic and lower eukaryotic systems. This was due to the more advanced genetic analyses first available in the primitive organisms. Recent advances in recombinant DNA technology have allowed the sophisticated analysis of mammalian gene expression to begin. In this chapter, the initial discussion will center on prokaryotic systems. The impressive genetic studies will not be described, but rather what may be termed the physiology of gene expression will be discussed. However, nearly all of the conclusions about this physiology have been derived from genetic studies.

Before the physiology can be explained, a few specialized genetic terms must be defined for prokaryotic systems.

The **cistron** is the smallest unit of genetic expression. As described in Chapter 9, some enzymes and other protein molecules are composed of 2 or more nonidentical subunits. Thus, the "one gene, one enzyme" concept is now known not to be necessarily valid. The cistron is the genetic unit coding for the structure of the subunit of a protein molecule, acting as it does as the smallest unit of genetic expression. Thus, the one gene, one enzyme idea might more accurately be regarded as a **one cistron, one subunit concept.**

An **inducible gene** is a gene whose expression increases in response to an **inducer,** a specific regulatory signal.

The expression of some genes is **constitutive,** meaning that they are expressed at a reasonably constant rate and not known to be subject to regulation. As the result of mutation, some inducible gene products become constitutively expressed. A mutation resulting in constitutive expression of what was formerly a regulated gene is called a constitutive mutation.

REGULATION IN PROKARYOTES

The Lac Operon

François Jacob and Jacques Monod in 1961 described their **operon** model in a classic paper. Their hypothesis was to a large extent based on observations on the regulation of lactose metabolism by the intestinal bacterium *E coli*. The molecular mechanisms responsible for the regulation of the genes involved in the metabolism of lactose are now among the best understood in any organism. β-Galactosidase hydrolyzes the β-galactoside lactose to galactose and glucose (Fig 31–2). The structural (Z) gene for β-galactosidase is

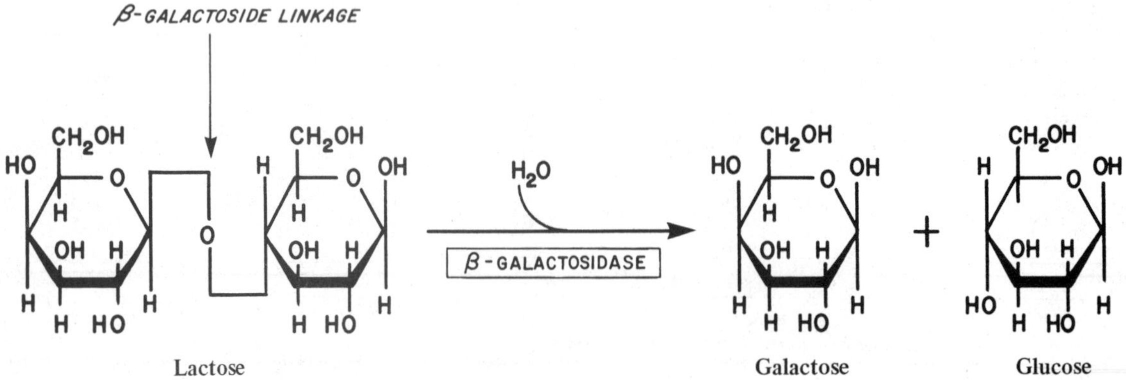

β-GALACTOSIDE LINKAGE

Lactose $+ H_2O$ β-GALACTOSIDASE   →   Galactose   +   Glucose

Figure 31–2. The hydrolysis by the enzyme β-galactosidase of lactose to galactose and glucose.

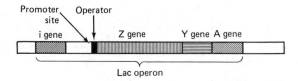

Figure 31–3. The positional relationships of the structural and regulatory genes of the lac operon.

clustered with the genes responsible for the permeation of galactose into the cell (Y) and for galactoside acetylase (A), whose function is not understood. The structural genes for these 3 enzymes are physically associated to constitute the **lac operon** as depicted in Fig 31–3. This genetic arrangement of the structural genes and their regulatory genes allows for the **coordinate expression** of the 3 enzymes concerned with lactose metabolism.

When *E coli* are presented with lactose or some specific lactose analogs, the expression of the activities of β-galactosidase, galactoside permease, and galactoside acetylase is increased 10-fold to 100-fold. This is a type A response, as seen in Fig 31–1. Upon removal of the signal, ie, the inducer, the rate of synthesis of these 3 enzymes declines. Since there is no significant degradation of these enzymes in bacteria, the level of β-galactosidase as well as those of the other 2 enzymes will remain the same unless they are diluted out by cell division.

When *E coli* are exposed to both lactose and glucose as sources of carbon, the organisms first metabolize the glucose and then temporarily cease growing until the genes of the lac operon become induced to provide the ability to metabolize lactose. This type of growth in the presence of 2 carbon sources such as glucose and lactose is biphasic; it is termed **diauxie** (Fig 31–4).

Although lactose is present from the beginning of the bacterial growth phase, the cell does not commence to induce those enzymes necessary for catabolism of lactose until the glucose has been exhausted. This

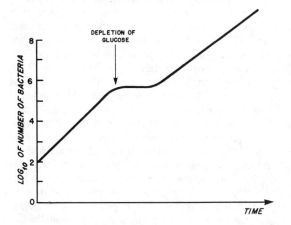

Figure 31–4. The diauxic growth of *E coli* on a mixture of glucose and lactose.

phenomenon was first thought to be attributable to the repression of the lactose operon by some catabolite of glucose; hence, it was termed **catabolite repression.** It is now known that "catabolite repression" is in fact mediated by a **catabolite gene activator protein (CAP)** and **cyclic AMP (cAMP).** The expression of many inducible enzyme systems or operons in *E coli* and other prokaryotes is sensitive to catabolite repression, as discussed below.

The physiology of the induction of the lac operon is well understood at the molecular level (Fig 31–5). The expression of the normal **i gene** of the lac operon is constitutive; it is expressed at a constant rate, resulting in the formation of the subunits of the **lac repressor.** Four identical subunits of MW 38,000 assemble into a lac repressor molecule. The repressor protein molecule, the product of the i gene, has a high affinity (K_d about 10^{-12} mol/L) for the operator locus. The **operator locus** is a region of double-stranded DNA 27 base pairs long with a 2-fold rotational symmetry (indicated by solid lines about the dotted axis) in a region that is 21 base pairs long, as shown below:

$$5'\text{-}\overline{AATTGTGAGC}\; \overset{.}{G}\; \overline{GATAACAATT}$$
$$3'\text{-}\underline{TTAACACTCG}\; \underset{.}{C}\; \underline{CTATTGTTAA}$$

The minimum effective size of an operator for lac repressor binding is 17 base pairs (boldface letters in above sequence). At any one time, only 2 subunits of the repressors appear to bind to the operator, and within the 17-base-pair region at least one base of each base pair is involved in the lac repressor recognition and binding. The binding occurs mostly in the **major groove** without interrupting the base-paired, double helical nature of the operator DNA. The amino acid residues in positions 1–52 of the repressor subunits seem to recognize DNA nonspecifically, whereas the amino acid residues in positions 53–58 of the repressor specifically bind to the 17-base-pair region, a region about 6–7 nm long. The amino acid residues in positions 74 and 75 are particularly involved in the binding of the inducer to the repressor molecule. The **operator locus** is between the **promoter site,** at which the DNA-dependent RNA polymerase attaches to commence transcription, and the beginning of the **Z gene,** the structural gene for β-galactosidase (Fig 31–3). When attached to the operator locus, the repressor molecule prevents the transcription of the operator locus as well as of the distal structural genes, Z, Y, and A. Thus, the repressor molecule is a **negative regulator;** in its presence the expression of the Z, Y, and A genes is prevented. There are normally present 20–40 repressor molecules and one or 2 operator loci per cell.

A lactose analog that is capable of inducing the lac operon while not itself serving as a substrate for β-galactosidase is called a **gratuitous inducer.** The addition of lactose or of a gratuitous inducer to bacteria growing on a limited carbon source (such as succinate) results in the prompt induction of β-galactosidase, permease, and acetylase. Small amounts of the

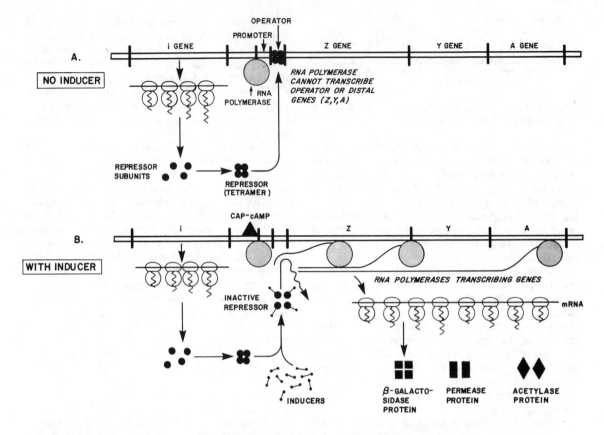

Figure 31–5. The mechanism of repression and derepression of the lactose operon. When no inducer is present *(A)*, the i gene products that are synthesized constitutively form a repressor molecule which binds at the operator locus to prevent the binding of RNA polymerase at the promoter locus and thus to prevent the subsequent transcription of the Z, Y, and A structural genes. When inducer is present *(B)*, the constitutively expressed i gene forms repressor molecules that are inactivated by the inducer and cannot bind to the operator locus. In the presence of cAMP and its binding protein (CAP), the RNA polymerase can transcribe the structural genes Z, Y, and A, and the polycistronic mRNA molecule formed can be translated into the corresponding protein molecules β-galactosidase, permease, and acetylase, allowing for the catabolism of lactose.

gratuitous inducer or of lactose are able to enter the cell even in the absence of permease. The repressor molecules, both those attached to the operator loci and those free in the cytosol, have an affinity for the inducer. The binding of the inducer to a repressor molecule attached to the operator locus will cause the repressor to detach. If DNA-dependent RNA polymerase has already attached to the template strand at the promoter site, transcription will commence. The polymerase generates a polycistronic mRNA, the 5′ terminus of which is complementary to the template strand of the operator. In such a manner, an inducer derepresses the lac operon and allows the transcription of the structural genes for galactosidase, galactoside permease, and galactoside acetylase. The translation of the polycistronic mRNA can occur even before the transcription is completed. The derepression of the lac operon allows the cell to synthesize the enzymes necessary to catabolize lactose as an energy source. In order for the RNA polymerase to attach at the promoter site, there must also be present the catabolite gene

activation protein (CAP) to which cAMP is attached. By an independent mechanism, the bacterium accumulates cAMP only when it is starved for a source of carbon. In the presence of glucose or of glycerol in concentrations sufficient for growth, the bacteria will lack sufficient cAMP to bind to CAP. Thus, in the presence of glucose or glycerol, cAMP-saturated CAP is lacking, so that the DNA-dependent RNA polymerase cannot commence the transcription of the lac operon. In the presence of the CAP-cAMP complex on the promoter site, transcription then occurs. Thus, the CAP-cAMP regulator is acting as a **positive regulator,** because its presence is required for gene expression. Hence, the lac operon is subject to both positive and negative regulation. This phenomenon accounts for the diauxic growth of *E coli* on glucose and lactose.

When the i gene has been mutated so that its product, the lac repressor, is not capable of binding to operator DNA, the organism will exhibit **constitutive expression** of the lac operon. In a contrary manner, an organism with an i gene mutation that prevents the binding of an inducer to the repressor will remain repressed even in the presence of the inducer molecule, because the inducer cannot bind to the repressor on the operator locus in order to derepress the operon.

Bacteria harboring mutations in their operator locus such that the operator sequence will not bind a normal repressor molecule are constitutive for the expression of the lac operon genes.

Bacteriophage Lambda (λ)

Some bacteria harbor viruses that can reside in a dormant state within the bacterial chromosome or can replicate within the bacterium and eventually lead to lysis and killing of the bacterial host. Some *E coli* harbor such a "temperate" virus, bacteriophage lambda (λ). When a lambda infects a sensitive *E coli*, it injects its 45,000-base-pair, double-stranded, linear DNA molecule into the cell (Fig 31–6). Depending upon the nutritional state of the cell, the lambda DNA will either **integrate** into the host genome (lysogenic pathway) and remain dormant until activated (see below), or it will commence **replicating** until it has made about 100 copies of complete, protein-packaged virus at which point it effects lysis of its host (lytic pathway). The newly generated virus particles can then infect other sensitive hosts.

When integrated into the host genome in its dormant state, lambda will remain in such a state until activated by exposure of its lysogenic bacterial host to DNA-damaging agents. In response to such a noxious stimulus, the dormant bacteriophage becomes "induced" and begins to transcribe and subsequently translate those genes of its own genome which are necessary for its excision from the host chromosome, its DNA replication, and its protein coat and lysis enzymes. This event acts like a trigger or type C (Fig 31–1) response; that is, once lambda has committed itself to induction, there is no turning back until the cell is lysed and the replicated bacteriophage released. This **switch** from a dormant or **prophage state** to a **lytic infection** is well understood at the genetic and molecular levels and will be described as a paradigm.

The switching event in lambda is centered around an 80-base-pair region in its double-stranded DNA molecule referred to as the "right operator" (O_R) (Fig 31–7A). The **right operator** is flanked on its left side by the structural gene for the lambda **repressor** and on its right side by the structural gene for another regulatory protein called **cro.** When lambda is in its prophage state, ie, integrated into the host genome, the **repressor gene** is the *only* lambda gene that is expressed. When the bacteriophage is undergoing lytic growth, the repressor gene is not expressed, but the cro gene, as well as many other genes in lambda, is expressed. That is, when the **repressor gene is on,** the **cro gene is off,** and when the **cro gene is on,** the **repressor gene is off.** As we shall see, these 2 genes regulate each other's expression.

The operator region can be subdivided into 3 discrete sites, each consisting of 17 base pairs of similar but not identical DNA sequence (Fig 31–7B). Each

of these 3 subregions, O_R1, O_R2, and O_R3, can bind either repressor or cro proteins in the major groove of the DNA double helix. The DNA region between the cro and repressor genes also contains 2 promoter sequences that direct the binding of RNA polymerase in a specified orientation, where it commences transcrib-

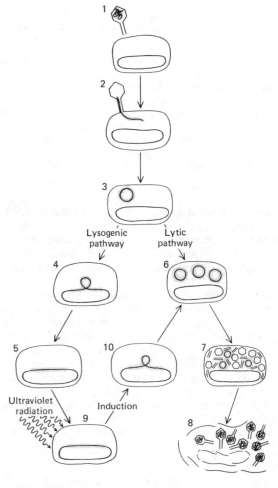

Figure 31–6. Infection of the bacterium *E coli* by the lambda virus begins when a virus particle attaches itself to the bacterial cell (1) and injects its DNA (shaded area) into the cell (2, 3). Infection can take either of 2 courses depending on which of 2 sets of viral genes is turned on. In the lysogenic pathway, the viral DNA becomes integrated into the bacterial chromosome (4, 5), where it replicates passively as the bacterial cell divides. The dormant virus is called a prophage, and the cell that harbors it is called a lysogen. In the alternative lytic mode of infection, the viral DNA replicates itself (6) and directs the synthesis of viral proteins (7). About 100 new virus particles are formed. The proliferating viruses lyse, or burst, the cell (8). A prophage can be "induced" by an agent such as ultraviolet radiation (9). The inducing agent throws a switch, so that a different set of genes is turned on. Viral DNA loops out of the chromosome (10) and replicates; the virus proceeds along the lytic pathway. (Reproduced, with permission, from Ptashne M, Johnson AD, Pabo CO: A genetic switch in a bacterial virus. *Sci Am* [Nov] 1982;**247**:128.)

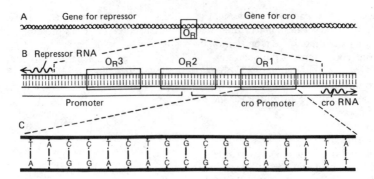

Figure 31–7. Right operator (O_R) is shown in increasing detail in this series of drawings. The operator is a region of the viral DNA some 80 base pairs long *(A)*. To its left lies the gene encoding lambda repressor, to its right the gene (cro) encoding the regulator protein cro. When the operator region is enlarged *(B)*, it is seen to include 3 subregions, O_R1, O_R2, and O_R3, each 17 base pairs long. They are recognition sites to which repressor and cro can bind. The recognition sites overlap 2 promoters: sequences of bases to which the enzyme RNA polymerase binds in order to transcribe a gene into mRNA (wavy lines), which is translated into protein. Site O_R1 is enlarged *(C)* to show its base sequence. (Reproduced, with permission, from Ptashne M, Johnson AD, Pabo CO: A genetic switch in a bacterial virus. *Sci Am* [Nov] 1982;**247**:128.)

ing the adjacent genes. One promoter directs RNA polymerase to commence transcription in the **rightward direction** and, thus, to transcribe cro and other distal genes, while the other promoter directs the transcription of the **repressor** gene in the **leftward direction** (Fig 31–7B).

The product of the repressor gene, the 236-amino-acid **repressor protein,** exists as a **2-domain** molecule in which the **amino-terminal domain binds to operator DNA** and the **carboxy-terminal domain promotes the association** of one repressor protein with another to form a dimer. A **dimer** of repressor molecules binds to **operator DNA** much more tightly than does the monomeric form (Fig 31–8A to C).

The product of the cro gene, the 66-amino-acid **cro protein,** has a single domain but also binds the operator DNA more tightly as a **dimer** (Fig 31–8D).

Obviously, the cro protein's single domain mediates both operator binding and dimerization.

In a lysogenic bacterium, ie, a bacterium containing a lambda prophage, the lambda repressor dimer binds **preferentially to O_R1** but in so doing, by a cooperative interaction (see Chapter 5), **enhances** the binding of another repressor dimer to O_R2 (Fig 31–9). The affinity of repressor for O_R3 is the least of the 3 operator subregions. The binding of repressor to O_R1 has 2 major effects. The occupation of O_R1 by repressor **blocks the binding of RNA polymerase to the rightward promoter** and thereby prevents the expression of the cro gene. Secondly, as mentioned above, repressor dimer bound to O_R1 enhances the binding of repressor dimer to O_R2. The binding of repressor to O_R2 has the important effect of **enhancing the binding of RNA polymerase to the leftward promoter**

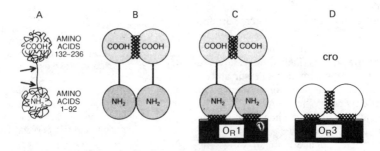

Figure 31–8. Lambda repressor protein is a chain of 236 amino acids. The chain folds itself into a dumbbell shape with 2 substructures: an amino-terminal (NH_2) domain and a carboxy-terminal (COOH) domain. The 2 domains are linked by a region of the chain that is susceptible to cleavage by proteases *(A)*. Single repressor molecules (monomers) tend to associate to form dimers *(B)*; a dimer can dissociate to form monomers again. A dimer is held together mainly by contact between the carboxy-terminal domains (hatching). Repressor dimers bind to (and can fall off) the recognition sites in the operator region; their greatest affinity is for site O_R1 *(C)*. It is the amino-terminal domain of the repressor molecule that makes contact with the DNA (hatching). Cro *(D)* has a single domain with sites that promote dimerization and other sites that promote binding of dimers to operator, preferentially to O_R3. (Reproduced, with permission, from Ptashne M, Johnson AD, Pabo CO: A genetic switch in a bacterial virus. *Sci Am* [Nov] 1982;**247**:128.)

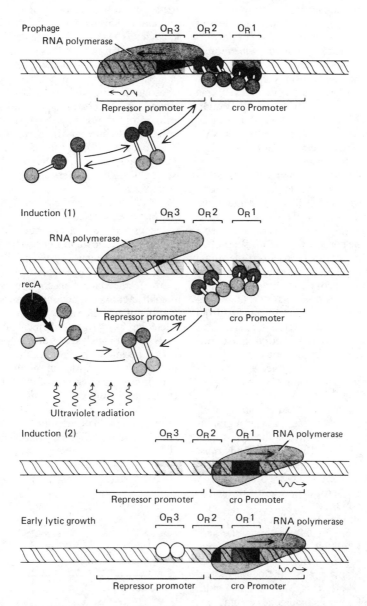

Figure 31–9. Configuration of the switch is shown at 4 stages of lambda's life cycle. The lysogenic path (in which the virus remains dormant as a prophage) is selected when a repressor dimer binds to O_R1, thereby making it likely that O_R2 will be filled immediately by another dimer. In the prophage (top), the repressor dimers bound at O_R1 and O_R2 prevent RNA polymerase from binding to the rightward promoter and so block the synthesis of cro (negative control). The repressors also enhance the binding of polymerase to the leftward promoter (positive control), with the result that the repressor gene is transcribed into RNA (wavy line) and more repressor is synthesized, maintaining the lysogenic state. The prophage is induced when ultraviolet radiation activates the protease recA, which cleaves repressor monomers. The equilibrium of free monomers, free dimers, and bound dimers is thereby shifted, and dimers leave the operator sites. Polymerase is no longer encouraged to bind to the leftward promoter, so that repressor is no longer synthesized. As induction proceeds, all the operator sites become vacant, and so polymerase can bind to the rightward promoter and cro is synthesized. During early lytic growth, a single cro dimer binds to O_R3, the site for which it has the highest affinity. Now polymerase cannot bind to the leftward promoter, but the rightward promoter remains accessible. Polymerase continues to bind there, transcribing cro and other early lytic genes. Lytic growth ensues. (Reproduced, with permission, from Ptashne M, Johnson AD, Pabo CO: A genetic switch in a bacterial virus. *Sci Am* [Nov] 1982;**247**:128.)

that overlaps O$_R$2 and thereby enhances the transcription and subsequent expression of the repressor gene. Thus, the lambda repressor is both a **negative regulator,** by preventing transcription of the cro gene, and a **positive regulator,** by enhancing the transcription of its own gene, the repressor gene. This dual effect of repressor is responsible for the stable state of the dormant lambda bacteriophage; not only does the repressor prevent the expression of the genes necessary for lysis, but it also promotes the expression of itself to stabilize this state of differentiation. In the event that the repressor protein concentration becomes very high, repressor can bind to O$_R$3 and by so doing diminish the transcription of the repressor gene from the leftward promoter, until the repressor concentration drops and repressor dissociates itself from O$_R$3.

When a DNA-damaging signal, such as ultraviolet light, strikes the lysogenic host bacterium, fragments of single-stranded DNA are generated that activate a specific **protease** coded by a bacterial gene and referred to as **recA** (Fig 31–9). The activated recA protease hydrolyzes the portion of the repressor protein that connects the amino-terminal and carboxy-terminal domains of that molecule. Such cleavage of the repressor domains causes the **repressor dimers to dissociate,** which in turn causes a **dissociation of the repressor molecules from O$_R$2** and eventually from O$_R$1. The effects of removal of repressor from O$_R$1 and O$_R$2 are predictable. RNA polymerase immediately has access to the rightward promoter and commences transcribing the **cro gene,** and the enhancement effect of the repressor at O$_R$2 on leftward transcription is lost (Fig 31–9).

The cro protein translated from the newly transcribed cro gene also binds to the operator region as dimers, but its order of preference is the opposite of that of repressor (Fig 31–9). That is, **cro binds most tightly to O$_R$3,** but there is no cooperative effect of cro at O$_R$3 on the binding of cro to O$_R$2. At increasingly higher concentrations of cro, the protein will bind to O$_R$2 and eventually to O$_R$1.

The occupancy of O$_R$3 by cro immediately turns off the transcription from the leftward promoter and, hence, **prevents any further expression of the repressor gene.** Thereby the switch is completely effected: the cro gene is now expressed, and the repressor gene is fully turned off. This event is irreversible, and the expression of other lambda genes commences as part of the lytic cycle. When cro repressor concentration becomes quite high, it will eventually occupy O$_R$1 and in so doing turn down the expression of its own gene, a process that is necessary in order to effect the final stages of the lytic cycle.

The 3-dimensional structure of the cro protein and that of the lambda repressor protein have been determined by x-ray crystallography, and models for their binding and effecting the above-described molecular and genetic events have been proposed and tested by Matthews et al and Ptashne et al. To date, this system provides the best understanding of the molecular events involved in gene regulation.

Attenuation in the Tryptophan Operon

Bacterial operons responsible for the biosynthesis of amino acids often have their expression modulated by a **transcriptional termination** process, termed **attenuation,** which is independent of promoter-operator regulation. This modulation occurs in response to various factors in the cell, particularly those responsible for the translation of codons specifying the amino acid products of the particular synthetic pathway. Regulation by the attenuation process involves translation, ribosome stalling, and shifts between alternative **RNA secondary structures** that form the transcriptional terminator or prevent the formation of the transcriptional terminator. In *E coli* and other bacteria, those operons involved in the biosynthesis of tryptophan, phenylalanine, histidine, threonine, leucine, isoleucine, and valine are all subject to modulation by attenuation.

Attenuation in the tryptophan (Trp) operon of *E coli* has been studied extensively by Yanofsky et al, and that system will be described. The topology of the Trp operon is shown in Fig 31–10. Regulation by the Trp promoter-operator system is analogous to that described above for the lac operon. Repression of the Trp operon can reduce transcription about 70-fold, but mutants **lacking** a functional repressor system are still **capable of responding to tryptophan starvation** by enhancing 8- to 10-fold their rate of synthesis of Trp mRNA. From analyses of other types of mutants in *E coli,* it became apparent that the attenuation process involved the **translation of tryptophan codons** rather than simply a recognition of the concentration of free tryptophan in the cell. It was soon established that within the TrpL region (Fig 31–10), transcriptional termination could occur prior to the transcription of the distal Trp genes (TrpEDCBA) in the operon. This

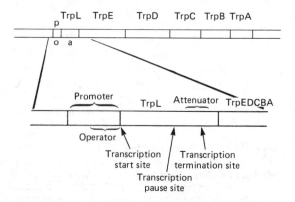

Figure 31–10. The regulatory and structural gene regions of the Trp operon of *E coli.* Transcription initiation is controlled at a promoter-operator. Transcription termination is regulated at an attenuator in the transcribed 162-base-pair leader region, TrpL. All RNA polymerase molecules transcribing the operon pause at the transcription pause site before proceeding further. (Reproduced, with permission, from Yanofsky C: Attenuation in the control of expression of bacterial operons. *Nature* 1981;**289**:751.)

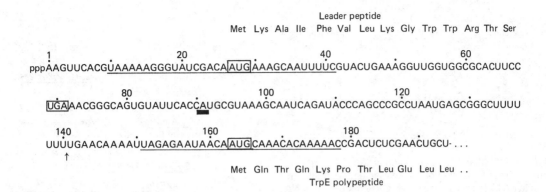

Figure 31–11. The nucleotide sequence of the 5′ end of Trp mRNA. The nonterminated transcript is presented. When transcription is terminated at the attenuator, a 140-nucleotide transcript is produced. Its 3′ terminus is marked by an arrow. The 3′ terminus of the pause transcript, at nucleotide 90, is underlined by a heavy bar. The two AUG-centered ribosome binding sites in this transcript segment are underlined. The boxed AUGs are where translation starts and the boxed UGA where it stops. The predicted amino acid sequence of the Trp leader peptide and the beginning of the TrpE protein are shown. (Reproduced, with permission, from Yanofsky C: Attenuation in the control of expression of bacterial operons. *Nature* 1981;**289**:751.)

transcriptional termination occurred when tryptophan codons within the TrpL region were translated at a "normal" rate. The "premature" termination (attenuation) generated a leader **transcript 140 nucleotides long** rather than a transcript of the entire polycistronic operon, as is necessary to generate the enzymes of the tryptophan synthetic pathway. Thus, the attenuation process is capable of detecting a **tryptophan deficiency** by a process involving translation of tryptophan codons and then **communicating this information to the transcribing RNA polymerase** in order that it transcribe beyond the attenuator into the structural genes of the operon. DNA recombinant technology allowed the construction of specific mutants within this attenuator region and the isolation of pure DNA molecules for nucleotide sequence analysis. The combination of genetics and recombinant DNA technology allowed the following picture to emerge.

At the Trp promoter, an RNA polymerase molecule that has escaped repressor control begins transcription of the operon and proceeds into the TrpL region, the sequence of which is shown in Fig 31–11, to nucleotide number 90 where it **pauses.** During this pause, a **ribosome attaches** at its own binding site centered on the AUG start codon at nucleotides 27–29 and commences translation of the 14-amino-acid **leader peptide.** At nucleotide 54 in this transcript appear 2 sequential **Trp codons** which, of course, require tryptophan-charged tRNA^{Trp} if the ribosome is going to proceed beyond these codons. Note that tryptophan is a rare amino acid and the occurrence of 2 sequential tryptophans in a peptide is extremely rare. Thus, the translation of this leader peptide provides a means of sensing the availability of appropriately charged tryptophan-tRNA^{Trp} molecules. When the RNA polymerase molecule resumes transcription beyond its pause site at nucleotide 90, the ribosome translating the leader will have proceeded to the trans-

lation stop codon centered at nucleotide 70 if adequate Trp-tRNA^{Trp} is available, or the ribosome will have **stalled** at the 2 Trp codons earlier in the peptide. The **position of the ribosome** on the leader transcript will determine which of the **2 alternative RNA secondary structures** will be formed in the transcript generated by the RNA polymerase.

The nucleotide sequence of the **leader transcript** is such that by the base-pairing rules (A:U, G:C) **2 hairpin loops** can be formed between regions designated 1 and 2 and between regions 3 and 4 (Fig 31–12). The hairpin loop between regions 3 and 4 generates a transcriptional termination signal that causes the RNA polymerase to stop transcribing beyond nucleotide 140 and to release a **140-nucleotide prematurely terminated transcript.**

However, the nucleotide sequences are such that **regions 2 and 3** are also capable of base pairing, generating an **alternative secondary structure** that **excludes the formation of the termination signal** by region 3 and 4. When the ribosome stalls at the 2 Trp codons in the leader sequence (Fig 31–12B), **region 1 is protected** and regions 2 and 3 can generate the hairpin loop that excludes the formation of a premature termination signal. This allows the RNA polymerase to transcribe beyond nucleotide 140 and thereby to generate the polycistronic messenger RNA for the synthesis of the enzymes of the tryptophan synthetic pathway.

In the event that there is adequate Trp-tRNA^{Trp} present and the ribosome proceeds through the Trp codons in the leader to the UGA translation stop signal in region 2, both **regions 1 and 2 are protected** by the ribosome. Therefore, regions 3 and 4 can base-pair to generate the premature **termination signal** beyond which RNA polymerase will not transcribe. Accordingly, a **140-nucleotide terminated transcript** is formed rather than the polycistronic message neces-

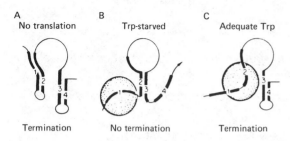

Figure 31–12. Model for attenuation in the *E coli* Trp operon. With excess tryptophan available, the ribosome (dotted circle) translating the newly transcribed leader RNA will synthesize the complete leader peptide. The ribosome will mask regions 1 and 2 of the RNA and will prevent the formation of stem and loop 1:2 or 2:3. Stem and loop 3:4 will be free to form, causing the RNA polymerase molecule (not shown) transcribing the leader region to terminate transcription. During tryptophan starvation, charged tRNA^Trp will be the limiting factor, and the ribosome will stall at the adjacent Trp codons in the leader peptide–coding region. Because only region 1 is masked, stem and loop 2:3 will be free to form and will exclude the formation of stem and loop 3:4 (required for termination). RNA polymerase will therefore continue transcription into the structural genes. Under conditions in which the leader peptide is not translated, stem and loop 1:2 can form, as regions 1 and 2 are synthesized. Formation of 1:2 will prevent the formation of 2:3 and will thereby permit the formation of stem and loop 3:4, causing transcription termination. (Reproduced, with permission, from Oxender D, Zurawski G, Yanofsky C: Attenuation in the *Escherichia coli* tryptophan operon: Role of RNA secondary structure involving the tryptophan codon region. *Proc Natl Acad Sci USA* 1979;**76**:5524.)

Phe, His, Leu, Thr, and Ilv leader peptides

PheA: Met-Lys-His-Ile-Pro-*PHE-PHE-PHE*-Ala-*PHE-PHE-PHE*-Thr-*PHE*-Pro

His: Met-Thr-Arg-Val-Gln-Phe-Lys-*HIS-HIS-HIS-HIS-HIS-HIS-HIS*-Pro-Asp

Leu: Met-Ser-His-Ile-Val-Arg-Phe-Thr-Gly-*LEU-LEU-LEU-LEU*-Asn-Ala-Phe-Ile-Val-Arg-Gly-Arg-Pro-Val-Gly-Gly-Ile-Gln-His

Thr: Met-Lys-Arg-*ILE*-Ser-*THR-THR-ILE-THR-THR-THR-ILE-THR-ILE-THR-THR*-Gly-Asn-Gly-Ala-Gly

Ilv: Met-Thr-Ala-*LEU-LEU*-Arg-*VAL-ILE*-Ser-*LEU-VAL-VAL-ILE*-Ser-*VAL-VAL-VAL-ILE-ILE-ILE*-Pro-Pro-Cys-Gly-Ala-Ala-Leu-Gly-Arg-Gly-Lys-Ala

Figure 31–13. The predicted amino acid sequences of the leader peptides of the PheA, His, Leu, Thr, and Ilv (isoleucine, leucine, valine) operons of *E coli* or *S typhimurium*. Amino acids that regulate the respective operons are in italicized capitals and are underlined. (Reproduced, with permission, from Yanofsky C: Attenuation in the control of expression of bacterial operons. *Nature* 1981;**289**:751.)

sary for the enzymes of the tryptophan operon. The formation of these **2 mutually exclusive secondary structures** between regions 2 and 3 or between regions 3 and 4 transmits to the RNA polymerase information concerning the ability of the cell to translate tryptophan codons.

The predicted amino acid sequences of the leader peptides of several other operons in *E coli* or *Salmonella typhimurium* are shown in Fig 31–13 and reveal the remarkable abundance of codons calling for the amino acid that is the end product of the pathway genetically dictated by the respective operons.

REGULATION IN EUKARYOTES

The nuclear membrane of eukaryotic cells physically segregates gene transcription from translation, since ribosomes exist only in the cytoplasm. Thus, processes such as the above-described transcription attenuation that are dependent upon the coupling of transcription and translation cannot occur in eukaryotic cells. In addition, there are many more steps, especially in RNA processing, involved in the expression of eukaryotic genes than of prokaryotic genes, and these steps provide sites for regulatory influences that

cannot exist in prokaryotes. These RNA processing steps in eukaryotes include capping of the 5′ end of the primary transcript, addition of a polyadenylate track to the 3′ end of transcripts, and excision of intron regions to generate spliced exons in the mature mRNA molecule. To date, the analyses of eukaryotic gene expression have provided evidence that regulation occurs at the level of **transcription, nuclear RNA processing,** and **mRNA stability.** In addition, **gene amplification** and **rearrangement** have been shown to occur and to influence gene expression.

Owing to the advent of recombinant DNA technology, much progress has been made in recent years in the understanding of eukaryotic gene expression. However, because most eukaryotic organisms contain so much more genetic information than do prokaryotes and the manipulation of their genes is so much more limited, molecular aspects of eukaryotic gene regulation are less well understood. This section briefly describes a few different types of eukaryotic gene regulation.

Gene Amplification During Development

During early development of metazoans, there is an abrupt increase in the need for specific generic molecules such as ribosomal RNAs and messenger RNA molecules for proteins that make up such organs as the eggshell. One way to increase the rate at which such molecules can be formed is to increase the number of genes available for transcription of these specific molecules. Among the repetitive DNA sequences described in Chapter 28 are thousands of copies of ribosomal RNA genes and tRNA genes. These genes preexist repetitively in the genomic material of the gametes and, thus, are transmitted in high copy number from generation to generation. In some

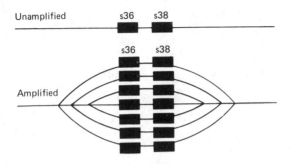

Figure 31–14. Amplification of chorion protein genes s36 and s38. (Reproduced, with permission, from Chisholm R: Gene amplification during development. *Trends Biochem Sci* 1982;7:161.)

specific organisms such as the fruit fly *(Drosophila)*, there occurs during oogenesis an amplification of a few preexisting genes, such as those for the chorion (eggshell) proteins. Subsequently, these amplified genes, presumably generated by a process of repeated initiations during DNA synthesis (compounded replication bubbles) provide multiple sites for gene transcription (Figs 28–17 and 31–14).

In recent years, it has been possible to promote the amplification of specific genetic regions in cultured mammalian cells. In some cases, a several thousand-fold increase in the copy number of specific genes can be achieved over a period of time involving increasing doses of selective drugs. In fact, it has been demonstrated in patients receiving methotrexate (see Chapter 10) for treatment of cancer that malignant cells can develop **drug resistance** by increasing the number of genes for dihydrofolate reductase, the target of methotrexate. Whether such gene amplification processes occur spontaneously in vivo, ie, in the absence of exogenously supplied selective agents, remains to be determined.

Immunoglobulin Gene Rearrangement

Some of the most interesting and perplexing questions raised by biologists in recent decades concern the genetic and molecular basis of antibody diversity (see Chapter 45). In addition, advances in immunology have made it apparent that as cells of the humoral immunity system differentiate, they produce antibodies with the same specificity but different effector functions. Within the last several years, many laboratories have contributed greatly to the understanding of the genetic basis of antibody diversity and regulation of the expression of immunoglobulin genes during development and differentiation.

As described in Chapter 29, the coding segments responsible for the generation of specific protein molecules are frequently not contiguous in the mammalian genome. The coding segments for the variable and the constant domains of the immunoglobulin (antibody) light chain were the first recognized to be separated in the genome. As described in more detail in

Chapter 45, immunoglobulin molecules are composed of 2 types of polypeptide chains, light (L) and heavy (H) chains (Fig 45–4). The L and H chains are each divided into N-terminal variable (V) and carboxy-terminal constant (C) regions. The V regions are responsible for the recognition of antigens (foreign molecules) and the constant regions for effector functions that determine how the antibody molecule will dispense with the antigen.

There are 3 unlinked families of genes responsible for immunoglobulin molecule structure. Two families are responsible for the light chains (λ and κ chains) and one family for heavy chains.

Each **light chain** is encoded by 3 distinct segments: the variable (V_L), the joining (J_L), and the constant (C_L) segments. The mammalian haploid genome contains over 500 V_L segments, five or six J_L segments, and perhaps ten or twenty C_L segments. During the differentiation of a lymphoid B cell, a V_L segment is brought from a distant site on the same chromosome to a position closer to the region of the genome containing the J_L and C_L segments. This **DNA rearrangement** then allows the V_L, J_L, and C_L segments to be transcribed as a single mRNA precursor and subsequently processed to generate the mRNA for a specific antibody light chain. By rearrangement of the various V_L, J_L, and C_L segments in the genome, the immunity system can generate an immensely diverse library of antigen-specific immunoglobulin molecules. This DNA rearrangement is referred to as **V-J joining** of the light chain.

The **heavy chain** is encoded by 4 gene segments: the V_H, the D (diversity), the J_H, and the C_H DNA segments. The variable region of the heavy chain is generated by joining the V_H with a D and a J_H segment. The resulting V_H-D-J_H DNA region is in turn linked to a C_H gene, of which there are 8. These C_H genes ($C\mu$, $C\delta$, $C\gamma3$, $C\gamma1$, $C\gamma2b$, $C\gamma2a$, $C\alpha$, and $C\epsilon$) determine the immunoglobulin class or subclass—IgM, IgG, IgA, etc—of the immunoglobulin molecule (see Chapter 45).

During its differentiation, a B cell that secretes antibody to a **specific antigen** will secrete antibodies of different classes having the same antigen specificity but different biologic roles. The different classes of immunoglobulins contain the same light chains and V_H regions but different C_H regions. Thus, a single B cell and its clonal derivatives can undergo "class switching." Class switching is the result of a second type of **DNA rearrangement** occurring during differentiation of the immunity system.

Developmentally and temporally, the **V-J joining** for light chain expression and the **V-D-J joining** for the heavy chain expression **precede the class-switching DNA rearrangement.**

V-J Joining

In the undifferentiated cell (eg, germ line cell), the κ-J gene (J_κ) is closely linked to the C_κ gene, but the gene segment for the κ-variable region (V_κ) is quite

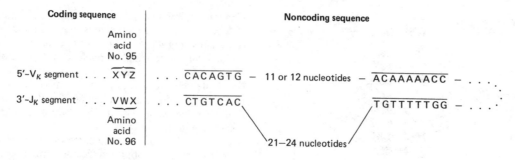

Figure 31–15. A possible arrangement of the conserved heptamers and nonamers in the noncoding, flanking regions of the V_κ and J_κ segments. Such an arrangement allows the coding regions of the genes to be juxtaposed for potential DNA rearrangement necessary to generate the gene for the V_L portion of the L chain.

distant on the same chromosome. In a lymphoid cell destined to make antibodies, one of the 100 or more V_κ gene segments (coding for amino acids 1–95 of the L chain) join to one of any of the four J_κ gene segments (amino acids 96–107) by a process that apparently involves deletion of the DNA originally separating the V_κ and J_κ genes. This results in formation of a V_κ region gene that encodes all 107 amino acids as an uninterrupted nucleotide sequence. The J_κ gene segment is sufficiently close to the C_κ gene so that the intervening sequence can be eliminated from the primary transcript during nuclear RNA processing (see Chapter 29).

Both the V_κ-J_κ and the similar V_λ-J_λ gene rearrangements seem to involve 2 short conserved sequences that exist in the direction **3′ to the V segment** and **5′ to the J segment,** close to the point of recombination. The 2 conserved sequences 3′ to the V segment are the heptamer CACAGTG and the nonamer ACAAAAACC. These 2 conserved sequences 3′ to the V segments are separated by 11 or 12 nonconserved bases in V_κ and by 22 or 23 bases in the V_λ segments.

The conserved sequences 5′ to the J_L segments are the heptamer CACTGTG and the nonamer GGTTTTTGT. In the J_κ segments, these 2 conserved sequences are separated by 21–24 bases and in the V_κ segments by 12 bases. There are 2 striking features of these conserved sequences. First, the conserved **sequences of the J_L segments are inverse complements of the conserved sequences in the V_L segments.** Second, the **length** of the nonconserved sequence separating the heptamers and the nonamers is highly conserved. Accordingly, the conserved sequences can be arranged as shown in Fig 31–15 to juxtapose the 2 segments that must be recombined in the differentiated B cell. Interestingly, the conserved lengths of spacers separating the conserved sequences are close to one or to 2 complete turns of a DNA double helix. It has been proposed that 2 different but closely related **joining proteins** recognize the one- and 2-turn separated sequences, form a complex with these sequences to catalyze the recombining or splicing of the DNA, and generate the rearranged variable region sequence.

The variable region of the heavy chain involves

three DNA segments, V_H, D, and J_H, which must be joined in a process involving two DNA rearrangements, since all 3 segments are separated. However, the J_H segments are found near the C_μ gene in the germ line genome. Remarkably, the conserved heptamer and nonamer sequences described for the light chain regions are found similarly placed in the noncoding regions 3′ to the V_H segment and 5′ to the J_H segment. In both of these positions, the conserved heptamer and nonamer sequences are interrupted by 22 or 23 nucleotides. The D segment, which is interspersed between the V_H and J_H segments in the rearranged genes, is flanked at both its 5′ and 3′ ends by the same conserved heptamer and nonamer sequences. However, the members of each of these sets of heptamers and nonamers are interrupted by 12 nucleotides. As depicted in Fig 31–16, this permits an arrangement of the V_H, D, and J_H segments analogous to that of the V_H-J_H segments shown in Fig 31–15. This might allow for the same joining proteins to recognize the one- and 2-turn spaced sequences for both the light and heavy chain VJ DNA rearrangements.

Class Switching

During the ontogeny of an immunoglobulin-secreting B cell and its clonal derivatives, including the terminally differentiated plasma cell, the sequence of immunoglobulin production and secretion commences with IgM and subsequently switches to IgA or IgG, etc. In the germ line genome, the J_H segments are next to the C_μ genes; thus, once the V_H-D-J_H rearrangement has occurred, no further DNA rearrangement is necessary to allow transcription of an mRNA precursor for a μ chain. However, as differentiation proceeds and immunoglobulin production switches from IgM to IgA, the V-D-J region of the parent B cell must be rearranged with a C_α gene to permit the transcription of an mRNA precursor for an α chain containing the same antigen-specific variable region.

The physical order of the 8 closely linked C_H genes is C_μ, C_δ, $C_\gamma3$, $C_\gamma1$, $C_\gamma2b$, $C_\gamma2a$, C_α, and C_ϵ. The **temporal order of the class switching is unidirectional** within this physical order, from left to right. In most cases studied to date, rearrangement of

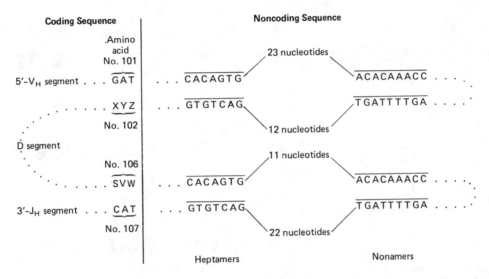

Figure 31–16. A possible arrangement of the conserved heptamers and nonamers in the noncoding, flanking regions of the V_H, D, and J_H segments. Such an arrangement allows the coding regions of the genes to be juxtaposed for potential DNA rearrangement necessary to generate the gene for the V_H portion of the H chain. Note the similarity to Fig 31–15.

the C_H genes seems to involve deletion of those C_H genes 5′ to (left of) the C_H gene joined to the V-D-J region.

An example of the recombination or rearrangement events leading to the complete γ2b gene is shown in Fig 31–17. The sequence first involves rearrangement of the V-D-J segments and subsequently the appropriate deletion or rearrangement of the C_H genes. The C region gene sequences coincide with the domains in the hinge region described in Chapter 45. The intervening sequences or introns that are transcribed and appear in the primary transcript are removed by RNA splicing events described in Chapter 29.

The switch sites appear to be different for different class switches but probably involve conserved sequences occurring in the appropriate flanking regions of the genes to be rearranged, analogous to those described above for V_L-J_L joining and V_H-D-J_H joining.

The information encoded in the genome can clearly be increased by this combinatorial joining of gene segments. This mechanism would not only increase the variable region diversity but would also effectively allow rearranged (useful or advantageous) information to be retained and perpetuated as a cell line alters its effector function during differentiation.

This seemingly complex DNA rearrangement during development and differentiation could be rather simply regulated by the appropriate induction and repression of specific joining proteins that recognize the highly conserved sequences flanking the coding sequences to be rearranged.

Transcription Control

In Chapter 29, a promoter is described as that region of a gene to which RNA polymerase attaches in order to commence transcription of a gene at a specific site. In general, promoters dictate precisely **where** the RNA polymerase is to start transcription, but the issue of **when** (ie, how frequently) to commence transcription is a more complex issue that is less well understood. In the extreme case of a zero rate of transcription, the where and when issues become indistinguishable and irrelevant, since transcription is not starting at all. Thus, the "where" signal is a potential signal and is meaningless if the more dominant "when" signal is "not now." As discussed in Chapter 28, there appear to be quite large regions of chromatin that are transcriptionally inactive, either constitutively or facultatively, while other areas of chromatin are potentially active chromatin. Also, as described in Chapter 28, there is evidence that the methylation of deoxycytidine residues in DNA may effect gross changes in chromatin so as to preclude its active transcription. For example, in mouse liver only the unmethylated ribosomal genes can be expressed, and there is evidence that many animal viruses are not transcribed when their DNA is methylated. However, it is *not* possible to generalize that methylated DNA is transcriptionally inactive, that all inactive chromatin is methylated, or that active DNA is not methylated.

In addition to gross changes in chromatin affecting transcriptional activity, there is increasing evidence that there are signals in DNA which exert influences on transcriptional activity of genes in smaller but not directly contiguous regions, ie, genes thousands of nucleotides removed from the signals. For example, in simian virus 40 (SV40) there exists immediately upstream from the promoter of the early genes a region of repeated 72-base-pair lengths that can greatly increase the expression of genes in vivo. These so-called **enhancer elements** can exert their positive influence on transcription even when separated by thousands of base pairs from a promoter and when oriented in either

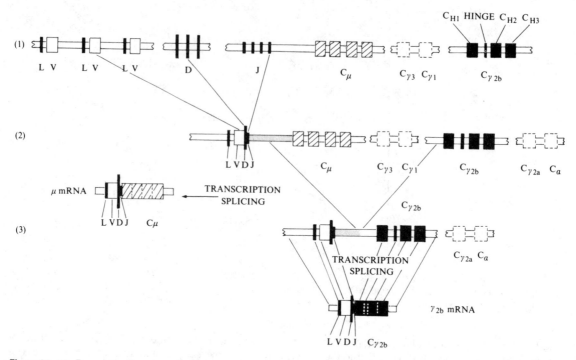

Figure 31–17. Recombination events leading to a complete γ2b gene. (1) The germ line DNA before rearrangement. There is a cluster of at least 50 genes (each with a short leader sequence L) coding for part of the variable (V) region, a cluster of D gene segments coding for most of the third hypervariable region, and some distance away there are four J segments that complete the V region coding sequence. The J segments lie about 8000 bases from the Cμ gene that lies at the start of a cluster containing all the C region genes. The C region gene sequences are interrupted by noncoding sequences to give a series of exons that coincide with the domains and the hinge region in the C region amino acid sequence. (2) In the first translocation event, one of each of the V, D, and J segments are recombined to give a complete μ chain transcription unit. The transcript is a copy of the gene as shown, but the noncoding sequences (introns) are removed by splicing events that lead to a continuous coding sequence in the μ mRNA. (3) A second translocation event, the heavy-chain switch, deletes the Cμ, Cγ3, and Cγ1 gene segments and places the V-D-J segment and part of the J-Cμ intron near the Cγ2b gene. Following transcription, the introns are removed by splicing, leading to a continuous coding sequence in the γ2b mRNA. (Reproduced, with permission, from Molgaard HV: Assembly of immunoglobulin heavy chain genes. *Nature* 1980;**286**:659.)

direction. The SV40 enhancer element can exert an influence on, for example, the transcription of β-(heme)globin by increasing its transcription 200-fold in cells containing both the enhancer and the β-globin gene on the same plasmid. The enhancer element does not seem to be producing a product that in turn acts on the promoter, since it is active only when it exists within the same DNA molecule as (ie, *cis* to) the promoter. Enhancer elements do appear to convey nuclease hypersensitivity to those regions where they reside (see Chapter 28).

Many genes have now been recognized to harbor enhancer elements in various locations relative to their coding regions. In addition to being able to enhance gene transcription, some of these enhancer elements clearly possess the ability to do so in a tissue-specific manner. Thus, the enhancer element associated with the immunoglobulin genes between the J and C regions enhances the expression of those genes preferentially in lymphoid cells. Enhancer elements associated with the genes for pancreatic enzymes are capable of enhancing even unrelated but physically ligated genes

preferentially in the pancreatic cells of mice into which the specifically engineered gene constructions were introduced microsurgically at the single-cell embryo stage.

By in vitro mutating, cutting, and splicing regions of DNA and then reintroducing the "genetically engineered" molecules into eukaryotic cells, one can determine which regions in the vicinity of structural genes have an influence on their expression. In many cases, it has been demonstrated that regions 5' to the transcriptional start site exert profound influence on when the RNA polymerase commences transcription. For example, **metallothionein** is a heavy metal-binding protein that contains many cysteine residues and exists in most organs of mammals. When an organism or its cultured cells are exposed to metal ions such as zinc or cadmium, there is an enhanced rate of transcription of the metallothionein gene and a subsequent increase in the metallothionein protein to bind the potentially toxic heavy metal. Using recombinant DNA technology, it has been possible to isolate the DNA region a few hundred base pairs proximal to the transcriptional start site of the metallothionein gene. Another structural gene, such as that for thymidine kinase, can then be ligated to this **"metallothionein promoter region"** and the synthetic construct introduced to cultured cells, a small number of which will integrate the DNA into its own genome. When those cells are exposed to heavy metals, the metallothionein promoter region effects an induction of thymidine kinase. A similar experiment has recently been conducted in mice. The metallothionein promoter region was ligated to the structural gene for thymidine kinase or to the structural gene for growth hormone. The engineered genetic constructions were introduced into the male pronuclei of single-cell mouse embryos and the embryos placed into the uterus of a surrogate mother to develop. Mice have been born, and in some the addition of zinc ions to their drinking water will effect an increase in liver thymidine kinase or growth hormone. In the latter case, the animals have responded to the high levels of growth hormone by becoming twice as large as their normal litter mates.

Glucocorticoids are one class of steroid hormones that regulate gene expression (see Chapter 40). Once glucocorticoids enter a mammalian cell, they bind to a steroid-specific receptor molecule that undergoes a conformational change in the cytoplasm and enters the nucleus. The glucocorticoid receptor complex in the nucleus seems to bind to a specific receptor recognition site on DNA a few hundred base pairs 5' upstream from the transcription start site for steroid-responsive genes, eg, mouse mammary tumor virus. The occupancy of this receptor recognition site on DNA appears to influence the efficiency of utilization of the promoter by RNA polymerase and thereby influence the expression of the steroid-responsive gene. Again by recombinant DNA technology, the DNA region that binds the glucocorticoid receptor complex can be molecularly cloned and ligated to other unrelated structural genes.

When the new constructions are introduced into cultured cells and integrated into their genome, the structural genes come under the regulatory influences of glucocorticoids added to the culture medium and, thus, are converted to steroid-inducible genes. By whittling away at the ends with nucleases and introducing changes (mutations) into the apparent regulatory region of the cloned DNA, molecular biologists can identify the specific DNA sequence to which the glucocorticoid receptor complex binds. In this case, it seems that the binding of the steroid receptor complex to the specific DNA sequence converts it to an active enhancer element. In the near future, we should understand at the molecular level in eukaryotes precisely how gene expression is regulated, for example, by steroid hormones.

In addition to regulating gene expression by affecting the efficiency of promoter utilization, eukaryotic cells can utilize **alternative RNA processing** to control gene expression. There are 2 general types of RNA processing control, **process versus discard** decisions and **differential processing.** Relative to the former, it is apparent that when primary transcripts contain introns, those intron sequences must be removed before the transcript can mature to a messenger RNA and appear in the cytoplasm for expression. There are **many more primary transcripts in the nucleus than are represented as messenger RNA molecules in the cytoplasm.** Thus, there must exist regulatory decisions as to which transcripts will ultimately be expressed and which will be discarded. There is no information available as to the mechanisms involved in such processes or even direct evidence that such decisions can be changed during differentiation or development or in response to environmental influences.

The direct evidence for differential processing of primary transcripts is derived from studies of the regulation of immunoglobulin synthesis.

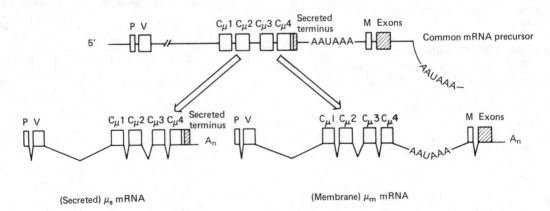

Figure 31–18. Splicing patterns deduced for μ_m and μ_s mRNAs. The μ_m and μ_s mRNAs are identical 5' to $C_\mu 4$. Raised boxes indicate exons. 3' Untranslated sequences are crosshatched. P refers to the signal peptide exon and V to the rearranged V_H exon. Bent lines indicate RNA splicing between exons. The signals for alternative poly(A) track (A_n) additions (AAUAAA) are indicated in the transcripts. (Reproduced, with permission, from Early P et al: Two mRNAs can be produced from a single immunoglobulin μ gene by alternative RNA processing pathways. *Cell* 1980;**20**:313.)

Differential RNA Processing

As described above, the first immunoglobulin synthesized by differentiating B cells is IgM. However, the IgM of the earliest B cell is not extruded all the way through the membrane to be secreted. Instead, the C-terminal region of the μ chain remains trapped in the membrane as an integral protein (see Chapter 32). The μ chain of **secreted IgM** is referred to as μ_S, and the μ chain of the **membrane-associated IgM** is called μ_m. The μ_S and μ_m chains of the same B cell or B cell lineage contain identical amino acid sequences up to the very C-terminal region of the $C_\mu 4$ domain (Fig 45–4). The μ_S chain has a 20-amino-acid **hydrophilic** C-terminal segment after the $C_\mu 4$ domain, while the μ_m chain has a C-terminal segment containing 38 **hydrophobic** amino acids followed by -Lys-Val-Lys. This hydrophobic amino acid sequence can thus embed itself in the membrane bilayer up to the charged Lys residues (see Chapter 32). Accordingly, μ_S and μ_m must be translated from different mRNA molecules.

These different mRNA molecules have been isolated and their nucleotide sequences determined indirectly by DNA sequencing. The μ_m mRNA consists of 2700 bases and the μ_S mRNA 2400 bases. By isolating and sequencing the genomic region coding for these μ mRNA molecules, it has been possible to demonstrate that they are both derived from a **common mRNA precursor** molecule as a result of **alternative RNA processing** pathways in the nucleus. Fig 31–18 depicts the 2 splicing patterns deduced for the μ_m and μ_S mRNA molecules transcribed from a single μ gene.

The common mRNA precursor contains **2 poly(A) addition sites** (see Chapter 29), one between the $C_\mu 4$ exon and the M exons and the other 3' to the M exons. Depending upon which potential poly(A) site is endonucleolytically cleaved in preparation for the addition of the poly(A) track, 2 μ heavy-chain mRNAs with different 3' region sequences can be formed, one for the μ_m chain and one for the μ_S chain. Thus, it may well be that the site chosen for poly(A) addition dictates which exons in the primary transcript shall be spliced.

Messenger RNA Stability

The stability of messenger RNA molecules in the cytoplasm can clearly affect the level of gene expression. It is becoming increasingly clear that the role of the **poly(A) tail** on a messenger RNA molecule is related to the **stability of the mRNA.** The half-life of the mRNA for the milk protein casein is greatly increased by exposing mammary cells to the hormone prolactin. The mechanisms involved are not understood.

Differential mRNA Translation

There are specific examples of organisms or cultured cells that appear to differentially translate mature mRNA molecules, the translation efficiencies of which cannot be distinguished using in vitro translation systems. This suggests that in these systems there exist molecules capable of recognizing specific mature mRNA molecules and affecting the rates at which they are translated relative to other messenger molecules.

Table 31–2 summarizes the frequency of various types of control of eukaryotic gene expression.

Table 31–2. Summary of frequency of various types of control.*

	Examples Proved or Strongly Suggested	Possible
Nuclear		
Transcriptional		
Initiation	Many, > 100	
Termination		
Premature (attenuation)	1	+
readthrough		
Nuclear RNA processing		
Poly(A) choice	~3	
Splicing choice	1	
Process versus discard		+
Cytoplasmic		
mRNA stability	~5 Specific, many general	
mRNA translation efficiency	~10 Specific, many general	

For those cases of control where only one or a few cases are proved, it is anticipated that these numbers will increase. It is not possible at present to even guess at the true frequency with which various mechanisms will be found ultimately to be used.

*Reproduced, with permission, from Darnell JE Jr: Variety in the level of gene control in eukaryotic cells. *Nature* 1982;**297:** 365. Copyright © 1982 by Macmillan Journals Ltd.

•   •   •

References

Banerji J et al: A lymphocyte-specific cellular enhancer is located downstream of the joining region in immunoglobulin heavy chain genes. *Cell* 1983;**33**:729.

Compere SJ, Palmiter RD: DNA methylation controls the inducibility of the mouse metallothionein-I gene in lymphoid cells. *Cell* 1981;**25**:233.

Darnell JE: Variety in the level of gene control in eukaryotic cells. *Nature* 1982;**297**:365.

Jacob F, Monod J: Genetic regulatory mechanisms in protein synthesis. *J Mol Biol* 1961;**3**:318.

Johnson AD et al: λ Repressor and cro: Components of an efficient molecular switch. *Nature* 1981;**294**:217.

Lee F et al: Glucocorticoids regulate expression of dihydrofolate reductase cDNA in mouse mammary tumor virus chimaeric plasmoids. *Nature* 1981;**294**:228.

Nordheim A, Rich A: Negatively supercoiled simian virus 40 DNA contains Z-DNA segments within transcriptional enhancer sequences. *Nature* 1983;**303**:67A.

Ptashne M, Johnson AD, Pabo CO: A genetic switch in a bacterial virus. *Sci Am* (Nov) 1982;**247**:128.

Seidman JG et al: Immunoglobulin V/J recombination is accompanied by deletion of joining site and variable region segments. *Proc Natl Acad Sci USA* 1980;**77**:6022.

Shimizu A, Honjo T: Immunoglobulin class switching. *Cell* 1984;**36**:801.

Sutcliffe JG et al: Control of neuronal gene expression. *Science* 1984;**225**:1308.

Swift GH et al: Tissue-specific expression of the rat pancreatic elastase I gene in transgenic mice. *Cell* 1984;**38**:639.

Varmus HE: Form and function of retroviral proviruses. *Science* 1982;**216**:812.

Wu R, Bahl CP, Narang SA: Lactose operator-repressor interaction. *Curr Top Cell Regul* 1978;**13**:137.

Yanofsky C: Attenuation in the control of expression of bacterial operons. *Nature* 1981;**289**:751.

Zaret KS, Yamamoto KR: Reversible and persistent changes in chromatin structure accompanying activation of a glucocorticoid-dependent enhancer element. *Cell* 1984;**38**:29.

32 | Membranes

David W. Martin, Jr., MD

Membranes are 2-dimensional oriented viscous solutions surrounding all living cells. By forming closed compartments around the cellular protoplasm, membranes separate one cell from another, thus permitting cellular individuality and differentiation. By separating the cell from its environment, membranes provide the main distinction between inside and outside. **Membranes act as barriers, with selective permeabilities to material and information** and thereby maintain the difference between inside and outside. The selective permeabilities are provided by **gates** and **pumps** as well as by specific **receptors** for enzymes, substrates, and signals such as hormones. Within cells, membranes form many of the morphologically distinguishable structures (organelles) such as mitochondria, endoplasmic and sarcoplasmic reticula, Golgi complexes, secretory granules, lysosomes, and the nuclear membrane. Membranes provide sites of energy transduction, such as in photosynthesis and oxidative phosphorylation.

Most membranes are composed predominantly of **lipids** and **proteins** but also contain **carbohydrates.** Different membranes have different ratios of proteins to lipids (Fig 32–1) that are dependent upon their specific functions. Membranes are asymmetric sheetlike enclosed structures with an inside and an outside. These sheetlike structures are noncovalent assemblies that are **thermodynamically stable but metabolically active.** Specific protein molecules are anchored in membranes, where they carry out specific functions of the organelle, the cell, and the organism.

LIPID COMPOSITION

The lipid elements of membrane composition are **phospholipids, glycolipids,** and **sterols**—cholesterol in mammalian membranes.

Phospholipids

Of the 2 major phospholipid groups present in membranes, **phosphoglycerides** are the more common and consist of a glycerol backbone to which are attached 2 fatty acids in ester linkage and a **phosphorylated** alcohol (Fig 32–2). The fatty acid constituents

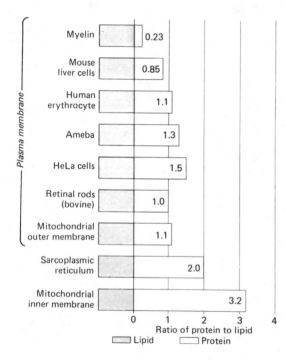

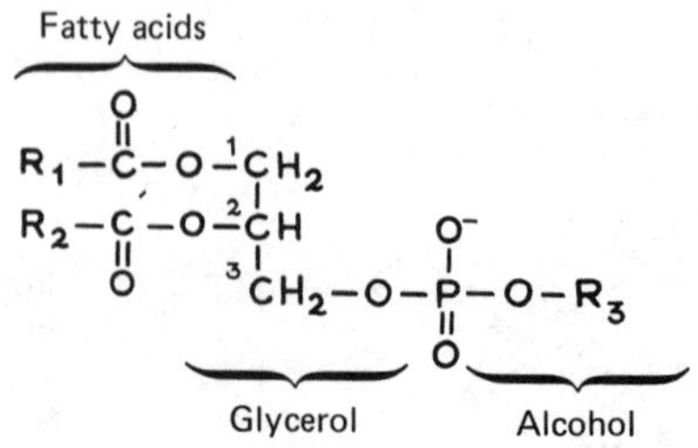

Figure 32–1. Proteins equal or exceed the quantity of lipid in nearly all membranes. The outstanding exception is myelin, thought to act as an insulator of the neuron—a function that would be incompatible with a high proportion of active (protein) molecules. (Reproduced, with permission, from Singer SJ: Architecture and topography of biologic membranes. Chapter 4 in: *Cell Membranes: Biochemistry, Cell Biology & Pathology.* Weissmann G, Claiborne R [editors]. HP Publishing Co., 1975.)

Figure 32–2. A phosphoglyceride showing the fatty acids (R_1 and R_2), glycerol, and phosphorylated alcohol components. In phosphatidic acid, R_3 is hydrogen.

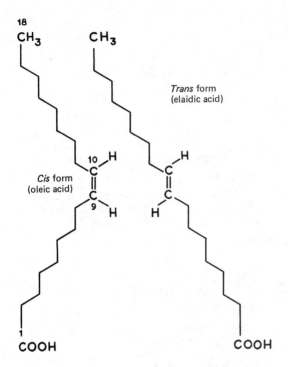

Figure 32–3. Geometric isomerism of oleic *(left)* and elaidic *(right)* acids.

rather than glycerol. A fatty acid is attached by an amide linkage to the amino group of sphingosine. The primary hydroxyl group of sphingosine is esterified to phosphorylcholine (Fig 32–5).

Glycolipids

The glycolipids, as the name implies, are sugar-containing lipids such as cerebrosides and gangliosides and are also derived from sphingosine. The cerebrosides and gangliosides differ from sphingomyelin by the nature of the moiety attached to the primary hydroxyl group of sphingosine. In sphingomyelin, a phosphorylcholine is attached to the alcoholic group. A **cerebroside** contains a single hexose moiety, glucose or galactose, at that site (Fig 32–5). A **ganglioside** contains a branched chain of up to 7 sugars attached to the primary alcohol moiety of sphingosine.

Sterols

The most common sterol in membranes is **cholesterol,** which exists almost exclusively in the plasma membranes of mammalian cells but can also be found in lesser quantity in mitochondria, Golgi complex, and nuclear membranes. Cholesterol is generally more abundant toward the outside of the plasma membrane.

All major lipids in membranes are **amphipathic** and are remarkably similar molecules, as can be seen from their space-filling models (Fig 32–6). An amphipathic molecule is one that contains both **hydrophobic** and **hydrophilic regions.** If the hydrophobic region were separated from the rest of the molecule, it would be insoluble in water but soluble in oil. Conversely, if the hydrophilic region were separated from the rest of the molecule, it would be insoluble in oil but soluble in water. The amphipathic membrane lipids have a polar head group and nonpolar tails; this can be represented as shown in Fig 32–7. **Detergents** are amphipathic molecules that have importance in biochemistry and in the household. The molecular structure of the detergent is not unlike that of a phospholipid.

are usually even-numbered carbon molecules, most commonly 14 or 16 carbons. They are unbranched and can be saturated or unsaturated. The unsaturated fatty acid is almost exclusively of the *cis* configuration (Fig 32–3). The simplest phosphoglyceride is phosphatidate, which is a diacylglycerol 3-phosphate, a key intermediate in the formation of all other phospholipids (see Chapter 17). In other phospholipids the 3-phosphate is esterified to an alcohol such as ethanolamine, choline, serine, glycerol, or inositol (Fig 32–4).

The second class of phospholipids are the **sphingomyelins,** which contain a sphingosine backbone

ORGANIZATION OF MEMBRANE LIPIDS

The amphipathic character of phospholipids suggests that the 2 regions of the molecule have incompatible solubilities; however, in a solvent such as water, phospholipids organize themselves into a form that thermodynamically satisfies both ends. A **micelle,** depicted in Fig 32–8, is a favored structure in which the hydrophobic regions are shielded from water while the hydrophilic polar groups are "happily" immersed in the aqueous environment. The stability of this structure is based on the fact that significant **free energy** is required to transfer a nonpolar molecule from a nonpolar medium to water. For example, 2.6 kcal of free energy is required to transfer 1 mol of methane from a nonpolar medium to an aqueous one. At the other end, much energy is required to transfer a polar moiety from

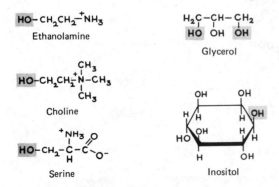

Figure 32–4. The alcohols attached to the 3-phosphoryl group of phosphoglycerides. The alcohol moieties that participate in the phosphoester bonds are shaded.

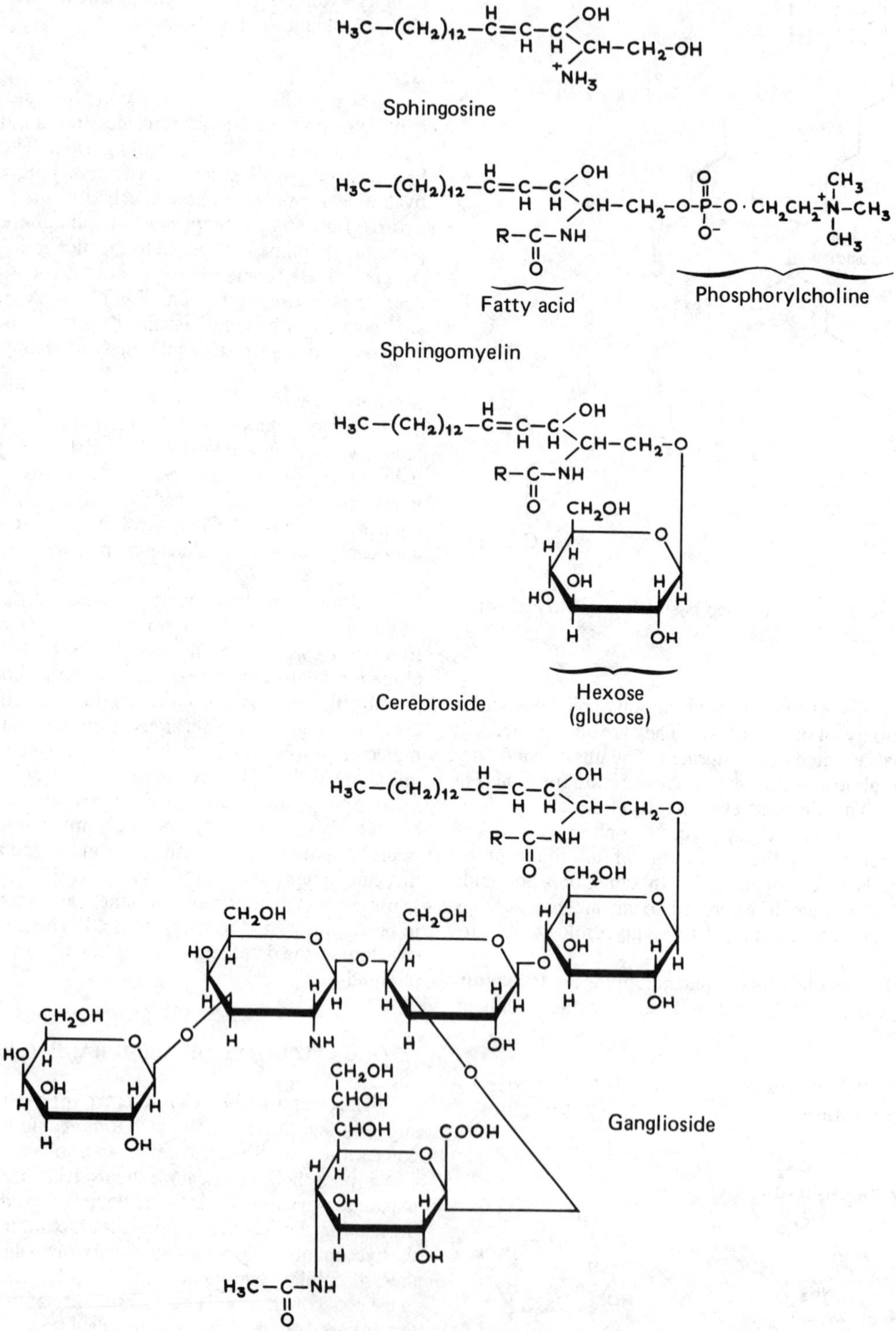

Figure 32–5. The structures of sphingosine, a sphingomyelin, a cerebroside, and a ganglioside.

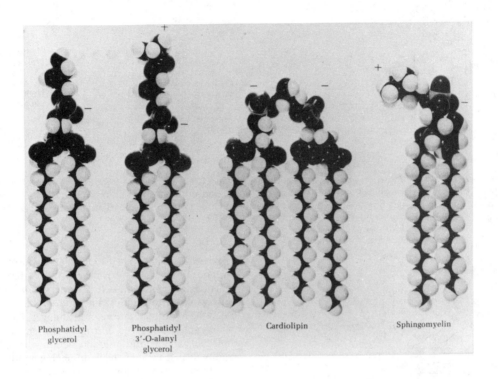

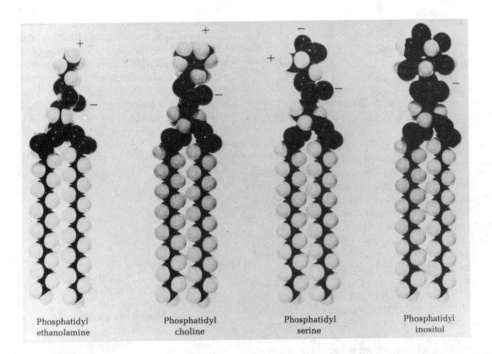

Figure 32—6. Space-filling models of the major phosphoglycerides. For convenience, all the fatty acid components are shown as palmitic acid. Sphingomyelin, although it is not a phosphoglyceride, is included to show its structural similarity. The electrical charges shown assume pH = 7.0. (Reproduced, with permission, from Lehninger AL: *Biochemistry,* 1st ed. Worth, 1970.)

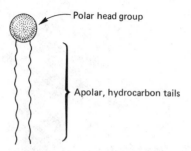

Figure 32–7. Diagrammatic representation of a phospholipid or other membrane lipid. The polar head group is hydrophilic, and the hydrocarbon tails are hydrophobic or lipophilic.

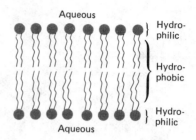

Figure 32–9. Diagram of a section of a bilayer membrane formed from phospholipid molecules. (Reproduced, with permission, from Stryer L: *Biochemistry,* 2nd ed. Freeman, 1981.)

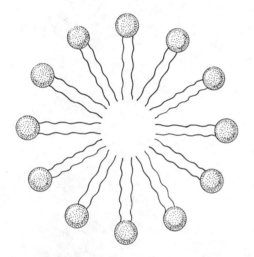

Figure 32–8. Diagrammatic cross section of a micelle. The polar head groups are bathed in water, whereas the hydrophobic hydrocarbon tails are surrounded by other hydrocarbons and thereby protected from water. Micelles are spherical structures.

water to a nonpolar medium. As an example, 6 kcal of free energy is required to transfer zwitterionic glycine from water to acetone. Thus, the micelle provides a minimal energy configuration and accordingly is **thermodynamically stable.** Compared to the above-described hydrophobic and hydrophilic interactions, hydrogen bonding and salt or electrostatic bonds are of only secondary importance to the micelle structure.

As recognized nearly 60 years ago by Gorter and Grendel, a bimolecular layer, or **bilayer,** can also satisfy the thermodynamic requirements of amphipathic molecules in an aqueous environment. A bilayer exists as a sheet in which the hydrophobic regions of the phospholipids are protected from the aqueous environment, while the hydrophilic regions are immersed in water (Fig 32–9). Only the ends or edges of the bilayer sheet are exposed to an unfavorable environment, but even those exposed edges can be eliminated by folding

the sheet back upon itself to form an **enclosed vesicle with no edges.** The closed bilayer provides the essential functions of membranes. It is **impermeable to most water-soluble molecules,** since they would be insoluble in the hydrophobic core of the bilayer. Gases such as oxygen, CO_2, and nitrogen, which are small molecules and exhibit little interaction with solvents, readily diffuse through the hydrophobic regions of the membrane. Organic nonelectrolyte molecules exhibit diffusion rates that are dependent upon their oil-water partition coefficients (Fig 32–10)—the greater the lipid solubility of a molecule, the greater will be its diffusion rate across the membrane. This bimolecular structure also allows for the interaction of amphipathic proteins with the membrane.

In biologic membranes, there is **inside-outside (transverse) asymmetry of the phospholipids.** The choline-containing phospholipids are located mainly in the outer molecular layer; the aminophospholipids are preferentially in the inner layer. Sphingomyelin and cholesterol are generally present in larger amounts on the outside than on the inside. Obviously, if this asymmetry is to exist at all, there must be **limited transverse mobility** (flip-flop) of the membrane phospholipids. In fact, phospholipids in synthetic bilayers exhibit an extraordinarily slow rate of flip-

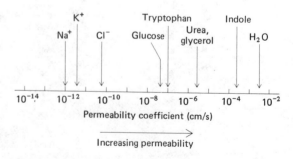

Figure 32–10. Permeability coefficients of some ions and molecules in lipid bilayer membranes. (Reproduced, with permission, from Stryer L: *Biochemistry,* 2nd ed. Freeman, 1981.)

flop; the half-life of the asymmetry can be measured in days or weeks. However, when certain membrane proteins such as the erythrocyte protein glycophorin are inserted artificially into synthetic bilayers, the frequency of phospholipid flip-flop may increase as much as 100-fold.

Even the enzymes involved in the synthesis of phospholipids and triglycerides are located on the cytoplasmic side of microsomal membrane vesicles, contributing a transverse asymmetry to the membrane.

MEMBRANE PROTEINS

The membrane phospholipids act as a **solvent** for the membrane proteins, creating an environment for the protein function. Of the 20 amino acids contributing to protein primary structure, the functional groups attached to the alpha carbon are strongly hydrophobic in 6, weakly hydrophobic in a few, and hydrophilic in the remainder. As described in Chapter 4, the α-helical structure of proteins minimizes the hydrophilic charac-

ter of the peptide bonds themselves. Thus, **proteins can be amphipathic** and form an integral part of the membrane by having hydrophilic regions protruding at the inside and outside faces of the membrane but connected by a hydrophobic region traversing the hydrophobic core of the bilayer. In fact, those portions of membrane proteins which do traverse membranes do contain substantial hydrophobic amino acids and high α-helical or β-pleated sheet content.

Different proteins provide different functions in membranes; there is no such thing as a typical membrane structure.

The asymmetry of membranes can be partially attributed to the **asymmetric distribution of proteins** within the membranes. An inside-outside asymmetry is provided also by the outside location of the carbohydrates attached to membrane proteins. In addition, specific enzymes are located exclusively on the outside or exclusively on the inside of membranes, as in the mitochondria and plasma membranes.

There are **regional asymmetries** in membranes. Some, such as the villous borders of mucosal cells, are

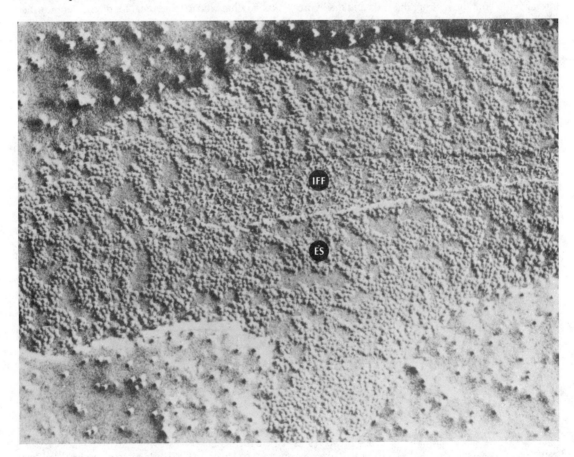

Figure 32–11. Electron micrograph of freeze-etched erythrocyte membrane shows "bumps" on both exterior surface (ES) and inner fracture face (IFF). ES bumps are ferritin-labeled agglutinin attached to protein-bound sugars; the "bumps" on the IFF are globules of protein within the membrane. Close examination reveals the pattern of "bumps" is apparently continuous across the 2 regions, suggesting that the 2 proteins are actually one. (Reproduced, with permission, from Marchesi VT: The structure and orientation of a membrane protein. Chapter 5 in: *Cell Membranes: Biochemistry, Cell Biology & Pathology.* Weissman G, Claiborne R [editors]. HP Publishing Co., 1975.)

almost macroscopically visible. Others, such as the gap junctions, tight junctions, and synapses, occupy much smaller regions of the membrane and generate local asymmetries.

Integral & Peripheral Membrane Proteins

Most membrane proteins are integral components of the membrane, and in fact all of those which have been adequately studied span the entire 5- to 10-nm transverse distance of the bilayer. These **integral proteins** are usually globular in shape and are themselves amphipathic. They consist of 2 hydrophilic ends separated by an intervening hydrophobic region that traverses the hydrophobic core of the bilayer.

Freeze-fracture etching techniques have visually demonstrated the existence of integral membrane proteins traversing the hydrophobic core of the membrane bilayer (Fig 32–11).

Nonionic detergents dissolve or bind to integral proteins—usually without concomitant loss of function, since the hydrophilic ends of the proteins are not bound by the detergent. However, ionic detergents interact with both the hydrophilic ends and the hydrophobic portion of integral proteins and inactivate their function as they do non-membrane-associated, water-soluble proteins.

Integral proteins are asymmetrically distributed across the membrane bilayer (Fig 32–12). If a membrane containing an asymmetrically distributed integral protein is dissolved in detergent and the detergent is then slowly removed, the phospholipids and the integral proteins will self-assemble, but the latter will lose their specific inside-outside orientation in the membrane. Thus, at least some proteins must be given

their asymmetric orientation in the membrane at the time of its insertion in the lipid bilayer. The hydrophilic external region of an amphipathic protein, which is clearly synthesized inside of the cell, must traverse the hydrophobic core of the membrane and eventually be found external to the membrane. The molecular mechanisms of membrane assembly are discussed below.

Peripheral proteins do not interact directly with the phospholipids in the bilayer but are instead **weakly bound** to the hydrophilic regions of **specific integral proteins.** For example, ankyrin, a peripheral protein, is bound to the integral protein "band III" of erythrocyte membrane. Spectrin, a cytoskeletal structure within the erythrocyte, is in turn bound to ankyrin and thereby plays an important role in the maintenance of the biconcave shape of the erythrocyte. The **immunoglobulin molecules** on the plasma membranes of lymphocytes are integral membrane proteins and can be released by the shedding of small fragments of the membrane. Many **hormone receptor molecules** are integral proteins, and the specific polypeptide hormones that bind to these receptor molecules may therefore be considered peripheral proteins. Peripheral proteins, such as peptide hormones, may even organize the distribution of integral proteins, such as their receptors, within the plane of the bilayer (see below).

THE FLUID MOSAIC MODEL OF MEMBRANE STRUCTURE

Functional membranes are 2-dimensional solutions of globular integral proteins dispersed in a fluid

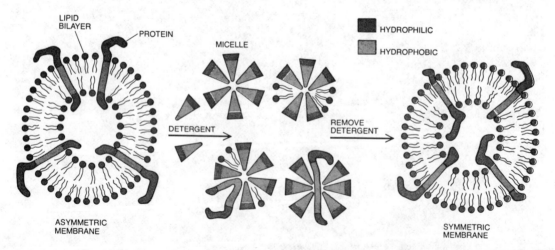

Figure 32–12. Self-assembly of a membrane preserves its basic structure but not its asymmetry. A membrane can be disrupted by a high concentration of a detergent, which is an amphipathic molecule that forms the small droplets called micelles. The detergent dissolves the components of the membrane by enveloping the hydrophobic portions of both lipids and proteins in micelles, where they are protected from contact with water. If the detergent is then removed, the lipids spontaneously form a new bilayer, incorporating the integral proteins in it. The proteins, however, generally assume random orientations. Experiments such as this one have shown that all membranes in the cell cannot be self-assembled; instead, at least some integral proteins must be inserted in a membrane that already exists and has a defined sidedness. (Reproduced, with permission, from Lodish HF, Rothman JE: The assembly of cell membranes. Sci Am [Jan] 1979;**240**:43.)

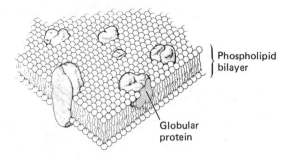

Phospholipid bilayer

Globular protein

Figure 32–13. Fluid mosaic model. Schematic 3-dimensional cross section. (Reproduced, with permission, from Singer SJ, Nicolson GL: The fluid mosaic model of the structure of cell membranes. *Science* 1972;**175**:720. Copyright ©1972 by the American Association for the Advancement of Science.)

phospholipid matrix. This **fluid mosaic model** of membrane structure was proposed in 1972 by Singer and Nicolson (Fig 32–13). At that time, the most compelling evidence suggesting the model was the rapid redistribution of species-specific integral proteins in the interspecies hybrid cell formed by the artificially induced fusion of their membranes (Fig 32–14). It has subsequently been demonstrated that phospholipids also undergo rapid redistribution in the plane of the membrane. This diffusion within the plane

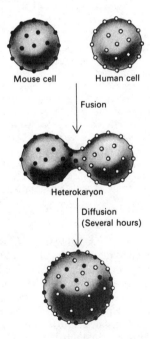

Mouse cell   Human cell

Fusion

Heterokaryon

Diffusion (Several hours)

Figure 32–14. The fusion of a mouse cell and a human cell, followed by diffusion of membrane components in the plane of the plasma membrane. The open and closed circles are completely intermingled after several hours. (Reproduced, with permission, from Stryer L: *Biochemistry,* 2nd ed. Freeman, 1981.)

of the membrane, referred to as **translational diffusion,** can be quite rapid for a phospholipid. In fact, within the plane of the membrane, one molecule of phospholipid can move several micrometers per second.

The **phase changes** and thus the **fluidity** of membranes are highly dependent upon the lipid composition of the membrane. In a lipid bilayer, the hydrophobic chains of the fatty acids can be highly aligned or ordered to provide a rather stiff structure. As the temperature is increased, the hydrophobic side chains will undergo a transition from the ordered state to a disordered one, taking on a more liquidlike or fluid arrangement. The temperature at which the structure undergoes the transition of **ordered to disordered** is called the **transition temperature.** The longer and more saturated fatty acid chains exhibit higher transition temperatures—ie, higher temperatures are required to increase the fluidity of the structure. Unsaturated bonds that exist in the *cis* configuration tend to increase the fluidity of a bilayer by decreasing the **compactness of the side chain packing** without diminishing hydrophobicity. Cellular membrane phospholipids contain at least one unsaturated fatty acid with at least one *cis* double bond.

Cholesterol also acts as a moderator molecule in membranes, producing **intermediate states of fluidity.** If the acyl side chains exist in a disordered phase, cholesterol will have a condensing effect; if the acyl side chains are ordered or in a crystalline phase, cholesterol will add disorder. At high cholesterol:phospholipid ratios, transition temperatures are abolished altogether.

The fluidity of a membrane has significant effects on its functions. As membrane fluidity increases, so does its permeability to water and other small hydrophilic molecules. The lateral mobility of integral proteins increases as the fluidity of the membrane increases. If an integral protein involved in some given function has its active site residing exclusively in its hydrophilic regions, there probably will be little effect of changing lipid fluidity on the protein's activity. However, if the protein is involved in a transport function in which transport components span the membrane, lipid phase effects may significantly alter the transport rate.

A state of fluidity and thus translational mobility in a membrane may be confined to certain regions of membranes under certain conditions. For example, protein-protein interaction may take place within the plane of the membrane such that the **integral proteins form a rigid matrix**—in contrast to the more usual situation, where the lipid acts as the matrix. Such regions of rigid protein matrix can exist side by side in the same membrane with the usual lipid matrix. **Gap junctions, tight junctions,** and **bacteriorhodopsin-containing regions** of the purple membranes of halobacteria are clear examples of such side-by-side coexistence of different matrices.

Some of the protein-protein interactions taking place within the plane of the membrane may be mediated by **interconnecting peripheral proteins,** such as cross-linking antibodies or lectins that are known to **patch** or **cap** on membrane surfaces. Thus, peripheral proteins, by their specific attachments, may restrict the mobility of integral proteins within the membrane.

MEMBRANE ASSEMBLY

As mentioned above, the enzymes responsible for the synthesis of phospholipids reside on the cytoplasmic aspects of the vesicles of endoplasmic reticulum. As phospholipids are synthesized at that site, they probably self-assemble into the thermodynamically stable bimolecular layers, thereby expanding the sheet of the vesicle. The lipid vesicles originating as endoplasmic reticulum seem to migrate to the Golgi apparatus, which in turn eventually fuses with the plasma membrane. Both the Golgi complex and the endoplasmic reticulum vesicles exhibit transverse asymmetries of both lipid and protein, and these asymmetries are maintained during fusion with the plasma membrane. **The inside of the vesicle after fusion becomes the outside of the plasma membrane,** and the cytoplasmic side of the vesicles remains the cytoplasmic side of the membrane (Fig 32–15). Since the transverse asymmetry of the membranes already exists in the vesicles of the endoplasmic reticulum well before they are fused to the plasma membrane, the major problem of the membrane assembly becomes how the integral proteins are to be **inserted** asymmetrically into the lipid bilayer of the endoplasmic reticulum.

Integral and secreted proteins frequently are synthesized with an **N-terminal leader sequence** of 15–30 mostly hydrophobic amino acids. Rarely, the hydrophobic "leader sequence" may be internal. The N-terminal leader sequence is usually removed from the protein during or after its integration into the membrane, producing the mature secreted or membrane protein (see Chapter 33).

There is strong evidence that the leader sequence is involved in the process of protein insertion. Mutant proteins containing altered leader sequences in which a hydrophobic amino acid is replaced by a hydrophilic one are not inserted into membranes. Nonmembrane proteins to which a leader sequence is attached by genetic engineering will be inserted into membranes or even secreted.

Two models have been proposed to describe the integration of proteins into membrane: the signal hypothesis and the membrane trigger hypothesis. The **signal hypothesis** proposes that the protein is inserted into the membrane simultaneously with the translation of its mRNA on polyribosomes, so-called cotranslational insertion. As the leader sequence of the protein emerges from the ribosome, it is recognized by a signal recognition particle (SRP) that blocks further translation after about 70 amino acids have been polymerized—40 buried in the large ribosomal complex and 30 exposed (Fig 32–16). The SRP contains 6

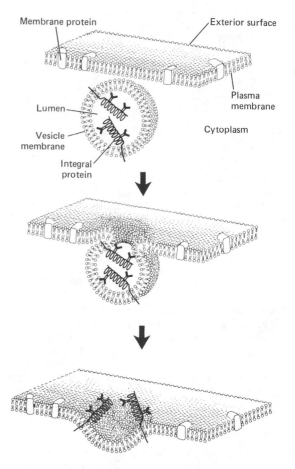

Figure 32–15. Fusion of a vesicle with the plasma membrane preserves the orientation of any integral proteins embedded in the vesicle bilayer. Initially, the N terminus of the protein faces the lumen, or inner cavity, of such a vesicle. After fusion, the N terminus is on the exterior surface of the plasma membrane. That the orientation of the protein has not been reversed can be perceived by noting that the other end of the molecule, the C terminus, is always immersed in the cytoplasm. The lumen of a vesicle and the outside of the cell are topologically equivalent. (Redrawn and modified, with permission, from Lodish HF, Rothman JE: The assembly of cell membranes. *Sci Am* [Jan] 1979;**240**:43.)

proteins and has associated with it a 7S RNA, which is closely related to the "Alu family" of highly repeated DNA sequences (see Chapter 28). The SRP-imposed block is not released until the SRP-leader sequence-ribosome complex has bound to the so-called docking protein (a receptor for the SRP) on the endoplasmic reticulum. Cotranslational insertion of the protein into the endoplasmic reticulum then commences at that site. The process of elongation of the remaining portion of the protein molecule drives the protein chain across the lipid bilayer as the ribosomes remain attached to the endoplasmic reticulum. Thus, the **rough** (or ribosome-studded) **endoplasmic reticulum** is formed. Ribosomes remain attached to the endoplasmic reticulum during synthesis of the membrane protein but are released and dissociated into their respective subunits as the protein is completed. The leader sequence is cleaved off and carbohydrate attached as the early synthesized portion of the protein enters the interior of the endoplasmic reticulum vesicle. (See Chapter 33.)

Integral membrane proteins do not completely cross the membrane and are probably prevented from doing so by a hydrophilic C-terminal anchor region. However, secreted proteins completely traverse the membrane bilayer and are discharged into the lumen of the endoplasmic reticulum. By the time they reach the interior of that vesicle, carbohydrate moieties have already been attached (see Chapter 33). Subsequently, the secretory proteins are found in the lumen of the Golgi apparatus, where their carbohydrate attachments are modified prior to their being directed to specific intracellular organelles or cellular membranes or being secreted. (See Chapter 33.)

Some proteins traverse one membrane and subsequently become anchored in a second juxtaposition membrane, such as the mitochondrial inner membrane.

The **membrane trigger hypothesis** minimizes the role of catalysis in membrane assembly and emphasizes the role of the leader sequence in altering the **folding pathway** of the protein itself. The leader sequence is said to promote an alternative folding of the usually hydrophobic integral protein, so that it can remain soluble in the aqueous environment of the cytoplasm where it is synthesized. The membrane lipid bilayer is said to **trigger the refolding** of the protein into a conformation which favors its insertion into that particular bilayer. Thus, the protein is triggered to self-assemble into the membrane in a manner that establishes the necessary transverse asymmetry. Once the protein is inserted or integrated, the leader is cleaved off. The trigger hypothesis does not require specific ribosome membrane interactions, but this still does not mean that protein synthesis on membranes cannot occur.

The major characteristics of the signal hypothesis and the trigger hypothesis are compared in Table 32–1.

It is clear that the signal mechanism and the trigger mechanism must both exist even in the same cell. Some membrane proteins and secreted proteins are synthesized on membrane-bound polysomes, while others are formed on free cytoplasmic polysomes. Some proteins will not enter the so-called assembly pathway to be secreted or inserted unless they interact with the membrane bilayer early in the process of their own synthesis on ribosomes. Some proteins such as the mitochondrial cytochrome b_5 can self-assemble or integrate in an oriented fashion into membranes after their synthesis is completed but still require the presence of a normal leader sequence. Some single-peptide chains or proteins such as bacteriorhodopsin can span a membrane back and forth several times, a phenomenon not easily attributed to the signal hypothesis. Finally, some integral proteins are oriented so that their C-terminal region is exterior while their N-terminal region is interior.

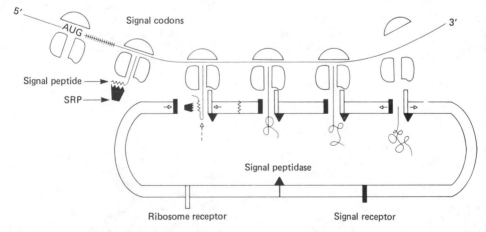

Figure 32–16. Diagram of the signal hypothesis for the transport of secreted proteins across the endoplasmic reticulum membrane. The ribosomes synthesizing a protein move along the messenger RNA specifying the amino acid sequence of the protein. (The messenger is represented by the line between 5' and 3'.) The codon AUG marks the start of the message for the protein; the hatched lines that follow AUG represent the codons for the signal sequence. As the protein grows out from the larger ribosomal subunit, the signal sequence is exposed and bound by the signal recognition particle (SRP). Translation is blocked until the complex binds to the "docking protein" (represented by the solid bar) on the endoplasmic reticulum membrane. There is also a receptor (open bar) for the ribosome itself. The interaction of the ribosome and growing peptide chain with the endoplasmic reticulum membrane results in the opening of a pore through which the protein is transported to the interior space of the endoplasmic reticulum. During transport, the signal sequence of most proteins is removed by an enzyme called the signal peptidase. The completed protein is eventually released by the ribosome, which then separates into its 2 components, the large and small ribosomal subunits. The protein ends up inside the endoplasmic reticulum. (Slightly modified and reproduced, with permission, from: Newly made proteins zip through the cell. *Science* 1980;**207**:164. Copyright © 1980 by the American Association for the Advancement of Science.)

Table 32–1. A comparison of 2 models for membrane assembly.*

Stage of Synthesis	Signal Hypothesis	Membrane Trigger Hypothesis
Site of initiation	Soluble polysomes	Soluble polysomes
Role of the leader peptide	Recognized by the protein transport channel	To alter the folding pathway
Association of the new protein with membrane	When leader peptide is complete *Place:* protein transport channel	During or after protein synthesis *Place:* receptor protein or lipid portions of the bilayer
Specific ribosome associations	With the protein transport channel	None
Catalysis for assembly	A specific pore	The effect of the leader peptide on conformation
Driving force for assembly	Polypeptide chain elongation	Protein-protein and protein-lipid associations: self-assembly
Removal of leader peptide	During polypeptide extrusion	During or after polypeptide assembly into bilayer
Final orientation	C terminus in, N terminus out	Specified by the primary sequence

*Modified and reproduced, with permission, from Wickner W: The assembly of proteins into biological membranes: The membrane trigger hypothesis. *Annu Rev Biochem* 1979;48:23.

TRANSPORT ACROSS MEMBRANES

The plasma membrane of cells acts as a selectively permeable interface between the cell and its environment and between its cytosol and intracellular organelles. Two major questions are then raised: How do molecules traverse the membrane to enter the cell or an organelle, and how is the selectivity effected? Three major mechanisms are responsible for satisfying the above requirements: **diffusion, active transport,** and **endocytosis.**

Diffusion

As described above, some solutes such as gases can enter the cell by diffusing down an electrochemical gradient across the membrane without requiring metabolic energy. The rate of simple diffusion of a solute across the membrane will not be limited and will be proportionate to the solubility of that solute in the hydrophobic core of the membrane bilayer. The fluidity of a membrane can significantly affect the diffusion of solutes, and even solvents such as water, through the membrane. The rate of diffusion is inversely proportionate to the number of hydrogen bonds that must be broken in order for a solute in the external aqueous phase to become partitioned into the hydrophobic bilayer. Electrolytes diffuse across membranes slowly for the above reason, and the greater their charge density, the slower the diffusion rate. In natural membranes, as opposed to synthetic membrane bilayers, there appear to be transmembrane channels or porelike structures generating ion-conductive pathways. The membranes of nerve cells contain well-studied ion channels that are responsible for the action potentials generated in the membrane. Some microbial peptides provide ion channels, or **ionophores,** that function as ion shuttles for the movement of ions across membranes. These ionophores contain hydrophilic centers that bind specific ions and are surrounded by peripheral hydrophobic regions, allowing them to dissolve effectively in the membrane and diffuse transversely therein (Fig 32–17). **Metabolic uncouplers** such as dinitrophenol similarly provide shuttles for **protons**

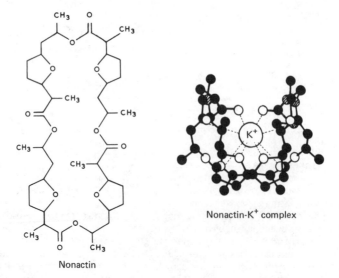

Nonactin-K⁺ complex

Nonactin

Figure 32–17. The ionophore nonactin and its complex with K⁺. (Reproduced, with permission, from Finean JB, Coleman R, Michell RH: *Membranes and Their Cellular Functions.* Wiley, 1974.)

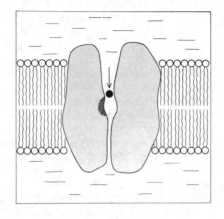 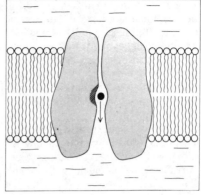

Figure 32–18. Active transport of molecule through membrane protein channel is visualized 2-dimensionally. Molecule impinges *(left)* on active site (hatched) of protein, following which some energy-yielding enzyme reaction triggers shift in subunit configuration *(right)* that "squeezes" the molecule through the membrane. (Reproduced, with permission, from Singer SJ: Architecture and topography of biologic membranes. Chapter 4 in: *Cell Membranes: Biochemistry, Cell Biology & Pathology.* Weissman G, Claiborne R [editors]. HP Publishing Co., 1975.)

across membranes, thereby collapsing proton gradients necessary for the generation of ATP, as described in the chemiosmotic theory of Mitchell (see Chapter 12). Microbial toxins such as diphtheria toxin and activated serum complement components (see Chapter 45) can generate large pores in cellular membranes, allowing macromolecules direct access to the internal milieu.

Some specific solutes diffuse down electrochemical gradients across membranes more rapidly than might be expected from their size, charge, or partition coefficients. Their diffusion is said to be **facilitated** and exhibits properties distinct from those of simple diffusion. The rate of diffusion can be **saturated;** ie, the number of sites involved in diffusion of the specific solutes appears finite. Many of the facilitated diffusion systems are stereospecific, and, like the simple diffu-

sion process, **no metabolic energy is required.**

From the above, it should be clear that the inside-outside asymmetry of membrane proteins is stable, and transverse mobility of proteins in the membrane is rare. Therefore, transverse mobility of specific carrier proteins is not likely to account for facilitated diffusion processes except those described above for microbial ionophores.

Fixed pore mechanisms involving a protein-lined pore that changes conformation upon binding specific ligands may account for the translocation of specific molecules across membranes (Fig 32–18). Peripheral and integral membrane proteins may function jointly to provide a facilitated diffusion system. The peripheral protein may provide specificity by its stereospecific binding of the ligand, while the integral protein provides the transmembrane pore (Fig 32–19).

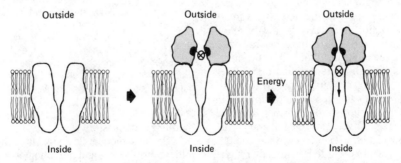

Figure 32–19. A schematic mechanism for the translocation event in active transport, where a peripheral binding protein is obligatorily involved. It is proposed that there are present in the membrane subunit aggregates of specific integral proteins which span the membrane, forming a water-filled pore. This pore *(left)* is initially closed to the diffusion of molecules other than water. A binding protein (shaded) with an active binding site (solid) for ligand X attaches specifically to the exposed surface of the integral protein *(center)*, the pore remaining closed. Some energy-yielding step results in a quaternary rearrangement of the subunits of this structure *(right)*, opening the pore and releasing X to the other side of the membrane. (Modified and reproduced, with permission, from Singer SJ: The molecular organization of membranes. *Annu Rev Biochem* 1974;**43**:805.)

Active Transport

The process of active transport differs from diffusion by requiring a continuous supply of **energy** and transporting molecules **unidirectionally,** frequently **against an electrochemical gradient.** In fact, only by transporting against an electrochemical gradient can a gradient be maintained. The maintenance of electrochemical gradients in biologic systems is so important that it consumes perhaps **30–40% of the total energy input** in a resting human.

In general, living cells maintain a low intracellular Na^+ concentration and a high intracellular K^+ concentration, along with a net **negative electric potential inside.** An integral part of the pump that maintains these gradients is an **ATPase** which is activated by Na^+ and K^+. The ATPase is an integral membrane protein and requires phospholipids for activity. The ATPase catalytic activity interacts with both ATP and Na^+ on the **cytoplasmic side** of the membrane, but the K^+ binding site is located on the **extracellular** side of the membrane. From the extracellular side of the membrane only, **ouabain** (digitalis) inhibits the ATPase that is catalytically active only on the cytoplasmic side of the membrane. Inhibition of ATPase by ouabain can be antagonized by extracellular K^+.

Nerve Impulse Transmission

The membrane forming the surface of neuronal cells maintains asymmetry of the inside-outside voltage (electric potential), as described above, and is "excitable." When appropriately stimulated by a chemical signal mediated by a specific membrane receptor (see Signal Transmission, below), gateways in the membrane can be opened to allow the rapid influx of Na^+ or Ca^{2+} followed by the efflux of K^+, so that the **voltage difference rapidly collapses.** However, as a result of the ion pumps in the membrane, the gradient is quickly restored.

When large areas of the membrane are "depolarized" in this manner, the electrochemical disturbance can propagate in wavelike form down the membrane, generating a nerve impulse. An electrical insulator surrounding most of the nerve will greatly speed up the propagation of the wave (signal) by allowing ions to flow in and out of the membrane only where the membrane is free of the insulation. **Myelin** sheets, formed by Schwann cells, wrap around nerve fibers and provide just such an insulation. Myelin is the membrane of the Schwann cell and, of course, includes phospholipids, cholesterol, proteins, and cerebrosides. There are relatively few integral and peripheral proteins associated with the myelin membrane structure; those present appear to hold together higher orders of membrane bilayers to form the hydrophobic electrically insulating structure that is impermeable to ions and water. **Anesthetics** are small lipophilic molecules that slow nerve impulse transmission by dissolving in the lipid coating of nerves and **disrupting the insulating properties.**

INTERCELLULAR CONTACT & COMMUNICATION

In a metazoan organism, there exist many areas of intercellular contact. This necessitates contact between the plasma membranes of the individual cells. Cells have developed specialized regions on their membranes for intercellular communication in close proximity. **Gap junctions** mediate and regulate the passage of ions and small molecules through a narrow **hydrophilic pore** connecting the cytoplasms of adjacent cells. These pores are composed of subunits called "connexons" that have been studied by x-ray crystallography. As diagrammed in Fig 32–20, connexons consist of 6 protein subunits that span the membrane and connect with the analogous structures on the adjacent cells. Each subunit is apparently rigid, and, in response to specific chemical stimuli, the subunits rearrange themselves relative to one another (see Hemoglobin, Fig 5–9) to provide a tangential central opening about 2 nm in diameter. It is through this central opening that ions and small molecules can pass from one cytoplasm to another in a regulated fashion.

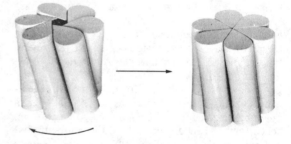

Figure 32–20. Simple model of the connexon, depicting the transition from the "open" to the "closed" configuration. It is proposed that the closure on the cytoplasmic face (uppermost) is achieved by the subunits sliding against each other, decreasing their inclination and hence rotating, in a clockwise sense, at the base. The darker shading on the side of the model indicates the portion that would be embedded in the membrane. The radial displacement of each subunit at the cytoplasmic end would be about 0.6 nm, given the observed inclination change of 5 degrees distributed over its 7.5-nm length. (Reproduced, with permission, from Unwin PNT, Zampighi G: Structure of the junction between communicating cells. *Nature* 1980;**283**:545.)

Signal Transmission

Specific biochemical signals such as neurotransmitters, hormones, and immunoglobulins bind to specific receptors (integral proteins) exposed to the outside of cellular membranes and transmit information through these membranes to the cytoplasm. For example, the β-adrenergic receptor, which stereospecifically binds catecholamines, is asymmetrically located on the outer aspect of plasma membranes of target cells, such as the erythrocytes. The binding of the catecholamine on the outside stimulates the catalytic activity of adenylate cyclase, asymmetrically located on the inside of the membrane. Adenylate cyclase generates cAMP from ATP (see Chapter 25). Thus, the information that a specific catecholamine is present on the outside is transmitted to the inside of the cell, where a second messenger, cAMP, takes up the role of further conveying the information (see Chapter 36).

There exist 3 main components of the coupled hormone receptor–adenylate cyclase system: the **receptor (R)**; the **coupling protein (N),** of which there are 2 types—one involved in the stimulation (N_s) of adenylate cyclase and the other involved in the inhibition (N_i) of adenylate cyclase; and the **catalytic (C) subunit** of adenylate cyclase. The receptor protein is an integral membrane glycoprotein, as described above. The coupling proteins, N_s and N_i, are made up of 3 subunits—alpha, beta, and gamma—of which beta and gamma are identical or nearly so for both N_s and N_i. The catalytic subunit when activated converts ATP to cAMP and pyrophosphate. The N and C components reside on the cytoplasmic aspect of the membrane.

The alpha subunit associated with N_s (ie, α_s) and that associated with N_i (ie, α_i) are both capable of binding GTP and possess GTPase activity, which allows them to convert GTP to GDP and phosphate.

In the membrane, the R is normally in contact with $N_s \cdot GDP$, under which conditions the R has a high affinity for its hormone, H. Upon binding of H to R, the conformation of N_s is changed such that the beta and gamma subunits dissociate, as does the GDP, allowing GTP to bind to the α_s. This process effects 2 subsequent changes: the R diminishes its affinity for H, and the $\alpha_s \cdot GTP$ activates C to catalyze the conversion of ATP to cAMP. The GTPase activity of α_s then converts GTP to GDP, which in turn effects 2 more changes: α_s loses its ability to activate the cyclase, and the beta and gamma subunits of N_s again bind to $\alpha_s \cdot GDP$ to regenerate $N_s \cdot GDP$. Thus, the binding of H to R activates indirectly the catalytic subunit of adenylate cyclase via N_s and GTP. This transmembrane coupling of receptor occupation to the production of the second messenger, ie, cAMP, is a widely used mechanism for signal transmission in prokaryotes and eukaryotes.

Similar coupling mechanisms are involved in inhibition of adenylate cyclase by specific ligand-receptor mechanisms. The inhibitory effect is mediated by the N_i component, which, similarly to the N_s, is dependent upon the binding of GTP to its alpha subunit (α_i). The $\alpha_i \cdot GTP$ signals the catalytic subunit, but in this case inhibiting its catalytic activity by an incompletely understood mechanism.

In animals, there are a number of interesting diseases in which a dysfunction of such signal transmission systems is probably causal. For example, it appears that in some cancers the loss of the α_s GTPase activity effects a constant stimulation of adenylate cyclase, resulting in uncontrolled proliferation of the cell harboring such an acquired change. In inherited conditions such as pseudohypoparathyroidism, the N_s component appears to be incapable of signaling the occupancy of the receptor to the adenylate cyclase. This disorder thus involves malfunctioning of the signal transmission for many hormones. In acquired hypothyroidism and hypoadrenalism there appear to be markedly diminished numbers of receptors and thus sluggish or absent responses to the presence of hormones in the environments of target cells.

Some toxins specifically interrupt this signaling process. For instance, cholera toxin inhibits the hydrolysis of GTP by α_s and thus can result in constant stimulation of adenylate cyclase in the intestine, an effect that results in excessive secretion of salt and water from the intestinal mucosal cells that the cholera toxin has entered. Pertussis toxin produced by the organism responsible for whooping cough apparently prevents the dissociation of GDP from N_i and thereby prevents the occupancy of N_i by GTP. Both of these toxins mediate their effects by catalyzing the covalent attachment of ADP (ADP ribosylation) to N proteins.

Recently, another type of signal transmission system has been discovered in mammalian cells. In this signaling system, inositol triphosphate acts as the second messenger, and its intracellular concentration is regulated by extracellular signals via a transmembrane receptor coupling. On the surface of most mammalian cells are specific receptors for a series of protein growth factors such as insulin, epidermal growth factor, and platelet-derived growth factor. When such a receptor is occupied by its respective effector molecule, a **kinase** activity that is an integral component of the transmembrane receptor molecule is activated on the cytoplasmic side of the membrane. This

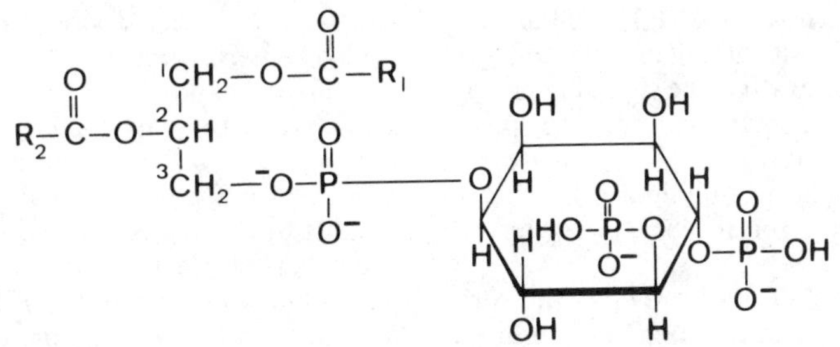

Figure 32–21. The structure of phosphatidylinositol 4,5-bisphosphate.

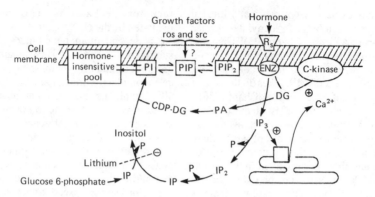

Figure 32–22. Proposed model for the role of the polyphosphatidylinositides in receptor activation. Binding of a hormone or neurotransmitter to its receptor (R_S) activates the enzyme (ENZ) that splits the polyphosphatidylinositide (PIP_2) to inositol triphosphate (IP_3), which releases calcium ions from internal stores, and diacylglycerol (DG), which activates protein kinase C. Resynthesis of PIP_2 involves the conversion of IP_3 to inositol by stepwise removal of the 3 phosphate groups to form first inositol bisphosphate (IP_2), then inositol phosphate (IP), and finally inositol. The last step is inhibited by the drug lithium. The diglyceride is converted to phosphatidic acid (PA) by the addition of a phosphate group and then to a cytosine nucleotide derivative (CDP-DG). Inositol and CDP-DG combine to produce phosphatidylinositol (PI), which is phosphorylated to PIP. Phosphorylation of PIP regenerates PIP_2. Growth factors and certain oncogene products with kinase activities may catalyze this latter phosphorylation. (Slightly modified and reproduced, with permission, from Marx JL: New view of receptor action. *Science* 1984;**224**:271. Copyright © by the American Association for the Advancement of Science.)

kinase is capable of phosphorylating phosphatidyl-inositol to phosphatidylinositol 4-phosphate and the latter compound to phosphatidylinositol 4,5-bisphosphate. Interestingly, several oncogenes, the expression of which can effect a malignant transformation of a cell, also possess kinase activities that can generate these **polyphosphatidylinositides.**

Other receptors on cell surfaces, such as those for acetylcholine or vasopressin, are, when occupied by their respective ligands, potent activators of **phospholipase C.** The latter catalyzes the hydrolysis of phosphatidylinositol 4,5-bisphosphate to inositol triphosphate and 1,2-diacylglycerol. The diacylglycerol is itself capable of activating a specific cytoplasmic kinase, **protein kinase C,** the activity of which is also dependent upon free ionic calcium. On the other hand, the **inositol triphosphate is an effective releaser of calcium** from intracellular storage sites such as the sarcoplasmic reticulum and mitochondria. Thus, the **hydrolysis of phosphatidylinositol 4,5-bisphosphate leads to activation of protein kinase C and promotes an increase in cytoplasmic calcium ion,** both of which promote cellular proliferation and other specific responses. In this signaling system, it appears that **calcium and 1,2-diacylglycerol are tertiary messengers** of the signal. Again, interestingly, some oncogenes appear to affect the signaling process indirectly, in this case by possessing phosphatidylinositol kinase activity, which increases the accumulation of polyphosphatidylinositides that in turn serve as precursors for secondary and tertiary messengers.

Equally interesting, **lithium prevents the recycling of inositol to phosphatidylinositol** by preventing the breakdown of inositol 1-phosphate. Lithium is a remarkably effective drug for the treatment of manic

disorders, which appear to result from hyperactivity in the central nervous system. It may well be that by diminishing the rate of synthesis of polyphosphatidylinositides lithium effectively diminishes an abnormal signaling process that occurs in affected persons.

Endocytosis

Endocytosis is a transport process that allows cells to internalize extracellular material and involves the formation of endocytotic vesicles during that process. **Endocytotic vesicles** are generated when segments of the plasma membrane invaginate, enclosing a volume of extracellular fluid, and then pinch off as the fusion of plasma membranes seals the neck of the vesicle and the original site of invagination (Fig 32–23). Subsequent fusion of the endocytotic vesicle with other membrane structures accomplishes the transport of its contents to other cellular compartments or even back to the cell exterior.

There are 2 general types of endocytosis. **Phagocytosis** (not discussed here) occurs only in specialized phagocytic cells such as macrophages and granulocytes present in blood. **Pinocytosis** is a property of all cells and leads to the cellular uptake of fluid and fluid contents. There are 2 types. **Adsorptive pinocytosis** is a receptor-mediated, selective process primarily responsible for the uptake of macromolecules for which there is a finite number of binding sites on the plasma membrane. These high-affinity receptors permit pinocytosis to **concentrate ligands** from the medium and to minimize the uptake of fluid or soluble unbound macromolecules. The vesicles formed in the process of adsorptive pinocytosis are derived from invaginations (pits) that are coated on the cytoplasmic side with a filamentous material. In many systems, **clathrin** is the filamentous material

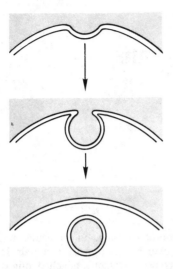

Figure 32–23. Formation of an endocytotic vesicle by the process of invagination at the cell plasma membrane.

and is probably a peripheral membrane protein.

For example, the LDL molecule and its receptor (Chapter 18) are internalized via coated pits containing the LDL receptor. These endocytotic vesicles containing LDL and its receptor fuse to lysosomes in the cell. The receptor is released and recycled back to the cell surface membrane, but LDL apoprotein is degraded and the cholesteryl esters metabolized. Synthesis of the LDL receptor is regulated by secondary or tertiary consequences of pinocytosis, ie, by metabolites of LDL. Disorders of the LDL receptor and its internalization are medically important and are discussed in Chapter 18.

Other macromolecules, including several hormones, are subject to adsorptive pinocytosis and form **receptosomes,** vesicles that avoid lysosomes and deliver their contents to other intracellular sites, such as the Golgi system.

Adsorptive pinocytosis of extracellular glycoproteins requires that the glycoproteins carry specific **carbohydrate recognition signals.** These recognition signals are bound by membrane receptor molecules, which play a role analogous to that of the LDL receptor. A galactosyl receptor on the surface of hepatocytes is instrumental in the adsorptive pinocytosis of asialoglycoproteins from the circulation. Acid hydrolases taken up by adsorptive pinocytosis in fibroblasts are recognized by their mannose 6-phosphate moieties. Interestingly, the mannose 6-phosphate moiety also seems to play an important role in the **intracellular targeting** of the acid hydrolases to the lysosomes of the cells in which they are synthesized.

The other type of pinocytosis is a nonselective fluid phase process in which the uptake of a solute is simply proportionate to its concentration in the surrounding medium. This **fluid phase pinocytosis** forms small vesicles and is an extraordinarily active process, utilizing up to 50% of the plasma membrane per hour in some cell types. These components of the membrane must be recycled in order to maintain cellular integrity.

●　●　●

References

Ashwell G, Harford J: Carbohydrate-specific receptors of the liver. *Annu Rev Biochem* 1982;**51**:531.

Bedouelle H et al: Mutations which alter the function of the signal sequence of the maltose binding protein of *Escherichia coli.* *Nature* 1980;**285**:78.

Berridge MJ, Irvine RF: Inositol triphosphate, a novel second messenger in cellular signal transduction. *Nature* 1984;**312**:315.

Blobel G et al: Translocation of proteins across membranes: The signal hypothesis and beyond. *Symp Soc Exp Biol* 1979;**33**:9.

Callahan JW, Lowden JA (editors): *Lysosomes and Lysosomal Storage Diseases.* Raven Press, 1981.

Dautry-Varsat A, Lodish HF: How receptors bring proteins and particles into cells. *Sci Am* (May) 1984;**250**:52.

Davis BD, Tai P-C: The mechanism of protein secretion across membranes. *Nature* 1980;**283**:433.

Hunter T: The proteins of oncogenes. *Sci Am* (Aug) 1984;**250**:70.

Kandel ER, Schwartz JH: Molecular biology of learning: Modulation of transmitter release. *Science* 1982;**218**:433.

Lefkowitz RJ et al: Mechanisms of membrane-receptor regulation. *N Engl J Med* 1984;**310**:1570.

Morell P, Norton WT: Myelin. *Sci Am* (May) 1980;**242**:88.

Op den Kamp JAF: Lipid asymmetry in membranes. *Annu Rev Biochem* 1979;**48**:47.

Pastan IH, Willingham MC: Receptor-mediated endocytosis of hormones in cultured cells. *Annu Rev Physiol* 1981;**43**:239.

Sabatini DD et al: Mechanisms for the incorporation of proteins in membranes and organelles. *J Cell Biol* 1982;**92**:1.

Schramm M, Selinger Z: Message transmission: Controlled adenylate cyclase system. *Science* 1984;**225**:1350.

Singer SJ, Nicolson GL: The fluid mosaic model of the structure of cell membranes. *Science* 1972;**175**:720.

Sly WS: Saccharide traffic signals in receptor-mediated endocytosis and transport of acid hydrolase. Page 433 in: *Structure and Function of the Gangliosides.* Svennerholm L et al (editors). Plenum Press, 1980.

Spiegel AM et al: Clinical implications of guanine nucleotide-binding proteins as receptor-effector couplers. *N Engl J Med* 1985;**312**:26.

Unwin N, Henderson R: The structure of proteins in biological membranes. *Sci Am* (Feb) 1984;**250**:78.

Walter P et al: Protein translocation across the endoplasmic reticulum. *Cell* 1984;**38**:5.

Wickner W: Assembly of proteins into membranes. *Science* 1980;**210**:861.

Willingham MC, Pastan I: The receptosome: An intermediate organelle of receptor-mediated endocytosis in cultured fibroblasts. *Cell* 1980;**21**:67.

33 | Glycoproteins, Proteoglycans, & Glycosaminoglycans

David W. Martin, Jr., MD

The descriptions of the biochemistry of glycoproteins, proteoglycans, and glycosaminoglycans are included in one chapter because these 3 types of molecules have several features in common, including aspects of their structure, synthesis, degradation, and even function. The 3 classes of molecules can be clearly defined, although in the past some confusion has existed because of overlapping terminology. **Glycoproteins** differ from other proteins in having oligosaccharide chains covalently attached to their polypeptide backbones. **Proteoglycans** are also proteins to which oligosaccharide chains are covalently attached to the polypeptide backbone, but the oligosaccharides differ chemically from those attached to glycoproteins (Fig 33–1). The oligosaccharide chains of proteoglycans consist of repeating disaccharide units that contain (1) glucosamine or galactosamine, (2) a uronic acid (except for keratan sulfate), *and* (3) covalently attached sulfate groups (except for hyaluronic acid). **Glycosaminoglycans** are oligosaccharide structures that have been removed from the protein backbone of their proteoglycan precursor. The structures, synthesis, degradation, and functions of each of these classes of molecules will be discussed in turn. All 3 classes of molecules exist mostly in the **extracellular space** but are synthesized intracellularly in close association with the intracellular membrane systems of the endoplasmic reticulum and Golgi complex (see Chapter 32). The oligosaccharide moieties appear to be important for both directing the export of these molecules and providing some specifically extracellular functional advantage, perhaps stability or localization.

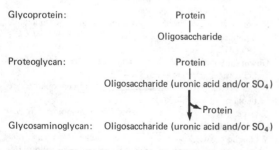

Figure 33–1. Similarities and relationships between glycoproteins, proteoglycans, and glycosaminoglycans.

GLYCOPROTEINS

Glycoproteins range in molecular weight from 15,000 to over 1 million, usually contain 15 or fewer sugar units per covalently attached oligosaccharide chain, and may have carbohydrate contents ranging from 1 to 85% by weight. Glycoproteins are present in most organisms, including plants, bacteria, fungi, viruses, and animals, and have several functions. As explained in Chapter 32, most membrane proteins and secreted proteins are glycoproteins. Table 33–1 sets forth a partial list of functions of different glycoproteins.

Table 33–1. Some functions served by glycoproteins.

Structural molecules
Cell walls
Collagen, elastin
Fibrins
Bone matrix
Lubricants and protective agents
Mucins
Mucous secretions
Transport molecules for
Vitamins
Lipids
Minerals and trace elements
Immunologic molecules
Immunoglobins
Histocompatibility antigens
Complement
Interferon
Hormones
Chorionic gonadotropin
Thyrotropin (TSH)
Enzymes
Proteases
Nucleases
Glycosidases
Hydrolases
Clotting factors
Cell attachment/recognition sites
Cell-cell
Virus-cell
Bacterium-cell
Hormone receptors
Antifreeze in antarctic fishes
Lectins

Structures of Oligosaccharides Attached to Glycoproteins

Nine different sugar residues are found in the oligosaccharide chains attached to the glycoproteins. Glucose (Glc) is found only in collagen, but galactose (Gal) and mannose (Man) are more common and widely distributed. The 2 most frequently found hexoses are N-acetylgalactosamine (GalNAc) and N-acetylglucosamine (GlcNAc). Fucose (Fuc), which is 6-deoxygalactose, is a common constituent. Two pentoses, arabinose (Ara) and xylose (Xyl), are found, and the ninth are the sialic acids (Sial), of which N-acetylneuraminic acid (Nana) is an example (see Chapter 13). In general, the N-acetylhexosamines are at the end of the oligosaccharide chains most proximal to the protein. The fucose and Nana residues are more distal in the chain, frequently at terminal sites.

The oligosaccharide chains are attached to the polypeptide backbone of glycoproteins at one of 5 amino acid residues: **asparagine** (Asn), **serine** (Ser), **threonine** (Thr), **hydroxylysine** (Hyl), or **hydroxyproline** (Hyp). There are 2 types of chemical bonds that provide the attachment sites, O-glycosidic links and N-glycosidic links.

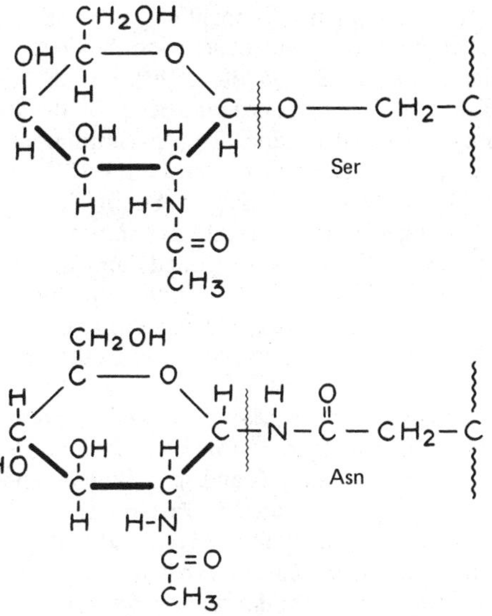

O-Glycosidic Links

Most of the O-glycosidic links occur through the free alcohol groups of Ser or Thr residues of the polypeptide (Fig 33–2), in a tripeptide sequence of Asn-Y-Ser(Thr), where Y is an amino acid other than aspartate. This specific tripeptide sequence is very common in proteins, but every such sequence is not glycosylated. The decision to glycosylate such Ser or

Figure 33–2. Linkage of N-acetylgalactosamine to serine and linkage of N-acetylglucosamine to asparagine.

Thr residues also is based on the protein conformation surrounding that tripeptide as it emerges through the endoplasmic reticulum (see Chapter 32).

The most common sugar residue attached directly to the Ser or Thr residue is GalNAc. About 6 different types of oligosaccharide structures can be found attached to this GalNAc-Ser(Thr) linkage. As shown in Table 33–2, many mucins, blood group substances,

Table 33–2. Glycopeptides linked through N-acetylgalactosamine to the hydroxyl group of serine and threonine.[*]

	Structure	Glycoprotein
A	Nana $\xrightarrow{\alpha 2,6}$ GalNAc $\longrightarrow$ Ser(Thr)	Submaxillary mucins
B	Gal $\xrightarrow{\beta 1,3}$ GalNAc $\longrightarrow$ Ser(Thr)	"Antifreeze" glycoprotein of antarctic fish; human IgA1; β subunit hCG; cartilage keratan sulfate; epiglycanin of TA$_3$-HA cells; lymphocyte, RBC, and milk fat globule membranes
C	Gal $\xrightarrow{\beta 1,3}$ GalNAc $\longrightarrow$ Ser(Thr) $\uparrow \alpha 2,3$ Nana	Bovine kininogen; epiglycanin of TA$_3$-HA cells; B$_{16}$ melanoma cells
D	Gal $\xrightarrow{\beta 1,3}$ GalNAc $\longrightarrow$ Ser(Thr) $\uparrow \alpha 2,3$ $\uparrow \alpha 2,6$ Nana Nana	Fetuin; human RBC membrane sialoglycoprotein; bovine kininogen; rat brain
E	Gal $\xrightarrow{\beta 1,3(4)}$ GlcNAc $\xrightarrow{1,2(4,6)}$ Gal $\xrightarrow{\beta 1,3(4)}$ GalNAc $\longrightarrow$ Ser(Thr) $\uparrow \alpha 2,3$ Nana	Epiglycanin
F	Gal $\xrightarrow{1,3}$ GlcNAc $\xrightarrow{1,3}$ Gal $\xrightarrow{1,3}$ GalNAc $\longrightarrow$ Ser(Thr) $\uparrow 1,6$ GlcNAc $\uparrow 1,4$ Gal	Human gastric mucin; core region of human and hog blood group substances

[*]Slightly modified and reproduced, with permission, from Lennarz WJ: *The Biochemistry of Glycoproteins and Proteoglycans.* Plenum Press, 1980.

and other common glycopeptides possess a Gal or Nana as the next residue attached to the GalNAc. The initiation and extension of these types of oligosaccharide chains of glycoproteins occur by the stepwise donation of sugar residues from pyrimidine or purine nucleotide sugars, as discussed below.

The O-glycosidic linkage to Ser or Thr may occur through sugars other than GalNAc. In yeast and fungi, Man-Ser(Thr) linkages are found, and human urine contains Fuc-Thr remnants of glycoproteins, providing evidence for their existence. As discussed below, Xyl-Ser(Thr) linkages are common in the proteoglycans.

Oligosaccharides may be linked to proteins via O-glycosidic bonds to Hyl or Hyp, which are amino acid residues uniquely found in **collagens** and some fibrous proteins of plants. Gal is frequently the lead sugar attached directly to the Hyl, and that linkage is common in basement membranes. As for other O-glycosidic linkages, the sugar moiety is donated by an "activated" nucleotide sugar.

N-Glycosidic Linkage to Polypeptide Chains

The N-glycosidic linkage of oligosaccharides to proteins occurs exclusively through a GlcNAc-Asn bond (Fig 33–2) where the Asn exists as part of an Asn-X-Ser(Thr) sequence, usually at a β turn of the folding protein molecule. The N-linked oligosaccharide consists of a core region with the structure Man-β-1,4-GlcNAc-β-1,4-GlcNAc-Asn. The sequence GlcNAc-β-1,4-GlcNAc-β-Asn is referred to as the **di-N-acetylchitobiose** sequence. The oligosaccharide chains attached to glycoproteins by way of this N-glycosidic core region are of 2 types: the high-mannose (simple) type and the complex type. A single protein can contain oligosaccharide chains of both high-mannose and complex types as well as the types employing O-glycosidic linkages described above.

The **high-mannose chains** contain only Man and GlcNAc residues, and all are remarkably similar in structure, as shown in Fig 33–3. Note that these high-mannose structures contain the same β-mannosyl-di-N-acetylchitobiose core structure and exhibit the same branching pattern of their outer α-Man residues. The outer chain **branch** is confined to the Man linked to the C_6 of the core β-Man residue.

Although all high-mannose oligosaccharides are synthesized from nucleotide sugars, there exists an important **lipid-linked precursor oligosaccharide** that is transferred en bloc from a lipid carrier to the Asn of the protein. The formation and function of the lipid-linked carrier is described below. The synthesis of the high-mannose glycoproteins occurs at the endoplasmic reticulum, as briefly described in Chapter 32 and in more detail below.

The **complex N-linked oligosaccharides** also contain the β-Man-di-N-acetylchitobiose core structure but consist also of a variable number of **outer**

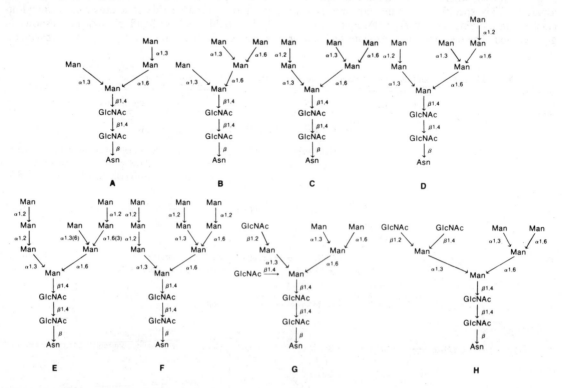

Figure 33–3. Structures of high-mannose chains. A, B, C, D, G, and H are from ovalbumin; B, C, E, and F are from Chinese hamster ovary cell membranes; and F is the A glycopeptide from bovine thyroglobulin. (Reproduced, with permission, from Lennarz WJ: *The Biochemistry of Glycoproteins and Proteoglycans.* Plenum Press, 1980.)

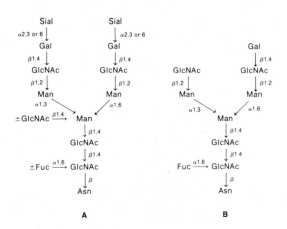

Figure 33–4. Structures of glycopeptides with complex N-linked oligosaccharides. *A* is a composite structure characteristic of many glycopeptides as described in the text, and *B* is from human IgG. (Reproduced, with permission, from Lennarz WJ: *The Biochemistry of Glycoproteins and Proteoglycans.* Plenum Press, 1980.)

chains containing Sial, Gal, and Fuc residues linked to the core. Usually, 2 α-Man residues are attached directly to the β-Man-N-acetylchitobiose structure (Fig 33–4). The outer chains most often consist of Sial-Gal-GlcNAc.

Complex N-linked oligosaccharide structures are found **only in higher animals,** whereas high-mannose structures are common in primitive organisms. Synthesis of the complex oligosaccharides occurs by way of the same lipid-linked precursor oligosaccharide that participates in synthesis of the high-mannose oligosaccharide. Thus, the **core regions** of both the high-mannose oligosaccharides and the complex oligosaccharides are **identical.** Clearly, the lipid-linked process used for the synthesis of the high-mannose oligosaccharides in ancestral organisms has been employed for the generation of the recently evolved complex oligosaccharide structures.

Lipid-Linked Oligosaccharide Precursor

Polyisoprenol compounds, occurring as free alcohols, exist in both bacteria and eukaryotic tissues. They participate in the synthesis of bacterial cell walls and of the glycoproteins and proteoglycans in eukary-

otic tissues. The polyisoprenol primarily used in eukaryotic tissues is **dolichol,** which is, next to rubber, the longest naturally occurring hydrocarbon made up of a single repeating unit. A space-filling model is illustrated in Fig 33–5. This very hydrophobic molecule extends approximately 10 nm, significantly greater than the width of the membrane bilayer where it is commonly found.

GlcNAc-pyrophosphoryl-dolichol (GlcNAc-P-P-Dol) is the key glycosyl lipid that acts as **acceptor** for other glycosyl units in the oligosaccharide-lipid assembly mechanism. It is also found in the membranes of a wide variety of tissues. This primary precursor is synthesized on the cytoplasmic aspect of microsomes from UDP-GlcNAc and dolichol phosphate in the following reaction:

$$\text{Dol-P} + \text{UDP-GlcNAc} \rightarrow \text{Dol-P-P-GlcNAc} + \text{UMP}$$

On the GlcNAc-P-P-Dol primer is built an oligosaccharide structure like the high-mannose type present in glycoproteins. The synthesis occurs as depicted in Fig 33–6. The penultimate GlcNAc is donated by UDP-GlcNAc to form a second (beta-linked) GlcNAc. The mannose is next added in a beta-linkage from GDP-α-Man in a reaction that involves an inversion of the glycosidic bond from alpha to beta. The subsequent Man moieties that become linked in the alpha configuration are donated by another dolichol

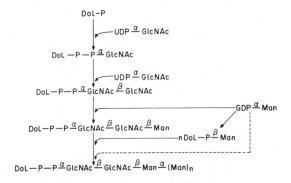

Figure 33–6. Pathway for assembly of oligosaccharide dolichol. (Reproduced, with permission, from Lennarz WJ: *The Biochemistry of Glycoproteins and Proteoglycans.* Plenum Press, 1980.)

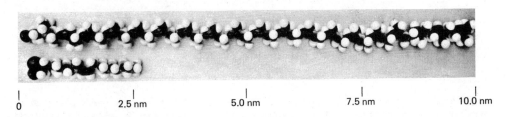

Figure 33–5. Molecular model of dolichol. In fully extended form it is 10 nm in length. Oleic acid (2.5 nm) is shown for comparison. (Reproduced, with permission, from Lennarz WJ: *The Biochemistry of Glycoproteins and Proteoglycans.* Plenum Press, 1980.)

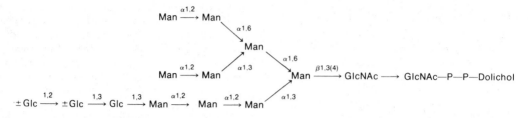

Figure 33–7. Proposed structure of the lipid-linked oligosaccharide precursor in glycoprotein synthesis. (Reproduced, with permission, from Lennarz WJ: *The Biochemistry of Glycoproteins and Proteoglycans.* Plenum Press, 1980.)

derivative, Man-P-Dol. The Man-P-Dol is formed in the following reaction:

$$Dol\text{-}P + GDP\text{-}\alpha\text{-}Man \rightarrow Dol\text{-}P\text{-}\beta\text{-}Man + GDP$$

It seems that some of the lipid-linked oligosaccharide precursors contain Glc residues donated by Glc-P-Dol, which have been generated similarly from UDP-Glc and P-Dol. In this way are generated the lipid-linked oligosaccharide precursors, with a structure taking the general form depicted in Fig 33–7.

Retinoic acid, a form of vitamin A, is also a polyisoprenoid compound widely distributed in animal tissues (see Chapter 11). Retinoic acid is capable of stimulating glycoprotein synthesis. An unknown metabolite of retinoic acid may also act as a carrier of β-Man-P and Gal-P. In a vitamin A–deficient state, rat liver accumulates low-molecular-weight oligosaccharide lipids, the major one being $(Man)_5(GlcNAc)_2$-Dol-P-P, whereas normal liver accumulates $(Glc)_3$-$(Man)_9(GlcNAc)_2$-Dol-P-P.

The high-mannose oligosaccharide moiety linked to pyrophosphoryl dolichol is **transferred en bloc** to form an N-glycosidic bond with the Asn moiety of a protein molecule emerging through the luminal aspect of the endoplasmic reticulum membrane (see Chapter 32). The reaction is catalyzed by an "oligosaccharide transferase," a membrane-associated enzyme. The transferase will recognize and transfer any glycolipid with the general structure R-(GlcNAc)$_2$-P-P-Dol. The recipient proteins in the endoplasmic reticulum have molecular weights ranging from 15,000 to 145,000 and include both secreted and integral membrane proteins. The intracellular soluble proteins are rarely if ever glycosylated. This transfer reaction is depicted in Fig 33–8.

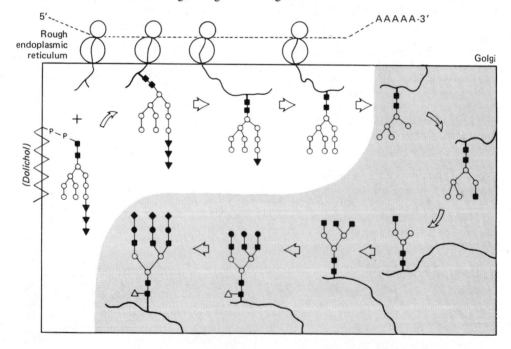

Figure 33–8. Proposed sequence for the processing of peptide-bound N-linked oligosaccharide chains: ■, *N*-acetylglucosamine residues; O, mannose residues; ▼, glucose residues; ●, galactose residues; ◆, sialic acid residues; and △, fucose residues. The wavy line represents the polypeptide chain; the broken line is the mRNA. The processes within the shaded area occur in the Golgi complex. (Modified and reproduced, with permission, from Lennarz WJ: *The Biochemistry of Glycoproteins and Proteoglycans.* Plenum Press, 1980.)

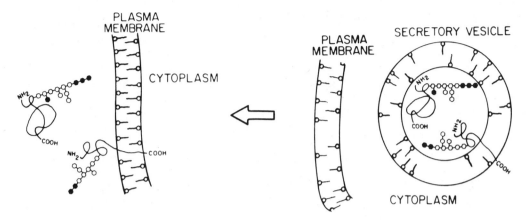

Figure 33–9. Depiction of the fusion of a secretory vesicle with the plasma membrane. The process provides integral plasma membrane glycoproteins and secretes luminal proteins to the extracellular space. (Reproduced, with permission, from Lennarz WJ: *The Biochemistry of Glycoproteins and Proteoglycans.* Plenum Press, 1980.)

The other product of the oligosaccharide transferase reaction is dolichol pyrophosphate, which is subsequently converted to dolichol phosphate. The dolichol phosphate can serve again as an acceptor for the synthesis of a lipid-linked oligosaccharide precursor. The synthesis of lipid-linked oligosaccharide is probably regulated by the availability of Dol-P.

The generation of the oligosaccharide dolichol precursor and the transfer of its oligosaccharide moiety occur in the rough endoplasmic reticulum. At that site, glycosylated integral membrane proteins remain within the endoplasmic reticulum membrane structure, while secretory proteins that have been glycosylated are extruded into the lumen of the endoplasmic reticulum. These glycosylated proteins, which contain the **high-mannose oligosaccharide moieties,** migrate to the Golgi complex, perhaps by lateral diffusion within the plane of the membrane. In the **Golgi complex,** the oligosaccharide moieties of these glycoproteins may be further modified to form complex oligosaccharides described above. This modification process involves glycosidase and glycosyltransferase enzymes and will be described in detail below. Vesicles are formed from the Golgi complex, and those so targeted will then fuse with a plasma membrane, as depicted in Fig 33–9. Luminal glycoproteins are secreted into the surrounding medium, while integral membrane proteins in secretory vesicles become integral components of the plasma membranes. Vesicles of similar structures deliver integral proteins to the internal membrane structures and provide glycoproteins to the lumens of internal membrane structures such as lysosomes. The mechanisms by which glycoproteins are targeted for specific structures or organelles are not understood but probably involve the oligosaccharide moieties of the glycoprotein. For example, a mannosyl 6-phosphate moiety is necessary for lysosomal enzymes to be delivered to lysosomal structures.

Synthesis of Dolichol

The isoprenol structure of dolichol is derived from mevalonate by the condensation of isopentenyl pyrophosphate and dimethylallyl pyrophosphate to form farnesyl pyrophosphate (see Chapter 18). The transfarnesyl pyrophosphate then acts as an acceptor of more isoprene units from isoprenyl pyrophosphate, eventually to form dolichol phosphate. As mentioned above, dolichol phosphate can also be regenerated from dolichol pyrophosphate, a by-product of the oligosaccharide transferase reaction in the endoplasmic reticulum.

There are a number of inhibitors of the synthesis of oligosaccharidepyrophosphoryl dolichol. The 2-deoxysugars such as 2-deoxyglucose, the fluorodeoxysugars, and the amino sugars can all inhibit formation of oligosaccharide moieties by mechanisms that are not clearly defined. The antibiotic **bacitracin** in bacteria blocks the dephosphorylation of undecaprenol pyrophosphate to form the necessary undecaprenol phosphate. In animal pancreas microsomes, bacitracin blocks the synthesis of GlcNAc-P-P-Dol.

Tunicamycin, an antibiotic from *Streptomyces*, also blocks the synthesis of GlcNAc-P-P-Dol from Dol-P and UDP-GlcNAc. Both of these antibiotics—particularly the latter—are useful in the study of the functional roles of glycoproteins. The regulation of dolichol phosphate synthesis appears to occur both at the level of synthesis of mevalonic acid and at the level of regeneration of dolichol phosphate from dolichol pyrophosphate.

The Synthesis of Complex Carbohydrates of Glycoproteins

The discovery of the mechanism of glycogen synthase established the role of nucleotides in the synthesis of complex carbohydrate molecules, such as starch and glycogen. The nucleotide sugars are formed from nucleoside triphosphates and sugar 1-phosphates in the following reaction:

$$NTP + P\text{-}1\text{-}Sugar \rightarrow NDP\text{-}Sugar + PP_i$$

The reaction is catalyzed by cytoplasmic enzymes. The sugar nucleotides formed by these reactions include the following:

UDP-α-Glc
UDP-α-Gal
UDP-α-GlcNAc
UDP-α-GalNAc
GDP-α-Man
GDP-β-Fuc

The nucleotide of sialic acid, CMP-Sial, is formed from CTP by sialyltransferases located in the Golgi complex and in the nucleoplasm.

In animal cells, the sugars are linked to the nucleotides by the alpha- linkage, with the exception of the beta- linkage of L-fucose to GDP. As mentioned above, during the transfer of the sugar moiety to the oligosaccharide, the alpha- bridges are inverted to beta- bridges and vice versa. Thus, GDP-α-Man provides a beta-linked mannose in the oligosaccharide. The GDP-α-Man can, however, form Man-β-P-Dol. When this beta-linked mannose is transferred from dolichol phosphate to the oligosaccharide, a second inversion occurs, thereby generating the alpha-Man bridges found in oligosaccharides.

A series of specific glycosyltransferase enzymes catalyze the transfer of the sugar moieties to generate the complex glycoproteins that have the general structure (Glc)$_X$(Man-α)$_Y$Man-β-1,4-GlcNAc-β-1,4-GlcNAc-Asn. These glycosyltransferases generally require divalent **manganese.** The order of addition is dictated by the substrate specificities of the glycosyltransferase enzymes. As depicted in Fig 33–8, by the time the high-mannose oligosaccharide-polypeptide has reached the Golgi complex, it may have had its sugar moieties trimmed such that only 5 mannosyl residues remain attached to the di-N-acetylchitobiose core.

A Golgi-localized enzyme, UDP-GlcNAc transferase I, can then donate a GlcNAc to a linear or branched α-Man moiety to form GlcNAc-β-1,2-Man linkages. A second transferase, UDP-GlcNAc transferase II, will donate its GlcNAc moiety **only to a branched structure** to which one GlcNAc has already been attached, such as by the transferase I enzyme. As depicted in Fig 33–8, the attachment of the first GlcNAc moiety seems to be followed by further trimming of the α-mannosyl residues from the oligosaccharide by membrane-associated mannosidases.

Fucosyltransferases can then act on the products of GlcNAc transferase I or transferase II but must have at least one GlcNAc residue on the Man$_3$GlcNAc$_2$Asn core. The galactosyltransferase enzymes are also located on the Golgi complex and attach a galactosyl residue usually to the end of a chain or occasionally

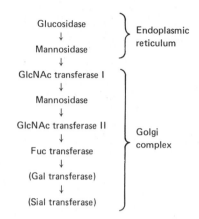

Figure 33–10. Order in which the specific glycosyltransferase enzymes act to form the specific complex type oligosaccharide structures of glycoproteins. The parentheses denote that either enzyme can act first. The locations of the enzymes are indicated.

penultimate to a sialic acid residue. The galactosyl residues are usually linked to GlcNAc by beta-1,4- linkages but occasionally by beta-1,6- linkages.

The galactosyltransferase enzyme is unique; in the presence of manganese and glucose or GlcNAc, it binds tightly to α-lactalbumin, present in colostrum and milk, and becomes the lactose synthase A enzyme per se.

At least 4 different sialyltransferase enzymes can be found in the Golgi complex and utilize CMP-sialic acid as donor for the sialation of protein-linked oligosaccharides. The Sial residues are always found linked to a subterminal Gal moiety at a nonreducing terminus in alpha- linkage, usually 2,3- or 2,6-.

This elongation process generating the complex type oligosaccharides of glycoproteins occurs exclusively in the Golgi complex. Each linkage appears to be carried out by a specific glycosyltransferase; thus, there seems to be a **"one linkage, one glycosyltransferase"** synthetic arrangement. The specific sequence in which the glycosyltransferases act is generalized in Fig 33–10. The ordered generation of the oligosaccharide and its location are depicted in Fig 33–8.

BLOOD GROUP ANTIGENS

The blood group antigens are oligosaccharides of specific medical interest. Their structures and syntheses will be described in detail. In 1900, **Landsteiner** described the **ABO blood groups.** Today, there are more than 20 blood group systems expressing more than 160 distinct antigens. The most commonly studied blood groups are those of the ABH(O) and the Lewis (Le) systems. These erythrocyte antigens are linked to specific membrane proteins by O-glycosidic bonds in which GalNAc is the most proximal sugar residue. The specific oligosaccharides forming these

Table 33–3. The 4 independent gene systems responsible for the expressions of the ABH(O) and Lewis (Le) blood group antigens.

Genetic Locus	Alleles
H	H, h
Secretor	Se, se
ABO	A, B, O
Lewis	Le, le

antigens occur in 3 forms: (1) as glycosphingolipids and glycoproteins on the surfaces of erythrocytes and other cells, (2) as oligosaccharides in milk and urine, and (3) as oligosaccharides attached to mucins secreted in the gastrointestinal, genitourinary, and respiratory tracts.

There are 4 independent gene systems related to the expressions of these oligosaccharide antigens (Table 33–3).

The H Locus

The **H locus** codes for the fucosyltransferase in hematopoietic tissues that attaches a fucose residue in alpha-1,2- linkage to a Gal residue, itself attached in either beta-1,4- or beta-1,3- linkage to an oligosaccharide. The fucosyltransferase catalyzes

$$\text{GDP-}\beta\text{-Fuc} + \text{Gal-}\beta\text{–R} \rightarrow \text{Fuc-}\alpha\text{-1,2-Gal-}\beta\text{–R} + \text{GDP}$$

The product, Fuc-α-1,2-Gal-β–R, is a **precursor** for the formation of both the A and B oligosaccharide antigens of erythrocytes. The h allele of the H locus codes for an inactive fucosyltransferase; therefore, individuals with the **hh genotype cannot generate this necessary precursor** of the A and B erythrocyte blood antigens. Accordingly, hh genotypic persons will be erythrocyte blood type O even though they may possess genes for the active A or active B glycosyltransferases described below.

The Secretor Locus

The **secretor locus (Se)** codes for a specific Fuc transferase in secretory organs, such as the exocrine glands, but *not* in the erythrocytes. Accordingly—for example—individuals with the SeSe or Sese genotype will generate the A and B antigen **precursor** in the exocrine glands that form saliva and will be secretors

of the A or B antigens (or both) when the A- or B-specific transferases are present (Table 33–4). Individuals who are sese genotype will **not secrete A or B** antigens, but if they possess an H allele and A or B alleles, their **erythrocytes will express** the A, B, or both antigens.

The ABO Locus

The ABO locus codes for 2 specific transferases that act to transfer specific Gal moieties to the Fuc-α-1,2-Gal-β–R precursor oligosaccharide formed by the action of the H or Se allele–coded fucosyltransferase. The A-specific transferase carries out the following reaction:

$$\text{UDP-}\alpha\text{-GalNAc} + \text{Fuc-}\alpha\text{-1,2-Gal-}\beta\text{–R} \rightarrow$$
$$\text{GalNAc-}\alpha\text{-1,3-(Fuc-}\alpha\text{-1,2)Gal-}\beta\text{–R} + \text{UDP}$$

The B allele–specific transferase catalyzes the reaction

$$\text{UDP-}\alpha\text{-Gal} + \text{Fuc-}\alpha\text{-1,2-Gal-}\beta\text{–R} \rightarrow$$
$$\text{Gal-}\alpha\text{-1,3-(Fuc-}\alpha\text{-1,2)Gal-}\beta\text{–R} + \text{UDP}$$

Accordingly, persons possessing an A allele will attach a **GalNAc moiety to the precursor generated by the 1,2-Fuc transferase,** and individuals possessing a B allele will transfer a **Gal moiety to the same precursor** (Fig 33–11). Individuals possessing both an A allele and a B allele will generate both oligosaccharides, ie, one with a GalNAc and another with a Gal moiety on the nonreducing terminus. Individuals lacking both A and B alleles (OO homozygotes) will not attach either GalNAc or Gal to the precursor. The

Table 33–4. A, B antigen expression.

Genotypes			Phenotypes	
ABO Locus	H Locus	Secretor Locus	Erythrocytes	Secretions
OO	Any	Any	O	O
A and/or B	HH or Hh	SeSe or Sese	A and/or B	A and/or B
A and/or B	HH or Hh	sese	A and/or B	O
A and/or B	hh	Any	O	O

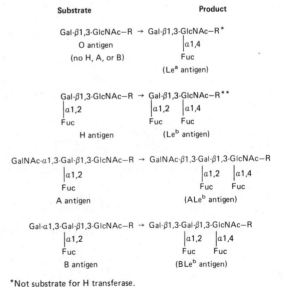

Substrate	Product

*Not substrate for H transferase.

**Not substrate for A or B transferase.

Figure 33–11. The A and B antigens and substrate specificity of the Lewis-dependent α-1,4-fucosyltransferase.

anti-A antiserum originally described by Landsteiner recognizes the specific oligosaccharide with the GalNAc nonreducing terminus. The anti-B antiserum recognizes the closely related oligosaccharide with the Gal nonreducing terminus. When neither GalNAc nor Gal is at the reducing terminus of this oligosaccharide, it will not be recognized by either anti-A or anti-B antisera, and the blood group antigen is said to be **type O.** It can be seen that individuals with the hh genotype and thus incapable of attaching the Fuc moiety to the appropriate Gal-β–R oligosaccharide would be incapable of expressing the A or the B antigen determinant and thus also would be considered to be of the O type blood group.

The Lewis Locus

The Le gene of the Lewis locus codes for an α-1,4-fucosyltransferase activity, which has a rather strict oligosaccharide substrate specificity. The Lewis-dependent transferase will attach, in alpha-1,4-linkage, a Fuc moiety to a GlcNAc residue that already has attached to it a β-**Gal in a 1,3-** **linkage** (Fig 33–11). Note that this Lewis fucosyltransferase will not utilize as a substrate a GlcNAc oligosaccharide that contains a β-Gal in a 1,4- linkage; it is that 4-moiety of the GlcNAc to which it must attach its own Fuc moiety. The Lewis-dependent fucosyltransferase is not specific about what is *not* attached to the Gal-1,3-β group. Thus, if the H or Se transferase has already put on a Fuc-1,2-α moiety, or even if the A-dependent

transferase or B-dependent transferase has attached GalNAc or Gal moieties, respectively, the Lewis transferase will still attach a Fuc in an alpha-1,4-linkage to that same GalNAc residue (Fig 33-11).

When no H allele is present (hh), the product of the Lewis α-1,4-fucosyltransferase is referred to as the Le^a antigen (Figs 33–11 and 33–12). When present, the H- or Se-dependent α-1,2-fucosyltransferase cannot act on the Le^a antigen, because of the prior attachment of the α-Fuc in 1,4- linkage to the penultimate GlcNAc residue. Thus, the Le^a antigen cannot have A or B antigenicity even when the A or B transferases are also present.

When both the H or Se allele and the Le allele fucosyltransferases have acted on the Gal-1,3–R oligosaccharide, the product is referred to as the Le^b antigen (Figs 33–11 and 33–12). The Le^b structure can in addition have A antigenicity or B antigenicity, since the Lewis α-1,4-fucosyltransferase can act on both the A oligosaccharide and the B oligosaccharide. However, if the Lewis fucosyl alpha-1,4- moiety is attached to the H or Se antigen before the A or B transferases have attached their sugar moieties, the A and B transferases will not be able to utilize that oligosaccharide containing the 2 juxtaposed α-Fuc residues (Fig 33–12). The Le^b antigen may also exist without A antigenicity or B antigenicity on the same molecule when (1) neither the A transferase nor the B transferase exists (OO genotype) or (2) when the Lewis α-1,4-fucosyltransferase acts on its substrate prior to

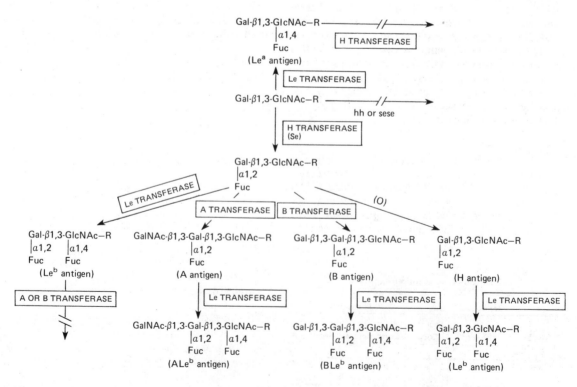

Figure 33–12. Pathways generating the antigenic oligosaccharides of the ABO-Lewis system. An interrupted arrow indicates a blocked pathway due to an inactive glycosyltransferase (hh, sese) or inappropriate substrate.

the action of the A transferase or B transferase on the same molecule (Fig 33–12).

The le allele codes for an inactive Lewis transferase, and thus neither Le^a nor Le^b antigens will be formed in a person with lele genotype (Fig 33–12).

PROTEOGLYCANS

The proteoglycans and the glycoproteins are molecules consisting of proteins to which oligosaccharide or polysaccharide chains are covalently attached. The distinction between proteoglycans and glycoproteins is based on the chemical nature of the attached polysaccharides. In proteoglycans, each polysaccharide consists of **repeating disaccharide units in which D-glucosamine or D-galactosamine is always present.** Each disaccharide unit in the proteoglycan polysaccharides (with the exception of keratan sulfate) contains a uronic acid, L-**glucuronic acid (GlcUA)** or its 5-epimer, L-**iduronic acid (IdUA).** With the exception of hyaluronic acid, all polysaccharides of proteoglycans contain **sulfate groups** either as O-esters or N-sulfate (in heparin and heparan sulfate).

The linkage of the proteoglycan polysaccharides to their polypeptide chain is one of 3 types:

(1) An O-glycosidic bond between the Xyl and Ser, a bond that is **unique to proteoglycans.**

(2) An O-glycosidic bond between GalNAc and Ser(Thr), present in keratan sulfate II.

(3) An N-glycosylamine bond between GlcNAc and the amide nitrogen of Asn.

The formation of the polysaccharide chains occurs in pathways quite similar to those responsible for the attachment and growth of the oligosaccharide chains of glycoproteins. A UDP-Xyl transferase attaches the Xyl of the nucleotide sugar to Ser to form the Xyl-Ser O-glycosidic bond. The formation of the O-glycosidic bond between GalNAc and Ser (or Thr) probably occurs by a similar UDP-GalNAc transferase. The N-glycosidic bond between GlcNAc and the amide nitrogen of Asn almost certainly involves the lipid-linked polysaccharide, dolichol-P-P polysaccharide, which, as discussed above, is responsible for the transfer of a preformed oligo- or polysaccharide in the formation of glycoproteins. However, the details of this reaction in the synthesis of proteoglycans have not been established.

The chain elongation process involves the nucleotidyl sugars acting as donors. The reactions are governed primarily by the substrate specificities of the specific glycosyltransferases. Again, the **"one enzyme, one linkage"** relationship seems to hold. The specificity of these reactions is dependent upon the nucleotide sugar donor, the acceptor oligosaccharide, and the anomeric configuration and position of the linkage. The enzyme systems involved in this chain elongation are capable of high-fidelity reproduction of complex polysaccharides.

The termination of polysaccharide chain growth

seems to result from (1) capping effects of **sialation** by the specific sialyltransferases; (2) **sulfation,** particularly at the 4- positions of the sugars, and (3) the progression of the particular polysaccharide **away from the site** in the membrane where the catalysis occurs.

After formation of the polysaccharide chain, there occur numerous chemical **modifications,** such as the introduction of sulfate groups onto GalNAc moieties of chondroitin sulfate and dermatan sulfate and the epimerization of GlcUA to IdUA residues in heparin and heparan sulfate.

An important aspect of the metabolism of proteoglycans is their **degradation.** Inherited defects in the degradation of the polysaccharide chains of proteoglycans lead to the group of diseases known as **mucopolysaccharidoses** and **mucolipidoses,** discussed below and in Chapter 13. These catabolic defects have allowed the study of specific degradation enzymes and their substrates. There exists a battery of exoglycosidases that act in a stepwise manner to remove the sulfate moieties and glycosyl groups. In addition, there are normally present endoglycosidases with different specificities. For example, **hyaluronidase** is a widely distributed enzyme that cleaves N-acetylhexosamine linkages in hyaluronic acid and chondroitin sulfates.

There are **7 types of polysaccharides** (glycosaminoglycans) found covalently attached to the proteins of proteoglycans. Six of them are structurally related and contain **alternating uronic acid and hexosamine residues** in repeating disaccharide units. All except hyaluronic acid contain **sulfated sugars.** The 7 types of polysaccharides can be distinguished by their **monomer composition,** their **glycosidic linkage,** and the amount and location of their **sulfate substituents.**

All of the glycosaminoglycans are **polyanions,** since they have acidic sulfate or carboxyl groups of uronic acids present throughout their structures. Many of their functions result from this particular characteristic.

The structures of the 7 glycosaminoglycans of the proteoglycan molecules are summarized in Fig 33–13.

Hyaluronic Acid

Hyaluronic acid consists of an unbranched chain of repeating disaccharide units containing GlcUA and GlcNAc. There is no firm evidence that hyaluronic acid is linked to a protein molecule, as are other connective tissue polysaccharides, but it is probably synthesized as a proteoglycan, as are the other glycosaminoglycans. Hyaluronic acid is present in bacteria and widely distributed among various animal organisms and tissues, including synovial fluid, the vitreous body of the eye, and loose connective tissue.

Chondroitin Sulfates

Chondroitin sulfates are proteoglycans that are a very prominent component of cartilage. The polysaccharide is linked to protein by the Xyl-Ser O-glycosidic bond. The structure of the chondroitin

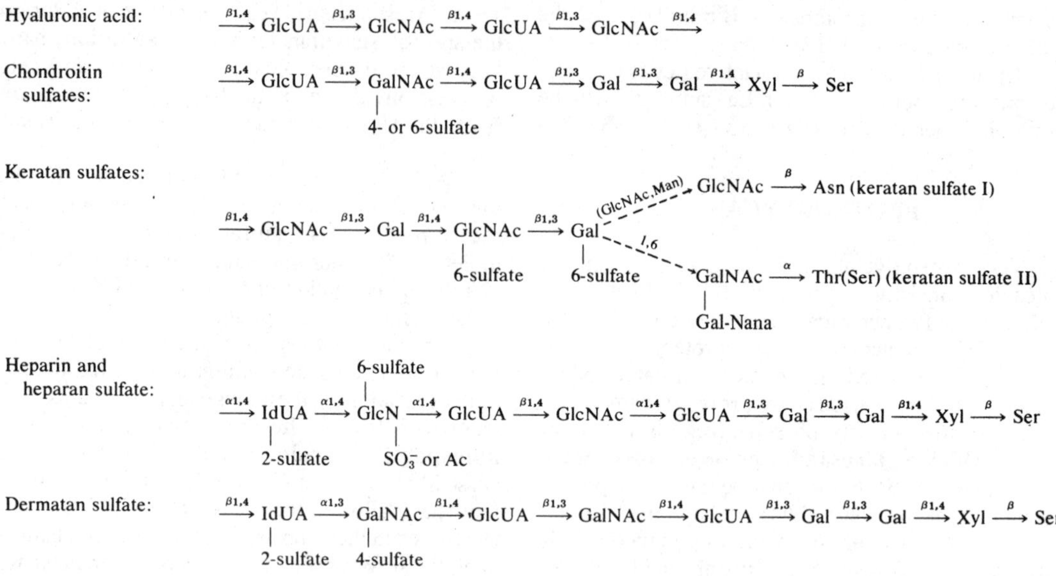

Hyaluronic acid:
$$\xrightarrow{\beta1,4} \text{GlcUA} \xrightarrow{\beta1,3} \text{GlcNAc} \xrightarrow{\beta1,4} \text{GlcUA} \xrightarrow{\beta1,3} \text{GlcNAc} \xrightarrow{\beta1,4}$$

Chondroitin sulfates:
$$\xrightarrow{\beta1,4} \text{GlcUA} \xrightarrow{\beta1,3} \text{GalNAc} \xrightarrow{\beta1,4} \text{GlcUA} \xrightarrow{\beta1,3} \text{Gal} \xrightarrow{\beta1,3} \text{Gal} \xrightarrow{\beta1,4} \text{Xyl} \xrightarrow{\beta} \text{Ser}$$
|
4- or 6-sulfate

Keratan sulfates:

$$\xrightarrow{\beta1,4} \text{GlcNAc} \xrightarrow{\beta1,3} \text{Gal} \xrightarrow{\beta1,4} \text{GlcNAc} \xrightarrow{\beta1,3} \text{Gal} \cdots$$

(GlcNAc,Man) — GlcNAc $\xrightarrow{\beta}$ Asn (keratan sulfate I)

1,6 → GalNAc $\xrightarrow{\alpha}$ Thr(Ser) (keratan sulfate II)
|
6-sulfate   6-sulfate

|
Gal-Nana

Heparin and heparan sulfate:

6-sulfate
|
$$\xrightarrow{\alpha1,4} \text{IdUA} \xrightarrow{\alpha1,4} \text{GlcN} \xrightarrow{\alpha1,4} \text{GlcUA} \xrightarrow{\beta1,4} \text{GlcNAc} \xrightarrow{\alpha1,4} \text{GlcUA} \xrightarrow{\beta1,3} \text{Gal} \xrightarrow{\beta1,3} \text{Gal} \xrightarrow{\beta1,4} \text{Xyl} \xrightarrow{\beta} \text{Ser}$$
| |
2-sulfate SO_3^- or Ac

Dermatan sulfate:

$$\xrightarrow{\beta1,4} \text{IdUA} \xrightarrow{\alpha1,3} \text{GalNAc} \xrightarrow{\beta1,4} \text{GlcUA} \xrightarrow{\beta1,3} \text{GalNAc} \xrightarrow{\beta1,4} \text{GlcUA} \xrightarrow{\beta1,3} \text{Gal} \xrightarrow{\beta1,3} \text{Gal} \xrightarrow{\beta1,4} \text{Xyl} \xrightarrow{\beta} \text{Ser}$$
| |
2-sulfate   4-sulfate

Figure 33–13. Summary of structures of proteoglycans and glycosaminoglycans. (GlcUA, D-glucuronic acid; IdUA, L-iduronic acid; GlcN, D-glucosamine; GalN, D-galactosamine; Ac, N-acetyl; Gal, D-galactose; Xyl, D-xylose; Ser, L-serine; Thr, L-threonine; Asn, L-asparagine; Man, D-mannose; Nana, N-acetylneuraminic acid.) The summary structures are qualitative representations only and do not reflect, for example, the uronic acid composition of hybrid polysaccharides such as heparin and dermatan sulfate, which contain both L-iduronic and D-glucuronic acid. Neither should it be assumed that the indicated substituents are always present, eg, whereas most iduronic acid residues in heparin carry a 2-sulfate group, a much smaller proportion of these residues are sulfated in dermatan sulfate. (Slightly modified and reproduced, with permission, from Lennarz WJ: *The Biochemistry of Glycoproteins and Proteoglycans.* Plenum Press, 1980.)

sulfates is summarized in Fig 33–13. The repeating disaccharide unit is very similar to that of hyaluronic acid, except that the hexosamine is GalNAc rather than GlcNAc. However, in both the chondroitin sulfates and hyaluronic acid, the uronic acid is GlcUA, and the bond positions and anomeric configurations are the same. In the chondroitin sulfates, the GalNAc carries a sulfate substituent in the 4- or 6- position. As a rule, both 4- and 6-sulfate substituents are present in the same molecule but not on the same monosaccharide residue. There is on the average about one sulfate substituent per disaccharide unit. Each chain of polysaccharide consists of about 40 repeating disaccharide units and thus has a molecular weight of about 20,000. Many such chains are attached to a single protein molecule, generating high-molecular-weight proteoglycans. For instance, the molecular weight of nasal cartilage chondroitin sulfate is approximately 2.5×10^6.

The chondroitin sulfates associate tightly with hyaluronic acid with the aid of 2 "link proteins" to generate very large aggregates in connective tissue. These aggregates can be observed in the electron microscope (Fig 33–14) and are diagrammatically presented in Fig 33–15.

The link proteins are strongly hydrophobic and interact both with hyaluronic acid and the proteoglycan.

The chondroitin sulfates contain 6 types of intersaccharide linkages and thus are synthesized by 6 dif-

ferent glycosyltransferase enzymes, one for each type of linkage. In addition, there are 2 types of sulfate esters, one on the 4- and another on the 6- position. Two sulfotransferases carry out these esterifications. The sulfate-containing substrate for these sulfotransferases is 3-phosphoadenyl 5'-phosphosulfate (PAPS).

Keratan Sulfate I & Keratan Sulfate II

As shown in Fig 33–13, the keratan sulfates consist of repeating Gal-GlcNAc disaccharide units and contain sulfates on the 6- position of GlcNAc residues and occasionally on the Gal 6- position. The polysaccharide of keratan sulfate I is attached to its polypeptide chain by a **GlcNAc-Asn** bond. It is abundant in the cornea.

Keratan sulfate II is a skeletal proteoglycan present along with chondroitin sulfate, attached to hyaluronic acid in loose connective tissue. Its polysaccharide chains are attached to its polypeptide chain by a **GalNAc-Thr(Ser)** linkage.

Heparin

Heparin is a classic proteoglycan in which several polysaccharide chains are linked to a common protein core. However, heparin is found stored in granules of mast cells and thus occurs **intracellularly.** Heparin has several other unique structural and functional features, including some that are of medical importance. Fig 33–16 illustrates some characteristic features of

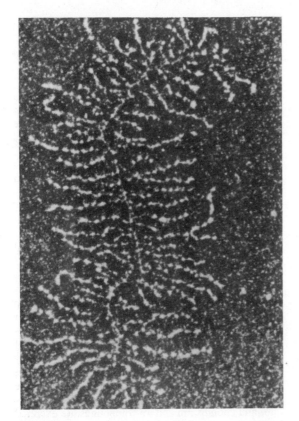

Figure 33–14. Darkfield electron micrograph of a proteoglycan aggregate of intermediate size in which the proteoglycan subunits and filamentous backbone are particularly well extended. (Reproduced, with permission, from Rosenberg L, Hellman W, Kleinschmidt AK: Electron microscopic studies of proteoglycan aggregates from bovine articular cartilage. *J Biol Chem* 1975;**250**:1877.)

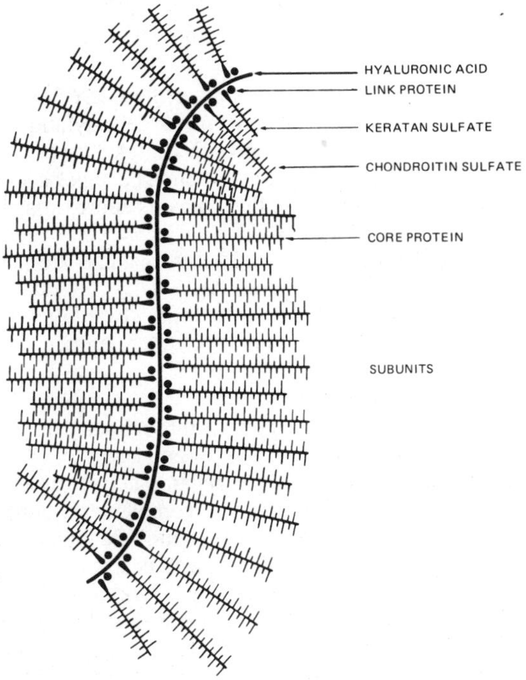

HYALURONIC ACID
LINK PROTEIN
KERATAN SULFATE
CHONDROITIN SULFATE
CORE PROTEIN
SUBUNITS

Figure 33–15. Schematic representation of proteoglycan aggregate. (Reproduced, with permission, from Lennarz WJ: *The Biochemistry of Glycoproteins and Proteoglycans.* Plenum Press, 1980.)

the heparin structure. The repeating disaccharide unit contains **glucosamine** (GlcN) and a uronic acid. Most of the amino groups of the GlcN residues are **N-sulfated**, but a few are **acetylated.** The GlcN also carries a C_6 sulfate ester.

Approximately 90% of the uronic acid residues are IdUA; only 10% are GlcUA. Initially, all of the uronic acids are GlcUA, but, as described below, a 5-epimerase converts approximately 90% of the GlcUA residues to IdUA residues after the polysac-

charide is formed. The IdUA residues are frequently sulfated at the 2- position.

The protein molecule of the heparin proteoglycan is unique, consisting exclusively of **serine and glycine** residues. Approximately two-thirds of the serine residues contain polysaccharide chains, usually with molecular weights of 5000–15,000 but occasionally as high as 100,000.

The polysaccharide chains of the heparin proteoglycans undergo a specific sequence of modification

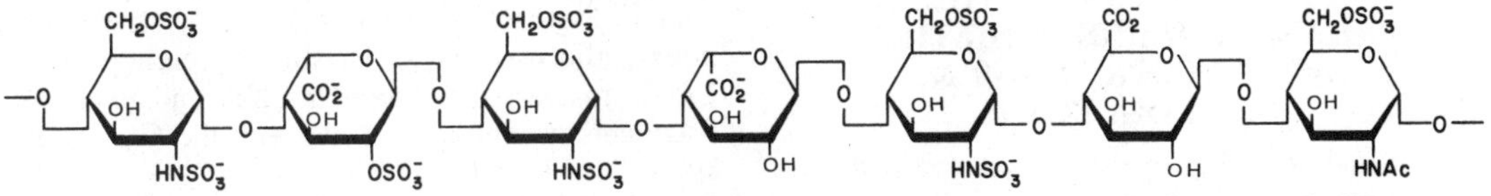

Figure 33–16. Structure of heparin. The polymer section illustrates structural features typical of heparin; however, the sequence of variously substituted repeating disaccharide units has been arbitrarily selected. In addition, non-*O*-sulfated or 3-*O*-sulfated glucosamine residues may also occur. (Modified, redrawn, and reproduced, with permission, from Lindahl U et al: Structure and biosynthesis of heparinlike polysaccharides. *Fed Proc* 1977;**36**:19.)

after the polymerization. This sequence of modifications occurs in the following way:

(1) The primary product is not sulfated but fully N-acetylated and thus is a polymer of (GlcUA-GlcNAc)n.

(2) Approximately 50% of the GlcNAc residues are N-deacetylated.

(3) The free amino groups of the GlcN are sulfated; subsequently, there is further deacetylation of about half of the remaining GlcNAc residues.

(4) The N-sulfated polymer then becomes a substrate for the 5-epimerase that converts approximately 90% of the GlcUA residues to IdUA.

(5) The recently formed IdUA residues are then O-sulfated on their C_2 positions.

(6) The modification is then completed by O-sulfation of the C_6 positions of GlcN units.

Heparan Sulfate

Heparan sulfate is present throughout cell surfaces as a proteoglycan and is **extracellular.** The polypeptide backbone of the heparan sulfate proteoglycan has a typical amino acid complement, unlike that for heparin. In the process of modification of its polysaccharide chains, there is less deacetylation of the GlcNAc residues, and thus it contains fewer N-sulfates. Because the 5-epimerase (as described above for the modification of heparin) requires the N-sulfate substituents on its substrate, heparan sulfate contains a lower content of IdUA but more GlcUA than does heparin. Accordingly, GlcUA is the predominant uronic acid in heparan sulfate, while IdUA is the predominant uronic acid in heparin.

Dermatan Sulfate

Dermatan sulfate is a proteoglycan widely distributed in animal tissues. Structurally, it resembles both chondroitin sulfates and heparan sulfate. Its structure is similar to that of chondroitin sulfate except that in place of a GlcUA in beta-1,3- linkage to GalNAc, dermatan sulfate contains an **IdUA** in an alpha-1,3-linkage to GalNAc. Formation of the IdUA occurs, as in heparin and heparan sulfate, by the 5-epimerization of GlcUA. As in the formation of heparin, the epimerization reaction is coupled tightly to the sulfation of hexosamine. Thus, the dermatan sulfate contains 2 types of repeating disaccharide units: IdUA-GalNAc and GlcUA-GalNAc.

DEGRADATION OF THE POLYSACCHARIDE MOIETIES OF GLYCOPROTEINS & PROTEOGLYCANS

Our understanding of the degradative pathways for glycoproteins, proteoglycans, and glycosaminoglycans has been greatly aided by discoveries of the specific enzyme deficiencies of inborn errors of human metabolism. Two groups of diseases whose study has contributed greatly are the mucopolysaccharidoses and the mucolipidoses. (For many years, what we now call proteoglycans were called mucopolysaccharides.) Table 33–5 lists the biochemical defects in the mucopolysaccharidoses, mucolipidoses, and related disorders.

Degradation of the polysaccharide chains is carried out by **endoglycosidases, exoglycosidases,** and **sulfatases.** In each case, the enzymes exhibit substrate specificities that allow one to deduce which of the polysaccharide chains will be subject to degradation by the particular glycosidase or sulfatase.

Hyaluronidase is a widely distributed endoglycosidase that cleaves hexosaminidic linkages. From hyaluronic acid, the hyaluronidase will generate a tetrasaccharide with the structure (GlcUA-β-1,3-GlcNAc-β-1,4)$_2$. Hyaluronidase acts on both **hyaluronic acid** and **chondroitin sulfate.** The tetrasaccharide described above can be further degraded by a β-glucuronidase and β-N-acetylhexosaminidase.

β-**Glucuronidase** is an exoglycosidase that removes both GlcUA and IdUA from nonreducing termini of tetrasaccharides or larger polysaccharides. In general, the disaccharides are poor substrates for β-glucuronidase. β-Glucuronidase, itself a glycoprotein, is localized in both **lysosomes** and **microsomes** of many mammalian cells. Its substrates include **dermatan sulfate, heparan sulfate, chondroitin sulfate,** and **hyaluronic acid.** In inherited β-glucuronidase deficiency in humans, dermatan sulfate, heparan sulfate, and chondroitin sulfate compounds are excreted in the urine, but hyaluronic acid is not. Apparently, there are other degradative pathways that can degrade the tetrasaccharide produced from hyaluronic acid by hyaluronidase.

β-D-**Acetylhexosaminidase** is an exoglycosidase present in many mammalian tissues. It cleaves from the nonreducing termini of polysaccharides GlcNAc and GalNAc when in beta- linkage. The substrates for the β-D-acetylhexosaminidase include **gangliosides** and **chondroitin sulfates, hyaluronic acid, dermatan sulfates,** and **keratan sulfates** I and II. There are 2 isozymes of β-D-acetylhexosaminidase. The **A isozyme** consists of 2 different types of subunits, the alpha subunit and the beta subunit $(\alpha\beta)_n$, while the **B isozyme** consists of only beta subunits $(\beta\beta)_n$. In **Tay-Sachs disease,** the alpha subunit is defective, and thus only the A isozyme is inactive. In **Sandoff disease,** the beta subunit is defective, resulting in a deficiency of both A and B isozymes.

β-**Galactosidases** exist in several forms in animal tissues. Both chondroitin sulfate and keratan sulfate contain β-galactosides and thus are substrates for the **acid galactosidases.** In the deficiency of acid β-galactosidase, both keratan sulfate and glycoprotein fragments accumulate, along with the G_{M1} gangliosides. (See Chapter 17.)

α-L-**Iduronidase** is a lysosomal hydrolase that removes IdUA from the nonreducing terminus of polysaccharide chains. This enzyme is deficient in **Hurler's syndrome.**

Mammalian tissues contain heparin and heparan sulfate-specific endoglycosidases, particularly an en-

Table 33–5. Biochemical defects in mucopolysaccharidoses, mucolipidoses and related disorders, and diagnostic tests.[*]

Name	Alternate Designation	Enzymatic Defect	Material for Enzyme Assay	Abnormal ^{35}S-Mucopolysaccharide Level in Fibroblasts	Urinary Metabolites
Mucopolysaccharidoses					
Hurler, Scheie, Hurler/Scheie	MPS I	α-L-Iduronidase	Fibroblasts, leukocytes, tissues, amniotic fluid cells	+	DS, HS
Hunter	MPS II	Iduronate sulfatase	Serum, fibroblasts, leukocytes, tissues, amniotic fluid cells, amniotic fluid	+	DS, HS
Sanfilippo A	MPS III A	HS N-sulfatase (sulfamidase)	Fibroblasts, leukocytes, tissues, amniotic fluid cells	±	HS (±)
Sanfilippo B	MPS III B	α-N-acetylglucosaminidase	Serum, fibroblasts, leukocytes, tissues, amniotic fluid cells	+	HS
Sanfilippo C	MPS III C	Acetyltransferase	Fibroblasts	+	HS
Morquio	MPS IV	N-acetylgalactosamine 6-sulfatase	Fibroblasts	−	KS
Morquiolike	None	β-Galactosidase	Fibroblasts	−	KS
Maroteaux-Lamy	MPS VI	N-acetylgalactosamine 4-sulfatase (arylsulfatase B)	Fibroblasts, leukocytes, tissues, amniotic fluid cells	+	DS
β-Glucuronidase deficiency	MPS VII	β-Glucuronidase	Serum, fibroblasts, leukocytes, amniotic fluid cells	+	DS, HS (±)
Unnamed disorder	MPS VIII	N-acetylglucosamine 6-sulfatase	Fibroblasts	+	HS, KS
Mucolipidoses and related disorders					
Sialidosis	ML I	Sialidase (neuraminidase)	Fibroblasts, leukocytes	−	GF
I-cell disease	ML II	UDP-N-acetylglucosamine: glycoprotein N-acetylgluco-saminylphosphotransferase (acid hydrolases thus lack phosphomannosyl residue)	Serum, fibroblasts, amniotic fluid cells	+	GF
Pseudo-Hurler polydystrophy	ML III	As for ML II but deficiency is incomplete	Serum, fibroblasts, amniotic fluid cells	±	GF
Multiple sulfatase deficiency	None	Arylsulfatase A and other sulfatases	Serum, fibroblasts, leukocytes, tissues, amniotic fluid cells	+	DS, HS
Mannosidosis	None	α-Mannosidase	Serum, fibroblasts, leukocytes, amniotic fluid cells	−	GF
Fucosidosis	None	α-L-Fucosidase	Serum, fibroblasts, leukocytes, amniotic fluid cells	−	GF

MPS = mucopolysaccharidosis; ML = mucolipidosis; DS = dermatan sulfate; KS = keratan sulfate; HS = heparan sulfate; GF = glycoprotein fragments.

[*]Reproduced, with permission, from DiNatale P, Neufeld EF: The biochemical diagnosis of mucopolysaccharidoses, mucolipidosis and related disorders. In: *Perspectives in Inherited Metabolic Diseases.* Vol 2. Barra B et al (editors). Editones Ermes (Milan), 1979.

doglucuronidase that exists in liver, intestinal mucosa, platelets, and lysosomes.

A large series of specific **sulfatases** exist for the removal of the sulfate substituents. There are 3 arylsulfatases: A, B, and C. **Arylsulfatase A** degrades the Gal-3-sulfate from ceramides. **Arylsulfatase B** removes the 4-sulfate from chondroitin sulfate and dermatan sulfate. However, patients with inherited deficiency of 4-sulfatase (**Maroteaux-Lamy syndrome**) spill only dermatan sulfate in urine. Distinct from arylsulfatases A and B is an enzyme that cleaves the 6-sulfate from GalNAc-6-sulfate. This sulfatase is deficient in patients with **Morquio's syndrome.** It normally will cleave the sulfate groups from both Gal-6-sulfate and GalNAc-6-sulfate. Thus, patients with

Morquio's syndrome excrete both keratan 6-sulfate and chondroitin 6-sulfate.

A deficiency of **N-acetylglucosamine 6-sulfatase** has been observed in mucopolysaccharidosis A. This enzyme can utilize as a substrate GlcNAc-6-sulfate and Glc-6-sulfate.

Iduronate sulfatase is a specific exoenzyme that will cleave the C_2 sulfate from an IdUA residue at the nonreducing end of heparin, heparan sulfate, and dermatan sulfate. This enzyme is present normally in serum, lymphocytes, fibroblasts, and amniotic fluid. The inherited deficiency of iduronate sulfatase causes **Hunter's syndrome.**

A specific **α-N-acetylglucosaminidase** can remove the specific alpha-linked GlcNAc residues present in heparin and heparan sulfate. The enzyme is normally present in fibroblasts but is missing in **Sanfilippo B syndrome.**

Heparin sulfamidase (heparan-N-sulfatase) is present in spleen, lung, and ileum. This enzyme is capable of removing a sulfate from GlcN-sulfates at a nonreducing terminus of heparin and heparan sulfate. It is deficient in **Sanfilippo A syndrome.** When the sulfates are removed, an α-glucosamine (GlcN), a free amino group, remains. This GlcN is not a substrate for the α-N-acetylglucosaminidase described above. The enzyme α-glucosamine:N-acetyltransferase **reacetylates** the free amino group of GlcN at a nonreducing terminus, using acetyl-CoA as the acetyl donor, and thereby renders its product susceptible to the action of the above-described α-N-acetylglucosaminidase. The acetyltransferase activity is absent in **Sanfilippo C syndrome.**

Functional Aspects of Glycosaminoglycans & Proteoglycans

The binding between glycosaminoglycans and other extracellular macromolecules contributes significantly to the structural organization of connective tissue matrix. Glycosaminoglycans can interact with extracellular macromolecules, plasma proteins, cell surface components, and intracellular macromolecules.

The binding of glycosaminoglycans is generally **electrostatic** in character because of their remarkable polyanionic nature. However, some binding interactions are more specific. Generally, the glycosaminoglycans containing IdUA, such as dermatan sulfate and heparan sulfate, bind proteins with greater affinities than do those containing GlcUA as their only uronic acid constituent.

Interactions With Extracellular Macromolecules

All glycosaminoglycans except those that lack sulfate groups (hyaluronate) or carboxyl groups (keratan sulfates) bind electrostatically to collagen at neutral pH. The presence of IdUA promotes tighter binding, and the proteoglycans interact more strongly than the corresponding glycosaminoglycans. Between 2 and 5 polysaccharide chains bind to each collagen monomer. The soluble collagens (types I, II, and III) all bind chondroitin sulfate proteoglycan.

Chondroitin sulfate and heparan sulfate bind specifically to elastin.

As mentioned above, chondroitin sulfate and keratan sulfate chains in their respective proteoglycans aggregate with the aid of link proteins with hyaluronic acid. As many as 100 proteoglycan molecules may bind to one hyaluronate molecule.

Interactions With Plasma Proteins

The intima of the arterial wall contains hyaluronate and chondroitin sulfate, dermatan sulfate, and heparan sulfate proteoglycans. Of these proteoglycans, **dermatan sulfate binds plasma lipoproteins.** In addition, dermatan sulfate appears to be the major glycosaminoglycan **synthesized by arterial smooth muscle cells.** As these smooth muscle cells are those that proliferate at the atherosclerotic lesion in arterial vessels, dermatan sulfate may play a significant role in development of the atherosclerotic plaque.

Heparin, although synthesized and stored in mast cells, is always in close proximity to blood vessels. Heparin, with its high negative charge density (due to the IdUA and sulfate residues), interacts strongly with several plasma components. Heparin specifically binds clotting factors IX and XI. More important in the **anticoagulant activity** of heparin is its interaction with a plasma alpha$_2$ glycoprotein called **antithrombin III.** The 1:1 stoichiometric binding of heparin to antithrombin III greatly accelerates the ability of the latter to inactivate serine proteases, particularly thrombin (see Chapter 42). The binding of heparin to Lys residues in antithrombin III appears to induce a conformational change that favors the binding of antithrombin III to the serine proteases. Such a scheme is diagrammatically depicted in Fig 33–17.

Commercially available heparin contains 2 components—a high-affinity heparin and a low-affinity heparin—both of which seem to bind to the same site of antithrombin III molecules. However, high-affinity heparin has an anticoagulant activity about 10 times higher than that of low-affinity material, and its binding constant is similarly greater. The N-desulfation or modification of the IdUA residues of heparin reduces its anticoagulant activity.

Heparan sulfate, the structure of which resembles that of heparin, is also capable of accelerating the action of antithrombin III, but it is much less potent than heparin.

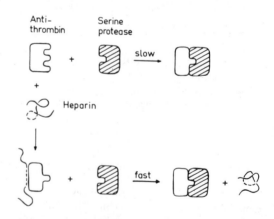

Figure 33–17. Schematic representation of inactivation by antithrombin III of serine proteases (eg, thrombin) participating in the coagulation mechanism. Heparin is believed to accelerate the inactivation by binding to antithrombin, thereby inducing a conformational change in the antithrombin molecule that facilitates its interaction with thrombin. (Binding of heparin to thrombin as well cannot be excluded.) The interaction requires a specific binding site (– – –) in the polysaccharide chain. (Reproduced, with permission, from Lennarz WJ: *The Biochemistry of Glycoproteins and Proteoglycans.* Plenum Press, 1980.)

Heparin can bind specifically to **lipoprotein lipase** present in capillary walls and cause a release of that triglyceride-degrading enzyme into the circulation. Similarly, hepatic lipase binds heparin and is released into the circulation, but it binds heparin with a lower affinity than does the lipoprotein lipase. Lipoprotein lipase will bind partially N-desulfated heparin better than antithrombin III will.

Glycosaminoglycans & Cell Surface Molecules

Heparin is capable of associating with many cell types, including blood platelets, arterial endothelial cells, and liver cells. Chondroitin sulfate, dermatan sulfate, and heparan sulfate bind to independent sites on surfaces of cells such as fibroblasts. At those sites, the glycosaminoglycans and proteoglycans are taken up by fibroblasts and degraded.

Hyaluronate is deposited by cells as they grow on the plastic substrata of culture dishes. In addition, hyaluronate appears to be involved in the cell-cell adhesion processes so important during the growth and development of metazoan organisms.

Some proteoglycans appear to serve as **receptors** and **carriers** for macromolecules, including the lipoproteins, lipases, and, as described above, antithrombin. Proteoglycans seem to be involved in the regulation of cell growth, the mediation of cell-cell communication, and the shielding of cell surface receptors.

Glycosaminoglycans & Intracellular Macromolecules

In addition to interacting with the enzymes involved in their biosynthesis and degradation, proteoglycans and their glycosaminoglycan components have effects on protein synthesis and intranuclear functions. Heparin particularly seems to have an effect on chromatin structure and can activate DNA polymerase activities in vitro. It is not clear how physiologic these actions are. Glycosaminoglycans are found in significant quantities in nuclei from different cell types, and in fact there is some suggestion that heparan sulfate has some role in the embryonic development of sea urchins.

Various lysosomal acid hydrolase activities can be affected in negative or positive ways by chondroitin sulfates, dermatan sulfates, and heparin. The acid hydrolases in lysosomes may be naturally complexed with glycosaminoglycans to provide a protected and inactive form.

Numerous storage or secretory granules such as the chromaffin granules in adrenal medulla, the prolactin secretory granules in the pituitary gland, and the basophilic granules in mast cells contain sulfated glycosaminoglycans. The glycosaminoglycan-peptide complexes that occur in these granules may play a role in the release of biogenic amines.

•   •   •

References

Buckwalter JA, Rosenberg LC: Electron microscopic studies of cartilage proteoglycans. *J Biol Chem* 1982;**257**:9830.

DiNatale P, Neufeld EF: The biochemical diagnosis of mucopolysaccharidoses, mucolipidosis and related disorders. In: *Perspectives in Inherited Metabolic Diseases.* Vol 2. Barra B et al (editors). Editiones Ermes (Milan), 1979.

Höök M et al: Cell-surface glycosaminoglycans. *Annu Rev Biochem* 1984;**53**:847.

Hubbard SC, Ivatt RJ: Synthesis and processing of asparagine-linked oligosaccharides. *Annu Rev Biochem* 1981;**50**:555.

Jaques LB: Heparin: An old drug with a new paradigm. *Science* 1979;**206**:528.

Kumazaki T, Yoshida A: Biochemical evidence that secretor gene, Se, is a structural gene encoding a specific fucosyl transferase. *Proc Natl Acad Sci USA* 1984;**81**:4193.

Lennarz WJ: *The Biochemistry of Glycoproteins and Proteoglycans.* Plenum Press, 1980.

Poole AR et al: Proteoglycans from bovine nasal cartilage: Immunochemical studies of link protein. *J Biol Chem* 1980; **255**:9295.

Reitman ML et al: Fibroblasts from patients with I-cell disease and pseudo-Hurler polydystrophy are deficient in uridine 5'-diphosphate-N-acetylglucosamine:glycoprotein N-acetylglucosaminylphosphotransferase activity. *J Clin Invest* 1981;**67**:1574.

Snider MD, Rogers OC: Transmembrane movement of oligosaccharide-lipids during glycoprotein synthesis. *Cell* 1984; **36**:753.

Wedgwood JF, Strominger JL: Enzymatic activities in cultured human lymphocytes that dephosphorylate dolichyl pyrophosphate and dolichyl phosphate. *J Biol Chem* 1980;**255**:1120.

34 | Contractile & Structural Proteins

David W. Martin, Jr., MD

Protein molecules in biologic systems may serve primary functions other than catalysis. The regulatory, signal transmission, and recognition functions of protein molecules have been described in earlier chapters. Protein molecules also provide important transducing and structural functions to biologic systems. Some of these latter roles, which are dependent upon the fibrous nature of specific protein molecules, are reviewed in this chapter.

MUSCLE

Muscle is the major biochemical transducer (machine) that converts potential (chemical) energy into kinetic (mechanical) energy. Muscle is the largest single tissue in the human body, comprising somewhat less than 25% of body mass at birth, more than 40% of body mass in the young adult, and somewhat less than 30% in the aged adult.

An effective **chemical-mechanical transducer** must meet several requirements: (1) There must exist a constant supply of chemical energy. In vertebrate muscle, ATP and creatine phosphate are the forms of chemical energy. (2) There must be a means of regulating the mechanical activity—ie, the speed, duration, and force of contraction in the case of muscle. (3) The machine must be connected to an operator, a requirement met in biologic systems by the nervous system. (4) If it is to be used more than once, there must be a way of returning the machine to its original state.

Muscle is only a pulling machine, not a pushing machine. Therefore, a given muscle must be antagonized by another group of muscles or another force such as gravity or elastic recoil.

In vertebrate organisms, the above requirements and the specific needs of the organisms are met by the existence of 3 types of muscles: skeletal muscle, cardiac muscle, and smooth muscle. Both **skeletal** and **cardiac muscle** appear **striated** upon microscopic observation; **smooth muscle** is **nonstriated.** Although

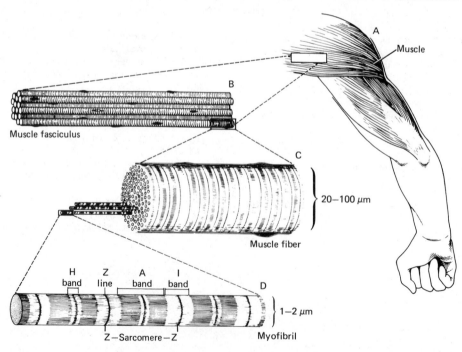

Figure 34–1. The structure of voluntary muscle. (Drawing by Sylvia Colard Keene. Reproduced, with permission, from Bloom W, Fawcett DW: *A Textbook of Histology,* 10th ed. Saunders, 1975.)

skeletal muscle is under **voluntary** nervous control, the control of both cardiac and smooth muscle is **involuntary.**

Muscle Structure

Striated muscle is composed of multinucleated muscle fiber cells surrounded by an electrically excitable membrane, the **sarcolemma.** When an individual muscle fiber cell, which may extend the entire length of the muscle, is examined microscopically, it will be found to contain a bundle of many **myofibrils** arranged in parallel; these are embedded in a type of intracellular fluid termed the **sarcoplasm.** Within this fluid is contained glycogen, the high-energy compounds ATP and phosphocreatine, and the enzymes of glycolysis.

The **sarcomere** is the functional unit of muscle. It is repeated along the axis of a fibril at distances of 1500–2300 nm (Fig 34–1). When the myofibril is examined by electron microscopy, alternating dark and light bands (A bands and I bands) can be observed. The central region of the A band (the H zone) appears less dense than the rest of the band. The I band is bisected by a very dense and narrow Z line. These structural details are illustrated in Fig 34–2.

The striated appearance of voluntary and cardiac muscles in light microscopic studies results from their high degree of organization in which most muscle fiber cells are aligned so that their sarcomeres are in parallel register (Fig 34–1).

When **cross sections** of a myofibril are examined in an electron micrograph, it appears that each myofibril is constructed of 2 types of longitudinal filaments. One type (the thick filament), confined to the A band, contains chiefly the protein **myosin.** These filaments are about 16 nm in diameter and arranged in cross section as a hexagonal array (Fig 34–2). The other filament (thin filament) lies in the I band and extends also into the A band but not into the H zone of the A band (Fig 34–2). The thin filaments are about 6 nm in diameter. They contain the proteins **actin, tropomyosin,** and **troponin.** In the A band, the thin filaments are arranged around the thick (myosin) filament as a secondary hexagonal array. Thus, as shown in Fig 34–2, each thin filament lies symmetrically between 3 thick filaments, and each thick filament is surrounded symmetrically by 6 thin filaments.

The thick and thin filaments interact via crossbridges that emerge at intervals of 14 nm along the

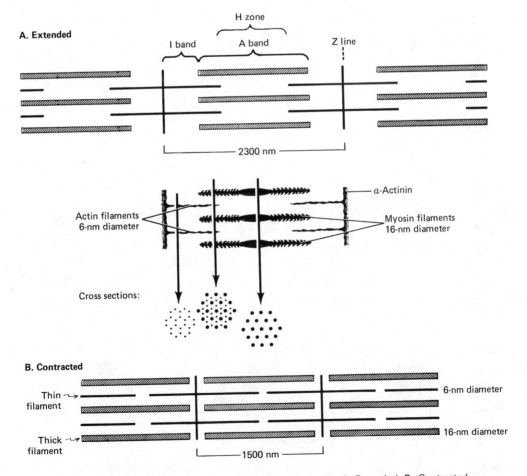

Figure 34–2. Arrangement of filaments in striated muscle. *A:* Extended. *B:* Contracted.

thick filaments. As depicted in Fig 34–2, the cross-bridges or "arrowheads" on the thick filaments have opposite polarities at the 2 ends of the filaments. The 2 poles of the filaments are separated by a 150-nm segment (the M band) that is free of projections.

When muscle contracts, there is no change in the lengths of the thick filaments or of the thin filaments, but the **H zone and the I bands shorten.** Thus, the **arrays of interdigitating filaments must slide past one another during muscle contraction.** The **cross-bridges generate and sustain the tension.** The tension developed during muscle contraction is proportionate to the filament overlap and thereby the number of cross-bridges. Each cross-bridge head is connected to the thick filament via a flexible fibrous segment that can bend outward from the thick filament to accommodate the interfilament spacing.

The Proteins of Muscle

The mass of a fresh muscle fibril is made up of 75% water and more than 20% protein. The 2 major muscle proteins are actin and myosin.

Monomeric (globular) actin (G-actin) is a 43,000-MW globular protein that comprises 25% of muscle protein by weight. At physiologic ionic strength and in the presence of magnesium, G-actin **polymerizes** noncovalently to form an insoluble double helical filament called F-actin (Fig 34–3). The **F-actin** fiber is 6–7 nm thick and has a pitch or repeating structure every 35.5 nm. Neither G- nor F-actin exhibits any catalytic activity.

In striated muscle, there are 4 other proteins that are minor in terms of their mass contribution but important in terms of their function. **Tropomyosin** is a fibrous molecule that consists of 2 chains, alpha and beta, that attach to the F-actin in the groove between the 2 polymers (Fig 34–3). **Tropomyosin is present in all muscle** and musclelike structures. The **troponin** system is unique to **striated muscle** and consists of 3 separate proteins. **Troponin T (TpT)** binds to tropomyosin as well as the other 2 troponin components (Fig 34–3). **Troponin I (TpI)** inhibits the F-actin-myosin interaction and also binds to the other components of troponin. **Troponin C (TpC)** is a calcium-binding protein that has a primary and secondary structure as well as a function quite analogous

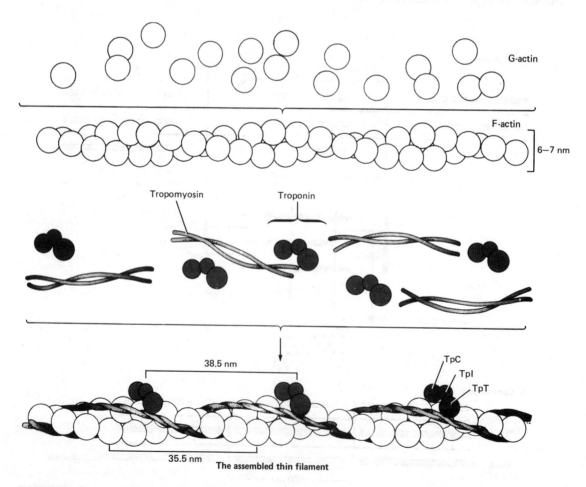

Figure 34–3. Schematic representation of the thin filament, showing the spatial configuration of the 3 major protein components—actin, tropomyosin, and troponin.

to **calmodulin,** a protein widely spread in nature. Four molecules of calcium ion are bound per molecule of troponin C or calmodulin, and both protein molecules have a molecular weight of 17,000. The thin filament of striated muscle consists of F-actin, tropomyosin, and the 3 components of troponin: TpC, TpI, and TpT (Fig 34–3). The repeat distance of the tropomyosin and troponin system is 38.5 nm.

Myosin contributes 55% of muscle protein by weight and forms the thick filaments. Myosin is an asymmetric hexamer with a molecular weight of 460,000. The myosin has a **fibrous portion** consisting of 2 intertwined helices, each with a **globular head** portion attached at one end (Fig 34–4). The **hexamer** consists of one pair of heavy chains (MW 200,000) and 2 pairs of light chains (MW 15,000–27,000). Skeletal muscle myosin exhibits **ATP-hydrolyzing (ATPase) activity** and binds to F-actin, an insoluble molecule.

Much has been learned from studies of the partial digestion products of myosin. When myosin is digested with trypsin, 2 myosin fragments (meromyosins) are generated. Light meromyosin (LMM) consists of aggregated, insoluble α-helical fibers (Fig 34–5). LMM exhibits no ATPase activity and will not bind to F-actin.

Heavy meromyosin (HMM) is a 340,000-MW soluble protein that has both a fibrous portion and a globular portion (Fig 34–5). HMM exhibits **ATPase activity** and **binds to F-actin.** The digestion of HMM with papain generates 2 subfragments, S-1 and S-2.

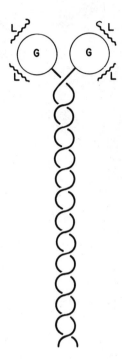

Figure 34–4. Diagram of a myosin molecule showing the 2 intertwined α-helices (fibrous portion), the globular region (G), and the light chains (L).

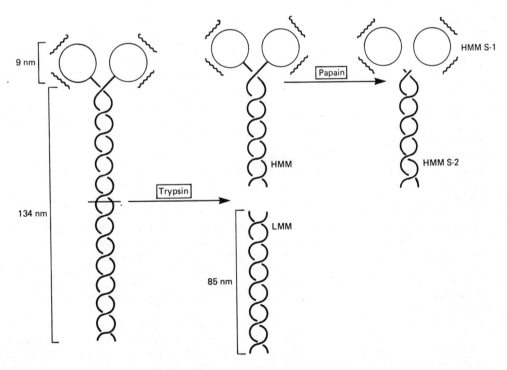

Figure 34–5. Enzymatic cleavage of myosin. (HMM, heavy meromyosin; LMM, light meromyosin; S-1, subfragment 1; S-2, subfragment 2.)

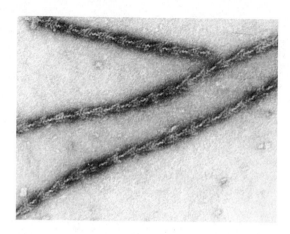

Figure 34–6. The decoration of actin filaments with the S-1 fragments of myosin to form "arrowheads." (Courtesy of Professor James Spudich, Stanford University.)

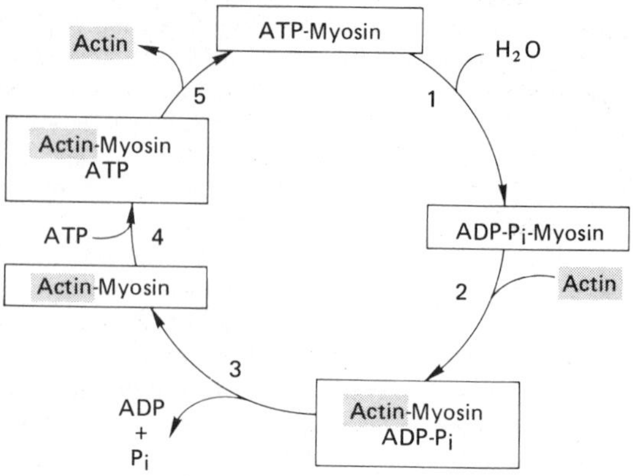

Figure 34–7. The hydrolysis of ATP drives the cyclic association and dissociation of actin and myosin in 5 reactions described in the text. (Modified from Stryer L: *Biochemistry,* 2nd ed. Freeman, 1981.)

The S-2 is fibrous in character, exhibits no ATPase activity, and does not bind to F-actin.

S-1 has a molecular weight of 115,000, exhibits **ATPase activity,** and in the absence of ATP will **bind to and decorate actin with "arrowheads"** (Fig 34–6). Although both S-1 and HMM exhibit ATPase activity, that **catalytic activity is accelerated 100- to 200-fold by the addition of F-actin.** As discussed below, F-actin greatly enhances the rate at which myosin ATPase releases its products, ADP and P_i. Thus, although F-actin does not affect the hydrolysis step per se, its ability to **promote the release of the ATPase products** greatly accelerates the overall rate of catalysis.

α-**Actinin** is a protein molecule found in the Z line to which the ends of the F-actin molecules of the thin filaments attach (Fig 34–2).

The Molecular Function of Muscle

The question of how the structure and function of muscle are related can be rephrased in biochemical terms: **How can ATP hydrolysis produce macroscopic movement?** It should be apparent from the above discussion that muscle contraction consists of the **cyclic attachment and detachment of the globular head portion of myosin to the F-actin filament.** The attachment is followed by a change in the actin-myosin interaction, so that the actin filaments and the myosin filaments slide past one another. The energy is supplied indirectly by ATP, which is hydrolyzed. ATP hydrolysis by the myosin ATPase is greatly accelerated by the binding of the myosin head to F-actin. The biochemical cycle of muscle contraction consists of 5 steps (Fig 34–7): (1) The myosin head alone can hydrolyze ATP to ADP + P_i, but it cannot release the products of this hydrolysis. Thus, the hydrolysis of ATP by the myosin head alone is stoichiometric rather than catalytic. (2) The myosin head containing ADP and P_i can rotate freely through large angles in order to

locate and bind to F-actin, making an angle of about 90 degrees with the fiber axis. This interaction (3) promotes the release of ADP and P_i from the actin-myosin complex. Because the conformation of lowest energy for the actomyosin bond is 45 degrees, the myosin changes its angle from 90 degrees to about 45 degrees by **pulling the actin** (10–15 nm) toward the center of the sarcomere. (4) A new ATP molecule binds to the myosin-F-actin complex. Myosin-ATP has a poor affinity for actin, and thus the myosin (ATP) **head is released** (5) from the F-actin. This last step is **relaxation,** a process clearly **dependent upon the binding of ATP** to the actin-myosin complex. The ATP is again hydrolyzed by the myosin head but without releasing ADP + P_i—to continue the cycle.

It should be clear that **ATP dissociates the myosin head from the thin filament and powers the contraction.** The efficiency of this contraction is about 50%; that of the internal combustion engine is less than 20%.

The Regulation of Muscle Contraction & Relaxation

The contraction of muscles from all sources occurs by the general mechanism described immediately above. Muscles from different organisms and from different cells and tissues within the same organism may have different molecular mechanisms responsible for the regulation of their contraction and relaxation. In all systems, **Ca^{2+} plays a key regulatory role.** There are 2 general mechanisms of regulation of muscle contraction: actin-based and myosin-based.

Actin-Based Regulation

Actin-based regulation of muscle occurs in vertebrate skeletal and cardiac muscles, both **striated.** In the general mechanism described above, the only potentially limiting factor in the cycle of muscle contraction might be ATP, not a seemingly ideal regulatory molecule, since it is required as the immediate energy source for contraction. The skeletal muscle system is inhibited at rest and is deinhibited to activate contraction. The **inhibitor of striated muscle is the troponin system,** which is bound to tropomyosin and F-actin in the thin filament (Fig 34–3). In striated muscle, there is no control of contraction (or ATPase as a biochemical indicator of contraction) unless the tropomyosin-troponin systems are present along with the actin and myosin filaments. As described above, tropomyosin lies along the groove of F-actin, and the 3 components of troponin—TpT, TpI, and TpC—are bound to the F-actin-tropomyosin complex. TpI prevents binding of the myosin head to its F-actin attachment site either by altering the conformation of F-actin via the tropomyosin molecules or by simply rolling tropomyosin into a position that directly blocks the sites on F-actin to which the myosin heads attach. Either way prevents the acceleration of the myosin ATPase that is mediated by binding of the myosin head to F-actin. Hence, the TpI system blocks the contraction cycle at step 2 of Fig 34–7. This accounts for the inhibited state of relaxed striated muscle.

The excitation of muscle contraction is mediated by Ca^{2+}. In resting muscle sarcoplasm, the concentration of Ca^{2+} is 10^{-7}–10^{-8} mol/L. Calcium is sequestered in the sarcoplasmic reticulum, a network of fine membranous sacs, by an active transport system utilizing a Ca^{2+}-binding protein called calsequestrin. The sarcomere is surrounded by an **excitable membrane** that has transverse (T) channels closely associated with the sarcoplasmic reticulum. When the sarcomere membrane is excited, such as by the occupation of an acetylcholine receptor by acetylcholine, **Ca^{2+} is rapidly released** into the sarcoplasm from the sarcoplasmic reticulum. The Ca^{2+} concentration in sarcoplasm rapidly rises to 10^{-5} mol/L. The Ca^{2+}-binding sites on TpC in the thin filament are quickly occupied by Ca^{2+}. The $TpC \cdot 4Ca^{2+}$ interacts with TpI and TpT to alter their interaction with tropomyosin. Accordingly, tropomyosin simply moves out of the way or alters the F-actin conformation so that the myosin head ADP-Pi can interact with F-actin to start the contraction cycle.

Relaxation occurs when (1) sarcoplasm Ca^{2+} falls below 10^{-7} mol/L owing to its resequestration in the sarcoplasmic reticulum by an energy-dependent Ca^{2+} pump; (2) $TpC \cdot 4Ca^{2+}$ loses its Ca^{2+}; (3) troponin, via its interaction with tropomyosin, inhibits further myosin head-F-actin interaction; and (4) in the presence of ATP, the myosin head detaches from the F-actin to induce relaxation. Thus, **Ca^{2+} controls muscle contraction by an allosteric mechanism** mediated in muscle by TpC, TpI, TpT, tropomyosin, and F-actin.

In cardiac muscle, the extracellular fluid is a major source of Ca^{2+} for excitation. In the absence of Ca^{2+} in the bathing extracellular fluid, cardiac muscle will cease contracting (beating) within 1 minute; skeletal muscle can contract for hours without extracellular Ca^{2+}.

The loss of ATP in the sarcoplasm has 2 major effects: (1) The Ca^{2+} pump in the sarcoplasmic reticulum ceases to maintain the low sarcoplasm Ca^{2+} concentration. Thus, the interaction of the myosin heads with F-actin is promoted. (2) The ATP-dependent detachment of myosin heads from F-actin cannot occur, and "rigor mortis" sets in.

Muscle contraction is not an all-or-none phenomenon, as anyone who can turn these pages will recognize. Muscle contraction is a delicate dynamic balance of the attachment and detachment of myosin heads to F-actin. The system is subject to fine regulation via the nervous system.

Myosin-Based Regulation of Contraction

As described above, all muscles contain actin, myosin, and tropomyosin, but **only vertebrate striated muscles contain the troponin system.** Thus, the mechanisms of regulating contraction must differ in various contractile systems.

Smooth muscles have molecular structures very similar to those in striated muscle, but the sarcomeres are not aligned in such a way as to generate the striated appearance. Smooth muscles contain α-actinin and tropomyosin molecules, as do skeletal muscles. They do not have the troponin system, and the light chains of smooth muscle myosin molecules differ from those of striated muscle myosin. However, like striated muscle, **smooth muscle contraction is regulated by Ca^{2+}.**

When smooth muscle myosin is bound to F-actin in the absence of other muscle proteins such as tropomyosin, there is no detectable ATPase activity. This absence of ATPase is quite unlike the situation described for striated muscle myosin and F-actin, which has abundant ATPase activity. Smooth muscle myosin contains a light chain (p-light chain) that prevents the binding of the myosin head to F-actin. The p-light chain must be phosphorylated before it allows F-actin to activate myosin ATPase. The **phosphorylation of p-light chain commences the attachment-detachment contraction cycle of smooth muscle.**

In smooth muscle sarcoplasm, there exists a **myosin light chain kinase. The myosin light chain kinase activity is calcium-dependent.** The Ca^{2+} activation of myosin light chain kinase requires binding of **calmodulin·$4Ca^{2+}$** to its 105,000-MW kinase subunit (Fig 34–8). The calmodulin·$4Ca^{2+}$-activated light chain kinase phosphorylates the p-light chain, which then ceases to inhibit the myosin–F-actin interaction. The contraction cycle then begins (Fig 34–8).

Relaxation of smooth muscle occurs when (1) sarcoplasm Ca^{2+} falls below 10^{-7} mol/L. The Ca^{2+} dissociates from calmodulin, which in turn dissociates from the myosin light chain kinase, (2) inactivating the kinase. (3) No new phosphates are attached to the p-light chain, and light chain protein phosphatase, which is continually active and calcium-independent, removes the existing phosphates from the p-light chain. (4) Dephosphorylated myosin p-light chain then inhibits the binding of myosin heads to F-actin and the ATPase activity. (5) The myosin head detaches from

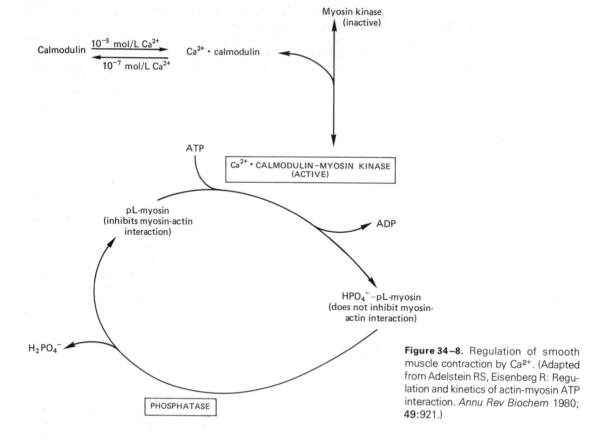

Figure 34–8. Regulation of smooth muscle contraction by Ca^{2+}. (Adapted from Adelstein RS, Eisenberg R: Regulation and kinetics of actin-myosin ATP interaction. *Annu Rev Biochem* 1980; 49:921.)

the F-actin in the presence of ATP, but it cannot reattach because of the presence of dephosphorylated p-light chain; hence, relaxation occurs.

Table 34–1 summarizes and compares the regulation of actin-myosin interactions (activation of myosin ATPase) in striated and smooth muscles.

The myosin light chain kinase is not directly affected or activated by cAMP. However, the usual cAMP-activated protein kinase (see Chapter 36) can phosphorylate the myosin light chain kinase (*not* the p-light chain itself). The phosphorylated myosin light chain kinase exhibits a significantly lower affinity for

Table 34–1. Actin-myosin interactions in striated and smooth muscle.

	Striated Muscle	Smooth Muscle (and Nonmuscle Cells)
Proteins of muscle filaments	Actin Myosin (hexamer) Tropomyosin Troponin (TpI, TpT, TpC)	Actin Myosin (hexamer)* Tropomyosin
Spontaneous interaction of F-actin and myosin *alone* (spontaneous activation of myosin ATPase by F-actin)	Yes	No
Inhibitor of F-actin–myosin interaction (inhibitor of F-actin–dependent activation of ATPase)	Troponin system (TpI)	Unphosphorylated myosin p-light chain
Contraction activated by	Ca^{2+}	Ca^{2+}
Direct effect of Ca^{2+}	$4Ca^{2+}$ bind to TpC	$4Ca^{2+}$ bind to calmodulin
Effect of protein-bound Ca^{2+}	TpC · $4Ca^{2+}$ antagonizes TpI inhibition of F-actin–myosin interaction (allows F-actin activation of ATPase).	Calmodulin · $4Ca^{2+}$ activates myosin light chain kinase that phosphorylates myosin p-light chain. The phosphorylated p-light chain no longer inhibits F-actin–myosin interaction (allows F-actin activation of ATPase).

*Light chains of myosin are different in striated and smooth muscles.

calmodulin·Ca^{2+} and thus is less sensitive to activation. Accordingly, an increase in cAMP dampens the contraction response of smooth muscle to a given elevation of sarcoplasm Ca^{2+}. This molecular mechanism can explain the relaxing effect of β-adrenergic stimulation on smooth muscle. The **phenothiazines,** widely used antipsychotic drugs, bind to calmodulin and prevent its attachment to calcium-dependent enzymes. Phenothiazines also relax smooth muscle.

Striated muscle from mollusks such as the scallop exhibits a myosin-based regulation of contraction. Like myosin and F-actin from smooth muscle, that from scallops also exhibits no ATPase, an effect of the inhibitory properties of the ''regulatory'' light chain of scallop myosin. The inhibition of scallop actin-myosin interaction is relieved when Ca^{2+} binds directly to a specific site on the myosin molecule. This regulation does not require covalent modification of myosin or the addition of a separate protein such as calmodulin or TpC to be Ca^{2+}-dependent.

Phosphorylation of Muscle Proteins

As described above, the phosphorylation of the light chain of smooth muscle myosin alleviates its inhibitory effect on the actin-myosin interaction and thereby commences the contraction cycle. Thus, phosphorylation is required for the actin-myosin interaction of smooth muscle.

One of the pairs of light chains of skeletal muscle myosin can also be phosphorylated, but this has no effect on the actin-activated ATPase of myosin, as it does on smooth muscle myosin. It has been proposed that the phosphate on the myosin light chains may form a chelate with the Ca^{2+} bound to the tropomyosin-TpC-actin complex, leading to an increased rate of formation of cross-bridges between the myosin heads and actin.

Some recent evidence suggests that phosphorylation of myosin heavy chains is a prerequisite for their assembly into the thick filaments in skeletal muscle, smooth muscle, and nonmuscle cells (see below).

The TpI and a peptide component of the sarcoplasmic reticulum Ca^{2+} pump in cardiac muscle can be phosphorylated by cAMP-dependent protein kinase. There is a rough correlation between the phosphorylation of TpI and the increased contraction of cardiac muscle induced by catecholamines. This mechanism may account for the inotropic effects (increased contractility) of the β-adrenergic compounds on the heart.

Muscle Metabolism

The ATP required as the constant energy source for the contraction-relaxation cycle of muscle can be generated by glycolysis, oxidative phosphorylation, creatine phosphate, or two ADP molecules. The ATP stores in skeletal muscle are short-lived during contraction, providing energy probably for less than 1 second of contraction. In **slow skeletal muscle,** which has abundant O_2 stores in myoglobin, **oxidative phosphorylation** is the major source of ATP regeneration. **Fast**

skeletal muscles regenerate ATP from glycolysis, mainly.

Phosphagens such as creatine phosphate prevent the rapid depletion of ATP by providing a readily available high-energy phosphate, which is all that is necessary to re-form ATP from ADP. Creatine phosphate is formed from ATP and creatine at times when the muscle is relaxed and ATP demands are not so great. The enzyme catalyzing the phosphorylation of creatine is creatine phosphokinase (CPK), a muscle-specific enzyme with clinical utility in the detection of acute or chronic disorders of muscle.

Skeletal muscle sarcoplasm contains large **glycogen** stores, located in granules close to the I bands. The release of glucose from glycogen is dependent upon a specific muscle glycogen phosphorylase enzyme (see Chapter 15). In order to generate glucose 6-phosphate for glycolysis in skeletal muscle, the glycogen phosphorylase b must be activated to phosphorylase a. The activation requires phosphorylation of phosphorylase b by the enzyme phosphorylase b kinase (Chapter 15). Ca^{2+} promotes the activation of phosphorylase b kinase, also by phosphorylation. Thus, Ca^{2+} not only activates muscle contraction but also activates a pathway to provide the necessary source of energy, ATP. Muscle glycogen phosphorylase b is missing in a specific disorder of muscle (McArdle's disease), a form of glycogen storage disease.

ATP is also available from oxidative phosphorylation in muscle tissue, a process dependent upon a constant oxygen supply. Muscles that have high oxygen demands as a result of sustained contraction (such as to maintain posture) have the ability to store oxygen in **myoglobin** (see Chapter 5). Because of the heme moiety to which oxygen is bound in myoglobin, muscles containing myoglobin are red, as compared to white skeletal muscle. Table 34–2 compares some of the properties of fast or white skeletal muscle with slow or red skeletal muscle.

Table 34–2. Characteristics of fast and slow skeletal muscle

	Fast Skeletal Muscle	Slow Skeletal Muscle
Myosin ATPase	High	Low
Energy utilization	High	Low
Color	White	Red
Myoglobin	No	Yes
Contraction rate	Fast	Slow
Duration	Short	Prolonged

Myoadenylate kinase, an enzyme present in muscle, catalyzes the formation of one ATP molecule and one AMP from two ADP molecules. This reaction is shown in Fig 34–9 coupled with the hydrolysis of ATP by myosin ATPase during muscle contraction. The relationships between these various sources of ATP and its consumption during muscle contraction are also depicted.

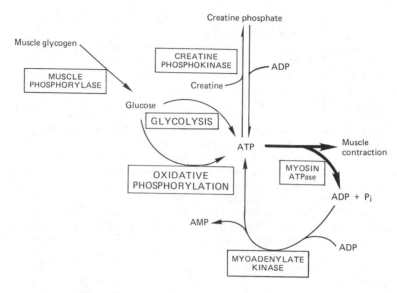

Figure 34–9. The multiple sources of ATP in muscle.

In humans, skeletal muscle protein is the major nonfat source of stored energy. This explains the very large losses of muscle mass, particularly in adults, resulting from prolonged caloric undernutrition.

The study of tissue protein breakdown in vivo is difficult, because amino acids released during intracellular breakdown of proteins can be extensively reutilized for protein synthesis within the cell, or the amino acids may be transported to other organs where they enter anabolic pathways. However, actin and myosin are methylated following synthesis of their peptide bonds, producing **3-methylhistidine** (3-MeHis). During intracellular breakdown of actin and myosin, 3-MeHis is released and excreted into the urine. When labeled material was administered to rats and humans, it was found that the urinary output of the methylated amino acid provides a reliable index of the rate of myofibrillar protein breakdown in the musculature of rats or human subjects. The fractional rate of muscle protein breakdown is not significantly different in the elderly as compared with young adults, but since muscle mass is less in the elderly, this tissue contributes less to the whole body protein breakdown that occurs with aging in humans.

As noted above, skeletal muscle is the major reserve of protein in the body. Also, this tissue is highly active in the degradation of certain amino acids as well as in the synthesis of others. In mammals, muscle appears to be the primary site of catabolism of the branched-chain amino acids. It oxidizes leucine to CO_2 and converts the carbon skeletons of aspartate, asparagine, glutamate, isoleucine, and valine into intermediates of the tricarboxylic acid cycle. The capacity of muscles to degrade branched-chain amino acids increases 3- to 5-fold during fasting and in diabetes.

Muscle also synthesizes and releases large amounts of alanine and glutamine. These compounds are synthesized utilizing amino groups that are generated in the breakdown of branched-chain amino acids, and the amino nitrogen is then transferred to α-ketoglutarate and to pyruvate by transamination. Glycolysis from exogenous glucose is the source of almost all of the pyruvate for synthesis of alanine. These reactions constitute the so-called glucose-alanine cycle, wherein alanine from muscle is utilized in hepatic gluconeogenesis while at the same time bringing amino groups to the liver for removal as urea.

The carbon skeletons of the amino acids that are degraded in muscle and enter the tricarboxylic acid cycle in muscle are converted mostly to glutamine and to pyruvate, which itself is further oxidized or converted to lactate. It thus appears that in fasting or the postabsorptive state, muscle releases most amino acids coming from net protein breakdown except for isoleucine, valine, glutamate, aspartate, and asparagine, which are used to contribute to the formation of glutamine, which itself is released for use by other tissues.

For many years, it has been observed that working muscle releases ammonia. It is now known that the immediate source of ammonia in skeletal muscle is AMP, which is deaminated to IMP, catalyzed by adenylate deaminase. IMP may be converted back to AMP by reactions utilizing aspartate and catalyzed by adenylosuccinate synthetase and adenylosuccinase (see Chapter 26).

CELL MOTILITY & THE CYTOSKELETON

It is apparent that nonmuscle cells perform mechanical work, including self-propulsion, morphogenesis, cleavage, endocytosis, exocytosis, intra-

(10–12 nm). Each of these types of filaments can be distinguished biochemically and electron microscopically by special techniques.

Nonmuscle Actin

The G-actin protein isolated from nonmuscle

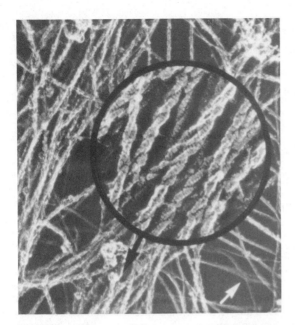

Figure 34–10. Replica of a freeze-dried cytoskeleton that was exposed to the myosin subfragment 1 (S-1) before quick-freezing. Nearly all the filaments in the lengthwise bundles, and many of the intervening filaments, have been thickened and converted into ropelike double helices (see *inset*). However, some of the filaments that travel by themselves, in between the bundles, remain totally undecorated (arrow); these are presumably intermediate filaments. × 70,000; *Inset,* × 200,000. (Reproduced, with permission, from Heuser JE, Kirschner MW: Filament organization revealed in platinum replicas of freeze-dried cytoskeletons. *J Cell Biol* 1980;**86**:212.)

cellular transport, and changing cell shape. These cellular functions are carried out by an extensive intracellular network of filamentous structures constituting the **cytoskeleton.** As will be shown, the cell cytoplasm is not a structural sac of fluid, as once thought. Essentially all eukaryotic cells contain 3 types of filamentous structures: **actin filaments** (7–9.5 nm in diameter), **microtubules** (25 nm), and **intermediate filaments**

Figure 34–11 (at right). Three moderately high powered views of ruffles or lamellipodia from fibroblasts that were fixed while whole (in *A*), were extracted with Triton before fixation (in *B*), or extracted with Triton after fixation (in *C*). In *A,* the plasma membrane is intact, and no internal structure can be seen. In *B,* the plasma membrane has been removed and an underlying web of "kinky" filaments revealed. In other experiments, these filaments decorate with S-1, but they are much more concentrated and much more extensively interdigitated than actin in other regions of the cell. In *C,* the plasma membrane has again been removed, but only after the cell was fixed with aldehyde. The delicate meshwork of underlying filaments appears coarser after the chemical fixation. *A,* × 140,000; *B* and *C,* × 115,000. (Reproduced, with permission, from Heuser JE, Kirschner MW: Filament organization revealed in platinum replicas of freeze-dried cytoskeletons. *J Cell Biol* 1980;**86**:212.)

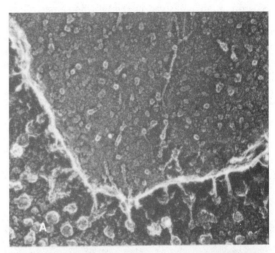

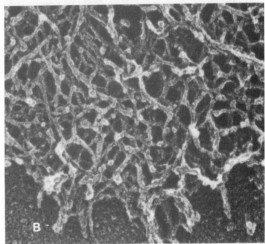

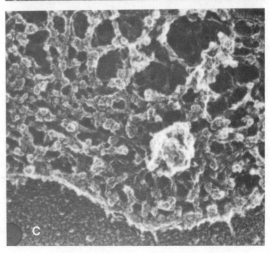

cells has a molecular weight of about 43,000 and contains, as does muscle actin (α-actin), N-methylhistidyl residues. In the presence of magnesium and potassium chloride, this actin will spontaneously polymerize to form the double helical **F-actin filaments** like those seen in muscle. There are at least 2 types of actin in nonmuscle cells: β-actin and γ-actin. Both types can coexist in the same cell and probably even copolymerize in the same filament. In the cellular cytoplasm, actin forms **microfilaments** of 7–9.5 nm that frequently exist as bundles of tangled-appearing meshwork. The bundles of microfilaments are prominent just underlying the plasma membrane of resting cells and are there referred to as **stress fibers.** These stress fibers will decorate with the S-1 portion of myosin to reveal their double helical character (Fig 34–10). The stress fibers disappear as cell motility increases or upon the malignant transformation of the cell by chemicals or oncogenic viruses.

Microfilaments are also tightly packed in a meshwork pattern underlying the leading edge or "ruffle" of a motile cell (Fig 34–11). Actin microfilaments are found in all cellular microprojections such as filopodia and microvilli. For instance, the microvilli of intestinal mucosal cells contain 20–30 actin microfilaments arranged longitudinally within the microvilli as diagrammed in Fig 34–12. These microfilaments will decorate with myosin S-1, demonstrating a uniform polarity (Fig 34–12). At the base of the microvilli, myosin filaments exist and are capable of pulling together the actin filaments projecting into the microvilli. The contraction process does not involve any change of length of actin or myosin and thus must occur, as in muscle, by the sliding filament mechanism of Huxley. As in smooth muscle, the activation of the actin-myosin interaction and thereby contraction is mediated by phosphorylation of the myosin light chain.

Actin and myosin are also both found between the spindle poles and the chromosomes and along the cleavage furrow of mitotic telophase.

Actin microfilaments are associated with other musclelike proteins in nonmuscle cells. α-**Actinin** is present at the plasma membrane sites to which microfilaments attach, such as the tips of microvilli. The geodesic domes—cytoskeletal scaffolding surrounding the nuclei of eukaryotic cells—consist of actin, α-actinin, and tropomyosin. α-Actinin is also found along actin microfilaments themselves.

As described above, **myosin** is found in association with actin microfilaments at the bases of microvilli. Myosin is also found along the actin fibers but as filaments thinner and shorter than in muscle. They seem to play a role in maintenance of the filamentous character of actin.

Tropomyosin, as mentioned above, participates in the formation of the geodomes surrounding nuclei. Tropomyosin along actin microfilaments seems to serve a structural rather than a motility function.

The regulation of nonmuscle actin function seems to depend upon several specialized proteins. **Profilin** prevents the polymerization of G-actin even in the

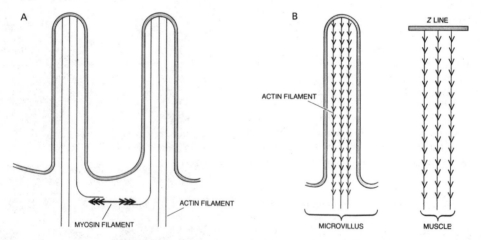

Figure 34–12. Microvilli are tiny cytoplasmic protrusions that extend out from the epithelial cells lining the small intestine, greatly increasing the surface for the absorption of nutrients. Microvilli contain both actin and myosin filaments and are known to contract much like muscle cells, and so they provide a convincing example of nonmuscle movement mediated by sliding filaments of actin and myosin. As is shown in *A,* bundles of actin filaments project upward inside each microvillus; the myosin filaments are localized at the base of the microvilli. In *B,* the orientation of the actin filaments was determined by treating the microvilli with isolated head fragments from muscle myosin, termed heavy meromyosin; these fragments retain the ability to bind to actin filaments. When the head fragments are applied to muscle cells, they form "arrowhead" complexes with the actin filaments that point in the direction of the filaments. When heavy meromyosin was added to microvilli, the head fragments formed arrowhead complexes with the actin filaments that pointed downward from the attachment sites in the tips of the microvilli. The actin filaments within the microvilli are therefore analogous to the actin filament arrays of muscle cells. (Reproduced, with permission, from Lazarides E, Revel JP: The molecular basis of cell movement. *Sci Am* [May] 1979;**240**:100.)

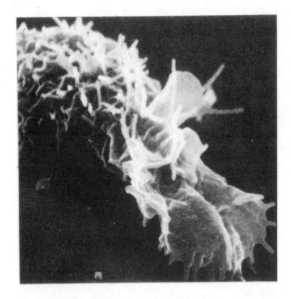

Figure 34–13. Individual cells in tissue culture are depicted. The delicate feathery structure at the bottom right is a "ruffle," or lamellipodium, which marks the leading edge of the cell. A cell is shown from an oblique angle as it moves across the substrate, extending its ruffle to form new adhesions. (Reproduced, with permission, from Lazarides E, Revel JP: The molecular basis of cell movement. *Sci Am* [May] 1979;**240**:100.)

presence of the proper concentrations of magnesium and potassium chloride. **Filamin** promotes the formation of an actin microfilament meshwork. **Tropomyosin** promotes the formation of bundles of actin stress fibers. **α-Actinin** promotes the attachment of actin microfilaments to membranes, substratum, and other cell organelles. **Cytochalasin** is a naturally occurring peptide that breaks microfilaments and prevents their polymerization. It is frequently used as a diagnostic test for the existence or function of microfilaments.

The actual motility of cells appears to be led by the **ruffle membrane,** or lamellipodium, that contains fingerlike projections called filopodia. The ruffle attaches at its tip to the substratum via the filopodia, and the cell then seems to pull in its rear margins. The ruffle releases and folds back over the top of the cell as new filopodia attach to the substratum (Fig 34–13).

Microtubules

Microtubules are an integral component of the cellular cytoskeleton. They consist of cytoplasmic tubes 25 nm in diameter and of indefinite length. Microtubules are necessary for the formation and function of the **mitotic spindle** and thus are present in all eukaryotic cells. Microtubules carry out a number of other cellular functions. They are responsible for the intracellular movement of endocytotic and exocytotic vesicles. They form the major structural component of **cilia and flagella.** Microtubules are a major protein component of **axons and dendrites,** where they main-

tain the structure and participate in the axoplasmic flow of material along these neuronal processes.

Microtubules are cylinders of 13 longitudinally arranged **protofilaments,** each consisting of dimers of **α-tubulin** and **β-tubulin** (Fig 34–14). α-Tubulin (MW 53,000) and β-tubulin (MW 55,000) are closely related protein molecules. The tubulin dimers assemble into protofilaments and subsequently into sheets and then cylinders, as depicted in Fig 34–15. The assembly of tubulin into microtubules requires two **GTP** molecules per tubulin dimer. Two proteins termed high-molecular-weight (HMW) protein and Tau promote the formation of microtubules but are not required for assembly. Calmodulin and phosphorylation may both play roles in microtubule assembly.

A number of particularly important alkaloids can prevent microtubule assembly. These include colchicine and its derivative demecolcine (used for treatment of acute gouty arthritis), vinblastine (a *Vinca* alkaloid used for treating cancer), and griseofulvin (an antifungal agent).

Microtubules "grow" with a polarity from specific sites (centrioles) within cells. On each chromatid of a chromosome (see Chapter 27) there exists a kinetochore that serves as a point of origin for microtubular growth. Many abnormalities of chromosomal segregation result from abnormal structure or function of kinetochores. The centrosome, which is at the center of the mitotic poles, also nucleates microtubular formation. The movement of chromosomes during anaphase of mitosis is dependent upon microtubules, but the molecular mechanism has not been delineated.

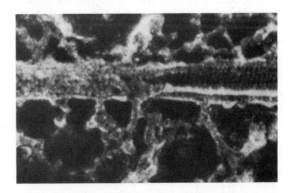

Figure 34–14. High magnification of a microtubule that was fractured and deep etched after quick-freezing. The left half of the field illustrates the outer surface of the microtubule, which displays longitudinal bands of bumps spaced 55 nm apart, which may represent the microtubule's protofilaments. To the right, the microtubule is fractured open to reveal its inner luminal walls, which display characteristic oblique striations separated by 40 nm. The reticulum surrounding the microtubule is thought to be unpolymerized tubulin and microtubule-associated proteins. (Reproduced, with permission, from Heuser JE, Kirschner MW: Filament organization revealed in platinum replicas of freeze-dried cytoskeletons. *J Cell Biol* 1980;**86**:212.)

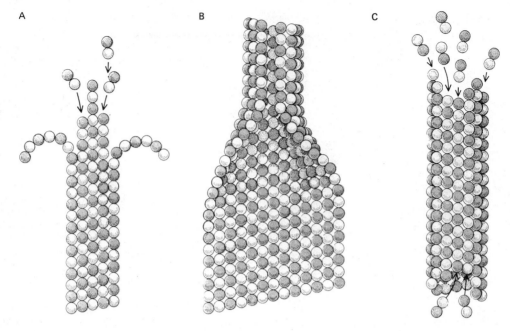

Figure 34–15. Assembly of microtubules in the laboratory begins with 2 protein molecules, α-tubulin and β-tubulin, which are globular molecules (probably more ovoid than these highly schematic spheres). The tubulins form dimers, or double molecules. If the dimers are present in a high enough concentration, they associate to form various intermediate structures, including double rings, spirals, and stacked rings; the equilibrium is biased in favor of either the isolated dimers or the intermediate structures, depending on the conditions. The next steps are not well established. It seems that the rings or spirals open up to form strands, called protofilaments, of linearly associated dimers, which assemble side by side in a sheet *(A);* sometimes the ends of protofilaments curve. When a sheet is wide enough, it forms a tube, perhaps by curling up *(B).* Once a short tube has formed *(C),* it is lengthened by the addition of dimers preferentially at one end. (Reproduced, with permission, from Dustin P: Microtubules. *Sci Am* [Aug] 1980;**243**:67.)

At the base of all eukaryotic **flagella and cilia** is a structure called the **basal body;** it is identical to the centriole and acts as a nucleation center for the formation of the 9-doublet array of microtubules in the flagella and cilia. These microtubular structures are specialized for motility. Each member of a doublet shares a common wall of 3 protofilaments with its partner, and the doublets are connected by a flexible protein, **nexin.** Movement is effected by the sliding of the doublets past one another causing distortion of the cilium in waves. Connected to one of the doublets in a cilium is a large protein, **dynein,** which possesses an ATPase necessary for the microtubular doublet sliding movement.

Intermediate Filaments

Recent studies have confirmed the existence of an intracellular fibrous system of filaments with an axial periodicity of 21 nm and 8–10 nm in diameter that are distinct from microfilaments (6 nm in diameter) and microtubules (23 nm in diameter). There are 6 major classes of these filaments that share an antigenic determinant and exhibit diameters **intermediate** in size between actin microfilaments and microtubules. Each intermediate filament consists of biochemically and immunologically distinct subunits. Intermediate filaments seem to form relatively **stable components** of the cytoskeleton, not undergoing rapid assembly and disassembly and not disappearing during mitosis as do

Table 34–3. Classes of intermediate filaments and their distributions.

Proteins	MW (Thousands)	Diameter (nm)	Distributions
Keratin type I and type II (tonofilaments)	40–65 (10–20 major proteins)	8	Epithelial cells (never cells of mesenchymal origin).
Desmin	50–55	10	Muscle (Z lines).
Vimentin	52	10	Mesenchymal and nonmesenchymal cells, eg, muscle, glial cells, epithelial cells.
Neurofilament	200 150 70	10	Neurons.
Glial filament	51	10	Glial cells.

actin and many microtubular filaments. Table 34–3 summarizes some properties and distributions of intermediate filaments.

There are 2 types of **keratin,** I and II, comprising 10–20 different polypeptides that are as different from one another as they are from the other 4 classes of intermediate filament proteins—desmin, vimentin, neurofilament, and glial filament. These latter 4 classes have a high degree of homology among them. A keratin filament will contain at least 2 different keratin polypeptides, whereas the other 4 classes of intermediate filaments are homopolymers. Each of the intermediate filaments consists of 4 α-helical domains separated from one another by regions of β-pleated sheets and flanked on both ends by nonhelical terminal domains. The nonhelical terminal domains are involved in end-to-end extension of protofilaments and side-to-side interprotofibrillar interactions. The ends of the microfibrillar keratins can be cross-linked through disulfide bonding to form insoluble filaments, such as those characteristic of wool.

It is apparent that some of the intermediate filaments, particularly those of muscle and mesenchymal origin, coexist in numerous tissues.

COLLAGEN

Collagen, the major macromolecule of connective tissues, is the most common protein in the animal world. It provides an extracellular framework for all metazoan animals and exists in virtually every animal tissue. There are at least **5 distinct types** of collagen in mammalian tissues; thus, they exist as a family of molecules sharing many properties. The most definitive property of collagen molecules is their **triple helix,** a coiled structure of 3 polypeptide subunits. Each polypeptide subunit, or alpha chain, is twisted into a **left-handed helix of 3 residues per turn.** Three of these left-handed helices are then wound to a right-handed superhelix to form a stiff rodlike molecule 1.4 nm in diameter and about 300 nm long. These triple helical molecules—unique to collagen—are then associated bilaterally and longitudinally into fibrils (Fig 34–16). The arrangement of collagen fibrils involves longitudinal staggering slightly less than one-quarter the length of the triple helix. Between the end of one triple helix and the beginning of the next is a gap that may provide a site for deposition of hydroxyapatite crystals in bone formation. Collagen fibrils range from 10 to 100 nm in diameter and are visible by microscopy as banded structures in the extracellular matrix of connective tissues.

The other striking characteristic of the collagen molecule is that **glycine constitutes every third residue** in the triple helical portion of each alpha chain. Glycine is the only amino acid small enough to exist in the limited space available down the central core of the triple helical molecule; thus, the central core of the triple helical molecule consists of glycine residues provided by each of the 3 alpha subunits. This repeat-

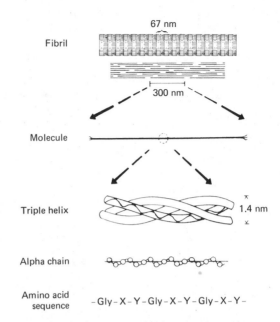

Figure 34–16. Molecular features of collagen structure from primary sequence up to the fibril. (Slightly modified and reproduced, with permission, from Eyre DR: Collagen: Molecular diversity in the body's protein scaffold. *Science* 1980;**207**:1315. Copyright © 1980 by the American Association for the Advancement of Science.)

ing structure can be represented by $(Gly-X-Y)_n$, where X and Y are amino acids other than glycine.

In mammalian collagen, about 100 of the X positions are **proline,** and 100 of the Y positions are **4-hydroxyproline.** These rigid imino acids limit rotation of the polypeptide backbone and thus increase the stability of the triple helix. The hydroxyproline residues contribute additional stability to the collagen triple helix by forming more intramolecular hydrogen bonds mediated through extra water molecules. Collagen also contains 3-hydroxyproline in some X positions and 5-hydroxylysine in Y positions.

The collagen triple helix is stabilized by multiple interchain cross-links between lysyl and hydroxylysyl residues. The chemical nature of these cross-links is described below. Mature collagen is a glycoprotein containing saccharides attached in O-glycosidic linkage to the hydroxylysine residues.

A summary of the vertebrate collagens, their tissue distributions, and distinctive features is presented in Table 34–4.

The Synthesis of Collagen

Collagen is an extracellular protein but is synthesized as an intracellular precursor molecule that undergoes posttranslational modification before becoming a mature collagen fibril. Like all secreted proteins, the precursor of collagen is processed as it passes through the endoplasmic reticulum and Golgi complex prior to appearing extracellularly (Chapters 32 and 33). The earliest collagen precursor is a **preprocolla-**

Table 34—4. Genetically distinct vertebrate collagens. At least 5 different molecules containing 7 genetically distinct a chains are present in higher animals.*

Type	Molecular Formula	Native Polymer	Tissue Distribution	Distinctive Features
I	$[a1(I)]_2 a2$	Fibril	Skin, tendon, bone, dentin, fascia; most abundant.	Low content of hydroxylysine; few sites of hydroxylysine glycosylation; broad fibrils.
II	$[a1(II)]_3$	Fibril	Cartilage, nucleus pulposus, notochord, vitreous body.	High content of hydroxylysine; heavily glycosylated; usually thinner fibrils than type I.
III	$[a1(III)]_3$	Fibril	Skin, uterus, blood vessels; "reticulin" fibers generally.	High content of hydroxyproline; low content of hydroxylysine; few sites of hydroxylysine glycosylation; interchain disulfides between cysteines at the carboxyl end of the helix; long carboxyl telopeptide.
IV	$[a1(IV)]_3$ (tentative, under dispute)	Basement lamina	Kidney glomeruli, lens capsule; Descemet's membrane; basement laminae of all epithelial and endothelial cells.	Very high content of hydroxylysine; almost fully glycosylated; relatively rich in 3-hydroxyproline; low alanine content; retains procollagen extension pieces.
V	$aA(aB)_2$ or $(aA)_3$ and $(aB)_3$	Unknown	Widespread in small amounts; basement laminae of blood vessels and smooth muscle cells; exoskeleton of fibroblasts and other mesenchymal cells?	High content of hydroxylysine; heavily glycosylated; low alanine content; fails to form native fibrils in vitro.

*Reproduced, with permission, from Eyre DR: Collagen: Molecular diversity in the body's protein scaffold. *Science* 1980;**207**:1315. Copyright © 1980 by the American Association for the Advancement of Science.

gen that contains a leader or signal sequence of approximately 100 amino acids at its amino terminus. Preprocollagen is generated by ribosomes attached to the endoplasmic reticulum. As the signal sequence penetrates into the vesicular space of the endoplasmic reticulum, the leader sequence is cleaved off and the amino-terminal end of **procollagen** continues to protrude into the endoplasmic reticular space. At this site, **prolyl 4-hydroxylase** and **lysyl hydroxylase** act on proline or lysine residues, respectively, in the Y position of the (Gly-X-Y)n peptide. A prolyl 3-hydroxylase acts on prolyl residues in the X position immediately preceding a 4-hydroxyproline in the Y position.

The procollagen molecule contains at its amino terminus a 20,000-MW peptide and at its carboxyl terminus a 30- to 35-thousand-MW peptide, neither of which is present in mature collagen. Both of these propeptides contain **cysteine** residues. While the amino-terminal propeptide collagen forms only intrachain disulfide bonds, the carboxy-terminal peptides form both intrachain and interchain disulfide bonds. Following the formation of these disulfide bonds, the procollagen molecules assemble as the triple helix.

After formation of the triple helix, further hydroxylation of prolyl and lysyl residues *cannot* occur. The glycosyltransferase activities that attach glucose or galactose to hydroxylysine residues also require that the procollagen alpha chains be nonhelical.

Following this intracellular processing, the glycosylated procollagen molecule reaches the outside of the cell by way of the Golgi complex. Extracellular **procollagen aminoprotease** and **procollagen carboxyprotease** remove the amino-terminal and carboxy-terminal propeptides, respectively. The

newly formed collagen molecules have approximately 1000 amino acids per chain and spontaneously assemble into **collagen fibrils** that are indistinguishable from the mature fibrils found in tissues.

These fibrils, however, do not have the tensile strength of mature collagen fibrils until they are **crosslinked by a series of covalent bonds.** The extracellular copper-containing enzyme lysyl oxidase oxidatively deaminates the ϵ-amino groups of certain lysyl and hydroxylysyl residues of collagen, yielding reactive aldehydes. The aldehydes can form Schiff bases with ϵ-amino groups of other lysines or hydroxylysines or even glycosylated hydroxylysines. These

Table 34—5. Order and location of processing the collagen precursor (containing repeating structure $[Gly-X-Y]_n$).

Intracellular (endoplasmic reticulum)
  (1) Cleavage of signal peptide.
  (2) 4-Hydroxylation of Y-prolyl residues.
  (3) 3-Hydroxylation of X-prolyl, where Y = 4-hydroxyprolyl residue.
  (4) 5-Hydroxylation of Y-lysyl residues.
  (5) Glycosylation of hydroxylysyl residues.
  (6) Formation of intrachain and interchain S–S bonds.
  (7) Formation of triple helix procollagen.

Extracellular
  (1) Cleavage of NH_2-terminal propeptide (MW 20,000).
  (2) Cleavage of COOH-terminal propeptide (MW 30–35,000).
  (3) Formation of immature collagen fibrils.
  (4) Oxidation of lysyl, hydroxylysyl, glycosylated hydroxylysyl residue to aldehydes.
  (5) Cross-linking of chains and helical molecules of fibrils via Schiff bases and aldol condensations.

Schiff bases are chemically rearranged and provide stable covalent cross-links such as new peptide bonds or secondary amine bridges. The aldehyde component derived from a hydroxylysine forms a more stable cross-link than does the aldehyde derived from a lysyl residue. Aldol bridges also provide intramolecular cross-links.

The intracellular and extracellular processing of the collagen precursor molecule is summarized in Table 34–5.

The same cells that secrete collagen also secrete **fibronectin,** a large glycoprotein present on cell surfaces, in the extracellular matrix, and in blood. Fibronectin binds to aggregating procollagen fibers and alters the kinetics of fibril formation in the pericellular matrix. Associated with fibronectin and procollagen in this matrix are the proteoglycans heparan sulfate and chondroitin sulfate (Chapter 33).

Cartilage is an extracellular matrix in which collagen contributes **tensile strength** and proteoglycans are responsible for its remarkable **resilience.**

Inherited Defects of Collagen & Its Assembly

The inherited diseases that result in abnormal collagen constitute an increasing number of variants of at least 4 different types of syndromes: **osteogenesis imperfecta, Marfan's syndrome, Ehlers-Danlos syndrome,** and **Menkes' (kinky-hair) syndrome.** Originally, these diseases were defined on the basis of having similar phenotypes, but as the understanding of collagen structure and function increases, it is becoming apparent that similar molecular defects may present dissimilar clinical syndromes and vice versa.

Many of the defects include defective processing of collagen precursors owing to abnormalities within the precursor or, in some cases, abnormalities of the processing enzyme per se. In many cases, understanding the nature of the molecular defect allows one to predict whether the disease is recessively or dominantly inherited. So far, only defects in type I and type III procollagen molecules have been recognized among the inherited diseases of collagen.

Table 34–6 summarizes defects and their consequences in some inherited human diseases of collagen, and Fig 34–17 depicts sites at which defects in procollagen type I are recognized.

Table 34–6. Consequences of molecular defects in 4 heritable diseases of collagen.[*]

Disease	Defect[†]	Consequences
Osteogenesis imperfecta		
Type I	$Pro\alpha1(I)^\circ$	Half normal amount of type 1 collagen
	$Pro\alpha2(I)^S$	Probably abnormal fibrils
	Other (unidentified)	
Type II	$Pro\alpha1(I)^S$	Unstable triple helix; increased synthesis of $pro\alpha1(III)$
	$Pro\alpha2(I)^S$ and $pro\alpha2(I)^\circ$	Uncertain
	Other (unidentified)	
Type III	$Pro\alpha2(I)^{CX}$	Synthesis of $pro\alpha1(I)$ trimers
	$Pro\alpha1(I)^{CX}$ or $pro\alpha2(I)^{CX}$	Increased mannose in C-propeptide and decreased solubility of type I procollagen
	Other (unidentified)	
Variant with characteristics of Ehlers-Danlos syndrome	$Pro\alpha2(I)^S$	Resistance to procollagen N-proteinase and persistence of pNcollagen[‡]
Marfan's syndrome	$Pro\alpha2(I)^L$	Probably abnormal cross-linking
	Other (unidentified)	
Ehlers-Danlos syndrome		
Type IV	$Pro\alpha1(III)^+$	Marked decrease in type III collagen
	$Pro\alpha1(III)^{SM}$	Unstable triple helix
	$Pro\alpha1(III)^X$	Decreased secretion rate of type III collagen
	Other (unidentified)	
Type VI	Lysine hydroxylase deficiency	Hydroxylysine-deficient collagen and defective cross-linking
	Other (unidentified)	
Type VII	Procollagen N-proteinase deficiency	Persistence of pNcollagen[‡]
	$Pro\alpha2(I)^X$	Resistance to procollagen N-proteinase and persistence of pNcollagen[‡]
Type IX	Defective copper metabolism	Lysine oxidase deficiency and defective cross-linking
Menkes' syndrome	Defective copper metabolism	Lysine oxidase deficiency and defective cross-linking

[*]Reproduced, with permission, from Prockop DJ, Kivirikko KI: Heritable diseases of collagen. *N Engl J Med* 1984;**311**:376.
[†]$Pro\alpha1(I)^\circ$, $pro\alpha2(I)^\circ$, and $pro\alpha1(III)^+$, nonfunctional or inefficiently functioning alleles for $pro\alpha$ chains; $pro\alpha1(I)^S$ and $pro\alpha2(I)^S$, shortened $pro\alpha$ chains; $pro\alpha2(I)^L$, lengthened $pro\alpha$ chains; $pro\alpha1(I)^{CX}$ and $pro\alpha2(I)^{CX}$, mutations altering the structure of the C-propeptides of $pro\alpha$ chains; $pro\alpha1(III)^{SM}$, an altered $pro\alpha1(III)$ chain that migrates slowly in electrophoretic gels; and $pro\alpha1(III)^X$ and $pro\alpha2(I)^X$, poorly defined mutations altering the structure of $pro\alpha$ chains.
[‡]Intermediate in the conversion of procollagen that contains the N-propeptides but not the C-propeptides.

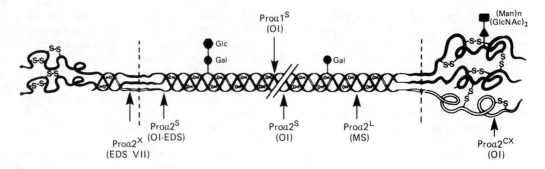

Figure 34–17. Approximate locations of mutations in the structure of type I procollagen. EDS, Ehlers-Danlos syndrome; MS, Marfan's syndrome; OI, osteogenesis imperfecta. For other abbreviations, see second footnote to Table 34 –6. (Reproduced, with permission, from Prockop DJ, Kivirikko KI: Heritable diseases of collagen. *N Engl J Med* 1984;**311:**376.)

• • •

References

Adelstein RS, Eisenberg R: Regulation and kinetics of actin-myosin ATP interaction. *Annu Rev Biochem* 1980;**49:**921.

Adelstein RS et al: Phosphorylation of muscle contractile proteins. *Fed Proc* 1980;**39:**1544.

Barany M, Barany K: Phosphorylation of the myofibrillar proteins. *Annu Rev Physiol* 1980;**42:**275.

Bornstein P, Sage H: Structurally distinct collagen types. *Annu Rev Biochem* 1980;**49:**957.

Caplan A: Cartilage. *Sci Am* (Oct) 1984;**250:**84.

Clark M, Spudich JA: Nonmuscle contractile proteins: The role of actin and myosin in cell motility and shape determination. *Annu Rev Biochem* 1977;**46:**797.

DeCrombrugghe B, Pastan I: Structure and regulation of a collagen gene. *Trends Biochem Sci* 1982;**7:**11.

Dustin P: Microtubules. *Sci Am* (Aug) 1980;**243:**67.

Eyre DR et al: Cross-linking in collagen and elastin. *Annu Rev Biochem* 1984;**53:**717.

Fuchs E, Hanukoglu I: Unraveling the structure of intermediate filaments. *Cell* 1983;**34:**332.

Heuser JE, Kirschner MW: Filament organization revealed in platinum replicas of freeze-dried cytoskeletons. *J Cell Biol* 1980;**86:**212.

Kleinman HK, Klebe RJ, Martin GR: Role of collagenous matrices in the adhesion and growth of cells. *J Cell Biol* 1981; **88:**473.

Lazarides E: Intermediate filaments: A chemically heterogeneous, developmentally regulated class of proteins. *Annu Rev Biochem* 1982;**51:**219.

Lazarides E, Revel JP: The molecular basis of cell movement. *Sci Am* (May) 1979;**240:**100.

Murray JM, Weber A: The cooperative action of muscle proteins. *Sci Am* (Feb) 1974;**230:**59.

Prockop DJ, Kivirikko KI: Heritable diseases of collagen. *N Engl J Med* 1984;**311:**376.

Sandberg LB, Soskel NT, Leslie JG: Elastin structure, biosynthesis, and relation to disease states. *N Engl J Med* 1981; **304:**566.

Characteristics of Hormone Systems | 35

Daryl K. Granner, MD

GENERAL FEATURES

A distinguishing characteristic of multicellular organisms is the presence of differentiated tissues that perform the specialized functions necessary for the survival of the organism. Mechanisms are required for intercellular communication to ensure the coordination of the responses necessary for adjusting to a constantly changing external and internal environment. Two general systems have evolved to serve these functions. These are the **nervous system,** often viewed as conducting signals or messages through a fixed, structural system; and the **endocrine system,** in which various **hormones** secreted by specific glands are transported as mobile messages to act on adjacent and distant tissue.

It is now clear that there is an exquisite convergence of these regulatory systems. Neural regulation of the endocrine system is very important; eg, epinephrine is produced and secreted by post-ganglionic cells in the adrenal medulla, and vasopressin is synthesized in the hypothalamus and transported by axons to the posterior pituitary from which it is released. Likewise, many **neurotransmitters** (catecholamines, dopamine, acetylcholine, etc) are similar to hormones with regard to their synthesis, release, transport, and mechanism of action. In fact, catecholamines are neurotransmitters in one tissue and hormones in other tissues. Finally, many hormones such as insulin, ACTH, vasoactive intestinal polypeptide (VIP), somatostatin, thyrotropin-releasing hormone (TRH), and cholecystokinin have recently been found in brain. It remains to be established whether all of these molecules are synthesized in brain and whether they act there as neuromodulators or as neurotransmitters. Since specific receptors for many of these hormones are found in brain, the possibility exists that these molecules act in brain.

The word hormone is derived from a Greek term meaning "to arouse to activity." By the classic definition, a hormone is a substance that is synthesized in one tissue and transported by the circulatory system to act on another organ. This original description is too restrictive; it is now appreciated that hormones act on adjacent cells in a given tissue **(paracrine function)** as well as on the cells in which they are synthesized **(autocrine function).**

The disciplines of basic and clinical endocrinology generally focus on the following glands and their products: pineal gland, neurohypophysis and adenohypophysis, adrenal cortex and medulla, ovaries, testes, placenta, thyroid, parathyroids, and pancreatic islets. Gastrointestinal and renal hormones, prostaglandins, and the newly discovered and rapidly expanding list of growth peptides are generally not included in discussions of the classic hormones, although in many respects they are similar.

The objective of this chapter is to impart an appreciation for the varied nature of the endocrine system and to define several of the fundamental concepts that will reappear in subsequent chapters.

DIVERSITY OF THE ENDOCRINE SYSTEM

One of the most remarkable features of the endocrine system is that it provides an organism with a number of different ways for solving problems. The purpose of this section is to present a very brief discussion of selected examples that highlight this diversity.

Derivation, Location, & Structure of Endocrine Glands

The endocrine glands are mostly derived from epithelial cells. Notable exceptions include the connective tissue origin of the testosterone-producing Leydig cells in the testis and the estrogen-producing granulosa cells in the ovary, and the neuronal origin of the secretory cells in the neurohypophysis. The **neural crest** has been suggested as the embryologic origin of a number of endocrine cell types. If true, this would provide a rational link between the central nervous system and the endocrine system. Since neural crest tissue can appear in any organ, this could explain why some hormones appear to be made in brain and in tissues predominantly derived from the midgut and foregut. It may also explain the **ectopic hormone syndromes,** in which there is production of hormones by the "wrong tissue" (eg, production of parathyroid hormone [PTH] and ACTH by malignant cells in the case of lung cancer). These syndromes generally involve a rather restricted number of peptide hormones but a large and apparently diverse number of tissues.

Although commonly thought to represent the activation of silent genes within a given cell, these syndromes could represent the activation of silent cells of common embryologic ancestry within a tissue. Another curious example is afforded by the **multiple endocrine neoplasia (MEN) syndromes,** in which there is a peculiar familial clustering of neoplasia of several endocrine glands. The production of excessive amounts of peptide or catecholamine hormones, often with one tissue making several, is a feature of these syndromes.

Hormone-producing cells are not randomly distributed; they are present in various tissues for specific reasons. Locally high concentrations of some hormones (ie, values in excess of plasma hormone levels) are often required for specific biologic processes. For example, a level of testosterone higher than that available in the plasma is required for spermatogenesis; thus, the testosterone-secreting Leydig cells and the seminiferous tubules are in juxtaposition. A very high concentration of estrogen is required for corpus luteum formation; hence, there is close proximity of this structure and the granulosa cells. A major action of insulin and glucagon is to regulate hepatic production of glucose; thus, there is close association of the pancreatic islets with the portal circulation. Cortisol, which is required in high concentration in the adrenal medulla for the induction of phenylethanolamine N-methyltransferase (a rate-limiting enzyme in catecholamine biosynthesis) reaches this site by a portal vascular system that originates in the adrenal cortex. There is an intimate association of the hypothalamus and anterior pituitary, so that high concentrations of the very labile hypothalamic releasing hormones can easily reach the pituitary target via another special portal vascular system. Finally, there is a unique anatomic relationship between the various cells of the pancreatic islets in which locally high gradients of somatostatin, pancreatic polypeptide, glucagon, and insulin interact to regulate the secretion of one another.

Endocrine glands are characterized by a profuse blood supply, and the cells are oriented toward the blood vessels with a distinctive **polarity** that is similar to that of other types of secretory cells. The basal cell membrane is located near a capillary, through which it derives the raw materials for hormone biosynthesis. The apical portion of the cell is oriented toward the venous end of the capillary, into which various hormones are released. A notable exception is the thyroid, wherein the hormones tri- and tetraiodothyronine (T_3 and T_4) are produced in thyroglobulin within a lumen surrounded by the apices of thyroid cells (see Fig 38–4). The thyroglobulin reenters the thyroid cells and is hydrolyzed, and T_4 and T_3 exit the cell via the basal membrane.

Features of protein hormone–producing cells include a well-developed rough endoplasmic reticulum, which is required for protein synthesis; a prominent Golgi apparatus in cells that produce glycoprotein hormones; and prominent secretory granules. Steroid hormone–producing cells, in contrast, have a profuse smooth endoplasmic reticulum and very little rough endoplasmic reticulum. These cells frequently contain abundant lipid droplets, which provide cholesterol, the precursor of steroid hormone biosynthesis.

Chemical Diversity of Hormones

Many hormones are derived from **lipid precursors.** These include the steroids and 1,25-dihydroxycholecalciferol, which come from cholesterol; and the prostaglandins, which are derived from arachidonic acid via the cyclooxygenase pathway. These lipophilic compounds enter target cells and act internally.

Thyroid hormones and the catecholamines are modifications of the amino acid **tyrosine.** Thyroid hormones enter cells and encounter a specific receptor in the nucleus, whereas the catecholamines interact with a cell surface receptor.

A final group consists of hormones characterized by having **peptide bonds.** These range from **tripeptides,** such as thyrotropin-releasing hormone, to **simple peptides,** such as antidiuretic hormone (9 amino acids), glucagon (29 amino acids), and ACTH (39 amino acids), to more **complex proteins,** such as parathyroid hormone (84 amino acids) and growth hormone (191 amino acids). Finally, there is a small class of **glycoprotein** hormones (TSH, FSH, LH, and hCG) that must contain carbohydrate moieties to be biologically active. All of these peptide hormones interact with cell surface receptors.

Hormone Biosynthesis & Modification

There is great diversity in the biosynthetic and postsynthetic mechanisms employed in the generation of active hormones. Hormones may be synthesized and secreted in final form; examples include aldosterone, hydrocortisone, T_3, estradiol, and the catecholamines. Others must be modified within the cell before they are secreted or before they have full biologic activity. Examples include insulin, which is synthesized as proinsulin, the prototype of **precursor proteins,** and parathyroid hormone (PTH), which has at least 2 precursor peptides (a prepro segment) that must be removed to achieve full biologic activity. A description of precursor proteins, their synthesis, and intracellular processing into the final product can be found in Chapter 32. Pro-opiomelanocortin (POMC), a 285-amino-acid peptide that is the product of a single gene, represents an even more complicated case. POMC is cleaved to form ACTH, β-lipotropin, β-endorphin, α-MSH, and β-MSH, and the parent or precursor molecule may contain sequences of peptide hormones as yet unidentified. The **processing** of the precursor molecule is tissue-specific (see Chapter 37).

Perhaps the most exaggerated example of a large precursor of a hormone is thyroglobulin. This is a large protein (MW 660,000) found in the lumen of the thyroid follicle. Among the 5000 amino acids of the thyroglobulin molecule, there are 120 tyrosyl residues, some of which are iodinated in the process of thyroid hormone biosynthesis (see Chapter 38). The entire thyroglobulin molecule must be degraded to release the few T_4 and T_3 molecules present.

Some hormones are converted into more active molecules in peripheral tissues. This can occur in target tissues, as is the case in conversion of T_4 to T_3 in liver and pituitary and in conversion of testosterone to dihydrotestosterone in secondary sex tissues. **Peripheral conversion** can also occur in nontarget tissues; dehydroepiandrosterone is synthesized in the adrenal and converted to androstenedione in the liver. This latter molecule can then be converted to testosterone or to estrone and estradiol in fat cells, liver, or skin. Combined target and nontarget tissue peripheral conversion of an inactive molecule to an active hormone occurs. This is illustrated by the conversion of vitamin D_3 (from skin) to 25-hydroxycholecalciferol in liver, with subsequent conversion to 1,25-dihydroxycholecalciferol in kidney (see Chapters 11 and 39).

Hormones that are secreted from very different tissues and have different target cell specificity may have structural similarities. The glycoprotein hormones from the pituitary and placenta (TSH, LH, FSH, and hCG) are heterodimers consisting of α and β subunits in which the α subunits are identical.

Hormone Transport

The hydrophobic steroid and thyroid hormones circulate bound to specific transport (carrier) proteins (Table 35–1). Although albumin and other plasma proteins bind hormones, the affinity of these interactions is low, and most binding is to specific transport globulins. Hormones bind to these specific transport globulins with less affinity and less specificity than to the cell-associated **receptors** (Table 35–2), yet the association is sufficient to bind most of the circulating hormone. The equilibrium between bound and free hormone is a function of the affinity of binding. Only the **free hormone** has biologic activity. These hormones cannot be metabolized when bound, and if they are not metabolized they cannot be excreted. These bound hormones also serve as circulating **reservoirs** of hormone in the immediate vicinity of the target cells. Because of this binding, an estimate of the total circulating level of thyroid and steroid hor-

mones, which is in the range of 10^{-7} to 10^{-9} mol/L, is not an accurate reflection of the amount of biologically active hormone, which in all cases is the free (unbound) hormone. Because of this binding, the **plasma half-life** of steroid hormones is a few hours, and that of thyroid hormones is a few days. In contrast, peptide and catecholamine hormones, which do not bind to carrier proteins, have plasma half-lives measured in minutes.

TARGET GLAND CONCEPT

A hormone may have one target tissue or it may affect a number of tissues. A target tissue was classically defined as having a unique biochemical or physiologic response to a hormone. For example, the thyroid is a specific target gland of TSH; TSH increases the number and size of the thyroid acinar cells and enhances all of the enzymatic steps involved in thyroid hormone biosynthesis. In contrast, insulin affects many tissues. Insulin enhances glucose uptake and oxidation in muscle, lipogenesis in fat, amino acid transport in liver and lymphocytes, and protein synthesis in liver and muscle, to name a few effects. More recently, with the delineation of specific cell surface and intracellular hormone receptors, the definition of a target has been expanded to include any tissue in which the hormone can be demonstrated to bind to a receptor, whether or not a classic biochemical or physiologic response has been determined (eg, insulin binding to endothelial cells). This definition is also incomplete, but it has heuristic merit, since it recognizes that not all actions of hormones have been elucidated.

Several factors determine the overall response of a target tissue to a hormone. The local concentration of a hormone around the target tissue depends upon (1) the rate of synthesis and secretion of the hormone; (2) the association-dissociation constants of the hormone with specific carrier proteins in the plasma, if such exist; (3) the rate of conversion of an inactive or suboptimally active form of the hormone into the active form; and (4) the rate of clearance of the hormone from blood by degradation or excretion, primarily accomplished by the liver and kidneys. The actual response then depends upon (1) the relative activity or state of occupancy of the specific hormone receptors on the plasma membrane or within the cytoplasm or nucleus; and (2) the postreceptor sensitization-desensitization of the cell. Alterations of any of these processes can result in a change of the hormonal activity on a given target tissue.

FEEDBACK CONTROL CONCEPT

Physiologic hormone levels in blood are maintained by a variety of homeostatic mechanisms that entail precise signaling between the hormone-secreting gland and the target tissue, and this often involves one or more intermediate glands. **Negative**

Table 35–1. Characteristics of hormone transport proteins.

Hormone	Primary Binding Protein	Percent Hormone Bound
Aldosterone	Albumin	50
Hydrocortisone	CBG	90
Estrogen	SHBG	Uncertain
Testosterone	SHBG/albumin	97
Triiodothyronine (T_3)	TBG	99.7
Thyroxine (T_4)	TBG	99.97

CBG, cortisol-binding globulin; SHBG, sex hormone–binding globulin; TBG, thyroid hormone–binding globulin.

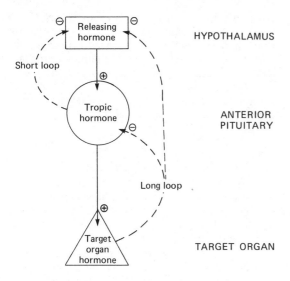

Figure 35–1. Example of the negative feedback control system used to regulate the function of the thyroid, adrenal, ovary, and testes.

feedback control is commonly employed, especially by the hypothalamic-pituitary target gland systems. An example is illustrated in Fig 35–1. A hypothalamic releasing hormone stimulates the synthesis and release of an anterior pituitary hormone, which in turn stimulates the production of the target organ hormone. High levels of the latter inhibit the system by decreasing hypothalamic hormone synthesis and action, while low levels result in the system being activated at the level of the hypothalamus. A unique feature of this particular axis is that the pituitary hormone may itself blunt the system by **"short-loop" feedback inhibition** of its own synthesis. This tonic system provides for exquisite control of the plasma hormone level and also illustrates that there are several hormones and several target tissues within one endocrine system. Such control loops are recognized for the adrenal, thyroid, testicular, and ovarian systems.

In other instances, negative feedback regulation is accomplished through various metabolites or substrates whose plasma concentration is changed as a result of a hormone acting on a target cell. For example, an increased plasma glucose concentration (hyperglycemia) provokes a measured release of insulin, which enhances glucose uptake and utilization by a number of tissues, thereby decreasing the plasma glucose to a normal level and, in turn, diminishing insulin release. Under certain pathologic conditions, the insulin response may be excessive, in which case hypoglycemia ensues. The physiologic response to this life-threatening condition is the release of catecholamines, growth hormone, glucagon, ACTH, vasopressin, and angiotensin II, all of which act to increase the plasma glucose concentration. Thus, a complex network has evolved to regulate a critical metabolite (in this example, glucose) which is required for brain function.

In other cases, hormones exert **positive feedback control.** For example, estrogen and progesterone are required for the acute burst of LH secretion that results in ovulation and follicular luteinization and the further production of these steroid hormones. In many instances, the feedback loops have not been established, usually because the end products of the action of the hormone are not known.

A number of **pathophysiologic events,** including shock, trauma, hypoglycemia, pain, and stress, affect the hypothalamic-pituitary target gland axis through higher brain centers. These stimuli have profound effects on catecholamine and growth hormone metabolism and on the function of the adrenal cortex, thyroid, and gonads, but the precise components of these circuits are still poorly defined.

Endocrine and metabolic diseases result from the disruption of these normal feedback control mechanisms, and diagnostic perturbations of these systems (eg, the metyrapone test; see p 554) are used to distinguish normal from pathologic conditions.

HORMONE RECEPTORS

General Features of Receptors

All hormones initiate their biologic effects by binding to specific cell-associated recognition molecules called receptors. A target tissue can be defined by its ability to bind selectively a given hormone via such a receptor. This can be quantitated by using radioactively labeled **ligands** that mimic hormone binding. Several features of this interaction are important. (1) The radioactivity must not alter the biologic activity of the ligand. (2) The binding should be specific, ie, displaceable by unlabeled **agonist** or **antagonist.** (3) Binding should be saturable. (4) Binding should occur within the concentration range of the expected biologic response. The receptors for peptide, protein, and glycoprotein hormones are located in the plasma membrane of the cell, and those for steroid and thyroid hormones are in the cytoplasmic or nuclear compartments.

Binding & Coupling Domains of Receptors

Receptors have 2 functional domains: one region recognizes and **binds the hormone** and the other **transduces a signal** that ultimately regulates an intracellular function, usually by changing the amount or activity of an enzyme. The demonstration that these 2 functions reside in a single molecule was accomplished very recently. The β-adrenergic receptor, which binds ligands with the appropriate specificity and affinity, was purified. The "activating" or "coupling" function of this preparation was demonstrated in an ingenious way. Red blood cells from the toad *Xenopus laevis* have no β-adrenergic receptors and thus do not show stimulation of adenylate cyclase in response to adrenergic agonists. These cells do have all of the other components of the adenylate cyclase system (see Chapter 36). The purified β-adrenergic receptor was incorporated into the plasma membrane of the toad erythrocytes. Membranes isolated from these cells bound the β-adrenergic ligand, and adenylate cyclase was then stimulated—thus demonstrating the bifunctional nature of the receptor.

In many cases, the amino acid sequences of these domains in peptide hormone receptors have been identified. Hormone analogs with specific amino acid substitutions have been used to define the 2 domains of the receptor and to alter the biologic activity of the hormone. It is the coupling of binding to signal transduction, so-called **receptor-effector coupling,** that provides the first step in the amplification of the hormonal response and distinguishes the target cell receptor from plasma carrier proteins, which only bind the hormone. This dual function ultimately defines a receptor and a target tissue.

Comparison of Receptors & Transport Proteins

It is important to distinguish the binding of hormones to receptors from the association hormones have with various transport (carrier) proteins. Table 35–2 illustrates several comparative features. Thousands of receptor molecules per cell bind the ligand, and there is high binding affinity and specificity. Receptors are capable of recognizing and selecting specific molecules against a concentration gradient of 10^6 or 10^7, and this binding is saturable at physiologic concentrations of the hormone. Receptor-hormone interactions exhibit a salt, temperature, and pH dependency that is characteristic for each hormone. Binding is by **hydrophobic** and **electrostatic** mechanisms and thus is readily reversible except in special cases.

Relationship Between Receptor Occupancy & Biologic Effect

The concentrations of hormone required for

Table 35–2. Comparison of hormone receptors with transport proteins.

Feature	Receptors	Plasma Transport Proteins
Concentration	Very low (thousands/cell)	Very high (billions/μL)
Binding affinity	Very high (10^{-11}–10^{-9} mol/L)	Low (10^{-7}–10^{-5} mol/L)
Binding specificity	High	Low
Saturability at physiologic concentrations	Yes	No
Reversibility	Yes	Yes
Signal transduction	Yes	No

half-maximal displacement of a radioactive ligand and for elicitation of a specific biologic response are often very similar (Fig 35–2A). This is especially true for steroid hormones, but some peptide hormones also exhibit the same characteristics. This is remarkable, considering the many steps that must occur between hormone binding and complex responses, such as enzyme induction, cell lysis, and amino acid transport. **In other instances, there is a marked dissociation of these 2 processes,** so that a maximal biologic effect occurs when only a small percentage of the receptors are occupied (Fig 35–2B, effect 2). Those receptors not involved in the elicitation of the response are said to be **spare receptors.**

Spare receptors are observed in the response of several polypeptide hormones and are thought to provide a means of increasing the sensitivity of a target cell to activation by low concentrations of hormone and to provide a reservoir of receptors. The concept of spare receptors is an operational one and may depend on which aspect of the response is examined and which tissue is involved. For example, there is excellent

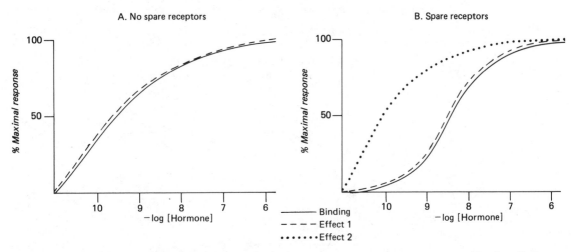

Figure 35–2. A comparison of hormone binding with biologic effect in the absence *(A)* or presence *(B,* effect 2) of spare receptors. In some cases, one biologic effect may be tightly coupled to binding in a tissue, whereas another effect shows the spare receptor phenomenon (compare effects 1 and 2 in *B*).

agreement between LH binding and cAMP production in granulosa cells (there generally are no spare receptors when any hormone activates adenylate cyclase), but steroidogenesis in these cells, which is cAMP-dependent, occurs when fewer than 1% of the receptors are occupied (compare effect 1 with effect 2, Fig 35–2B). Transcription of the phosphoenolpyruvate carboxykinase gene is repressed when far fewer than 1% of liver cell insulin receptors are occupied, whereas in thymocytes there is a high correlation between insulin binding and amino acid transport. Other examples of the dissociation of receptor binding and biologic effects include the effects of catecholamines on muscle contraction, lipolysis, and ion transport. The presumption is that these end responses reflect a cascade or multiplier effect of the hormone. Variable sensitivities of different responses even within the same cell have been noted. Successively greater degrees of occupancy of the adipose cell insulin receptor increase (in sequence) lipolysis, glucose oxidation, amino acid transport, and protein synthesis.

Regulation of Receptors

The number of receptors on or in a cell is in a dynamic state and can be regulated physiologically or be influenced by diseases or therapeutic measures. Most is known about the plasma membrane receptors. Both the receptor concentration and the affinity of hormone binding can be regulated in plasma membrane. These changes can be acute and can significantly affect hormone responsiveness of the cell. For instance, cells exposed to β-adrenergic agonists for minutes to hours no longer activate adenylate cyclase in response to the addition of more agonist, and the biologic response is lost. This **desensitization** occurs by 2 mechanisms. The first involves a loss of receptors from the plasma membrane. This **"down regulation"** involves the internal sequestration of receptors,

thereby segregating them from the other components of the response system including the regulatory and catalytic subunits of adenylate cyclase (see Chapter 36). Removal of the agonist results in the return of receptors to the cell surface and restoration of hormonal sensitivity. A second form of desensitization of the β-adrenergic system involves the covalent modification of receptor by phosphorylation. This cAMP-dependent process entails no change in receptor number and no translocation. Reconstitution experiments, similar to those described above, show that the phosphorylated receptor is unable to activate cyclase, so that the activation and hormone binding functions are uncoupled. Other examples of physiologic adaptation accomplished through "down regulation" of receptor number by the homologous hormone include insulin, glucagon, TRH, growth hormone, LH, FSH, and catecholamines. A few hormones, such as angiotensin II and prolactin, **"up regulate"** their receptors. These changes in receptor number can occur rapidly (minutes to hours) and are probably an important means of regulating biologic responses.

How the loss of receptors affects the biologic response elicited at a given hormone concentration depends on whether or not there are spare receptors. Fig 35–3 illustrates the effects of a 5-fold loss of receptors on the concentration-response curve in both conditions. In condition A (with no spare receptors), the maximal response obtained is 20% that of control; hence, the effect is on the "V_{max}." In condition B (with spare receptors), the maximal response is obtained but at 5 times the originally effective hormone concentration, analogous to a "K_m" effect.

Structure of Receptors

The structure of the acetylcholine receptor has been identified through molecular cloning techniques and is known to consist of 4 protein subunits. Much

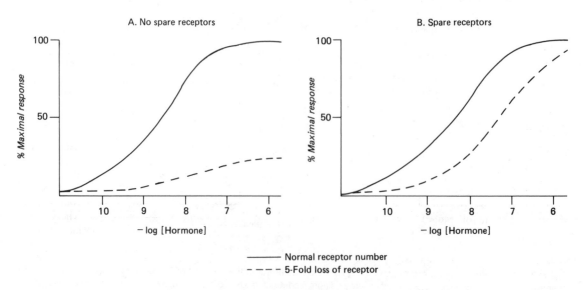

Figure 35–3. Effect of a 5-fold loss of receptors on a biologic effect in a system that lacks *(A)* or has *(B)* spare receptors.

less is known about the structure of other peptide hormone receptors, although details are accumulating about the insulin and growth peptide receptors (see Chapter 42). Peptide hormone receptors are assumed to have a fundamental protein component, because of their sensitivity to a variety of peptidases and proteolytic enzymes. Hormone binding appears to require disulfide bonds, phospholipid, and carbohydrate moieties in many instances. Steroid hormone receptors are also proteins, some of which are heterodimers (eg, progesterone receptor), while others are relatively large single proteins. Receptors are present in very small amounts; thus, purification and characterization have been difficult. Recombinant DNA techniques may provide the requisite amounts of material for such studies.

Receptor Movement in Target Cells

There is some evidence that peptide hormone receptors move within the plasma membrane after ligand binding occurs, but the relationship of this movement to the action of the hormone is not clear. Most is known about the movement of insulin receptors. Conditions that decrease membrane fluidity (ie, an increased incorporation of saturated fatty acids into the membrane) decrease receptor mobility and decrease insulin binding. Support for the notion that insulin induces receptors to aggregate and therefore to move is provided by experiments in which various anti-insulin receptor antibodies were used. The intact, bivalent IgG binds to and cross-links receptors and mimics the antilipolytic action of insulin in the adipocyte. A monovalent Fab' antibody fragment, which cannot cross-link, binds to the receptor but does not mimic insulin action. However, if there is a subsequent addition of anti-F(ab)'$_2$ antiserum, which cross-links the Fab'-receptor complexes, an insulinlike action results.

Apart from the exceptional example of **epidermal growth factor (EGF),** there is little to suggest that the hormone-receptor complex must enter the cell to act. Intact insulin (along with other hormones) is certainly found within the cell, often in association with lysosomes and other organelles, but this may represent degradative or "down regulation" pathways. The cytoplasmic and nuclear receptors for steroids and thyroid hormones are a different case, as discussed in detail in Chapter 36.

HORMONE RECEPTORS & DISEASE

The realization that **certain diseases involve abnormalities of receptor function** followed the basic elucidation of the role that receptors play in hormone action. Three general categories of receptor-related defects are shown in Table 35–3. In the first category,

Table 35–3. Hormone receptors and disease.

Disease	Receptor	Problem
Graves' disease (hyperthyroidism)	TSH	Antibody stimulates TSH receptor
Acanthosis nigricans with insulin resistance	Insulin	Antibody blocks insulin binding to receptor
Myasthenia gravis	Acetylcholine	Antibody enhances turnover of the acetylcholine receptor
Asthma	β-Adrenergic receptor	Antibody blocks β-adrenergic binding
Congenital nephrogenic diabetes insipidus	ADH	Receptor deficiency
Testicular feminization syndrome	Androgen	Receptor deficiency
Pseudohypoparathyroidism	PTH	Receptor deficiency
Vitamin D – resistant rickets type II	Calcitriol	Receptor deficiency
Obesity	Insulin	Hormone binding decreased
Diabetes mellitus type II (non – insulin-dependent diabetes mellitus [NIDDM])	Insulin	Hormone binding decreased

antibodies directed against a specific hormone receptor are responsible for the disease. These antibodies of the IgG class can block hormone binding (acanthosis nigricans with insulin resistance; asthma), mimic hormone binding (Graves' disease), or enhance receptor turnover (myasthenia gravis).

In the second category, no hormone binding to receptor can be detected. Whether receptors are absent in these diseases or present but defective cannot be determined as yet, since the assays for most receptors depend upon hormone binding.

The third category consists of diseases involving abnormal receptor regulation. Patients with obesity and those with type II diabetes mellitus and obesity often manifest glucose intolerance and insulin resistance in spite of elevated plasma insulin levels. These individuals have fewer insulin receptors ("down regulation") on target cells such as fat, liver, and muscle. With weight reduction, the plasma insulin level decreases, the number of receptors increases, insulin sensitivity improves, and glucose intolerance is reduced. Recent studies of the molecular basis of cancer strongly suggest that abnormalities of growth factor receptor-effector coupling can account for the uncontrolled growth of malignant cells. These examples are illustrative of the many hormone receptor-mediated diseases.

•   •   •

References

Ginsberg BH: Synthesis and regulation of receptors for polypeptide hormones. Pages 59–97 in: *Biological Regulation and Development*. Vol 3B. Yamamoto K (editor). Plenum Press, 1985.

Granner DK, Lee F: The multiple endocrine neoplasia syndromes. Chapter 76 in: *Comprehensive Textbook of Oncology*. Moosa AR, Robson MC, Schimpff SC (editors). Williams & Wilkins, 1984.

Mishina M et al: Expression of functional acetylcholine receptor from cloned cDNAs. *Nature* 1984;**307**:604.

Roth J, Taylor SI: Receptors for peptide hormones: Alterations in disease of humans. *Annu Rev Physiol* 1982;**44**:639.

Roth J et al: The evolutionary origins of hormones, neurotransmitters, and other extracellular messengers. *N Engl J Med* 1982;**306**:523.

Hormone Action | 36

Daryl K. Granner, MD

CLASSIFICATION OF HORMONES

Hormone action at the cellular level begins with the association of the hormone and its specific receptor. Hormones can be classified by the location of the receptor and by the nature of the signal used to mediate hormone action within the cell. Such a classification is illustrated in Table 36–1.

The hormones in group I are all lipophilic and, with the exception of T_3 and T_4, are derived from cholesterol. These hormones readily traverse the plasma membrane and encounter receptors either in the cytosol or in the nucleus. The ligand-receptor complex is assumed to be the intracellular messenger in this group.

The second major group of hormones consists of those that bind to the plasma membrane of the target cell. Hormones that bind to the surface of cells communicate with intracellular metabolic processes through intermediary molecules, so-called **second messengers** (the hormone itself is the first messenger), which are generated as a consequence of the ligand-receptor interaction. The second-messenger concept arose from Sutherland's observation that epinephrine binds to the plasma membrane of pigeon erythrocytes and increases intracellular cAMP. This was followed by a series of experiments in which cAMP was found to mediate the metabolic effects of many hormones. Hormones that clearly employ this mechanism are shown in group II.A. Several hormones, many of which were previously thought to affect cAMP, appear to use calcium or phosphatidylinositide metabolites (or both) as the intracellular signal. These are shown in group II.B. The intracellular messenger has not been definitively identified for group II.C, a large and very interesting class of hormones. Several candidates have

Table 36–1. Classification of hormones by mechanism of action.

Group I. Hormones that bind to intracellular receptors	
Glucocorticoids	Androgens
Mineralocorticoids	Thyroid hormones (T_3 and T_4)
Estrogens	Calcitriol ($1,25[OH]_2$-D_3)
Progestins	

Group II. Hormones that bind to cell surface receptors	
A. The second messenger is cAMP:	
Adrenocorticotropic hormone (ACTH)	Parathyroid hormone (PTH)
Luteinizing hormone (LH)	Calcitonin
Follicle-stimulating hormone (FSH)	Glucagon
Thyroid-stimulating hormone (TSH)	β-Adrenergic catecholamines
Human chorionic gonadotropin (hCG)	α_2-Adrenergic catecholamines
Melanocyte-stimulating hormone (MSH)	Somatostatin
Lipotropin (LPH)	Corticotropin-releasing hormone (CRH)
Angiotensin II	Opioids
Antidiuretic hormone (ADH)	
B. The second messenger is calcium or phosphatidylinositides (or both):	
Vasopressin	Angiotensin II
Thyrotropin-releasing hormone (TRH)	Gonadotropin-releasing hormone (GnRH)
α_1-Adrenergic catecholamines	Acetylcholine (muscarinic)
C. The intracellular messenger is unknown:	
Insulin	Nerve growth factor (NGF)
Insulinlike growth factors (IGF-I, IGF-II)	Epidermal growth factor (EGF)
	Fibroblast growth factor (FGF)
Growth hormone (GH)	Oxytocin
Prolactin (PRL)	
Chorionic somatomammotropin (CS)	

been proposed as mediators of the actions of insulin—eg, cAMP, cGMP, H_2O_2, calcium, several small peptides, a phospholipid, insulin itself, and the insulin receptor—but none of these fulfill the necessary criteria as yet. It would not be surprising if a number of mediators or different mechanisms are involved in the action of this group of hormones. A few hormones fit into more than one category, and assignments change with new information.

MECHANISM OF ACTION OF GROUP I HORMONES

STEROL-DERIVED HORMONES

The general features of the action of this group of hormones are illustrated in Fig 36–1. These lipophilic molecules diffuse through the plasma membrane of all cells but only encounter their specific, high-affinity receptor in target cells. The hormone-receptor complex next undergoes a temperature- and salt-dependent "activation" reaction that results in size, conformation, and surface charge changes that render it able to bind to chromatin. Whether this association and "activation" process occurs in the cytoplasm or nucleus is debatable but not crucial to understanding the whole process. The hormone-receptor complex binds to specific regions of DNA and activates or inactivates specific genes. **By selectively affecting gene transcription and the production of the respective mRNAs, the amounts of specific proteins are changed and metabolic processes are influenced.** The effect of each of these hormones is quite specific; generally, the hormone affects less than 1% of the proteins or mRNA in a target cell. This discussion has concentrated on nuclear actions of steroid hormones because these are quite well defined. Direct actions in the cytoplasm and upon various organelles and membranes have also been described.

An effect of estrogens and glucocorticoids on mRNA degradation has been demonstrated, and it is known that glucocorticoids affect posttranslational processing of some proteins. However, most evidence suggests that these hormones exert their predominant effect on gene transcription. Although the biochemistry of gene transcription in mammalian cells is not well understood, a general model of the structural requirements for steroid regulation of gene transcription can be drawn (Fig 36–2). Steroid-regulated genes must be in regions of "open" or transcriptionally active chromatin (depicted as the bubble in Fig 36–1), as defined by their susceptibility to digestion by the enzyme **DNase I. The genes studied to date have at least 2**

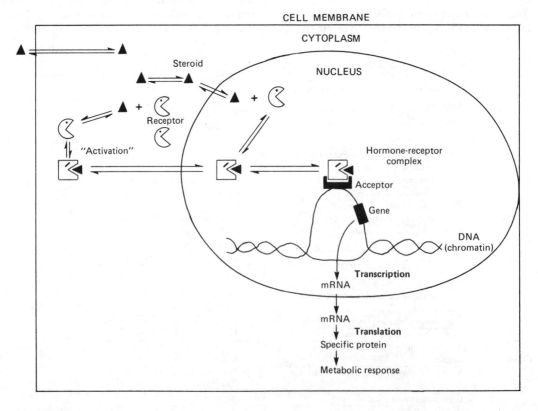

Figure 36–1. The steroid binds to an intracellular receptor and causes a conformational change of the latter. This complex then binds to a specific region on chromatin, which results in the activation of a restricted number of genes.

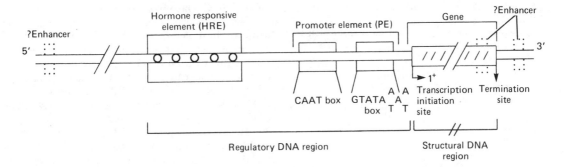

Figure 36–2. Structural requirements for steroid regulation of gene transcription.

separate regulatory elements (control sites) in the DNA sequence immediately 5′ of the transcription initiation site (Fig 36–2). The first of these, the **promoter element (PE),** is generic, since it is present in all genes. This element specifies the site of RNA polymerase II attachment to DNA and therefore the accuracy of transcript initiation (see Chapter 31).

A second element, the **hormone responsive element (HRE),** has been identified in many genes regulated by steroid hormones. This is located slightly farther 5′ than the PE and may consist of several discrete elements. The HRE presumably modulates the frequency of transcript initiation and is less dependent on position and orientation; in these respects, it resembles the transcription **enhancer elements** found in other genes (see Chapter 31). Generally, the HRE is found within 250 nucleotides of the transcription initiation site. However, the precise location of the HRE varies from gene to gene, ranging from −20 to −10 for the pro-opiomelanocortin (POMC) gene to about −2600 for the uteroglobin gene.

The identification of an HRE requires that it bind the hormone-receptor complex more avidly than does surrounding DNA or DNA from another source. In the cases just cited, such specific binding has been demonstrated. The HRE must also confer hormone responsiveness. Putative regulatory sequence DNA can be ligated to reporter genes to assess this point. Usually, these **"fusion genes"** contain reporter genes not ordinarily influenced by the hormone, and often these genes are not normally expressed in the tissue being tested. Commonly used reporter genes are globin, thymidine kinase, and bacterial chloramphenicol acetyltransferase. The "fusion gene" is transfected into a target cell, and if the hormone now regulates the transcription of the reporter gene, one has functionally defined an HRE. Position, orientation, and base substitution effects can be precisely defined using this technique. Exactly how the hormone-receptor interaction with the HRE affects transcription is an area of active investigation. Transcript initiation is a probable control site, but effects on elongation and termination might also occur. Control sites farther 5′ from the initiation site, or 3′ downstream, either within or beyond the gene, have been proposed. Finally *trans*-acting control mechanisms (eg, from another chromosome) may also be operative.

IODOTHYRONINE HORMONES

Thyroid hormones probably act in a manner similar to that of steroids (Fig 36–1). The exception to the general mechanism discussed above has been that the association of T_3 with its high-affinity receptor occurs entirely within the nucleus rather than in the cytoplasm. (The progesterone receptor has recently been shown to reside in the nucleus; if this proves true of other steroid hormones, this distinction will not apply.) Thyroid hormones also affect the amount of specific mRNAs (growth hormone, malic enzyme, fatty acid synthase), but the latency of such effects has made more precise studies of the mechanism more difficult than in the case of the steroid hormones.

MECHANISM OF ACTION OF GROUP II (PEPTIDE) HORMONES

The general features of peptide hormone receptors are discussed in Chapter 35. The mechanism of action of this group of hormones can best be discussed in terms of their intracellular messengers rather than by any distinguishing features of their receptors, if there are any.

cAMP AS THE SECOND MESSENGER

cAMP (cyclic AMP, 3′,5′-adenylic acid; see p 178), a ubiquitous nucleotide derived from ATP through the action of the enzyme adenylate cyclase, **plays a crucial role in the action of a number of hormones.** The intracellular level of cAMP is increased or decreased by various hormones (Table 36–2), and this effect varies from tissue to tissue.

Table 36–2. Subclassification of group II.A hormones.

Hormones That Stimulate Adenylate Cyclase (H$_s$)	Hormones That Inhibit Adenylate Cyclase (H$_i$)
Glucagon	Somatostatin
β-Adrenergics	Angiotensin II
ACTH	α$_2$-Adrenergics
CRH	Opioids
LH	
FSH	
TSH	
ADH	
PTH	
hCG	
MSH	
LPH	
Calcitonin	

Epinephrine causes large increases of cAMP in muscle and relatively small changes in liver. The opposite is true of glucagon. Tissues that respond to several hormones of this group do so through unique receptors converging upon a single adenylate cyclase molecule. The best example of this is the adipose cell, in which epinephrine, ACTH, TSH, glucagon, MSH, and vasopressin (ADH) stimulate adenylate cyclase and increase cAMP. Combinations of maximally effective concentrations are not additive, and treatments that destroy one receptor have no effect on the cellular response to other hormones.

Adenylate Cyclase System

The components of this system in mammalian cells are illustrated in Fig 36–3. **The interaction of the hormone with its receptor results in the activation or inactivation of adenylate cyclase.** This process is mediated by at least 2 GTP-dependent regulatory proteins, designated G$_s$ (stimulatory) and G$_i$ (inhibitory) (sometimes referred to as N$_s$ and N$_i$), each of which is composed of 3 subunits, α, β, and γ (Fig 36–4). Adenylate cyclase, located on the inner surface of the plasma membrane, catalyzes the formation of cAMP from ATP in the presence of magnesium (see Fig 25–14).

What was originally conceived of as a single protein with 2 functional domains is now viewed as a system of extraordinary complexity. Over the past 15 years, a number of studies have established the biochemical uniqueness of the hormone receptor and GTP regulatory and catalytic domains of the adenylate cyclase complex, a current model of which is illustrated in Fig 36–3. This model explains how different peptide hormones can either stimulate (s) or inhibit (i) the production of cAMP (Table 36–2).

Two parallel systems, a stimulatory (s) one and an inhibitory (i) one, converge upon a single catalytic molecule (C). Each consists of a receptor, R$_s$ or R$_i$, and regulatory complex, G$_s$ and G$_i$. G$_s$ and G$_i$ are each trimers composed of α, β, and γ subunits (Fig 36–4). The β and γ subunits in G$_s$ appear to be identical to their respective counterparts in G$_i$. Because the α sub-

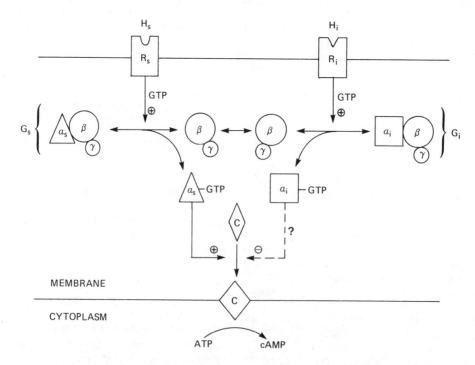

Figure 36–3. The hormone-receptor signal is transmitted through a stimulatory (s) or inhibitory (i) regulatory complex (G$_s$ or G$_i$) to either stimulate (s) or inhibit (i) the activity of adenylate cyclase (C). Adenylate cyclase catalyzes the formation of cAMP from ATP. (Modified, with permission, from Gilman AG: G proteins and dual control of adenylate cyclase. *Cell* 1984;**36**:577. Copyright © the Massachusetts Institute of Technology.)

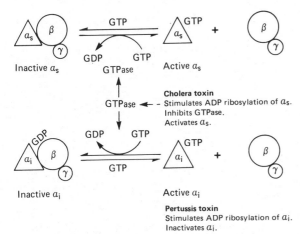

Figure 36–4. An expanded version of the regulatory components of adenylate cyclase. GTP activates G_S by dissociating α_S from β and γ. GTPase reverses this effect, and cholera toxin permanently activates α_S by inhibiting GTPase activity. GTP activates α_i by exchanging with bound GDP. Pertussis toxin acts on the complex through an undefined mechanism.

unit in G_s differs from that in G_i, the proteins are designated α_s (MW 45,000) and α_i (MW 41,000). The binding of a hormone to R_s or R_i results in a receptor-mediated activation of G, which entails Mg^{2+}-dependent binding of GTP by α and the concomitant dissociation of β and γ.

$$\alpha\beta\gamma \xrightleftharpoons[\text{[H--R]}]{\text{GTP}} \alpha \cdot \text{GTP} + \beta\gamma$$

The α_s has intrinsic GTPase activity, and the active form, $\alpha_s \cdot$ GTP, is inactivated upon hydrolysis of the GTP to GDP, and the trimeric G_s complex is reformed. Cholera toxin, known to be an irreversible **activator** of cyclase, causes ADP ribosylation of α_s and in so doing inactivates the GTPase; therefore, α_s is frozen in the active form. The α_i also has a GTPase activity; however, GDP does not freely dissociate from $\alpha_i \cdot$ GDP. The α_i is reactivated by an exchange of GTP for GDP. Pertussis toxin irreversibly activates adenylate cyclase by promoting the ADP ribosylation of α_i, which prevents the α_i subunit from being activated. NaF, another irreversible activator of cyclase, presumably acts on the α_s or α_i subunit, because it affects G_s and G_i similarly. The exact role of each of the α, β, and γ subunits has not been defined. Two possibilities have been tested. The α_s and α_i could interact noncompetitively with C, causing opposite effects; the net effect would depend on the balance of active α_s and active α_i. Unfortunately, active α_i has little inhibitory effect on C in isolated systems. The second possibility, therefore, is that the β subunit of G_i inhibits α_s. In this model, α_i would be an anti-inhibitor of adenylate cyclase by binding β and, as such, would have no direct effect. A role for α_i

in other hormone-mediated membrane processes, such as calcium flux or phosphatidylinositol metabolism, has not been excluded. Many of these components have been purified, including C, which recently was isolated from brain. It is a single polypeptide of MW ~ 120,000. There may be a family of G proteins. **Transducin,** which is important in coupling light to photoactivation in the retina, is closely related to the α subunit of adenylate cyclase, as are the products of the ras oncogenes.

The importance of these components is underscored by an experiment of nature. **Pseudohypoparathyroidism** is a syndrome consisting of a number of congenital defects with associated hypocalcemia and hyperphosphatemia, the biochemical hallmarks of hypoparathyroidism. Some individuals with this syndrome do not have defective parathyroid function; indeed, they secrete large amounts of biologically active PTH. These individuals have target organ resistance on the basis of a receptor defect (see Chapter 35 and Table 35–3). Others are deficient in G protein (probably only the α_s subunit) and thus fail to couple binding to cyclase stimulation. This is a partial defect, and not surprisingly such patients often have evidence of defective responses to other hormones, including TSH, glucagon, and β-adrenergic agents.

Protein Kinase

In **prokaryotic cells,** cAMP binds to a specific protein, called **catabolite regulatory protein (CRP),** which binds directly to DNA and influences gene expression. The analogy of this to steroid hormone action described above is apparent. In **eukaryotic cells,** cAMP binds to a **protein kinase** that is a heterotetrameric molecule consisting of 2 **regulatory** subunits (R) and 2 **catalytic** subunits (C). cAMP binding results in the following reaction:

$$4 \text{ cAMP} + R_2C_2 \rightleftharpoons 2 (R - 2 \text{ cAMP}) + 2 C$$

The R_2C_2 complex has no enzymatic activity, but the binding of cAMP by R dissociates R from C, thereby activating the latter (Fig 36–5). The active C subunit catalyses the transfer of the γ phosphate of ATP (Mg^{2+}) to a serine or threonine residue in a variety of proteins. The consensus phosphorylation sites are -Arg-Arg-X-Ser- and -Lys-Arg-X-X-Ser-, where X can be any amino acid.

Protein kinase activities were originally described as being **cAMP-dependent** or **cAMP-independent.** Table 36–3 shows that this too has become considerably more complex, as protein phosphorylation is now recognized as being an important regulatory mechanism. The kinases listed are all unique molecules and show considerable variability with respect to subunit composition, molecular weight, autophosphorylation, K_m for ATP, and substrate specificity.

The cAMP-dependent protein kinases I and II have been studied in greatest detail. These kinases share a common C subunit and have different R sub-

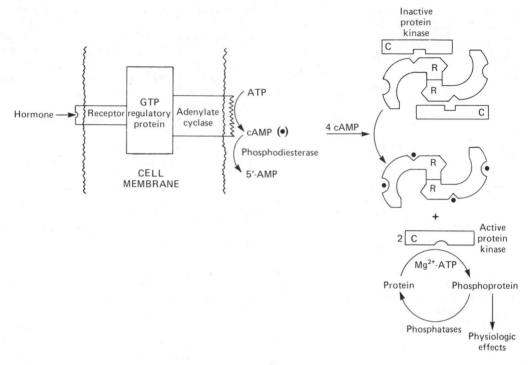

Figure 36—5. Hormonal regulation of cellular processes through cAMP-dependent protein kinases. (Courtesy of J Corbin.)

units. They were originally classified by type on the basis of their different surface charges and hence differential elution from ion exchange chromatography columns (type I is less acidic and elutes at a lower salt concentration than does type II). Most tissues have both forms, but there is a marked species-to-species and tissue-to-tissue variation in the distribution of the 2 isozymes. Recent studies suggest that types I and II respond differently to various combinations of cAMP

Table 36—3. Purified protein kinases.

Hormone-responsive
  cAMP-dependent kinases I and II
  Phosphorylase kinase
  Myosin light chain kinase
  Epidermal growth factor–dependent tyrosine kinase
  Insulin-dependent tyrosine kinase
  Pyruvate dehydrogenase kinase
  Insect cyclic nucleotide–dependent kinase
  Calcium-calmodulin–dependent kinase
  Calcium-phospholipid–dependent kinase
Not known to be hormone-responsive
  cGMP-dependent kinase
  Hemin-dependent eIF-2α kinase
  dsRNA-dependent eIF-2α kinase
  Casein kinases I and II
  Viral tyrosine kinases I, II, and III
  Rhodopsin kinase
  Protease-activated kinase I
May be hormone-responsive
  Casein kinase I
  Protease-activated kinase II

analogs, and this approach may be useful in defining which isozyme mediates a specific biologic response. There is also some evidence that hormone stimulation selectively enhances either type I or type II kinase activity.

Several other protein kinases are involved in hormone action. The role some of these play is illustrated in Figs 36–6 and 36–7 and in the later parts of this chapter. The epidermal growth factor and insulin-dependent kinases are unique in that the enzymatic activity resides within the hormone receptor and depends upon ligand-receptor binding for activation (see Chapter 42). Another distinguishing feature is that these kinases preferentially phosphorylate tyrosine residues, and tyrosine phosphorylation is infrequent in mammalian cells. The role these receptor-associated kinases play in hormone action is not clear, but it is possible that the hormone initiates a phosphorylation cascade and that one or more products of the cascade are the intracellular messenger.

Phosphoproteins

The effects of cAMP in eukaryotic cells are all thought to be mediated by protein phosphorylation-dephosphorylation. The control of any of the effects of cAMP, including such diverse processes as steroidogenesis, secretion, ion transport, carbohydrate and fat metabolism, enzyme induction, gene regulation, and cell growth and replication, could be conferred by a specific protein kinase, a specific **phosphatase,** or by specific substrates for phosphorylation. In some instances, a **phosphoprotein** that is a known

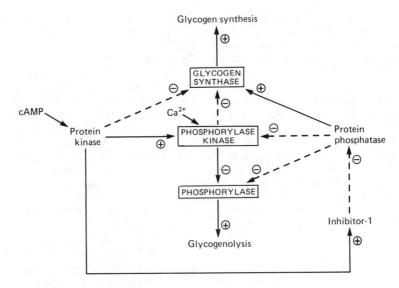

Figure 36–6. The regulation of glycogen metabolism by phosphorylation-dephosphorylation reactions. This is a simplified scheme in which the 3 interconvertible enzyme systems are shown in boxes. Actions of either the protein kinases or the protein phosphatases that lead to an increase in activity are shown by the solid arrows, and those that lead to a decrease in activity are shown by the broken arrows. This proposed scheme shows the dephosphorylation reactions that lead to activity changes of the interconvertible enzymes as mediated by a single protein phosphatase. Also shown in this scheme is the possibility that phosphorylase kinase may play a significant role in the phosphorylation of glycogen synthase. (Slightly modified and reproduced, with permission, from Lee EY et al: The phosphoprotein phosphatases. *Adv Cyclic Nucleotide Res* 1980;**13**:95.)

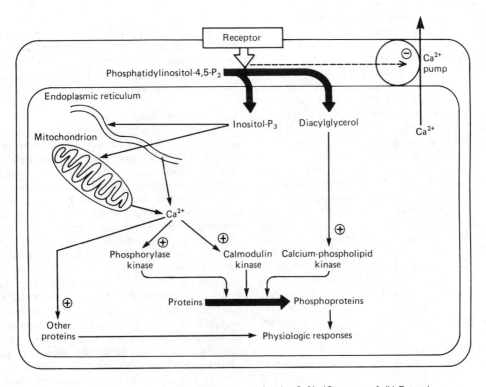

Figure 36–7. The regulation of hormone action by Ca^{2+}. (Courtesy of JH Exton.)

participant in a metabolic pathway has been identified; however, in most processes cited above, the phosphoproteins involved have not been identified. These substrates may help define a target tissue and certainly are involved in defining the extent of the response within a given cell. Many proteins can be phosphorylated, including casein, histones, and protamine; these may be epiphenomena, although they are useful for assaying protein kinase activity. Until recently, the only actions of cAMP that had been defined were actions that occurred outside the nucleus. Effects of cAMP on the transcription of the prolactin, phosphoenolpyruvate carboxykinase, tyrosine aminotransferase, and discoidin genes have now been described. Whether these nuclear actions of cAMP occur by protein phosphorylation or by a CRP-like mechanism is not known.

Phosphodiesterases

Actions caused by hormones that increase cAMP concentration can be terminated in a number of ways, including the hydrolysis of cAMP by **phosphodiesterases.** The presence of these hydrolytic enzymes ensures a rapid turnover of the signal (cAMP) and hence a rapid termination of the biologic process once the hormonal stimulus is removed. cAMP phosphodiesterases exist in low and high K_m forms and are themselves subject to regulation by hormones as well as by intracellular messengers such as calcium, probably acting through calmodulin. For example, acetylcholine decreases the intrathyroidal cAMP concentration by such a mechanism. Inhibitors of phosphodiesterase, most notably methylated xanthine derivatives such as caffeine, increase intracellular cAMP and mimic or prolong the actions of hormones.

Phosphoprotein Phosphatases

Another means of controlling hormone action is the regulation of the protein dephosphorylation reaction. The **phosphoprotein phosphatases** are themselves subject to regulation by phosphorylation-dephosphorylation and by a variety of other substances. Most is known about the role of phosphatase in regulation of glycogen metabolism in muscle. In this tissue, 2 types of phosphoprotein phosphatases have been described. Type I preferentially dephosphorylates the β subunit of phosphorylase kinase, whereas type II dephosphorylates the α subunit. Two heat-stable protein inhibitors regulate type I phosphatase activity. Inhibitor-1 is phosphorylated and activated by cAMP-dependent protein kinase, and inhibitor-2, which may be a subunit of the inactive phosphatase, is also phosphorylated, possibly by glycogen synthase kinase-3. Phosphorylation of inhibitor-2 also results in activation of the phosphatase. This system is even more complex, since activity of the phosphatases appears to be affected by glycogen, glucose 6-phosphate, adenylate, uridylate, and various metals.

This difficult topic is summarized in Chapter 19 and Fig 36–6, which shows how the cAMP-sensitive protein phosphatase and inhibitor-1 protein regulate the activity of many of the enzymes involved in glycogen metabolism.

Extracellular cAMP

Some cAMP leaves cells and can be readily detected in extracellular fluids. The action of glucagon on liver and vasopressin or PTH on kidney is reflected in elevated levels of cAMP in plasma and urine, respectively; this has led to diagnostic tests of target organ responsiveness. Extracellular cAMP has little if any biologic activity in mammals, but it is an extremely important intercellular messenger in lower eukaryotes and prokaryotes.

Guanylate Cyclase; cGMP; cGMP-Dependent Protein Kinase

cGMP is found in most cells and for a time was thought to be the counterpart of cAMP. The enzyme **guanylate cyclase** is found in the cytosol and is stimulated by nitroprusside and related compounds, but attempts to find hormones that directly regulate this enzyme have been generally unsuccessful. There is no compelling evidence that cGMP is involved in any of the familiar hormone responses or as a negative feedback inhibitor to counteract cAMP. cGMP kinase has some structural homology with cAMP-dependent protein kinase, but it is a single-chain peptide without separate regulatory and catalytic subunits.

HORMONES THAT ACT THROUGH CALCIUM OR PHOSPHATIDYLINOSITIDES

Ionized calcium is an important regulator of a variety of cellular processes including muscle contraction, stimulus-secretion coupling, the blood clotting cascade, enzyme activity, and membrane excitability. It is also an intracellular messenger of hormone action.

Calcium Metabolism

The extracellular calcium (Ca^{2+}) concentration is about 1.2 mmol/L and is very rigidly controlled (see Chapter 39). The intracellular concentration of this free ion is much lower, 0.1–10 μmol/L, and the concentration associated with intracellular organelles such as mitochondria and endoplasmic reticula is in the range of 1–20 μmol/L. In spite of this large concentration gradient and a favorable transmembrane electrical gradient, Ca^{2+} is restrained from entering the cell, and an active Ca^{2+}/Mg^{2+}-ATPase-dependent pump extrudes Ca^{2+} in exchange for H^+. There are 2 ways of changing cytosolic Ca^{2+} concentration. The first is to alter plasma membrane permeability or the Ca^{2+}/Mg^{2+}-ATPase-dependent pump (or both). The second is to mobilize (or deposit) Ca^{2+} from the mitochondrial and endoplasmic reticulum pools. **Certain hormones (class II.B) enhance membrane permeability to Ca^{2+} and increase Ca^{2+} influx.**

Two observations led to the current understanding of how Ca^{2+} serves as an intracellular messenger of hormone action. First was the ability to quantitate the rapid changes of intracellular Ca^{2+} concentration that are implicit in its role as an intracellular messenger. This was provided by a variety of techniques, including the use of Quin 2, a fluorescent Ca^{2+} chelator. The acetoxymethylester of Quin 2 readily enters cells, wherein the ester is hydrolyzed. The free compound emits fluorescence in a Ca^{2+}-dependent manner. Rapid changes of intracellular Ca^{2+} in the submicromolar range can be quantitated using this technique. Defining the intracellular target of Ca^{2+} action was the second important observation linking this ion to hormone action. The discovery of a Ca^{2+}-dependent regulator of phosphodiesterase activity provided the basis for understanding how Ca^{2+} and cAMP interact within cells.

Calmodulin

The calcium-dependent regulatory protein is now referred to as **calmodulin**, a 17,000-MW protein that is homologous to the muscle protein troponin C in structure and function (see Chapter 34). Calmodulin has four Ca^{2+} binding sites, and full occupancy of these sites leads to a marked conformational change, so that most of the molecule assumes an alpha-helical structure. This conformational change is presumably linked to calmodulin's ability to activate or inactivate enzymes. The interaction of Ca^{2+} with calmodulin (with the resultant change of activity of the latter) is conceptually similar to the binding of cAMP to protein kinase and the subsequent activation of this molecule. Calmodulin is often one of numerous subunits of complex proteins and is particularly involved in regulating various kinases and enzymes of cyclic nucleotide generation and degradation. A partial list of the enzymes regulated directly or indirectly by Ca^{2+}, probably through calmodulin, is given in Table 36–4.

In addition to its effects on enzymes and ion transport, Ca^{2+}/calmodulin regulates the activity of many structural elements in cells (see Chapter 34). These include the actin-myosin complex of smooth muscle, which is under β-adrenergic control, and various microfilament-mediated processes in noncontractile cells including cell motility, conformation changes, mitosis, granule release, and endocytosis.

Calcium as a Mediator of Hormone Action

A role for ionized calcium in hormone action is suggested by the observations that the effect of many

Table 36–4. Enzymes regulated by calcium/calmodulin.

Adenylate cyclase	NAD kinase
Guanylate cyclase	Ca^{2+}-dependent protein kinase
Cyclic nucleotide phospho-	Glycogen synthase
diesterase	Phosphorylase kinase
Ca^{2+}/Mg^{2+}-ATPase	Pyruvate dehydrogenase
Phospholipase A_2	Ca^{2+}-phospholipid–dependent
Glycerol 3-phosphate dehy-	protein kinase
drogenase	Pyruvate kinase
Pyruvate carboxylase	Myosin kinase

hormones (1) is blunted in Ca^{2+}-free media or when intracellular calcium is depleted; (2) can be mimicked by agents that increase cytosolic Ca^{2+}, such as the Ca^{2+} ionophore A23187; and (3) influences cellular calcium flux. These processes have been studied in some detail in pituitary, smooth muscle, platelets, and salivary gland, but most is probably known about how vasopressin and α-adrenergic catecholamines regulate glycogen metabolism in liver. This is shown schematically in Figs 15–10 and 15–11.

Addition of α_1 agonists or vasopressin to isolated hepatocytes results in a 3-fold increase of cytosolic Ca^{2+} (from 0.2 to 0.6 μmol/L) within a few seconds. This change precedes and equals the increase in phosphorylase a activity, and the hormone concentrations required for both processes are comparable. This effect on Ca^{2+} is inhibited by α_1 antagonists, and removal of the hormone results in a prompt decline of both cytosolic Ca^{2+} and phosphorylase a. The initial source of the Ca^{2+} appears to be the intracellular organelle reservoirs, which seem to be sufficient for the early effects of the hormones. More prolonged action appears to require enhanced influx or inhibition of Ca^{2+} efflux through the Ca^{2+} pump. The latter may depend upon concomitant increases of cAMP.

Phosphorylase activation results from the conversion of phosphorylase b to phosphorylase a through the action of the enzyme phosphorylase b kinase. This enzyme contains calmodulin as its δ subunit, and its activity is increased through a Ca^{2+} concentration range of 0.1–1 μmol/L, the range through which hormones increase Ca^{2+} in liver. The link between Ca^{2+} and phosphorylase activation is definite.

A number of critical metabolic enzymes are regulated by Ca^{2+}, phosphorylation, or both, including glycogen synthase, pyruvate kinase, pyruvate carboxylase, glycerol 3-phosphate dehydrogenase, and pyruvate dehydrogenase. It is uncertain whether calmodulin is directly involved or whether the newly discovered Ca^{2+}-calmodulin–dependent or Ca^{2+}-phospholipid–dependent protein kinases are responsible.

Role of Phosphatidylinositide Metabolism in Ca^{2+}-Dependent Hormone Action

Some signal must provide communication between the hormone receptor on the plasma membrane and the intracellular Ca^{2+} reservoirs. The best candidates appear to be products of phosphatidylinositide metabolism. Phosphatidylinositol-4,5-P_2 is hydrolyzed to **myo-inositol 1,4,5-P_3** and **diacylglycerol** through the action of a phosphodiesterase (Fig 36–7). This reaction occurs within seconds after the addition of either vasopressin or epinephrine to hepatocytes. Myo-inositol-P_3, at 0.1–0.4 μmol/L, releases Ca^{2+} from a variety of membrane and organelle preparations with appropriately rapid kinetics. Attempts to mimic hormone action using this compound, an essential step in establishing this relationship, have met with mixed success, perhaps because it is difficult to get the compound into cells and because it is rapidly hydrolyzed intracellularly. Another product of phosphatidylinositide hydrolysis, 1,2-diacylglycerol, activates a Ca^{2+}-phospholipid-dependent protein kinase by decreasing the K_m of the enzyme for Ca^{2+}. The role this process plays in the action of Ca^{2+}-dependent hormones is under investigation.

Steroidogenic agents all increase the amount of phosphatidic acid, phosphatidylinositol, and polyphosphatidylinositides. These include ACTH and cAMP in the adrenal cortex; angiotensin II, K^+, serotonin, ACTH, and dibutyryl cAMP in the zona glomerulosa of the adrenal; LH in the ovary; and LH and cAMP in the Leydig cells of the testes. These effects occur in vivo and in vitro at physiologic concentrations of the effector and with the proper temporal relationship. Certain phospholipids, namely, diphosphatidylinositide, triphosphatidylinositide, and cardiolipin, mimic the actions of ACTH. They increase cholesterol side-chain cleavage, the rate-limiting step in steroidogenesis. These compounds also enhance the binding of cholesterol to cytochrome $P-450_{scc}$ in vitro, but other mechanisms may be equally important, including the translocation of cholesterol within the mitochondrion.

Several other examples can be cited. The addition of TRH to pituitary cells is followed, within 5–10 seconds, by a marked increase of inositol degradation by phospholipase C. The intracellular levels of inositol diphosphate and triphosphate increase markedly, and this results in mobilization of intracellular calcium. The calcium-dependent protein kinase is activated, which in turn phosphorylates several proteins, one of which is presumably involved in TSH release. Calcium also appears to be the intracellular mediator of GnRH action on LH release. This reaction probably also involves calmodulin.

The roles that Ca^{2+} and phosphatidylinositide breakdown products might play in hormone action are presented in Fig 36–7. In this scheme, the phosphatidylinositide products are the second messengers and Ca^{2+} is actually a tertiary messenger. It is likely that this particular complex networking of the intracellular messengers is not unique.

HORMONES FOR WHICH THE INTRACELLULAR MESSENGER IS UNKNOWN

A large number of important hormones have no identified intracellular messenger. It is curious that these hormones cluster into 2 groups. One group consists of insulin, the insulinlike growth factors (IGF-I and IGF-II), and a variety of other growth factors, all of which may share a common ancestor. The other major group consists of proteins from the growth hormone gene family (growth hormone, prolactin, chorionic somatomammotropin), which clearly are related to one another (see Chapter 37). There is some overlap between these 2 groups, since many of the actions of growth hormone appear to be mediated by IGF-I. Oxytocin appears to stand alone.

Much effort has been directed toward finding the intracellular mediator of insulin action. A variety of candidates including cAMP, cGMP, H_2O_2, Ca^{2+}, and insulin itself have been proposed. Various "mediator" substances of peptide or phospholipid derivation have been found in tissue extracts, but to date these have not been purified or characterized. The recent observation that the insulin receptor has intrinsic tyrosine kinase activity has spurred interest in finding a phosphorylation cascade that might explain the actions of this hormone. This is not an isolated observation, since the epidermal growth factor receptor is also a tyrosine kinase; indeed, this observation led to the studies of the insulin receptor. Finally, the platelet-derived growth factor is also a tyrosine kinase that closely resembles v-sis and c-sis, specific virus-associated and cell-associated oncogene products. Stimulation of platelet-derived growth factor target cells (fibroblasts, glial cells, smooth muscle cells) results in the production of several gene products that appear to be involved in the replication of those cells.

It is probable that entirely different mechanisms of intracellular signaling are employed by this large group of hormones. The traditional messengers certainly do not seem to be involved.

●　　●　　●

References

Anderson JE: The effect of steroid hormones on gene transcription. In: *Biological Regulation and Development*. Goldberger RF, Yamamoto KR (editors). Vol 3B: Hormone Action. Plenum Press, 1985.

Blackmore PF, Exton JH: Mechanisms involved in the actions of calcium dependent hormones. In: *Biochemical Action of the Hormones*. Vol 12. Litwack G (editor). Academic Press, 1985.

Catt KJ, Dufau ML: Hormone action: Control of target-cell function by peptide, thyroid, and steroid hormones. Pages 61–105 in: *Endocrinology and Metabolism*. Felig P et al (editors). McGraw-Hill, 1981.

Codina J et al: Mechanism in the vectorial receptor–adenylate cyclase signal transduction. *Adv Cyclic Nucleotide Res* 1984;**17**:111.

Enhancers and eukaryotic gene expression. In: *Current Communications in Molecular Biology*. Gluzman Y, Shenk T (editors). Cold Spring Harbor Press, 1983.

Gilman A: G proteins and dual control of adenylate cyclase. *Cell* 1984;**36**:577.

Means AR, Chafouleas JG: Calmodulin in endocrine cells. *Annu Rev Physiol* 1982;**44**:667.

Niall HD: The evolution of peptide hormones. *Annu Rev Physiol* 1982;**44**:615.

O'Malley BW: Steroid hormone action in eukaryotic cells. *J Clin Invest* 1984;**74**:307.

Rasmussen H: Calcium and cyclic nucleotides as universal second messengers. *Cell Tissue Interactions* 1978;**32**:243.

Pituitary & Hypothalamic Hormones | 37

Daryl K. Granner, MD

GENERAL STRUCTURE OF THE PITUITARY

The human pituitary, a structure weighing 0.5–0.8 g, is located in the sella turcica at the base of the brain. It lies just behind and below the optic chiasm as an extension from the floor of the hypothalamus and is connected to the diencephalic region of the brain by the pituitary stalk. The pituitary, a gland of tremendous structural and functional complexity, consists of 2 major components: the **adenohypophysis,** which differentiates from Rathke's pouch and the nasopharynx; and the **neurohypophysis,** which is derived from the diencephalon (Fig 37–1). The adenohypophysis consists of the anterior lobe or anterior pituitary; the pars tuberalis, which forms part of the pituitary stalk; and the intermediate lobe, which is rudimentary in humans. The neurohypophysis consists of the infundibular process, or posterior lobe, and the infundibular stem, which also forms part of the **pituitary stalk.** The pituitary stalk is important for 2 reasons. It contains the axons of neurons that reside in the supraoptic and paraventricular nuclei of the hypothalamus. These axons transport the neurohypothalamic hormones ADH and oxytocin and terminate around capillaries in the posterior lobe. The pituitary stalk also contains the **vascular portal system** through which the various hypothalamic regulatory hormones are transported to the anterior lobe.

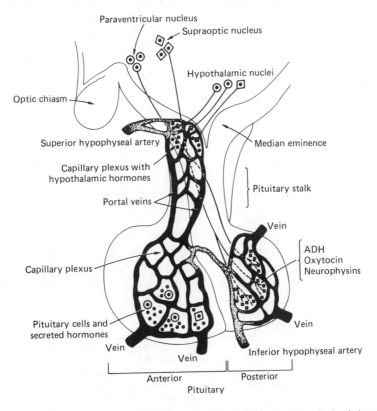

Figure 37–1. Structure of the human pituitary gland and illustration of transport of hypothalamic hormones to the anterior and posterior pituitary. Note that the posterior pituitary has an arterial blood supply, whereas the anterior pituitary is nourished by a portal system.

Table 37–1. Hypothalamic-hypophyseal hormones.

Hypothalamic Hormone (or Factor)	Acronym	Pituitary Hormone Affected*
Corticotropin-releasing hormone	CRH or CRF	ACTH (LPH, MSH, endorphins)
Thyrotropin-releasing hormone	TRH or TRF	TSH (PRL)
Gonadotropin-releasing hormone	GnRH (LHRH, FSHRH)	LH, FSH
Growth hormone –releasing hormone	GHRH or GHRF; GRH or GRF	GH
Growth hormone release – inhibiting hormone; somatostatin; somatotropin release – inhibiting hormone	GHRIH or GHRIF; SRIH or SRIF	GH (TSH, FSH, ACTH)
Prolactin release – inhibiting hormone; ? dopamine	PRIH or PRIF; PIH or PIF	PRL

*The hypothalamic hormone has a secondary or lesser effect on the hormones in parentheses.

HYPOTHALAMIC HORMONES

The anterior pituitary secretes a number of hormones (trophic hormones) that regulate the growth and function of other endocrine glands or influence metabolic reactions in other target tissues. The loss of anterior pituitary function (panhypopituitarism) results in atrophy of the thyroid, adrenal cortex, and gonads. Secondary actions due to the absence of the hormones secreted by these target glands affect most body organs and tissues and many general processes such as protein, fat, carbohydrate, and fluid and electrolyte metabolism.

The release (and in some cases production) of each of the pituitary hormones listed in Table 37–1 is under tonic control by at least one hypothalamic hormone. The hypothalamic hormones are released from the hypothalamic nerve fiber endings around the capillaries of the hypothalamic-hypophyseal system in the pituitary stalk and reach the anterior lobe through the special portal system that connects the hypothalamus and the anterior lobe (Fig 37–1). The structures of several hypothalamic hormones are illustrated in Table 37–2.

The hypothalamic hormones are released in a pulsatile manner, and isolated anterior pituitary target cells respond better to pulsatile administration of these hormones than to continuous exposure. The release of LH and FSH is controlled by the concentration of one releasing hormone, GnRH; this in turn is primarily a function of circulating levels of gonadal hormones that reach the hypothalamus (see the feedback loop in Fig 35–1). The release of ACTH is primarily controlled by CRH, but a number of other hormones, including ADH, catecholamines, VIP, and angiotensin II, may be involved. CRH release is influenced by cortisol, a glucocorticoid hormone secreted by the adrenal. TSH release is primarily affected by TRH, which in turn is regulated by the thyroid hormones T_3 and T_4; but TSH release is also inhibited by somatostatin (see Fig 38–5). Growth hormone release and production are

Table 37–2. Structures of hypothalamic releasing hormones.

Hormone	Structure
TRH	(pyro)Glu-His-Pro-NH$_2$
Somatostatin	Ala-Gly-Cys-Lys-Asn-Phe-Phe-Trp-Lys-Thr-Phe-Thr-Ser-Cys-NH$_2$ (S—S bridge between the two Cys residues)
GnRH	(pyro)Glu-His-Trp-Ser-Tyr-Gly-Leu-Arg-Pro-Gly-NH$_2$
PRIH (? dopamine)	HO— (dihydroxyphenyl ring) —CH$_2$CH$_2$NH$_2$
Ovine CRH	Ser-Gln-Glu-Pro-Pro-Ile-Ser-Leu-Asp-Leu-Thr-Phe-His-Leu-Leu-Arg-Glu-Val-Leu-Glu-Met-Thr-Lys-Ala-Asp-Gln-Leu-Ala-Gln-Gln-Ala-His-Ser-Asn-Arg-Lys-Leu-Leu-Asp-Ile-Ala-NH$_2$
Human GHRH	Tyr-Ala-Asp-Ala-Ile-Phe-Thr-Asn-Ser-Tyr-Arg-Lys-Val-Leu-Gly-Gln-Leu-Ser-Ala-Arg-Lys-Leu-Leu-Gln-Asp-Ile-Met-Ser-Arg-Gln-Gln-Gly-Glu-Ser-Asn-Gln-Glu-Arg-Gly-Ala-Arg-Ala-Arg-Leu-NH$_2$

under tonic control by both stimulating and inhibiting hypothalamic hormones. In addition, a peripheral feedback loop is involved in GH regulation. IGF-I (somatomedin C), which mediates some of the effects of GH, stimulates the release of somatostatin (GHRIH) while inhibiting the release of GHRH (Fig 37–5). The regulation of prolactin release appears to be unique, since no known peripheral feedback loop is involved. Release of prolactin is under tonic inhibition by prolactin release–inhibiting hormone, which may be dopamine. A releasing hormone has been searched for but not found.

Many of the hypothalamic hormones, in particular TRH, CRH, and somatostatin, are found in other portions of the nervous system and in a variety of peripheral tissues. The concentration of somatostatin is higher in the pancreas than in the hypothalamus. In the pancreas, it is produced by the D cells of the islets of Langerhans and probably regulates glucagon and insulin secretion. Somatostatin is also one of the more than 40 peptides produced by neurons of the central and peripheral nervous systems.

Although cAMP was originally thought to mediate the action of releasing hormones on the adenohypophysis, recent studies with GnRH and TRH suggest that a calcium-phospholipid mechanism, similar to that described above, is involved (see Fig 36–7). Whether the releasing hormones also affect the synthesis of the corresponding pituitary hormone has been argued, but recently GHRH has been shown to stimulate the rate of transcription of the GH gene, and TRH has a similar effect on the prolactin gene.

ANTERIOR PITUITARY HORMONES

The anterior pituitary produces a large number of hormones that stimulate a variety of physiologic and biochemical processes in target tissues. In addition, the placenta produces hormones that are closely related to some anterior lobe hormones. These hormones have traditionally been discussed individually, but recent studies dealing with the mechanism of synthesis and with the intracellular mediators of action (see Table 36–1) allow one to classify these hormones into 3 categories: (1) the growth hormone–prolactin–chorionic somatomammotropin group, (2) the glycoprotein hormone group, and (3) the pro-opiomelanocortin peptide family.

THE GROWTH HORMONE–PROLACTIN–CHORIONIC SOMATOMAMMOTROPIN GROUP

Growth hormone (GH), prolactin (PRL), and **chorionic somatomammotropin (CS; placental lactogen)** are a family of protein hormones having considerable sequence homology. GH, CS, and PRL range in size from 190 to 199 amino acids in different species. Each has a single tryptophan residue (locus 85 in GH and CS; locus 91 in PRL), and each has 2 homologous disulfide bonds. The amino acid homology between hGH and hCS is 85%, whereas that between hGH and hPRL is 35%. In view of this homology, it is not surprising that these 3 hormones share common antigenic determinants and that all have growth-promoting and lactogenic activity. The hormones are produced in a tissue-specific manner, with GH and PRL produced in the anterior pituitary and CS in the syncytiotrophoblast cells of the placenta. Each appears to be under different regulation (see below).

On the basis of these striking similarities, it was postulated several years ago that these hormones may have arisen by duplication of an ancestral gene. Recombinant DNA technology has revealed that there are multiple genes for GH and CS in primates and humans; that the single PRL gene, while encoding a very similar protein, is 5 times as large as those for GH and CS; that hCS is a variant of hGH; and that the GH-CS group in humans is located on chromosome 17, while PRL in humans is found on chromosome 6. There is marked evolutionary divergence of these genes. Rat and bovine tissues have a single copy of GH and PRL per haploid genome, and humans have a single PRL gene. Humans have one functional GH gene (GH-N) and a variant (GH-V), two CS genes that are expressed (CS-A and CS-B), and one CS gene that is not expressed (CS-L). Several simian species have at least 4 of the genes from the GH-CS family. The coding sequence of all of these genes is organized into 5 exons interrupted by 4 introns (Fig 37–2). The genes are highly homologous in the 5′ flanking regions and the coding sequence areas (~93% homology in the latter) and diverge in the 3′ flanking regions. The

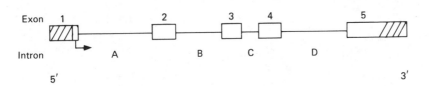

Figure 37–2. Schematic representation, drawn to scale, of the structure of the human growth hormone gene. The gene is about 45 kb in length and consists of 5 exons and 4 introns. Cross-hatching represents noncoding regions in exons 1 and 5. Arrow indicates direction of transcription.

5'   3'

Figure 37–3. Location and orientation of the human GH-CS gene family on chromosome 17. Relative positions of hGH and hCS genes are shown in a 5' to 3' orientation. Arrows indicate direction of transcription.

splice junctions are highly conserved, even though the introns in the PRL gene are much longer.

The human GH-CS gene family is located on a linkage group in region q22–24 on the long arm of chromosome 17. Fig 37–3 indicates the relative positions of each of these genes in a 5' to 3' orientation. The genes are all transcribed in the 5' to 3' direction, and GH-N is separated from CS-B by about 45 kb.

The GH-N coding sequence matches the amino acid sequence for circulating GH, and the gene is DNase I–sensitive, signifying its location in a region of **"active chromatin."** The GH-V gene, if expressed, would encode for a protein with 13 amino acid differences. This gene is DNase I–resistant, and thus it may not be active. The GH-V gene is present in patients who lack the GH-N gene (inherited GH deficiency), but since these persons have complete GH deficiency, the GH-V gene either is silent or is producing an inactive GH molecule. The first possibility is most likely, because these individuals form antibodies in response to exogenous GH, an indication that this molecule has not previously been seen by the immune system.

The CS-A and CS-B genes are expressed in placenta; CS-L is silent.

Growth Hormone (GH)

A. Synthesis and Structure: Growth hormone is synthesized in **somatotropes,** a subclass of the pituitary acidophilic cells; somatotropes are the most abundant cell in the gland. The concentration of GH in the pituitary is 5–15 mg/g, which is much higher than the μg/g quantities of other pituitary hormones. Growth hormone is a single polypeptide, with a molecular weight of about 22,000 in all mammalian species. The 191-amino-acid sequence of human growth hormone is shown in Fig 37–4. Although there is a high degree of sequence homology between various mammalian growth hormones, only human growth hormone or that of other higher primates is active in humans.

B. Regulation of Secretion and Synthesis: GH secretion is influenced by a variety of stimuli (eg, sleep, stress) and, like that of many of the pituitary hormones, is episodic and pulsatile. Plasma GH levels may change as much as 10-fold within a few minutes. One of the largest increases occurs shortly after the onset of sleep, lending support to the adage "If you don't get your sleep, you won't grow." Other stimuli include stress (pain, cold, apprehension, surgery), exercise, severe hypoglycemia or fasting, a protein meal, and the amino acid arginine. The stress responses may be mediated by catecholamines acting through the hypothalamus. These and many other effectors may be a consequence of the major physiologic action of GH to spare glucose. In stress, hypogly-

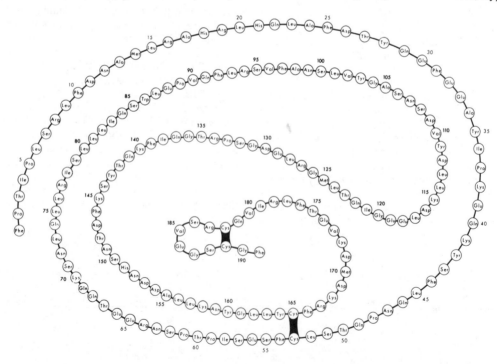

Figure 37–4. Structure of human growth hormone. The numbers identify the amino acid residues, starting from the N terminus.

cemia, sleep, or fasting, GH promotes lipolysis (delivery of fatty acids to cells) and amino acid entry into cells (potential gluconeogenic substrates), thus sparing glucose for brain metabolism. The intracellular glucose (or metabolite) level in the GH-regulating region of the ventromedial nucleus of the hypothalamus may be key. The glucose analog 2-deoxyglucose inhibits normal glycolysis of glucose and prompts the release of GH. Since this glucose analog also tends to increase the blood glucose, which ordinarily suppresses GH release, it appears that the regulatory signal is the intracellular metabolism of glucose, not the circulating level of glucose per se. The stimulation of GH release by protein-rich meals or arginine provides a mechanism for clearing amino acids from the plasma and for promoting incorporation into protein and other energy storage forms.

A variety of other agents influence GH release, including estrogens, dopamine, α-adrenergic agents, serotonin, opiate polypeptides, gut hormones, and glucagon. All of these appear to converge in the ventromedial nucleus of the hypothalamus, where GH release is regulated by the feedback system illustrated in Fig 37–5. In this system, the **short loop** involves the positive regulator GHRH and the negative regulator GHRIH (somatostatin); the **peripheral loop** involves insulinlike growth factor I (IGF-I; also known as somatomedin C and sulfation factor).

The growth-promoting actions of GH are presumably mediated by IGF-I, which is produced in the liver. IGF-I regulates GH secretion by inhibiting the release of GHRH from the hypothalamus and stimulating the release of somatostatin. Short-loop feedback inhibition is provided by GH itself, which inhibits the release of GHRH. GHRH is produced in the median eminence and, in addition to its effects on release, has recently been shown to stimulate transcription of the GH gene. Some effects of GHRH are duplicated by dopamine, which also increases GH production.

Negative control of GH release is provided by **somatostatin.** Somatostatin also inhibits the release of glucagon, insulin, TSH, FSH, ACTH, and many gut hormones but has no effect on PRL. This tetradecapeptide has a disulfide bridge but is active in either the linear or cyclic form (Table 37–2). Somatostatin is synthesized as part of an 11,500-MW prohormone that has biologic activity, as does a 28-amino-acid precursor. Secretion of somatostatin is increased by such substances as Ca^{2+}, Na^+, thyroid hormones, cAMP, and vasoactive intestinal peptide (VIP) and is decreased by atropine, acetylcholine, and GABA. The effect of GABA is reversed by picrotoxin and the benzodiazepine class of drugs. Exactly how these agents affect hypothalamic release of somatostatin and GH remains to be elucidated. Since somatostatin is produced in a variety of tissues, there may be many different types of control of its synthesis and release.

Somatostatin appears to inhibit GH by inhibiting calcium mobilization. Whether this occurs by changing Ca^{2+} influx or by stabilizing intracellular stores is uncertain. It also inhibits K^+ efflux, which in turn might decrease Ca^{2+} influx.

C. Physiologic and Biochemical Actions: GH is essential for postnatal growth and for normal carbohydrate, lipid, nitrogen, and mineral metabolism. As mentioned above, the growth-related effects are primarily mediated by **IGF-I,** a member of the insulinlike gene family. This was originally known as "sulfation factor" because of its ability to enhance the incorporation of sulfate into cartilage. It next was known as somatomedin C. Structurally, it is similar to proinsulin (see Chapter 42 and Fig 42–9). Another closely related peptide found in human plasma, **IGF-II,** has activity similar or identical to what is often referred to in the rat as multiplication-stimulating activity (MSA). IGF-I and IGF-II both bind to membrane receptors; however, they can be differentiated on the basis of specific radioimmunoassays. IGF-I has 70 amino acids, and IGF-II has 67. Plasma levels of IGF-II are twice those of IGF-I, but it is IGF-I that correlates most directly with GH effects. Individuals who lack sufficient IGF-I but have IGF-II (GH-deficient dwarfs and pygmies; see Table 37–3) fail to grow normally.

1. Protein synthesis–GH increases the transport of amino acids into muscle cells and also increases protein synthesis by a mechanism separate from the transport effect. Animals treated with GH show positive nitrogen balance, reflecting a generalized increase in protein synthesis and a decrease in plasma and urinary levels of amino acids and urea. This is accompanied by increased synthesis of RNA and DNA in some tissues. In these respects, GH actions resemble some of the actions of insulin.

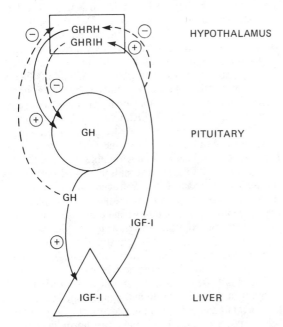

Figure 37–5. Feedback system regulating growth hormone release. Dashed lines show inhibitory effects; solid lines show stimulatory effects. See text for description.

Table 37–3. Relationship of GH, IGF-I, and IGF-II to dwarfism.

	Plasma Levels			Response to GH Stimulation
	GH	IGF-I	IGF-II	
GH-deficient dwarfs	Low	Low	Low to normal	Yes
Pygmies	Normal	Low	Normal	No
Laron type dwarfs	High	Low	Low	No

2. Carbohydrate metabolism–GH generally antagonizes the effects of insulin. Hyperglycemia after growth hormone administration is the combined result of decreased peripheral utilization of glucose and increased hepatic production via gluconeogenesis. In liver, GH increases liver glycogen, probably from activation of gluconeogenesis from amino acids. Impairment of glycolysis may occur at several steps, and GH may also inhibit the transport of glucose. Whether the latter is a direct effect on transport or a result of the inhibition of glycolysis has not yet been established. The mobilization of fatty acids from triacylglycerol stores may also contribute to the inhibition of glycolysis in muscle. Prolonged administration of GH may result in diabetes mellitus.

3. Lipid metabolism–GH promotes the release of free fatty acids and glycerol when incubated in vitro with adipose tissue. The in vivo administration of GH causes a rapid (30–60 minutes) increase of circulating free fatty acids and increased oxidation of fatty acids in the liver. Under conditions of insulin deficiency (eg, diabetes), increased ketogenesis may occur. These effects and those on carbohydrate metabolism probably are not mediated by IGF-I.

4. Mineral metabolism–GH, or more likely IGF-I, promotes a positive calcium, magnesium, and phosphate balance and causes the retention of Na^+, K^+, and Cl^-. The first effect probably relates to the action of GH in bone, where it promotes growth of long bones at the epiphyseal plates in growing children and appositional or acral growth in adults. In children, GH also increases formation of cartilage.

5. Prolactinlike effects–GH binds to lactogenic receptors and thus has many of the properties of prolactin, such as stimulation of the mammary glands, lactogenesis, and stimulation of the pigeon crop sac.

D. Pathophysiology: Deficient amounts of GH, whether from panhypopituitarism or isolated GH deficiency, are most serious in infancy because affected infants fail to grow properly. The other metabolic effects are less troublesome. Several types of dwarfism help illustrate the importance of the various steps in GH action (Table 37–3). **GH-deficient dwarfs** respond normally to exogenous GH. Two types of target organ resistance have been described. **Laron type dwarfs** have excessive amounts of GH-N, but they lack hepatic GH receptors. **Pygmies** apparently have a post-GH receptor defect, and this may be limited to the action GH exerts through IGF-I.

GH excess, usually from an acidophilic tumor, causes **gigantism** if it occurs before the epiphyseal plates close, since there is accelerated growth of the long bones. **Acromegaly** results from excessive release of GH that begins after epiphyseal closure and the cessation of long bone growth. Acral bone growth causes the characteristic facial changes (protruding jaw, enlarged nose) and enlargement of the hands, feet, and skull. Other findings include enlarged viscera, thickening of the skin, and a variety of metabolic problems, including diabetes mellitus.

A knowledge of GH regulation allows one to understand the clinical tests used to confirm these diagnoses. GH-deficient patients fail to increase GH levels in response to induced hypoglycemia or administration of arginine or levodopa. Patients with increased GH from a tumor (gigantism or acromegaly) fail to suppress GH levels in response to glucose administration.

Prolactin (PRL; Lactogenic Hormone, Mammotropin, Luteotropic Hormone)

A. Synthesis and Structure: PRL is a protein hormone with a molecular weight of about 23,000; its primary structure is illustrated in Fig 37–6. It is secreted by **lactotropes,** which are acidophilic cells in the anterior pituitary. The number of these cells and their size increase dramatically during pregnancy. The similarities between the structures and functions of PRL, GH, and CS are noted above.

B. Regulation of Secretion: An early and important observation about the control of PRL secretion was that—as is not true of other pituitary hormones—PRL secretion increased when the gland was removed from the sella turcica or when the pituitary stalk was completely transected. PRL thus seemed to be under tonic inhibition due to a prolactin release-inhibiting hormone (PRIH), which may, in fact, be dopamine. Pituitary cells have dopamine receptors, and dopamine decreases PRL release and inhibits PRL gene transcription, possibly mediated by decreasing cAMP levels. Levodopa, the dopamine precursor used in clinical testing, inhibits PRL release while stimulating GH release. The presence of a positive releasing factor (prolactin-releasing hormone; PRH) is less well established. Molecules that resemble fragments of oxytocin release PRL, and stimuli that cause oxytocin release also increase PRL. Estrogens stimulate PRL release, possibly by decreasing the number of dopaminergic receptors in the pituitary, and they also stimulate PRL gene transcription. PRL levels rise during late pregnancy and lactation. The physiologic stimulus for PRL release is nipple stimulation, but stress, sleep, and sexual intercourse also promote release.

C. Physiologic and Biochemical Actions: PRL is involved in the initiation and maintenance of lactation in mammals. Physiologic levels act only upon breast tissue primed by female sex hormones, but excessive levels can trigger breast development in ovariectomized females or in males. In rodents, PRL is capable of maintaining the corpus luteum—hence the

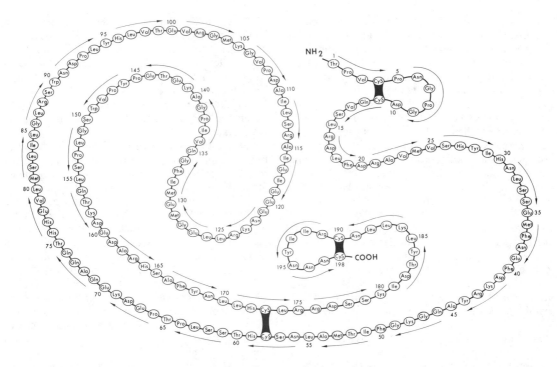

Figure 37–6. Structure of ovine prolactin.

name **luteotropic hormone.** Related molecules appear to be responsible for the adaptation of salt-water fish to fresh water, for the molting of reptiles, and for crop-sac milk production in birds. The intracellular mediator of PRL action is unknown. A peptide has been proposed, but this has not been verified.

D. Pathophysiology: Tumors of prolactin-secreting cells cause **amenorrhea** (cessation of menses) and **galactorrhea** (breast discharge) in women. Excessive PRL has been associated with **gynecomastia** (breast enlargement) and **impotence** in men.

Chorionic Somatomammotropin (CS; Placental Lactogen)

The final member of the GH-PRL-CS family has no definite function in humans. In bioassays, CS has lactogenic and luteotropic activity and metabolic effects that are qualitatively similar to those of growth hormone, including inhibition of glucose uptake, stimulation of free fatty acid and glycerol release, enhancement of nitrogen and calcium retention (despite increased urinary calcium excretion), and reduction in the urinary excretion of phosphorus and potassium. It may provide growth-supporting activity to the developing fetus, but pregnancies in which the fetus and placenta lack all the genes in the GH-CS group except GH-N and CS-L result in infants with normal in utero development and normal growth in the neonatal period. Since the human CS-L gene is not expressed, there is no possible source of CS in such individuals.

THE GLYCOPROTEIN HORMONE GROUP

The most complex protein hormones yet discovered are the pituitary and placental glycoproteins: **thyroid-stimulating hormone (TSH), luteinizing hormone (LH), follicle-stimulating hormone (FSH),** and **chorionic gonadotropin (CG).** These hormones affect diverse biologic processes and yet have remarkable structural similarities. This class of hormones is found in all mammals. Hormones with similar action are found in lower forms, and molecules with TSH- and hCG-like activities have been found in bacteria. These molecules, like other peptide and protein hormones, interact with cell surface receptors and activate adenylate cyclase; thus, they employ cAMP as their intracellular messenger.

Each of these hormones consists of 2 subunits, α and β, joined by noncovalent bonding. The α subunits are identical for all of these hormones within a species, and there is considerable interspecies homology. The specific biologic activity is determined by the β subunit, which also is highly conserved between hormones but to a lesser extent than that noted for the α subunit. The β subunit is not active by itself, and receptor recognition involves the interaction of regions of both subunits. Interhormone and interspecies hybrid molecules are fully active; eg, $TSH\alpha LH\beta = LH$ activity, and $hTSH\alpha mTSH\beta =$ mouse TSH activity. Thus, interspecies differences between α and β do not affect subunit association or the biologic function domain on β. Each subunit is synthesized from unique mRNAs from separate genes. It is thought that all hormones in this class evolved from a common ancestral gene that resulted in 2 molecules, α and β, and that the latter evolved further to provide the separate hormones.

A great deal is known about the structure of these molecules. For example, the carboxy-terminal pentapeptide of α is essential for receptor binding but not for $\alpha\beta$ association. The feature that distinguishes hormones in the glycoprotein group from hormones in other groups is their glycosylation. In each glycoprotein hormone, the α subunit contains 2 complex asparagine-linked oligosaccharides, and the β subunit has either one or 2. The glycosylation may be necessary for $\alpha\beta$ interaction. The α subunit has five S–S bridges, and the β moiety has 6.

Free α subunits are found in the pituitary and placenta. This finding and the observation that α and β are translated from separate mRNAs support the concept that the syntheses of α and β are under separate control and that β is limiting for the production of the complete hormone. All are synthesized as preprohormones and are subject to posttranslational processing within the cell to yield the glycosylated proteins.

The Gonadotropins (FSH, LH, & hCG)

These hormones are responsible for gametogenesis and steroidogenesis in the gonads. Each is a glycoprotein with a molecular weight of about 25,000.

A. Follicle-Stimulating Hormone (FSH): FSH binds to specific receptors on the plasma membranes of its target cells, the **follicular cells** in the ovary and the **Sertoli cells** in the testis. This results in activation of adenylate cyclase and increased cAMP production. FSH promotes follicular growth, prepares the follicle for the ovulation-inducing action of LH, and enhances the LH-induced release of estrogen. In the male, it binds to the Sertoli cells, where it induces the synthesis of an **androgen-binding protein** that appears to be involved in transporting testosterone to the seminiferous tubule and epididymis, a mechanism important for achieving the high local level of testosterone required for spermatogenesis. FSH stimulates seminiferous tubule and testicular growth and is important in initiating spermatogenesis. In the absence of FSH, the testes are atrophic and sperm production is absent. FSH also stimulates estradiol production in isolated Sertoli cells. The role of this in male physiology is unclear. Plasma FSH concentrations increase through puberty from the low levels of infancy. The appearance of the pulsatile release of FSH and LH, particularly during sleep, may signal the onset of puberty. In the female, there is marked cycling of levels, with peak values 10-fold or more over basal level at or slightly before the time of ovulation.

B. Luteinizing Hormone (LH): LH binds to specific plasma membrane receptors and stimulates the production of progesterone by **corpus luteum cells** and of testosterone by the **Leydig cells.** The intracellular signal of LH action is cAMP. This nucleotide mimics the actions of LH, which include enhanced conversion of acetate to squalene (the precursor for cholesterol synthesis) and enhanced conversion of cholesterol to 2α-hydroxycholesterol, a necessary step in the formation of progesterone and testosterone. There is tight coupling between the binding of LH and the production of cAMP, but steroidogenesis occurs when very small increases of cAMP have occurred. There thus are spare receptors in this response (see Fig 35–2). Prolonged exposure to LH results in desensitization, perhaps owing to "down regulation" of LH receptors.

An estradiol-dependent LH spike in midcycle triggers human ovulation, and LH is required for maintenance of the corpus luteum, which is the transformed follicle that begins to make progesterone as well as estradiol. This function of LH is later assumed by the placental hormone hCG if fertilization and implantation occur. For the first 6–8 weeks, the corpus luteum maintains the pregnancy, and then the placenta makes sufficient progesterone to continue the pregnancy, but production of hCG continues throughout.

In males, LH stimulates testosterone production, which with FSH promotes spermatogenesis. Systemic actions include the development of secondary sex characteristics and development and maintenance of accessory sex organs including the prostate, vasa deferentia, and seminal vesicles.

LH can stimulate interstitial cells in ovarian nongerminal tissues to produce a number of androgens and androgen precursors, including androstenedione, dehydroepiandrosterone, and testosterone. Patients with **polycystic ovaries** (Stein-Leventhal syndrome) have elevated LH levels, increased androgen production, poor fertility, and increased body and facial hair growth. This syndrome is presumed to be secondary to overactivity of the ovarian struma.

C. Human Chorionic Gonadotropin (hCG): hCG is a glycoprotein synthesized in the **syncytiotrophoblast cells** of the placenta. It has the $\alpha\beta$ dimer structure characteristic of this class of hormones and most closely resembles LH. It increases in blood and urine shortly after implantation (see above); hence, its detection is the basis of many pregnancy tests.

D. Regulation of LH and FSH Release: LH and FSH secretion are regulated by a classic negative feedback loop regulated by the gonadal steroid hormones. Sex hormones given over a prolonged period inhibit the secretion of LH and FSH. Castration or physiologic atrophy of the ovary at menopause results in hypersecretion of both LH and FSH. Positive feedback control may also be involved, since estradiol (progesterone or 20α-hydroxyprogesterone in some species) is responsible for, or permits, the ovulatory burst of LH release. LH and FSH are released episodically; this is especially notable during puberty. There are great fluctuations in mean plasma levels as well, with midmenstrual cycle peaks of both FSH and LH.

The secretion of LH and FSH is regulated by a single hypothalamic releasing factor generally referred to as **gonadotropin-releasing hormone (GnRH)**. GnRH is a decapeptide whose N-terminal amino acid, pyroglutamate, is a cyclized derivative of glutamate (Table 37–2). GnRH release is inhibited by the target organ hormones testosterone and estradiol and by endorphin. Its release is stimulated by dopamine, α-adrenergic agents, and prostaglandins. Inhibition of prostaglandin production has been linked to decreased ovulation. GnRH acts directly on the anterior pituitary to effect gonadotropin release through a calcium-phospholipid–dependent mechanism. Although separate releasing factors have not been found, plasma FSH and LH do not always change concordantly. Men in whom spermatogenesis fails to proceed beyond the secondary spermatocyte stage have elevated FSH levels. This finding and other observations have led to the hypothesis that a testicular factor, termed **inhibin,** inhibits FSH release. Various GnRH analogs are being tested for the contrary purposes of promoting fertility or contraception.

Thyroid-Stimulating Hormone (TSH)

A. Structure and Mechanism of Action: TSH is a glycoprotein of $\alpha\beta$ dimer structure with a molecular weight of about 30,000. Like other hormones of this class, TSH binds to plasma membrane receptors and activates adenylate cyclase. The consequent increase of cAMP is responsible for the action of TSH in thyroid hormone biosynthesis. Its relationship to the trophic effects of TSH on the thyroid is less certain.

TSH has several acute effects on thyroid function. These occur in minutes and involve increases of all phases of T_3 and T_4 biosynthesis, including iodide concentration, organification, coupling, and thyroglobulin hydrolysis. TSH also has several chronic effects on the thyroid. These require several days and include increases in the synthesis of proteins, phospholipids, and nucleic acids and in the size and number of thyroid cells. Long-term metabolic effects of TSH are due to the production and action of the thyroid hormones.

B. Regulation of TSH Release: TSH release is governed by a negative feedback system that includes the target gland hormones T_3 and T_4 and the hypothalamic hormone thyrotropin-releasing hormone (TRH). The details of this system are illustrated in Fig 38–5. T_3 is probably the biologically active thyroid hormone, even though T_4 is secreted in larger amounts. T_4 is converted to T_3 in peripheral tissues, including the pituitary. T_3 inhibits TRH action on the thyrotropic cells of the anterior lobe and may inhibit TRH production by the hypothalamus. When free T_3 is low, the system is activated at the level of TRH release from the hypothalamus. T_3 and T_4 both stimulate somatostatin release, which in turn inhibits TSH release, thereby decreasing T_3 and T_4 production. Additional fine-tuning may be accomplished by somatostatin via the growth hormone feedback loop. It is curious to note that children treated for short stature with GH occasionally develop hypothyroidism, perhaps owing to the convergence of the GH and TSH feedback loops. TRH also stimulates prolactin release. The physiologic importance of this is not known.

TRH is a neutral tripeptide consisting of pyroglutamic acid, histidine, and prolinamide (Table 37–2).

The TRH peptide shows no species specificity, and synthetic 3-methylation of histidine increases its activity 8-fold. TRH increases TSH release and cAMP levels within 1 minute, but its action appears to be more closely related to a Ca^{2+}-phospholipid–dependent mechanism, as is the case for GnRH. Prolonged exposure of cells to TRH also results in desensitization.

Estrogens increase the TSH response of the pituitary to TRH, an observation that may explain why women respond to TRH better than men do. TSH secretion is increased by α-adrenergic agents, which may mediate the increased production of thyroid hormones observed in cold-induced stress.

TRH, like somatostatin, is found in many extrahypothalamic locations, where it may serve as a neurotransmitter. TRH is used to distinguish between hypothyroidism of pituitary versus hypothalamic origin, since a person with the latter increases TSH in response to exogenous TRH whereas a person with the former does not. Because of its rapid plasma disappearance time ($t_{1/2} \cong 4$ minutes), TRH is not useful for long-term therapy.

THE PRO-OPIOMELANOCORTIN (POMC) PEPTIDE FAMILY

The **POMC family** consists of peptides which act as hormones (ACTH, LPH, MSH) and others which may serve as neurotransmitters or neuromodulators (endorphins). POMC is synthesized as a precursor molecule of $\sim$285 amino acids and is processed differently in various regions of the pituitary. One gene is responsible for POMC expression, and the general organization of this gene, obtained from human, bovine, rat, and mouse tissue, has been determined.

The POMC Gene

There is remarkable structural similarity between the POMC genes of various species and between the human genes for POMC and proenkephalin (Fig 37–7). There are general similarities between the organization of these genes and those which encode other hormones, including corticotropin-releasing hormone (CRH), nerve growth factor (NGF), glucagon, ADH, and calcitonin.

These genes have large 3' end exons containing the coding sequences for the active peptides and have repeated regions of intrasequence homology. In POMC there are 3 such regions, each about 50 nucleotides in length, which code for α-, β-, and γ-MSH. Proenkephalin has 7 regions, each about 25 nucleotides in length, which encode the enkephalins. POMC and proenkephalin have small exons, located about 3 kb upstream from the large 3' exon, which code for the N-terminal peptide, the signal peptide, and a 5' nontranslated region.

Distribution, Processing, and Functions of the POMC Gene Products

The POMC gene is expressed in the anterior and

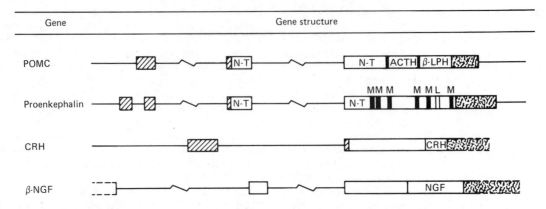

Figure 37–7. Similarities in structure of pro-opiomelanocortin (POMC) gene and related genes. CRH, corticotropin-releasing hormone; NGF, nerve growth factor; N-T, N-terminal peptide of POMC and proenkephalin proteins; ACTH, adrenocorticotropic hormone; LPH, lipotropin; M (dark bars), Met-enkephalin coding regions; L, Leu-enkephalin coding regions. Solid lines represent introns, and boxed areas represent exons; dashed and stippled boxes indicate nontranslated regions of mature mRNA. (Modified and reproduced, with permission, from Douglass J, Civelli O, Herbert E: Polyprotein gene expression: Generation of diversity of neuroendocrine peptides. *Annu Rev Biochem* 1984;**53**:665. Copyright © 1984 by Annual Reviews, Inc.)

intermediate lobes of the pituitary. The most conserved sequences between species are within the N-terminal fragment, the ACTH region, and the β-endorphin region. POMC or related products are found in several other vertebrate tissues, including the brain, placenta, gastrointestinal tract, reproductive tract, lung, and lymphocytes. This is presumably due to gene expression in these tissues (rather than to absorption from plasma) but has only been proved for brain, placenta, and testes. Related peptides have also been found in many invertebrate species.

The POMC protein is processed differently in the anterior lobe than in the intermediate lobe. The intermediate lobe is rudimentary in adult humans, but it is active in human fetuses and in pregnant women during late gestation and is also active in many animal species. Processing of the POMC protein in the peripheral tissues (gut, placenta, male reproductive tract) resembles that in the intermediate lobe. There are 3 basic peptide groups: (1) ACTH, which can give rise to

α-MSH and corticotropinlike intermediate lobe peptide (CLIP); (2) β-lipotropin (β-LPH), which can yield γ-LPH, β-MSH, and β-endorphin (and thus α- and γ-endorphins); and (3) a large N-terminal peptide, which generates γ-MSH. The diversity of these products is due to the many dibasic amino acid clusters that are potential cleavage sites for trypsinlike enzymes. Each of the peptides mentioned is preceded by Lys-Arg, Arg-Lys, Arg-Arg, or Lys-Lys residues. The prehormone segment is cleaved, and modification by glycosylation, acetylation, and phosphorylation occurs after translation. The next cleavage, in both anterior and intermediate lobes, is between ACTH and β-LPH, resulting in an N-terminal peptide with ACTH and a β-LPH segment (Fig 37–8). $ACTH_{1-39}$ is subsequently cleaved from the N-terminal peptide, and in the anterior lobe essentially no further cleavages occur. In the intermediate lobe, $ACTH_{1-39}$ is cleaved into α-MSH (residues 1–13) and CLIP (18–39); β-LPH (42–134) is converted to γ-LPH (42–101) and

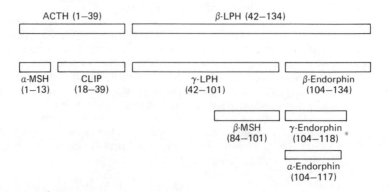

Figure 37–8. Products of pro-opiomelanocortin (POMC) cleavage. MSH, melanocyte-stimulating hormone; CLIP, corticotropinlike intermediate lobe peptide; LPH, lipotropin.

Table 37–4. Postulated functions of POMC peptides.*

Peptide	Function
ACTH	Adrenal growth and steroid production†
α-MSH	Melanin dispersion in amphibians†
	Learning and sexual behavior
	Growth and function of the testicular Sertoli cells
β-LPH	Lipolysis and fatty acid mobilization
β-Endorphin	Analgesia†
	Behavior (feeding, emotion, learning)
	Temperature and blood pressure regulation
	Contraction of reproductive tract muscles
N-terminal fragment	Potentiation of ACTH action on steroidogenesis

*Adapted, with permission, from Krieger DT: The multiple faces of pro-opiomelanocortin, a prototype precursor mulecule. *Clin Res* 1983;**31**:342.

†Established functions.

β-endorphin (104–134). β-MSH (84–101) is derived from γ-LPH.

There are extensive additional modifications of these peptides. Much of the N-terminal peptide and ACTH$_{1-39}$ in the anterior pituitary is glycosylated. α-MSH is found predominantly in an N-acetylated and carboxy-terminal amidated form; deacetylated α-MSH is much less active. β-Endorphin is rapidly acetylated in the intermediate lobe; acetylated β-endorphin, in contrast to α-MSH, is 1000 times less active than the unmodified form. β-Endorphin may therefore be inactive in the pituitary. In the hypothalamus, these molecules are not acetylated and presumably are active. β-Endorphin is also trimmed at the C-terminal end to form α- and γ-endorphin (Fig 37–8). These form the 3 major endorphins in the rodent intermediate lobe. The large N-terminal fragment is probably also extensively cleaved, but while γ-MSH has been found in rat and bovine pituitaries, less is known about this fragment. This structural information has come largely from studies of the rodent pituitary, but the general scheme is thought to apply to other species.

Precise functions for most of the POMC peptides have not been established. Postulated actions are listed in Table 37–4.

Regulation of POMC Production

About 5% of the cells of the anterior pituitary synthesize POMC, whereas all of the intermediate lobe cells synthesize this peptide. The regulation of synthesis and secretion is very different in the 2 areas.

A. Anterior Lobe: Corticotropin-releasing hormone (CRH) is the major factor controlling POMC release from the anterior pituitary. It works through a cAMP-mediated system in which Ca^{2+} is required. The stimulatory effects of CRH on POMC secretion are directly prevented by glucocorticoid hormones. In addition, glucocorticoids may act on the hypothalamus by inhibiting CRH production, CRH release, or both. Adrenalectomy (which causes decreased glucocorticoid and increased CRH levels) re-

sults in a 20-fold increase of POMC gene transcription. Through the concurrent administration of a glucocorticoid, however, the increase of POMC gene transcription can be inhibited, presumably through a receptor-mediated process. The inhibition of ACTH secretion by glucocorticoids occurs more rapidly than the effect on POMC gene transcription, so that these effects are presumably mediated independently. Minor effects on anterior lobe POMC (ACTH) secretion include direct stimulation by vasopressin and α-adrenergic agents, indirect stimulation (via the central nervous system) by serotonin and acetylcholine, and inhibition by GABA. Dopamine has no effect.

B. Intermediate Lobe: This lobe is poorly vascularized and is not reached by the hypothalamic-hypophyseal portal system; thus, it is unaffected by CRH. This tissue also has no glucocorticoid receptors, and thus glucocorticoids do not regulate POMC. The lobe is heavily innervated by dopaminergic fibers, and it also has serotoninergic and catecholaminergic nerve endings. Dopamine agonists (ergocryptine) decrease and antagonists (haloperidol) increase POMC mRNA and the release of POMC peptides. The time and magnitude of these changes are consistent with production-secretion coupling. These agents have no effect in the anterior lobe. POMC release is stimulated by serotonin and β-adrenergic agents in the intermediate lobe.

C. Other Tissues: Little is known about the regulation of POMC in other tissues. Hypophysectomy, adrenalectomy, CRH, and glucocorticoids do not affect POMC in these tissues. Chronic stress (eg, in immobilization) increases plasma ACTH and decreases pituitary ACTH, while brain POMC is unchanged. In contrast, acute stress decreases hypothalamic β-endorphin. Estrogens may promote β-endorphin release from the hypothalamus.

Action & Regulation of Specific Peptides

A. Adrenocorticotropic Hormone (ACTH):

1. Structure and mechanism of action– ACTH, a single-chain polypeptide consisting of 39 amino acids (Fig 37–9), regulates the growth and function of the adrenal cortex. The 24 N-terminal amino acids are required for full biologic activity and are invariant between species, whereas the 16 C-terminal amino acids are quite variable. A synthetic ACTH$_{1-24}$ analog is widely used in diagnostic testing.

ACTH increases the synthesis and release of adrenal steroids by enhancing the conversion of cholesterol to pregnenolone. This step entails the conversion from a C$_{27}$ to a C$_{21}$ steroid by removal of a 6-carbon side chain. Since pregnenolone is the precursor of all adrenal steroids (see Fig 40–4), prolonged ACTH stimulation results in excessive production of glucocorticoids, mineralocorticoids, and dehydroepiandrosterone (an androgen precursor). However, the contribution of ACTH to the last 2 classes of steroids is minimal under physiologic conditions. ACTH increases adrenal cortical growth (the trophic effect) by enhancing protein and RNA synthesis.

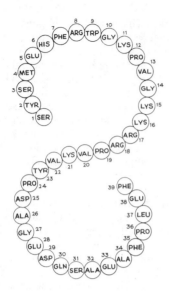

Figure 37–9. Structure of human ACTH.

ACTH, like other peptide hormones, binds to a plasma membrane receptor. Within a few seconds of this interaction, intracellular cAMP levels increase markedly. cAMP analogs mimic the action of ACTH, but calcium also is involved.

ACTH activates adenylate cyclase in adipose cells and results in a cAMP-mediated activation of lipase and increased lipolysis. ACTH also stimulates insulin release from the pancreas, but these extra-adrenal effects are small and require supraphysiologic concentrations of the hormone.

2. Regulation–The production of ACTH from the POMC precursor protein and the regulation of synthesis and secretion of the latter have been discussed above. Primary regulation is accomplished through a negative feedback loop that involves glucocorticoids and CRH. Excessive levels of ACTH may also inhibit CRH production through a "short loop." The central nervous system is prominently involved in the regulation of ACTH production and secretion. This is accomplished through a variety of neurotransmitters including norepinephrine, serotonin, and acetylcholine. The ACTH response, which stimulates the glucocorticoids necessary for adaptation to stresses such as hypoglycemia, surgery, physical or emotional trauma, cold, and pyrogens, is probably mediated by these neurotransmitters. Lesions in the median eminence decrease ACTH release and prevent the response to stress.

The secretion of ACTH is episodic and pulsatile, with bursts that last a few minutes. There is a diurnal rhythm to this pattern; secretion is greatest between 1:00 AM and 4:00 AM and reaches a nadir at about 1 hour after the onset of sleep. Glucocorticoid secretion follows the same pattern with about a 1-hour delay. Disruption of this pattern is an important factor in "night-shift flu" and "jet lag."

3. Pathophysiology–Excessive production of ACTH by the pituitary or by ectopic production from a tumor results in **Cushing's syndrome.** The weak MSH-like activity of ACTH or associated release of β- or α-MSH results in hyperpigmentation. The metabolic manifestations are due to excessive production of adrenal steroids and include (1) negative nitrogen, potassium, and phosphorus balance; (2) sodium retention, which can result in hypertension, edema, or both; (3) glucose intolerance or overt diabetes mellitus; (4) increased plasma fatty acids; and (5) decreased circulating eosinophils and lymphocytes, with increased polymorphonuclear leukocytes. Patients with Cushing's syndrome may have muscle atrophy and a peculiar redistribution of fat, ie, truncal obesity. Loss of ACTH owing to tumor, infection, or infarction of the pituitary results in an opposite constellation of findings.

B. β-Lipotropin (β-LPH): This peptide consists of the carboxy-terminal 91 amino acids of POMC (Fig 37–8). β-LPH contains the sequences of β-MSH, γ-LPH, Met-enkephalin, and β-endorphin. Of these, β-LPH, γ-LPH, and β-endorphin have been found in human pituitary but β-MSH has not been detected. β-LPH is found only in the pituitary, since it is rapidly converted to γ-LPH and β-endorphin in other tissues. β-LPH contains a 7-amino-acid sequence (β-LPH$_{47-53}$) that is identical to ACTH$_{4-10}$ (Fig 37–10). β-LPH causes lipolysis and fatty acid mobilization, but its physiologic role is minimal. It probably serves only as the precursor for β-endorphin.

C. Endorphins: β-Endorphin consists of the carboxy-terminal 31 amino acids of β-LPH (Fig 37–8). The α- and γ-endorphins are modifications of β-endorphin from which 15 and 14 amino acids, respectively, are removed from the C-terminal end. These peptides are found in the pituitary, but they are acetylated there (see above) and probably are inactive. In other sites (eg, central nervous system neurons), they are not modified and hence probably serve as neurotransmitters or neuromodulators. Endorphins bind to the same central nervous system receptors as do the morphine opiates and may play a role in endogenous control of pain perception. They have higher analgesic potencies (18–30 times on a molar basis) than morphine. The sequence for enkephalin is present in POMC, but it is not preceded by dibasic amino acids and presumably is not cleaved or expressed.

D. Melanocyte-Stimulating Hormone (MSH): MSH stimulates **melanogenesis** in some species by causing the dispersion of intracellular melanin granules, resulting in darkening of the skin. Three different MSH molecules, α, β, and γ, are contained within the POMC molecule, and 2 of these, α and β, are secreted in some nonhuman species. In humans, the actual circulating MSH activity is contained within the larger molecules γ- or β-LPH. α-MSH contains an amino acid sequence that is identical to ACTH$_{1-13}$, but it has an acetylated N terminus. α-MSH (and CLIP) are generally found in animals that have a well-developed

-Tyr-Ser-Met-Glu-His-Phe-Arg-Trp-Gly-Lys-Pro-

ACTH$_{2-12}$

-Tyr-Lys-Met-Glu-His-Phe-Arg-Trp-Gly-Ser-Pro-

β-LPH$_{45-55}$

Figure 37–10. A comparison of the amino acid sequences of portions of the ACTH and β-LPH molecules. Underlined residues indicate the differences. The entire ACTH molecule consists of 39 amino acids, and β-LPH has 91 amino acids.

intermediate lobe. These peptides are not found in postnatal humans.

Patients with insufficient production of glucocorticoids **(Addison's disease)** have hyperpigmentation associated with increased plasma MSH activity. This could be due to ACTH but is more likely the result of concomitant secretion of β- and γ-LPH, with their associated MSH activity.

POSTERIOR PITUITARY HORMONES

The posterior pituitary contains 2 active hormones, vasopressin and oxytocin. **Vasopressin,** originally named because of its ability to increase blood pressure when administered in pharmacologic amounts, is more appropriately called **antidiuretic hormone (ADH)** because its most important physiologic action is to promote reabsorption of water from the distal renal tubules. **Oxytocin** is also named for an effect of questionable physiologic significance, the acceleration of birth by stimulation of uterine smooth muscle contraction. Its probable physiologic role is to promote milk ejection from the mammary gland.

Both hormones are produced in the hypothalamus and transported by axoplasmic flow to nerve endings in the posterior pituitary where, upon appropriate stimulation, the hormones are released into the circulation (Fig 37–1). The probable reason for this arrangement is to escape the blood-brain barrier. ADH is primarily synthesized in the **supraoptic nucleus** and oxytocin in the **paraventricular nucleus.** Each is transported through axons in association with specific carrier proteins called **neurophysins.** Neurophysins I and II are synthesized with oxytocin and ADH, respectively, each as a part of a single protein (sometimes referred to as propressophysin) from a single gene. Neurophysins I and II are unique proteins with molecular weights of 19,000 and 21,000, respectively. ADH and oxytocin are secreted separately into the bloodstream along with their appropriate neurophysins. They circulate unbound to proteins and have very short plasma half-

lives, on the order of 2–4 minutes. The structures for ADH and oxytocin are shown below.

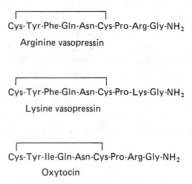

Cys-Tyr-Phe-Gln-Asn-Cys-Pro-Arg-Gly-NH$_2$
Arginine vasopressin

Cys-Tyr-Phe-Gln-Asn-Cys-Pro-Lys-Gly-NH$_2$
Lysine vasopressin

Cys-Tyr-Ile-Gln-Asn-Cys-Pro-Arg-Gly-NH$_2$
Oxytocin

Each is a nonapeptide containing cysteine molecules at positions 1 and 6 linked by an S–S bridge. Most animals have arginine vasopressin; however, the hormone in pigs and related species has a lysine substituted in position 8. Because of the close structural similarity, it is not surprising that ADH and oxytocin each exhibit some of the effects of the other molecule. These peptides are primarily metabolized in the liver, although renal excretion of ADH accounts for a significant part of its loss from blood.

OXYTOCIN

Regulation of Secretion

The neural impulses that result from stimulation of the nipples are the primary stimulus for oxytocin release. Vaginal and uterine distention are secondary stimuli. PRL is released by many of the stimuli that release oxytocin, and a fragment of oxytocin has been proposed as prolactin-releasing factor. Estrogen stimulates the production of oxytocin and of neurophysin I, and progesterone inhibits the production of these compounds.

Mechanism of Action

The mechanism of action of oxytocin is unknown. It causes contraction of uterine smooth muscle and thus is used in pharmacologic amounts to induce labor in humans. Interestingly, pregnant animals in which the hypothalamic-hypophyseal tract has been destroyed do not necessarily have trouble delivering their young. The most likely physiologic function of oxytocin is to stimulate contraction of myoepithelial cells surrounding the mammary alveoli. This promotes the movement of milk into the aveolar duct system and allows for milk ejection. Membrane receptors for oxytocin are found in both uterine and mammary tissues. These receptors are increased in number by estrogens and decreased by progesterone. The concomitant rise in estrogens and fall in progesterone occurring immediately before parturition probably explains the onset of lactation prior to delivery. Progesterone derivatives are commonly used to inhibit postpartum lactation in humans. Oxytocin and neurophysin I appear to be produced in the ovary, wherein oxytocin may inhibit steroidogenesis.

The chemical groups important for oxytocin action include the primary amino group of the N-terminal cysteine; the phenolic group of tyrosine; the 3 carboxamide groups of asparagine, glutamine, and glycinamide; and the disulfide (S–S) linkage. By deleting or substituting these groups, numerous analogs of oxytocin have been produced. For example, deletion of the free primary amino group of the terminal half cysteine residue (position 1) results in desamino oxytocin, which has 4–5 times the antidiuretic activity of oxytocin.

ANTIDIURETIC HORMONE
(ADH; VASOPRESSIN)

Regulation of Secretion

The neural impulses that trigger ADH release are activated by a number of different stimuli. Increased osmolality of plasma is the primary physiologic stimulus. This is mediated by **osmoreceptors** located in the hypothalamus and by **baroreceptors** located in the heart and other regions of the vascular system. Hemodilution (decreased osmolality) has the opposite effect. Other stimuli include emotional and physical stress and pharmacologic agents including acetylcholine, nicotine, and morphine. Most of these effects involve increased synthesis of ADH and neurophysin II, since the depletion of stored hormone is not associated with this action. Epinephrine and agents that expand plasma volume inhibit ADH secretion, as does ethanol.

Mechanism of Action

The most important physiologic target cells of ADH in mammals are those of the distal convoluted tubules and collecting structures of the kidney. These ducts pass through the renal medulla, in which the extracellular solute pool has an osmolality gradient up to 4 times that of plasma. These cells are relatively impermeable to water, so that in the absence of ADH, the urine is not concentrated and may be excreted in amounts exceeding 20 L/d. ADH increases the permeability of the cells to water and permits osmotic equilibration of the collecting tubule urine with the hypertonic interstitium, resulting in urine volumes in the range of 0.5–1 L/d. ADH receptors exist on the mucosal (urinary) membrane of these epithelial cells. This receptor is linked to adenylate cyclase, and cAMP is thought to mediate the effects of ADH in the renal tubule. This physiologic action is the basis of the name "antidiuretic hormone." cAMP and inhibitors of phosphodiesterase activity mimic the actions of ADH. In vivo, an elevated level of calcium in the medium bathing the mucosal surface of the tubular cells inhibits the action of ADH on water movement, apparently by inhibiting the action of adenylate cyclase, since it does not diminish the action of cAMP per se. This may account, in part, for the excessive volumes of urine that are characteristic of patients with hypercalcemia.

Arginine vasopressin (and neurophysin II) may be produced in the testis. There are arginine vasopressin receptors in this tissue, and the hormone inhibits 17-hydroxylase activity and steroidogenesis in the testis. High concentrations of ADH act as secretagogues for other anterior pituitary hormones; however, this is probably of negligible physiologic importance. High concentrations of ADH also increase blood pressure, because of the vasopressor effect. Its vasoconstricting properties have led to its use in the management of shock and of severe gastrointestinal or postpartum hemorrhage.

Pathophysiology

Abnormalities of ADH secretion or action lead to **diabetes insipidus,** which is characterized by the excretion of large volumes of dilute urine. Primary diabetes insipidus, an insufficient amount of the hormone, is usually due to destruction of the hypothalamic-hypophophyseal tract from a basal skull fracture, tumor, or infection, but it can be hereditary. In **hereditary nephrogenic diabetes insipidus,** ADH is secreted normally but the target cell is incapable of responding, presumably because of a receptor defect (see Table 35–3). This hereditary lesion is distinguished from **acquired nephrogenic diabetes insipidus,** which most often is due to the pharmacologic administration of lithium for manic-depressive illness. The **inappropriate secretion of ADH** occurs in association with ectopic production by a variety of tumors (usually tumors of the lung) but can also occur in conjunction with diseases of the brain, pulmonary infections, or hypothyroidism. It is called inappropriate secretion because ADH is produced at a normal or increased rate in the presence of hypo-osmolality, thus causing a persistent and progressive dilutional hyponatremia with excretion of hypertonic urine.

●   ●   ●

References

Anterior Pituitary Hormones

Douglass J, Civelli O, Herbert E: Polyprotein gene expression: Generation of diversity of neuroendocrine peptides. *Annu Rev Biochem* 1984;**53**:665.

Eiper BA, Mains RE: Structure and biosynthesis of Pro-ACTH/ endorphin and related peptides. *Endocr Rev* 1980;**1**:1.

Frantz AG: Prolactin. *N Engl J Med* 1978;**298**:201.

Frohman LA: Diseases of the anterior pituitary. Pages 151–232 in: *Endocrinology and Metabolism*. Felig P et al (editors). McGraw-Hill, 1981.

Krieger DT: The multiple faces of pro-opiomelanocortin, a prototype precursor molecule. *Clin Res* 1983;**3**:342.

Krulich L: Central neurotransmitters and the secretion of prolactin, GH, LH, and TSH. *Annu Rev Physiol* 1979;**41**:603.

Pierce JG, Parsons TF: Glycoprotein hormones: Structure and function. *Annu Rev Biochem* 1981;**50**:465.

Seeburg P: The human growth hormone gene family: Structure and evolution of the chromosomal locus. *Nucleic Acids Res* 1983;**11**:3939.

Simpson ER, MacDonald PC: Endocrine physiology of the placenta. *Annu Rev Physiol* 1981;**43**:163.

Posterior Pituitary Hormones

Chord IT: The posterior pituitary gland. *Clin Endocrinol* 1975;**4**:89.

Robertson GL: Regulation of vasopressin function in health and disease. *Recent Prog Horm Res* 1977;**33**:333.

Sawyer WH, Manning M: Synthetic analogs of oxytocin and the vasopressins. *Annu Rev Pharmacol* 1973;**13**:1.

Soloff MS: Minireview: Regulation of oxytocin action at the receptor level. *Life Sci* 1979;**25**:1453.

Hypothalamic Hormones

Imura H et al: Effect of CNS peptides on hypothalamic regulation of pituitary secretion. *Adv Biochem Psychopharmacol* 1981;**28**:557.

Jackson IMD: Thyrotropin-releasing hormone. *N Engl J Med* 1982;**306**:145.

Koop GF, Bloom FE: The role of the central nervous system in the control of ovarian function in higher primates. *Annu Rev Physiol* 1982;**44**:571.

Labrie F et al: Mechanism of action of hypothalamic hormones in the adenohypophysis. *Annu Rev Physiol* 1979;**41**:555.

Mayo KE et al: Expression-cloning and sequence of a cDNA encoding human growth hormone–releasing factor. *Nature* 1983;**306**:86.

Reichlin S: Systems for the study of regulation of neuropeptide secretion. In: *Neurosecretion and Brain Peptides: Implications for Brain Function and Neurological Disease*. Martin JB, Reichlin S, Bick KL (editors). Raven Press, 1981.

38 | The Thyroid Hormones

Daryl K. Granner, MD

STRUCTURE & GENERAL FEATURES

The thyroid gland produces 2 iodoamino acid hormones, **3,5,3'-triiodothyronine (T$_3$)** and **3,5,3',5'-tetraiodothyronine (T$_4$, thyroxine)**, which have long been recognized for their importance in regulating general metabolism, development, and tissue differentiation. These structures are illustrated in Fig 38-1.

The thyroid is the largest endocrine gland in humans, weighing about 20 g. It consists of 2 lobes, one on each side of the trachea, connected by an isthmus. The thyroid is generally described as being composed of discrete follicles but is actually a continuous epithelial mass. The cells lining the follicles are generally cuboidal or columnar, depending on the degree of stimulation by TSH. These cells originate from epithelium at the base of the tongue and must be distinguished from the **thyroidal C cells** that make calcitonin (see Chapter 39). C cells are found scattered within the follicular basement membrane and are derived from a different source, the ultimobranchial organ. Thyroid cells are typical **polarized cells** (see Chapter 35). The basal portion of the follicular cell approximates the rich capillary network of the thyroid, while the apical plasma membranes of adjacent cells, with their numerous microvilli, define the follicular lumen.

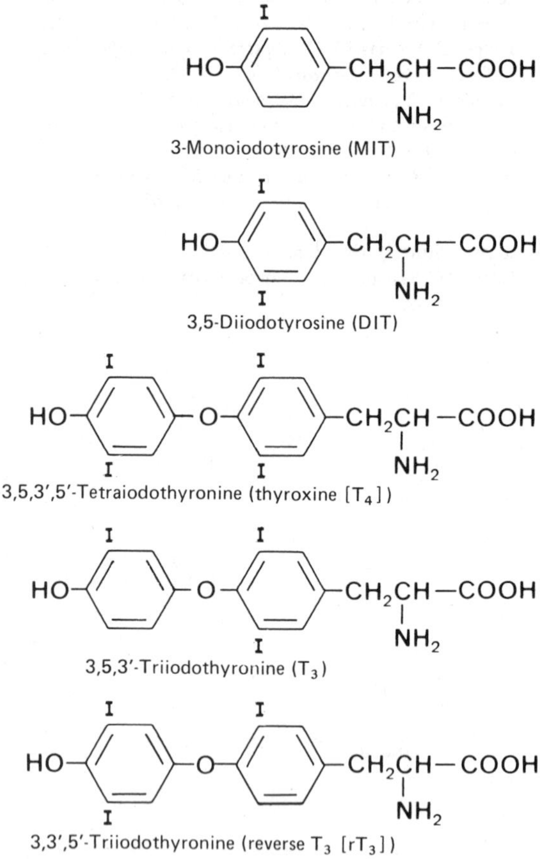

THYROID HORMONE BIOSYNTHESIS

Thyroid hormones are unique in that they require the trace element **iodine** for biologic activity. In most parts of the world, iodine is a scarce component of soil, and hence there is little in food. A complex mechanism has evolved to acquire and retain this crucial element and to convert it into a form suitable for incorporation into organic compounds. At the same time, the thyroid must synthesize thyronine, and this synthesis takes place in thyroglobulin. These processes will be discussed separately, although they occur concurrently.

Figure 38-1. Structure of thyroid hormones and related compounds.

THYROGLOBULIN METABOLISM

Biosynthesis

Thyroglobulin is the precursor of T$_4$ and T$_3$. It is a large, iodinated, glycosylated protein with a molecular weight of 660,000. Carbohydrate accounts for 8–10% of the weight of thyroglobulin and iodide for about 0.2–1%, depending upon the iodine content in the diet. Thyroglobulin is probably composed of 2 subunits. It contains 115 tyrosine residues, each of which is a potential site of iodination. About 70% of the iodide in thyroglobulin exists in the inactive precursors, **monoiodotyrosine (MIT)** and **diiodotyrosine (DIT),** while 30% is in the **iodothyronyl** residues, T_4 and T_3. When iodine supplies are sufficient, the $T_4:T_3$ ratio is about 7:1. In **iodine deficiency,** this ratio decreases, as does the DIT:MIT ratio. The reason for synthesizing a molecule of 5000 amino acids to generate a few molecules of a modified diamino acid seems to be that the conformation of this large structure is required for tyrosyl coupling or iodide organification. The physical pathway of thyroglobulin metabolism in the thyroid is bidirectional; it is synthesized from the basal portion of the cell toward the lumen, where it is stored in the extracellular **colloid,** and it reenters the cell and moves in an apical to basal direction during its hydrolysis into the active T_3 and T_4 hormones.

Amino acids for thyroglobulin synthesis, including tyrosine, enter the cell through the basal membrane and are incorporated into nascent thyroglobulin subunits by polyribosomes attached to the endoplasmic reticulum. The addition of carbohydrate starts in the cisternae of the rough endoplasmic reticulum but continues in the Golgi apparatus. Each molecule contains over 20 carbohydrate chains, which may be short or long and simple or branched. Packaging, including polymerization, continues in the Golgi vesicles, which migrate toward the apical membrane of the cell. Thyroglobulin is secreted by exocytosis into the follicular lumen. All of these steps are probably enhanced by TSH, and this hormone (or cAMP) also enhances transcription of the thyroglobulin gene.

Hydrolysis

Thyroglobulin is a storage form of T_3 and T_4 in the colloid; a several weeks' supply of these hormones exists in the normal thyroid. Existing thyroglobulin is displaced toward the center of the follicle by the newly synthesized product; hence, the newest thyroglobulin is most susceptible to **pinocytosis** back into the follicular cell (the "last come, first served" model). This intrafollicular heterogeneity is matched by an interfollicular heterogeneity of thyroglobulin metabolism; smaller follicles seem to be more active than larger ones.

Within minutes after the stimulation of the thyroid by TSH (or cAMP), there is a marked increase of microvilli on the apical membrane. This microtubule-dependent process entraps thyroglobulin, and subsequent pinocytosis brings it back into the follicular cell. These phagosomes fuse with lysosomes to form **phagolysosomes** in which various acid proteases and peptidases hydrolyze the thyroglobulin into amino acids, including the iodothyronines. T_4 and T_3 are discharged from the basal portion of the cell, perhaps by a facilitated process, into the blood. The $T_4:T_3$ ratio in this blood is lower than that in thyroglobulin, so that some selective deiodination of T_4 must occur in the thyroid. About 50 μg of thyroid hormone iodide is secreted each day. With an average uptake of iodide (25–30% of the iodide ingested), the daily iodide requirement is between 150 and 200 μg.

As mentioned above, most of the iodide in thyroglobulin is not in iodothyronine; about 70% is in the inactive compounds MIT and DIT. These amino acids are released when thyroglobulin is hydrolyzed and the iodide is scavenged by an environmentally conscious enzyme, **deiodinase.** This NADPH-dependent enzyme is also present in kidney and liver. The iodide removed from MIT and DIT constitutes an important pool within the thyroid, as distinguished from that I^- which enters from blood. Under steady-state conditions, the amount of iodide that enters the thyroid matches the amount that leaves. If one-third of the iodide in thyroglobulin leaves (as T_4 and T_3), it follows that two-thirds of the iodide available for biosynthesis comes from the deiodination of MIT and DIT within the thyroid.

IODIDE METABOLISM

Iodide metabolism involves a number of discrete steps, as illustrated in Fig 38–2.

Concentration of Iodide (I^-)

The thyroid, along with several other epithelial tissues including mammary gland, chorion, salivary gland, and stomach, **is able to concentrate I^- against a strong electrochemical gradient.** This is an energy-dependent process and is linked to the ATPase-dependent Na^+/K^+ pump. The activity of the **thyroidal I^- pump** can be isolated from subsequent steps in hormone biosynthesis by inhibiting organification of I^- with drugs of the thiourea class (Fig 38–3). The ratio of iodide in thyroid to iodide in serum (T:S ratio) is a reflection of the activity of this pump or concentrating mechanism. This activity is primarily controlled by TSH and ranges from 500 in animals chronically stimulated with TSH to 5 or less in hypophysectomized animals. The T:S ratio in humans on a normal iodine diet is about 25.

A very small amount of iodide also enters the thyroid by diffusion. Any intracellular I^- that is not incorporated into MIT or DIT (generally < 10%) is free to leave by this mechanism.

The transport mechanism is inhibited by 2 classes of molecules. The first group consists of perchlorate (ClO_4^-), perrhenate (ReO_4^-), and pertechnetate (TcO_4^-), all anions with the same partial specific volume as I^-. These anions compete with I^- for its carrier and are concentrated by the thyroid. A radioisotope of TcO_4^- is commonly used to study iodide transport in humans. The linear anion thiocyanate (SCN^-), an example of the second class, is a competitive inhibitor of I^- transport but is not concentrated by the thyroid. These inhibitors of I^- transport unmask the rapid diffusion of exchangeable I^- from the thyroid and are used to diagnose organification deficiencies. After the acute administration of a blocking concentration of a transport inhibitor, the amount of accumulated I^- (usually measured as the isotope ^{131}I) that leaves the thyroid is directly related to the unbound, or nonorganified, frac-

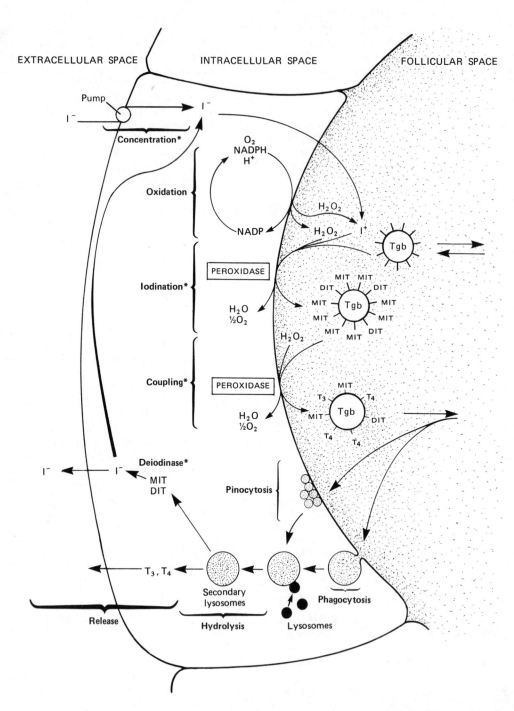

Figure 38–2. Model of iodide metabolism in the thyroid follicle. A follicular cell is shown facing the follicular lumen (stippled area) and the extracellular space (at left). Iodide enters the thyroid by a pump and by passive diffusion. Thyroid hormone synthesis occurs in the follicular space through a series of reactions, many of which are peroxidase-mediated. Thyroid hormones are released from thyroglobulin by hydrolysis. Tgb, thyroglobulin; MIT, monoiodotyrosine; DIT, diiodotyrosine; T_3, triiodothyronine; T_4, tetraiodothyronine. Asterisks indicate inherited enzyme deficiencies that cause congenital goiter and often result in hypothyroidism.

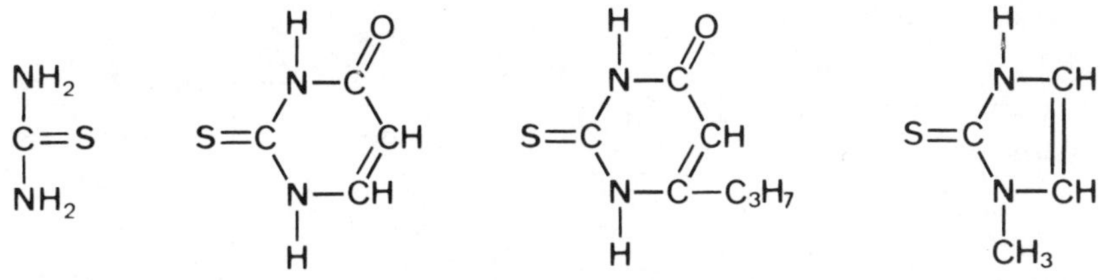

Figure 38-3. Thiourea class of antithyroid drugs.

tion. Individuals with incomplete organification will "discharge" more ^{131}I than will normal persons in response to ClO_4^-.

I^- Oxidation

The thyroid is the only tissue that can oxidize I^- to a higher valence state, an obligatory step in I^- organification and thyroid hormone biosynthesis. This step involves a heme-containing peroxidase and occurs at the luminal surface of the follicular cell.

Thyroperoxidase, a tetrameric protein with a molecular weight of 60,000, requires hydrogen peroxide as an oxidizing agent. The H_2O_2 is produced by an NADPH-dependent enzyme resembling cytochrome c reductase. A number of compounds inhibit I^- oxidation and therefore its subsequent incorporation into MIT and DIT. The most important of these clinically are the thiourea drugs, some of which are shown in Fig 38-3. They are known as **antithyroid drugs** because of their ability to inhibit thyroid hormone biosynthesis at this step.

Iodination of Tyrosine

Oxidized iodide reacts with the tyrosyl residues in thyroglobulin in a reaction that probably also involves thyroperoxidase. The 3 position of the aromatic ring is iodinated first and then the 5 position to form MIT and DIT, respectively. This reaction occurs within seconds in luminal thyroglobulin. Free tyrosine can be iodinated, but it is not incorporated into proteins, since no tRNA recognizes iodinated tyrosine.

Coupling of Iodotyrosyls

The coupling of two DIT molecules to form T_4 or of an MIT and DIT to form T_3 occurs within the thyroglobulin molecule, although the addition of a free MIT or DIT to a bound DIT has not been conclusively excluded. A separate coupling enzyme has not been found, and since this is an oxidative process, it is assumed that the same thyroperoxidase catalyzes this reaction by stimulating free radical formation of iodotyrosine. This hypothesis is supported by the observation that the same drugs which inhibit I^- oxidation also inhibit coupling. The formed thyroid hormones remain as integral parts of thyroglobulin until the latter is degraded, as described above. Thyroglobulin hydrolysis is stimulated by TSH but is **inhibited by I^-**; this latter effect is occasionally exploited by using KI to treat hyperthyroidism (see below).

Autoregulation of Thyroid Function

The thyroid increases the concentration of iodide during iodide deficiency even in the absence of TSH (hypophysectomy). The T:S ratio of hypophysectomized rats fed a normal iodine diet is 4, but if the animals are placed on an iodine-deficient diet, their T:S ratio is 12. By this mechanism, the thyroid accumulates the same amount of iodide even though the serum iodide level in the iodide-deficient animals is one-third that of those fed a normal iodine diet. This **autoregulation** is thought to be related to the decrease of an intrathyroidal iodide-containing organic compound that inhibits iodide transport. Another compensatory mechanism also occurs in iodide deficiency. The MIT:DIT ratio increases, and hence relatively more T_3 is made, thereby sparing an iodide molecule and making a more potent hormone molecule.

The thyroid also has intrinsic mechanisms for adjusting to increased intrathyroidal levels of iodide that would otherwise result in excessive thyroid hormone production. Above a certain level, intrathyroidal I^- inhibits organic binding, the so-called **Wolff-Chaikoff effect.** After a time, a secondary adaptive response occurs: as thyroidal I^- concentration decreases, intracellular levels of I^- fall, escape from the Wolff-Chaikoff effect occurs, and hormone synthesis resumes. In some individuals, this escape mechanism fails, leading to an **iodide-induced goiter** (a goiter is an enlarged thyroid), often with hypothyroidism.

TRANSPORT & METABOLISM OF THYROID HORMONES

One-half to two-thirds of T_4 and T_3 in the body is extrathyroidal, and most of this circulates in bound form, ie, bound to 2 specific binding proteins, **thyroxine-binding globulin (TBG)** and **thyroxine-binding prealbumin (TBPA).** TBG, a glycoprotein of 50,000 MW, is quantitatively the more important. It binds T_4 and T_3 with 100 times the affinity of TBPA and has the capacity to bind 20 $\mu g/dL$ of plasma. Under normal circumstances, TBG binds, noncovalently, nearly all of the T_4 and T_3 in plasma (Table 38-1). The small, unbound (free) fraction is responsible for the biologic activity. In spite of the great difference in total amount, the free fraction of T_3 approxi-

Table 38–1. Comparison of T_4 and T_3 in plasma.

Total Hormone (μg/dL)	Free Hormone			$t\frac{1}{2}$ in Blood (days)
	Percent of Total	ng/dL	Molarity	
T_4 8	0.03	~ 2.24	3.0×10^{-11}	6.5
T_3 0.15	0.3	~ 0.4	$~0.6 \times 10^{-11}$	1.5

mates that of T_4, but the plasma half-life of T_4 is 4–5 times that of T_3.

TBG is also subject to regulation, an important consideration in diagnostic testing of thyroid function, since most assays of T_4 or T_3 measure the total amount in plasma rather than the free hormone. TBG is produced in liver, and its synthesis is increased by estrogens (pregnancy and birth control pills). Decreased production of TBG occurs following androgen or glucocorticoid therapy and in certain liver diseases. Inherited increases or decreases of TBG also occur. All of these conditions result in changes of total T_4 and T_3 without a change of the free level. Phenytoin and salicylates compete with T_3 and T_4 for binding to TBG. This decreases the total level of hormone without changing the free fraction and must be considered when interpreting diagnostic tests.

Extrathyroidal deiodination converts T_4 to T_3. Since T_3 binds to the thyroid receptor in target cells with 10 times the affinity of T_4, T_3 is thought to be the preponderant metabolically active form of the molecule. About 80% of circulating T_4 is converted to

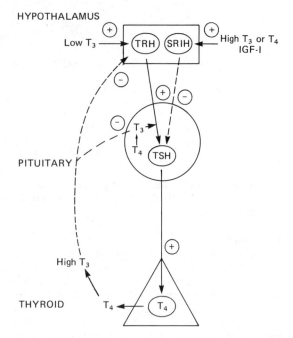

Figure 38–5. Feedback regulation of thyroid hormone biosynthesis. Solid lines and $\oplus$ symbols indicate stimulatory pathways and dashed lines and $\ominus$ symbols indicate inhibitory pathways. IGF-I, insulinlike growth factor I; SRIH, somatostatin; TRH, thyrotropin-stimulating hormone; TSH, thyroid-stimulating hormone.

T_3 or reverse T_3 (rT_3) in the periphery, and this conversion accounts for most of the production of T_3 (Fig 38–4). Reverse T_3 is a very weak agonist that is made in relatively larger amounts in chronic disease, in carbohydrate starvation, and in the fetus. Propylthiouracil and propranolol decrease the conversion of T_4 to T_3.

Other forms of thyroid hormone metabolism include total deiodination and inactivation by deamination or decarboxylation. Hepatic glucuronidation and sulfation result in a more hydrophilic molecule that is excreted into bile, reabsorbed in the gut, deiodinated in the kidney, and excreted as the glucuronide conjugate in the urine.

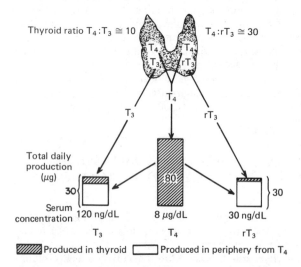

Figure 38–4. Quantitative outline of thyroidal secretion and peripheral conversions of thyroxine (T_4) and thyroidal and peripheral production of triiodothyronine (T_3) and reverse triiodothyronine (rT_3). The approximate serum concentrations of T_3 and rT_3 derived from thyroidal and peripheral production are also shown. (Reproduced, with permission, from Schimmel M, Utiger RD: Thyroidal and peripheral production of thyroid hormones. *Ann Intern Med* 1977; 87:760.)

REGULATION OF THYROID HORMONE SYNTHESIS & RELEASE

The primary components of the negative feedback loop consist of T_4, T_3, TSH, and TRH (Fig 38–5). T_4 and T_3 cause feedback inhibition of their own synthesis. T_3 may be the actual feedback mediator, since T_4 is converted to T_3 in the pituitary. Feedback at this level inhibits TSH release. T_3 (or possibly T_4) may also inhibit the release and production of TRH by the hypothalamus. The stimulus for

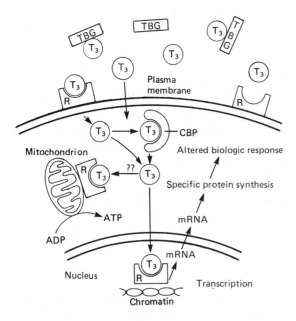

Figure 38–6. Proposed mechanism of thyroid hormone action. T_3 enters the cell directly or by a cell surface receptor. An interaction with low-affinity cytoplasmic protein may occur, and the hormone may interact with mitochondrial receptors, but the major action, which results in selective gene activation, involves combination with nuclear receptors. (Modified and reproduced, with permission, from Katzung BG [editor]: *Basic & Clinical Pharmacology,* 2nd ed. Lange, 1984. Courtesy of JA Williams.)

MECHANISM OF ACTION OF THYROID HORMONES

Thyroid hormones bind to specific high-affinity receptors in the target cell nucleus; T_3 binds with approximately 10 times the affinity of T_4. The question as to whether all biologic activity of the thyroid hormones is mediated by T_3 is thus moot; both T_3 and T_4 are active. A comparison of various thyroid hormone analogs shows a high correlation between binding affinity and ability to elicit a biologic response. Thyroid hormones bind to low-affinity sites in cytoplasm, but this is apparently not the same protein as the nuclear receptor. The cytoplasmic binding may serve to keep thyroid hormones "in the neighborhood." Plasma membrane binding of T_3 has been described; the role this plays in hormone transport is uncertain. A general model of thyroid hormone action is illustrated in Fig 38–6.

The general metabolic function of thyroid hormones is to increase oxygen consumption. This effect is seen in all organs except those that are most critical such as the brain, reticuloendothelial system, and gonads. This observation directed attention to the mitochondria, where T_4 was shown to cause morphologic changes and to uncouple oxidative phosphorylation. These observed effects require massive amounts of T_4 and almost certainly are not physiologic events. Thyroid hormones induce mitochondrial α-glycerophosphate dehydrogenase, and this may be related to the effects on O_2 consumption.

Edelman and coworkers have recently hypothesized that much of the energy utilized by a cell is for driving the **Na^+/K^+-ATPase pump.** Thyroid hormones enhance the function of this pump by increasing the number of pump units. Since all cells have this pump and virtually all cells respond to thyroid hormones, this increased utilization of ATP and the associated increase of oxygen consumption via oxidative phosphorylation could be the basic mechanism of thyroid hormone action.

Thyroid hormones, like steroids, induce proteins through an enhanced gene transcription mechanism. Although few specific examples are known, this is presumed to be the mechanism by which T_3 enhances general protein synthesis and causes positive nitrogen balance. Here again there is a curious association between the 2 classes of hormones related to growth, the thyroid hormones and growth hormone itself. T_3 and glucocorticoids enhance transcription of the GH gene, so that more GH is produced. This explains a classic observation in which the pituitaries of T_3-deficient animals were found to lack GH, and it may account for some of the general anabolic effects of T_3. Very high concentrations of T_3 inhibit protein synthesis and cause negative nitrogen balance.

Thyroid hormones are known to be important modulators of developmental processes. This is

increased release of TRH and TSH is a decrease of free thyroid hormone in the blood. Even if thyroid hormone biosynthesis is completely blocked, as with antithyroid drug therapy, enhanced release of TRH and TSH does not occur immediately. The thyroid contains several weeks' supply of preformed hormone, and there are also substantial extrathyroidal stores (in liver and bound to TBG) that first must be depleted. In addition, the thyroid autoregulatory mechanism described above helps compensate when iodine deficiency threatens to decrease hormone biosynthesis.

There is an interesting entwining of the thyroid and growth hormone feedback loops that accounts for the regulatory mechanisms shown in Fig 38–5. T_3 and T_4 enhance the release of somatostatin (SRIH) from the hypothalamus, and this peptide inhibits TSH release from the pituitary. Somatostatin is involved in another way. Levels of somatostatin increase in response to increased plasma IGF-I, which in turn is stimulated by GH (see Chapter 37 and Fig 37–5). Children treated with GH for short stature occasionally develop hypothyroidism, presumably because the increase in IGF-I stimulates somatostatin release, which in turn shuts off TSH release. Adrenergic and dopaminergic agents inhibit TRH release, and the latter may also inhibit TSH release.

most apparent in amphibian metamorphosis. Thyroid hormones are required for the conversion of a tadpole into a frog, a process that involves resorption of the tail, limb-bud proliferation, conversion from fetal to adult hemoglobin, stimulation of urea cycle enzymes (carbamoyl phosphate synthase) so that urea is excreted rather than ammonia, and epidermal changes. Thyroid hormones are required for normal development in humans. Intrauterine or neonatal hypothyroidism results in **cretinism,** a condition characterized by multiple congenital defects and severe, irreversible mental retardation.

PATHOPHYSIOLOGY

GOITER

Any enlargement of the thyroid is referred to as a **goiter.** Simple goiter represents an attempt to compensate for decreased thyroid hormone production; thus, in all of these situations, elevated TSH is the common denominator. Causes include iodide deficiency; iodide excess, when the Wolff-Chaikoff escape mechanism fails; and a variety of rare inherited metabolic defects that illustrate the importance of various steps in thyroid hormone biosynthesis. These defects include (1) I^- transport defect; (2) iodination defect; (3) coupling defect; (4) deiodinase deficiency; and (5) production of abnormal iodinated proteins. Partial deficiencies of these functions may cause simple goiter in adults. Any of these causes of simple goiter can, when severe, cause hypothyroidism. Simple goiter is treated with exogenous thyroid hormone. Supplementation or restriction of iodide intake is appropriate for specific types of goiter.

HYPOTHYROIDISM

Insufficient amounts of free T_3 or T_4 result in the clinical condition known as **hypothyroidism.** This is usually due to thyroid failure but can be due to disease of the pituitary or hypothalamus. In hypothyroidism, the basal metabolic rate is decreased, as are other processes dependent upon thyroid hormones. Prominent features include slow heart rate, diastolic hypertension, sluggish behavior, sleepiness, constipation, sensitivity to cold, dry skin and hair, and a sallow complexion. Other features depend upon the age at onset. Cretinism is discussed above. Hypothyroidism later in childhood results in short stature but no mental retardation. The various kinds of hypothyroidism are treated with exogenous thyroid hormone replacement.

HYPERTHYROIDISM

Hyperthyroidism, or **thyrotoxicosis,** is due to the excessive production of thyroid hormone. There are many causes, but most cases in the USA are due to **Graves' disease,** which results from the production of **thyroid-stimulating IgG (TSI)** that activates the TSH receptor (see Table 35–3). This causes a diffuse enlargement of the thyroid and excessive, uncontrolled production of T_3 and T_4, since the production of TSI is not under feedback control. Findings are multisystemic and include rapid heart rate, widened pulse pressure, nervousness, inability to sleep, weight loss in spite of increased appetite, weakness, excessive sweating, sensitivity to heat, and red, moist skin. The hyperthyroidism of Graves' disease is treated by blocking hormone production with an antithyroid drug, by ablating the gland with a radioactive isotope of iodide (such as ^{131}I), or by a combination of these 2 methods. Occasionally, the gland is removed surgically.

• • •

References

Cheron RG, Kaplan MM, Larson PR: Physiological and pharmacological influences on T_4 to T_3 conversion and nuclear T_3 binding in rat anterior pituitary. *J Clin Invest* 1979;**64**:1402.

Chopra IJ et al: Pathways of metabolism of thyroid hormones. *Recent Prog Horm Res* 1978;**34**:531.

Jackson IMD: Thyrotropin-releasing hormone. *N Engl J Med* 1982;**306**:145.

Larsen PR: Thyroid-pituitary interaction: Feedback regulation of thyrotropin secretion by thyroid hormones. *N Engl J Med* 1982;**396**:23.

Lo GS et al: Dependence of renal (Na^+ and K^+)-ATPase activity on thyroid status. *J Biol Chem* 1976;**251**:7826.

Nakashima T, Taurog A, Riesco G: Mechanism of action of thioureylene antithyroid drugs. *Endocrinology* 1978; **103**:2187.

Oppenheimer JH: Thyroid hormone action at the cellular level. *Science* 1979;**203**:971.

Oppenheimer JH: Thyroid hormone action at the nuclear level. *Ann Intern Med* 1985;**102**:374.

Robins J et al: Thyroxine transport proteins of plasma: Molecular properties and biosynthesis. *Recent Prog Horm Res* 1978; **34**:477.

Silver TM et al: Inhibition by somatostatin on the release of TSH induced in man by TRH. *J Clin Endocrinol Metab* 1974; **38**:742.

Hormones That Regulate Calcium Metabolism | 39

Daryl K. Granner, MD

GENERAL FEATURES

There is approximately 1 kg of calcium in the human body. Ninety-nine percent of this is located in bone where, with phosphate, it forms the **hydroxyapatite crystals** that provide the inorganic and structural component of the skeleton. Bone is a dynamic tissue, and it undergoes constant remodeling as stresses change; in the steady-state condition, there is a balance between new bone formation and bone resorption. Most of the calcium in bone is not freely exchangeable with **extracellular fluid (ECF) calcium.** Thus, in addition to its mechanical role, bone serves as a large reservoir of calcium. About 1% of skeletal Ca^{2+} is in a freely exchangeable pool and this, with another 1% of the total found in the periosteal space, constitutes the **miscible pool of Ca^{2+}.** These features are depicted in Fig 39–1. The hormones discussed in this chapter regulate the amount of calcium in the ECF by influencing the transport of calcium across the membrane that separates the ECF space from the periosteal fluid space. This transport is primarily stimulated by parathyroid hormone (PTH), but calcitriol is also involved. Calcitonin may counteract these effects.

Calcium ion regulates a number of important physiologic and biochemical processes including **neuromuscular excitability, blood coagulation, secretory processes, membrane integrity and plasma membrane transport, enzyme reactions, the release of hormones and neurotransmitters,** and the **intracellular action** of a number of hormones. In addition, the proper ECF and periosteal concentrations of Ca^{2+} and PO_4^{3-} are required for **bone mineralization.** To ensure that these processes operate normally, the plasma Ca^{2+} concentration is maintained within *very* narrow limits.

Plasma calcium exists in 3 forms: (1) **complexed** with organic acids; (2) **protein-bound;** and (3) **ionized.** About 6% of total calcium is complexed with citrate, phosphate, and other anions. The remainder is divided nearly equally between a protein-bound form (bound primarily to albumin) and an ionized (unbound) form. The ionized calcium (Ca^{2+}), which is maintained at concentrations between 1.1 and 1.3 mmol/L in most mammals, birds, and fresh-water fish, is the biologically active fraction. The organism has very little tolerance for significant deviation from this normal range. If the ionized calcium level falls, the animal becomes increasingly hyperexcitable and may develop tetanic convulsions. A marked elevation of plasma calcium may result in death owing to muscle paralysis and coma.

Calcium ion and the counter-ion, phosphate, exist at or near their solubility product in plasma; hence, protein binding may protect against precipitation and **ectopic calcification.** An alteration of the plasma protein concentration (primarily albumin, but globulins also bind calcium) results in parallel changes in total plasma calcium. For example, hypoalbuminemia re-

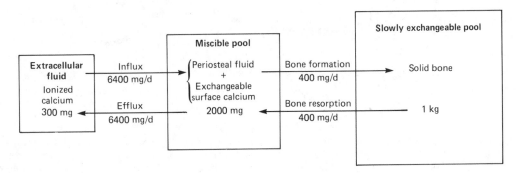

Figure 39–1. Dynamics of calcium homeostasis. Calcium exits in 3 pools: (1) the ECF; (2) miscible bone; and (3) a slowly exchangeable bone pool. The daily movement of calcium between these pools in a normal human is shown.

sults in a decrease of total plasma calcium of approximately 0.8 mg/dL for each g/dL of albumin decrease. The converse is noted when the plasma albumin is increased. The association of calcium with plasma proteins is pH-dependent; acidosis favors the ionized form, whereas alkalosis enhances binding and causes a concomitant decrease in Ca^{2+}. The latter probably accounts for the numbness and tingling associated with the **hyperventilation syndrome,** which causes acute respiratory alkalosis.

CALCIUM HOMEOSTASIS

The primordial sea consisted primarily of K^+ and Mg^{2+}, so proteins evolved with the ability to function best in that ionic milieu. With time, the composition of the sea changed, and Na^+ and Ca^{2+} became relatively more abundant. Thus, in order to preserve intracellular protein function in the changing environment, it became necessary to limit the intracellular concentrations of sodium and calcium while conserving the potassium and magnesium environment. This was achieved by the development of membrane-associated pumps for sodium and calcium which, in the case of Ca^{2+}, maintain about a 1000-fold concentration gradient between cytosol and extracellular fluid. Na^+ and Ca^{2+} now constitute the major extracellular ionic environment of multicellular animals. Hormones and other effectors

cause rapid, transient changes in the flux of calcium ion across the cellular plasma membrane and from one intracellular compartment to another. **Thus, calcium ion serves as an intracellular mediator in a variety of metabolic reactions** (see Chapter 36).

The movement from an aquatic environment rich in Ca^{2+} to a terrestrial environment relatively deficient in this element necessitated the development of an intricate homeostatic mechanism to extract calcium from dietary sources and to ensure against marked changes of the Ca^{2+} concentration in ECF. This mechanism involves the actions of 3 hormones—**parathyroid hormone (PTH), calcitriol** [1,25(OH)₂-D₃], and **calcitonin (CT)**—acting on 3 organs—bone, kidney, and intestine. A schematic view of this is illustrated in Fig 39–2. The parathyroid glands increase the secretion of PTH when the level of ionized calcium in plasma falls below the lower limit of the normal range (< 1.1 mmol/L). PTH stimulates the movement of calcium and phosphate **from bone to blood** and acts upon the **kidney to increase calcium resorption and phosphate excretion.**

A second important action of PTH on the kidney is to stimulate the formation of 1,25(OH)₂-D₃. This compound, currently referred to as calcitriol, is the active form of what previously was called vitamin D. **Calcitriol acts upon the intestine to increase calcium absorption** and probably plays a permissive role in the actions of PTH on bone and kidney. The concerted actions of these agents are to raise the level of Ca^{2+} in ECF while maintaining or decreasing the

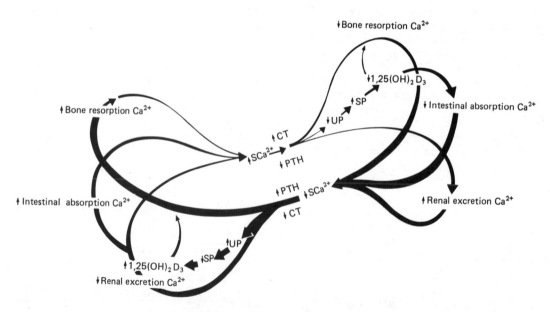

Figure 39–2. Regulation of calcium homeostasis. Three overlapping control loops interlock and relate to one another through the level of blood concentrations of Ca^{2+}, PTH, and CT. Each loop involves a calciotropic hormone target organ (bone, intestine, kidney). The limbs of the 3 loops that describe physiologic events which increase blood concentrations of calcium (SCa²⁺) are on the left; the limbs that describe events which decrease blood concentrations of calcium are on the right. UP, urine phosphorus; SP, serum phosphorus. (Modified and reproduced, with permission, from Arnaud CD: Calcium homeostasis: Regulatory elements and their integration. *Fed Proc* 1978;**37**:2557.)

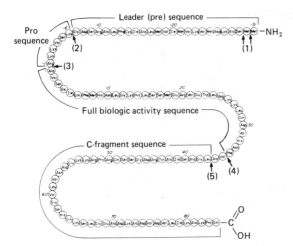

Figure 39–3. Structure of bovine preproparathyroid hormone. Arrows indicate sites cleaved by processing enzymes in the parathyroid gland (1–5) and in the liver after secretion of the hormone (4–5). The biologically active region of the molecule is flanked by sequence not required for activity on target organ receptors. (Slightly modified and reproduced, with permission, from Habener JF: Recent advances in parathyroid hormone research. *Clin Biochem* 1981;**14**:223.)

concentration of phosphate. There is a feedback inhibition of PTH secretion when extracellular Ca^{2+} reaches the normal level. An increase of Ca^{2+} also inhibits the formation of calcitriol (in part by lowering PTH) and increases the production of inactive metabolites of this compound. This results in decreased intestinal calcium absorption and decreased PTH action on bone and kidney. In some animals, an elevation of extracellular Ca^{2+} stimulates the secretion of calcitonin (CT) from C cells of the thyroid or the ultimobranchial bodies. The role of CT in normal calcium homeostasis is obscure in humans, but in some in vitro test systems CT appears to inhibit bone resorption.

HORMONES INVOLVED IN CALCIUM HOMEOSTASIS

PARATHYROID HORMONE (PTH)

Glandular Origin

Human PTH is produced by 4 small glands having a total weight of 0.05–0.3 g. An upper pair develops from the fourth branchial pouch and a lower pair from the third branchial pouch. Because of this derivation, the parathyroids can be found anywhere in the neck or upper mediastinum but usually are located just behind the posterior thyroid capsule. The small size, variable location, and delicate vascular supply of the parathyroids make them particularly liable to damage or removal during thyroid or parathyroid surgery.

The function of the parathyroid glands is to secrete PTH, which (with calcitriol) maintains the concentration of ionized calcium in the plasma within a very narrow range despite wide fluctuations in calcium intake, excretion, and deposition in bone.

Structure

PTH is an 84-amino-acid single-chain peptide (MW 9500) that contains no carbohydrate or other covalently bound molecules (Fig 39–3). Full biologic activity resides in the N-terminal third of the molecule; PTH_{1-34} has full biologic activity. The region 25–34 is primarily responsible for receptor binding.

PTH is synthesized as a 115-amino-acid precursor molecule (Fig 39–3). The immediate precursor of PTH is **proPTH,** which differs from the native hormone by having an N-terminal highly basic hexapeptide extension whose function is obscure. The primary gene product and the immediate precursor for proPTH is **preproPTH.** This differs from proPTH by having an additional 25-amino-acid N-terminal extension that, in common with the other leader or signal sequences characteristic of secreted proteins, is hydrophobic. The complete structure of preproPTH and the sequences of proPTH and PTH are illustrated in Fig 39–3.

PTH was the first preprohormone identified, and the sequence of events involved in the conversion of this to PTH is shown in schematic form in Fig 39–4. PreproPTH is transferred to the cisternal space of the endoplasmic reticulum while the molecule is still being translated from PTH mRNA by the ribosomes. During this transfer, the 25-amino-acid prepeptide (signal or leader peptide) is removed to yield proPTH. ProPTH is then transported to the Golgi apparatus, where an enzyme removes the pro-extension to yield the mature PTH molecule. The PTH released from the Golgi apparatus in secretory vesicles has 3 possible fates: (1) transport into a storage pool; (2) degradation; or (3) immediate secretion.

Role in Mineral Homeostasis

A. Calcium Homeostasis: The central role of PTH in calcium metabolism is underscored by the observation that the first evolutionary appearance of this hormone was in animals attempting to adapt to a terrestrial existence. The physiologic maintenance of calcium balance depends on the long-term effects of PTH acting on intestinal absorption through the formation of calcitriol. If in the face of prolonged dietary Ca^{2+} deficiency intestinal calcium absorption is inadequate, a complex regulatory system involving PTH is brought into play. PTH restores normal ECF calcium concentration by acting directly on bone and kidney and by acting indirectly on the intestinal mucosa (through stimulation of synthesis of calcitriol). PTH (1) increases the rate of dissolution of bone, including both organic and inorganic phases, which moves Ca^{2+} into ECF; (2) reduces the renal clearance or excretion of calcium, hence increasing the ECF concentration of this cation; and (3) increases the efficiency of calcium

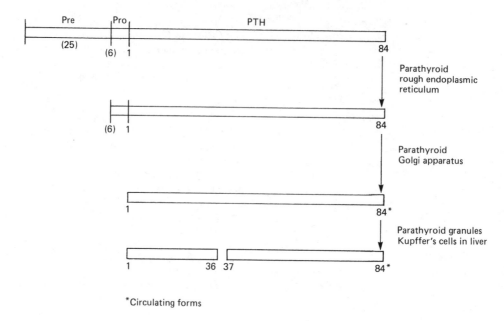

Figure 39–4. The precursors and cleavage products of PTH and the location of these steps in the parathyroid gland and liver.

absorption from the intestine by promoting the synthesis of calcitriol. The most rapid changes occur through the action on the kidney, but the largest effect is from bone. Therefore, although PTH prevents hypocalcemia in the face of dietary calcium deficiency, it does so at the expense of bone substance.

B. Phosphate Homeostasis: The usual counter-ion for Ca^{2+} is phosphate, and the hydroxyapatite crystal in bone consists of calcium phosphate. Phosphate is released with calcium from bone whenever PTH increases dissolution of the mineral matrix. PTH increases renal phosphate clearance; thus, the net effect of PTH on bone and kidney is to increase the ECF calcium concentration and decrease the ECF phosphate concentration. Importantly, this prevents the development of a supersaturated concentration of calcium and phosphate in plasma.

Biochemistry

A. Regulation of Synthesis: The rate of synthesis and degradation of proPTH is unaffected by the ambient Ca^{2+} concentration, even though the rate of formation and secretion of PTH is always markedly enhanced at low Ca^{2+} concentrations. Indeed, 80–90% of the proPTH synthesized cannot be accounted for as intact PTH in cells or in the incubation medium of experimental systems. This led to the conclusion that most of the proPTH synthesized is quickly degraded. It was later discovered that this rate of degradation decreases when Ca^{2+} concentrations are low and increases when Ca^{2+} concentrations are high. This indicates that **calcium affects PTH production through control of degradation and not synthesis.** The constitutive synthesis of proPTH is reflected in

PTH mRNA levels, which also do not change in spite of wide fluctuations of extracellular Ca^{2+}. It appears that the only way that the organism can enhance PTH synthesis is to increase the size and number of PTH-producing chief cells in the parathyroid glands.

B. Regulation of Metabolism: The degradation of PTH begins about 20 minutes after proPTH is synthesized, is initially unaffected by the Ca^{2+} concentration, and occurs after the hormone is in secretory vesicles, as shown in Fig 39–5. Newly formed PTH can either be secreted immediately or be placed in storage vesicles for subsequent secretion. Degradation occurs as soon as the secretory vesicle begins to enter the storage compartment.

Very specific fragments of PTH are generated during its proteolytic digestion (Figs 39–3 and 39–4), and large amounts of carboxy-terminal fragments of PTH are found in the circulation. These molecules, with molecular weights of about 7000, consist of PTH$_{37-84}$ and lesser amounts of PTH$_{34-84}$. Most of the newly synthesized PTH is degraded. About 2 mol of the C-terminal fragments is secreted for each mole of intact PTH; hence, the bulk of circulating PTH consists of the C-terminal molecules. No biologic function for the C-terminal fragment of PTH has been defined, but it may prolong the half-life of the hormone in the circulation. A number of proteolytic enzymes, including **cathepsins B and D,** have been identified in parathyroid tissue. Cathepsin B cleaves PTH into 2 fragments, PTH$_{1-36}$ and PTH$_{37-84}$. PTH$_{37-84}$ is not further degraded; however, PTH$_{1-36}$ is rapidly and progressively cleaved into di- and tripeptides. ProPTH has never been found in circulation, and little (if any) PTH$_{1-34}$ escapes from the gland. PreproPTH was iden-

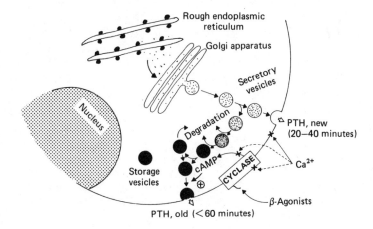

Figure 39–5. Processing, secretion, and degradation of PTH in a parathyroid cell. (Modified and reproduced, with permission, from Cohn DV, Elting J: Biosynthesis, processing, and secretion of parathormone and secretory protein–1. *Recent Prog Horm Res* 1983;**39**:181.)

tified by deciphering the coding sequence of the PTH gene.

Most of the proteolysis of PTH occurs within the gland; however, there are a number of studies which confirm that PTH, once secreted, is proteolytically degraded in other tissues. The exact contribution of extraglandular proteolysis has not been defined, nor is it clear whether the proteolytic enzymes in the 2 sites are similar or whether the patterns and products of cleavage are identical.

The liver and kidneys are involved in peripheral metabolism of secreted PTH. After hepatectomy, no 34–84 or 37–84 fragments are detected, indicating that the liver is the principal organ involved in the generation of these fragments. The role of the kidneys may be to remove and excrete these fragments. The principal site of **peripheral proteolysis** appears to be the **Kupffer cells** lining the intrasinusoidal passages of the liver. The endopeptidase responsible for the initial cleavage into the amino- and carboxy-terminal fragments is located on the surface of these macrophagelike cells, which are in intimate contact with plasma. This enzyme, also a cathepsin B, cleaves PTH between residues 36 and 37; as in the parathyroid, the resulting carboxy-terminal fragment continues to circulate, whereas the amino-terminal fragment is rapidly degraded.

C. Regulation of Secretion: PTH secretion is inversely related to the ambient concentration of ionized calcium and magnesium, as is the circulating level of immunoreactive PTH. Fig 39–6 illustrates that serum PTH declines in a rectilinear fashion in relation to serum calcium levels between 4 mg/dL and 10.5 mg/dL. The presence of biologically active PTH when the serum calcium level is 10.5 mg/dL or greater is an indication of **hyperparathyroidism.**

A variety of agents that increase intracellular cAMP enhance the secretion of PTH (Fig 39–5). These include β-adrenergic agonists, prostaglandins

E_1 and E_2, dopamine, secretin, cholera toxin, cAMP derivatives, and agents that inhibit cAMP phosphodiesterase activity. β-Adrenergic antagonists inhibit secretion. There is a linear relationship between PTH release and the parathyroid intracellular level of cAMP. The intracellular Ca^{2+} level may be involved in this process, since there is an inverse relationship between the intracellular concentrations of calcium and cAMP. Calcium may exert this effect through its known action on phosphodiesterase (via Ca^{2+}/ calmodulin–dependent protein kinase) or through a similar mechanism by inhibiting adenylate cyclase (Fig 39–5). Phosphate has no effect on PTH secretion.

Bovine parathyroid glands have relatively few

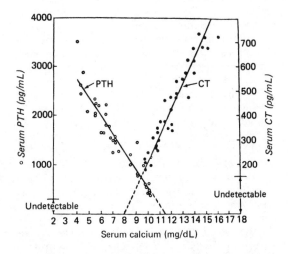

Figure 39–6. Concentration of calcitonin (CT) and parathyroid hormone (PTH) as a function of serum calcium level. (Modified and reproduced, with permission, from Aurbach GD et al: Polypeptide hormones and calcium metabolism. *Ann Intern Med* 1969;**70**:1243.)

storage granules and contain enough hormone to maintain maximal secretion for only 1.5 hours. This is in contrast to the pancreatic islets, which contain insulin stores sufficient for several days, and to the thyroid, which contains hormone stores adequate for several weeks. PTH must therefore be continually synthesized and secreted.

Mechanism of Action

A. The PTH Receptor: PTH binds to a single membrane receptor protein of approximately 70,000 MW. This receptor appears to be identical in bone and kidney, and it is not found in nontarget cells. The hormone-receptor interaction initiates a typical cascade: activation of adenylate cyclase → increased intracellular cAMP → increased intracellular calcium → phosphorylation of specific intracellular proteins by kinases → activation of the intracellular enzymes or proteins that finally mediate the biologic actions of the hormone. The PTH response system, like that for many other peptide and protein hormones, is subject to **"down regulation"** of receptor number and to **"desensitization,"** which may involve a post-cAMP mechanism.

B. Effects of PTH on Bone: PTH has multiple effects on bone and apparently influences several types of bone cells. The net effect is bone destruction, with the concomitant release of calcium, phosphate, and organic matrix elements, including collagen breakdown products. The cell responsible for this may be the **osteoclast,** which certainly can destroy bone when stimulated chronically with PTH, or the **osteocyte,** which also can resorb bone. PTH may stimulate the differentiation of precursor cells into bone-resorbing cells. At low concentrations, perhaps within the physiologic range, PTH has an anabolic effect and is responsible for bone remodeling. At these concentrations, **osteoblasts** increase in number, there is an increase in alkaline phosphatase activity that reflects new bone formation, and the incorporation of radioactive sulfate into cartilage is promoted. Calcitriol may play a permissive role in the action of PTH on bone.

Ca^{2+} may be the intracellular messenger for PTH. The earliest action of PTH is to decrease pericellular Ca^{2+} while increasing intracellular Ca^{2+}. Increased intracellular calcium promotes bone cell RNA synthesis and the release of enzymes associated with bone resorption. These processes appear to be mediated through the binding of calcium to calmodulin. In the absence of extracellular calcium, PTH still increases cAMP but no longer stimulates bone resorption. Thus, a major requirement for PTH stimulation of bone resorption may be a paradoxic increase of the uptake of ionized calcium into the bone-resorbing cells.

C. Effects of PTH on Kidney: PTH has many effects on the kidney; it influences the transport of several ions and regulates the synthesis of calcitriol. Under normal conditions, Ca^{2+} resorption exceeds 90% of the filtered load, and **PTH increases Ca^{2+} resorption** to greater than 98%. Phosphate resorption varies between 75 and 90%, since it is more dependent

on dietary intake and other factors, but **PTH inhibits phosphate resorption** whatever the basal rate. PTH also inhibits sodium, potassium, and bicarbonate transport. The effects of PTH on calcitriol metabolism (see below and Chapter 11) may occur at the same cellular sites as its effects on mineral resorption.

An infusion of PTH results in a prompt increase of intracellular cAMP in renal cells and in the prompt excretion of cAMP in urine. This response precedes the characteristic phosphaturia and is presumed to be responsible for the latter. The PTH-stimulated adenylate cyclase is in the basolateral portion of renal cortical tubular cells and is distinct from the renal adenylate cyclase that is stimulated by calcitonin, catecholamines, and ADH. The intracellular receptor proteins for cAMP (presumably protein kinases) are found in the brush border of these cells on the luminal surface of the tubule. The cAMP generated by PTH stimulation therefore migrates from the basolateral aspect of the cell to the luminal surface, where it facilitates ion transport.

Calcium may also be involved in the renal mechanism of action of PTH. Indeed, the first physiologic effect of PTH administration is to decrease extracellular fluid Ca^{2+} while intracellular Ca^{2+} increases. These changes, however, occur after the changes in cAMP, so that the association of Ca^{2+} flux to PTH action is not so clear in the kidney.

D. Effects of PTH on Intestinal Mucosa: PTH probably has no direct effect on Ca^{2+} transport across the intestinal mucosa, but **it is critically involved in the biosynthesis of calcitriol** (see below) and certainly has an important indirect effect on the intestine.

Pathophysiology

Insufficient amounts of PTH result in **hypoparathyroidism.** The biochemical hallmarks of this condition are decreased serum ionized calcium and elevated serum phosphate levels. Symptoms include neuromuscular irritability which, when mild, causes muscle cramps and **tetany.** Severe, acute hypocalcemia results in tetanic paralysis of the respiratory muscles, laryngospasm, severe convulsions, and death. Long-standing hypocalcemia results in cutaneous changes, cataracts, and calcification of the basal ganglia of the brain. The usual cause of hypoparathyroidism is accidental removal or damage of the glands during neck surgery (secondary hypoparathyroidism), but the disorder occasionally results from **autoimmune destruction** of the glands (primary hypoparathyroidism).

Pseudohypoparathyroidism is discussed in Chapter 36. Biologically active PTH is produced in this inherited disorder, but there is end-organ resistance to its effects. The biochemical consequences are the same, however. There are usually associated developmental anomalies including short stature, short metacarpal or metatarsal bones, and mental retardation. There are several types of pseudohypoparathyroidism, and they have been attributed to (1) an altered or deficient PTH receptor, (2) deficiency of the G_s

adenylate cyclase regulatory protein, and (3) a defective step beyond the formation of cAMP.

Hyperparathyroidism, the excessive production of PTH, is usually due to the presence of a functioning **parathyroid adenoma** but can be due to **parathyroid hyperplasia** or to **ectopic production** of PTH in a malignant tumor. The biochemical hallmarks of hyperparathyroidism are elevated serum ionized calcium and PTH and depressed serum phosphate levels. In long-standing hyperparathyroidism, findings include extensive resorption of bone and a variety of renal effects, including kidney stones, nephrocalcinosis, frequent urinary tract infections, and (in severe cases) decreased renal function. **Secondary hyperparathyroidism,** characterized by hyperplasia of the glands and hypersecretion of PTH, may be seen in patients with progressive renal failure. Hyperparathyroidism in these patients is presumably due to the decreased conversion of $25OH-D_3$ to $1,25(OH)_2-D_3$ in the diseased renal parenchyma, which results in inefficient calcium absorption in the gut and the secondary release of PTH in a compensatory attempt to maintain normal ECF calcium levels.

CALCITRIOL ($1,25[OH]_2-D_3$)

General Role in Calcium Homeostasis

A. Historical Perspective: Rickets, a childhood disorder characterized by deficient mineralization of the skeleton and severe, crippling bone deformities, was epidemic in North America and Western Europe early in this century. Results of a series of studies suggested that rickets was due to a dietary deficiency. After the discovery that rickets could be prevented by ingestion of cod-liver oil and that the active ingredient in this agent was not vitamin A, the preventive factor was termed fat-soluble **vitamin D.** About the same time, it was found that ultraviolet light, either artificial or from sunlight, would also prevent the disorder. It was subsequently determined that there was an adult equivalent to rickets. **Osteomalacia,** in which there is a failure to mineralize bone, also responded to vitamin D. Clues to further developments resulted from the observation that patients with liver or kidney disease did not respond normally to vitamin D. For the last 50 years, efforts to elucidate the structure of vitamin D and to define its mechanism of action have proceeded, greatly accelerated during the last 10 years.

B. Homeostatic Role: The principal biologic role of calcitriol is **to stimulate intestinal absorption of calcium and phosphate.** Calcitriol is the only hormone which can promote this translocation of calcium against the concentration gradient that exists across the intestinal cell membrane. Since the production of calcitriol is tightly regulated (Fig 39–7), a fine mechanism exists for controlling ECF Ca^{2+} in spite of marked fluctuations of the calcium content of food. This assures a proper concentration of calcium and phosphate for deposition, as hydroxyapatite crystals, onto the collagen fibrils in bone. In vitamin D deficiency (calcitriol deficiency), new bone formation slows and bone remodeling is also impaired. These processes are primarily regulated by PTH acting on bone cells, but small concentrations of calcitriol are also required. Calcitriol may also augment the actions of PTH on renal calcium reabsorption.

Biochemistry

A. Biosynthesis: Calcitriol is a hormone in every respect. It is produced by a complex series of enzymatic reactions that involve the plasma transport of precursor molecules to a number of different tissues (Fig 39–7). The active molecule, calcitriol, is transported to other organs where it activates biologic processes in a manner similar to that employed by other steroid hormones.

1. Skin–Small amounts of **vitamin D** occur in food (fish-liver oil, egg yolk), but most of the vitamin D available for calcitriol synthesis is produced in the malpighian layer of the epidermis from 7-dehydrocholesterol in an ultraviolet light–mediated, nonenzymatic **photolysis reaction.** The extent of this conversion is directly related to the intensity of the exposure and inversely related to the extent of pigmentation in the skin. There is an age-related loss of 7-dehydrocholesterol in the epidermis that may be related to the negative calcium balance associated with old age.

2. Liver–A specific transport protein called the **D-binding protein** binds vitamin D_3 and its metabolites and moves D_3 from the skin or intestine to the liver where it undergoes 25-hydroxylation, the first obligatory reaction in the production of calcitriol. 25-Hydroxylation occurs in the endoplasmic reticulum in a reaction that requires magnesium, NADPH, molecular oxygen, and an uncharacterized cytoplasmic factor. Two enzymes, an NADPH-dependent cytochrome P-450 reductase and a cytochrome P-450, are involved. This reaction is not regulated, and it also occurs with low efficiency in kidney and intestine. The $25OH-D_3$ enters the circulation, where it is the major form of vitamin D found in plasma, and is transported to the kidney by the D-binding protein.

3. Kidney–$25OH-D_3$ is a weak agonist and must be modified by hydroxylation at position C_1 for full biologic activity. This is accomplished in mitochondria of the renal proximal convoluted tubule in a complex, 3-component monooxygenase reaction that requires NADPH, Mg^{2+}, molecular oxygen, and at least 3 enzymes: (1) a flavoprotein, renal ferredoxin reductase; (2) an iron sulfur protein, renal ferredoxin; and (3) cytochrome P-450. This system produces $1,25(OH)_2-D_3$, which is the most potent naturally occurring metabolite of vitamin D.

4. Other tissues–The placenta has a 1α-hydroxylase that appears to be an important extrarenal source of calcitriol. Enzyme activity is found in a variety of other tissues, including bone; however, the physiologic significance of this appears to be minimal, since very little calcitriol is found in nonpregnant, nephrectomized animals.

B. Regulation of Metabolism and Synthesis:

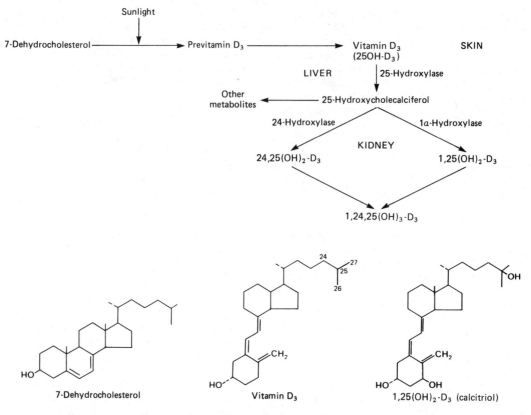

Figure 39–7. Formation and hydroxylation of vitamin D_3. 25-Hydroxylation takes place in the liver, and the other hydroxylations occur in the kidneys. $25,26(OH)_2$-D_3 and $1,25,26(OH)_3$-D_3 are probably formed as well. The formulas of 7-dehydrocholesterol, vitamin D_3, and $1,25(OH)_2$-D_3 (calcitriol) are also shown. (Reproduced, with permission, from Ganong WF: *Review of Medical Physiology,* 12th ed. Lange, 1985.)

Like other steroid hormones, calcitriol is subject to tight feedback regulation (Fig 39–7 and Table 39–1). Low-calcium diets and hypocalcemia result in marked increases of 1α-hydroxylase activity in intact animals. This effect requires PTH, which is also released in response to hypocalcemia. The action of PTH is as yet unexplained, but it stimulates 1α-hydroxylase activity in both vitamin D–deficient and vitamin D–treated animals. Low-phosphorus diets and hypophosphatemia also induce 1α-hydroxylase activity, but this appears to be a weaker stimulus than that provided by hypocalcemia.

Calcitriol is an important regulator of its own production. High levels of calcitriol inhibit renal 1α-hydroxylase and stimulate the formation of a 24-hydroxylase that leads to the formation of $24,25(OH)_2$-D_3, an apparently inactive by-product. Estrogens, progestins, and androgens cause marked increases of 1α-hydroxylase in ovulating birds. The role that these hormones, along with insulin, growth hormone, and prolactin, play in mammals is uncertain.

The basic sterol molecule can be modified by **alternative metabolic pathways,** ie, by hydroxylation at positions 1, 23, 24, 25, and 26 and by the formation of a number of lactones. Over 20 metabolites have been found; none have unequivocally been shown to have biologic activity.

Mechanism of Action

Calcitriol acts at the cellular level in a manner similar to other steroid hormones (Fig 39–8). Studies using radioactive calcitriol revealed localization in the nuclei of intestinal villus and crypt cells, osteoblasts, and distal renal tubular cells. There also is nuclear accumulation of this hormone in cells not previously suspected of being targets, including cells in the malpighian layer of the skin; pancreatic islet cells; some brain cells; some cells in the pituitary, ovary,

Table 39–1. Regulation of renal 1α-hydroxylase.

Primary Regulators	Secondary Regulators
Hypocalcemia	Estrogens
PTH	Androgens
Calcitriol	Progesterone
Hypophosphatemia	Insulin
	Growth hormone
	Prolactin
	Thyroid hormone

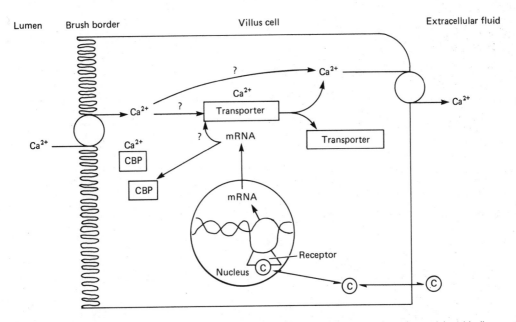

Figure 39–8. Calcitriol (C) acts like other steroid hormones. It induces several gene products (eg, calcium-binding protein, CBP) that promote the movement of calcium from the intestinal lumen to the extracellular fluid.

testis, placenta, uterus, mammary gland, and thymus; and myeloid precursors. Calcitriol binding has also been noted in parathyroid cells, which leads to the intriguing possibility that it might be involved in PTH metabolism.

A. The Calcitriol Receptor: An intestinal cell protein with a molecular weight of 90,000–100,000 binds calcitriol with high affinity and low capacity. This binding is saturable, specific, and reversible. This protein, which meets the basic criteria for being a receptor, has been found in many of the tissues listed above.

When examined under physiologic salt conditions, most of the unoccupied receptor is found in the nucleus in association with chromatin. This resembles the cases of receptors for T_3 and progesterone, if not for all steroid hormones. It is not certain whether the association of the calcitriol-receptor complex with chromatin requires an activation step, as do typical steroid hormone–receptor complexes.

B. Calcitriol-Dependent Gene Products: It has been known for several years that the response of intestinal transport to calcitriol requires RNA and protein synthesis. The observation of binding of the calcitriol receptor to chromatin in the nucleus suggests that calcitriol stimulates gene transcription and the formation of specific mRNAs. One such example, the induction of an mRNA that codes for a calcium-binding protein (CBP), has been reported.

There are several cytosolic proteins that bind Ca^{2+} with high affinity. One group, comprised of several proteins of different molecular weight, antigenicity, and tissue location (intestine, skin, and bone), is calcitriol-dependent. Of these, intestinal CBP has been studied most intensively. No CBP is found in the intestine of vitamin D–deficient rats, and the concentration of CBP is highly correlated with the extent of nuclear localization of calcitriol.

C. Effects of Calcitriol on Intestinal Mucosa: The transfer of Ca^{2+} or PO_4^{3-} across the intestinal mucosa requires (1) uptake across the brush border and microvillar membrane; (2) transport across the mucosal cell membrane; and (3) efflux across the basal lateral membrane into the ECF. It is clear that calcitriol enhances one or more of these steps, but the precise mechanism has not been established. CBP was thought to be actively involved until it was observed that Ca^{2+} translocation occurs within 1–2 hours after administration of calcitriol, well before CBP increases in response to calcitriol. CBP may bind Ca^{2+} and protect the mucosal cell against the large fluxes of Ca^{2+} coincident with the transport process. Several investigators are searching for other proteins that may be involved in Ca^{2+} transport, whereas others suggest that the process, particularly the early increase of Ca^{2+} flux, may be mediated by a membrane change. Phosphatidylinositide metabolites have been implicated.

D. Effects of Calcitriol on Other Tissues: Much less is known about the action of calcitriol in other tissues. Nuclear receptors are present in bone cells, and the increase in ECF Ca^{2+} following treatment with calcitriol requires concomitant RNA and protein synthesis. The gene products presumably induced by calcitriol are unknown, as is the mechanism by which PTH and calcitriol interact in bone cells.

An interesting role of calcitriol in cellular differentiation is suggested by studies demonstrating that this hormone promotes the conversion of promyelocytic leukemia cells into macrophages. Since osteoclasts are thought to be related to or derived from

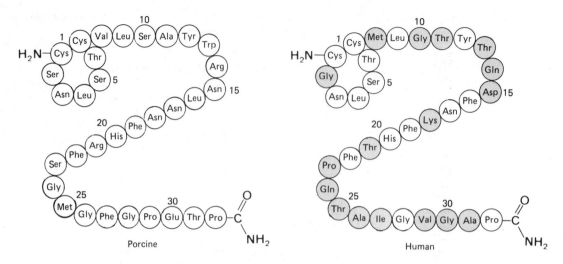

Figure 39–9. Structure of porcine and human calcitonin. Differences in amino acids are shaded in the human calcitonin structure.

macrophages, calcitriol may be involved in promoting the differentiation of bone cells.

Pathophysiology

Rickets is a childhood disorder characterized by low plasma calcium and phosphorus levels and by poorly mineralized bone with associated skeletal deformities. Rickets is most commonly due to **vitamin D deficiency.** There are 2 types of **vitamin D-dependent rickets. Type I** is an inherited autosomal recessive trait characterized by a defect in the conversion of 25OH-D_3 to calcitriol. **Type II** is an autosomal recessive disorder in which there is apparent absence of the calcitriol receptor.

Vitamin D deficiency in the adult results in **osteomalacia.** Calcium and phosphorus absorption are decreased, as are the ECF levels of these ions. Consequently mineralization of osteoid to form bone is impaired, and such undermineralized bone is structurally weak.

When substantial renal parenchyma is lost or diseased, the formation of calcitriol is reduced and calcium absorption decreases. When hypocalcemia ensues, there is a compensatory increase of PTH, which acts on bone in an attempt to increase ECF Ca^{2+}. The associated extensive bone turnover, structural changes, and symptoms are known as **renal osteodystrophy.** Early treatment with vitamin D will blunt this process.

CALCITONIN (CT)

Origin & Structure

Calcitonin (CT) is a 32-amino-acid peptide (Fig 39–9) secreted by the parafollicular C cells of the human thyroid (less commonly, the parathyroid or thymus) or by similar cells located in the ultimobran-

chial gland of other species. These cells originate in the neural crest and are biochemically related to cells in a variety of other endocrine glands.

The entire CT molecule, including the 7-member N-terminal loop, is required for biologic activity. There is tremendous interspecies variation of the amino acid sequence of CT (human and porcine CT share only 14 of 32 amino acids), but in spite of these differences there is cross-species bioactivity. The most potent naturally occurring CT is isolated from salmon.

Regulation of Secretion

CT and PTH secretion are inversely related (Fig 39–6), and both are controlled by the ECF ionized calcium (and probably magnesium) level. CT secretion increases linearly when calcium concentrations are between 9.5 and 15 mg/dL. Glucagon and pentagastrin are potent CT secretagogues, and the latter is used as a provocative test for medullary thyroid cancer, a malignant tumor of the parafollicular C cells.

Mechanism of Action

CT has a history unmatched by any other hormone. Within a 7-year span (1962–1968), CT was discovered, isolated, sequenced, and synthesized; yet its role in human physiology is still uncertain. Removal of the thyroid in animals does not result in hypercalcemia, and the injection of CT into healthy adults has little calcium-lowering effect.

In test systems, the primary target of CT is bone, where it decreases matrix resorption and therefore decreases the release of calcium and phosphate. In this action, CT is independent of PTH; it increases bone cAMP, presumably in cells other than those affected by PTH.

CT also has significant effects on phosphate metabolism. It causes phosphate to enter bone cells and the periosteal fluid while reducing the movement of calcium from bone to blood plasma. This entry of phosphate may be accompanied by calcium, since the hypocalcemic effects of CT depend upon phosphate. This action and the apparent ability of CT to inhibit osteoclast-mediated bone resorption probably account for its effectiveness in treating the hypercalcemia of cancer.

Pathophysiology

No clinical manifestations of CT deficiency have been described. CT excess occurs in **medullary thyroid carcinoma (MTC),** which can be sporadic or familial. CT levels in MTC are often thousands of times greater than normal, yet hypocalcemia is a very rare occurrence in MTC. Although the biologic importance of these elevated CT levels is obscure, the observation has important diagnostic implications. Measurement of plasma CT, often coupled to a calcium or pentagastrin challenge, allows early diagnosis of this potentially fatal disease at a time when it is curable.

• • •

References

Cohn DV, Elting J: Biosynthesis, processing, and secretion of parathormone and secretory protein–1. *Recent Prog Horm Res* 1983;**39**:181.

Copp CH: Parathyroids, calcitonin and control of plasma calcium. *Recent Prog Horm Res* 1964;**20**:59.

Deftos LJ: Calcitonin in clinical medicine. *Adv Intern Med* 1978;**34**:159.

DeLuca HF: Metabolism and molecular mechanism of action of vitamin D: 1981. *Biochem Soc Trans* 1982;**10**:147.

DeLuca HF, Schnoes HK: Vitamin D: Recent advances. *Annu Rev Biochem* 1983;**52**:411.

Massry SG: Pharmacology of magnesium. *Annu Rev Pharmacol Toxicol* 1977;**17**:67.

Norman AW, Roth J, Orci L: The vitamin D endocrine system: Steroid metabolism, hormone receptors, and biological response (calcium binding). *Endocr Rev* 1982;**3**:331.

Potts JT Jr, Kronenberg HM, Rosenblatt M: Parathyroid hormone: Chemistry, biosynthesis and mode of action. *Adv Protein Chem* 1982;**35**:323.

Rosenblatt M: Pre-proparathyroid hormone, proparathyroid hormone, and parathyroid hormone. *Clin Orthop* 1982;**170**:260.

Talmadge RV, VanderWiel CJ, Matthews JL: Calcitonin and phosphate. *Mol Cell Endocrinol* 1981;**24**:235.

40 | Hormones of the Adrenal Gland

Daryl K. Granner, MD

STRUCTURE OF THE ADRENAL GLAND

The mammalian adrenal actually consists of 2 glands: the **cortex** and the **medulla.** These have different embryologic origins and produce different kinds of hormones. The cortex originates from the retroperitoneal mesoderm and makes the **glucocorticoid, mineralocorticoid,** and **androgenic** steroids. The medulla is derived from the neural crest and makes the **catecholamine** hormones.

VASCULAR ANATOMY

The adrenal cortex receives blood through the many capsular arteries that form a plexus in the outer layer of the cortex (Fig 40–1). This plexus is drained by capillaries that traverse the cortex and form a second plexus in the zona reticularis, or deep layer, of the cortex. This second plexus becomes the **adrenal portal system,** which supplies the medulla with blood that is enriched with glucocorticoids, an important feature in epinephrine biosynthesis (see p 565). The capillaries of the medulla drain into the central adrenal vein. The central adrenal vein has a unique structural feature. It contains longitudinal muscle fibers that, by contracting and swelling, occlude venous effluent. Adrenal hormones are released in spurts, since this vein contracts or relaxes under neurogenic control.

ZONES OF THE ADRENAL CORTEX

The adult cortex has 3 distinct layers or zones. The subcapsular area is called the **zona glomerulosa** and is associated with the production of mineralocorticoids. Next is the **zona fasciculata,** which, with the **zona reticularis,** produces glucocorticoids and androgens. Human fetuses have a very large cortex that cannot easily be divided into zones; most of the fetal gland is devoted to the production of androgens. The fetal cortex rapidly involutes after birth and is replaced by the layered cortex.

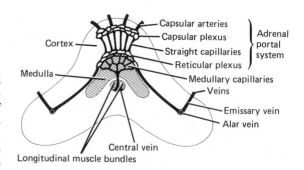

Figure 40–1. Anatomy of the human adrenal gland.

THE ADRENAL MEDULLA

The cells of the medulla are called **pheochromocytes** or **chromaffin** cells because they stain avidly with dichromate, which oxidizes the intracellular catecholamines and results in brown pigmentation of the cells. The origin and structure of the medulla are discussed in more detail below.

THE ADRENAL CORTEX

HORMONES

Some 50 steroids have been isolated and crystallized from adrenal tissue. Most of these are intermediates; only a small number are secreted in significant amounts; and few have significant hormonal activity. The adrenal cortex makes 3 general classes of steroid hormones, which are grouped according to their dominant action. There is an overlap of biologic activity, since all natural glucocorticoids have mineralocorticoid activity and vice versa. The **glucocorticoids** are 21-carbon steroids with many actions, the most important of which is to promote gluconeogenesis. **Cortisol** is the predominant glucocorticoid in humans, and it is made in the zona fasciculata. **Corticosterone,** made in the zonae fasciculata and glomerulosa, is less abundant in humans, but it is the

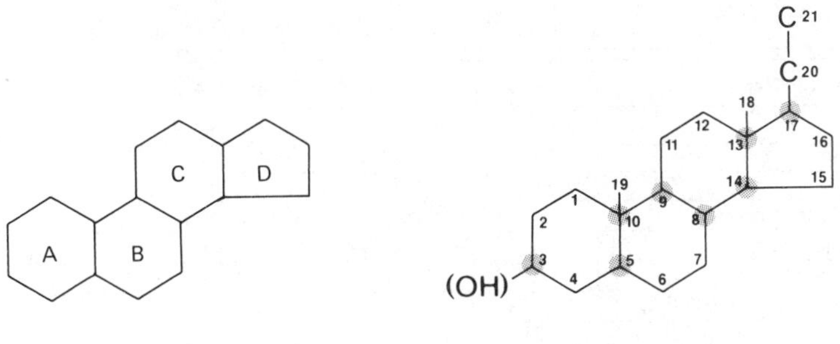

Cyclopentanoper-
hydrophenanthrene
nucleus

Numbering of the carbon
atoms. Asymmetric car-
bons are shaded.

Figure 40–2. Structural features of steroid molecules.

dominant glucocorticoid in rodents. **Mineralocorticoids** are also 21-carbon steroids. The primary action of these hormones is to promote retention of Na^+ and excretion of K^+ and H^+, particularly in the kidney. **Aldosterone** is the most potent hormone in this class, and it is made exclusively in the zona glomerulosa. The zonae fasciculata and reticularis of the adrenal cortex also produce significant amounts of the androgen precursor **dehydroepiandrosterone** and of the weak androgen **androstenedione.** These steroids are converted into more potent androgens in extra-adrenal tissues and become pathologic sources of androgens when specific steroidogenic enzymes are deficient. Estrogens are not made in the normal adrenal in significant amounts, but in certain cancers of the adrenal they may be produced, and androgens of adrenal origin are important precursors of estrogen (converted by peripheral aromatization) in postmenopausal women.

NOMENCLATURE & CHEMISTRY OF STEROIDS

All steroid hormones have in common the 17-carbon **cyclopentanoperhydrophenanthrene** structure with the 4 rings labeled A–D (Fig 40–2). Additional carbons can be added at positions 10 and 13 or as a side chain attached to C_{17}. Steroid hormones and their precursors and metabolites differ in number and type of substituted groups, number and location of double bonds, and stereochemical configuration. A precise nomenclature for designating these chemical formulations has been devised. The asymmetric carbon atoms (shaded on the C_{21} molecule in Fig 40–2) allow for **stereoisomerism.** The angular methyl groups (C_{19} and C_{18}) at positions 10 and 13 project in front of the ring system and serve as the point of reference. Nuclear substitutions in the same plane as these groups are designated *cis* or "β" and are represented in drawings by solid lines. Substitutions that project behind the plane of the ring system are designated *trans* or "α" and are represented as a dashed line. Double bonds are referred to by the number of the

preceding carbon (eg, Δ^3-Δ^4). The steroid hormones are named according to whether they have one angular methyl group (estrane, 18 carbons), 2 angular methyl groups (androstane, 19 carbons), or 2 angular groups plus a 2-carbon side chain at C_{17} (pregnane, 21 carbons). This information (Fig 40–3), together with the glossary provided in Table 40–1, should allow one to understand the chemical names of the natural and synthetic hormones listed in Table 40–2.

BIOSYNTHESIS OF ADRENAL STEROID HORMONES

Steroid Precursors & General Enzymatic Steps

The adrenal steroid hormones are synthesized from cholesterol that is mostly derived from the plasma, but a small portion is synthesized in situ from acetyl-CoA via mevalonate and squalene. Much of the cholesterol in the adrenal is esterified and stored in

Table 40–1. Nomenclature of steroids.

Prefix	Suffix	Chemical Nature
Hydroxy-	-ol	Alcohols
Dihydroxy-	-diol	
Oxo-	-one	Ketones (eg, -dione = 2 keto groups)
Cis-		Arrangement of 2 groups in same plane as C_{19}
Trans-		Arrangement of 2 groups in opposing plane to C_{19}
α-		A group *trans* to the 19-methyl
β-		A group *cis* to the 19-methyl
Deoxy-		Lacking a hydroxy group
Iso- or epi-		Isomerism at a C–C, C–OH, or C–H bond, eg, androsterone (5α) versus isoandrosterone (5β)
Dehydro-		Removal of 2 hydrogen atoms to form a double bond
Dihydro-		Addition of 2 hydrogen atoms to a double bond
Allo-		*Trans* configuration of the A and B rings

Table 40–2. Trivial and chemical names of some steroids.

Trivial Name	Chemical Name
Aldosterone	$11\beta,21$-Dihydroxy-3,20-dioxo-4-pregnen-18-al
Androstenedione	4-Androstene-3,17-dione
Cholesterol	5-Cholesten-3β-ol
Corticosterone (compound B)	$11\beta,21$-Dihydroxy-4-pregnene-3,20-dione
Cortisol (compound F)	$11\beta,17\alpha,21$-Trihydroxy-4-pregnene-3,20-dione
Cortisone (compound E)	$17\alpha,21$-Dihydroxy-4-pregnene-3,11,20-trione
Dehydroepiandrosterone (DHEA)	3β-Hydroxy-5-androsten-17-one
11-Deoxycorticosterone (DOC)	21-Hydroxy-4-pregnene-3,20-dione
11-Deoxycortisol (compound S)	17,21-Dihydroxy-4-pregnene-3,20-dione
Dexamethasone	9α-Fluoro-16α-methyl-$11\beta,17\alpha,21$-trihydroxypregna-1,4-diene-3,20-dione
Estradiol	1,3,5,(10)-Estratriene-3,17β-diol
Estriol	1,3,5,(10)-Estratriene-3,16α,17β-triol
Estrone	3-Hydroxy-1,3,5(10)-estratriene-3-ol-17-one
Etiocholanolone	3α-Hydroxy-5β-androstan-17-one
9α-Fluorocortisol	9α-Fluoro-$11\beta,17\alpha,21$-trihydroxypregn-4-ene,3,20-dione
Prednisone	$17\alpha,21$-Dihydroxypregna-1,4-diene-3,11,20-trione
Prednisolone	$11\beta,17\alpha,21$-Trihydroxypregna-1,4-diene-3,20-dione
Pregnanediol	5β-Pregnane-3α,20α-diol
Pregnanetriol	5β-Pregnane-3α,17α,20α-triol
Pregnenolone	3β-Hydroxy-5-pregnen-20-one
Progesterone	4-Pregnene-3,20-dione
Testosterone	17β-Hydroxy-4-androsten-3-one
Triamcinolone	9α-Fluoro-$11\beta,16\alpha,17\alpha,21$-tetrahydroxypregna-1,4-diene-3,20-dione

cytoplasmic lipid droplets. Upon stimulation of the adrenal by ACTH (cAMP), an esterase is activated, and the free cholesterol formed is transported into the mitochondrion where a **cytochrome P-450 side chain cleavage enzyme** (P-450$_{scc}$) converts cholesterol to pregnenolone. Cleavage of the side chain involves sequential hydroxylations, first at C_{22} and then at C_{20},

followed by side chain cleavage (removal of the 6-carbon fragment isocaproaldehyde) to give the 21-carbon steroid (Fig 40–3). An ACTH-dependent protein may bind and activate cholesterol or P-450$_{scc}$. Aminoglutethimide is a very efficient inhibitor of P-450$_{scc}$ and of steroid biosynthesis.

All mammalian steroid hormones are formed

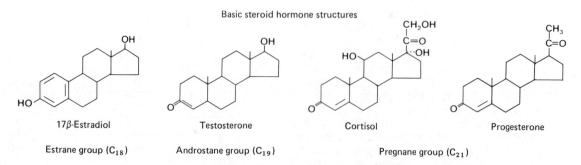

Figure 40–3. Cholesterol side-chain cleavage and basic steroid hormone structures.

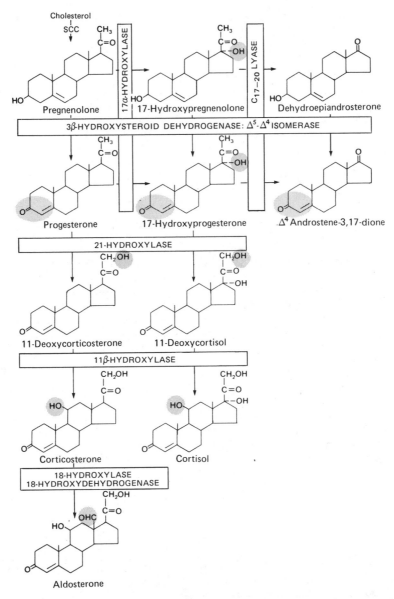

Figure 40–4. Pathways involved in the synthesis of the 3 major classes of adrenal steroids. Enzymes are shown in the rectangular boxes, and the modifications at each step are shaded. (Slightly modified and reproduced, with permission, from Harding BW. Page 1135 in: *Endocrinology.* Vol 2. DeGroot LJ [editor]. Grune & Stratton, 1979.)

from cholesterol via pregnenolone through a series of reactions that occur in either the mitochondria or endoplasmic reticulum of the adrenal cell. **Hydroxylases** that require molecular oxygen and NADPH are essential, and **dehydrogenases,** an **isomerase,** and a **lyase** are also necessary for certain steps. There is some cellular specificity in steroidogenesis. For instance, 18-hydroxylase and 18-hydroxysteroid dehydrogenase, which are required for aldosterone synthesis, are found only in glomerulosa cells, so that the biosynthesis of this mineralocorticoid is confined to this region. A schematic representation of the pathways involved in the synthesis of the 3 major classes of adrenal

steroids is presented in Fig 40–4. The enzymes are shown in the rectangular boxes, and the modifications at each step are shaded.

Mineralocorticoid Synthesis

Synthesis of aldosterone follows the mineralocorticoid pathway and occurs in the zona glomerulosa. Pregnenolone is converted to progesterone by the action of 2 smooth endoplasmic reticulum (SER) enzymes, **3β-hydroxysteroid dehydrogenase (3β-OHSD)** and **Δ^5-Δ^4 isomerase.** Progesterone is hydroxylated at the C_{21} position to form 11-deoxycorticosterone (DOC), which is an active (Na$^+$-retaining)

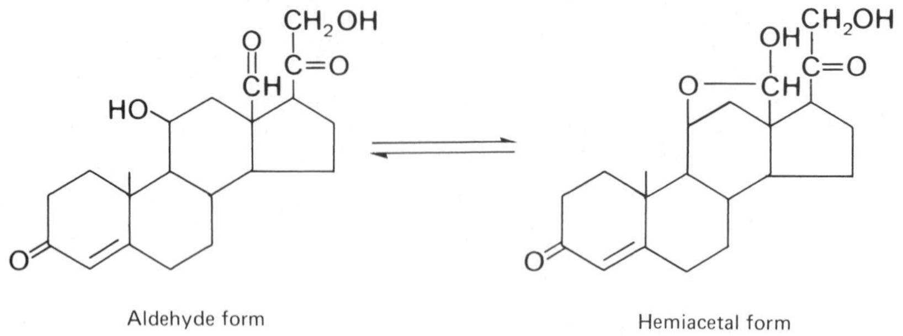

Aldehyde form   Hemiacetal form

Figure 40–5. Equilibrium forms of aldosterone.

mineralocorticoid. The next hydroxylation, at C_{11}, produces corticosterone, which has glucocorticoid activity and is a weak mineralocorticoid (it has less than 5% of the potency of aldosterone). In some species (eg, rodents), it is the most potent glucocorticoid. C_{21} hydroxylation is necessary for both mineralocorticoid and glucocorticoid activity, but most steroids with a C_{17} hydroxyl group have more glucocorticoid and less mineralocorticoid action. In the zona glomerulosa, which does not have the SER enzyme $\cdot 17\alpha$-hydroxylase, a mitochondrial 18-hydroxylase is present. The **18-hydroxylase** acts on corticosterone to form 18-hydroxycorticosterone, which is changed to aldosterone by the conversion of the 18-alcohol to an aldehyde. The final product, aldosterone, exists in 2 equilibrium forms, as shown in Fig 40–5. This unique distribution of enzymes and the special regulation of the zona glomerulosa (see below) have led some investigators to suggest that, in addition to the adrenal being 2 glands, the adrenal cortex is actually 2 separate organs.

Glucocorticoid Synthesis

Cortisol synthesis requires 3 hydroxylases that act sequentially on the C_{17}, C_{21}, and C_{11} positions. The first 2 reactions are rapid, while C_{11} hydroxylation is relatively slow. If the C_{21} position is hydroxylated first, the action of 17α-hydroxylase is impeded and the mineralocorticoid pathway is followed (forming corticosterone or aldosterone, depending on the cell type). 17α-Hydroxylase is an SER enzyme that acts upon either progesterone or, more commonly, pregnenolone. 17α-Hydroxyprogesterone is hydroxylated at C_{21} to form 11-deoxycortisol, which is then hydroxylated at C_{11} to form cortisol, the most potent natural glucocorticoid hormone in humans. The **21-hydroxylase** is an SER enzyme, whereas the **11β-hydroxylase** is a mitochondrial enzyme. Steroidogenesis thus involves the repeated shuttling of substrates into and out of the mitochondria of the fasciculata and reticularis cells (Fig 40–6).

The compound **metyrapone** is an effective inhibitor of 11β-hydroxylase and is used in a diagnostic test of hypothalamic-pituitary reserve. The test takes advantage of the fact that cortisol is the only steroid that causes feedback inhibition of ACTH release (Fig

40–7). When cortisol synthesis is blocked by giving a normal person an oral dose of metyrapone (usually at midnight to take advantage of the early morning ACTH burst), there is excessive release of ACTH; steroidogenesis is stimulated; and 11-deoxycortisol accumulates, since cortisol cannot be formed. A specific radioimmunoassay is used to quantitate plasma **11-deoxycortisol,** which does not increase if corticotropin-releasing hormone or ACTH release is impaired.

Androgen Synthesis

The major androgen or androgen precursor produced by the adrenal cortex is **dehydroepiandros-**

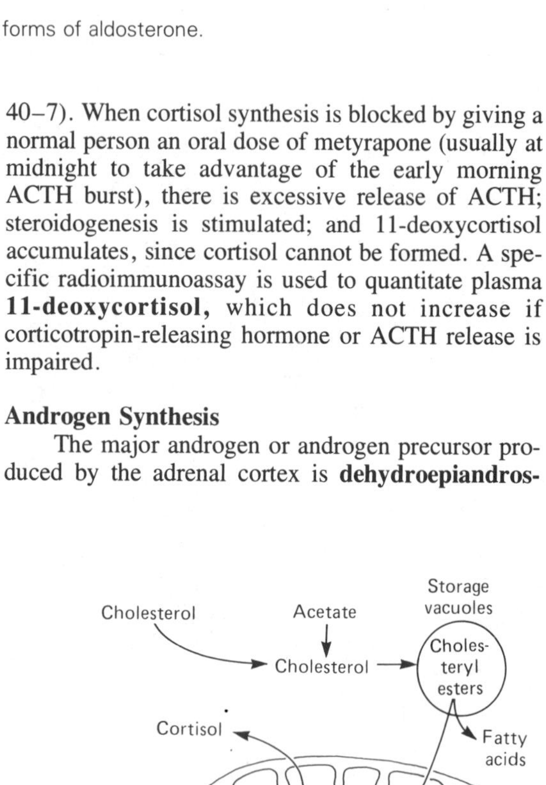

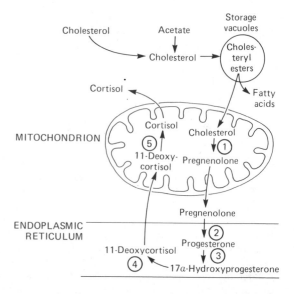

Figure 40–6. Subcellular compartmentalization of glucocorticoid biosynthesis. Adrenal steroidogenesis involves the shuttling of precursors between mitochondria and the endoplasmic reticulum. The enzymes involved are (1) C_{20-22} lyase, (2) 3β-hydroxysteroid dehydrogenase and Δ^5-Δ^4 isomerase, (3) 17α-hydroxylase, (4) 21-hydroxylase, and (5) 11β-hydroxylase. (Slightly modified and reproduced, with permission, from Harding BW. Page 1135 in: *Endocrinology.* Vol 2. DeGroot LJ [editor]. Grune & Stratton, 1979.)

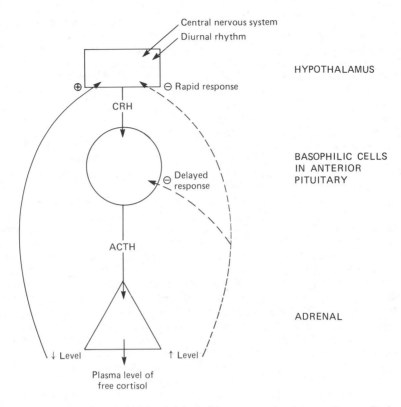

Figure 40–7. Feedback regulation of cortisol biosynthesis. Solid arrows = stimulatory pathways. Dashed arrows = inhibitory pathways.

terone **(DHEA).** Most 17-hydroxypregnenolone follows the glucocorticoid pathway, but a small fraction is subjected to oxidative fission and removal of the 2-carbon side chain through the action of 17,20-lyase. This enzyme is found in the adrenals and gonads and acts exclusively on 17α-hydroxy–containing molecules. Adrenal androgen production increases markedly if glucocorticoid biosynthesis is impeded by the lack of one of the hydroxylases (see adrenogenital syndrome, below). Most DHEA is rapidly modified by the addition of sulfate, about half of which occurs in the adrenal and the rest in the liver. DHEA sulfate is inactive, but removal of the sulfate results in reactivation. DHEA is really a prohormone, since the actions of 3β-OHSD and Δ^5-Δ^4 isomerase convert the weak androgen DHEA into the more potent **androstenedione.** Small amounts of androstenedione are also formed in the adrenal by the action of the lyase on 17α-hydroxyprogesterone. Reduction of androstenedione at the C_{17} position results in the formation of **testosterone,** the most potent adrenal androgen. Small amounts of testosterone are produced in the adrenal by this mechanism, but most of this conversion occurs in other tissues.

Small amounts of other steroids can be isolated from adrenal venous blood, including 11-deoxycorticosterone, progesterone, pregnenolone, 17α-hydroxyprogesterone, and a very small amount of estradiol (from the aromatization of testosterone). None of these amounts are important in relation to production from other glands, however.

SECRETION, TRANSPORT, & METABOLISM OF ADRENAL STEROID HORMONES

Secretion

There is little, if any, storage of steroid hormones within the adrenal (or gonad) cell, since these hormones are released into the plasma when they are made. Cortisol release occurs with a periodicity that is regulated by the **diurnal rhythm** of ACTH release. Plasma cortisol begins to increase shortly after midnight and reaches its peak plasma value (approximately 15 μg/dL) between 6:00 and 8:00 AM. About 70% of the secreted cortisol is released between midnight and 8:00 AM. After 8:00 AM, cortisol secretion gradually declines, as does the plasma level, and it reaches a nadir of about 6 μg/dL between 6:00 PM and midnight. During this time, cortisol is not secreted continuously; release occurs in bursts with the greatest frequency and magnitude during the early morning hours. During stress, this diurnal rhythm is overridden, and plasma cortisol levels may exceed 25 μg/dL. At this point, the capacity of the main plasma binding protein, corticosteroid-binding globulin, is exceeded (see below) and the free cortisol level is increased.

Plasma Transport

A. Glucocorticoids: Cortisol circulates in plasma in protein-bound and free forms. The main plasma binding protein is an α-globulin called **transcortin** or **corticosteroid-binding globulin (CBG)**. CBG is produced in the liver, and its synthesis, like that of thyroid-binding globulin (TBG), is increased by estrogens. During pregnancy and under other high-estrogen conditions, there is an increase in the level of CBG and therefore in the total plasma cortisol level. CBG and total plasma cortisol levels decrease in certain liver diseases and when excessive amounts of protein are lost in the urine (nephrotic syndrome). CBG binds most of the hormone when plasma cortisol levels are within the normal range (see Table 35–1); much smaller amounts of cortisol are bound to albumin. The avidity of binding helps determine the biologic half-lives of various glucocorticoids. Cortisol binds tightly to CBG and has a $t_{1/2}$ of 1.5–2 hours, while corticosterone, which binds less tightly, has a $t_{1/2}$ of less than 1 hour. Binding to CBG is not restricted to glucocorticoids. Deoxycorticosterone and progesterone interact with CBG with sufficient affinity to compete for cortisol binding. The unbound, or free, fraction constitutes about 8% of the total plasma cortisol and represents the biologically active fraction of cortisol.

B. Mineralocorticoids: Aldosterone, the most potent natural mineralocorticoid, does not have a specific plasma transport protein, but it forms a very weak association with albumin. Corticosterone and 11-deoxycorticosterone, other steroids with mineralocorticoid effects, bind to CBG. These observations are important in understanding the mechanism of action of aldosterone (see p 561).

Metabolism & Excretion

A. Glucocorticoids: Cortisol and its metabolites constitute about 80% of the 17-hydroxycorticoids in plasma; the other 20% consist of cortisone and 11-deoxycortisol. About half of the cortisol (as well as cortisone and 11-deoxycortisol) circulates in the form of the reduced dihydro- and tetrahydro- metabolites that are produced from reduction of the A ring double bond by NADPH-requiring hydrogenases and from reduction of the 3-ketone group by a reversible dehydrogenase reaction. Substantial amounts of all of these compounds are also modified by conjugation at the C_3 position with glucuronide or, to a lesser extent, with sulfate. These modifications occur primarily in the liver and make the lipophilic steroid molecule water-soluble and excretable. In humans, most of the conjugated steroids that enter the intestine by biliary excretion are reabsorbed by the enterohepatic circulation. About 70% of the conjugated steroids are excreted in the urine, 20% leave in feces, and the rest exit through the skin.

B. Mineralocorticoids: Aldosterone is very rapidly cleared from the plasma by the liver, no doubt because it lacks a plasma carrier protein. The liver forms tetrahydroaldosterone 3-glucuronide, which is excreted in the urine.

C. Androgens: Androgens are excreted as 17-keto compounds including DHEA (sulfate) as well as androstenedione and its metabolites. Testosterone, secreted in small amounts by the adrenal, is not a 17-keto compound, but the liver converts about 50% of testosterone to androsterone and etiocholanolone, which are 17-keto compounds.

REGULATION OF SYNTHESIS OF ADRENAL STEROID HORMONES

Glucocorticoid Hormones

The secretion of cortisol is dependent on ACTH, which in turn is regulated by corticotropin-releasing hormone (CRH). These hormones are linked by a classic negative feedback loop (Fig 40–7). Excessive levels of free cortisol exert both rapid and delayed negative feedback control (inhibition) on the anterior pituitary, the hypothalamus, or both. The rapid response appears to be triggered by the rate of increase of cortisol levels and may involve an action of cortisol on the cell membrane, presumably at the hypothalamus, since CRH can overcome this inhibition. The delayed effect seems to be dependent on the absolute level of cortisol and is exerted on the basophilic cells of the anterior pituitary, probably through inhibition of pro-opiomelanocortin (POMC) mRNA production.

Abnormally low levels of free cortisol activate the system by enhancing CRH release from the hypothalamus. This 41-amino-acid peptide reaches the basophilic cells of the anterior pituitary by the portal system described in Fig 37–1 and stimulates the production and release of ACTH (from the precursor POMC molecule as described in Chapter 37). In the adrenal cortex, ACTH enhances the rate of cholesterol side chain cleavage, the rate-limiting step in steroidogenesis. This completes one side of the negative feedback loop. The restoration of a normal free cortisol level results in reduced release of CRH from the hypothalamus, decreased release of ACTH from the pituitary, and diminished production of cortisol, thereby completing the other side of the loop. This intricate mechanism provides for rapid adjustments of the circulating level of cortisol.

Prolonged stimulation of the adrenal by ACTH results in an increase of cell size and number and may determine the magnitude of the steroidogenic response to an acute ACTH stimulus. Conversely, prolonged lack of ACTH results in atrophy of the adrenal cortex, decreased steroidogenesis, and very sluggish response to ACTH.

ACTH release (and cortisol secretion) is controlled by neural input from a number of sites within the nervous system. There is an endogenous rhythm that controls the release of CRH and therefore ACTH. This circadian cycle is normally set to provide for an increase of plasma cortisol shortly after the onset of sleep. The plasma cortisol level gradually increases during the sleeping hours, peaks shortly after waking,

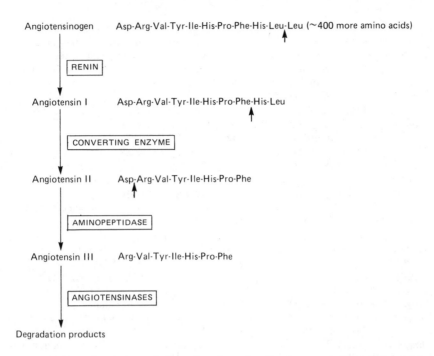

Figure 40–8. Formation and metabolism of angiotensins. Small arrows indicate cleavage sites.

gradually falls over the next several hours, and reaches a nadir in late afternoon and early evening. This general pattern is due to a series of episodic, pulsatile bursts of cortisol release, which are preceded by bursts of ACTH release (see Chapter 37). This is a complex cycle, and it is affected by the period of light exposure and feeding-fasting cycles as well as the sleep-wake cycle. Loss of the diurnal variation in steroid secretion is often seen in association with diseases of the adrenal-pituitary system and some types of depressive illness. Neural input from the suprachiasmatic nucleus drives this rhythm.

Cortisol secretion is also affected by physical and emotional stress. Input from the nuclei of the amygdala mediates the ACTH response to emotional stress, apprehension, fear, and anxiety, while fibers from the spinothalamic pathway and reticular formation mediate the response to pain. These responses can override both the negative feedback system and the diurnal rhythm.

Mineralocorticoid Hormones

The production of aldosterone by the glomerulosa cells is regulated in a completely different manner. The primary regulators are the **renin-angiotensin system** and potassium. Sodium, ACTH, and neural mechanisms are also involved.

A. The Renin-Angiotensin System: This system is involved in the regulation of blood pressure and electrolyte metabolism. The primary hormone in these processes is **angiotensin II,** an octapeptide made from **angiotensinogen** (Fig 40–8). Angiotensinogen, an α_2-globulin made in liver, is the substrate for renin, an enzyme produced in the **juxtaglomerular cells** of the

renal afferent arteriole. The position of these cells makes them particularly sensitive to blood pressure changes, and many of the physiologic regulators of renin release act through renal **baroreceptors** (Table 40–3). The juxtaglomerular cells are also sensitive to changes of Na^+ and Cl^- concentration in the renal tubular fluid; therefore, any combination of factors that decreases fluid volume (dehydration, decreased blood pressure, fluid or blood loss) or decreases NaCl concentration stimulates renin release. Renal sympathetic nerves that terminate in the juxtaglomerular cells mediate the central nervous system and postural effects on renin release independent of the baroreceptor and salt effects, a mechanism that involves the β-adrenergic receptor.

Renin acts upon the substrate angiotensinogen to produce the decapeptide **angiotensin I.** The synthesis of angiotensinogen in liver is enhanced by glucocorticoids and estrogens. Hypertension associated with these hormones may be due in part to increased plasma levels of angiotensinogen. Since this protein circulates

Table 40–3. Factors that influence renin release.

Stimulators	Inhibitors
Decreased blood pressure	Increased blood pressure
Change from supine to erect posture	Change from erect to supine posture
Salt depletion	Salt loading
β-Adrenergic agents	β-Adrenergic antagonists
Prostaglandins	Prostaglandin inhibitors
	Potassium
	Vasopressin
	Angiotensin II

at about the K_m for renin, small changes could markedly affect the generation of angiotensin II.

Angiotensin-converting enzyme, a glycoprotein found in lung, endothelial cells, and plasma, removes 2 carboxy-terminal amino acids from the decapeptide angiotensin I to form angiotensin II in a step that is not thought to be rate-limiting. Various nonapeptide analogs of angiotensin I inhibit converting enzyme and are used to treat **renin-dependent hypertension.** Converting enzyme also degrades **bradykinin,** a potent vasodilator; thus, this enzyme increases blood pressure in 2 distinct ways.

Angiotensin II increases blood pressure by causing vasoconstriction of the arteriole and is the most potent vasoactive substance known. It inhibits renin release from the juxtaglomerular cells and is a potent stimulator of aldosterone production. Although angiotensin II stimulates the adrenal directly, it has no effect on cortisol production.

In some species, angiotensin II is converted to the des-Asp[1] heptapeptide **angiotensin III** (Fig 40–8), an equally potent stimulator of aldosterone production. In humans, the plasma level of angiotensin II is 4 times greater than that of angiotensin III, so most effects are exerted by the octapeptide. Angiotensins II and III are rapidly inactivated by **angiotensinases.**

Angiotensin II binds to specific glomerulosa cell receptors. The concentration of these receptors is "up regulated" by potassium and the hormone itself and "down regulated" by a low potassium concentration; hence, this ion plays a central role in the action of angiotensin II on the adrenal. The hormone-receptor interaction does not activate adenylate cyclase, and cAMP does not appear to mediate the action of this hormone. The actions of angiotensin II, which are to stimulate the conversion of cholesterol to pregnenolone and of corticosterone to 18-hydroxycorticosterone and aldosterone, may involve changes in the concentration of intracellular calcium and of phospholipid metabolites by mechanisms similar to those described in Chapter 36. **Prostaglandin biosynthesis** may also be involved, since prostaglandins E_1 and E_2 stimulate aldosterone release while $F_{1\alpha}$ and $F_{2\alpha}$ are inhibitory, a pattern typical of prostaglandin-mediated responses. Indomethacin, an inhibitor of prostaglandin biosynthesis, inhibits basal and angiotensin II–stimulated aldosterone release.

B. Potassium: Aldosterone secretion is sensitive to changes in plasma potassium level; an increase as small as 0.1 meq/L stimulates production, whereas a similar decrease reduces aldosterone production and secretion. The effects of K^+ are independent of Na^+ and the plasma level of angiotensin II. Prolonged hyperkalemia results in hypertrophy of the zona glomerulosa and increased sensitivity of glomerulosa cells to the ion. K^+ affects the same enzymatic steps as does angiotensin II, although the mechanism involved is obscure. Like angiotensin II, K^+ does not affect the biosynthesis of cortisol.

C. ACTH: An acute decrease in the level of ACTH (eg, following hypophysectomy or glucocor-

ticoid suppression) has little effect on aldosterone production in humans, but long-term ACTH deficiency may reduce the effect other regulators (angiotensin II, Na^+, K^+) have on aldosterone. ACTH appears to be more important in aldosterone production in other species (eg, rats), and it does stimulate cAMP and the early steps of steroidogenesis in isolated glomerulosa cells.

D. Sodium: Na^+ deficiency increases and Na^+ loading decreases aldosterone production, but these effects are largely mediated through the renin-angiotensin system. Na^+ can influence aldosterone synthesis directly, but this regulation requires high Na^+ concentrations and the effects are small and transient.

METABOLIC EFFECTS OF ADRENAL STEROID HORMONES

Loss of adrenal cortical function results in death unless replacement therapy is instituted. In humans, treatment of adrenal insufficiency with mineralocorticoids is generally not sufficient; glucocorticoids seem to be more critical in this regard. Rats, in contrast, do quite well with mineralocorticoid replacement. Excessive or deficient plasma levels of either of these classes of hormones, whether due to disease or therapeutic use, cause a number of serious complications directly related to their metabolic actions. Only selected biochemical and physiologic effects are discussed in this chapter.

Glucocorticoid Hormones
A. Intermediary Metabolism:
1. Gluconeogenesis–Glucocorticoid hormones are named for their ability to promote glucose production. This is accomplished through a concerted action that involves a number of tissues, several complex biochemical pathways, and both catabolic and anabolic actions; such processes are summarized in Fig 40–9.

Glucocorticoids promote hepatic glucose production (1) by increasing the rate of gluconeogenesis; (2) by releasing amino acids, the gluconeogenic substrate, from peripheral tissues such as muscle and lymphoid cells through catabolic actions; and (3) by "permitting" other hormones to stimulate key metabolic processes, including gluconeogenesis, at maximal efficiency. The basal rate of gluconeogenesis is not reduced in fed adrenalectomized animals, but the response of these animals to catecholamines and glucagon is impaired. Fasted or diabetic adrenalectomized animals have reduced rates of gluconeogenesis, and glucocorticoids reverse this. Glucocorticoids are thus active in fasted or insulin-deficient animals and are required for the maximal action of other hormones in fed animals. Glucocorticoid hormones also inhibit glucose uptake and utilization by extrahepatic tissues, so that the net effect is an elevated plasma glucose

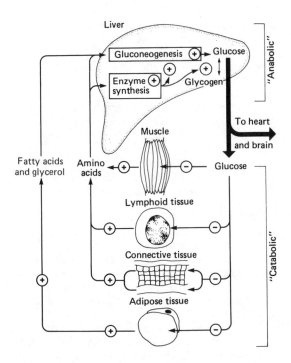

Figure 40-9. Metabolic effects of glucocorticoids. $\ominus$, Inhibition; $\oplus$, stimulation. (Modified and reproduced, with permission, from Baxter JD, Forsham PH: Tissue effects of glucocorticoids. *Am J Med* 1972;**53**:573.)

level. In normal animals, this is counteracted by the release of insulin, which has effects opposite to those of glucocorticoids. These counterbalancing effects usually result in a normal blood glucose level, but the insulin-deficient animal develops hyperglycemia in response to glucocorticoids. Conversely, the glucocorticoid-deficient animal has decreased glucose production and decreased glycogen reserves and is particularly sensitive to insulin.

Glucocorticoid hormones enhance gluconeogenesis by increasing the amount (and activity) of several key hepatic enzymes. The induction of several enzymes that catalyze rate-limiting steps in amino acid degradation (alanine aminotransferase, tryptophan oxygenase, and tyrosine aminotransferase) has been studied in detail. Although these studies provide examples of how glucocorticoids regulate gene transcription, these enzymes probably have modest effects on gluconeogenesis. The rate-limiting enzyme in gluconeogenesis is **phosphoenolpyruvate carboxykinase (PEPCK)** (see Fig 14-6). The synthesis of PEPCK is increased by glucagon (acting through cAMP) and to a lesser extent by glucocorticoids. These hormones in combination result in an additive response. Insulin inhibits the synthesis of PEPCK and overrides the action of the 2 inducers. All of these effects are exerted at the level of gene transcription.

2. Glycogen synthesis–Glucocorticoids increase glycogen deposition in the liver of fasted or fed animals (an effect that led to the development of an

assay for glucocorticoid potency) by promoting the conversion of glycogen synthase from its inactive to active (b to a) form, possibly by activating a phosphatase that enhances this conversion (see Fig 36-6).

3. Lipid metabolism–Excessive amounts of glucocorticoids promote lipolysis in some areas of the body (extremities) and lipogenesis in others (face and trunk). It is not clear whether the lipogenic action is a direct steroid effect or one mediated by the increased plasma insulin that accompanies glucocorticoid excess. In any case, there seems to be some tissue specificity, because not all areas show increased fat deposition or lipolysis.

Plasma free fatty acid levels increase in humans given glucocorticoids. This effect may be due in part to a direct effect on lipolysis, since these hormones do release fatty acids from isolated hepatocytes. Glucocorticoids decrease glucose uptake and utilization in adipose tissue and thus cause a decrease in production of glycerol. Since glycerol is required for the reesterification of fatty acids, this decrease results in the release of fatty acids into the plasma. The net increase of plasma free fatty acids, coupled with their enhanced conversion to ketones, favors the development of ketosis, particularly in insulin-deficient animals. Such responses are important, but the most significant action of the glucocorticoids in lipid metabolism derives from their ability to augment the lipolytic actions of the catecholamines and growth hormone. This "permissive effect" of the glucocorticoids is discussed below.

4. Protein and nucleic acid metabolism– Glucocorticoids generally have anabolic effects on protein and RNA metabolism in liver and catabolic effects at other sites including muscle, lymphoid tissues, adipose tissue, skin, and bone. This pattern is in keeping with the general action of these hormones, which is to provide the optimal milieu for gluconeogenesis. The anabolic effects are reasonably well described; they involve the stimulation of specific gene products, which in turn results in corresponding increases in the rate of synthesis of specific proteins. The catabolic effects have not been extensively characterized at the molecular level.

B. Effects of Glucocorticoids on Host Defense Mechanisms:

1. Immune response–High concentrations of glucocorticoids suppress the host immune response. These steroids kill lymphocytes and cause involution of lymphoid tissue, effects that are dependent upon species and cell type. For example, mouse lymphocytes are much more sensitive to this killing effect than are human lymphocytes, and precursor cells seem to be spared in all species. Glucocorticoids affect the proliferative response of lymphocytes to antigens and, to a lesser extent, to mitogens. Steroids may also affect several other steps in the immune response, including the processing of antigen by macrophages, antibody production by B lymphocytes, suppressor and helper T lymphocyte functions, and antibody metabolism. Most of these effects require glucocorticoids in supraphysiologic levels, eg, in doses used to treat autoimmune diseases or suppress transplant rejection. The role of physiologic levels of these hormones in modulating immune function is not clear.

2. Anti-inflammatory response–The ability of glucocorticoids to suppress the inflammatory response is well known and provides the basis for the major therapeutic use of this class of hormones. In rodents, glucocorticoids decrease the number of circulating lymphocytes, monocytes, and eosinophils, presumably by cell lysis. In humans, this change is not due to cell death but rather to a shift of the cells from the vascular compartment to sites such as bone marrow, lymphoid tissue, and spleen. These hormones enhance the release of polymorphonuclear leukocytes from bone marrow, thus increasing the number of these cells in circulation. Glucocorticoids also inhibit the accumulation of leukocytes at the site of inflammation and cause substances involved in the inflammatory response (eg, kinins, plasminogen-activating factor, prostaglandins, and histamine) to be released from the leukocytes. Suppression of phagocytosis and chemotaxis has been noted in vitro, but it is uncertain whether this effect occurs in vivo. Glucocorticoids inhibit fibroblast proliferation at the site of an inflammatory response and can inhibit some fibroblast functions, such as the production of collagen and fibronectin. The combination of these effects accounts for the poor wound healing, increased susceptibility to infection, and decreased inflammatory response that are characteristically seen in patients with glucocorticoid excess.

C. Effects of Glucocorticoids on Other Functions:

1. Cardiovascular function–Glucocorticoids are necessary for maintenance of normal blood pressure and cardiac output. These responses may not reflect direct physiologic effects but may represent examples of how glucocorticoids are required for the maximal action of other hormones, the catecholamines in this case. (See "Permissive Effect" of Glucocorticoids, below.)

2. Fluid and electrolyte metabolism–Humans with glucocorticoid deficiency are unable to excrete water normally. This may be related to ADH secretion. Glucocorticoids have been observed to inhibit ADH release; thus, in the absence of glucocorticoids, ADH levels may increase and contribute to water retention. The glomerular filtration rate decreases in glucocorticoid deficiency, and this can result in decreased free water clearance.

Glucocorticoids mimic the action of mineralocorticoids in that they increase angiotensinogen, which in turn increases angiotensin II; thus, they increase blood pressure, promote sodium retention, and cause potassium excretion. Some portion of the effects of glucocorticoids on electrolyte metabolism are due to the intrinsic mineralocorticoid activity of these molecules.

3. Calcium metabolism–Glucocorticoids reduce intestinal calcium absorption. This is probably not a direct effect, since it appears to be due to the inhibition of calcitriol formation, perhaps at the step of 25-hydroxylation (see Fig 39–7). Glucocorticoids also inhibit renal reabsorption of calcium and promote movement of calcium from the extracellular fluid into the cell.

4. Growth and development of connective tissue, muscle, and bone–High concentrations of glucocorticoids are catabolic. Fibroblast growth and replication are inhibited, as is formation of collagen and fibronectin. The skin substratum is therefore weakened, leading to development of the thin skin, easy bruising, and poor wound healing characteristic of glucocorticoid excess.

Muscle is the major source of amino acids, the gluconeogenic substrates; hence, it is a primary target of glucocorticoid action. Protein, RNA, and DNA synthesis are inhibited by glucocorticoids, and the rate of degradation of RNA and protein is enhanced. Severe muscle atrophy and weakness are typical findings in patients with prolonged exposure to excessive amounts of corticosteroids.

Glucocorticoids inhibit bone cell replication and function (collagen deposition) and augment the effect of PTH on bone. The net result of prolonged exposure to these hormones is decreased bone mass (**osteoporosis**).

D. "Permissive Effect" of Glucocorticoids: Glucocorticoid hormones augment the effects of several hormones on many biologic processes in numerous tissues. In some cases, the actions of the primary hormone are not observed unless the tissue has first been exposed to a glucocorticoid. Examples (with the primary effector or effectors in parentheses) include gluconeogenesis (glucagon, epinephrine), glycogenolysis (epinephrine, glucagon), glycogenesis (insulin), lipolysis (epinephrine, ACTH, GH), and cardiovascular function (catecholamines). In other instances, the glucocorticoid has a strong effect itself and exhibits a synergistic effect in combination with another hormone. Examples of this include glucose uptake by lymphocytes (epinephrine), erythropoiesis (erythropoietin), growth hormone synthesis (thyroid hormones), and cell growth (growth factors). In other cases, such as the development and differentiation of several tissues, virus synthesis, and brain sensory functions, the primary effectors have not yet been identified, but glucocorticoids are known to magnify effects. The molecular mechanisms by which glucocorticoids "permit" these and other metabolic processes to attain maximal rates have not been elucidated.

E. Role of Glucocorticoids in the "Stress Response": The "**fight or flight**" response is discussed in detail below, under the adrenal medulla, since it is a complex entwining of a number of physiologic responses primarily mediated by catecholamine hormones. Many components of this response require glucocorticoids for maximal activity, as described in the previous section.

Glucocorticoids are more directly involved in the

response to the acute stress occasioned by surgery, trauma, or infection. Cortisol secretion increases severalfold in such circumstances, and a deficient response markedly reduces the chances for survival. Mineralocorticoid replacement helps in such situations, but glucocorticoid therapy is required for optimal results.

Mineralocorticoid Hormones

Mineralocorticoid hormones act in the kidney to stimulate active Na^+ transport by the distal convoluted tubules and collecting tubules, the net result being Na^+ retention. These hormones also promote the secretion of K^+, H^+, and NH_4^+ by the kidney and affect ion transport in other epithelial tissues including sweat glands, intestinal mucosa, and salivary glands. Aldosterone is 30–50 times more potent than 11-deoxycorticosterone (DOC) and 1000 times more potent than cortisol or corticosterone. As the most potent naturally occurring mineralocorticoid, aldosterone accounts for most of this action in humans. Cortisol, although far less potent, has a much higher production rate and thus has a significant effect on Na^+ retention and K^+ excretion. Since the amount of DOC produced is very small, it is much less important in this regard.

The regulation of cation transport by aldosterone occurs without changes in renal blood flow or glomerular filtration rate, and thus it appears to be a direct effect. RNA and protein synthesis are required for the action of aldosterone, which appears to involve the production of specific gene products (see below).

The kidney is the primary site of aldosterone action in humans. There is evidence that aldosterone-mediated antinatriuresis and kaliuresis are not due to the straight exchange of Na^+ for K^+ via Na^+/K^+-ATPase. Na^+ and K^+ fluxes are separable in humans and in a number of in vitro test systems. Micropuncture studies show that Na^+ reabsorption and K^+ secretion occur at separate locations and may be temporally uncoupled. Dactinomycin, which inhibits RNA synthesis, prevents the antinatriuretic effect of aldosterone but not the effect on H^+ or K^+ flux. Finally, aldosterone promotes Na^+ retention by amphibian kidney, bladder, skin, and colon but has no effect on K^+ flux in these tissues. The exact mechanism involved in these transport processes has not been elucidated, but it is suspected to involve the synthesis of specific proteins (see below).

CLASSIFICATION & MECHANISM OF ACTION OF ADRENAL STEROID HORMONES

Glucocorticoid Hormones

A. General Features of Hormone Action: The general features of glucocorticoid hormone action are described in Chapter 36 and illustrated in Fig 36–1. Numerous examples support the concept that this class of hormones affects specific cellular processes by influencing the amount of critical proteins, usually enzymes, within the cell. Glucocorticoids accomplish this by regulating the rate of transcription of specific genes in the target cell. This process requires that the steroid-receptor complex bind to specific regions of DNA in the vicinity of the transcription initiation site and that such regions confer specificity to the response. How this interaction actually enhances or inhibits transcription, how tissue specificity is accomplished, and how a given gene can be stimulated in one tissue and inhibited in another are a few of the important questions that remain unanswered.

Control of the rate of gene transcription appears to be the major action of the glucocorticoid hormones, but it is not the sole mechanism employed. The ability to measure specific processes has revealed that these hormones also regulate the processing and transport of nuclear transcripts (eg, α_1-acid glycoprotein), the rate of degradation of specific mRNAs (eg, growth hormone and phosphoenolpyruvate-carboxykinase), and posttranslational processing (various mammary tumor virus proteins). It would appear that these and other classes of steroid hormones can act at any level of the "information flow" from DNA to protein and that the relative importance of each varies from system to system.

B. Classes of Glucocorticoid Hormones: Glucocorticoid hormones initiate their action in a target cell by interacting with a specific receptor. This interaction results in "activation" of the receptor, a step thought to be necessary for DNA binding. There is generally a high correlation between the association of a steroid with receptor and the elicitation of a given biologic response (Fig 40–10). This correlation holds true for a wide range of activities, so that a steroid with one-tenth the binding affinity evokes a correspondingly decreased biologic effect at a given steroid concentration (compare 2 with 1, or 3 with 2, in Fig 40–10). There are generally no "spare receptors" involved in steroid hormone action.

The biologic effect of a steroid depends upon both its ability to bind to the receptor and the concentration of free hormone in the plasma. Cortisol, corticosterone, and aldosterone all bind with high affinity to the glucocorticoid receptor, but in physiologic circumstances cortisol is the dominant glucocorticoid because of its much greater plasma concentration. Corticosterone is an important glucocorticoid in certain pathologic conditions (17α-hydroxylase deficiency), but aldosterone never reaches a concentration in plasma sufficient to exert glucocorticoid effects.

A comparison of the ability of a number of steroids to mediate a well-known glucocorticoid effect, the induction of the liver enzyme tyrosine aminotransferase (TAT), revealed that these hormones can be divided into 4 classes: **agonists, partial agonists, antagonists,** and **inactive steroids** (Table 40–4).

Agonists elicit the maximal response, although different concentrations may be required (Figs 40–10 and 40–11A). Partial agonists evoke an incomplete response, even when very large concentrations of the hormone are employed, as illustrated in Fig 40–11B.

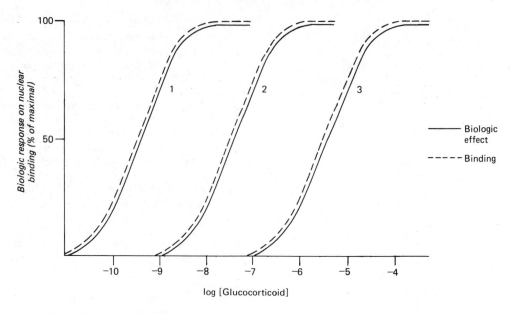

Figure 40–10. Concordance of nuclear binding and biologic effect of steroid hormones. Within a class of steroid hormones different molecules may have different potency, but there is usually a high correlation between the binding of a given molecule to the nuclear receptor protein (dashed lines) and the elicitation of a biologic effect (solid lines).

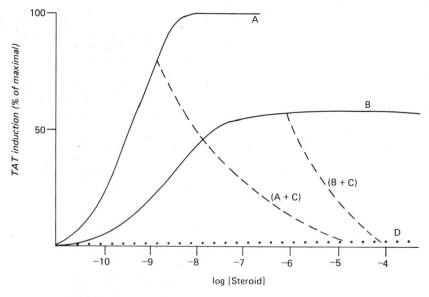

Figure 40–11. Classification of steroids according to their glucocorticoid activity. Steroids can be classified as agonists (line A), partial agonists (line B), antagonists (lines A + C and B + C), or inactive agents (dotted line D). In this example, the biologic action measured was the induction of the enzyme tyrosine aminotransferase (TAT).

Antagonists generally have no effect themselves, but they competitively inhibit the action of agonists or partial agonists (Fig 40–11 A+C or B+C). A large group of compounds elicit no effect at all and have no effect on the action of the agonists or antagonists. These are classified as inactive steroids (Fig 40–11D).

An interesting hypothesis regarding glucocor-

ticoid receptor function resulted from these observations—namely, in addition to binding to the receptor, a ligand must also facilitate a change in this molecule so that it can bind to DNA. Agonists bind to and fully activate the receptor and elicit the maximal biologic response. Partial agonists fully occupy the receptor but afford incomplete activation and a partial response.

Table 40–4. Classification of steroids according to their glucocorticoid action.

Agonists
Dexamethasone
Cortisol
Corticosterone
Aldosterone
Partial agonists
11β-Hydroxyprogesterone
21-Deoxycortisol
17α-Hydroxyprogesterone
Progesterone
Antagonists
Testosterone
17β-Estradiol
19-Nortestosterone
Cortisone
Inactive steroids
11α-Hydroxyprogesterone
Androstenedione
11α,17α-Methyltestosterone
Tetrahydrocortisol

Antagonists fully occupy the receptor, but this complex is unable to bind to DNA and elicits no response.

Partial agonists also compete with agonists for binding to or activating the receptor, in which case they become **partial antagonists.** The extent of inhibition of agonist activity caused by partial or complete antagonists depends on the relative concentration of the various steroids. Generally, much higher concentrations of antagonist are required to inhibit an agonist than are necessary for the latter to exert its maximal

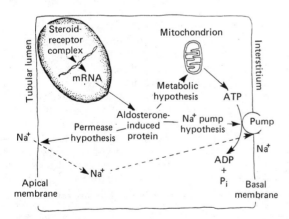

Figure 40–12. Mechanism of action of aldosterone. The steroid induces the formation of one or more proteins that in turn increase the permeability of the apical (luminal) membrane to Na$^+$, increase the active transport of Na$^+$ out of the cell across the basal and lateral membranes into the interstitium, or increase the energy available to the pump. (Modified from Edelman IS: Candidate mediators in the action of aldosterone on Na$^+$ transport. In: *Membrane Transport Processes.* Vol I. Hoffman JF [editor]. Raven Press, 1978.)

effect. Such concentrations are rarely (if ever) achieved in vivo; however, in vitro studies of this phenomenon have provided useful data on the mechanism of action of glucocorticoid hormones.

Mineralocorticoid Hormones

A. General Features of Hormone Action: The general features of aldosterone action are similar to those of other steroid hormones (Fig 40–12). Target cells contain specific receptors that bind aldosterone. The hormone-receptor complex binds to chromatin and alters the rate of transcription of specific genes. Although specific gene products have not been isolated, protein and RNA synthesis are known to be required for aldosterone action, and it is presumed that specific proteins are involved in mediating the effects of aldosterone on ion transport.

B. Aldosterone Receptor Binding: Receptors that bind aldosterone with high affinity (K$_d$ ~1 nmol/L) are found in the cytoplasm and nuclei of target cells. The total binding capacity in the cytoplasm exceeds that in the nucleus by a factor of 80–100; however, the specificity and affinity of nuclear binding is much greater than that of the total cytosol binding activity. In vitro studies have shown that there are actually 3 types of cytosol receptors. Types I and II both bind aldosterone with high affinity, while type III has a low affinity for aldosterone. Type I is a mineralocorticoid receptor, whereas type II appears to be a glucocorticoid receptor that coincidentally binds aldosterone. The type I receptor avidly binds aldosterone but also binds DOC and corticosterone very well. Given the fact that the plasma level of aldosterone is much lower than that of either of the other 2 steroids, one might suppose that these would preferentially occupy the type I sites and that aldosterone would exert little effect. Recall that DOC and corticosterone are avidly bound to corticosteroid-binding globulin, the plasma glucocorticoid transport protein, while aldosterone has no specific carrier protein. Consequently, the effective "free" concentration of aldosterone in plasma is greater than that of either corticosterone or DOC. Aldosterone therefore is readily able to enter cells, and this ensures a competitive advantage for aldosterone with respect to occupying the type I receptor in vivo.

C. Actions of Aldosterone on Ion Transport: The molecular mechanisms of aldosterone action on Na$^+$ transport have not been elucidated, but several studies point to the general model illustrated in Fig 40–12. Na$^+$ from the luminal fluid bathing the apical surface of the renal cell enters passively through Na$^+$ channels. Na$^+$ is then transported into the interstitial fluid through the serosal side of the cell by the Na$^+$/K$^+$-dependent ATPase pump. ATP provides the energy required for this active process.

Aldosterone increases the number of apical membrane Na$^+$ channels, and this presumably increases intracellular Na$^+$. Aldosterone also increases the activity of several mitochondrial enzymes, and this could result in the generation of the ATP required to drive the serosal membrane Na^+/K^+ pump. The NADH:NAD ratio increases as a result of aldosterone action, as do the activities of several mitochondrial enzymes including malate dehydrogenase, glutamate dehydrogenase, glutamic-oxaloacetic aminotransferase, and citrate synthase. The increased activity of citrate synthase involves a true induction (perhaps mediated by the gene transcription effects alluded to above), and the temporal increase of this protein correlates highly with the effect of aldosterone on Na^+ transport. Aldosterone has not been shown to have an effect on the Na^+ pump itself; therefore, it appears that the hormone increases the intracellular concentration of Na^+ and creates the energy source required for removal of this ion through the serosal pump. Other mechanisms, involving different aldosterone-regulated proteins, may be involved in the handling of K^+ and H^+.

PATHOPHYSIOLOGY OF THE ADRENAL CORTEX

Disorders Involving Glucocorticoid Hormones

Primary adrenal insufficiency (**Addison's disease**) results in hypoglycemia, extreme sensitivity to insulin, intolerance to stress, anorexia, weight loss, nausea, and severe weakness. Patients with Addison's disease have low blood pressure, decreased glomerular filtration rate, and decreased ability to excrete a water load. They often have a history of salt craving. Plasma Na^+ levels are low, K^+ levels are high, and blood lymphocyte and eosinophil counts are increased. Such patients often show increased pigmentation of skin and mucous membranes because of the exaggerated compensatory secretion of ACTH and associated products of the POMC gene. **Secondary adrenal insufficiency** is due to a deficiency of ACTH resulting from tumor, infarction, or infection. This results in a similar metabolic syndrome without hyperpigmentation.

Glucocorticoid excess, commonly called **Cushing's syndrome,** is usually due to the pharmacologic use of steroids, but it may result from an ACTH-secreting pituitary adenoma, from adrenal adenomas or carcinomas, or from the ectopic production of ACTH by a neoplasm. Patients with Cushing's syndrome typically lose the diurnal pattern of ACTH/cortisol secretion. They have hyperglycemia or glucose intolerance (or both) because of accelerated gluconeogenesis. Related to this are severe protein catabolic effects, which result in thinning of the skin, muscle wasting, osteoporosis, extensive lymphoid tissue involution, and generally a negative nitrogen balance. There is a peculiar redistribution of fat, with truncal obesity and the typical "buffalo hump." Resistance to infections and inflammatory responses is impaired, as is wound healing. Several findings, including hypernatremia, hypokalemia, alkalosis, edema, and hypertension, are due to the mineralocorticoid actions of cortisol.

Disorders Involving Mineralocorticoid Hormones

Small adenomas of the glomerulosa cells result in **primary aldosteronism (Conn's syndrome),** the classic manifestations of which include hypertension, hypokalemia, hypernatremia, and alkalosis. Patients with primary aldosteronism do not have evidence of glucocorticoid hormone excess, and plasma renin and angiotensin II levels are suppressed.

Renal artery stenosis, with the attendant decrease in perfusion pressure, can lead to hyperplasia and hyperfunction of the juxtaglomerular cells and cause elevated levels of renin and angiotensin II. This action results in **secondary aldosteronism,** which resembles the primary form, except for the elevated renin and angiotensin II levels.

Congenital Adrenal Hyperplasia

Insufficient amounts of steroidogenic enzymes result in the deficiency of end products, the accumulation of intermediates, and the exaggerated production of steroids from alternative pathways. A common feature of most of these syndromes, which develop in utero, is deficient cortisol production with ACTH overproduction and adrenal hyperplasia—hence, the term **congenital adrenal hyperplasia.** The overproduction of adrenal androgens is another common feature. This hormone excess results in increased body growth, virilization, and ambiguous external genitalia—hence, the alternative designation **adrenogenital syndrome.** The virilizing aspect of the pathophysiology of congenital adrenal hyperplasia can be understood by referring to the discussion of sexual differentiation in Chapter 41. Other symptoms depend on whether there is excessive or deficient production of aldosterone with hypertension or salt wasting, respectively.

Two types of **21-hydroxylase deficiency** (partial, or simple virilizing, and complete, or salt wasting) account for more than 90% of cases of congenital adrenal hyperplasia, and most of the rest are due to **11β-hydroxylase deficiency.** Only a few cases of other deficiencies (3β-hydroxysteroid dehydrogenase, 17α-hydroxylase, cholesterol desmolase, 18-hydroxylase, and 18-dehydrogenase) have been described. The **18-hydroxylase and -dehydrogenase deficiencies** affect only aldosterone biosynthesis and so do not cause adrenal hyperplasia. The **cholesterol desmolase deficiency** prevents any steroid biosynthesis and so is usually incompatible with extrauterine life.

THE ADRENAL MEDULLA

THE SYMPATHOADRENAL SYSTEM

The **sympathoadrenal** system consists of the **parasympathetic** nervous system with its cholinergic pre- and postganglionic nerves, the **sympathetic** ner-

Table 40–5. Physiologic responses in the "fight or flight" response.

Organ	Process or Result
Brain	Increased blood flow
	Increased glucose metabolism
Cardiovascular system	Increased rate and force of contraction
	Peripheral vasoconstriction
Pulmonary system	Increased oxygen supply
	Bronchodilatation
	Increased ventilation
Muscle	Increased glycogenolysis
	Increased contraction
Liver	Increased glucose production
	↑ Gluconeogenesis
	↑ Glycogenolysis
	↓ Glycogen synthesis
Adipose tissue	Increased lipolysis
	↑ Fatty acids and glycerol
Skin	Decreased blood flow
Skeleton	Decreased glucose uptake and utiliza-
Gastrointestinal and	tion
genitourinary tracts	Decreased protein synthesis
Lymphoid tissue	Increased proteolysis

vous system with cholinergic preganglionic and adrenergic postganglionic nerves, and the **adrenal medulla.** The latter is actually an extension of the sympathetic nervous system, since preganglionic fibers from the splanchnic nerve terminate in the adrenal medulla where they innervate the chromaffin cells that produce the catecholamine hormones **dopamine, norepinephrine,** and **epinephrine.** The adrenal medulla is thus a specialized ganglion without axonal extensions. Its chromaffin cells synthesize, store, and release products that act on distant sites, so that it also functions as an endocrine organ—a perfect illustration of the enmeshing of the nervous and endocrine systems alluded to in Chapter 36.

Role in the "Fight or Flight" Response

The hormones of the sympathoadrenal system, while not necessary for life, are required for adaptation to acute and chronic stress. Epinephrine, norepinephrine, and dopamine are the major elements in the **"fight or flight" response** (as occurs, for example, when one encounters a bear in a blueberry patch). The response to such a threat involves an acute, integrated adjustment of many complex processes in the organs vital to the response (brain, muscles, cardiopulmonary system, and liver) at the expense of other organs that are less immediately involved (skin, gastrointestinal system, and lymphoid tissue). The processes affected are listed in Table 40–5. Catecholamines do not facilitate the "fight or flight" response alone but are aided by the glucocorticoids, growth hormone, vasopressin, angiotensin II, and glucagon.

ORIGIN & STRUCTURE OF THE ADRENAL MEDULLA

Embryology

The sympathoadrenal system is derived from the neural crest. The primitive cells from this structure (sympathogonia) develop further into either neuroblasts, which are precursors for the mature sympathetic ganglion cells, or pheochromoblasts, which differentiate into the mature pheochromocytes (chromaffin cells) of the adrenal medulla. In the 7-week-old human fetus, the primitive neuroectodermal sympathogonia invade the tissue that will become the adrenal cortex. At birth, there are large masses of chromaffin tissue in addition to the adrenal medulla, but this extramedullary tissue rapidly involutes, and the medulla becomes the predominant tissue. This extramedullary tissue, usually found around the sympathetic nerve plexuses, is important because it may become functional if both adrenal medullas are removed or destroyed by disease and because functioning tumors (pheochromocytomas) can arise from these sites.

The development of the sympathoadrenal system depends upon nerve growth factor (NGF). Injection of a specific NGF antiserum at or just before birth prevents the development of the sympathoadrenal system (immunosympathectomy). In addition to increasing the number of cells, NGF also induces the critical enzymes tyrosine hydroxylase and dopamine β-hydroxylase (see below). Thus, it stimulates cell proliferation and differentiation.

Structure

The mature human adrenal gland weighs 5–7 g, and the medulla makes up about 10% of this. The medulla is surrounded by the cortex (Fig 40–1) and is bathed in the rich blood supply characteristic of this gland. Vascular effluent from the cortex empties into the medullary sinuses (the adrenal portal system, illustrated in Fig 40–1), which eventually drain into the central adrenal vein. This arrangement provides for a high medullary concentration of glucocorticoid hormones that stimulate the production of phenylethanolamine N-methyltransferase, the enzyme which converts norepinephrine to epinephrine. This biosynthetic step distinguishes the adrenal medulla from all other sympathetic tissues.

BIOSYNTHESIS OF CATECHOLAMINES

The catecholamine hormones dopamine, norepinephrine, and epinephrine are 3,4-dihydroxy derivatives of phenylethylamine. These amines are synthesized in the chromaffin cells of the adrenal medulla, so named because they contain granules that develop a red-brown color when exposed to potassium dichromate. Collections of these cells are also found in the heart, liver, kidney, gonads, adrenergic neurons of the postganglionic sympathetic system, and central nervous system.

The major product of the adrenal medulla is epinephrine. This compound constitutes about 80% of the catecholamines in the medulla, and it is not made in extramedullary tissue. In contrast, most of the norepinephrine present in organs innervated by sympathetic nerves is made in situ (~80% of the total), and most of the rest is made in other nerve endings and reaches the target sites via the circulation. Epinephrine and norepinephrine may be produced and stored in different cells in the adrenal medulla and other chromaffin tissues.

The conversion of tyrosine to epinephrine requires 4 sequential steps: (1) ring hydroxylation; (2) decarboxylation; (3) side chain hydroxylation; and (4) N-methylation. The biosynthetic pathway and the enzymes involved are illustrated in Fig 40–13, and a schematic representation is illustrated in Fig 40–14.

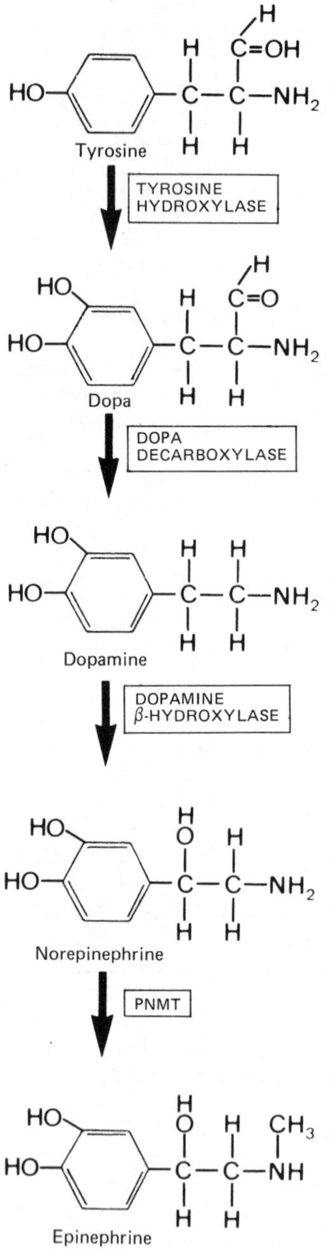

Tyrosine Hydroxylase (TH)

Tyrosine is the immediate precursor of catecholamines, and **tyrosine hydroxylase (TH)** is the rate-limiting enzyme in catecholamine biosynthesis. TH is found in both soluble and particle-bound forms; it functions as an oxidoreductase, with tetrahydropteridine as a cofactor, to convert L-tyrosine to L-dihydroxyphenylalanine (L-dopa). As the rate-limiting enzyme, TH is regulated in a variety of ways. The most important mechanism involves feedback inhibition by the catecholamines, which compete with the enzyme for the pteridine cofactor by forming a Schiff base with the latter. TH is also competitively inhibited by a series of tyrosine derivatives, including α-methyltyrosine. This compound is occasionally used to treat catecholamine excess in pheochromocytoma, but other agents are more effective and have fewer side effects. A third group of compounds inhibit TH by chelating iron and thus removing available cofactor. An example is α,α'-dipyridyl.

Catecholamines cannot cross the blood-brain barrier; hence, norepinephrine in the brain must be synthesized locally. In certain central nervous system diseases, eg, Parkinson's disease, there is a local deficiency of norepinephrine synthesis. L-Dopa, the precursor of norepinephrine, readily crosses the blood-brain barrier and so is an important agent in the treatment of Parkinson's disease.

Dopa Decarboxylase (DD)

In contrast to tyrosine hydroxylase, which is found only in tissues that synthesize catecholamines, **dopa decarboxylase** is found in all tissues. This soluble enzyme requires pyridoxal phosphate for the conversion of L-dopa to 3,4-dihydroxyphenylethylamine (dopamine). Compounds that resemble L-dopa, such as α-methyldopa, are competitive inhibitors of this reaction. Halogenated compounds form a Schiff base with L-dopa and also inhibit the decarboxylase reaction.

α-Methyldopa and other decarboxylase inhibitors are not effective in treating the severe hypertension that accompanies the excessive production of epineph-

Figure 40–13. Biosynthesis of catecholamines. PNMT, phenylethanolamine-N-methyltransferase. (Reproduced, with permission, from Goldfien A: The adrenal medulla. In: *Basic & Clinical Endocrinology.* Greenspan FS, Forsham PH [editors]. Lange, 1983.)

rine and norepinephrine in pheochromocytoma. Concentrations sufficient to inhibit the enzyme apparently cannot be achieved in the neurons or medullary cells. α-Methyldopa is effective in treating other kinds of hypertension. This was initially thought to be due to a **"false transmitter"** action, since a metabolite of α-methyldopa (α-methylnorepinephrine) is taken up

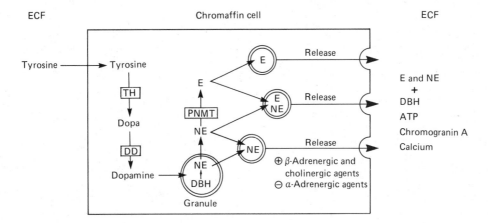

Figure 40–14. Schematic representation of catecholamine biosynthesis. TH, tyrosine hydroxylase; DD, dopa decarboxylase; PNMT, phenylethanolamine-N-methyltransferase; DBH, dopamine β-hydroxylase; ATP, adenosine triphosphate. The biosynthesis of catecholamines occurs within the cytoplasm and in various granules of the adrenal medullary cell. Some granules contain epinephrine (E), others have norepinephrine (NE), while still others have both hormones. Upon stimulation all the contents of the granules are released into the extracellular fluid (ECF).

by central and peripheral nerves and released in place of norepinephrine. Other "false transmitters" are 3-hydroxytyramine (from tyramine), α-methyltyrosine, and metaraminol. The antihypertensive action of these metabolites is now thought to result from their ability to stimulate the α-adrenergic receptor (see below) of the corticobulbar system in the central nervous system. This results in reduced peripheral sympathetic nerve discharge and decreased blood pressure.

Dopamine β-Hydroxylase (DBH)

Dopamine β-hydroxylase (DBH) is a mixed-function oxidase that catalyzes the conversion of dopamine to norepinephrine. DBH uses ascorbate as an electron donor, copper at the active site, and fumarate as modulator. DBH is in the particulate fraction of the medullary cells, probably in the secretion granule; thus, the conversion of dopamine to norepinephrine occurs in this organelle. DBH is released from the adrenal medulla or nerve endings with norepinephrine, but (unlike norepinephrine) it cannot reenter nerve terminals via the reuptake mechanism.

Phenylethanolamine-N-Methyltransferase (PNMT)

The soluble enzyme phenylethanolamine-N-methyltransferase (PNMT) catalyzes the N-methylation of norepinephrine to form epinephrine in the epinephrine-forming cells of the adrenal medulla. Since PNMT is soluble, it is assumed that norepinephrine-to-epinephrine conversion occurs in the cytoplasm. The synthesis of PNMT is induced by glucocorticoid hormones that reach the medulla via the intra-adrenal portal system described above. This system provides for a 100-fold steroid concentration gradient over systemic arterial blood, and this high intra-adrenal concentration appears to be necessary for the induction of PNMT.

STORAGE & RELEASE OF CATECHOLAMINES

Storage

The adrenal medulla contains the **chromaffin granules**—organelles capable of the biosynthesis, uptake, storage, and secretion of catecholamines. These granules contain a number of substances in addition to the catecholamines, including ATP-Mg^{2+}, Ca^{2+}, DBH, and the protein chromogranin A. Catecholamines enter the granule via an ATP-dependent transport mechanism and bind this nucleotide in a 4:1 ratio (hormone:ATP). Norepinephrine is stored in these granules but can exit to be N-methylated; the epinephrine formed then enters a new population of granules.

Release

Neural stimulation of the adrenal medulla results in the fusion of the membranes of the storage granules with the plasma membrane, and this leads to the exocytotic release of norepinephrine and epinephrine. This is a calcium-dependent process and, like most exocytotic events, is stimulated by cholinergic and β-adrenergic agents and inhibited by α-adrenergic agents (Fig 40–14). Catecholamines and ATP are released in proportion to their intragranular ratio, as are the other contents including DBH, calcium, and chromogranin A.

Neuronal reuptake of catecholamines is an important mechanism for conserving these hormones and for quickly terminating hormonal or neurotransmitter activity. The adrenal medulla, unlike the sympathetic nerves, does not have a mechanism for the reuptake and storage of discharged catecholamines. The epinephrine discharged from the adrenal goes to the liver and skeletal muscle but then is rapidly metabolized. Very little adrenal norepinephrine reaches distal tissues. Catecholamines circulate in plasma in a loose

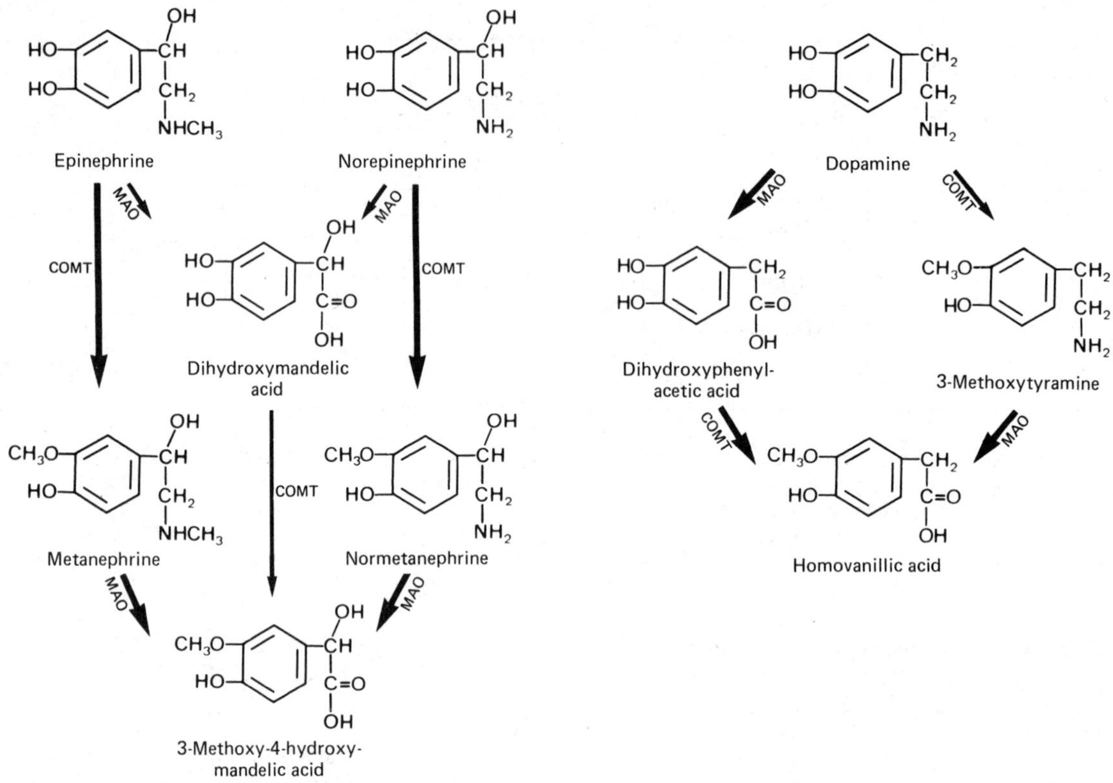

Figure 40–15. Metabolism of catecholamines by catechol-O-methyltransferase (COMT) and monoamine oxidase (MAO). (Reproduced, with permission, from Goldfien A: The adrenal medulla. In: *Basic & Clinical Endocrinology.* Greenspan FS, Forsham PH [editors]. Lange, 1983.)

association with albumin. They have an extremely short biologic half-life (10–30 seconds).

METABOLISM OF CATECHOLAMINES

Very little epinephrine ($< 5\%$) is excreted in the urine. Catecholamines are rapidly metabolized by catechol-O-methyltransferase (COMT) and monoamine oxidase (MAO) to form the inactive O-methylated and deaminated metabolites (Fig 40–15). Most catecholamines are substrates for both of these enzymes, and these reactions can occur in any sequence.

Catechol-O-methyltransferase (COMT) is a cytosol enzyme found in many tissues. It catalyzes the addition of a methyl group, usually at the 3 position (meta) on the benzene ring, to a variety of catecholamines. The reaction requires a divalent cation, and S-adenosylmethionine is the methyl donor. The result of this reaction, depending on the substrate, is the production of homovanillic acid, normetanephrine, and metanephrine.

Monoamine oxidase (MAO) is an oxidoreductase that deaminates monoamines. It is located in many

tissues, but it occurs in highest concentrations in the liver, stomach, kidney, and intestine. At least 2 isozymes of MAO have been described. MAO-A is found in neural tissue and deaminates serotonin, epinephrine, and norepinephrine, while MAO-B is found in extraneural tissues and is most active against 2-phenylethylamine and benzylamine. Dopamine and tyramine are metabolized by both forms. Much research effort is directed at correlating affective disorders with increases or decreases of the activity of these isozymes. MAO inhibitors have been used to treat hypertension and depression, but serious reactions with foods or drugs that contain sympathomimetic amines limit their usefulness.

O-Methoxylated derivatives are further modified by conjugation with glucuronic or sulfuric acid.

A bewildering number of metabolites of catecholamines are formed. Two classes of these have diagnostic significance, since they are found in readily measurable amounts in urine. **Metanephrines** represent the methoxy derivatives of epinephrine and norepinephrine, while the O-methylated deaminated product of epinephrine and norepinephrine is **3-methoxy-4-hydroxymandelic acid** (also called **vanillylmandelic acid [VMA]**) (Fig 40–15). The concentration of metanephrines or VMA in urine is elevated in more than 95% of patients with pheochromocytoma. These tests have excellent diagnostic precision, particularly when coupled with a measurement of plasma or urine catecholamines.

REGULATION OF SYNTHESIS OF CATECHOLAMINES

Stimulation of the splanchnic nerve, which supplies the preganglionic fibers to the adrenal medulla, results in the exocytotic release of catecholamines, the granule carrier protein, and DBH. Such stimulation is controlled by the hypothalamus and brain stem, but the exact feedback loop has not been described. Ganglionic blocking agents prevent and nicotine mimics the response. In addition, centers in the spinal cord at the level of the first cervical vertebra are known to be involved in the response, since this cervical cord center is necessary for the release of epinephrine in response to hypoglycemia.

Nerve stimulation also results in increased synthesis of catecholamines. Norepinephrine synthesis increases after acute stress, but the amount of TH is unchanged even though TH activity increases. TH is a substrate for cAMP-dependent protein kinase, and so this activation may involve phosphorylation. Prolonged stress accompanied by chronic sympathetic nerve activity results in an induction (increased amount) of TH. A similar induction of DBH has also been reported. The induction of these enzymes of the catecholamine biosynthetic pathway is a means of adapting to physiologic stress and depends upon neural (TH and DBH induction) and endocrine (PNMT induction) factors.

CLASSIFICATION & MECHANISM OF ACTION OF CATECHOLAMINES

Classification

The mechanism of action of the catecholamines has attracted the attention of investigators for nearly a century. Indeed, many of the general concepts of receptor biology and hormone action can be traced to these early studies.

The catecholamines act through 2 major classes of receptors. These are designated α-adrenergic and β-adrenergic, and each consists of 2 subclasses, ie, alpha$_1$, alpha$_2$, beta$_1$, and beta$_2$. This classification is based on the relative order of binding of various agonists and antagonists as described in Table 40–6. For example, the beta$_2$ receptor binds isoproterenol more avidly than epinephrine; epinephrine is bound much more avidly than norepinephrine; and phenylephrine is bound very inefficiently. The binding of the synthetic agonist isoproterenol best distinguishes beta from alpha receptors; this catecholamine binds more avidly to beta receptors than do epinephrine and norepinephrine, whereas it binds very poorly to alpha receptors. Epinephrine binds to and activates both

Table 40—6. Classification of adrenergic hormone receptors.*

Receptor	Agonists†	Antagonists	Mechanism of Action
Alpha$_1$	E ⩾ NE ≫ PE ≫ I	Prazosin	Promotes calcium flux
Alpha$_2$	E ⩾ NE ≫ PE ≫ I	Yohimbine Rauwolscine	Inhibits cyclase
Beta$_1$	I > E ⩾ NE > PE	Propranolol Alprenolol Metoprolol	Stimulates cyclase
Beta$_2$	I > E ≫ NE > PE	Propranolol Alprenolol Pindolol	Stimulates cyclase

*Modified and reproduced, with permission, from Lefkowitz RJ, Stadel JM, Caron MG: Adenylate cyclase–coupled β-adrenergic receptors: Structure and mechanisms of activation and desensitization. *Annu Rev Biochem* 1983;52:159. Copyright © 1983 by Annual Reviews Inc.

†E, epinephrine; NE, norepinephrine; I, isoproterenol; PE, phenylephrine.

alpha and beta receptors, so that its action in a tissue which has both depends on the relative affinity of these receptors for the hormone. Norepinephrine at physiologic concentrations primarily binds to alpha receptors.

Mechanism of Action

Three of these adrenergic receptor subgroups are coupled to the adenylate cyclase system. Hormones that bind to the beta$_1$ and beta$_2$ receptors activate adenylate cyclase, whereas hormones that bind to alpha$_2$ receptors inhibit this enzyme (see Fig 36–3 and Table 36–2). Alpha$_1$ receptors are coupled to processes that alter intracellular calcium concentrations or modify phosphatidylinositide metabolism (or both). (See Chapter 36.) A partial list of the biochemical and physiologic effects mediated by each of these receptors is provided in Table 40–7, and the effects of catecholamines on the secretion of other hormones are shown in Table 40–8.

Activation of phosphoproteins by cAMP-dependent protein kinase (see Fig 36–5) accounts for many of the biochemical effects of epinephrine. In muscle, and to a lesser extent in liver, epinephrine stimulates glycogenolysis by activating a protein kinase that, in turn, activates the phosphorylase cascade (see Fig 15–11). Conversely, phosphorylation of glycogen synthase decreases glycogen synthesis. In heart muscle, epinephrine increases cardiac output by increasing the force (**inotropic effect**) and rate (**chronotropic effect**) of contraction, which are also related to increased cAMP.

In adipose tissue, epinephrine increases cAMP, which converts the hormone-sensitive lipase into the active (phosphorylated) form. This enzyme promotes lipolysis and release of fatty acids into the circulation. These fatty acids serve as an energy source in muscle and can activate gluconeogenesis in liver.

Table 40—7. Actions mediated through various adrenergic receptors.

Alpha$_1$	Alpha$_2$	Beta$_1$	Beta$_2$
Increased glycogenolysis	Smooth muscle relaxation	Stimulation of lipolysis	Increased hepatic gluconeogenesis
Smooth muscle contraction	Gastrointestinal tract	Myocardial contraction	Increased hepatic glycogenolysis
Blood vessels	Smooth muscle contraction	Increased rate	Increased muscle glycogenolysis
Genitourinary tract	Some vascular beds	Increased force	Increased release of:
	Inhibition of:		Insulin
	Lipolysis		Glucagon
	Renin release		Renin
	Platelet aggregation		Smooth muscle relaxation
	Insulin secretion		Bronchi
			Blood vessels
			Genitourinary tract
			Gastrointestinal tract

In the "fight or flight" reaction discussed above, epinephrine (1) rapidly provides fatty acids as the primary fuel for muscle action; (2) mobilizes glucose as an energy source for the brain by increasing glycogenolysis and gluconeogenesis in the liver and by decreasing glucose uptake in the muscle and other organs; and (3) decreases insulin release, which also prevents glucose from being taken up by peripheral tissues and thus preserves it for the central nervous system. Studies of the mechanism of action of epinephrine on glycogenolysis led to the discovery of cAMP, which in turn resulted in the second messenger hypothesis. The actions of norepinephrine are predominantly associated with alpha receptors (Table 40–6) and tend to be exerted in the peripheral vascular bed rather than on metabolic processes. Norepinephrine does activate hepatic glycogenolysis through the alpha$_1$ receptor in a cAMP-independent process that apparently involves changes in calcium flux, phosphatidylinositide metabolism, or both (see Fig 36–7).

Table 40—8. Effects of catecholamines on hormone secretion.*

Endocrine Organ	Hormone	Receptor	Feedback Loop
Pancreatic Islets			
A cells	Glucagon	Beta$_2$	Plasma glucose
B cells	Insulin	Beta$_2$	Plasma glucose
Thyroid			
Follicle cells	T$_4$–T$_3$	Beta$_2$	TSH
C cells	Calcitonin	Beta	Plasma Ca^{2+}
Parathyroid	PTH	Beta$_1$	Plasma Ca^{2+}
Kidney			
Juxtaglomerular cells	Renin	Beta$_2$	Distal tubule Na$^+$
Cells not known	Erythropoietin	Beta$_2$	Arterial P$_{O_2}$
Gastric antral and duodenal G cells	Gastrin	Beta	Gastric pH

*Modified and reproduced, with permission, from Young JB, Landsberg L: Catecholamines and the regulation of hormone secretion. *Clin Endocrinol Metab* 1977;**6**:657.

PATHOPHYSIOLOGY OF THE ADRENAL MEDULLA

Pheochromocytomas are tumors of the adrenal medulla that are usually not detected unless they produce and secrete enough epinephrine or norepinephrine to cause a severe hypertension syndrome. The ratio of norepinephrine to epinephrine is often increased in pheochromocytoma. This may account for differences in clinical presentation, since norepinephrine is thought to be primarily responsible for hypertension and epinephrine for hypermetabolism. Extraadrenal pheochromocytomas generally produce only norepinephrine. Pheochromocytomas can be sporadic or familial. Familial pheochromocytoma is often part of multiple endocrine neoplasia type II (**Sipple's syndrome**).

•　　•　　•

References

General

Feiser LF, Feiser M: *Steroids*. Reinhold, 1959.

Samuels LT, Nelson DH: Biosynthesis of the corticosteroids. In: *Handbook of Physiology*. Section 7: Endocrinology. Vol 6: Adrenal Gland. American Physiological Society, Washington, DC, 1975.

Renin-Aldosterone System

Barajas L: Anatomy of the juxtaglomerular apparatus. *Am J Physiol* 1979;**237**:F333.

Brown JJ et al: Angiotensin II, aldosterone, and arterial pressure: A quantitative approach. *Hypertension* 1979; **1**:159.

Davis JO, Freeman RM: Mechanisms regulating renin release. *Physiol Rev* 1976;**56**:1.

Morris DJ: The metabolism and mechanism of action of aldosterone. *Endocr Rev* 1981;**2**:234.

Wilson M et al: Blood pressure, the renin-aldosterone system and sex steroids throughout normal pregnancy. *Am J Med* 1980;**68**:97.

Glucocorticoids

Baxter JD, Forsham PH: Tissue effects of glucocorticoids. *Am J Med* 1972;**53**:573.

Gill GN: Mechanism of ACTH action. *Metabolism* 1972; **21**:571.

Granner DK: The role of glucocorticoid hormones as biological amplifiers. In: *Glucocorticoid Hormone Action*. Baxter JD, Rousseau GG (editors). Springer-Verlag, 1979.

New MI et al: An update of congenital adrenal hyperplasia. *Recent Prog Horm Res* 1981;**37**:105.

Samuels HH, Tomkins GM: Relation of steroid structure to enzyme induction in hepatoma tissue culture cells. *J Mol Biol* 1970;**52**:57.

Adrenal Medulla

Cryer PE: Diseases of the adrenal medulla and sympathetic nervous system. Pages 511–550 in: *Endocrinology and Metabolism*. Felig P et al (editors). McGraw-Hill, 1981.

Exton JH: Mechanisms involved in α-adrenergic phenomena: Role of calcium ion in actions of catecholamines in liver and other tissues. *Am J Physiol* 1980;**238**:E3.

Lefkowitz RJ: Clinical physiology of adrenergic receptor regulation. *Am J Physiol* 1982;**243**:E43.

Perlman FL, Chalfie M: Catecholamine release from the adrenal medulla. *Clin Endocrinol Metab* 1977;**6**:551.

Stiles GL, Caron MG, Lefkowitz RK: The β-adrenergic receptor: Biochemical mechanisms of physiological regulation. *Physiol Rev* 1984;**64**:661.

Young JB, Landsberg L: Catecholamines and intermediary metabolism. *Clin Endocrinol Metab* 1977;**6**:599.

Young JB, Landsberg L: Catecholamines and the regulation of hormone secretion. *Clin Endocrinol Metab* 1977;**6**:657.

41 | Hormones of the Gonads

Daryl K. Granner, MD

HORMONES OF THE TESTES

The testes are bifunctional organs that produce testosterone (the male sex hormone) and spermatozoa (the male germ cells). These functions are carried out by 3 specialized cell types: (1) the **spermatogonia** and more differentiated germ cells, which are located in the seminiferous tubules; (2) the **Leydig cells** (also called interstitial cells), which are scattered in the connective tissue between the coiled seminiferous tubules and which produce testosterone in response to LH; and (3) the **Sertoli cells,** which form the basement membrane of the seminiferous tubules and provide the environment necessary for germ cell differentiation and maturation, including the secretion of androgen-binding protein (ABP) in response to FSH. Spermatogenesis is stimulated by FSH and LH from the pituitary. It requires an environment conducive to germ cell differentiation and a concentration of testosterone in excess of that found in the systemic circulation—requirements that are met by local secretion of ABP and testosterone by the Sertoli and Leydig cells, respectively.

BIOSYNTHESIS & METABOLISM OF TESTICULAR HORMONES

Synthesis

Testicular androgens are synthesized in the interstitial tissue by the Leydig cells; these cells contain virtually all of the 3β-hydroxysteroid dehydrogenase found in the testis, and this enzyme catalyzes the key step in testosterone biosynthesis.

A. Biosynthetic Pathways:

1. Testosterone–The immediate precursor of the gonadal steroids, as with the adrenal steroids, is cholesterol. The rate-limiting step, as in the adrenal, is cholesterol side chain cleavage. The conversion of cholesterol to pregnenolone is identical in adrenal, ovary, and testis. In the latter 2 tissues, however, the reaction is promoted by LH rather than ACTH.

The conversion of pregnenolone to testosterone requires the action of 5 enzymes: (1) 3β-hydroxysteroid dehydrogenase (3β-OHSD); (2) Δ^5-Δ^4 isomerase; (3) 17α-hydroxylase; (4) C_{17-20} lyase; and (5) 17β-hydroxysteroid dehydrogenase (17β-OHSD). This sequence, referred to as the pro-

gesterone (or Δ^4) pathway, is shown on the right side of Fig 41–1. Pregnenolone can also be converted to testosterone by the dehydroepiandrosterone (or Δ^5) pathway, which is illustrated on the left side of Fig 41–1. The Δ^4 route appears to be preferred in human

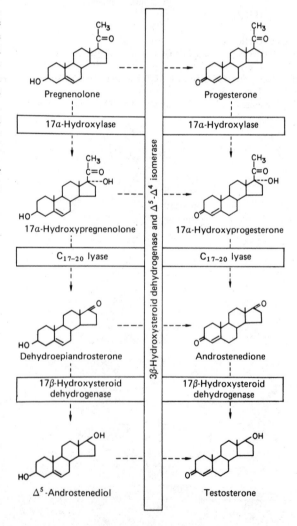

Figure 41–1. Pathways of testosterone biosynthesis. The pathway on the left side of the figure is called the Δ^5 or dehydroepiandrosterone pathway; the pathway on the right side is called the Δ^4 or progesterone pathway.

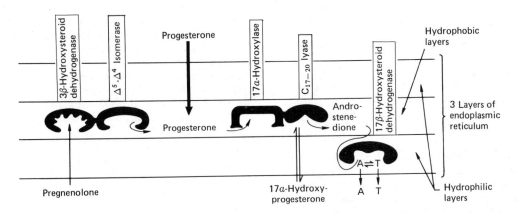

Figure 41–2. Schematic representation of androgen biosynthesis in the testicular microsomal membrane. The membrane is shown as horizontal, which may be the case in the cell; in microsomal preparations, however, it forms vesicles. A, androstenedione; T, testosterone. (Reproduced, with permission, from DeGroot LJ: *Endocrinology.* Vol 3. Grune & Stratton, 1979.)

testes; however, since these are seldom available for study, most information about these pathways comes from studies in other animals. There may be significant species differences.

The 5 enzymes are localized in the microsomal fraction in rat testes, and **there is a close functional association between the activities of 3β-OHSD and Δ⁵-Δ⁴ isomerase and between those of 17α-hydroxylase and C_{17-20} lyase.** These enzyme pairs are shown in the general reaction sequence in Fig 41–1 and in the schematic representation of androgen biosynthesis in the testicular microsomal membrane in Fig 41–2. The latter shows how the various substrates for testosterone biosynthesis can enter the microsomal compartment and how they might proceed via the Δ^4 pathway from one reaction to the next. Since there are 4 potential substrates for what appears to be a single 3β-OHSD, multiple alternative pathways exist; thus, the route taken probably depends on the substrate concentration in the vicinity of the various enzymes. Partitioning in the microsomal membrane may provide these gradients.

2. Other testicular hormones–Dihydrotestosterone (DHT) is formed from testosterone by the reduction of the A ring through the action of the enzyme **5α-reductase.** Human testes secrete about 50–100 μg of DHT per day, but most DHT is derived from peripheral conversion (see below).

The testes also make small but significant amounts of 17β-estradiol (E_2), the female sex hormone, but most of the E_2 produced by the male is derived from peripheral aromatization of testosterone and androstenedione. The Leydig cells, the Sertoli cells, and the seminiferous tubules are thought to be involved in E_2 production. The role of E_2 in the male has not been determined, but it may contribute to FSH regulation. Abnormally high plasma levels of E_2 and changes in the free E_2:testosterone ratio have been associated with pubertal or postpubertal gynecomastia

(male breast enlargement), particularly in older individuals and in patients with chronic liver disease or hyperthyroidism.

B. Age-Related Changes in Testicular Hormone Production: Testosterone is the dominant hormone in the fetal and neonatal rat, but the testes make only androsterone soon after birth. The ability to produce testosterone is restored at puberty and continues throughout life. Similar observations have been made in other species, and these age-related changes may also occur in humans.

Secretion & Transport

A number of steroids are present in testicular venous blood, but **testosterone is the major steroid secreted by the adult testes.** The secretion rate is about 5 mg/d in normal adult men. Although a small amount of testosterone is secreted by the adrenals, most comes from the testes. Castration or Leydig cell destruction thus results in a marked decrease in the testosterone secretion rate. Testosterone production is decreased by supine positioning, stress, and anesthesia—effects that may involve decreased blood flow to the testes. There is no apparent regulation of the secretion of testicular steroids; like other steroid hormones, testosterone seems to be released as it is produced.

Most mammals, humans included, have a plasma β-globulin that binds testosterone with specificity, relatively high affinity, and limited capacity (Table 41–1). This protein, usually called **sex hormone-binding globulin (SHBG) or testosterone-estrogen-binding globulin (TEBG),** is produced in the liver. Its production is increased by estrogens (women have twice the serum concentration of SHBG as men), certain types of liver disease, and hyperthyroidism; it is decreased by androgens, advancing age, and hypothyroidism. Many of these conditions also affect the production of CBG (see Chapter 40) and

Table 41–1. Hormone binding to sex hormone–binding globulin (SHBG).

Steroids Bound	Steroids Not Bound
Testosterone	Conjugated androgens
17β-Estradiol	17α-Testosterone
Dihydrotestosterone	Dehydroisoandrosterone
Other 17β-hydroxysteroids	Cortisol
Estrone	Progesterone

TBG (see Chapter 38). Since SHBG and albumin bind 97–99% of circulating testosterone, only a small fraction of the hormone in circulation is in the free (biologically active) form. The primary function of SHBG may be to restrict the free concentration of testosterone in the serum. Testosterone binds to SHBG with higher affinity than does estradiol (Table 41–2). Therefore, a change in the level of SHBG causes a greater change in the free testosterone level than in the free estradiol level. An increase of SHBG may contribute to the increased free E_2:testosterone ratio noted in aging, cirrhosis, and hyperthyroidism and hence contribute to the attendant signs and symptoms of "estrogenization" alluded to above.

Peripheral Metabolism & Excretion

A. Metabolic Pathways: Testosterone is metabolized by 2 pathways. One involves oxidation at the 17-position, and the other involves reduction of the A ring double bond and the 3-ketone. Metabolism via the first pathway occurs in many tissues, including liver, and produces 17-ketosteroids that are generally inactive or less active than the parent compound. Metabolism via the second pathway, which is less efficient, occurs primarily in target tissues and produces the potent metabolite DHT as well as estradiol and androstanediol. Etiocholanolone and androsterone are 5β-reduced products of androgens.

B. Metabolites of Testosterone: The most significant metabolic product of testosterone is DHT, since in many tissues, including seminal vesicles, prostate, external genitalia, and some areas of the skin, this is the active form of the hormone. The plasma content of DHT in the adult male is about one-tenth that of testosterone, and approximately 400 μg of DHT is produced daily, as compared to about 5 mg of testosterone. The reaction is catalyzed by 5α-reductase, and NADPH-dependent enzyme. (See below.)

Testosterone can thus be considered a prohormone, since it is converted into a much more potent compound (dihydrotestosterone) and since most of this conversion occurs outside the testes. A small percentage of testosterone is also converted into estradiol by aromatization, a reaction that is especially important in the brain, where these hormones help determine the sexual behavior of the animal. Androstanediol, another potent androgen, is also produced from testosterone.

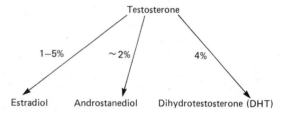

The major 17-ketosteroid metabolites, androsterone and etiocholanolone, are conjugated with glucuronide and sulfate in the liver to make water-soluble, excretable compounds. Quantification of urinary 17-ketosteroids was employed as an assay for androgen activity, but this is now recognized to be a poor reflection of the in vivo status of this class of hormones.

REGULATION OF TESTICULAR FUNCTION

Regulation of Steroidogenesis

Testicular function is regulated by LH and FSH (Fig 41–3). LH stimulates steroidogenesis and testosterone production by binding to receptors on the plasma membrane of the Leydig cells (an analogous LH receptor is found on cells of the corpus luteum) and activating adenylate cyclase, thus increasing intracellular cAMP. This action enhances the rate of cholesterol side chain cleavage. It is not clear whether this cleavage results from activation or induction of the enzyme or from enhanced transport of cholesterol to the enzyme; the induction of a protein that facilitates this process has been proposed. The similarity between this action of LH and that of ACTH on the adrenal is apparent. Although LH (or hCG) has been shown to induce other steroidogenic enzymes, including 3β-

Testosterone

5α-Reductase
NADPH

Dihydrotestosterone (DHT)

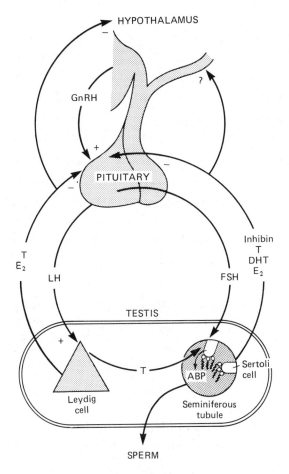

Figure 41–3. Feedback regulation of testicular function. GnRH, gonadotropin-releasing hormone; LH, luteinizing hormone; FSH, follicle-stimulating hormone; T, testosterone; DHT, dihydrotestosterone; ABP, androgen-binding protein; E₂, 17β-estradiol; +, positive influence; −, negative influence. (Reproduced, with permission, from Braunstein GD: The testes. In: *Basic & Clinical Endocrinology.* Greenspan FG, Forsham PH [editors]. Lange, 1983.)

OHSD, C_{17-20} lyase, and 5α-reductase, the primary effect appears to occur somewhere in the course of cholesterol conversion to pregnenolone.

The interaction of testosterone with its receptor probably provides for feedback control of gonadotropin release (Figs 41–3 and 41–4). This feedback appears to be accomplished at the hypothalamus through inhibition of GnRH release, GnRH production, or both, although inhibition of the action of GnRH on the LH-producing cells in the anterior pituitary cannot be excluded.

GnRH is normally released in a pulsatile fashion, and maximal production of the gonadotropins (LH and FSH) in experimental systems occurs only when this pulsatile pattern of GnRH release is simulated. Prolonged exposure to constantly elevated levels of GnRH appears to result in target cell desensitization and a profound suppression of LH and FSH release;

thus, long-acting GnRH analogs are being tested as contraceptive agents.

Prior to puberty, serum testosterone levels are very low. An early event in this developmental process is an increase in sleep-associated, pulsatile bursts of LH and FSH release. When serum testosterone levels rise, growth and development of the secondary sex organs ensue. The signal that initiates this process has not been deciphered, but the prevailing hypothesis is that the hypothalamic centers responsible for GnRH production become less sensitive to feedback inhibition by gonadal steroid hormones.

Regulation of Spermatogenesis

This complex subject will be discussed only in terms of the feedback regulation of FSH secretion. **FSH binds to the Sertoli cells and promotes the synthesis of androgen-binding protein (ABP).** ABP is a glycoprotein that binds testosterone, but it is distinct from SHBG and the intracellular androgen receptor. ABP is secreted into the lumen of the seminiferous tubule, and in this process testosterone produced by the Leydig cells is transported in very high concentration to the site of spermatogenesis (Fig 41–3). This appears to be a critical step, since normal systemic levels of testosterone, such as might be achieved by replacement therapy, do not support spermatogenesis.

Although only one GnRH has been identified, **there is evidence for selective release of FSH and LH.** In men with selective destruction of seminiferous tubules or with arrested spermatogenesis due to various causes, there are normal LH and testosterone levels but elevated FSH levels. A substance from the seminiferous tubules or the Sertoli cells that would regulate FSH release, an **"inhibin,"** has been sought. Part of this feedback effect on FSH release may be mediated by estradiol, which is made in small amounts by the Leydig and Sertoli cells. Production of estradiol in these cells is stimulated by FSH, and this steroid does result in feedback inhibition of FSH under certain test conditions. These possible mechanisms of FSH regulation are illustrated in Fig 41–3.

PHYSIOLOGIC ACTION OF TESTICULAR HORMONES

The androgens, principally testosterone and DHT, are involved in (1) sexual differentiation, (2) spermatogenesis, (3) development of secondary sexual organs and ornamental structures, (4) anabolic metabolism and gene regulation, and (5) male-pattern behavior (Fig 41–4). It is therefore difficult to define target and nontarget tissues, since so many are involved. In a more specific sense, such target tissues must also be defined according to whether they are affected by testosterone or DHT. The classic target cells for DHT (and those which coincidentally have the highest 5α-reductase activity) are the prostate, seminal vesicles, external genitalia, and genital skin. Targets for testosterone include the embryonic wolffian structures,

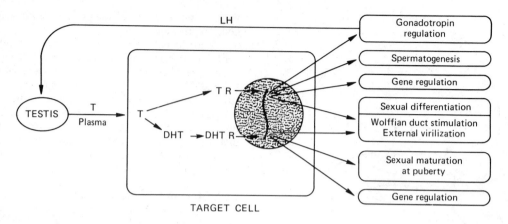

Figure 41–4. Mechanism of androgen action. LH, luteinizing hormone; T, testosterone; DHT, dihydrotestosterone; R, androgen receptor. (Modified and reproduced, with permission, from Wilson JD et al: The endocrine control of male phenotypic development. *Aust J Biol Sci* 1983;**36**:101.)

spermatogonia, muscles, bone, kidney, and brain. The specific androgen involved in regulating the many other processes mentioned above has not been determined.

Sexual Differentiation

Sexual differentiation is a major action of the androgens, and since it represents a unique opportunity to discuss how specific hormones influence tissue differentiation, it is discussed separately below.

Spermatogenesis

The requirement for testosterone in spermatogenesis is unquestioned, yet its precise role in this process has not been defined. Testosterone may affect a relatively late stage, since it does not initiate spermatogenesis in the immature testis, nor does it restore sperm production in hypophysectomized animals in which the process has been allowed to regress.

Maturation of Secondary Sex Tissues

The increased production of testosterone at puberty results in the maturation of secondary sex tissues. The phallus, prostate, and seminal vesicles enlarge. The texture of skin and hair changes from the soft, smooth, infantile variety to a coarser form, beard growth commences, vocal cords thicken, and sebaceous glands enlarge. Castration causes most of these processes to revert toward the prepubertal form.

Anabolic Metabolism

Rapid growth of the musculoskeletal system is associated with puberty. Cartilage in the epiphyseal plates enlarges, and new bone formation ensues. This increase in height is accompanied by a marked increase in skeletal muscle mass. These effects are difficult to analyze on a molecular level, but some clues exist. Androgens appear to induce the synthesis of protein in target tissues by the now well-accepted mechanism employed by other steroid hormones in which the

hormone-receptor complex recognizes specific regions of chromatin and selectively activates certain genes. (See Chapter 36.) This appears to be true for ABP, aldolase, and the enzymes involved in polyamine biosynthesis. Similar mechanisms may be involved in androgen-mediated muscle hypertrophy, but as yet the specific proteins (genes) involved have not been identified.

Actions of Androgen Antagonists

Several potent androgen antagonists have been synthesized. These inhibit androgen action by competing with androgen for binding to the target cell receptor rather than by inhibiting androgen biosynthesis or metabolism. Some of these compounds, such as cyproterone acetate, are steroids, whereas others, such as flutamide, are not.

Cyproterone acetate

Flutamide

The androgen antagonists are not extensively used for clinical purposes but have been useful experimentally in determining aspects of androgen action in animals. For example, the administration of an androgen antagonist during embryogenesis was observed to block certain aspects of male sexual development. The normal pattern of development is described under Gonadal Hormones & Sexual Differentiation (below).

MECHANISM OF ACTION OF TESTICULAR HORMONES

The current concept of androgen action is shown in Fig 41–4. Free testosterone enters cells through the plasma membrane by either passive or facilitated diffusion. Target cells retain testosterone, presumably because the hormone associates with a specific intracellular receptor. Although there is considerable tissue-to-tissue variability, most of the retained hormone is found in the cell nucleus. The cytoplasm of many (but not all) target cells contains the enzyme 5α-reductase, which converts testosterone to DHT. Whether there are distinct receptors for testosterone and DHT has been a point of controversy, but the consensus is that while there is but a single class of receptors, the affinity of the receptor for DHT exceeds that for testosterone. Single gene mutations in mice result in loss of binding of both testosterone and DHT to the receptor in various tissues, suggesting that a single protein is involved. The affinity difference, coupled with the ability of a target tissue to form DHT from testosterone, may determine whether the testosterone-receptor complex or the DHT-receptor complex is active.

Nuclear localization of the testosterone/DHT-receptor complex is a prerequisite for androgen action. Binding of the receptor-steroid complex to chromatin may involve a prior activation step, and some specificity or acceptor function is certainly supplied by chromatin. The nature of the nuclear acceptor for the active receptor-steroid complex has not been elucidated.

In keeping with other steroid (and some peptide) hormones, **the testosterone/DHT receptor presumably activates specific genes,** and the protein products of these mediate many (if not all) of the effects of the hormone. Testosterone stimulates protein synthesis in male accessory organs, an effect that is usually associated with increased accumulation of total cellular RNA, including mRNA, tRNA, and rRNA. A more specific example involves the effect of testosterone on the synthesis of ABP. The hormone increases the rate of transcription of the ABP gene, which results in an increased amount of the mRNA that codes for this protein. Another well-studied example is α_{2u} globulin, the major protein excreted in the urine of male rats. It is synthesized by the liver of mature (> 40-day-old) male rats but is not synthesized by female rats or castrated male rats unless they are given testosterone. Estrogen

inhibits the production of α_{2u} globulin, and maximal rates of production require the concerted action of hormones including GH, thyroid hormones, insulin, and glucocorticoids. The rate of synthesis of α_{2u} globulin is directly related to the amount of the cognate mRNA, which in turn is related to the rate of transcription of the α_{2u} globulin gene.

The kidney is a major target tissue for androgens. These hormones cause a general enlargement of the kidney and induce the synthesis of a number of enzymes—including L-gulonolactonase, β-glucuronidase, and ornithine decarboxylase—in various species.

An interesting potential anabolic effect results from the action of androgens on the submaxillary gland, which appears to be an unlikely target organ. Androgens, however, increase the production of nerve growth factor, epidermal growth factor, and protease D by the submaxillary gland. Saliva containing these proteins may aid in wound healing—and this may be the biologic precursor of the healing kiss.

Other more complex actions of androgens, such as their effects on muscle hypertrophy and glandular secretion, could be exerted through a different mechanism. **Androgens also stimulate the replication of cells in some target tissues,** an effect that is poorly understood. Testosterone or DHT, in combination with E_2, appears to be implicated in the extensive and uncontrolled division of prostate cells that results in **benign prostatic hypertrophy,** a condition that afflicts as many as 75% of men over the age of 60 years.

PATHOPHYSIOLOGY OF THE MALE REPRODUCTIVE SYSTEM

The lack of tetosterone synthesis is called **hypogonadism.** If this occurs before puberty, secondary sex characteristics fail to develop, and if it occurs in adults, many of these features regress. **Primary hypogonadism** is due to processes that affect the testes directly and cause testicular failure, whereas **secondary hypogonadism** is due to defective secretion of the gonadotropins. Many of the genetic deficiencies that affect the male reproductive system are discussed in the context of sexual differentiation at the end of this chapter.

HORMONES OF THE OVARIES

The ovaries are bifunctional organs that produce estrogens and progestins (the female sex hormones) and ova (the female germ cells). The most active naturally occurring hormones of these classes are 17β-estradiol (E_2) and progesterone.

17β-Estradiol

Progesterone

The ovary contains a number of specific cell types organized into a variety of structures with unique functions. The ovary is organized into cortical and medullary regions, but these are usually not very distinct. The cortex is derived from the coelomic epithelium; it contains the primitive germ cells, which migrate from the hindgut, and the progenitors of the granulosa cells. The medulla is derived from the urogenital mesenchyma and contains cells that will become interstitial and theca cells. Like all endocrine glands, the ovary has an abundant vascular supply.

The cortical region of the ovary increases in size after birth owing to the enlargement of the **primary follicles,** each of which contains a germ cell surrounded by **granulosa cells.** After a follicle ruptures and releases its ovum, these granulosa cells hypertrophy and luteinize (accumulate a yellow pigment and lipid) to form a structure known as the **corpus luteum.** This structure regresses after an ovulatory cycle or pregnancy and becomes a scarlike structure called the **corpus atreticum.** The medullary stroma also enlarges with development, and in so doing it invades the cortex. Theca cells line the primordial follicles, making it difficult to distinguish the cortex from the medulla in the adult.

BIOSYNTHESIS & METABOLISM OF OVARIAN HORMONES

Synthesis

The estrogens are a family of hormones synthesized in ovarian and extraovarian tissues. 17β-Estradiol is the primary estrogen of ovarian origin. In some species, estrone is more abundant but is of extraovarian origin. In pregnancy, relatively more estriol is produced, but this too is extraovarian. The general pathway and the subcellular localization of the enzymes involved in the early steps of estradiol synthesis are the same as are found in the adrenal glands and testes. Features unique to the ovary are illustrated in Fig 41–5.

Estrogens are formed by the aromatization of androgens in a complex process that involves 3 hydroxylation steps, each of which requires O_2 and NADPH. The aromatase enzyme complex is thought to include a P-450 mixed-function oxidase. Estradiol is formed if the substrate of this enzyme complex is testosterone, whereas estrone results from the aromati-

zation of androstenedione (this generally occurs in extraovarian tissues).

The cellular source of the various ovarian steroids has been difficult to unravel, but it now appears that 2 cell types are involved. Theca cells are the major sources of 17α-hydroxyprogesterone and of androstenedione (the principal androgen produced by the ovary), and granulosa cells are the major source of estradiol. Progesterone is produced and secreted by the corpus luteum, which also makes some estradiol.

Significant amounts of estrogens are produced by the peripheral aromatization of androgens. In human males, the peripheral aromatization of testosterone to estradiol (E_2) accounts for 80% of the production rate of the latter. In females, adrenal androgens are important substrates, since as much as 50% of the E_2 produced during pregnancy comes from the aromatization of DHEA sulfate, and the conversion of androstenedione to estrone is the major source of estrogens in postmenopausal women. Aromatase activity is present in adipose cells and also in liver, skin, and other tissues. Increased activity of this enzyme may contribute to the "estrogenization" that characterizes diseases like cirrhosis of the liver, hyperthyroidism, aging, and obesity.

Catechol estrogens are the major metabolites of estrogen in all mammalian species. They result from hydroxylation at position 2 of the aromatic ring. The catechol estrogens have weak estrogenic activity but are potent agents in the central nervous system, where they are also found.

Secretion & Transport

The rate of secretion of ovarian steroids varies considerably during the menstrual (or estrous) cycle and is directly related to rate of production in the ovary. There is no storage of these compounds; they are secreted when they are produced.

Estrogens and progestins, like other steroids, are bound in varying degrees to plasma transport proteins. Estrogens are bound to SHBG and progestins to CBG. SHBG binds estradiol about 5 times less avidly than it binds testosterone or DHT, but progesterone and cortisol have little affinity for this protein (Table 41–2). In contrast, progesterone and cortisol bind with nearly equal affinity to CBG, which in turn has little avidity for estradiol and even less for testosterone, DHT, or estrone.

These plasma transport proteins play no apparent

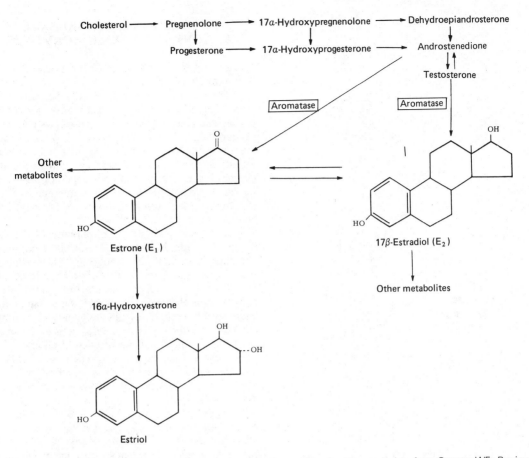

Figure 41–5. Biosynthesis of estrogens. (Slightly modified and reproduced, with permission, from Ganong WF: *Review of Medical Physiology,* 12th ed. Lange, 1985.)

role in the mechanism of action of these hormones at the cellular level, and (as with other steroids) probably only the free hormone has biologic activity. The binding proteins do provide a circulating reservoir of hormone, and because of the relatively large binding capacity, they buffer against sudden changes in the plasma level. The metabolic clearance rates of these steroids are inversely related to the affinity of their binding to SHBG; hence, estrone is cleared more rapidly than estradiol, which in turn is cleared more rapidly than testosterone or DHT. In this regard, the conjugated derivatives of these hormones (see below) are not bound by either SHBG or CBG. SHBG has an additional role in that, given the difference in binding affinity of estradiol and testosterone or DHT, it can affect the amount of these sex hormones available for interaction with target tissues. The factors that regulate the production of SHBG are discussed above.

Metabolism & Excretion

A. Estrogens: The liver converts estradiol and estrone to estriol by the pathways shown in Fig 41–5. Estradiol, estrone, and estriol are substrates for hepatic enzymes that add glucuronide or sulfate moieties. Activity of these conjugating enzymes varies among species. Rodents have such active metabolizing enzyme systems, particularly hydroxylating systems, that estrogens are almost completely metabolized by the liver and thus are essentially without activity when given orally. These enzyme systems are less active in primates, so that oral estrogens are more effective. The

Table 41–2. Approximate affinities of steroids for serum-binding proteins.*

	SHBG†	CBG†
Estradiol	5	>10
Estrone	>10	>100
Androstenedione	. . .	. . .
Testosterone	2	>100
Dihydrotestosterone	1	>100
Progesterone	>100	2
Cortisol	>100	3

*Adapted from Siiteri PK, Febres F: Ovarian hormone synthesis, circulation and mechanisms of action. Page 1401 in: *Endocrinology.* Vol 3. DeGroot LJ (editor). Grune & Stratton, 1979.

†Affinity expressed as K_d of molar quantity $\times 10^9$.

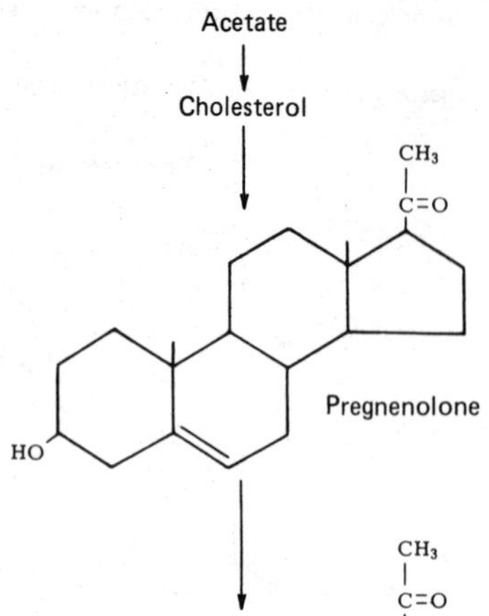

Acetate

↓

Cholesterol

↓

Pregnenolone

↓

Progesterone

↓

Pregnanediol

↓

Sodium pregnanediol-20-glucuronide

Figure 41–6. Biosynthesis of progesterone and major pathway for its metabolism. Other metabolites are also found. (Slightly modified and reproduced, with permission, from Ganong WF: *Review of Medical Physiology,* 12th ed. Lange, 1985.)

conjugated steroids are water-soluble and do not bind to transport proteins; thus, they are excreted readily in the bile and feces and to a lesser extent in the urine.

B. Progestins: Because the liver actively metabolizes progesterone to several compounds, progesterone is ineffective when given orally. Sodium pregnanediol-20-glucuronide is the major progestin metabolite found in human urine (Fig 41–6). Certain synthetic steroids, eg, derivatives of 17α-hydroxyprogesterone and 17α-alkyl-substituted 19-nortestosterone compounds, have progestational activity and avoid hepatic metabolism. Thus, they are widely used in oral contraceptives.

REGULATION & PHYSIOLOGIC ACTIONS OF OVARIAN HORMONES

Maturation & Maintenance of the Female Reproductive System

The major function of the ovarian hormones is to prepare the structural determinants of the female reproductive system (see below) for reproduction by (1) maturing the primordial germ cells; (2) developing the tissues that will allow for implantation of the blastocyst; (3) providing the "hormonal timing" for ovulation; (4) establishing, with placental hormones, the milieu required for the maintenance of pregnancy; and (5) providing the hormonal influences for parturition and lactation.

Estrogens stimulate the development of tissues involved in reproduction. In general, these hormones stimulate the size and number of cells by increasing the rate of synthesis of protein, rRNA, tRNA, mRNA, and DNA. Under estrogen stimulation, the vaginal epithelium proliferates and differentiates; the uterine endometrium proliferates and the glands hypertrophy and elongate; the myometrium develops an intrinsic, rhythmic motility; and breast ducts proliferate. Estradiol also has anabolic effects on bone and cartilage, and so it is growth-promoting. By affecting peripheral blood vessels, estrogens typically cause vasodilatation and heat dissipation.

Progestins generally require the previous or concurrent presence of estrogens; thus, the 2 classes of hormones often act synergistically, although they can be antagonists. Progestins reduce the proliferative activity of the estrogens on the vaginal epithelium and convert the uterine epithelium from proliferative to secretory (increased size and function of secretory glands and increased glycogen content), thus preparing the uterine epithelium for implantation of the fertilized ovum. Progestins enhance development of the acinar portions of breast glands after estrogens have stimulated ductal development. Progestins decrease peripheral blood flow, thereby decreasing heat loss, so that body temperature tends to increase during the luteal phase of the menstrual cycle, when these steroids are produced. This temperature spike, usually ~0.5 °C, is used as an indicator of ovulation.

The number of oogonia in the human fetal ovary reaches a maximum of 6–7 million at about the fifth month of gestation. This decreases to about 2 million by birth and is further diminished to 100–200 thousand by the onset of menarche. Some 400–500 of these develop into mature oocytes; the rest are gradually lost through a process that is not understood, although ovarian androgens have been implicated. Follicular maturation begins in infancy, and the ovaries gradually enlarge in prepubertal years owing to increased volume of the follicles because of the growth of granulosa cells, to the accumulation of tissue from atretic follicles, and to the increased mass of medullary stromal tissue with the interstitial and theca cells that will produce the steroids.

The concentration of sex hormones is low in

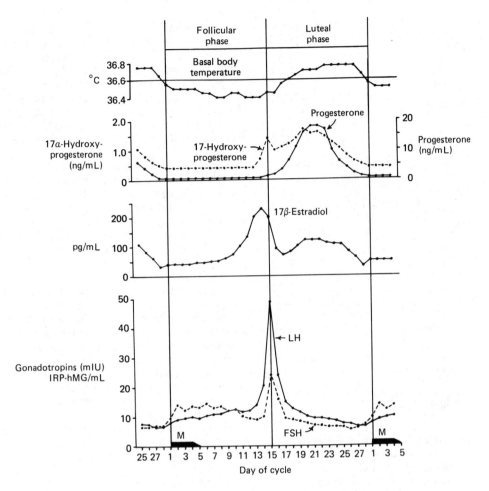

Figure 41–7. Hormonal and physiologic changes during a typical human menstrual cycle. M, menstruation; IRP-hMG, international reference standard for gonadotropins. (Reproduced, with permission, from Midgley AR in: *Human Reproduction.* Hafez ESE, Evans TN [editors]. Harper & Row, 1973.)

childhood, although exogenous gonadotropins increase production; hence, the immature ovary has the capacity to synthesize estrogen. It is thought that these low levels of sex steroids inhibit gonadotropin production in prepubertal girls and that at puberty the hypothalamic-pituitary system becomes less sensitive to suppression. At puberty, the pulsatile release of GnRH begins; LH causes a dramatic increase of ovarian hormone production; FSH, the main stimulus for estrogen secretion, stimulates a follicle to ripen, and ovulation ensues.

The Menstrual Cycle

Hormones determine the frequency of ovulation and receptivity to mating. Monestrous species ovulate and mate once a year, whereas polyestrous species repeat this cycle several times a year. Primates have menstrual cycles, with shedding of the endometrium at the end of each cycle, and mating behavior is not tightly coupled to ovulation. The human menstrual cycle results from a complex interaction between the hypothal-

amus, pituitary, and ovary. **The cycle normally varies between 25 and 35 days in length (average, 28 days). It can be divided into a follicular phase, a luteal phase, and menstruation** (Fig 41–7).

A. Follicular Phase: For reasons that are not clear, a particular follicle begins to enlarge under the general influence of FSH. E_2 levels are low during the first week of the follicular phase, but they begin to rise progressively as the follicle enlarges. E_2 reaches its maximal level 24 hours before the LH (FSH) peak and sensitizes the pituitary to GnRH. LH is either released in response to this high level of E_2 in a "positive feedback" manner or in response to a sudden decline of E_2 from this high level. Continuous administration of high doses of estrogen (as in oral contraceptives) suppress LH and FSH release and inhibit the action of GnRH on the pituitary. Progesterone levels are very low during the follicular phase. The LH peak heralds the end of the follicular phase and precedes ovulation by 16–18 hours.

B. Luteal Phase: After ovulation, the granulosa

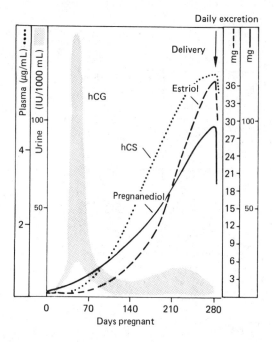

Figure 41–8. Hormone levels during normal pregnancy. hCG, human chorionic gonadotropin; hCS, human chorionic somatomammotropin. (Data from various authors.) (Reproduced, with permission, from Ganong WF: *Review of Medical Physiology,* 12th ed. Lange, 1985.)

cells of the ruptured follicle luteinize and form the corpus luteum, a structure that soon begins to produce progesterone and some estradiol. Estradiol peaks about midway through the luteal phase and then declines to a very low level. **The major hormone of the luteal portion of the cycle is progesterone,** which (as noted above) is required for preparation and maintenance of the secretory endometrium that provides early nourishment for the implanted blastocyst. **LH is required for the early maintenance of the corpus luteum,** and the pituitary supplies it for about 10 days. If implantation occurs (day 22–24 of the average cycle), this LH function is assumed by chorionic gonadotropin (hCG), a placental hormone that is very similar to LH and is made by the cytotrophoblastic cells of the implanted early embryo (see Chapter 37). hCG supports progesterone synthesis by the corpus luteum until the placenta begins making large amounts of this steroid. In the absence of implantation (and hCG), the corpus luteum regresses and menstruation ensues; after the endometrium is shed, a new cycle commences. The luteal phase is always 14 ± 2 days in length. Variations in cycle length are almost always due to an altered follicular phase.

Pregnancy & Placental Hormones

The implanted blastocyst forms the trophoblast, which is subsequently organized into the placenta. The placenta provides the nutritional connection between the embryo and the maternal circulation and produces a number of hormones.

A. Human Chorionic Gonadotropin (hCG): The primary function of the glycoprotein hormone hCG is to support the corpus luteum until the placenta produces amounts of progesterone sufficient to support the pregnancy. hCG can be detected within a few days of implantation, and this provides the basis of early diagnostic tests for pregnancy. Peak hCG levels are reached in the middle of the first trimester, after which there is a gradual decline throughout the remainder of pregnancy. Changes in hCG and other hormone levels in pregnancy are illustrated in Fig 41–8.

B. Progestins: The corpus luteum is the major source of progesterone for the first 6–8 weeks of the pregnancy, and then the placenta assumes this function. The corpus luteum continues to function, but late in pregnancy the placenta makes 30–40 times more progesterone than does the corpus luteum. The placenta cannot synthesize cholesterol and so depends upon a maternal supply.

C. Estrogens: Plasma concentrations of estradiol, estrone, and estriol gradually increase throughout pregnancy. **Estriol is produced in the largest amount, and its formation reflects a number of fetoplacental functions.** The fetal adrenal produces DHEA and DHEA sulfate, which are converted to 16α-hydroxy derivatives by the fetal liver. These are converted to estriol by the placenta; travel via the placental circulation to the maternal liver, where they are conjugated to glucuronides; and then are excreted in the urine (Fig 41–9). The measurement of urinary estriol levels is used to document the function of a number of maternal-fetal processes.

Another interesting exchange of substrates is required for fetal cortisol production. The fetal adrenal lacks the familiar 3β-hydroxysteroid dehydrogenase/Δ^5-Δ^4 isomerase complex and hence depends upon the placenta for the progesterone required for cortisol synthesis. The pregnenolone required for DHEA synthesis also comes from the placenta (Fig 41–9).

D. Placental Lactogens: The placenta makes a hormone called placental lactogen (PL). PL is also called chorionic somatomammotropin or placental growth hormone because it has biologic properties of prolactin and growth hormone. The genetic relationship of these hormones is discussed in Chapter 37. The physiologic function of PL is uncertain, since women who lack this hormone appear to have normal pregnancies and deliver normal babies.

Parturition

Pregnancy lasts a predetermined number of days for each species, but the factors responsible for its termination are unknown. Hormonal influences are suspected but unproved. Estrogens and progestins are candidates, since they affect uterine contractility, and there is evidence that catecholamines are involved in induction of labor. Since oxytocin stimulates uterine contractility, it is used to facilitate delivery, but it will not initiate labor unless the pregnancy is at term. There are 100 times more oxytocin receptors in the uterus at

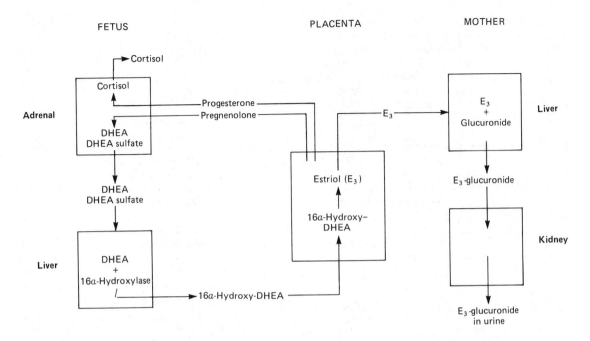

Figure 41–9. Steroid metabolism by the fetal-maternal unit. DHEA, dehydroepiandrosterone.

term than there are at the onset of pregnancy. The increase correlates with the increased amount of estrogens at term, which increase the number of oxytocin receptors (see Chapter 37). Once labor begins, the cervix dilates, initiating a neural reflex that stimulates oxytocin release and hence further uterine contraction. Mechanical factors, such as the amount of stretch or force applied to the muscle, may be important. A sudden and dramatic change in the hormonal milieu of both the mother and newborn occurs with parturition, and plasma levels of progesterone (measured as pregnanediol) and estriol decline rapidly after the placenta is delivered (Fig 41–8).

Mammary Gland Development & Lactation

The differentiation and function of the mammary gland are regulated by the concerted action of several hormones. The female sex hormones initiate this process, since estrogens are responsible for ductal growth and progestins stimulate alveolar proliferation. Some growth of glandular tissue occurs during puberty, along with deposition of adipose tissue, but extensive development occurs during pregnancy when glandular tissue is exposed to high concentrations of estradiol and progesterone. Complete differentiation, studied mostly in rat mammary gland explants, requires the additional action of prolactin, a glucocorticoid, insulin or a growth peptide, and an unidentified serum factor. Of these hormones, only the concentration of prolactin changes dramatically in pregnancy; it increases from < 2 ng/dL to > 200 ng/dL in late pregnancy. The effects of these hormones on the synthesis of various milk proteins, including lactalbumin, lactoglobulin, and casein, have been studied in

detail. These hormones increase the rate of synthesis of these proteins by increasing amounts of the specific mRNAs, and in the case of casein at least, this is due to an increase in gene transcription. Interestingly, gene transcription is not increased unless cortisol, prolactin, and insulin are all added to the explant cultures.

Progesterone, required for aveolar differentiation, inhibits milk production and secretion in late pregnancy. Lactation commences when levels of this hormone decrease abruptly after delivery. Prolactin levels also fall rapidly postpartum but are stimulated with each episode of suckling (see Chapter 37), thereby ensuring continual lactation. Lactation gradually decreases if suckling is not allowed and can be rapidly terminated by administration of a large parenteral dose of an androgen before suckling is allowed.

Suckling also results in the release of oxytocin from the posterior pituitary. Oxytocin stimulates contraction of the myoepithelial cells that surround the alveolar ducts, thus expelling milk from the gland. The regulation of oxytocin synthesis and secretion is discussed in Chapter 37.

Menopause

Women in the western hemisphere cease having regular menstrual cycles at about age 53, coincident with loss of all follicles and ovarian function. There is no alternative source of progesterone, but substantial amounts of a weak estrogen, estrone, are produced by the peripheral aromatization of the adrenal steroid androstenedione (Fig 41–5). The levels of estrone are not sufficient to suppress pituitary gonadotropin levels; thus, marked increases of LH and FSH are characteristic of the postmenopausal years. Postmenopausal women are particularly prone to 2 problems associated with tissue catabolism. Estrone is not always able to prevent the **atrophy of secondary sex tissues,** particularly the epithelium of the lower urinary tract and vagina. **Osteoporosis** is a major health problem in older individuals, and women with the most severe decrease in bone mass have lower than normal estrone levels.

Synthetic Agonists & Antagonists

A. Estrogens: Several synthetic compounds have estrogenic activity and one or more favorable pharmacologic features. Most modifications are designed to retard hepatic metabolism, so that the compounds can be given orally. One of the first developed was diethylstilbestrol. Other examples of modified steroids include 17α-ethinyl estradiol and mestranol, which are used in oral contraceptives.

Clomiphene citrate

Clomiphene was originally designed as an antifertility drug, but it has the opposite effect. Clomiphene competes with estradiol for hypothalamic receptor sites; thus, GnRH release is not restrained and excessive amounts of LH and FSH are released. Multiple follicles often mature simultaneously in response to clomiphene, and multiple pregnancies can ensue. Nafoxidine, a nonsteroidal compound, and tamoxifen combine with the estrogen receptor to form very stable complexes with chromatin; hence, the receptor cannot recycle and these agents inhibit the action of estradiol for prolonged periods. These antagonists are used in the treatment of estrogen-dependent breast cancer.

B. Progestins: It has been difficult to synthesize compounds that have progestin activity but no estrogenic or androgenic action. The 17α-alkyl-substituted 19-nortestosterone derivatives (eg, norethindrone) have minimal androgenic activity in most women and are used in oral contraceptives. Another potent progestin is medroxyprogesterone acetate (Provera). Medroxyprogesterone inhibits ovulation for several months when given as an intramuscular depot injection, but it is more frequently used for treating well-differentiated endometrial carcinoma. It is believed to affect the replication of normal and malignant endometrial cells by forming a very stable complex with the progesterone receptor and thereby inhibiting action of the natural hormone.

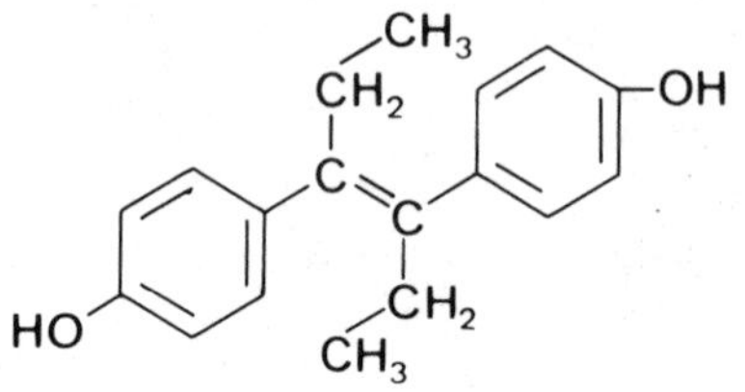

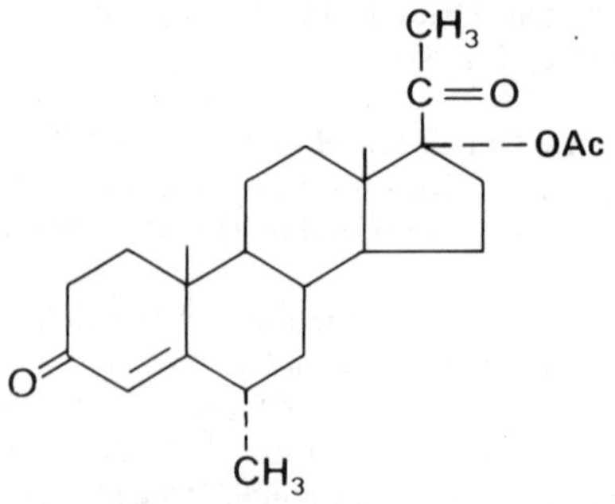

Diethylstilbestrol

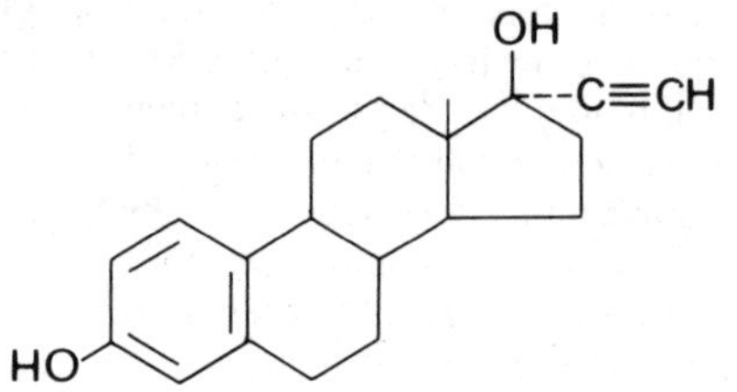

17α-Ethinyl estradiol

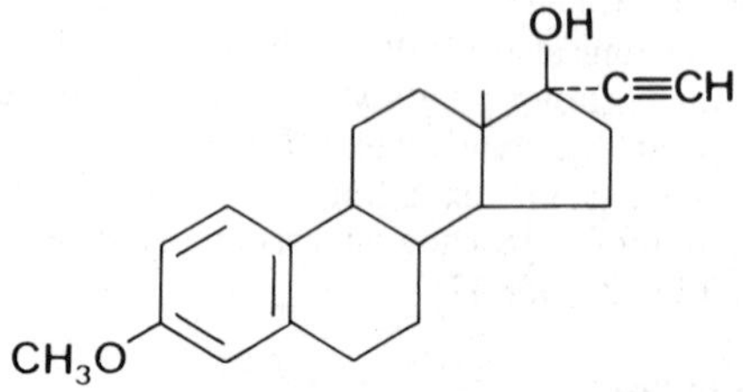

Mestranol

Medroxyprogesterone acetate

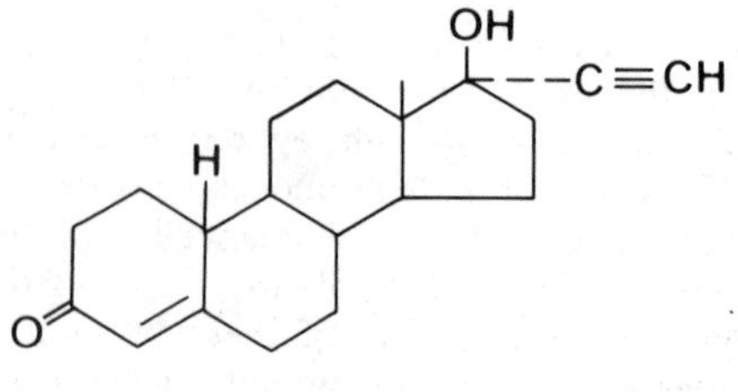

Norethindrone

Numerous compounds with antiestrogenic activity have been synthesized, and several of these have clinical applications. Most of these antagonists act by competing with estradiol for its intracellular receptor (see below). Clomiphene citrate (Clomid) has a particular affinity for the estrogen receptor in the hypothalamus.

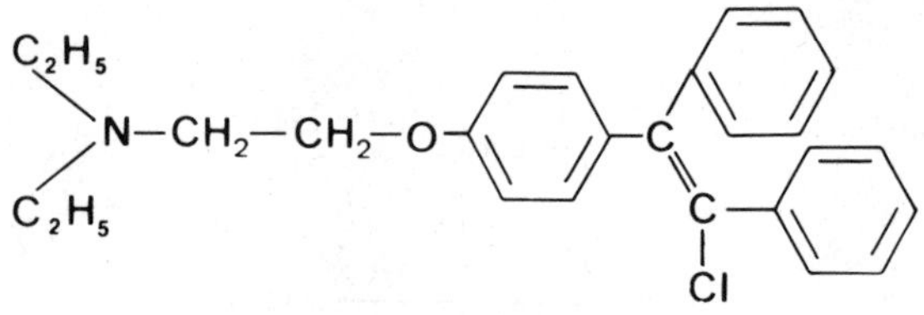

MECHANISM OF ACTION OF OVARIAN HORMONES

Studies of the mechanism of action of the sex steroids have given impetus to the field of hormone action, starting with the demonstration that radiolabeled estradiol is selectively retained in the cells of target tissues.

Estrogens and progestins exert major effects through their ability to combine with intracellular receptors which then bind to specific regions of chromatin or DNA (or both) to effect changes in the rate of transcription of specific genes. Much information has been learned from the analysis of how estradiol and progesterone stimulate transcription of the avian egg-white protein genes, especially ovalbumin and conalbumin. The determination of exactly how these hormones activate gene transcription is under intense investigation.

Special Features

Some points, which may have application to the mechanism of action of other hormones, bear noting: (1) There is considerable cross talk between the sex hormone receptors. Progesterone binds to the androgen receptor and thus is a weak androgen; some androgens bind to the estrogen receptor and mimic the action of the latter in the uterus. (2) Estrogens increase the concentration of both the estrogen and the progesterone receptor. (3) Progesterone appears to enhance the rate of turnover of its receptor. (4) So-called weak estrogens, such as estriol, act as potent estrogens when given frequently.

Receptor-Independent Actions of Sex Hormones

Whether all actions of steroid hormones are mediated by receptors has been debated since their discovery. **Recent evidence suggests that some actions may be receptor-independent and probably do not involve nuclear effects.**

A. Estrogens: Estrogen may act independently of its receptor. Various estrogens stimulate uterine blood flow with a relative potency that does not match their binding to the receptor, nor does this effect require RNA synthesis. Direct effects on histamine release and prostaglandin production have been proposed to explain this effect, which, although not so well defined as the membrane effect of progesterone (see below), is an important physiologic action of estrogens.

B. Progestins: The interaction of progesterone with the membrane of amphibian oocytes results in a hormone- and time-dependent increase of intracellular calcium, which in turn stimulates the synthesis of specific cytoplasmic proteins that appear to be involved in oocyte maturation; these proteins, when transferred to other immature oocytes, stimulate maturation. This effect is observed in enucleated oocytes (hence, gene transcription is not involved), and the effect is not obtained if the progesterone is injected directly into the egg. This is probably not a unique example. The membrane anesthetic and anti-inflammatory actions of progesterone in mammalian cells may be other examples of receptor-independent actions of this hormone.

PATHOPHYSIOLOGY OF THE FEMALE REPRODUCTIVE SYSTEM

A discussion of all of the disorders that affect the female reproductive system is beyond the scope of this chapter, but a few illustrative disorders follow. **Primary hypogonadism** is due to processes that directly involve the ovaries and thus cause ovarian deficiency (decreased ovulation, decreased hormone production, or both), whereas **secondary hypogonadism** is due to the loss of pituitary gonadotropin function. **Gonadal dysgenesis (Turner's syndrome)** is a relatively frequent genetic disorder in which individuals have an XO karyotype, female internal and external genitalia, several developmental abnormalities, and delayed puberty.

Several syndromes are related to abnormal amounts of hormones. The most frequent is **polycystic ovary syndrome** (Stein-Leventhal syndrome), in which overproduction of androgens causes hirsutism, obesity, irregular menses, and impaired fertility. The rare **Leydig cell and arrhenoblastoma tumors** produce testosterone; **granulosa-theca cell tumors** produce estrogens; and **intraovarian adrenal rests** produce cortisol. Persistent trophoblastic tissue results in the benign **hydatidiform mole** or a malignant transformation of this—**choriocarcinoma;** both of these produce enormous quantities of hCG. The radioimmunoassay of hCG is a diagnostic test for these dangerous conditions and can also be used to monitor efficacy of therapy.

GONADAL HORMONES & SEXUAL DIFFERENTIATION

Sexual differentiation involves a series of sequential, ordered processes that can be described by the paradigm chromosomal sex → gonadal sex → phenotypic sex. This progression provides an excellent example of how hormones are involved in the differentiation and development of tissues, and an analysis of defects at several steps emphasizes the importance of various processes in overall androgen function.

CHROMOSOMAL SEX

Chromosomal sex, the first phase of sexual differentiation, is established at fertilization and is the

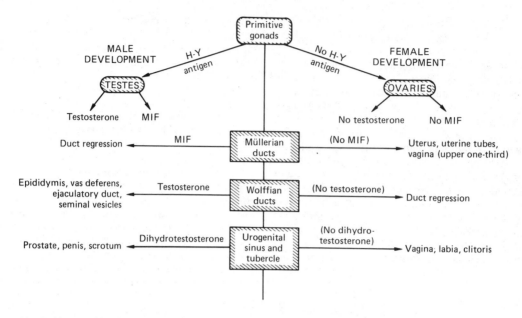

Figure 41–10. Hormonal involvement in sexual differentiation. MIF, müllerian inhibiting factor. (Modified and reproduced, with permission, from Fox SI. Page 631 in: *Human Physiology*. William C. Brown, 1984.)

only immutable portion of the paradigm. **A heterogametic distribution of sex chromosomes (XY) dictates the male genotype, whereas a homogametic complement (XX) specifies the female genotype.** In patients with ambiguous external genitalia or in whom a dissociation between phenotypic and genotypic sex is suspected, this fact is established by a Barr body analysis of buccal mucosal cells, fibroblasts, or leukocytes. **The Barr body is an area of condensed chromatin that represents an inactivated X chromosome.** The number of Barr bodies per cell is directly related to the number of X chromosomes. X chromosome number $-1 = $ Barr body number; so that XY = 0, XX = 1, XXY = 1, XXX = 2. There is no known hormonal influence on chromosomal sex.

GONADAL SEX

During the initial stages of gestation, the development of male and female embryos is indistinguishable. In humans, the germ cells begin to migrate from the yolk sac to the genital ridges between the 35th and 50th days of gestation. This process results in the formation of the **primitive gonad.** The primitive gonad is ambiguous and consists of the primordial germ cells, connective or interstitial tissue, and a covering epithelial layer. At about day 56, hormones become involved, and gonadal differentiation begins. The exact initiating mechanism is not clear, but one fact is certain. **In the absence of a positive event, ie, the differentiation of the primitive gonad into a testis, all embryos develop into phenotypic females.** A male-specific cell surface antigen, the so-called **H-Y antigen,** has been associated with

differentiation of the primitive gonad into a testis (Fig 41–10).

If the genetic sex is male, the Leydig cells appear in the connective tissue, testosterone synthesis begins, and development of the male reproductive tract starts. **In the absence of the Y chromosome effect, the female system develops** with a slight lag in time and is essentially completed by the 90th day of gestation. This sequence, in which the structural and functional development of the testis precedes development of the male phenotype and in which the ovary and female phenotype occur in the absence of testicular differentiation, is common to all mammals and is shown in schematic form in Fig 41–10. This scheme was first elucidated in rabbits, but the extrapolation to humans and other species has been subsequently validated.

PHENOTYPIC SEX

Internal Genital Structures

Male sex hormones are directly involved in the differentiation of the **primordial genital duct system** (wolffian and müllerian) and of the anlage for the external genitalia. The male internal genital tract develops from the primitive **wolffian duct system,** and the female tract is derived from the **müllerian duct system** (Fig 41–10).

The distinction between wolffian and müllerian development depends on the production of a testicular factor called **müllerian inhibiting factor (MIF).** MIF, a glycoprotein of MW ∼ 70,000, is formed in the spermatogenic tubules and constitutes the first endocrine function of the testis. The mechanism by which MIF suppresses müllerian duct formation is not

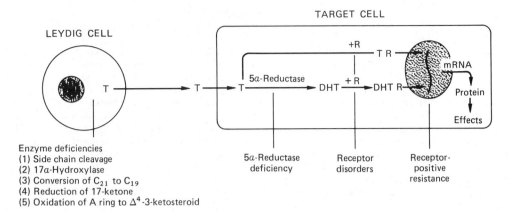

Figure 41–11. Steps involved in androgen resistance. Four stages at which mutations have been identified are shown. T, testosterone; DHT, dihydrotestosterone; R, androgen receptor. (Modified and reproduced, with permission, from Wilson JD et al: The endocrine control of male phenotypic development. *Aust J Biol Sci* 1983;**36**:101.)

known, but it is clear that this is an active process unrelated to subsequent actions of testosterone.

External Genital Structures

The nature of the external genital structures, which develop from a common anlage, is determined by the presence or absence of another testicular hormone, testosterone, and its derivative, dihydrotestosterone (DHT).

Testosterone synthesis immediately precedes the initiation of fetal virilization. In the male rabbit embryo, testosterone synthesis begins between day 17 and day 17.5 and is associated with marked increases of cholesterol side chain cleavage enzyme and 3β-hydroxysteroid dehydrogenase/Δ^5-Δ^4 isomerase complex—key enzymes in testosterone biosynthesis; the other steroidogenic enzymes are always present in the primitive gonad. Estrogen synthesis begins in the ovary at exactly the same time. This coincidence suggests that perhaps female differentiation is not entirely passive, since estrogen synthesis by the immature gonad could play a role in stimulating the replication of the primordial germ cells or their differentiation into oogonia. The switch that determines the onset of steroidogenesis has not been determined, nor is it clear whether at early stages this process is regulated by other hormones. Later in embryogenesis, as in postnatal life, LH regulates steroidogenesis by controlling the rate of side chain cleavage of cholesterol.

Until the discovery of DHT, it was assumed that the development of the male reproductive tract depended entirely on testosterone. That both DHT and testosterone are required for this process came from studies of embryonic tissues in which it was determined that, just before the onset of virilization, 5α-reductase activity was highest in the anlage that specified the prostate and external genitalia, whereas this enzyme was undetectable in wolffian tissue at that time. This biochemical observation received genetic support when patients lacking 5α-reductase activity were identified. Such individuals are genetic males, have normal wolffian structures, and have an external female phenotype, except that the vagina is incompletely developed.

Genetic Evidence for the Role of Testosterone & Dihydrotestosterone in Sexual Differentiation

Persons with abnormal sexual differentiation illustrate the point that isolated genetic deficiencies help to establish the importance of specific steps in a metabolic pathway. Fig 41–11 represents the pathway involved in sexual differentiation from testosterone biosynthesis through postreceptor actions of testosterone and DHT. At least 5 distinct genetic defects in testosterone biosynthesis have been described; the 5α-reductase deficiency is known; there are a number of instances in which either no testosterone/DHT receptor is detected or the receptor is abnormal in some manner; and there are a number of cases in which all measurable entities, including the receptor, are normal, but the patients (always genetic males) have variable degrees of feminization. The extent of the abnormality of differentiation is related to the severity of the deficit. Persons who completely lack a biosynthetic enzyme appear to be phenotypic females but have an XY genotype, while the mildest cases may have only an abnormally located penile urethra. Genetic males who completely lack functioning receptors have testes and produce testosterone but have complete feminization of the external genitalia (the so-called **testicular feminization syndrome**), which illustrates the separate roles of MIF and testosterone. It is interesting that no comparable deficiencies in estrogen synthesis or action have been identified. Indeed, this may be the only hormone about which this can be stated.

References

General

Chan L, O'Malley BW: Mechanism of action of the sex steroid hormones. (3 parts.) *N Engl J Med* 1976;**294:**1322, 1372, 1430.

Huggins C: Two principles in endocrine therapy of cancer: Hormone deprival and hormone interference. *Cancer Res* 1965;**25:**1163.

Murphy BEP: Protein binding and the assay of nonantigenic hormones. *Recent Prog Horm Res* 1969;**25:**563.

O'Malley BW: Steroid hormone action in eucaryotic cells. *J Clin Invest* 1984;**74:**307.

Samuels LT: Metabolism of steroid hormones. In: *Metabolic Pathways,* 2nd ed. Vol I. Greenberg DM (editor). Academic Press, 1960.

Testicular Hormones

Hall PF: Testicular hormones: Synthesis and control. Pages 1511–1520 in: *Endocrinology.* Vol 3. DeGroot LJ (editor). Grune & Stratton, 1979.

Hall PF: Gonadotropic regulation of testicular function. Pages 1511–1519 in: *The Androgens of the Testis.* Eik-Nes KB (editor). Dekker, 1970.

Ito T, Horton R: The source of plasma dihydrotestosterone in man. *J Clin Invest* 1971;**50:**1621.

Longcope C, Kato T, Horton R: Conversion of blood androgens to estrogen in normal men and women. *J Clin Invest* 1969;**48:**2191.

Mainwaring WIP: *The Mechanism of Action of Androgens.* Springer, 1977.

Samuels LT, Matsumoto K: Localization of enzymes involved in testosterone biosynthesis by the mouse testis. *Endocrinology* 1974;**94:**55.

Wilson J: Metabolism of testicular androgens. Chap 25, pp 491–508, in: *Handbook of Endocrinology.* Section 7: *Endocrinology.* Vol 5: *Male Reproductive System.* Hamilton DW, Greep RO (editors). American Physiological Society, Washington DC, 1975.

Ovarian Hormones

Channing CP, Coudert SP: The role of granulosa cells and follicular fluid in estrogen secretion by the monkey ovary in vivo. *Endocrinology* 1976;**98:**590.

Channing CP, Tsafriri A: Mechanism of action of luteinizing hormone and follicle-stimulating hormone on the ovary in vitro. *Metabolism* 1977;**26:**413.

Jensen EV, Jacobson HI: Basic guides to the mechanism of estrogen action. *Recent Prog Horm Res* 1962;**18:**387.

Siiteri PK, Febres F: Ovarian hormone synthesis, circulation and mechanisms of action. Pages 1401–1417 in: *Endocrinology.* Vol 3. DeGroot LJ (editor). Grune & Stratton, 1979.

Toft D, Gorski J: A receptor molecule for estrogens. *Proc Natl Acad Sci USA* 1966;**55:**1574.

Westphal U: *Steroid-Protein Interactions.* Springer-Verlag, 1971.

Sexual Differentiation

Bullock LP, Barden CW, Ohno S: The androgen insensitive mouse: Absence of intranuclear androgen retention in the kidney. *Biochem Biophys Res Commun* 1971;**44:**1537.

Jost A et al: Studies in sex differentiation in mammals. *Recent Prog Horm Res* 1973;**29:**1.

Ohno S: Major regulatory genes for mammalian sexual development. *Cell* 1976;**7:**315.

Ohno S: The role of H-Y antigen in primary sex determination. *JAMA* 1978;**239:**217.

Wilson JD, Walker JD: The conversion of testosterone to 5α-androsten-17β-ol-3-one (dihydrotestosterone) by skin slices of man. *J Clin Invest* 1969;**48:**371.

Wilson JD et al: The endocrine control of male phenotypic development. *Aust J Biol Sci* 1983;**36:**101.

Sex Hormones & the Central Nervous System

Naftolin F et al: The formation of estrogens by central neuroendocrine tissues. *Recent Prog Horm Res* 1975;**31:**295.

Ohno S, Geller LN, Lai EVY: *Tfm* mutation and masculinization versus feminization of the mouse central nervous system. *Cell* 1974;**3:**235.

Daryl K. Granner, MD

PANCREATIC HORMONES

Structure & Function of the Pancreas

The pancreas is 2 very different organs contained within one structure. The acinar portion has an **exocrine** function, secreting into the duodenal lumen the enzymes and ions used for the digestive process. The **endocrine** portion consists of the islets of Langerhans. The 1–2 million islets of the human pancreas make up 1–2% of its weight and are scattered throughout the pancreas but are most concentrated in the tail of this organ. The islets are small (75 × 175 μm), ovoid, highly vascular collections of the several different cell types listed in Table 42–1. These cells are not evenly distributed in the islets. The A and D cells form a rim around a central core of B cells, and the F cells are more randomly dispersed.

The pancreatic islets secrete at least 4 hormones: insulin, glucagon, somatostatin, and pancreatic polypeptide. The hormones are released into the pancreatic vein, which empties into the portal vein—a convenient arrangement, since the liver is the primary site of action of insulin and glucagon. These 2 hormones are chiefly involved in regulating carbohydrate metabolism but affect many other processes. Somatostatin, first identified in the hypothalamus as the hormone that inhibits growth hormone secretion, is present in higher concentration in the pancreatic islets than in the hypothalamus and is involved in the local regulation of insulin and glucagon secretion. Pancreatic polypeptide affects gastrointestinal secretion.

Table 42–1. Cell types in the islets of Langerhans.

Cell Type	Relative Abundance	Hormone Produced
A (or α)	∼ 25%	Glucagon
B (or β)	∼ 70%	Insulin
D (or δ)	< 5%	Somatostatin
F	Trace	Pancreatic polypeptide

INSULIN

Historical Perspective

Langerhans identified the islets in the 1860s but did not understand their function—nor did von Mering and Minkowski, who demonstrated in 1889 that pancreatectomy produced diabetes. The link between the islets and diabetes was suggested by de Mayer in 1909 and by Sharpey-Schaffer in 1917, but it was Banting and Best who proved this association in 1921. After ligating the pancreatic duct in dogs, which resulted in atrophy of the exocrine pancreas, these investigators used acid-ethanol to extract from the remaining tissue an islet cell factor that had potent hypoglycemic activity. The factor was named insulin, and it was quickly learned that bovine and porcine islets contained insulin that was active in humans. Within a year, insulin was in widespread use for the treatment of diabetes and proved to be lifesaving.

Having large quantities of bovine or porcine insulin to study had an equally dramatic effect on biomedical research. Insulin was the first protein proved to have hormonal action, the first protein crystallized

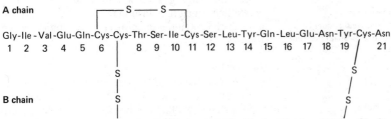

Figure 42–1. Covalent structure of human insulin. (Reproduced, with permission, from Ganong WF: *Review of Medical Physiology*, 12th ed. Lange, 1985.)

(Abel, 1926), the first protein sequenced (Sanger et al, 1955), the first protein synthesized by chemical techniques (Du et al; Zahn; Katsoyanis; ~1964), the first protein shown to be synthesized as a larger precursor molecule (Steiner et al, 1967), and the first protein prepared for commercial use by recombinant DNA technology. In spite of this impressive list of "firsts," less is known about how insulin works at the molecular level than about how most other hormones work at that level.

Chemistry

Insulin is a polypeptide consisting of 2 chains, A and B, linked by 2 interchain disulfide bridges that connect A7 to B7 and A20 to B19. A third intrachain disulfide bridge connects residues 6 and 11 of the A chain. The location of these 3 disulfide bridges is invariant, and the A and B chains have 21 and 30 amino acids, respectively, in most species. The covalent structure of human insulin (MW 5734) is illustrated in Fig 42–1, and a comparison of the amino acid substitutions found in a variety of species is presented in Table 42–2. Substitutions occur at many positions within either chain without affecting bioactivity and are particularly common in positions 8, 9, and 10 of the A chain. Thus, this region is not crucial for bioactivity. **Several positions and regions are highly conserved,** however, including (1) the positions of the 3 disulfide bonds, (2) the hydrophobic residues in the C-terminal region of the B chain, and (3) the N- and C-terminal regions of the A chain. Chemical modification or substitution of specific amino acids in these regions has allowed investigators to formulate a composite active region (Fig 42–2). The C-terminal hydrophobic region of the B chain is also involved in the dimerization of insulin.

Table 42–2 reveals the close similarity between human, porcine, and bovine insulins. Porcine insulin differs by a single amino acid, an alanine for threonine substitution at B30, while bovine insulin has this modification plus the substitutions of alanine for threonine at A8 and valine for isoleucine at A10. These modifications result in no appreciable change in biologic activity and very little antigenic difference.

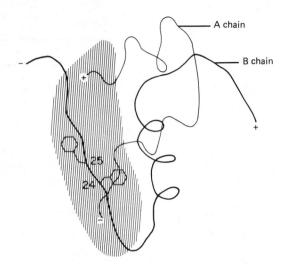

Figure 42–2. Region of the insulin molecule required for biologic activity. Diagrammatic structure of insulin as determined by x-ray crystallography. The shaded area illustrates the portion of insulin that is thought to be most important in conferring biologic activity to the hormone. The Phe residues B24 and B25 are the sites of mutations that affect insulin bioactivity (see p 592). The N termini of the insulin A and B chains are indicated by +, whereas the C termini are indicated by −. (Redrawn and reproduced, with permission, from Tager HS: Abnormal products of the human insulin gene. *Diabetes* 1984;**33**:693.)

Although all patients given heterologous insulin develop low titers of circulating antibodies against the molecule, few develop clinically significant titers. Porcine and bovine insulins were standard therapy for diabetes mellitus until human insulin was produced by recombinant DNA technology. Despite a wide variation in primary structure, biologic activity is about 25–30 IU/mg dry weight for all insulins.

Insulin forms very interesting complex structures. Zinc is present in high concentration in the B cell and forms complexes with insulin and proinsulin. Insulins from all vertebrate species form isologous dimers through hydrogen bonding between the peptide groups of the B24 and B26 residues of 2 monomers, and at high concentrations these are organized as hexamers, each with 2 atoms of zinc. This higher-order structure is illustrated in Fig 42–3 and has made studies of the crystalline structure of insulin feasible. Insulin is probably in the monomeric form at physiologic concentrations.

Biosynthesis

A. Precursors of Insulin: Insulin is synthesized as a preprohormone (MW ~11,500) and is the prototype for peptides that are processed from larger precursor molecules. The sequence and subcellular location of these biosynthetic events are depicted in Fig 42–4. The hydrophobic 23-amino-acid pre-, or leader, sequence directs the molecule into the cisternae of the endoplasmic reticulum and then is removed. This re-

Table 42–2. Variations in the structure of insulin in mammalian species.*

	Variations From Human Amino Acid Sequence	
	A-Chain Position	B-Chain Position
Species	8 9 10	30
Human	Thr-Ser-Ile	Thr
Pig, dog, sperm whale	Thr-Ser-Ile	Ala
Rabbit	Thr-Ser-Ile	Ser
Cattle, goat	Ala-Ser-Val	Ala
Sheep	Ala-Gly-Val	Ala
Horse	Thr-Gly-Ile	Ala
Sei whale	Ala-Ser-Thr	Ala

*Modified and reproduced, with permission, from Ganong WF: *Review of Medical Physiology*, 12th ed. Lange, 1985.

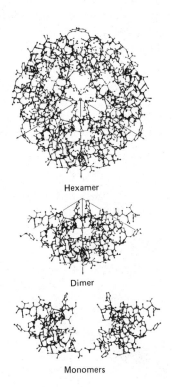

Figure 42–3. Higher-order structure of insulin. Complete hexamer of porcine insulin showing the development of dimers from monomers and their organization into the hexamer. (Reproduced, with permission, from Blundell T et al: Insulin: The structure in the crystal and its reflection in chemistry and biology. *Adv Protein Chem* 1972;**26**:279.)

sults in the 9000-MW proinsulin molecule that provides the conformation necessary for forming the proper disulfide bridges. As shown in Fig 42–5, the arrangement of proinsulin, starting from the amino terminus, is B chain—connecting (C) peptide—A chain. The proinsulin molecule undergoes a series of site-specific peptide cleavages that result in the formation of equimolar amounts of mature insulin and C peptide. These enzymatic cleavages, summarized in Fig 42–6, start with a protease with trypsinlike activity that cleaves at the carboxy-terminal end of 2 sequential basic amino acids at 2 separate sites (Arg 31–Arg 32↓, and Lys 64–Arg 65↓ in human proinsulin) within the C peptide. A second enzyme with carboxypeptidase B–like activity then removes the C-terminal basic amino acids from what will become insulin and the C peptide. The model illustrated in Fig 42–6 accounts for all of the intermediates found in the B cell secretion granule and can be duplicated by adding trypsin and chymotrypsin B to proinsulin.

B. Precursors of Other Islet Cell Hormones: The synthesis of other islet cell hormones also requires posttranslational enzymatic processing of higher-molecular-weight precursor molecules. Diagrammatic structures of pancreatic polypeptide, glucagon, and somatostatin are compared with that of

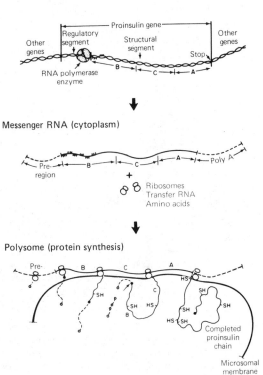

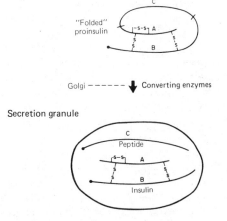

Figure 42–4. Biosynthesis of insulin via a short-lived preproinsulin. The letters A, B, and C identify the A and B chains of insulin and the connecting (C) peptide. A 23-amino-acid leader sequence transcribed by a segment of mRNA next to the portion that transcribes the B chain (dashed lines) is formed and then split off, possibly before the formation of the rest of the proinsulin molecule is completed. (Reproduced, with permission, from Steiner DF: Errors in insulin biosynthesis. *N Engl J Med* 1976;**294**:952.)

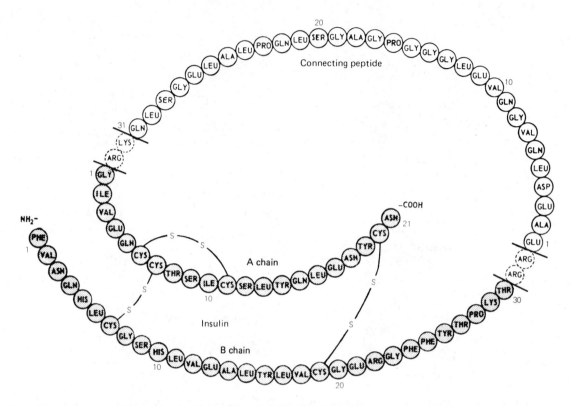

Figure 42–5. Structure of human proinsulin. Insulin and C-peptide molecules are connected at 2 sites by dipeptide links. (Slightly modified and reproduced, with permission, from Karam JH, Salber PR, Forsham PH: Pancreatic hormones and diabetes mellitus. In: *Basic & Clinical Endocrinology.* Greenspan FS, Forsham PH [editors]: Lange, 1983.)

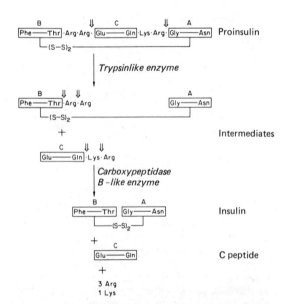

Figure 42–6. Stages in the cleavage of human proinsulin by the combined action of trypsinlike and carboxypeptidase B-like proteases. ⇓, cleavage sites. (Redrawn and reproduced, with permission, from Steiner DF, Tager HS. Page 927 in: *Endocrinology.* Vol 2. DeGroot LJ [editor]. Grune & Stratton, 1979.)

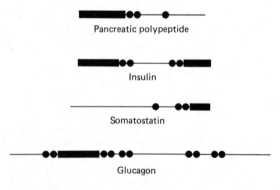

Figure 42–7. Diagrammatic structures of the precursors for the 4 major endocrine cell products of the pancreatic islet. Portions of the precursors that correspond to the named hormones are indicated by heavy bars, whereas portions that correspond to peptide extensions are indicated by lines; dibasic amino acid residues (arginine or lysine) corresponding to precursor conversion sites are shown as filled circles. Note that proinsulin has been drawn in an extended form that does not show disulfide bonds; the structure of proinsulin illustrated has the sequence B chain–C peptide–A chain. (Redrawn and reproduced, with permission, from Tager HS: Abnormal products of the human insulin gene. *Diabetes* 1984;**33**:693.)

insulin in Fig 42–7. Several combinations of endo-proteolytic (trypsinlike) and exoproteolytic (carboxy-peptidase B-like) cleavages are involved, since the hormone sequence may occur at the carboxyl terminus of the precursor (somatostatin), at the amino terminus (pancreatic polypeptide), at both ends (insulin), or in the middle (glucagon).

C. Subcellular Localization of Insulin Synthesis and Granule Formation: Insulin synthesis and the packaging of the hormone into secretion granules proceeds in orderly fashion (Fig 42–8). Proinsulin is synthesized by ribosomes on the rough endoplasmic reticulum, and the enzymatic removal of the leader peptide (pre- segment), disulfide bond formation, and folding (Fig 42–4) occur in the cisternae of this organelle. The proinsulin molecule is transported to the Golgi apparatus wherein proteolysis and packaging into the secretory granules begin. Granules continue to mature as they traverse the cytoplasm toward the plasma membrane. Proinsulin and insulin both combine with zinc to form hexamers, but since about 95% of the proinsulin is converted to insulin, it is the crystals of the latter that confer morphologic distinctness to the granules. Equimolar amounts of C peptide are present within these granules, but these molecules do not form a crystalline structure. Upon appropriate

stimulation (see below), the mature granules fuse with the plasma membrane and discharge their contents into the extracellular fluid by **emiocytosis.**

D. Properties of Proinsulin and C Peptide: Proinsulins vary in length from 78 to 86 amino acids, with the variation occurring in the length of the C-peptide region. Proinsulin has the same solubility and isoelectric point as insulin; it also forms hexamers with zinc crystals, and it reacts strongly with insulin antisera. **Proinsulin has less than 5% of the bioactivity of insulin,** indicating that most of the active site of the latter is occluded in the precursor molecule. Some proinsulin is released with insulin and in certain conditions (islet cell tumors) in larger than usual amounts. Since the plasma half-life of proinsulin is significantly longer than that of insulin and since proinsulin is strongly cross-reactive with insulin antisera, a radio-immunoassay for "insulin" may occasionally overestimate the bioactivity of "insulin" in plasma.

The C peptide has no known biologic activity. It is a distinct molecule from an antigenic standpoint. Thus, C-peptide immunoassays can distinguish insulin secreted endogenously from insulin administered exogenously and can quantitate the former when anti-insulin antibodies preclude the direct measurement of insulin. The C peptides of different species have a high

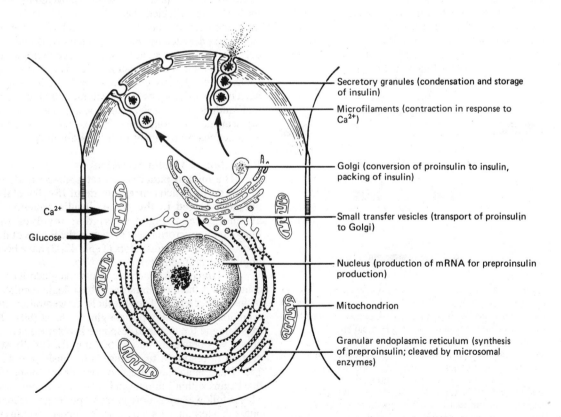

Ca²⁺

Glucose

Secretory granules (condensation and storage of insulin)

Microfilaments (contraction in response to Ca²⁺)

Golgi (conversion of proinsulin to insulin, packing of insulin)

Small transfer vesicles (transport of proinsulin to Golgi)

Nucleus (production of mRNA for preproinsulin production)

Mitochondrion

Granular endoplasmic reticulum (synthesis of preproinsulin; cleaved by microsomal enzymes)

Figure 42–8. Structural components of the pancreatic B cell involved in glucose-induced biosynthesis and release. Schematic representation of secretory granular alignment on microfilament "tracks" that contract in response to calcium. (Based on data presented by Orci L: A portrait of the pancreatic B cell. *Diabetologia* 1974; **10**:163.) (Modified and reproduced, with permission, from Junqueira LC, Carneiro J: *Basic Histology,* 4th ed. Lange, 1983.)

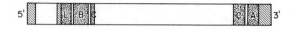

rate of amino acid substitution, an observation which underscores the statement that this fragment probably has no biologic activity.

E. Precursors of Insulin-Related Peptides: The structural arrangement of the precursor molecule is not unique to insulin; very closely related peptide hormones (relaxin and the insulinlike growth factors) show the same arrangement (Fig 42–9). All of these hormones have highly homologous B- and A-chain regions at the amino and carboxyl termini of a precursor molecule, and these are joined by a connecting segment. In the relaxin and insulin precursor peptides, this connecting segment is bound on both ends by 2 basic amino acids. After the B and A chains are joined by disulfide bonds, this piece is removed by endoproteolytic action, and these molecules are converted to 2-chain peptide hormones. The insulinlike growth factors, though highly homologous to insulin and relaxin in primary structure, lack these dibasic cleavage sites and thus remain single-chain peptide hormones.

F. The Human Insulin Gene: The human insulin gene (Fig 42–10) is located on the short arm of chromosome 11. Most mammals express a single insulin gene that is organized like the human gene, but rats and mice have 2 nonallelic genes. Each codes for a unique proinsulin that is processed into 2 distinct, active insulin molecules.

G. Abnormal Human Insulin Gene Products: Knowledge of the structure of the insulin gene and of the insulin molecule makes it possible to detect abnormal gene products, and this in turn provides additional information about the function of this hormone. Three

Figure 42–10. Diagrammatic structure of the human insulin gene. Areas with diagonal stripes correspond to untranslated regions of the corresponding mRNA; open regions correspond to intervening sequences; and stippled regions correspond to coding sequences. L, B, C, and A identify coding sequences for the leader (or signal) peptide, the insulin B chain, the C peptide, and the insulin A chain, respectively. Note that the coding sequence for the C peptide is split by an intervening sequence. The diagrammatic structure is drawn to scale. (Redrawn and reproduced, with permission, from Tager HS: Abnormal products of the human insulin gene. *Diabetes* 1984;**33**:693.)

cases of gene mutation have been documented, and the molecular basis of each defect has been defined. In one case, serine replaced phenylalanine at B24, owing to a single-base mutation. In another case, leucine replaced phenylalanine at B25, again because of a single-base mutation. One proinsulin processing mutation has been discovered. In this case, there was faulty cleavage at the 3' terminus of the C peptide that abuts the A-chain peptide. The Lys-Arg at this site (Fig 42–6) was converted to Lys-X, so that trypsinlike cleavage could not occur. These cases were discovered because the mutations affected the active site of the insulin molecule; hence, the individuals had (1) hyperinsulinemia, detected by radioimmunoassay; (2) no evidence of insulin resistance; (3) decreased biologic activity of the circulating insulin; and (4) a normal response to exogenous insulin. At least 4 other single nucleotide substitutions have been identified in "normal" individuals, but since these occurred in intervening sequences or noncoding regions, they resulted in no functional impairment of the insulin molecule.

Regulation of Insulin Secretion

The human pancreas secretes 40–50 units of insulin daily, which represents about 15–20% of the hormone stored in the gland. Insulin secretion is an energy-requiring process that involves the microtubule-microfilament system in the B cells of the islets. A number of mediators (Table 42–3) have been implicated in insulin release.

A. Glucose: An increase in plasma glucose concentration is the most important physiologic regulator of insulin secretion. The threshold concentration for secretion is the fasting plasma glucose level (80–100 mg/dL), and the maximal response is obtained at glucose levels between 300 and 500 mg/dL. **Insulin secretion in response to glucose is biphasic** (Fig 42–11). There is an immediate, or first-phase, response that begins within 1 minute and lasts for 5–10 minutes. This is followed by a more gradual, prolonged second phase that terminates soon after the glucose stimulus is removed. It is postulated that these 2 phases reflect the existence of 2 intracellular compartments, or pools, of insulin. The **absolute** plasma glucose concentration is not the sole determinant of insulin secretion; the B cell

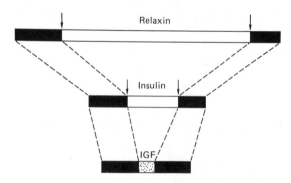

Figure 42–9. Diagrammatic structures of precursors for insulin-related peptides. Homologous regions of relaxin, insulin, and insulinlike growth factor are shown as solid bars. Amino acid sequences connecting B-chain and A-chain sequences in the precursors for relaxin and insulin are shown as open bars; these sequences are removed during processing of the precursors to their corresponding 2-chained products (vertical arrows). The amino acid sequence of insulinlike growth factor that corresponds to these connecting peptides, but which is not removed by proteolytic processing events, is shown as a stippled bar; insulinlike growth factor is a single-chain peptide hormone. (Redrawn and reproduced, with permission, from Tager HS: Abnormal products of the human insulin gene. *Diabetes* 1984;**33**:693.)

Table 42–3. Regulation of insulin release in humans.*

Stimulants of insulin release
  Glucose, mannose, fructose
  Leucine
  Vagal stimulation
  Sulfonylureas
Amplifiers of glucose-induced release
  Enteric hormones
    Gastrin inhibitory polypeptide
    Cholecystokinin, glucagon
    Secretin, gastrin
  Neural amplifiers
    β-Adrenergic agonists
    Acetylcholine
  Amino acids
    Arginine
    Lysine
  β-Ketoacids and fatty acids
  cAMP
Inhibitors of insulin release
  Neural inhibitors
    α-Adrenergic agonists of catecholamines
    β-Adrenergic antagonists
  Humoral inhibitors
    Somatostatin
  Drugs
    Diazoxide, phenytoin, vinblastine, colchicine, thiazides
  Sugar analogs
    2-Deoxyglucose, mannoheptulose

*Modified and reproduced, with permission, from Karam JH, Salber PR, Forsham PH: Pancreatic hormones and diabetes mellitus. In: *Basic & Clinical Endocrinology.* Greenspan FS, Forsham PH (editors). Lange, 1983.

responds to the **rate of change** of plasma glucose concentrations as well.

Glucose is much more effective in releasing insulin when given orally than intravenously; hence, various gastrointestinal hormones including secretin, cholecystokinin, glucagon, and gastrin have been implicated in insulin release, but gastric inhibitory polypeptide (GIP) is now thought to play the major role in this process.

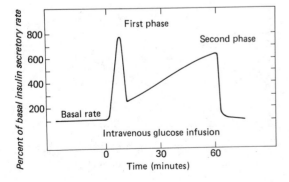

Figure 42–11. The biphasic pattern of insulin release in response to an increased plasma glucose concentration.

Two different mechanisms have been proposed to explain how glucose regulates insulin secretion. One hypothesis suggests that glucose combines with a receptor, possibly located on the B cell membrane, that activates the release mechanism. The second hypothesis suggests that intracellular metabolites or the rate of metabolite flux through a pathway such as the pentose-phosphate shunt, the citric acid cycle, or the glycolytic pathway, is involved. There is experimental evidence to support both positions.

Other sugars that are readily metabolized, such as mannose and fructose, stimulate insulin secretion, whereas nonmetabolizable sugars, such as galactose, L-arabinose, and D-xylose, do not. Analogs that inhibit glucose metabolism, such as 2-deoxyglucose and mannoheptulose, inhibit the effect of glucose on insulin secretion.

B. Amino Acids, Fatty Acids, and Ketone Bodies: High-protein meals stimulate insulin release, and arginine, lysine, and leucine are potent insulin secretagogues. Whether these amino acids act in the absence of glucose is unclear (leucine may), but combinations of amino acids and glucose certainly give synergistic responses. Physiologic concentrations of short- and long-chain fatty acids and of ketone bodies are weak secretagogues in most species.

C. Hormonal Factors: Numerous hormones affect insulin release. α-Adrenergic agonists, principally epinephrine, inhibit insulin release even when this process has been stimulated by glucose. β-Adrenergic agonists stimulate insulin release, probably by increasing intracellular cAMP (see below). This is the probable mechanism by which GIP increases insulin release and may explain the actions of high concentrations of TSH, ACTH, gastrin, secretin, cholecystokinin, and enteroglucagon.

Chronic exposure to excessive levels of growth hormone, cortisol, placental lactogen, estrogens, and progestins also increases insulin secretion. It is therefore not surprising that insulin secretion increases markedly during the later stages of pregnancy.

D. Pharmacologic Agents: Many drugs stimulate insulin secretion, but the **sulfonylurea compounds** are used most frequently for therapy in humans. Drugs such as tolbutamide stimulate insulin release by a mechanism different from that employed by glucose and have achieved widespread use in the treatment of type II (non-insulin-dependent) diabetes mellitus.

$$H_3C-\hspace{-2pt}\underset{}{\bigcirc}\hspace{-2pt}-SO_2-NH-\underset{\underset{O}{\|}}{C}-NH-(CH_2)_3-CH_3$$

Tolbutamide

E. Intracellular Mediators of Secretion: Oxygen consumption and ATP utilization increase as glucose stimulates insulin release. This is associated with a K^+-induced depolarization of the membrane that results in the rapid entry of Ca^{2+} via a voltage-dependent channel. The fusion of insulin-containing secretory granules with the plasma membrane, and thus insulin secretion, is calcium-dependent. Metabolites of phosphatidylinositol (see Chapter 36) have been linked to glucose-stimulated insulin secretion.

cAMP is associated with insulin secretion, and this nucleotide potentiates the actions of glucose and amino acids. cAMP may release Ca^{2+} from intracellular organelles or it may activate a kinase that phosphorylates a component of the microfilament-microtubule system, thereby rendering this structure Ca^{2+}-sensitive and contractile. Replacement of extracellular Na^+ with another monovalent cation blunts the effects of glucose and other secretagogues; Na^+ may regulate the intracellular concentration of Ca^{2+} through a cotransport system.

Metabolism of Insulin

Unlike the insulinlike growth factors, **insulin has no plasma carrier protein;** thus, its plasma half-life is less than 3–5 minutes under normal conditions. The major organs involved in insulin metabolism are the liver, kidneys, and placenta; about 50% of insulin is removed in a single pass through the liver. **Mechanisms involving 2 enzyme systems are responsible for the metabolism of insulin.** The first involves an insulin-specific **protease** found in many tissues but in highest concentration in those listed above. This protease has been purified from skeletal muscle and is known to be sulfhydryl-dependent and active at physiologic pH. The second mechanism involves hepatic **glutathione-insulin transhydrogenase.** This enzyme reduces the disulfide bonds, and then the individual A and B chains are rapidly degraded. It is not clear which of these mechanisms is most active under physiologic conditions, nor is it clear whether either process is regulated.

Physiologic Effects of Insulin

The central role of insulin in carbohydrate, lipid, and protein metabolism can be best appreciated by examining the consequences of insulin deficiency in humans. The cardinal manifestation of **diabetes mellitus** is **hyperglycemia,** which results from (1) decreased entry of glucose into cells, (2) decreased utilization of glucose by various tissues, and (3) increased production of glucose (gluconeogenesis) by the liver. Each of these is discussed in more detail below.

Polyuria, polydipsia, and weight loss in spite of adequate caloric intake are the major symptoms of insulin deficiency. How is this explained? The plasma glucose level rarely exceeds 120 mg/dL in normal humans, but much higher levels are routinely found in patients with deficient insulin action. After a certain plasma glucose level is attained (generally > 180 mg/dL in humans), the maximum level of renal tubular reabsorption of glucose is exceeded, and sugar is excreted in the urine (glycosuria). The urine volume is increased owing to osmotic diuresis and coincident obligatory water loss (polyuria), and this in turn leads

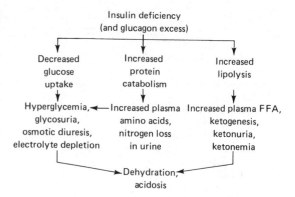

Figure 42–12. Pathophysiology of insulin deficiency. (Courtesy of RJ Havel.)

to dehydration (hyperosmolarity), increased thirst, and excessive drinking (polydipsia). Glycosuria causes a substantial loss of calories (4.1 kcal for every gram of glucose excreted); this loss, when coupled with the loss of muscle and adipose tissue, results in severe weight loss in spite of increased appetite (polyphagia) and normal or increased caloric intake.

Protein synthesis decreases in the absence of insulin, partly because the transport of amino acids into muscle is diminished (the amino acids serve as gluconeogenic substrates). Thus, insulin-deficient persons are in negative nitrogen balance. The antilipolytic action of insulin is lost, as is its lipogenic effect; hence, plasma fatty acid levels rise. When the capacity of the liver to oxidize fatty acids to CO_2 is exceeded, **β-hydroxybutyric acid and acetoacetic acid accumulate (ketosis).** The organism initially compensates for the accumulation of these organic acids by increasing respiratory losses of CO_2, but if unchecked by the administration of insulin, severe **metabolic acidosis** supervenes and the patient dies of **diabetic coma.** The pathophysiology of insulin deficiency is summarized in Fig 42–12.

A. Effects on Membrane Transport: The intracellular free glucose concentration is very low com-

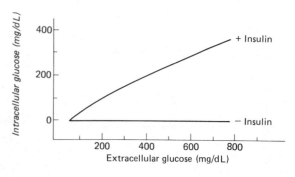

Figure 42–13. Entry of glucose into muscle cells. (Courtesy of CR Park.)

pared with the extracellular concentration. Most studies suggest that **the rate of glucose transport across the plasma membrane of muscle and adipose cells determines the rate of glucose phosphorylation of glucose and its further metabolism.** D-Glucose and other sugars with a similar configuration at the C_1–C_3 positions (galactose, D-xylose, and L-arabinose) enter cells by **carrier-mediated facilitated diffusion,** a process enhanced in many cells by insulin (Fig 42–13). This involves a V_{max} effect (increased number of transporters) rather than a K_m effect (increased affinity of binding). Data suggest that in adipose cells this is accomplished by recruiting **glucose transporters** from an inactive pool in the Golgi fraction and then moving them to an active site in the plasma membrane. This transporter translocation is temperature- and energy-dependent and is protein synthesis–independent (Fig 42–14).

The hepatic cell represents a notable exception to this scheme. Insulin does not promote the facilitated diffusion of glucose into hepatocytes, but it indirectly enhances net inward flux by converting intracellular glucose to glucose 6-phosphate through the action of glucokinase, an enzyme induced by insulin.

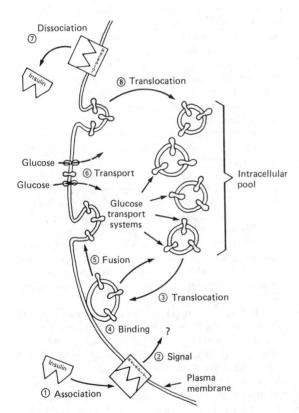

Figure 42–14. Translocation of glucose transporters by insulin. (Reproduced, with permission, from Karnieli E et al: Insulin-stimulated translocation of glucose transport systems in the isolated rat adipose cell. *J Biol Chem* 1981;256:4772. Courtesy of S Cushman.)

This rapid phosphorylation keeps the free glucose concentration very low in the hepatocyte, thus favoring entry by simple diffusion down a concentration gradient.

Insulin also promotes the entry of amino acids into cells, particularly in muscle, and enhances the movement of K^+, Ca^{2+}, nucleosides, and inorganic phosphate. These effects are independent of the action of insulin on glucose entry.

B. Effects on Glucose Utilization: Insulin influences the intracellular utilization of glucose in a number of ways, as illustrated below.

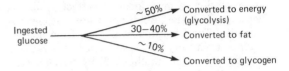

In a normal person, about half of the glucose ingested is converted to energy through the glycolytic pathway and about half is stored as fat or glycogen. Glycolysis decreases in the absence of insulin, and the anabolic processes of glycogenesis and lipogenesis are impeded. Indeed, only 5% of an ingested glucose load is converted to fat in an insulin-deficient diabetic.

Insulin increases hepatic glycolysis by increasing the activity and amount of several key enzymes including glucokinase, phosphofructokinase, and pyruvate kinase. Enhanced glycolysis increases glucose utilization and thus indirectly decreases glucose release into plasma. Insulin also decreases the activity of glucose 6-phosphatase, an enzyme found in liver but not in muscle. Since glucose 6-phosphate cannot exit from the plasma membrane, this action of insulin results in the retention of glucose within the liver cell.

Insulin stimulates lipogenesis in adipose tissue by (1) providing the acetyl-CoA and NADPH required for fatty acid synthesis; (2) maintaining a normal level of the enzyme acetyl-CoA carboxylase, which catalyzes the conversion of acetyl-CoA to malonyl-CoA; and (3) providing the glycerol involved in triacylglycerol synthesis. In insulin deficiency, all of these are decreased; thus, lipogenesis decreases. Another reason for the decreased lipogenesis in insulin deficiency is that fatty acids, released in large amounts by several hormones when unopposed by insulin, feedback-inhibit their own synthesis by inhibiting acetyl-CoA carboxylase. The net effect of insulin on fat is therefore anabolic.

The final action of insulin on glucose utilization involves another anabolic process. In liver and muscle, insulin stimulates the conversion of glucose to glucose 6-phosphate, which then undergoes isomerization to glucose 1-phosphate and is incorporated into glycogen by the enzyme glycogen synthase, the activity of which is stimulated by insulin. This action is indirect and dual in nature. Insulin decreases intracellular cAMP levels by activating a phosphodiesterase. Since cAMP-dependent phosphorylation inactivates glycogen synthase, low levels of this nucleotide allow the enzyme to stay in the active form. Insulin also activates a phosphatase that dephosphorylates glycogen synthase, thereby resulting in the activation of this enzyme (see Fig 36–6). Finally, insulin inhibits phosphorylase by a mechanism involving cAMP and phosphatase as described above, and this decreases glucose liberation from glycogen. The net effect of insulin on glycogen metabolism is also anabolic.

C. Effects on Glucose Production (Gluconeogenesis): The actions of insulin on glucose transport, glycolysis, and glycogenesis occur within seconds or minutes, since they primarily involve the activation or inactivation of enzymes by phosphorylation or dephosphorylation. A more long-term effect on plasma glucose involves **the inhibition of gluconeogenesis by insulin.** The formation of glucose from noncarbohydrate precursors involves a series of enzymatic steps, many of which are stimulated by glucagon (acting through cAMP), by glucocorticoid hormones, and to a lesser extent by α- and β-adrenergic agents, angiotensin II, and vasopressin. Insulin inhibits these same steps. The key gluconeogenic enzyme in the liver is phosphoenolpyruvate carboxykinase (PEPCK), which converts oxaloacetate to phosphoenolpyruvate. Recent studies (see below) show that insulin decreases the amount of this enzyme by selectively inhibiting transcription of the gene that codes for PEPCK mRNA.

D. Effects on Glucose Metabolism: The net action of all of the above effects of insulin is to decrease the blood glucose level. In this action, insulin stands alone against an array of hormones that attempt to counteract this effect. This no doubt represents one of the organism's most important defense mechanisms, since prolonged hypoglycemia poses a potentially lethal threat to the brain and must be avoided.

E. Effects on Lipid Metabolism: The lipogenic actions of insulin were discussed in the context of glucose utilization. Insulin also is a potent inhibitor of lipolysis in liver and adipose tissue and thus has an indirect anabolic effect. This is partly due to the ability of insulin to decrease tissue cAMP levels (which are increased in these tissues by the lipolytic hormones glucagon and epinephrine) but also to the fact that insulin inhibits hormone-sensitive lipase activity. This inhibition is presumably due to the activation of a phosphatase that dephosphorylates and thereby inactivates the lipase or cAMP-dependent protein kinase. Insulin therefore decreases circulating free fatty acids. This contributes to the action of insulin on carbohydrate metabolism, since fatty acids inhibit glycolysis at several steps and stimulate gluconeogenesis. This illustrates the point that one cannot discuss metabolic regulation in the context of a single hormone or metabolite. Regulation is a complex process in which the flux through a given pathway is the result of the interplay of a number of hormones and metabolites.

In patients with insulin deficiency, lipase activity increases, resulting in enhanced lipolysis and increased concentration of free fatty acids in plasma and liver. Glucagon levels also increase in these patients,

and this enhances the release of free fatty acids. (Glucagon opposes most of the actions of insulin, and the metabolic state in the diabetic is a reflection of the relative levels of glucagon and insulin.) A portion of the free fatty acids is metabolized to acetyl-CoA (the reverse of lipogenesis) and then to CO_2 and H_2O via the citric acid cycle. In patients with insulin deficiency, the capacity of this process is rapidly exceeded and the acetyl-CoA is converted to acetoacetyl-CoA and then to acetoacetic and β-hydroxybutyric acids. Insulin reverses this pathway.

Insulin apparently affects the formation or clearance of VLDL and LDL, since levels of these particles, and consequently the level of cholesterol, are often elevated in poorly controlled diabetics. Accelerated atherosclerosis, a serious problem in many diabetics, is attributed to this metabolic defect.

The actions of insulin can be inferred by inspecting Fig 42–15, which depicts the flux through several critical pathways in the absence of the hormone.

F. Effects on Protein Metabolism: Insulin generally has an anabolic effect on protein metabolism in that it stimulates protein synthesis and retards protein degradation. Insulin stimulates the uptake of type A neutral amino acids into muscle, an effect that is not linked to glucose uptake or to subsequent incorporation of the amino acids into protein. The effects of insulin on general protein synthesis in skeletal and cardiac muscle and in liver are thought to be exerted at the level of mRNA translation.

In recent years, insulin has been shown to influence the synthesis of specific proteins by effecting changes in the corresponding mRNAs. This action of insulin, which may ultimately explain many of the effects the hormone has on the activity or amount of specific proteins, is discussed in more detail below.

G. Effects on Cell Replication: Insulin stimulates the proliferation of a number of cells in culture, and it may also be involved in the regulation of growth in vivo. Cultured fibroblasts are the most frequently used cells in studies of growth control. In such cells, insulin potentiates the ability of fibroblast growth factor (FGF), platelet-derived growth factor (PDGF), epidermal growth factor (EGF), tumor-promoting phorbol esters, prostaglandin $F_{2\alpha}$ ($PGF_{2\alpha}$), vasopressin, and cAMP analogs to stimulate cell cycle progression of cells arrested in the G_1 phase of the cycle by serum deprivation.

The temporal requirements for the various growth factors have led to the concept that there are 2 classes. One class, including PDGF, FGF, $PGF_{2\alpha}$, and phorbol esters, is thought to cause a biochemical change early in G phase that, when established, removes the requirement for the growth factor and makes the cells **"competent"** for replication. The second class, including insulin, allows the cells to **"progress"** to and through S phase and must be present at all times. This model describes events in 3T3 fibroblasts, and its universality is not established. It also is not clear whether insulin acting through the insulin receptor is involved or whether insulin mediates this "progres-

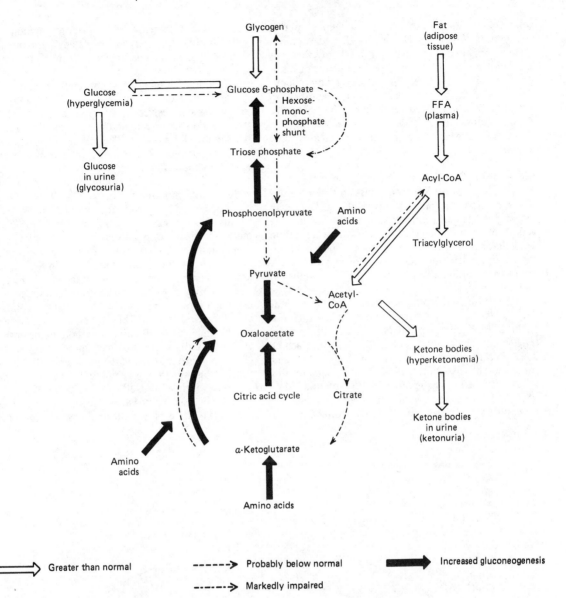

Figure 42–15. Metabolic consequences of insulin deficiency.

sion'' through an insulinlike growth factor (IGF) receptor, especially since IGF-I is also a ''progression'' factor.

Insulin supports the growth and replication of many cells of epithelial origin, including hepatocytes, hepatoma cells, adrenocortical tumor cells, and mammary carcinoma cells. Insulin stimulates replication at very low concentrations of the hormone, apparently through the insulin receptor, and often in the absence of other peptide growth factors. Indeed, insulin is a critical ingredient in all ''defined'' tissue culture media, so that a role in growth and replication is certain.

The biochemical actions of insulin in cell replication have not been established but have been linked to its known anabolic actions. Thus, effects on the uptake of glucose, phosphate, type A neutral amino acids, and cations have been implicated. The hormone might affect replication through its established ability to activate or inactivate enzymes by controlling the rate and extent of protein phosphorylation or by regulating enzyme synthesis.

An exciting new area of research involves the investigation of tyrosine kinase activity. The insulin receptor, along with receptors for many other growth-promoting peptides including those of PDGF and EGF, has tyrosine kinase activity. Interestingly, at least 10 oncogene products, many of which are suspected to be involved in stimulating malignant cell replication, are also tyrosine kinases. Mammalian cells contain analogs of these oncogenes (**proto-oncogenes**), which may be involved in the replication of normal cells. Support for the theory that they are involved comes from recent observations that the expression of at least 2 proto-oncogene products, c-fos and c-myc, increases following addition of serum to growth-arrested cells. PDGF has also been shown to stimulate the production of specific mRNAs. Whether insulin acts in a similar way remains to be established.

Mechanism of Action of Insulin

A. The Insulin Receptor: Insulin action begins when the hormone binds to a specific glycoprotein receptor on the surface of the target cell. The diverse actions of the hormone (Fig 42–16) can occur within seconds or minutes (transport, protein phosphorylation, enzyme activation and inhibition) or after a few hours (protein and RNA synthesis, DNA synthesis, and cell growth).

The insulin receptor has been studied in great detail and is known to be a heterodimer consisting of 2 subunits, designated α and β, in the configuration α_2-β_2, linked by disulfide bonds (Fig 42–16). Each of these glycoprotein subunits has a unique structure and function. The α subunit (MW 135,000) binds insulin to an extracellular domain. The β subunit (MW 95,000) is a transmembrane (or integral membrane) protein that performs the second major function of a receptor (see Chapter 36), ie, signal transduction. Both subunits are extensively glycosylated, and removal of sialic acid and galactose decreases insulin binding and insulin action.

The insulin receptor is constantly being synthesized and degraded, and its half-life is 7–12 hours. The receptor is synthesized as a single-chain peptide in the rough endoplasmic reticulum and is rapidly glycosylated in the Golgi region. The precursor has a molecular weight of 190,000 and is cleaved to form the mature α and β subunits.

Insulin receptors are found on most mammalian cells, in concentrations of up to 20,000 per cell, and often on cells not typically thought of as being insulin targets. Insulin has a well-known set of effects on metabolic processes but also is involved in growth and replication of cells (see above) as well as in fetal organogenesis and differentiation and in tissue repair and regeneration. The structure of the insulin receptor and the ability of different insulins to bind to receptors and elicit biologic responses are virtually identical in all cells and all species. Thus, porcine insulin is always 10–20 times more effective than porcine proinsulin, which in turn is 10–20 times more effective than guinea pig insulin, even in the guinea pig. The insulin receptor has apparently been highly conserved, more so than even insulin itself.

When insulin binds to the receptor, several events occur. (1) There is a conformational change of the

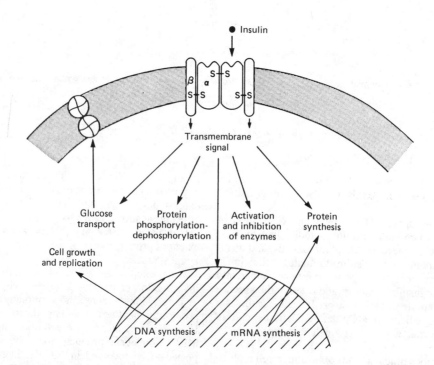

Figure 42–16. Relationship of the insulin receptor to insulin action. (Courtesy of CR Kahn.)

receptor; (2) the receptors cross-link and form microaggregates, patches, or caps; (3) the receptor is internalized; and (4) some signal is generated. The significance of the conformational change is unknown, and internalization probably represents a means of controlling receptor concentration and turnover. In conditions in which plasma insulin levels are high, eg, obesity or acromegaly, the number of insulin receptors is decreased and target tissues become less sensitive to insulin. This "down regulation" results from the loss of receptors by internalization, the process whereby insulin-receptor complexes enter the cell through endocytosis in clathrin-coated vesicles (see Chapter 31). "Down regulation" explains part of the insulin resistance in obesity and type II diabetes mellitus.

Receptor mobility and the cross-linking of receptors are discussed in Chapter 36. These and the generation of an intracellular signal or mediator are strongly linked to insulin action.

B. Intracellular Mediators: Although the mechanism of insulin action has been under investigation for 60 years, certain critical points, such as the nature of the intracellular signal, remain obscure. Insulin is not unique in this respect—the intracellular messenger has not been identified for a large number of hormones (see Table 36–1). A variety of different molecules have been proposed as the intracellular second messenger or mediator. These include insulin itself, calcium, cyclic nucleotides (cAMP, cGMP), H_2O_2, membrane-derived peptides, membrane phospholipids, monovalent cations, and tyrosine kinase (the insulin receptor). None has withstood rigorous testing.

Current interest centers on the observation that the insulin receptor is itself an insulin-sensitive enzyme, since it undergoes autophosphorylation in response to insulin binding. This function is conferred by the β subunit, which acts as a protein kinase in transferring the γ-phosphate of ATP to a tyrosine residue in the β subunit (Fig 42–17). Insulin increases the V_{max} of this enzymatic reaction, and divalent cations, particularly Mn^{2+}, decrease the K_m for ATP.

Tyrosine phosphorylation is unusual in mammalian cells (phosphotyrosine accounts for only 0.03% of the phosphoamino acid content of normal cells), and it is perhaps more than coincidental that the EGF, PDGF, and IGF-I receptors also have tyrosine kinase activity. Tyrosine kinase activity is thought to be an essential factor in the action of a number of viral oncogene products; the relationship of this and of cellular oncogene analogs with similar properties in malignant and normal cell growth was discussed above. As structures are elucidated, a high degree of homology between receptors and oncogenes is becoming apparent, eg, between the EGF receptor and erb-B, between the PDGF receptor and v-sis, and between the insulin receptor and c-ros.

Tyrosine kinase activity has not been proved to be involved in transduction of the insulin-receptor signal, but it could accomplish this by phosphorylating a specific protein that initiates insulin action, by initiating a phosphorylation-dephosphorylation cascade, by changing some property of the cell membrane, or by generating a membrane-related product, eg, a phospholipid.

C. Protein Phosphorylation-Dephosphorylation: Many of the metabolic effects of insulin, particularly those which occur rapidly, are mediated by influencing protein phosphorylation and dephosphorylation reactions that in turn alter the enzymic activity of the protein. A list of enzymes affected in this way is

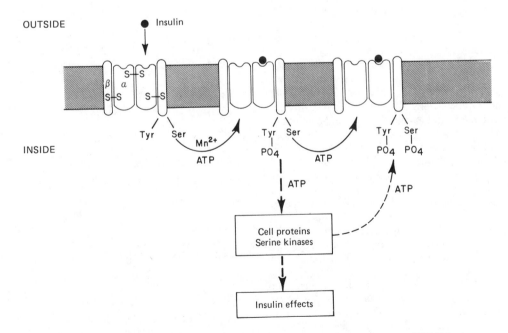

Figure 42–17. The insulin receptor as a protein (tyrosine) kinase. (Courtesy of CR Kahn.)

Table 42–4. Enzymes whose degree of phosphorylation and activity are altered by insulin.*

Enzyme	Change in Activity	Possible Mechanism
cAMP metabolism		
Phosphodiesterase (low K_m)	Increase	Phosphorylation
Protein kinase (cAMP-dependent)	Decrease	Association of R and C subunits
Glycogen metabolism		
Glycogen synthase	Increase	Dephosphorylation
Phosphorylase kinase	Decrease	Dephosphorylation
Phosphorylase	Decrease	Dephosphorylation
Glycolysis and gluconeogenesis		
Pyruvate dehydrogenase	Increase	Dephosphorylation
Pyruvate kinase	Increase	Dephosphorylation
6-Phosphofructo 2-kinase	Increase	Dephosphorylation
Fructose 2,6-bisphosphatase	Decrease	
Lipid metabolism		
Acetyl-CoA carboxylase	Increase	Phosphorylation
HMG-CoA reductase	Increase	Dephosphorylation
Triacylglycerol lipase	Decrease	Dephosphorylation
Other		
Tyrosine kinase (the insulin receptor)	?	Phosphorylation

*Modified and reproduced, with permission, from Denton RM et al: A partial view of the mechanism of insulin action. *Diabetologia* 1981;**21**:347.

presented in Table 42–4. In some instances, insulin decreases intracellular cAMP levels (by activating a cAMP-phosphodiesterase), thereby decreasing the activity state of cAMP-dependent protein kinase; examples of this action include glycogen synthase and phosphorylase. In other instances, this action is independent of cAMP and is exerted by activating other protein kinases (as is the case with the insulin receptor, tyrosine kinase); by inhibiting other protein kinases (see Table 36–3); or, more commonly, by stimulating the activity of phosphoprotein phosphatases. Dephosphorylation increases the activity of a number of key enzymes (Table 42–4). These covalent modifications allow for almost immediate changes in the activity of enzymes.

D. Effects on mRNA Translation: Insulin is known to affect the activity or amount of at least 50 proteins in a variety of tissues, and many of these effects involve covalent modification. A role for insulin in the translation of mRNA has been proposed, largely based on studies of ribosomal protein S6, a component of the 40S ribosomal subunit. Such a mechanism could account for the general effect insulin has on protein synthesis in liver, skeletal muscle, and cardiac muscle.

E. Effects on Gene Expression: The actions of insulin discussed heretofore all occur at the plasma membrane level or in the cytoplasm. In addition, insulin affects specific nuclear processes, presumably through its intracellular mediator. The enzyme phos-

phoenolpyruvate carboxykinase (PEPCK) catalyzes a rate-limiting step in gluconeogenesis. The synthesis of PEPCK is decreased by insulin; hence, gluconeogenesis decreases. Recent studies show that the rate of transcription of the PEPCK gene is selectively decreased within minutes after the addition of insulin to cultured hepatoma cells (Fig 42–18). The decrease in transcription accounts for the decreased amount of the primary transcript and of mature $mRNA^{PEPCK}$, which in turn is directly related to the decreased rate of PEPCK synthesis. This effect occurs at physiologic levels of insulin (10^{-12} to 10^{-9} mol/L), is mediated through the insulin receptor, and appears to be due to a decreased rate of $mRNA^{PEPCK}$ transcript initiation.

Although studies of PEPCK regulation provided the first example of an effect of insulin on gene transcription, this case is no longer unique. Indeed, it appears that regulation of mRNA synthesis is a major action of insulin. A number of specific mRNAs are affected by insulin (Table 42–5). In several instances, including those of ovalbumin, albumin, and casein, the hormone is known to affect gene transcription.

This effect of insulin involves enzymes retained in the cells, secreted enzymes and proteins, proteins involved in the reproductive process, and structural proteins (Table 42–5). A number of organs or tissues are involved, and the effect occurs in many species. The regulation of specific mRNA transcription by insulin is now well established, and as a means of modulating enzyme activity, it may soon rival phosphorylation-dephosphorylation in importance. The effect of insulin on gene transcription may also explain its effect

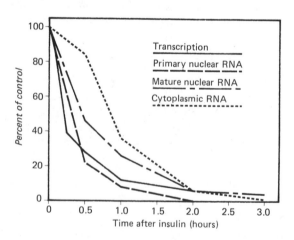

Figure 42–18. Effect of insulin on specific gene transcription. The addition of insulin to H4IIE hepatoma cells results in a rapid decrease in the rate of transcription of the PEPCK gene. This is followed by decreases in the amounts of primary transcript in the nucleus and mature $mRNA^{PEPCK}$ The rate of synthesis of PEPCK protein declines after the amount of cytoplasmic $mRNA^{PEPCK}$ decreases. (Reproduced, with permission, from Sasaki K et al: Multihormonal regulation of phosphoenolpyruvate carboxykinase gene transcription. *J Biol Chem* 1984;**259**:15242.)

Table 42–5. Messenger RNAs regulated by insulin.

Intracellular enzymes
  Tyrosine aminotransferase*
  Phosphoenolpyruvate carboxykinase†
  Fatty acid synthase
  Pyruvate kinase
  Glucokinase
Secreted proteins and enzymes
  Albumin†
  Amylase
  α_{2u} globulin
  Growth hormone
Proteins involved in reproduction
  Ovalbumin†
  Casein†
Structural proteins
  δ-Crystallin

---

*Insulin may regulate the rate of transcription.
†Insulin regulates the rate of specific mRNA transcription.

Table 42–6. Comparison of insulin and the insulinlike growth factors. (Courtesy of CR Kahn.)

	Insulin	IGF-I	IGF-II
Other names	. . .	Somatomedin C	Multiplication-stimulating activity (MSA)
Number of amino acids	51	70	67
Source	Pancreatic B cells	Liver and other tissues	Diverse tissues
Level regulated by	Glucose	Growth hormone, nutritional status	Unknown
Plasma levels	0.3–2 ng/mL	ng/mL range	ng/mL range
Plasma binding protein	No	Yes	Yes
Major physiologic role	Control of metabolism	Skeletal and cartilage growth	Unknown; perhaps a role in embryonic development

on embryogenesis, differentiation, and growth and replication of cells.

Pathophysiology

Insulin deficiency or resistance to the action of insulin results in **diabetes mellitus.** About 90% of persons with diabetes have **non-insulin dependent (type II) diabetes mellitus (NIDDM).** Such patients are usually obese, have elevated plasma insulin levels, and have "down-regulated" insulin receptors. The other 10% have **insulin-dependent (type I) diabetes mellitus (IDDM).** The metabolic derangements discussed earlier most typically apply to the type I diabetic.

Certain rare conditions illustrate essential features about insulin action. A few individuals produce antibodies directed against their insulin receptors. These antibodies prevent insulin from binding to the receptor, so that such persons develop a syndrome of severe insulin resistance (see Table 35–3). Tumors of B cell origin cause hyperinsulinism and a syndrome characterized by severe hypoglycemia. The role of insulin (or perhaps of IGF-I or IGF-II) in organogenesis and development is illustrated by the rare cases of **leprechaunism.** This syndrome is characterized by low birth weight, decreased muscle mass, decreased subcutaneous fat, elfin facies, insulin resistance with markedly elevated plasma levels of biologically active insulin, and early death. Several individuals with leprechaunism have been shown to lack insulin receptors or to have defective receptors.

INSULINLIKE GROWTH FACTORS

The insulinlike growth factors (IGF-I and IGF-II) are not pancreatic hormones but are related to insulin in structure and function. It is difficult to separate the effects of insulin on cell growth and replication from

similar actions exerted by IGF-I and IGF-II. Indeed, insulin and the IGFs may interact in this process. The structural similarity of these proteins was alluded to above and in Fig 42–9. A more detailed comparison is presented in Table 42–6. IGF-I and IGF-II are single-chain polypeptides of 70 and 67 amino acids, respectively. There is 62% homology between IGF-I and IGF-II, and these 2 hormones are identical with insulin in 50% of their residues. These molecules have unique antigenic sites and are regulated in different ways (Table 42–6). Insulin is the more potent metabolic hormone, whereas the IGFs are more potent in stimulating growth. Each hormone has a unique receptor. The IGF-I receptor, like the insulin receptor, is a heterodimer of α_2-β_2 structure and is a tyrosine kinase. The IGF-II receptor, in contrast, is a single-chain polypeptide of MW 260,000 and is not a tyrosine kinase.

There is some cross talk between these hormones and their receptors, and this probably accounts for the mixed biologic activity of these hormones (Table 42–7). In general, the growth-promoting effects of these hormones correlate best with their affinity for binding to the IGF-I or IGF-II receptor.

Table 42–7. Binding of insulin, IGF-I, and IGF-II to various receptors.

Hormone	Receptor		
	Insulin	IGF-I	IGF-II
Insulin	High	Low	Negligible
IGF-I	Moderate	High	Moderate
IGF-II	Negligible	Low	High

GLUCAGON

The early commercial preparations of insulin increased the plasma glucose level before lowering it, owing to the presence of a contaminating peptide, glucagon, which was the second pancreatic islet cell hormone discovered.

Chemistry

Glucagon is a single-chain polypeptide (MW 3485) consisting of 29 amino acids (Fig 42–19). Glucagon contains no cysteine residues and thus has no disulfide bonds. Glucagon shares some immunologic and physiologic properties with enteroglucagon, a peptide extracted from the duodenal mucosa, and 14 of the 27 amino acid residues of secretin are identical to those of glucagon (Table 42–14).

Biosynthesis & Metabolism

Glucagon is synthesized mainly in the A cells of the pancreatic islets, although significant amounts may come from other sites in the gastrointestinal tract. Glucagon is synthesized as a much larger (MW ~9000) proglucagon precursor. Molecules larger than this have been detected, but whether they represent glucagon precursors or closely related peptides is unclear. Only 30–40% of the immunoreactive "glucagon" in plasma is pancreatic glucagon; the rest consists of biologically inactive larger molecules.

Glucagon circulates in plasma in the free form. Since it does not associate with a transport protein, its plasma half-life is short (~5 minutes). Glucagon is inactivated by the liver, which has an enzyme that removes the first 2 amino acids from the N-terminal end by cleaving between Ser 2 and Gln 3. Since the liver is the first stop for glucagon after it is secreted and since the liver rapidly inactivates the hormone, the level of glucagon in the portal vein is much higher than that in the peripheral circulation.

Regulation of Secretion

The secretion of glucagon is inhibited by glucose, an action that emphasizes the opposing metabolic roles of glucagon and insulin. It is not clear whether glucose

Table 42–8. Factors affecting glucagon secretion.*

Stimulators	Inhibitors
Amino acids (particularly the gluconeo-genic amino acids: alanine, serine, glycine, cysteine, and threonine)	Glucose
	Somatostatin
	Secretin
Gastrin, cholecystokinin	Free fatty acids
Cortisol	Ketones
Exercise	Insulin
β-Adrenergic agonists	Phenytoin
Theophylline	α-Adrenergic
Acetylcholine	agonists

*Slightly modified and reproduced, with permission, from Ganong WF: *Review of Medical Physiology,* 12th ed. Lange, 1985.

directly inhibits glucagon secretion or whether this is mediated through the actions of insulin or IGF-I, since both of these islet cell hormones directly inhibit glucagon release. Many other substances, including amino acids, fatty acids and ketones, gastrointestinal tract hormones, and neurotransmitters, affect glucagon secretion (Table 42–8). Some of these agents stimulate both glucagon and insulin release, while others have more selective effects.

Physiologic Effects

In general, the actions of glucagon oppose those of insulin. Whereas insulin promotes energy storage by stimulating glycogenesis, lipogenesis, and protein synthesis, glucagon causes the rapid mobilization of potential energy sources into glucose by stimulating glycogenolysis and into fatty acids by stimulating lipolysis. Glucagon is also the most potent gluconeogenic hormone, and it is ketogenic.

The liver is the primary target of glucagon action. Glucagon binds to specific receptors in the hepatic cell plasma membrane, and this activates adenylate cyclase. The cAMP generated activates phosphorylase, which enhances the rate of glycogen degradation while inhibiting glycogen synthase and thus glycogen formation (see Chapter 36). There is hormone and tissue specificity in this effect, since glucagon has no effect on glycogenolysis in muscle, whereas epinephrine is active in both muscle and liver.

The elevated cAMP level stimulates the conversion of amino acids to glucose by inducing a number of enzymes involved in the gluconeogenic pathway. Principal among these is PEPCK. Glucagon, through cAMP, increases the rate of transcription of mRNA from the PEPCK gene, and this stimulates the synthesis of more PEPCK. This is the opposite of the effect of insulin, which decreases PEPCK gene transcription. Other examples are illustrated in Table 42–9. The net action of glucagon in the liver is increased glucose production; since much of this glucose exits the liver, the plasma glucose concentration increases in response to glucagon.

Glucagon is a potent lipolytic agent; it increases adipose cell cAMP levels, and this activates the

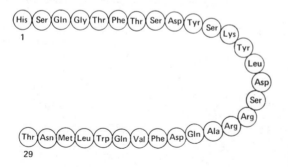

Figure 42–19. Amino acid sequence of glucagon. (Reproduced, with permission, from Katzung BG [editor]: *Basic & Clinical Pharmacology,* 2nd ed. Lange, 1984.)

Table 42–9. Enzymes induced or repressed by insulin or glucagon.*

Enzymes induced by a high insulin:glucagon ratio and repressed by a low insulin:glucagon ratio
  Glucokinase
  Citrate cleavage enzyme
  Acetyl-CoA carboxylase
  HMG-CoA reductase
  Pyruvate kinase
  6-Phosphofructo 1-kinase
  6-Phosphofructo 2-kinase/fructose 2,6-bisphosphatase
Enzymes induced by a low insulin:glucagon ratio and repressed by a high insulin:glucagon ratio
  Glucose 6-phosphatase
  Phosphoenolpyruvate carboxykinase (PEPCK)
  Fructose 1,6-bisphosphatase

*Slightly modified and reproduced, with permission, from Karam JH, Salber PR, Forsham PH: Pancreatic hormones and diabetes mellitus. In: *Basic & Clinical Endocrinology.* Greenspan FS, Forsham PH (editors). Lange, 1983.

hormone-sensitive lipase. The increased fatty acids can be metabolized for energy or converted to the ketone bodies acetoacetate and β-hydroxybutyrate. This is an important aspect of metabolism in the diabetic, since glucagon levels are always increased in insulin deficiency.

SOMATOSTATIN

Somatostatin, so-named because it was first isolated from the hypothalamus as the factor that inhibited growth hormone secretion, is a cyclic peptide secreted by and synthesized in the D cells of the pancreatic islets. The large somatostatin prohormone (MW ~11,500) is first processed into a 28-amino-acid peptide and finally into a molecule that has a molecular weight of 1640 and contains 14 amino acids (Fig 42–20). All forms have biologic activity.

In addition to its presence in the hypothalamus and pancreatic islets, somatostatin is found in many gastrointestinal tissues, where it is thought to regulate a variety of functions, and in multiple sites in the central nervous system, where it may be a neurotransmitter.

Virtually all of the agents listed in Tables 42–3 and 42–8 affect somatostatin release. Somatostatin, in turn, inhibits the release of the other islet cell hormones through a paracrine action (Fig 42–21).

In pharmacologic amounts, somatostatin significantly blunts the ketosis associated with acute insulin

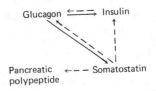

Figure 42–21. Effects of islet cell hormones on the secretion of other islet cell hormones. Solid arrows indicate stimulation; dashed arrows indicate inhibition. (Reproduced, with permission, from Ganong WF: *Review of Medical Physiology,* 12th ed. Lange, 1985.)

deficiency. This is apparently due to its ability to inhibit the glucagon release that accompanies insulinopenia. It also decreases the delivery of nutrients from the gastrointestinal tract into the circulation, because it (1) prolongs gastric emptying, (2) decreases gastrin secretion and therefore gastric acid production, (3) decreases pancreatic exocrine (digestive enzyme) secretion, (4) decreases splanchnic blood flow, and (5) slows sugar absorption. Little is known about the biochemical and molecular actions of this hormone.

PANCREATIC POLYPEPTIDE

Pancreatic polypeptide, a 36-amino-acid peptide (MW ~42,000), is a recently discovered product of the pancreatic F cells. Its secretion in humans is increased by a protein meal, fasting, exercise, and acute hypoglycemia and is decreased by somatostatin and intravenous glucose. The function of pancreatic polypeptide is unknown, but effects on hepatic glycogen levels and gastrointestinal secretion have been suggested.

GASTROINTESTINAL HORMONES

The gastrointestinal tract secretes many hormones, perhaps more than any other single organ. The purpose of the gastrointestinal tract is to propel foodstuffs to sites of digestion, to provide the proper milieu (enzymes, pH, salt, etc) for the digestive process, to move the digested products across the intestinal mucosa through the mucosal cells and into the extracellular space, and to move those products to

Figure 42–20. Amino acid sequence of somatostatin. (Reproduced, with permission from Karam JH, Salber PR, Forsham PH: Pancreatic hormones and diabetes mellitus. In: *Basic & Clinical Endocrinology.* Greenspan FS, Forsham PH [editors]. Lange, 1983.)

distant cells via the circulation. The gastrointestinal hormones assist in all of these functions.

Historical Perspective

The discipline of endocrinology began with the discovery of a gastrointestinal hormone. In 1902, Bayliss and Starling instilled hydrochloric acid into a denervated loop of a dog's jejunum and showed that this increased the secretion of fluid from the pancreas. Intravenous injection of HCl did not mimic this effect, but the intravenous injection of an extract of the jejunal mucosa did. These investigators postulated that "secretin," released from the mucosa of the upper intestine in response to a stimulus, moved to the pancreas through the circulation, where it exerted its effect. Bayliss and Starling were the first to use the word "hormone," and secretin was the first hormone whose function was identified.

Although the activity of secretin was identified in 1902, it took 60 years before its chemical identity was proved. In the meantime, many "younger" hormones were discovered, sequenced, and synthesized, often in

a matter of a few years (eg, calcitonin; see Chapter 39). The reasons for this 60-year time span are now apparent; families of closely related gastrointestinal peptides have overlapping chemical structures and biologic functions, and most of these peptides exist in multiple forms. Isolation techniques developed only recently are able to differentiate among them.

Features of the Gastrointestinal Hormones

More than a dozen peptides with unique actions have been isolated from gastrointestinal tissues (Table 42–10). These peptides of the gastrointestinal hormone system differ in many respects from those of more typical hormone systems, and some of these differences are discussed below.

A. Diversity of Actions: Many of the gastrointestinal peptides fit the classic definition of a hormone, as discussed in Chapter 35. Examples include gastrin, secretin, gastric inhibitory polypeptide (GIP), and possibly cholecystokinin (CCK), motilin, pancreatic polypeptide (PP), and enteroglucagon (Table 42–10). Other gastrointestinal peptides are thought to have **paracrine** actions (see Chapter 35) or to act in a **neurocrine** fashion (as local neurotransmitters or neuromodulators). This is based on the observation that although these substances are found in high concentration in neurons or in various cells in the gastrointestinal tract, they either are not found in the circulation under normal conditions or have such short plasma half-lives that they would not be effective. Peptides

Table 42–10. Gastrointestinal hormones.*

	Mechanism of Action†			Major Action
	E	N	P	
Gastrin	+	(+)	−	Gastric acid and pepsin secretion.
Cholecystokinin (CCK)	(+)	(+)	−	Pancreatic amylase secretion.
Secretin	+	−	−	Pancreatic bicarbonate secretion.
Gastric inhibitory polypeptide (GIP)	+	−	−	Enhances glucose-mediated insulin release. Inhibits gastric acid secretion.
Vasoactive intestinal polypeptide (VIP)	−	+	(−)	Smooth muscle relaxation. Stimulates pancreatic bicarbonate secretion.
Motilin	(+)	−	−	Initiates interdigestive intestinal motility.
Somatostatin	−	+	(+)	Numerous inhibitory effects.
Pancreatic polypeptide (PP)	(+)	−	(+)	Inhibits pancreatic bicarbonate and protein secretion.
Enkephalins	−	+	(+)	Opiatelike actions.
Substance P	−	+	(+)	Physiologic actions uncertain.
Bombesinlike immunoreactivity (BLI)	−	+	(+)	Stimulates release of gastrin and CCK.
Neurotensin	−	+	(+)	Physiologic actions unknown.
Enteroglucagon	(+)	(+)	(+)	Physiologic actions unknown.

*Slightly modified and reproduced, with permission, from Deveney CS, Way LW: Regulatory peptides of the gut. In: *Basic & Clinical Endocrinology.* Greenspan FS, Forsham PH (editors). Lange, 1983.
†E, endocrine; N, neurocrine; P, paracrine; ( ), suggested but not proved; +, yes; −, no.

Table 42–11. Distribution of gastrointestinal hormones.*

	Endocrine Cell†	Localization	Localized in Gut Nerves
Gastrin	G	Gastric antrum, duodenum	(?)
CCK	I	Duodenum, jejunum	Yes
Secretin	S	Duodenum, jejunum	No
GIP	K	Small bowel	No
VIP	D_1	Pancreas	Yes
Motilin	EC_2	Small bowel	No
Substance P	EC_1	Entire gastrointestinal tract	Yes
Neurotensin	N	Ileum	(?)
Somatostatin	D	Stomach, duodenum, pancreas	Yes
Enkephalins	...	Stomach, duodenum, gallbladder	Yes
BLI	P	Stomach, duodenum	Yes
PP	D_2F	Pancreas	No
Enteroglucagon	A	Pancreas	No
	L	Small intestine	

*Slightly modified and reproduced, with permission, from Deveney CS, Way LW: Regulatory peptides of the gut. In: *Basic & Clinical Endocrinology.* Greenspan FS, Forsham PH (editors). Lange, 1983.
†Endocrine cells identified with a specific hormone are identified by a letter. EC, enterochromaffin cell. Note that several peptides are found both in nerves and in endocrine cells. VIP has been found only in nerves. The cells containing enkephalins have yet to be named.

with neurocrine action include vasoactive intestinal peptide (VIP), somatostatin, substance P, the enkephalins, bombesinlike peptides, and neurotensin (Table 42–10). Many of these substances are thought to have paracrine actions in vivo because they affect various cells when added to tissue or organ cultures.

B. Location of Gastrointestinal Peptide-Producing Cells: A unique aspect of the gastrointestinal endocrine system is that the cells are scattered throughout the gastrointestinal tract rather than collected in discrete organs as in more typical endocrine glands. The distribution of the gastrointestinal hormones is outlined in Table 42–11, which also includes the cellular nomenclature.

Since many of the gastrointestinal peptides are found in the nerves in gastrointestinal tissues, it is not surprising that most of them are also present in the central nervous system (Table 42–12). Synthesis of the peptides by central nervous system tissue has often been difficult to prove, but new techniques of molecular biology should establish whether genes coding for these substances are active. The function of these peptides in the central and peripheral nervous systems is under investigation.

C. Precursors and Multiple Forms: Of the major gastrointestinal hormones, only secretin exists in a single form (Table 42–13). The presence of multiple forms of gastrointestinal peptides in gastrointestinal tissues and in the circulation impeded the definition of the number and nature of these molecules. The concept of precursor molecules helped clarify this issue; much of tissue heterogeneity is due to this feature. Other help came from the construction of synthetic molecules that could be prepared free of contaminating peptides and then used to define the function of specific peptides.

D. Overlapping Structure and Function of Gastrointestinal Peptides: The amino acid sequences of gastrointestinal peptides have been determined

Table 42–13. Multiple forms of gastrointestinal hormones.

Hormone	In Tissue	In Plasma
Secretin	27 Amino acids (S27)	S27
Gastrin	Large precursor	
	34 Amino acids (G34)	G34
	17 Amino acids (G17)	G17
	14 Amino acids (G14)	G14
Cholecystokinin	Large precursor	
	39 Amino acids (CCK39)	
	33 Amino acids (CCK33)	
	12 Amino acids (CCK12)	CCK12
	8 Amino acids (CCK8)	CCK8
	4 Amino acids (CCK4)	
GIP	Large precursor	Large form
	43 Amino acids (GIP43)	GIP43
Somatostatin	11,500-MW prohormone	
	28 Amino acids	
	14 Amino acids	

(Table 42–14). Many of these hormones can be placed in one of 2 families based on sequence and functional similarity. These are the **gastrin family,** which consists of gastrin and CCK, and the **secretin family,** which includes secretin, glucagon, GIP, VIP, and glicentin (which has glucagonlike immunoreactivity but is a distinct peptide). The neurocrine peptides neurotensin, bombesinlike peptides, substance P, and somatostatin bear no structural similarity to any other gastrointestinal peptide. A final general characteristic of this last group of molecules is that they have very short plasma half-lives and may play no physiologic role in plasma.

E. Mechanism of Action: Studies of the mechanism of action of the gastrointestinal peptide hormones have lagged behind those of other hormones, no doubt because most attention to date has been directed toward cataloging the various molecules and establishing their physiologic action. A notable exception to this statement involves the regulation of secretion of enzymes by the pancreatic acinar cell.

Six different classes of receptors on pancreatic acinar cells have been identified (Fig 42–22). These are for (1) muscarinic cholinergic agents, (2) the gastrin-CCK family, (3) bombesin and related peptides, (4) the physalaemin–substance P family, (5) secretin and VIP, and (6) cholera toxin.

Fig 42–22 illustrates that these peptide-receptor complexes activate 2 distinct intracellular mechanisms. One involves the mobilization of intracellular calcium stores, and the other involves the activation of adenylate cyclase and the generation of cAMP. These mechanisms do not cross over; ie, gastrin does not alter cAMP levels, nor does secretin affect the intracellular Ca^{2+} level. The 2 systems converge at some point, however, since combinations of secretagogues that act by these different mechanisms have a synergistic effect on enzyme secretion.

The peptides that cause Ca^{2+} mobilization in the pancreatic acinar cells also affect the metabolism of phosphatidylinositol and enhance its conversion to

Table 42–12. Peptides found in gut and central nervous system.*

Isolated from both brain and gut
    Substance P
    Neurotensin
    Secretin
    Somatostatin
    CCK
Isolated from either brain or gut: immunoreactivity
    found in the other organ
    VIP
    PP and motilin
    Enkephalins and endorphins
    BLI
    Insulin
    Glucagon

---

*Slightly modified and reproduced, with permission, from Deveney CS, Way LW: Regulatory peptides of the gut. In: *Basic & Clinical Endocrinology.* Greenspan FS, Forsham PH (editors). Lange, 1983.

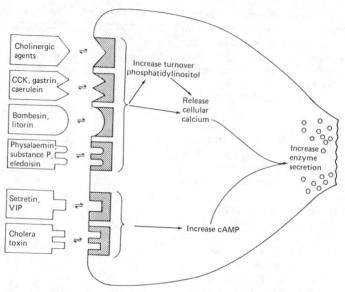

Figure 42–22. Mechanism of action of secretagogues on enzyme secretion from pancreatic acinar cells. There are 4 classes of receptors for secretagogues that can cause mobilization of cellular calcium and 2 classes of receptors for secretagogues that can cause activation of adenylate cyclase and increase cellular generation of cAMP. The interaction of these 2 pathways is described in the text. (Slightly modified and reproduced, with permission, from Gardner JD, Jensen RT: Gastrointestinal peptides: The basis of action at the cellular level. *Recent Prog Horm Res* 1983;**39**:211.)

diacylglycerol and various inositol phosphates. These changes precede those of Ca^{2+} mobilization and thus may be involved in the primary response. These effects are associated with depolarization of the acinar cell, which may be involved in amylase secretion. The molecular basis of the cAMP-mediated secretion has not been elucidated. The convergence of the actions of cAMP and Ca^{2+} and phospholipids on amylase secretion is similar in many respects to that of others discussed in Chapter 36.

THE SECRETIN FAMILY

Secretin

Secretin, a 27-amino-acid peptide synthesized and released by the S cells in the duodenum and proximal jejunum in response to duodenal acidification, contains 4 arginine residues and one histidine and is basic. Its structure is identical to that of glucagon in 14 of 27 amino acids and quite similar to the structures of GIP and VIP (Table 42–14). The entire 27-amino-acid structure is required for stimulation of bicarbonate and water secretion from the pancreas.

Gastric Inhibitory Polypeptide

Gastric inhibitory polypeptide (GIP) is a 43-amino-acid peptide released from the duodenal and jejunal mucosa in response to glucose. Although GIP inhibits gastric motility and secretion, its major action appears to be the stimulation of insulin release. GIP is probably the physiologic B cell–stimulating hormone of the gastrointestinal tract. This action requires concomitant hyperglycemia.

Vasoactive Intestinal Polypeptide

Vasoactive intestinal polypeptide (VIP) is a basic 28-amino-acid peptide whose physiologic role has not been defined. It is present in the nerves of the submucosal plexus, the myenteric plexus, and blood vessels; it may be involved in gut motility, sphincter relaxation, and blood flow. At high concentration, VIP stimulates secretion by the pancreas and small intestine. Tumors that produce this peptide, **VIPomas,** cause a syndrome of watery diarrhea, hypokalemia, and achlorhydria.

Glucagon

Glucagon is the final member of this family; its chemical nature and actions were discussed above. It is made by gastric and duodenal A cells as well as by pancreatic A cells.

THE GASTRIN-CHOLECYSTOKININ FAMILY

Gastrin is produced by G cells located in the antral gastric mucosa and to a lesser extent in the duodenal mucosa. Gastrin exhibits more heterogeneity in size (number of forms) than any other gastrointestinal hormone (Table 42–13); in addition, each of these forms of gastrin has a sulfated and nonsulfated form (at the single Tyr residue; see explanatory note in Table 42–14). The carboxy-terminal 14 amino acids of G34, G17, and G14 are identical. G34 is more abundant in the circulation than G17, probably because its plasma half-life (15 minutes) is 5–7 times that of G17. The latter is thought to be the main stimulus for gastric acid

Table 42–14. Amino acid sequences of gastrointestinal peptides.*†

1 CCK	2 Gastrin	3 GIP	4 Glucagon	5 Secretin	6 VIP	7 Motilin	8 Substance P	9 Bombesin	10 Somatostatin
Tyr		Tyr	His	-	-	Phe	Arg	(pyro)Glu	Ala
Ile		Ala	Ser	-	-	Val	Pro	Gln	Gly
Gln		Glu	Gln	Asp	-	Pro	Lys	Arg	Cys
Gln		Gly	-	-	Ala	Ile	Pro	Leu	Lys
Ala		Thr	-	-	Val	Phe	Gln	Gly	Asn
Arg	(pyro)Glu	Phe	-	-	-	Thr	Gln	Asn	Phe
→Lys	Leu	Ile	Thr	-	-	Tyr	Phe	Gln	Phe
Ala	Gly	Ser	-	-	Asp	Gly	Phe	Trp	-
Pro	-	Asp	-	Glu	Asn	Glu	Gly	Ala	Lys
Ser	Gln	Tyr	-	Leu	Tyr	Leu	-	Val	Thr
Gly	-	Ser	-	-	Thr	Gln	Met-NH₂	Gly	Phe
Arg	His	Ile	Lys	Arg	-	-		His	Thr
Val	Pro	Ala	Tyr	Leu	-	Met		Leu	Ser
Ser	-	Met	Leu	Arg	-	Gln		Met-NH₂	Cys
Met	Leu	Asp	-	-	Lys	Glu			
Ile	Val	Lys	Ser	-	Gln	Lys			
Lys	Ala	Ile	Arg	Ala	Met	Glu			
Asn	Asp	Arg	-	-	Ala	Arg			
Leu	Pro	Gln	Ala	Leu	Val	Asn			
Gln	Ser	Gln	-	-	Lys	-			
Ser	Lys	Asp	-	Arg	Lys	Gly			
Leu	→Lys	Phe	-	Leu	Tyr	Gln			
Asp	Gln	Val	-	Leu	-				
Pro	Gly	Asn	Gln	-	Asn				
Ser	Pro	Trp	-	Gly	Ser				
His	→Trp	Leu	-	-	Ile				
→Arg	Leu	-	Met	Val-NH₂	Leu				
→Ile	Glu	Ala	Asp		Asn-NH₂				
Ser	Glu	Gln	Thr						
Asp	Glu	Gln							
→Arg	Glu	Gln							
Asp	Glu	Lys							
Tys	Ala	Gly							
Met	Tys	Lys							
→Gly	→	Lys							
→Trp	-	Ser							
Met		Asp							
Asp		Trp							
Phe-NH₂		Lys							
		His							
		Asn							
		Ile							
		Thr							
		Gln							

*Slightly modified and reproduced, with permission, from Grossman MI: The gastrointestinal hormones: An overview. In: *Endocrinology.* James VHT (editor). Excerpta Medica, 1977.

†Tys, tyrosine sulfate; -, same as preceding column; →, point of cleavage to form a smaller variant.

secretion, which is under negative feedback control, since acidification of the antral region of the stomach decreases gastrin release. Gastrin also stimulates pepsin secretion and results in hypertrophy of the gastric mucosa. The carboxyl end of gastrin is responsible for biologic activity; the carboxy-terminal pentapeptide has the full range of physiologic action of G17 but is one-tenth as potent on a weight basis.

The homology between gastrin and cholecystokinin (CCK) is particularly prominent in the C-terminal region, since the last 5 amino acids in these molecules are identical (Table 42–14). Both have a sulfated tyrosine residue, but this residue is not essential for gastrin activity (stimulation of gastric acid and pepsin secretion), whereas a 7-amino-acid C-terminal fragment with a sulfated tyrosine is required for maximal CCK activity (stimulation of pancreatic enzyme secretion and contraction of the gallbladder). This subtle change makes a large physiologic difference.

Gastrin-secreting tumors, **gastrinomas,** cause excessive gastric acid production and intractable peptic ulcer disease. The C-terminal pentapeptide, **pentagastrin,** causes calcitonin release and is used as a provocative test in the diagnosis of medullary thyroid cancer.

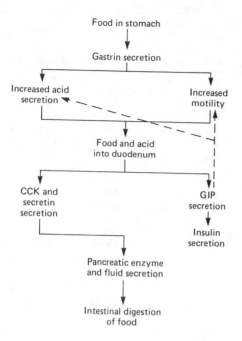

Figure 42–23. Integrated action of gastrointestinal hormones in regulating digestion and utilization of absorbed nutrients. Dashed arrows indicate inhibition. (Reproduced, with permission, from Ganong WF: *Review of Medical Physiology,* 12th ed. Lange, 1985.)

CCK exists in at least 5 molecular forms (Table 42–13), of which CCK8 appears to be the most abundant and potent form in the circulation. CCK is made in I cells in the mucosa of the duodenum and proximal jejunum and is released in response to peptides, amino acids, long-chain fatty acids, calcium, and acid. Its physiologic actions are to cause gallbladder contraction and to stimulate pancreatic enzyme secretion. Like all gastrointestinal peptides, it has numerous secondary actions, an intriguing one of which is to cause satiety (CCK8 is the form found in the brain).

Fig 42–23 illustrates how the integrated actions of gastrin, CCK, secretin, GIP, and insulin regulate digestion and utilization of foodstuffs.

OTHER GASTROINTESTINAL PEPTIDES

Several other peptides have been isolated from the gastrointestinal tract and appear to be involved in the regulation of digestion—probably by paracrine or neurocrine mechanisms, since appreciable concentrations are not found in the circulation. It should be emphasized that no certain physiologic role has been assigned to any of these molecules.

Substance P was the first peptide found in both the gut and the brain. The 5 carboxy-terminal amino acids of this 11-amino-acid peptide are required for its action, which appears to be stimulation of smooth muscle contraction in the intestine. **Bombesin** is found in frog skin, but a similar peptide, often called **gastrin-releasing peptide (GRP),** has been isolated from endocrine cells in the gut, gut neurons, and brain. The amino acids at positions 5–14 of bombesin are identical to those at positions 18–27 of gastrin-releasing peptide except at one residue. Bombesin stimulates gastric and pancreatic secretion and increases motility of the gallbladder and intestine. **Motilin,** a 22-amino-acid peptide, is made in the intestinal mucosa. It stimulates acid and pepsin secretion by gastric mucosa and is a stimulator of intestinal smooth muscle contraction. **Somatostatin** is produced in gastric D cells and inhibits (by paracrine action) the release of gastrin, secretin, CCK, motilin, and GIP. **Glucagon** is made in the gastric mucosa A cells and is thought to contribute to the metabolic action of pancreatic glucagon. Other peptides with glucagonlike immunoreactivity (GLI) have been isolated from the L cells of the ileum and colon. The major component of GLI is a large 100-amino-acid peptide called **glicentin,** which contains the exact sequence of pancreatic glucagon. Glicentin may mimic the actions of glucagon.

Neurotensin (a 13-amino-acid peptide), **Met-** and **Leu-enkephalins,** and **serotonin** are found in intestinal cells and may be active in these tissues. Some 40 peptides have been found in neural tissues, and it is likely that more gastrointestinal peptides will be discovered.

•   •   •

References

Pancreatic Hormones

Chance RE, Ellis RM, Bromer WW: Porcine proinsulin: Characterization and amino acid sequence. *Science* 1968; **161:**165.

Cohen P: The role of protein phosphorylation in neural and hormonal control of cellular activity. *Nature* 1982;**296:** 613.

Czech MP: Molecular basis of insulin action. *Annu Rev Biochem* 1977;**46:**359.

Docherty K, Steiner DF: Post-translational proteolysis in polypeptide hormone biosynthesis. *Annu Rev Physiol* 1982;**44:**625.

Gerich JE: Somatostatin: Another islet hormone. *Adv Exp Med Biol* 1979;**124:**63.

Granner DK, Andreone T: Insulin modulation of gene expression. In: *Diabetes and Metabolism Reviews.* Vol 1. DeFronzo R (editor). Wiley, 1985.

Hedeskov CJ: Mechanism of glucose-induced insulin secretion. *Physiol Rev* 1980;**60:**442.

Kahn CR: Current concepts of the molecular mechanism of insulin action. *Annu Rev Med* 1985. [In press.]

Kono T: Action of insulin on glucose transport and cAMP phosphodiesterase in fat cells: Involvement of two distinct molecular mechanisms. *Recent Prog Horm Res* 1983; **30:**519.

Owerbach D et al: The insulin gene is located on chromosome 11 in humans. *Nature* 1980;**286:**82.

Steiner DF, Tager HS: Biosynthesis of insulin and glucagon.

In: *Endocrinology.* Vol 2. DeGroot LJ (editor). Grune & Stratton, 1979.

Straus DS: Growth-stimulatory actions of insulin in vitro and in vivo. *Endocr Rev* 1984;**5:**356.

Tager HS: Abnormal products of the human insulin gene. *Diabetes* 1984;**33:**693.

Unger RH, Dobbs RE: Insulin, glucagon, and somatostatin: Secretion in the regulation of metabolism. *Annu Rev Physiol* 1978;**40:**307.

Unger RH, Orci L: Glucagon and the A cell. (2 parts.) *N Engl J Med* 1981;**304:**1518, 1575.

Gastrointestinal Hormones

Bloom SR, Polak JM: *Gut Hormones,* 2nd ed. Churchill Livingstone, 1981.

Boden G: Gastrointestinal hormones. Pages 1175–1190 in: *Endocrinology and Metabolism.* Felig P et al (editors). McGraw-Hill, 1981.

Buchanan KD: Gastrointestinal hormones: General concepts. *Clin Endocrinol Metab* 1979;**8:**249.

Chen WY, Gutierrez JG: The endocrine control of gastrointestinal function. *Adv Intern Med* 1978;**23:**61.

Gardner JD, Jensen RT: Gastrointestinal peptides: The basis of action at the cellular level. *Recent Prog Horm Res* 1983; **39:**211.

Walsh JH: Gastrointestinal hormones and peptides. In: *Physiology of the Gastrointestinal Tract.* Johnson LR (editor). Raven Press, 1981.

43 | The Chemistry of Respiration

David W. Martin, Jr., MD

The term respiration is here applied to the interchange of 2 gases, oxygen and carbon dioxide (CO_2), between the body and its environment. Respiration may be divided into 4 major processes: (1) pulmonary ventilation, ie, the inflow and outflow of air between the atmosphere and the alveoli; (2) the diffusion of oxygen and CO_2 between the alveoli and the blood; (3) the transport of oxygen and CO_2 to and from the cells of the organism via the blood; and (4) the regulation of ventilation.

The process of pulmonary ventilation per se will not be discussed in this text, although it is necessary to note that during the introduction of atmospheric air into the alveoli of the lungs, the air is warmed to body temperature and maximally humidified.

CHEMICAL & PHYSIOLOGIC EVENTS AFFECTING DIFFUSION OF OXYGEN & CARBON DIOXIDE

To understand the processes of gas diffusion and gas transport, it is necessary to comprehend the **physics of ideal gases.** If the temperature and mass (molar quantity) of a gas in a chamber remain constant but the volume of the chamber is increased or decreased, the pressure of the gas within that chamber will vary inversely with the volume, ie,

$$Pressure = Constant \div Volume$$
$$(or, rearranged)$$
$$Pressure \times Volume = Constant$$

at a fixed mass and temperature of an ideal gas.

For example, at 0 °C and 1 atm of pressure (760 mm Hg), one gram-mole of gas occupies 22.4 L; if the volume of the gas is reduced by one-half, ie, 11.2 L, then the pressure would increase to 2 atm, or 1520 mm Hg. Conversely, if the volume of the gas is expanded to 44.8 L, the pressure would be reduced to 0.5 atm, or 380 mm Hg. This relationship is known as **Boyle's law.**

Given a fixed mass of gas at a constant pressure, when the temperature changes, the volume of the gas also changes proportionately to the increase or decrease in temperature (expressed in absolute or Kelvin [K] degrees of temperature):

$$Volume = Constant \times Temperature (°K)$$

As an example, 1 gram-mole of an ideal gas at 273 °K (0 °C) occupies a volume of 22.4 L; if the temperature of the gas is increased to 310 °K (37 °C), it would occupy a volume of 25.4 L. This relationship is referred to as **Gay-Lussac's law.**

The combination of Gay-Lussac's law and Boyle's law generates the relationship

$$PV = nRT$$

where P = pressure,
V = volume,
n = the mass quantity of the gas,
R is a constant, and
T = temperature in absolute or Kelvin degrees.

The above expression is called the **ideal gas law.** When P is expressed in mm Hg, V in liters, n in gram-moles, and T in absolute degrees, the value of the **gas constant** = 62.36.

On a clear, cool day, atmospheric air contains 78.62% nitrogen, 20.84% oxygen, 0.04% carbon dioxide, and 0.5% water. In a mixture of gases in air, each gas exerts its own partial pressure. For example, the partial pressure of oxygen at sea level would be 20.84% of the total pressure of 760 mm Hg, or 159 mm Hg. However, when atmospheric air is inhaled, by the time it has reached the alveoli it has been saturated with water in the gas phase. Since the water vapor has mass, it occupies space, and yet the pressure in the lungs at the end of inspiration will not exceed that of the atmosphere (760 mm Hg). It follows that the partial pressures of the other components of the inspired air must be appropriately reduced. **At 37 °C, the water vapor pressure is 47 mm Hg,** an important number to remember. Therefore, the sum of the partial pressures of the other components of air must contribute 760 – 47, or 713 mm Hg. In Table 43–1 are shown the partial pressures of the respiratory gases in atmospheric air and in humidified air at 37 °C.

At a liquid-gas interface, the number of mole-

Table 43—1. Partial pressures of respiratory gases in air. (Values in parentheses are percentage concentrations.)

| | mm Hg (%) | | | | |
	N$_2$	O$_2$	CO$_2$	H$_2$O	Total
Atmospheric air	597.0 (78.62)	159.0 (20.84)	0.3 (0.04)	3.7 (0.50)	760.0 (100)
Humidified air	563.4 (74.09)	149.3 (19.67)	0.3 (0.04)	47.0 (6.2)	760.0 (100)
Alveolar air	569.0 (74.9)	104.0 (13.6)	40.0 (5.3)	47.0 (6.2)	760.0 (100)
Expired air	566.0 (74.5)	120.0 (15.7)	27.0 (3.6)	47.0 (6.2)	760.0 (100)

cules of gas entering the liquid phase will eventually equal the number of dissolved gas molecules leaving the liquid phase and entering the gaseous phase, a condition referred to as a **steady-state equilibrium.** At equilibrium, the quantity of gas dissolved in a liquid phase will be determined by 2 factors: (1) the partial pressure of the gas surrounding the water, and (2) the solubility of the gas in the liquid at the given temperature. More specifically, **at equilibrium, the volume of dissolved gas equals the product of the partial pressure of that gas and its solubility coefficient (α) in that particular liquid.** The solubilities of the respiratory gases in water at 37 °C and 1 atm of pressure are shown in Table 43–2.

Table 43—2. Solubility coefficients (α values) of respiratory gases in water at 37 °C and 1 atm of pressure.

Oxygen	0.024
Carbon dioxide	0.57
Carbon monoxide	0.018
Nitrogen	0.012
Helium	0.008

At equilibrium, the force exerted by the gas attempting to enter the liquid will equal the force exerted by the same gas attempting to leave the liquid. The **pressure exerted by the gas attempting to escape from the liquid is referred to as its tension.** This is expressed as P_{O_2}, P_{CO_2}, P_{N_2}, etc. Thus, it can be said that at equilibrium, **the partial pressure of a gas equals the tension** of that gas in the liquid. It should be evident that a gas which is highly soluble in a given liquid will be present at much higher **concentrations** in the liquid before it would exert a **tension** equal to its partial pressure in the gas phase. As is true for any solute dissolved in a liquid, the ability of each gas to dissolve in a liquid is independent of the presence of any other gas. As an important example, the quantity of CO_2 dissolved in a body fluid does not significantly affect the quantity of oxygen that can be dissolved in the same fluid (in the absence of any competition for a common carrier molecule such as hemoglobin).

When a gas is introduced into a chamber containing a liquid such as water, the gas molecules will collide with the liquid phase in an attempt to enter and to establish a condition of equilibrium such that the tension of the gas within the liquid will be equal to its partial pressure in the gaseous phase. The collision and

entrance of the gas molecules into the liquid occur by a process known as **diffusion.**

The rate at which the diffusion process occurs will be influenced by several factors in addition to the difference between the partial pressure of the gas above the liquid and its tension within it. The greater the cross-sectional **area** of the gas-liquid interphase, the greater will be the diffusion rate. The greater **distance** the molecules must diffuse, the longer it will take to achieve equilibrium. The greater the **solubility** of the gas in the liquid, the greater will be the number of molecules available for diffusion at any given pressure difference. Finally, the greater the velocity or **kinetic movement** of the molecules (a property that is dependent upon the molecular weight of the gas and its temperature), the greater will be the rate of diffusion.

All of the above factors influencing the diffusion rate (DR) can be expressed in a single equation:

$$DR \propto \frac{PD \times A \times S}{D \sqrt{MW}}$$

where PD = the pressure difference of the gas between the 2 phases,

A = the cross-sectional area of the interfaces,

S = the solubility of the gas in a particular liquid,

D = the distance through which the gas must diffuse, and

MW = the molecular weight of the gas.

It will be noted that the diffusion rate for any given **gas** in a given liquid will be proportionate to $S \div \sqrt{MW}$, a property that is termed its **diffusion coefficient.** Relative to oxygen, the diffusion coefficients for other respiratory gases in the aqueous body fluids are as follows:

Carbon dioxide, 20.3

Carbon monoxide, 0.81

Nitrogen, 0.53

These gases of respiratory importance are highly soluble in lipids and thus also highly soluble in cell membranes. Therefore, the major control on the movement of gases in body tissues is the rate at which gases can diffuse through the tissue fluids, which for practical purposes can be considered as water.

As shown in Table 43–1, the partial pressures and percentage concentrations of the respiratory gases are different in alveolar air than in humidified air. These differences are due to the following factors:

(1) The constant absorption of oxygen from the alveolar air.

(2) The constant diffusion of CO_2 from the pulmonary blood into the alveoli.

(3) The relatively slow replacement of alveolar air during normal ventilation.

In the total of both lungs of a normal human, there are approximately 300 million alveoli where gas exchange occurs. Each alveolus has extremely thin alveolar walls in a near-solid network of interconnecting capillaries such that the alveolar gases are in extraordinarily close proximity to the blood in the pulmonary capillaries. The **total surface area** of the functional respiratory membranes approximates 70 m², an area equivalent to a flat surface 10 m long by 7 m wide. The amount of blood present in the capillaries of the lungs at any given moment is approximately 100 mL, an amount that is effectively spread over the entire 70 m² surface area. As described above for the diffusion of a gas into water in a chamber, the diffusion of the respiratory gases into the blood in the pulmonary capillaries will be dependent upon (1) the functional alveolar surface area and (2) the distance through which the gases must diffuse, the so-called **respiratory membrane.** Obviously, pathologic states that decrease the effective surface area for gas exchange (such as emphysema) or thicken the effective functional respiratory membrane (such as increased interstitial fluid) will severely impair gas exchange and thus the process of respiration.

The overall ability of the total respiratory membrane to bring about the exchange of gases between the alveoli and pulmonary blood can be expressed as the **diffusing capacity,** ie, the volume of a gas that diffuses through the respiratory membrane in 1 minute at a pressure difference of 1 mm Hg. The diffusing capacity for oxygen is approximately 21 mL/min in an average young adult male under resting conditions. The normal difference in mean oxygen pressure across the respiratory membrane is approximately 11 mm Hg. Thus, the oxygen diffusing through the respiratory membrane each minute would equal 11 × 21, or 231 mL of oxygen. Importantly, during strenuous exercise, the diffusing capacity for oxygen can increase to a maximum of about 65 mL/min in young male adults. This 3-fold increase in diffusing capacity is due to an increased surface area of the blood perfusing the lungs as a result of the opening of previously dormant capillaries and dilatation of previously patent capillaries. In addition, the stretching of the alveolar membranes increases their surface area and decreases thickness.

As described above, the diffusion coefficient of CO_2 in water is 20 times higher than that of oxygen. In fact, the diffusing capacity of CO_2 is so great that it is immeasurable. This high diffusing capacity of CO_2 allows for virtually instantaneous equilibration of the pulmonary blood P_{CO_2} with the alveolar CO_2. Thus, the difference between plasma and alveolar CO_2 is normally less than 1 mm Hg. The diffusing capacity for CO_2 can be reduced to a degree where it causes significant clinical symptoms only when lung damage

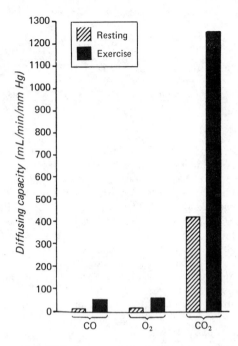

Figure 43–1. Diffusing capacities of carbon monoxide, oxygen, and carbon dioxide in the normal lungs. (Redrawn and reproduced, with permission, from Guyton AC: *Textbook of Medical Physiology,* 5th ed. Saunders, 1976.)

is so severe that it would ordinarily lead to death. This may occur when a patient's life is being maintained by intensive oxygen therapy necessary to overcome an equally severe, although more significant, reduction in oxygen-diffusing capacity.

In Fig 43–1 are depicted the diffusing capacities of carbon monoxide, oxygen, and CO_2 in normal lungs at rest and during exercise.

Exchange of Oxygen & CO_2 During Respiration

As can be seen in Table 43–3, the P_{O_2} of the blood as it enters the pulmonary capillary is 40 mm Hg, whereas the P_{O_2} in the alveolus is 104 mm Hg. Because of the large surface area of the respiratory membrane and the fact that the membrane is extremely thin, the uptake of oxygen from the alveolus into the pulmonary capillary blood occurs so rapidly that the P_{O_2} values are equal in the pulmonary capillary and alveolus even before the blood has reached the midpoint of the capillary (Fig 43–2). The time-integrated aver-

Table 43–3. Partial pressures and tensions (in mm Hg) of oxygen, CO_2, and water in the pulmonary system.

	Pulmonary Artery	Alveolus	Pulmonary Vein
Oxygen	40	104	104
Carbon dioxide	45	40	40
Water	47	47	47

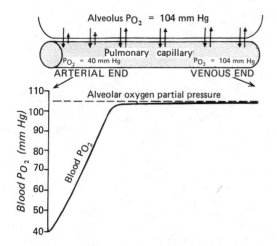

Figure 43–2. Uptake of oxygen by the pulmonary capillary blood. (The curve in this figure was constructed from data in Milhorn HT Jr, Pulley PE Jr: Theoretical study of pulmonary capillary gas exchange and venous admixture. *Biophys J* 1968;**8**:337.) (Reproduced, with permission, from Guyton AC: *Textbook of Medical Physiology,* 5th ed. Saunders, 1976.)

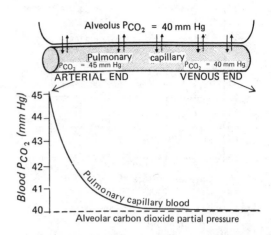

Figure 43–3. Diffusion of carbon dioxide from the pulmonary blood into the alveolus. (This curve was constructed from data in Milhorn HT Jr, Pulley PE Jr: Theoretical study of pulmonary capillary gas exchange and venous admixture. *Biophys J* 1968;**8**:337.) (Reproduced, with permission, from Guyton AC: *Textbook of Medical Physiology,* 5th ed. Saunders, 1976.)

age pressure difference during normal respiration is about 11 mm Hg. During exercise, the increased cardiac output greatly reduces the time blood remains in the pulmonary capillary bed. However, this reserve transit distance within the capillary bed still permits almost complete saturation of the blood with oxygen by the time it leaves the pulmonary capillaries. In addition, as shown in Fig 43–1, the diffusing capacity for oxygen increases with exercise, providing a further safety margin to allow the rapid diffusion of oxygen through the respiratory membrane.

In the periphery, as the oxygenated blood passes through the tissue capillaries, the process occurs in reverse. The high P_{O_2} in arterial blood (about 95 mm Hg) diffuses by this gradient into the interstitial fluids, where the P_{O_2} averages about 40 mm Hg. By the time the blood has passed the tissue capillaries, its P_{O_2} has approached the 40 mm Hg oxygen tension of the interstitial fluid.

Arterial blood entering the tissue capillaries contains CO_2 at a tension of 40 mm Hg. Because of the high diffusion coefficient for CO_2, the relatively low gradient of CO_2 tension between interstitial fluid and the capillary blood is still sufficient to assure rapid equilibration of the P_{CO_2}. As a result, the P_{CO_2} of the venous blood is about 45 mm Hg.

As the blood arrives in the pulmonary capillaries, the P_{CO_2} is approximately 45 mm Hg (Table 43–3), whereas the P_{CO_2} in the alveolar air is 40 mm Hg. Thus, the gradient of P_{CO_2} is far less than that of oxygen between the alveolar gas and pulmonary artery (also, of course, it is in the opposite direction). Again, because the diffusion coefficient of CO_2 is 20-fold greater than that of oxygen, the CO_2 in the blood is rapidly equilibrated with that in the alveoli; furthermore, it occurs during less than the first half of

the transit time of the blood through the pulmonary capillary (Fig 43–3).

TRANSPORT OF OXYGEN IN BLOOD

From the partial pressures of the respiratory gases shown in Table 43–3 and their solubilities as shown in Table 43–2, the expected content of these dissolved gases in blood can be calculated. A comparison of this **calculated** content with the **actual** content (Table 43–4) reveals that there is a marked difference. Thus, it should be evident that substantial quantities of oxygen as well as CO_2 are carried in the blood in other than simple solution.

Hemoglobin is the principal molecule responsible for transport in the blood of both oxygen and CO_2 (see Chapter 5). It is the hemoglobin contained within the erythrocytes that accounts for all of the "extra" oxygen content of the blood and a significant portion of the "extra" CO_2.

Normally, about 97–98% of the oxygen transported from the lungs to the tissues is carried in reversible combination with the hemoglobin molecule. This may be represented in simplistic terms by the equation

$$Hb + O_2 \rightleftarrows HbO_2$$

where Hb = deoxygenated hemoglobin and
HbO_2 = oxyhemoglobin.

The combination of hemoglobin and oxygen is not that of a compound or of a chemical combination such as an oxide. The nature of the oxygen-hemoglobin affinity was, in fact, not understood until the

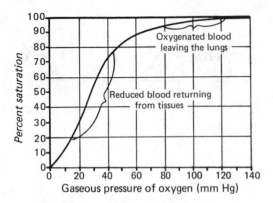

Figure 43–4. The oxygen-hemoglobin dissociation curve. (Reproduced, with permission, from Guyton AC: *Textbook of Medical Physiology,* 5th ed. Saunders, 1976.)

discoveries of the molecular events of the hemoglobin-oxyhemoglobin interchange were made by Perutz. This is discussed in detail in Chapter 5.

The degree of combination of oxygen with hemoglobin or of its reversal, ie, dissociation of oxyhemoglobin to release oxygen or association of oxygen with hemoglobin, is determined by the tension (P_{O_2}) of the oxygen in the medium surrounding the hemoglobin. At the tension of oxygen in the blood as it is leaving the pulmonary capillaries (104 mm Hg), hemoglobin is approximately 97% saturated (Fig 43–4). However, when the blood that has perfused peripheral tissues has returned to the lungs and enters the pulmonary capillary, it has a P_{O_2} of 40 mm Hg; at this tension, hemoglobin is about 70% saturated (Fig 43–4). The relationship between the percentage saturation of the hemoglobin in blood and the oxygen tension of the blood shown in Fig 43–4 depicts the **oxygen dissociation curve of hemoglobin.** The oxygen dissociation curves of hemoglobin are somewhat dependent upon the P_{CO_2} in the blood, as discussed below.

When fully saturated, each gram of hemoglobin combines with approximately 1.34 mL of oxygen. Assuming a hemoglobin concentration of 14.5 g/dL of blood, the total oxygen that could be carried as oxyhemoglobin would be

$$14.5 \times 1.34 = 19.4 \text{ mL/dL blood}$$

This amount, when added to the amount of oxygen physically dissolved in the blood (0.33 mL/dL), yields the **total oxygen capacity** of blood, which is approximately 20 mL/dL. It is evident that the oxygen-carrying capacity of the blood is almost entirely a function of the blood **hemoglobin concentration.**

As can be perceived from Fig 43–4, the shape of the oxygen-hemoglobin dissociation curve is **sigmoid.** This property of the hemoglobin-oxygen interaction results from 2 properties important to the transport of oxygen. First, the relatively flat portion of the dissociation curve above an oxygen tension of 70–80 mm Hg results in minimal loss of oxygen from hemoglobin

despite rather significant changes in P_{O_2} above 70–80 mm Hg. Second, the precipitous change of the dissociation curve below a P_{O_2} of 40 mm Hg ensures that a disproportionately greater release of oxygen from hemoglobin will occur at any given decline in P_{O_2}. These 2 characteristics of hemoglobin-oxygen dissociation minimize the effects of small changes in pulmonary P_{O_2} on the oxygen content of the blood and maximize the delivery of oxygen to the oxygen-depleted peripheral tissues.

Under normal conditions (when the P_{O_2} of arterial blood is approximately 100 mm Hg and that of venous blood returning to the heart is 40 mm Hg), 5–6 mL of oxygen is delivered to the peripheral tissues by each 100 mL of blood. During strenuous exercise, the P_{O_2} in peripheral tissues may fall to as low as 15 mm Hg, which allows delivery of approximately 15 mL of oxygen per 100 mL of blood.

The hemoglobin-oxygen dissociation curve depicted in Fig 43–4 is that of normal, average blood, pH 7.4 and P_{CO_2} 40 mm Hg, at sea level. However, several factors can shift the hemoglobin-oxygen dissociation curve to the right or to the left. A **shift of the dissociation curve to the right** results in greater release of oxygen from the oxyhemoglobin at a given oxygen tension. In other words, **a shift to the right decreases the affinity** of hemoglobin for oxygen. Conversely, **a shift to the left increases the affinity** of hemoglobin for oxygen; accordingly, it results in a decreased release of oxygen from the hemoglobin at a given oxygen tension.

There are 4 major factors that bring about **a rightward shift** of hemoglobin-oxygen dissociation: (1) increased hydrogen ion or acidity (decreased blood pH), (2) increased CO_2 tension, (3) increased temperature, and (4) increased erythrocyte concentration of 2,3-diphosphoglycerate (DPG, also called 2,3-bisphosphoglycerate). All of the first 3 of these circumstances occur in situations where there are increased demands for oxygen by the tissue. The result is to bring about enhancement of delivery of oxygen. As discussed below, increased erythrocyte DPG concentrations occur under stressful situations such as a decreased atmospheric pressure; as is the case with increased CO_2 tension, the effect of DPG on oxygen affinity is also advantageous to the organism.

As shown in Fig 43–5, decreasing blood pH causes a small but significant rightward shift of the curve.

Shift of the hemoglobin-oxygen dissociation curve to the right by increasing CO_2 tension is termed the **Bohr effect.** It is due chiefly to the increased hydrogen ion concentration resulting from increased carbonic acid generation, as discussed below.

2,3-Diphosphoglycerate (DPG) is a metabolic intermediate in the Embden-Meyerhof pathway of glycolysis (see also Chapter 5). In the erythrocyte, 1 molecule of DPG binds noncovalently to the α-amino groups of the N-terminal valine residues of the 2 β chains of deoxyhemoglobin but not to those of oxygenated hemoglobin (see Chapter 5). Thus, in effect,

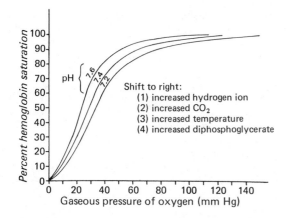

Figure 43–5. Shift of the oxygen-hemoglobin dissociation curve to the right by increases in (1) hydrogen ions, (2) CO₂, (3) temperature, or (4) diphosphoglycerate. (Reproduced, with permission, from Guyton AC: *Textbook of Medical Physiology,* 5th ed. Saunders, 1976.)

DPG pulls the equilibrium between oxyhemoglobin and deoxyhemoglobin plus oxygen to the right, favoring the deoxygenated state of hemoglobin:

$$HbO_2 \xrightleftharpoons[]{DPG} Hb \cdot DPG + O_2$$

The higher the DPG, the more favored will be the deoxyhemoglobin state and thus the farther to the right will be the shift of the hemoglobin-oxygen dissociation curve. In fact, the normal DPG concentration in erythrocytes shifts the dissociation curve somewhat to the right at all times.

Erythrocyte DPG levels are increased by chronic hypoxia, such as that occurring at altitudes above 2500–2750 m, in anemia, and in some disorders in which inherited abnormalities of hemoglobin alter the interaction of hemoglobin with oxygen and thereby diminish oxygen transport. It is not clear, however, whether the increased DPG concentrations are important in the adaptation to hypoxic conditions, because the presence of excess DPG diminishes also the affinity of hemoglobin for oxygen in the lungs.

One cause of a shift of the hemoglobin-oxygen dissociation curve to the left is an increased content of fetal hemoglobin (hemoglobin F) in the erythrocytes. An increased affinity for oxygen is characteristic of erythrocyte hemoglobin F. Obviously, this property is advantageous to the fetus, which normally is exposed to the diminished oxygen tension of the placental blood. It was once thought that this increased affinity of hemoglobin F for oxygen was an intrinsic property of the fetal hemoglobin molecule; however, an alteration in its oxygen affinity has not been demonstrable in vitro in purified preparations of hemoglobin F. It is now recognized that while hemoglobin F does not differ in its affinity for oxygen, when compared to

hemoglobin A, hemoglobin F has a significantly reduced affinity for DPG. It is this fact that results in an *apparent* increased affinity for oxygen in the presence of normal concentrations of DPG.

The rate of transport of oxygen to tissues depends on the oxygen utilization per unit volume, ie, the oxygen utilization coefficient, as well as the cardiac output. The normal utilization of oxygen, as mentioned above, is approximately 5 mL/dL blood; the oxygen content is normally 20 mL/dL blood. Thus, the utilization coefficient normally is 25%, but it can be increased another 3-fold—as, for instance, during strenuous exercise. In addition, the cardiac output can be increased 5-fold during exercise, resulting in nearly a 15-fold increase in the rate of oxygen transport to peripheral tissues.

In peripheral tissues, the utilization of oxygen is controlled not merely by its availability but more importantly by the intracellular concentration of ADP available for the process of oxidative phosphorylation. Whenever the oxygen tension in peripheral tissues is greater than 4 mm Hg, the cellular chemical reactions can proceed without regard to the availability of oxygen.

TRANSPORT OF CO₂ IN BLOOD

From the data in Table 43–4, it should be apparent that the content of CO₂ in blood, like that of oxygen, depends on factors other than simply its solution in the aqueous component of whole blood. In fact, only about 6% of the CO₂ present in blood is in the form of dissolved CO₂. According to the following equation,

$$CO_2 + H_2O \rightleftharpoons H_2CO_3$$

CO₂ reacts with water in the blood to form carbonic acid (H_2CO_3), although the reaction is very slow in the absence of catalytic activity. It is the enzyme carbonic anhydrase present in erythrocytes that catalyzes the rapid equilibration of the above reaction. Carbonic acid rapidly and spontaneously dissociates into hydrogen ion and bicarbonate ion and, because it goes to about 99.9% completion, only 0.1% of the carbonic acid remains in the undissociated form. Since an increase in hydrogen ion concentration is severely detri-

Table 43–4. Comparison of calculated content with actual content (in mL/dL) of oxygen, CO₂, and nitrogen in the blood.

	Oxygen	Carbon Dioxide	Nitrogen
Calculated content	0.33	3.0	0.9
Actually present			
Arterial blood	20.0	50.0	1.7
Venous blood	14.0	56.0	1.7

mental to an organism, a buffer must be available to remove the free proton.

Hemoglobin is the major buffer in blood that removes the free hydrogen ion from blood to form a protonated hemoglobin, "freeing" an equimolar quantity of bicarbonate ion, as depicted in the reaction,

$$H^+ + HCO_3^- + KHb \rightleftharpoons HHb + K^+ + HCO_3^-$$

This reaction, of course, occurs only within the red cell, which is highly impermeable to potassium ion but readily permeable to bicarbonate anion. As the bicarbonate anion diffuses out of the erythrocyte into the plasma, another anion must enter the erythrocyte in equimolar quantities in order to maintain electrical neutrality across the erythrocyte membrane. This is chloride ion; thus, the exchange between bicarbonate and chloride ions across the erythrocyte membrane is designated the **chloride shift** (Fig 43–6). It accounts for the greater chloride content in venous erythrocytes than in arterial erythrocytes, where the CO_2 tension is less. The conversion of CO_2 (via carbonic acid) to bicarbonate ion accounts for about 70% of the CO_2 transport. When carbonic anhydrase activity is inhibited, such as by acetazolamide, CO_2 transport from the tissues is inhibited. As a result, the CO_2 tension may rise to 70 or 80 mm Hg.

In addition to being transported in simple solution and as bicarbonate ion, CO_2 can combine (carbamino binding) in a rather loose covalent structure with the α-amino groups of the N-terminal valine residues of all 4 chains of the hemoglobin molecule. Since DPG binds to 2 of the amino termini of hemoglobin, clearly there is antagonism between the binding of CO_2 and that of diphosphoglycerate to the hemoglobin molecule. However, even though hemoglobin is the principal macromolecule for CO_2 transport, its role is minor when compared to the transport of CO_2 in the form of bicarbonate.

The carbamino-hemoglobin formed by the interaction of CO_2 with the amino termini of the hemoglobin molecule is independent of P_{CO_2} once that tension is greater than 15 mm Hg; but it is significantly influenced by the degree of oxygen saturation of the hemoglobin. The binding of oxygen to hemoglobin displaces CO_2, a phenomenon referred to as the **Haldane effect.**

The Haldane effect has a quantitatively greater importance in promoting CO_2 transport than the Bohr effect has in promoting oxygen transport. The Haldane effect results from the fact that oxyhemoglobin is a stronger acid than is deoxyhemoglobin, because the oxygenation of hemoglobin promotes the release of protons (hydrogen ions) from the hemoglobin molecule. The displacement of CO_2 from blood following the oxygenation of hemoglobin results from

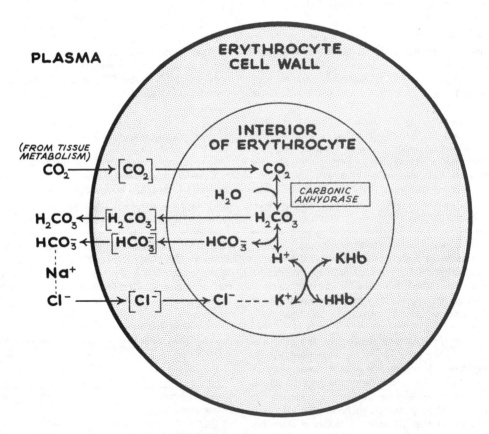

Figure 43–6. The chloride shift.

this increased availability of protons to combine with bicarbonate ions to form carbonic acid. Carbonic acid in the presence of carbonic anhydrase can be released as CO_2. The more acidic oxyhemoglobin also has a lesser tendency to form carbamino-hemoglobin from CO_2 and accounts for what has been referred to as the "oxylabile" carbamate.

The contribution of the carbamino-CO_2 to transport of CO_2 in an adult at rest is only about 10%. The Haldane effect nearly doubles the quantity of CO_2 that is released from the blood upon its oxygenation in the lungs, and upon the deoxygenation of hemoglobin in the peripheral tissues, the Haldane effect nearly doubles the uptake of CO_2.

The **respiratory exchange (RE) ratio** is the ratio of CO_2 released in the lungs divided by the rate of oxygen uptake in the lungs,

$$\frac{CO_2 \text{ release}}{O_2 \text{ uptake}} = RE \text{ ratio}$$

The respiratory exchange ratio changes under different metabolic conditions. In tissues utilizing carbohydrate as an energy source, there exists a 1:1 relationship between CO_2 production and oxygen consumption. However, the CO_2 production is diminished for each oxygen molecule consumed during the oxidation of fats as an energy source. For persons consuming a diet average in the quantities of carbohydrates, fats, and proteins, the respiratory exchange ratio (formerly termed respiratory quotient, RQ) is approximately 0.825.

Regulation of Respiration

Although the regulation of the hemoglobin affinity for oxygen, ie, the relative position of the hemoglobin-oxygen dissociation curve, is brought about by changes in blood pH and not by CO_2 tension, the regulation of respiration through a central nervous system mechanism is mediated predominantly by the **CO_2 tension of the blood.** An increase in P_{CO_2} as it exceeds 40 mm Hg causes an almost linear increase in the alveolar ventilation. The **oxygen tension alters ventilatory rate only when the CO_2 tension is abnormally low or exceedingly high.**

RESPIRATORY REGULATION OF ACID-BASE BALANCE

As described in Chapter 2, the buffering power of a buffer system is greatest at a pH equal to its pK_a. The pH of extracellular body fluids is 7.4, while the pK_a of the bicarbonate-CO_2 buffer system is 6.1. From the Henderson-Hasselbalch equation, it can be seen that at pH 7.4, the concentration of bicarbonate ion is 20 times greater than that of dissolved CO_2, a state which a priori would not provide significant buffering power. This can be seen by the following calculation, applying the Henderson-Hasselbalch equation to conditions in the blood.

$$7.4 = \text{pH of blood}$$

$$6.1 = pK_a \text{ of } H_2CO_3$$

$$pH = pK_a + \log \frac{(\text{salt})}{(\text{acid})}$$

$$7.4 = 6.1 + \log \frac{(HCO_3^-)}{(H_2CO_3)}$$

$$1.3 = \log \frac{(HCO_3^-)}{(H_2CO_3)}$$

$$\text{antilog } 1.3 = 20$$

$$\frac{(HCO_3^-)}{(H_2CO_3)} = \frac{20}{1}$$

However, because the concentration of each of these 2 components of the bicarbonate–carbonic acid system can be physiologically regulated, it provides a very powerful buffering system for the organism, as described below.

The CO_2 tension can be increased in blood by either increased production from the peripheral tissues or decreased removal by ventilation. From the Henderson-Hasselbalch equation, it should also be apparent that increased CO_2 tension will lead to a lower pH and acidosis. Acidosis due to the retention of excessive CO_2 results from ventilation that is inadequate for the rate of CO_2 production. For example, reducing ventilation at rest to one-fourth of normal rates *increases* the CO_2 tension and drops the pH from 7.4 to about 7.0. On the other hand, increasing the rate of alveolar ventilation (hyperventilation) 2-fold will *diminish* the CO_2 tension and lead to an increase of blood pH to about 7.6. Since alveolar ventilation can be reduced to nil or increased to about 15 times normal, it is readily understandable how changes in ventilation can severely affect the pH of extracellular fluid, which verifies the important role of the bicarbonate-CO_2 buffering system.

An acidosis due to *decreased* ventilation and the consequential *increase* in CO_2 tension is referred to as **respiratory acidosis.** An alkalosis due to hyperventilation and reduction of CO_2 tension in blood is referred to as **respiratory alkalosis.** However, because of the rapidity with which the respiratory system can change the blood pH, this system is frequently called upon to make rapid adjustments to pH changes that are generated by metabolic rather than by respiratory causes. The **respiratory-mediated readjustments of pH are rapid but incomplete.** On the other hand, **renal mechanisms can completely readjust the pH but are slow to act.**

Disturbances in acid-base balance due to alterations in the content of bicarbonate in the blood are said to be metabolic in origin. A deficit of bicarbonate without any change in H_2CO_3 will produce a **metabolic acidosis;** an excess of bicarbonate, a **metabolic alkalosis. Compensation** will occur by adjustments of the carbonic acid concentrations, in the first instance by elimination of more CO_2 (hyperventilation) and in the latter instance by retention of CO_2 (hypoventilation). The CO_2 content of the plasma will obviously be lower than normal in metabolic acidosis and higher than normal in metabolic alkalosis.

Causes of Disturbances in Acid-Base Balance

A. Metabolic Acidosis: Metabolic acidosis is caused by a decrease in the bicarbonate fraction, with either no change or a relatively smaller change in the carbonic acid fraction. This is the most common, classic type of acidosis. It occurs in uncontrolled diabetes with ketosis, in renal insufficiency, in poisoning by an acid salt, and in excessive loss of intestinal fluids (particularly from the lower small intestine and colon, as in diarrhea or colitis). Increased respirations (hyperpnea) may be an important sign of an uncompensated acidosis and is an attempt to reestablish the 20:1 ratio of $HCO_3^-:H_2CO_3$ by appropriately reducing the CO_2 tension of blood.

B. Respiratory Acidosis: Respiratory acidosis is caused by an increase in carbonic acid relative to bicarbonate. This may occur in any disease that impairs respiration, such as pneumonia, emphysema, congestive failure, asthma, or in depression of the respiratory center (as by morphine poisoning). A poorly functioning mechanical respirator may also contribute to respiratory acidosis.

C. Metabolic Alkalosis: Metabolic alkalosis occurs when there is an increase in the bicarbonate fraction, with either no change or a relatively smaller change in the carbonic acid fraction. A simple alkali excess leading to alkalosis is produced by the ingestion of large quantities of alkali, such as might occur in patients under treatment for peptic ulcer. But this type of alkalosis occurs much more commonly as a consequence of high intestinal obstruction (as in pyloric stenosis), after prolonged vomiting of acidic stomach contents, or after the excessive removal of gastric secretions containing hydrochloric acid (as in gastric suction). The common denominator in this form of alkalosis is a chloride deficit caused by the removal of gastric secretions that are low in sodium but high in chloride (ie, as hydrochloric acid). The chloride ions that are lost are then replaced by bicarbonate. This type of metabolic alkalosis is aptly termed "hypochloremic" alkalosis. Potassium deficiency is frequently associated with the development of hypochloremic alkalosis due to the unavailability of H^+ for the exchange with Na^+ from the lumen of the renal tubule.

In all types of uncompensated alkalosis, the respirations are slow and shallow; the urine may be alkaline, but usually, because of a concomitant deficit of sodium and potassium, will give an acid reaction even though the blood bicarbonate is elevated. This paradox is attributable in part to the fact that the excretion of the excess bicarbonate by the kidney will require an accompanying loss of sodium which under the conditions described (low sodium) cannot be spared. Thus, the kidney defers to the necessity of maintaining sodium concentrations in the extracellular fluid at the expense

of acid-base balance. However, an equal—if not, in the usual situations, a more important—cause of the excretion of an acid urine in the presence of an elevated plasma bicarbonate is the effect mentioned above of a potassium deficit on the excretion of hydrogen ions by the kidney. Metabolic alkalosis as encountered clinically is almost always associated with a concomitant deficiency of potassium.

D. Respiratory Alkalosis: Respiratory alkalosis occurs when there is a decrease in the carbonic acid fraction with no corresponding change in bicarbonate. This is brought about by hyperventilation, either voluntary or forced. Examples are hysterical hyperventilation, central nervous system disease affecting the respiratory system, the early stages of salicylate poisoning, and injudicious use of respirators. Respiratory alkalosis may also occur in patients in hepatic coma.

Measurement of Acid-Base Balance; pH of Blood

The existence of uncompensated acidosis or alkalosis is most accurately determined by measurement of the pH of the blood. However, determination of the pH of the blood may not be feasible in some clinical circumstances. Furthermore, it is necessary to know in what manner the electrolyte pattern of the blood is disturbed in order to prescribe the proper corrective therapy. For these reasons, a determination of the CO_2 derived from a sample of blood plasma after treatment with acid (CO_2 capacity or CO_2 combining power) is also used. This measures essentially the total quantity of H_2CO_3 and of bicarbonate in the plasma but gives no information as to the ratio of distribution of the 2 components of the bicarbonate buffer system. Because of the properties of the Henderson-Hasselbalch equation, knowing any 2 out of the 3 variables—P_{CO_2}, bicarbonate concentration, and pH—or even knowing only the pH and the total CO_2 content permits determination of the remaining unknown variable (Fig 43–7). Accordingly, knowing 2 of the 3 variables also permits diagnosis of the nature of the acid-base disturbance by utilizing diagrams such as that shown in Fig 43–8.

For example, in **acute respiratory failure,** the retention of CO_2 would produce an **uncompensated respiratory acidosis.** The conditions of the blood might be transformed from the normal at point A to point B (Fig 43–8) with a P_{CO_2} of 60 mm Hg. The pH would be 7.3, and because of the requirement that the Henderson-Hasselbalch relationship be satisfied, the bicarbonate must rise minimally to 28 meq/L. If the respiratory failure is prolonged, the kidneys may well compensate for the acidosis, at least partially, by retaining bicarbonate. The condition of the blood might then move to point C, which would return the blood pH to the normal 7.4. This would accomplish what is termed a **compensated respiratory acidosis.**

Were hyperventilation to be induced, the P_{CO_2} might fall to 20 mm Hg—point D—with an ensuing **uncompensated respiratory alkalosis.** Again, owing to the requirement that the Henderson-Hasselbalch

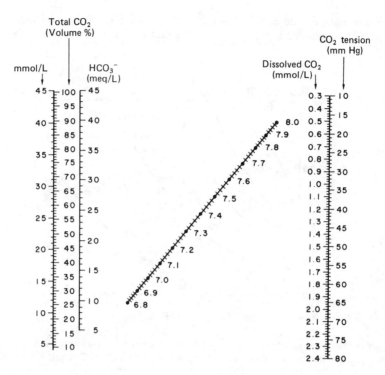

Figure 43–7. Nomogram of relationships between components of HCO_3^--CO_2 buffering system in the blood. (Reproduced, with permission, from Davenport HW: *The ABC of Acid-Base Chemistry*, 6th ed. University of Chicago Press, 1974.)

equation be satisfied, the bicarbonate concentration must accordingly fall to about 20 meq/L. The kidney, by excreting excess bicarbonate, might bring about a change in the status of the blood to point E, which is nearly that of a normal pH of 7.4. This would then result in a **compensated respiratory alkalosis.** As mentioned above, these renal-mediated compensations for respiratory acidosis or respiratory alkalosis occur slowly and thus would be seen only in chronic respiratory abnormalities.

In an **acute metabolic alkalosis** such as that due to an infusion of sodium bicarbonate, the condition of the blood might change from normal point A to point F, with a bicarbonate concentration of 34 meq/L and a P_{CO_2} of slightly greater than 40 mm Hg. This mild elevation of the P_{CO_2} is due to the requirement that the conditions of the Henderson-Hasselbalch equation be satisfied at any given pH. Thus, at point F, with a plasma pH of 7.5, decreased respiration (retaining CO_2) could change the condition from point F to point C by increasing the P_{CO_2} to 60 mm Hg. This would result in a **compensated metabolic alkalosis,** but the previous state of the blood must be known in order to determine whether the condition at point C was due to a compensated metabolic alkalosis or a compensated respiratory acidosis, as described immediately above.

An **acute metabolic acidosis** might result in a situation wherein the blood is transformed from normal point A to point G, with a pH of 7.3. Hyperventilation would reduce the P_{CO_2} to 20 mm Hg and thereby

compensate for the metabolic acidosis by changing the condition of the blood to condition E. Once again it should be emphasized that finding the blood in the condition at point E still would not allow a distinction to be made between **compensated metabolic acidosis** and compensated respiratory alkalosis unless the previous condition of the blood were known.

The Role of the Kidney in Acid-Base Balance

In addition to carbonic acid, which is eliminated by the respiratory organs as CO_2, other acids, which are not volatile, are produced by metabolic processes. These include lactic and pyruvic acids and the more important inorganic acids, hydrochloric, phosphoric, and sulfuric. About 50–150 meq of these inorganic acids are eliminated by the kidneys in a 24-hour period. It is of course necessary that these acids be partially buffered with cation, largely sodium; but in the distal tubules of the kidney some of this cation is reabsorbed (actually exchanged for hydrogen ion), and the pH of the urine is allowed to fall. This acidification of the urine in the distal tubule is a valuable function of the kidney in conserving the reserves of cation in the body.

Another device used by the kidney to buffer acids and thus to conserve fixed base (cation) is the production of ammonia from amino acids. The ammonia is substituted for alkali cations, and the amounts of ammonia mobilized for this purpose may be markedly increased when the production of acid within the body is excessive (eg, as in metabolic acidosis occurring as a result of the ketosis of uncontrolled diabetes).

When alkali is in excess, the kidney excretes an alkaline urine to correct this imbalance.

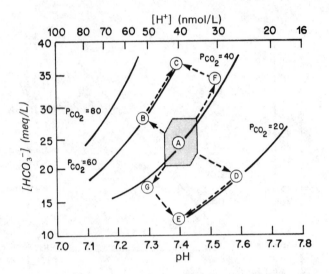

Figure 43–8. Diagram of relationships between HCO_3^-, P_{CO_2}, H^+, and pH of blood under normal conditions (shaded area, A) and in the presence of uncompensated and compensated acidosis and alkalosis. See text for details.

• • •

References

Anderson OS: The acid-base status of the blood. *Scand J Clin Lab Invest* 1963;**15 (Suppl 70)**:1.

Astrup P: A new approach to acid-base metabolism. *Clin Chem* 1961;**7**:1.

Best CH, Taylor NB: *The Physiological Basis of Medical Practice*, 9th ed. Williams & Wilkins, 1973.

Christensen HN: *Body Fluids and the Acid-Base Balance*. Saunders, 1964.

Davenport HW: *The ABC of Acid-Base Chemistry*, 6th ed. Univ of Chicago Press, 1974.

Filley GF: *Acid-Base and Gas Regulation*. Lea & Febiger, 1971.

Goldberger E: *A Primer of Water, Electrolyte, and Acid-Base Syndromes*, 5th ed. Lea & Febiger, 1975.

Hills AG: *Acid-Base Balance: Chemistry, Physiology, Pathophysiology*. Williams & Wilkins, 1973.

Michel CC: The transport of oxygen and carbon dioxide by the blood. Page 67 in: *Physiology*, Series One. Guyton AC (editor). University Park Press, 1974.

Robinson JR: *Fundamentals of Acid-Base Regulation*, 5th ed. Blackwell, 1975.

Digestion/Absorption in the Gastrointestinal Tract | 44

Peter A. Mayes, PhD, DSc

Most foodstuffs are ingested in forms that are unavailable to the organism, since they cannot be absorbed from the digestive tract until they have been broken down into smaller molecules. This disintegration of the naturally occurring foodstuffs into assimilable forms constitutes the process of digestion.

The chemical changes incident to digestion are accomplished with the aid of hydrolase enzymes of the digestive tract, which catalyze the hydrolysis of native proteins to amino acids, of starches to monosaccharides, and of triacylglycerols to monoacylglycerols, glycerol, and fatty acids. In the course of these digestive reactions, the minerals and vitamins of the foodstuffs are also made more assimilable. For example, the lipid-soluble vitamins are not absorbed efficiently unless fat digestion is proceeding normally.

A systematic account of the nature and functions of the gastrointestinal hormones is given in Chapter 42.

DIGESTION IN THE ORAL CAVITY

Constituents of the Saliva

The oral cavity contains saliva secreted by 3 pairs of salivary glands: parotid, submaxillary, and sublingual. The saliva consists of about 99.5% water, although the content varies with the nature of the factors exciting its secretion. It acts as a lubricant for mastication in the oral cavity and for swallowing. Adding water to dry food provides a medium in which food molecules can dissolve and in which hydrolases can initiate digestion. Mastication subdivides the food, increasing its solubility and surface area for enzyme attack. The saliva is also a vehicle for the excretion of certain drugs (eg, ethanol and morphine), of inorganic ions such as K^+, Ca^{2+}, HCO_3^-, thiocyanate (SCN^-), and iodine, and of immunoglobulins (IgA).

The pH of the saliva is usually slightly on the acid side, about 6.8, although it may vary on either side of neutrality.

Salivary Digestion

Saliva contains a starch-splitting enzyme, **salivary amylase (ptyalin).** Although saliva is capable of bringing about the hydrolysis of starch and glycogen to maltose, this is of little significance in the body be-cause of the short time it can act on the food. Salivary amylase is readily inactivated at pH 4.0 or less, so that digestive action on food in the mouth will soon cease in the acid environment of the stomach. Furthermore, pancreatic amylase, which has a similar enzymatic action and specificity, is capable of accomplishing complete starch digestion. In many animals, a salivary amylase is entirely absent. A lingual lipase secreted by the dorsal surface of the tongue (Ebner's glands) has been reported.

DIGESTION IN THE STOMACH

Gastric Constituents & Gastric Digestion

In the mucosa of the stomach wall, 2 types of secretory glands are found: those exhibiting a single layer of secreting cells (the chief cells) and those with cells arranged in layers (the parietal cells) which secrete directly into the gastric glands. The mixed secretion is known as **gastric juice.** It is normally a clear, pale yellow fluid of high acidity, 0.2–0.5% HCl, with a pH of about 1.0. The gastric juice is 97–99% water. The remainder consists of mucin and inorganic salts, the digestive enzymes (pepsin and rennin), and a lipase.

A. Hydrochloric Acid: The parietal cells are the sole source of gastric hydrochloric acid. HCl originates according to the reactions shown in Fig 44–1.

The process is similar to that of the "chloride shift" described for the red blood cell on p 616. There is also a resemblance to the renal tubular mechanisms for secretion of H^+, wherein the source of H^+ is also the **carbonic anhydrase**-catalyzed formation of H_2CO_3 from H_2O and CO_2. An alkaline urine often follows the ingestion of a meal ("alkaline tide"), as a result of the formation of bicarbonate in the process of hydrochloric acid secretion by the stomach in accordance with reactions shown in Fig 44–1. Secretion of H^+ into the lumen is an active process driven by a membrane-located K^+-ATPase that is ouabain-insensitive. HCO_3^- passes into the plasma in exchange for Cl^-, which is coupled to the secretion of H^+ into the lumen.

As a result of contact with gastric HCl, proteins are denatured; ie, the tertiary protein structure is lost as a result of the destruction of hydrogen bonds. This

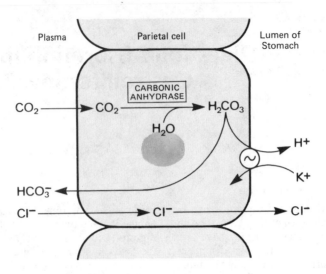

Figure 44–1. Production of gastric hydrochloric acid. ($\sim$, K^+-ATPase.)

allows the polypeptide chain to unfold, making it more accessible to the actions of proteolytic enzymes (proteases). The low pH also has the effect of destroying most microorganisms entering the gastrointestinal tract.

B. Pepsin: The chief digestive function of the stomach is the initiation of protein digestion. Pepsin is produced in the chief cells as the inactive zymogen, **pepsinogen.** This is activated by the presence of H^+ ions, then by the proteolytic attack of another acid-activated pepsinogen molecule that splits off the protective polypeptide to expose active pepsin; and by pepsin, which rapidly activates further molecules of pepsinogen (**autocatalysis**). Pepsin transforms denatured protein into proteoses and then peptones, which are large polypeptide derivatives. Pepsin is an **endopeptidase,** since it hydrolyzes peptide bonds within the main polypeptide structure rather than adjacent to N- or C-terminal residues, which is characteristic of **exopeptidases.** It is specific for peptide bonds formed by aromatic or dicarboxylic amino acids and is characterized by the presence of 2 reactive aspartic acid residues at the active site.

C. Rennin (Chymosin, Rennet): The enzyme causes the coagulation of milk. This is important in the digestive processes of infants, because it prevents the rapid passage of milk from the stomach. In the presence of calcium, rennin changes irreversibly the casein of milk to a paracasein which is then acted on by pepsin. Rennin is said to be absent from the stomach of adults. It is used in the making of cheese.

D. Lipase: The heat of the stomach is important in liquidizing the bulk of dietary lipids; emulsification takes place aided by peristaltic contractions. Although it does contain a lipase capable of hydrolyzing triacylglycerols of short and medium chain length, the lipolytic action of gastric juice is not important. However, the lingual lipase can continue its activity at the low pH of the stomach, where because of the retention time of

2–4 hours, about 30% of dietary triacylglycerol may be digested. Lingual lipase is more active on triacylglycerol having shorter-chain fatty acids and is more specific for the ester linkage in the *sn*-3 position rather than position 1. Milk fat contains short- and medium-chain fatty acids, which tend to be esterified in the *sn*-3 position. Therefore, milk fat seems to be a particularly good substrate for this enzyme. The released hydrophilic short-chain fatty acids are absorbed via the stomach wall and enter the portal vein, whereas longer-chain fatty acids dissolve in the fat droplets.

PANCREATIC & INTESTINAL DIGESTION

The stomach contents, or **chyme,** which are of a thick creamy consistency, are intermittently introduced during digestion into the duodenum through the pyloric valve. The pancreatic and bile ducts open into the duodenum at a point very close to the pylorus. The alkaline content of pancreatic and biliary secretions neutralizes the acid of the chyme and changes the pH of this material to the alkaline side; this shift of pH is necessary for the activity of the enzymes contained in pancreatic and intestinal juice, but it inhibits further action of pepsin.

THE BILE

In addition to many functions in intermediary metabolism, the liver, by producing bile, plays an important role in digestion. The gallbladder, a saccular organ attached to the hepatic duct, stores a certain amount of the bile produced by the liver between meals. In humans, the gallbladder is a dispensable organ. During digestion, the gallbladder contracts and supplies bile rapidly to the small intestine by way of the common bile duct. The pancreatic secretions mix with the bile, since they empty into the common duct shortly before its entry into the duodenum.

Composition of Bile

The composition of hepatic bile differs from that of gallbladder bile. As shown in Table 44–1, the latter is more concentrated.

Table 44–1. The composition of hepatic and of gallbladder bile.

| | Hepatic Bile (as secreted) | | Bladder Bile |
	Percent of Total Bile	Percent of Total Solids	Percent of Total Bile
Water	97.00	. . .	85.92
Solids	2.52	. . .	14.08
Bile acids	1.93	36.9	9.14
Mucin and pigments	0.53	21.3	2.98
Cholesterol	0.06	2.4	0.26
Esterified and nonesterified fatty acids	0.14	5.6	0.32
Inorganic salts	0.84	33.3	0.65
Specific gravity	1.01	. . .	1.04
pH	7.1–7.3	. . .	6.9–7.7

Bile Acids

The primary bile acids are synthesized in the liver from cholesterol by several intermediate steps. **Cholic acid** is the bile acid found in the largest amount in the bile itself. Both cholic acid and **chenodeoxycholic acid** are formed from a common precursor, itself derived from cholesterol (Fig 44–2).

The 7α-hydroxylation of cholesterol is the first committed step in the biosynthesis of bile acids, and it is probably this reaction that is rate-limiting in the pathway for synthesis of the acids. The α-hydroxylation reaction is catalyzed by a microsomal system; it requires oxygen and NADPH, and it is partially inhibited by carbon monoxide. This system appears similar to that for the monooxygenases previously described in connection with hydroxylation of steroids and of certain drugs (see p 132). It appears that cytochrome P-450 is a component of the system, as it is for subsequent hydroxylation steps. Vitamin C deficiency interferes with bile acid formation at the 7α-hydroxylation step and leads to cholesterol accumulation, hypercholesterolemia, and increased atherosclerosis in guinea pigs.

Under normal circumstances in humans, bile acids are synthesized by the liver at the relatively low rate of 200–500 mg/d. This rate is regulated to just replace the daily loss of bile acids in the feces. The bile acids are the end products of cholesterol catabolism in the body. Because the tissues cannot break down the steroid nucleus, these compounds, together with cholesterol itself, which is also present in the bile, represent the only significant route for **elimination of cholesterol from the body.** Measurement of the fecal output of bile acids plus neutral steroids is therefore the most accurate way to estimate the amount of cholesterol lost from the body.

The bile acids normally enter the bile as glycine or taurine conjugates. The newly synthesized primary bile acids are considered to exist within the liver cell as esters of CoA, ie, cholyl- or chenodeoxycholyl-CoA (Fig 44–2). The CoA derivatives are formed with the aid of an activating enzyme occurring in the microsomes of the liver. A second enzyme catalyzes conjugation of the activated bile acids (the CoA derivatives) with glycine or taurine to form glycocholic or glycochenodeoxycholic and taurocholic or taurochenodeoxycholic acids. These are the **primary bile acids.** In humans, the ratio of the glycine to the taurine conjugates is normally 3:1.

Since bile contains significant quantities of sodium and potassium and the pH is alkaline, it is assumed that the bile acids and their conjugates are actually in a salt form—hence the term **"bile salts."**

The Enterohepatic Circulation

A portion of the primary bile acids in the intestine may be subjected to some further changes by the activity of the intestinal bacteria. These include deconjugation and 7α-dehydroxylation, which produces the **secondary bile acids,** deoxycholic acid from cholic acid, and lithocholic acid from chenodeoxycholic acid (Fig 44–2). Although fat digestion products are normally absorbed in the first 100 cm of small intestine, the primary and secondary bile acids are absorbed almost exclusively in the ileum, returning to the liver by way of the portal circulation about 99% of the bile acids secreted into the intestine. This is known as the **enterohepatic circulation** (Fig 44–3). However, lithocholic acid, because of its insolubility, is not reabsorbed to any significant extent.

A small fraction of the bile salts—perhaps only as little as 500 mg/d—escapes absorption and is therefore eliminated in the feces. Even though this is a very small amount, it nonetheless represents a major pathway for the elimination of cholesterol. The enterohepatic circulation of the bile salts is so efficient that each day the relatively small pool of bile acids (about 3–5 g) can be cycled through the intestine 6–10 times with only a small amount lost in the feces, ie, approximately 1% per pass through the enterohepatic circulation. However, **each day, an amount of bile acid equivalent to that lost in the feces is synthesized from cholesterol** by the liver, so that a pool of bile acids of constant size is maintained. This is accomplished by a system of feedback control.

Hepatic synthesis of cholesterol, in addition to being subject to feedback regulation by dietary intake of cholesterol, is also under regulatory control by the bile acids in the enterohepatic circulation. Changes in the rate of synthesis of bile acids are nearly always paralleled by corresponding changes in the rate of cholesterol synthesis in the liver. The principal rate-limiting step in the biosynthesis of bile acids is at the **7α-hydroxylase reaction,** and in the biosynthesis of cholesterol it is at the HMG-CoA reductase step (Fig

Table 44—2. Summary of digestive processes.

Source of Secretion and Stimulus for Secretion	Enzyme	Method of Activation and Optimal Conditions for Activity	Substrate	End Products or Action
Salivary glands: Secrete saliva in reflex response to presence of food in oral cavity.	Salivary amylase	Chloride ion necessary. pH 6.6—6.8.	Starch Glycogen	Maltose plus 1:6 glucosides (oligosaccharides) plus maltotriose.
Lingual glands	Lingual lipase	pH range 2.0—7.5; optimal, 4.0—4.5.	Short-chain primary ester link at *sn*-3	Fatty acids plus 1,2-diacylglycerols.
Stomach glands: Chief cells and parietal cells secrete gastric juice in response to reflex stimulation and chemical action of gastrin.	Pepsin A (fundus) Pepsin B (pylorus)	Pepsinogen converted to active pepsin by HCl. pH 1.0—2.0.	Protein	Proteases. Peptones.
	Rennin	Calcium necessary for activity. pH 4.0.	Casein of milk	Coagulates milk.
Pancreas: Presence of acid chyme from the stomach activates duodenum to produce (1) secretin, which hormonally stimulates flow of pancreatic juice; (2) cholecystokinin, which stimulates the production of enzymes.	Trypsin	Trypsinogen converted to active trypsin by enterokinase of intestine at pH 5.2—6.0. Autocatalytic at pH 7.9.	Protein Proteoses Peptones	Polypeptides. Dipeptides.
	Chymotrypsin	Secreted as chymotrypsinogen and converted to active form by trypsin. pH 8.0.	Protein Proteases Peptones	Same as trypsin. More coagulating power for milk.
	Elastase	Secreted as proelastase and converted to active form by trypsin.	Protein Proteoses Peptones	Polypeptides. Dipeptides.
	Carboxypeptidase	Secreted as procarboxypeptidase, activated by trypsin.	Polypeptides at the free carboxyl end of the chain	Lower peptides. Free amino acids.
	Pancreatic amylase	pH 7.1.	Starch Glycogen	Maltose plus 1:6 glucosides (oligosaccharides) plus maltotriose.
	Lipase	Activated by bile salts, phospholipids, colipase. pH 8.0.	Primary ester linkages of triacylglycerol	Fatty acids, monoacylglycerols, diacylglycerols, glycerol.
	Ribonuclease		Ribonucleic acid	Nucleotides.
	Deoxyribonuclease		Deoxyribonucleic acids	Nucleotides.
	Cholesteryl ester hydrolase	Activated by bile salts.	Cholesteryl esters	Free cholesterol plus fatty acids.
	Phospholipase A_2	Secreted as proenzyme, activated by trypsin and Ca^{2+}.	Phospholipids	Fatty acids, lysophospholipids.
Liver and gallbladder: Cholecystokinin, a hormone from the intestinal mucosa—and possibly also gastrin and secretin—stimulate the gallbladder and secretion of bile by the liver.	(Bile salts and alkali)		Fats—also neutralize acid chyme	Fatty acid–bile salt conjugates and finely emulsified neutral fat–bile salt micelles.
Small intestine: Secretions of Brunner's glands of the duodenum and glands of Lieberkühn.	Aminopeptidase		Polypeptides at the free amino end of the chain	Lower peptides. Free amino acids.
	Dipeptidases		Dipeptides	Amino acids.
	Sucrase	pH 5.0—7.0.	Sucrose	Fructose, glucose.
	Maltase	pH 5.8—6.2.	Maltose	Glucose.
	Lactase	pH 5.4—6.0.	Lactose	Glucose, galactose.
	Trehalase		Trehalose	Glucose.
	Phosphatase	pH 8.6.	Organic phosphates	Free phosphate.
	Isomaltase or 1:6 glucosidase		1:6 glucosides	Glucose.
	Polynucleotidase		Nucleic acid	Nucleotides.
	Nucleosidases (nucleoside phosphorylases)		Purine or pyrimidine nucleosides	Purine or pyrimidine bases, pentose phosphate.

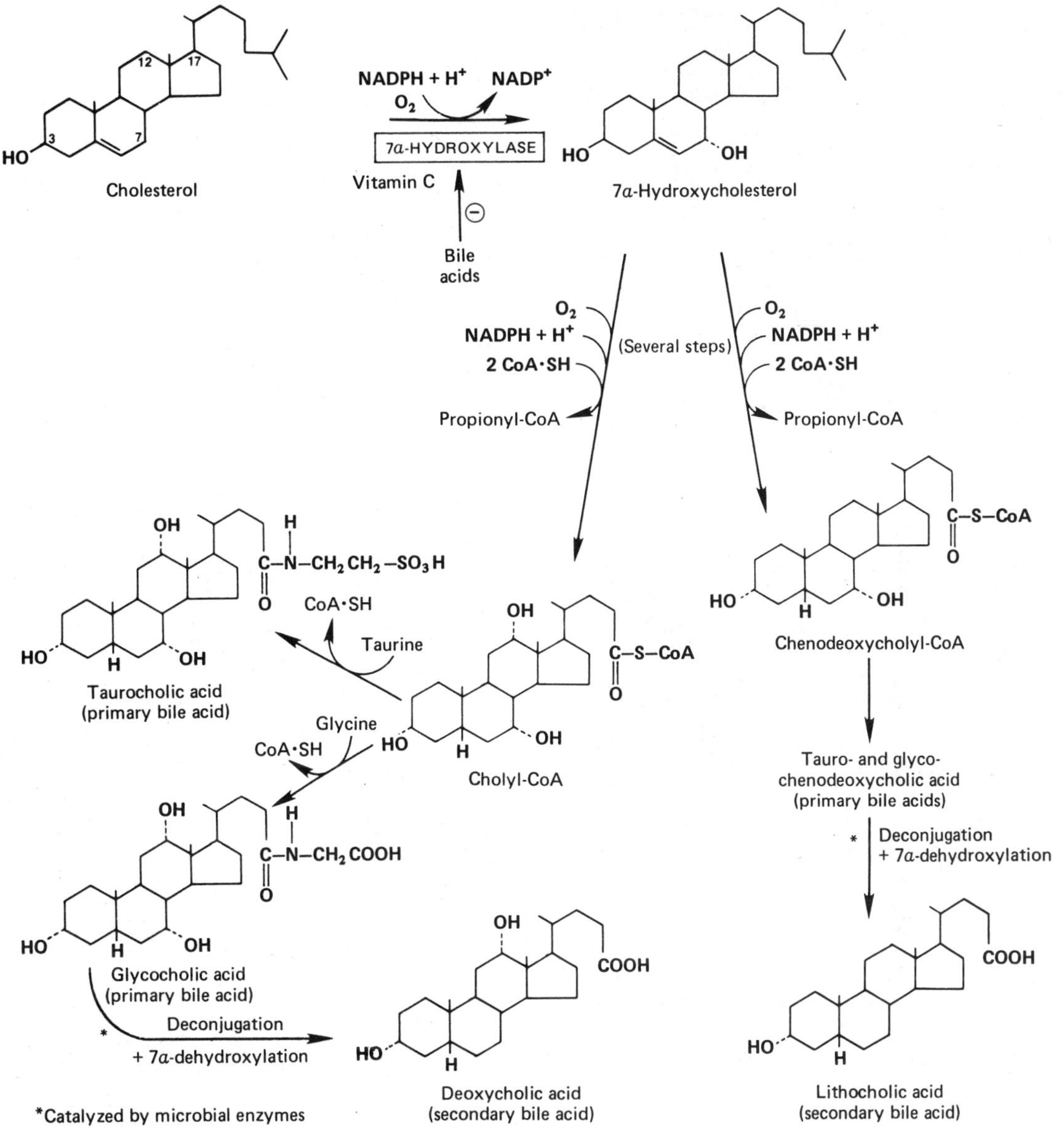

Figure 44-2. Biosynthesis and degradation of bile acids.

18–14). The activities of these 2 enzymes change in parallel, and consequently it is difficult to ascertain whether inhibition of bile acid synthesis takes place primarily at the HMG-CoA reductase step or at the 7α-hydroxylase reaction. Bile acids do not seem to regulate these enzyme activities by a direct allosteric mechanism. However, recent work indicates that 7α-hydroxylase (as well as HMG-CoA reductase) can be controlled by covalent phosphorylation-dephosphorylation. In contrast to HMG-CoA reductase, it is the phosphorylated form that results in increased activity of 7α-hydroxylase. The ability to suppress cholesterol synthesis after feeding cholesterol varies with different human subjects.

There is lower excretion of bile acids in patients with familial hypercholesterolemia (see p 255) that is reflected by lower synthesis of cholic acid. A similar pattern is observed in hepatic cirrhosis and cholestasis in which cholic and deoxycholic acid formation and presence in bile are reduced, whereas chenodeoxycholic acid production is normal. It has been reported (Halloran et al, 1978) that in humans, when the enterohepatic circulation has been interrupted by a bile fistula, free cholesterol in plasma HDL (high-density lipoprotein) was the preferred source of both biliary cholesterol and chenodeoxycholic acid.

Clinically, hypercholesterolemia may be treated by interrupting the enterohepatic circulation of bile acids. It is reported that significant reductions of plasma cholesterol can be effected by this procedure,

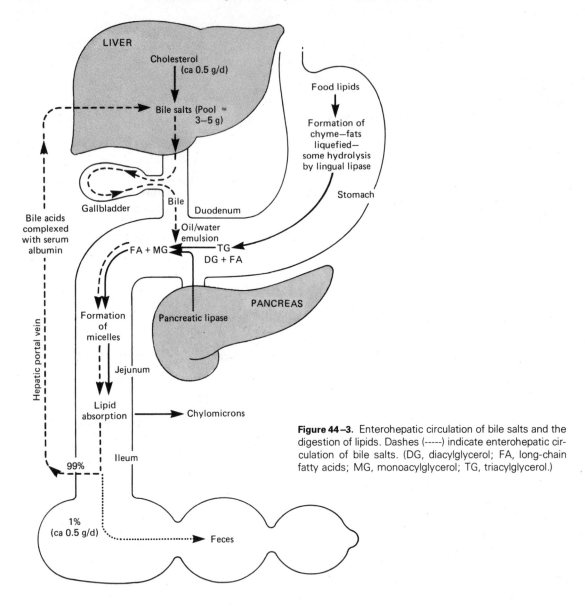

Figure 44–3. Enterohepatic circulation of bile salts and the digestion of lipids. Dashes (-----) indicate enterohepatic circulation of bile salts. (DG, diacylglycerol; FA, long-chain fatty acids; MG, monoacylglycerol; TG, triacylglycerol.)

which can be accomplished by the use of cholestyramine resin (Questran) or surgically by the ileal exclusion operations. Both procedures cause a block in the reabsorption of bile acids. Then, because of release from feedback regulation normally exerted by bile acids, the conversion of cholesterol to bile acids is greatly enhanced in an effort to maintain the pool of bile acids.

Functions of Bile

A. Emulsification: The bile salts have considerable ability to lower surface tension. This enables them to emulsify fats in the intestine and to dissolve fatty acids and water-insoluble soaps. The presence of bile in the intestine is an important adjunct to accomplish the digestion and absorption of fats as well as the absorption of the fat-soluble vitamins A, D, E, and K. When fat digestion is impaired, other foodstuffs are

also poorly digested, since the fat covers the food particles and prevents enzymes from attacking them. Under these conditions, the activity of the intestinal bacteria causes considerable putrefaction and production of gas.

B. Neutralization of Acid: In addition to its functions in digestion, the bile is a reservoir of alkali, which helps to neutralize the acid chyme from the stomach.

C. Excretion: As stated above, bile is an important vehicle for cholesterol excretion, but it also removes many drugs, toxins, bile pigments, and various inorganic substances such as copper, zinc, and mercury (see Chapter 46).

D. Cholesterol Solubility in Bile; Formation of Gallstones: Free cholesterol is totally insoluble in water; consequently, it is incorporated into a lecithin–bile salt micelle (see p 206). Indeed, lecithin, the predominant phospholipid in bile, is itself insoluble in aqueous systems but can be dissolved by bile salts in micelles. The large quantities of cholesterol present in the bile of humans are solubilized in these water-soluble mixed micelles, allowing cholesterol to be transported in bile via the biliary tract to the intestine. However, the actual solubility of cholesterol in bile depends on the relative proportions of bile salt, lecithin, and cholesterol. The solubility also depends on the water content of bile. This is especially important in dilute hepatic bile.

Using triangular coordinates (Fig 44–4), Redinger and Small were able to determine the maximum solubility of cholesterol in human gallbladder bile. The diagram was constructed from studies of bile salt, lecithin, and cholesterol mixtures in water to illustrate the limits of cholesterol solubility in this quaternary system. For cholesterol solubility, reference to the figure indicates that any triangular point falling above the line ABC would represent a bile whose composition is such that cholesterol is either supersaturated or precipitated.

It is believed that at some time during the life of a patient with gallstones there is formed an abnormal bile that has become supersaturated with cholesterol.

With time, various factors such as infection, for example, serve as seeding agents to cause the supersaturated bile to precipitate the excess cholesterol as crystals. Unless the newly formed crystals are promptly excreted into the intestine with the bile, the crystals will grow to form stones. When the activities of key enzymes in bile acid formation were measured in the livers of patients with gallstones, cholesterol synthesis was elevated but bile acid synthesis was reduced, causing liver cholesterol concentrations to increase. It seems that decreased 7α-hydroxylase activity leads to a diminished enterohepatic bile acid pool that signals the liver to produce more cholesterol. The bile then becomes overloaded with cholesterol, which is unable to dissolve completely in the mixed micelles.

The above information concerning cholesterol solubility has been used in attempts to dissolve gallstones or to prevent their further formation. Chenodeoxycholic acid appears to offer specific medical treatment for asymptomatic radiolucent gallstones in functioning gallbladders because of its specific inhibition of HMG-CoA reductase in the liver, with consequent reduction in cholesterol synthesis.

E. Bile Pigment Metabolism: The origin of the bile pigments from hemoglobin is discussed on p 341.

Digestion by Pancreatic Secretion

Pancreatic secretion is a nonviscid watery fluid that is similar to saliva in its content of water and contains some protein and other organic and inorganic compounds —mainly Na^+, K^+, HCO_3^-, and Cl^-, but Ca^{2+}, Zn^{2+}, HPO_4^{2-}, and SO_4^{2-} are also present in small amounts. The pH of pancreatic secretion is distinctly alkaline, 7.5–8.0 or higher.

Many enzymes are found in pancreatic secretion; some are secreted as zymogens.

A. Trypsin, Chymotrypsin, and Elastase: The proteolytic action of pancreatic secretion is due to the 3 endopeptidases trypsin, chymotrypsin, and elastase, which attack protein, proteoses, and peptones released from the stomach, to produce polypeptides. Trypsin is specific for peptide bonds of basic amino acids, and chymotrypsin is specific for peptide bonds containing uncharged amino acid residues such as aromatic amino acids, whereas elastase, in spire of its name, has rather broad specificity in attacking bonds next to small amino acid residues such as glycine, alanine, and serine. All 3 enzymes are secreted as zymogens. Activation of **trypsinogen** is due to another proteolytic enzyme, **enterokinase,** secreted by the intestinal mucosa. This hydrolyzes a lysine peptide bond in the zymogen, releasing a small polypeptide that allows the molecule to unfold as active trypsin. Once trypsin is formed, it will attack not only additional molecules of trypsinogen but also the other zymogens in the pancreatic secretion, **chymotrypsinogen, proelastase,** and **procarboxypeptidase,** liberating chymotrypsin, elastase, and **carboxypeptidase,** respectively.

B. Carboxypeptidase: The further attack on the polypeptides produced by the action of endopeptidases is carried on by the exopeptidase carboxypeptidase,

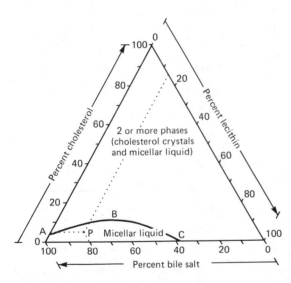

Figure 44–4. Method for presenting 3 major components of bile (bile salts, lecithin, and cholesterol) on triangular coordinates. Each component is expressed as a percentage mole of total bile salt, lecithin, and cholesterol. Line ABC represents maximum solubility of cholesterol in varying mixtures of bile salt and lecithin. Point P represents normal bile composition, containing 5% cholesterol, 15% lecithin, and 80% bile salt, and falls within the zone of a single phase of micellar liquid. Bile having a composition falling above the line would contain excess cholesterol in either supersaturated or precipitated form (crystals or liquid crystals). (Reproduced, with permission, from Redinger RN, Small DM: Bile composition, bile salt metabolism, and gallstones. *Arch Intern Med* 1972;**130**:620. Copyright © 1972. American Medical Association.)

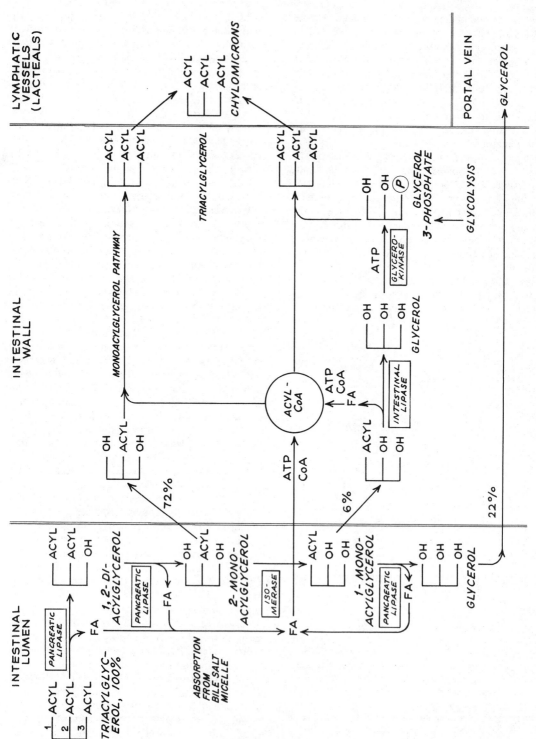

Figure 44–5. Chemical mechanisms of digestion and absorption of triacylglycerols. FA, long-chain fatty acid. (Modified from Mattson FH, Volpenheim RA: The digestion and absorption of triglycerides. *J Biol Chem* 1964;**239**:2772.)

which attacks the carboxy-terminal peptide bond, liberating single amino acids.

C. Amylase: The starch-splitting action of pancreatic secretion is due to a pancreatic α-amylase. It is similar in action to salivary amylase, hydrolyzing starch and glycogen to maltose, maltotriose [three α-glucose residues linked by $\alpha(1\rightarrow4)$ bonds], and a mixture of branched (1:6) oligosaccharides (α-limit dextrins), nonbranched oligosaccharides, and some glucose.

D. Lipase: The pancreatic lipase acts at the oil-water interface of the finely emulsified lipid droplets formed by mechanical agitation in the gut in the presence of the products of lingual lipase activity, bile salts, **colipase** (a protein present in pancreatic secretion), **phospholipids,** and **phospholipase A$_2$** (also present in the pancreatic secretion). Phospholipase A$_2$ and colipase are secreted in pro- forms and require activation by tryptic hydrolysis of specific peptide bonds. Ca^{2+} is necessary for phospholipase A$_2$ activity. A limited hydrolysis of the ester bond in the 2 position of the phospholipid by phospholipase A$_2$ (see Fig 17–21) results in the binding of lipase to the substrate interface and a rapid rate of hydrolysis of triacylglycerol. Colipase binds to the bile salt–triacylglycerol/water interface, providing a high-affinity anchor for the lipase. The complete hydrolysis of triacylglycerols produces glycerol and fatty acids. However, the second and third fatty acids are hydrolyzed from the triacylglycerols with increasing difficulty. Pancreatic lipase is virtually specific for the hydrolysis of primary ester linkages, ie, at positions 1 and 3 of triacylglycerols.

Because of the difficulty of hydrolysis of the secondary ester linkage in the triacylglycerol, it is probable that the digestion of triacylglycerol proceeds by removal of the terminal fatty acids to produce 2-monoacylglycerol. Since this last fatty acid is linked by a secondary ester bond, its removal requires isomerization to a primary ester linkage. This is a relatively slow process; as a result, 2-monoacylglycerols are major end products of triacylglycerol digestion, and less than one-fourth of the ingested triacylglycerol is completely broken down to glycerol and fatty acids (Fig 44–5).

E. Cholesteryl Ester Hydrolase (Cholesterol Esterase): This enzyme may either catalyze the esterification of free cholesterol with fatty acids or, depending upon the conditions of equilibrium, it may catalyze the opposite reaction, ie, hydrolysis of cholesteryl esters. Under the conditions within the lumen of the intestine, the enzyme catalyzes the hydrolysis of cholesteryl esters, which are thus absorbed from the intestine in a nonesterified, free form.

F. Ribonuclease (RNase) and **Deoxyribonuclease (DNase)** have been prepared from pancreatic tissue (see Chapters 28 and 29).

G. Phospholipase A$_2$: Phospholipase A$_2$ hydrolyzes the ester bond in the 2 position of glycerophospholipids of both biliary and dietary origins to form lysophospholipids.

Digestion by Intestinal Secretion

The intestinal juice secreted by the glands of Brunner and of Lieberkühn also contains digestive enzymes, including the following:

(1) **Aminopeptidase,** which is an exopeptidase attacking peptide bonds next to N-terminal amino acids of polypeptides and oligopeptides; and **dipeptidases** of various specificity, some of which may be within the intestinal epithelium. The latter complete digestion of dipeptides to free amino acids.

(2) Specific **disaccharidases** and **oligosaccharidases,** ie, α-glucosidase **(maltase),** which removes single glucose residues from $\alpha(1\rightarrow4)$ linked oligosaccharides and disaccharides, starting from the nonreducing ends; **isomaltase (α-dextrinase),** which hydrolyzes $1\rightarrow6$ bonds in α-limit dextrins; β-**galactosidase (lactase)** for removing galactose from lactose; **sucrase** for hydrolyzing sucrose; and **trehalase** for hydrolyzing trehalose.

(3) A **phosphatase,** which removes phosphate from certain organic phosphates such as hexosephosphates, glycerophosphate, and the nucleotides derived from the diet and the digestion of nucleic acids by nucleases.

(4) **Polynucleotidases,** which split nucleic acids into nucleotides.

(5) **Nucleosidases** (nucleoside phosphorylases), one of which attacks only guanine- and hypoxanthine-containing nucleosides. The pyrimidine nucleosides (uridine, cytidine, and thymidine) are broken down by another enzyme that differs from the purine nucleoside phosphorylase.

(6) The intestinal secretion is also said to contain a **phospholipase** that attacks phospholipids to produce glycerol, fatty acids, phosphoric acid, and bases such as choline.

The Major Products of Digestion

The final result of the action of the digestive enzymes described is to reduce the foodstuffs of the diet to forms that can be absorbed and assimilated. These end products of digestion are, for carbohydrates, the monosaccharides (principally glucose); for proteins, the amino acids; for triacylglycerol, the fatty acids, glycerol, and monoacylglycerols; and for nucleic acids, the nucleobases, nucleosides, and pentoses.

The plant cell wall polysaccharides and lignin of the diet that cannot be digested by mammalian enzymes constitute **dietary fiber** and make up the bulk of the residues from digestion. Fiber performs an important function in adding bulk to the diet and is discussed further on p 670.

ABSORPTION FROM THE GASTROINTESTINAL TRACT

There is little absorption from the stomach, even of smaller molecules like glucose that are absorbed directly from the intestine. Although water is not absorbed to any extent from the stomach, considerable gastric absorption of ethanol is possible.

The small intestine is the main digestive and absorptive organ. About 90% of the ingested foodstuffs is absorbed in the course of passage through the small intestine, and water is absorbed at the same time. Considerably more water is absorbed after the foodstuffs pass into the large intestine, so that the contents, which were fluid in the small intestine, gradually become more solid in the colon.

There are 2 pathways for the transport of materials absorbed by the intestine: the **hepatic portal system,** which leads directly to the liver; and the **lymphatic vessels,** which lead to the blood by way of the thoracic duct.

Absorption of Carbohydrates

The products of carbohydrate digestion are absorbed from the jejunum into the blood of the portal venous system in the form of monosaccharides, chiefly the hexoses (glucose, fructose, mannose, and galactose), although the pentose sugars, if present in the food ingested, will also be absorbed. The oligosaccharides (compounds derived from starches that yield 3–10 monosaccharide units upon hydrolysis) and the disaccharides are hydrolyzed by appropriate enzymes derived from the mucosal surfaces of the small intestine, which may include pancreatic amylase adsorbed onto the mucosa. There is little free disaccharidase activity in the intestinal lumen. Most of the activity is associated with small "knobs" on the brush border of the intestinal epithelial cell.

Two mechanisms are responsible for the absorption of monosaccharides: active transport against a concentration gradient and simple diffusion. However, the absorption of some sugars does not fit clearly into one or the other of these mechanisms. The molecular configurations that seem necessary for active transport, which are present in glucose and galactose, are the following: the OH on carbon 2 should have the same configuration as in glucose, a pyranose ring should be present, and a methyl or substituted methyl group should be present on carbon 5. Fructose is absorbed more slowly than glucose and galactose. Its absorption appears to proceed by diffusion with the concentration gradient, which is different from the energy-dependent active transport mechanism for glucose, which is against a concentration gradient.

The brush border of the enterocyte contains several transporter systems, some very similar to those of the renal brush border membranes, which specialize in the uptake of the different amino acids and sugars. To explain the active absorption of glucose, a carrier has been postulated which binds both glucose and Na$^+$ at separate sites and which transports them both through the plasma membrane of the intestinal cell. It is envisaged that both glucose and Na$^+$ are released into the cytosol, allowing the carrier to take up more "cargo." The Na$^+$ is transported down its concentration gradient and at the same time causes the carrier to transport glucose against its concentration gradient. The free energy required for this active transport is obtained from the hydrolysis of ATP linked to a sodium pump that expels Na$^+$ from the cell in exchange for K$^+$ (Fig 44–6). The active transport of glucose is inhibited by ouabain (cardiac glycoside), an inhibitor of the sodium pump, and by phlorhizin, a known inhibitor of glucose reabsorption in the kidney tubule. Phlorhizin, a plant glycoside, probably displaces Na$^+$ from its binding site on the glucose carrier. The ratio of Na$^+$:glucose transported varies but may be consistent with 2 carriers—a 1:1 and a 3:1 carrier operating in parallel. There is also an Na$^+$-independent carrier of glucose.

Hydrolysis of polysaccharides, oligosaccharides, and disaccharides is a rapid process; therefore, the absorptive mechanisms for glucose and fructose are quickly saturated. A conspicuous exception is the hydrolysis of lactose, which proceeds at only half the rate for sucrose, accounting for the fact that digestion of lactose does not lead to saturation of the transport mechanisms for glucose and galactose.

Defects in Digestion & Absorption of Carbohydrates

A. Lactase Deficiency: Intolerance to lactose, the sugar of milk, may be attributable to a deficiency of lactase. The syndrome should not be confused with intolerance to milk resulting from a sensitivity to milk proteins, usually to the β-lactoglobulin. The signs and symptoms of lactose intolerance are the same regard-

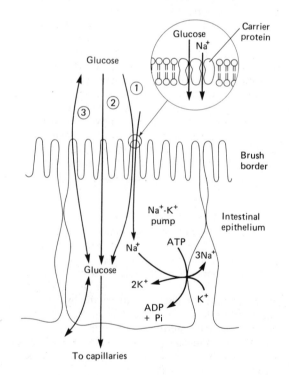

Figure 44–6. Transport of glucose across the intestinal epithelium. Active glucose transport is coupled to the Na$^+$-K$^+$ pump, (1), or to an Na$^+$-independent system, (2). Diffusion is represented by (3).

less of the cause. These include abdominal cramps, diarrhea, and flatulence. They are attributed to accumulation of lactose, which is osmotically active, so that it holds water, and to the fermentative action on the sugar of the intestinal bacteria which produce gases and other products that serve as intestinal irritants.

There are 3 types of lactase deficiency:

1. Inherited lactase deficiency–In this syndrome, which is relatively rare, symptoms of intolerance to milk such as diarrhea and wasting, incident to fluid and electrolyte disturbances as well as inadequate nutrition, all develop very **soon after birth.** The feeding of a lactose-free diet results in disappearance of the symptoms. Occasionally, infants who appear to be able to digest and absorb lactose nonetheless develop severe symptoms after ingestion of milk or lactose. The occurrence of lactose in the urine is a prominent feature of this syndrome, which appears to be attributable to an effect of lactose on the intestine.

2. Secondary low-lactase activity–Because digestion of lactose is limited even in normal humans, intolerance to milk is not uncommon as a consequence of intestinal diseases. These include many gastrointestinal conditions prevalent in tropical as well as nontropical countries. Examples are tropical and nontropical (celiac) sprue, kwashiorkor, colitis, and gastroenteritis. The disorder may be noted also after surgery for peptic ulcer.

3. Primary low-lactase activity–This is a relatively common syndrome, particularly among nonwhite populations in the USA as well as other parts of the world. Since intolerance to lactose was not a feature of the early life of adults with this disorder, it is presumed to represent a gradual decline in activity of lactase in susceptible individuals.

B. Sucrase Deficiency: There are a number of reports of an inherited deficiency of the disaccharidases sucrase and isomaltase. These 2 deficiencies coexist, because sucrase and isomaltase occur together as a complex enzyme. Symptoms occur in early childhood following ingestion of the sugars in question. The symptoms are the same as those described in lactase deficiency.

C. Disacchariduria: An increase in the excretion of disaccharides may be observed in some patients with disaccharidase deficiencies. As much as 300 mg or more of disaccharide may be excreted in the urine of these people and in patients with intestinal damage (eg, sprue).

D. Monosaccharide Malabsorption: There is a congenital condition in which glucose and galactose are absorbed only slowly, owing to a defect in the carrier mechanism. Because fructose is not absorbed via the carrier, its absorption is normal.

Absorption of Lipids

The 2-monoacylglycerols, fatty acids, and small amounts of 1-monoacylglycerols leave the oil phase of the lipid emulsion and diffuse into the mixed micelles consisting of bile salts, lecithin, and cholesterol, furnished by the bile (Fig 44–3). Because the micelles are soluble, they allow the products of digestion to be transported through the aqueous environment of the intestinal lumen to the brush border of the mucosal cells, where they are absorbed into the intestinal epithelium. The bile salts pass on to the ileum, where most are absorbed into the enterohepatic circulation (Fig 44–3). Phospholipids of dietary and biliary origin (eg, lecithin) are hydrolyzed by phospholipase A_2 of the pancreatic secretion to fatty acids and lysophospholipids, which are also absorbed from the micelles. Cholesteryl esters are hydrolyzed by cholesteryl ester hydrolase of the pancreatic juice, and the free cholesterol, together with most of the biliary cholesterol, is absorbed through the brush border after transportation in the micelles. Over 98% of dietary lipid is normally absorbed.

Within the intestinal wall, 1-monoacylglycerols are further hydrolyzed to produce free glycerol and fatty acids by a lipase, which is distinct from pancreatic lipase, whereas 2-monoacylglycerols may be reconverted to triacylglycerols via the **monoacylglycerol pathway** (Fig 44–5). The utilization of fatty acids for resynthesis of triacylglycerols requires first their "activation." This is accomplished by formation of a coenzyme A (acyl) derivative of the fatty acid (see p 109). The reaction (which also requires ATP) is catalyzed by the enzyme **acyl-CoA synthetase.**

$$CoA \cdot SH$$

$$R - COOH \xrightarrow[\underset{Mg^{2+}}{\overset{\boxed{\text{ACYL-CoA SYNTHETASE}}}{}]{}} R - \overset{\overset{O}{\|}}{C} \sim S - CoA$$

$$ATP \quad AMP + PP_i$$

It is likely that the synthesis of triacylglycerols proceeds in the intestinal mucosa in a manner similar to that which takes place in other tissues, as described on p 224. The absorbed lysophospholipids, together with much of the absorbed cholesterol, are also reacylated with acyl-CoA to regenerate phospholipids and cholesteryl esters.

The free glycerol released in the intestinal lumen (from approximately 22% of the total amount of triacylglycerol originally present) is not reutilized but passes directly to the portal vein. However, the glycerol released within the intestinal cells can be reutilized for triacylglycerol synthesis by activation by ATP to glycerol 3-phosphate. Thus, all long-chain fatty acids absorbed in intestinal wall mucosal cells are ultimately utilized in the re-formation of triacylglycerols.

Triacylglycerols, having been synthesized in the intestinal mucosa, are not transported to any extent in the portal venous blood. Instead, the great majority of absorbed lipids, including phospholipids, cholesteryl esters, and cholesterol, appear in the form of **chylomicrons** that pass to the lymphatic vessels of the abdominal region and later to the systemic blood (see also Fig 18–5).

The majority of absorbed fatty acids of more than 10 carbon atoms in length, irrespective of the form in which they are absorbed, are found as esterified fatty acids in the lymph of the thoracic duct. Fatty acids with carbon chains **shorter than 10–12 carbons** are transported in the portal venous blood as unesterified (free) fatty acids.

Of the plant sterols (phytosterols), none are absorbed from the intestine except activated egosterol (provitamin D).

Chyluria is an abnormality in which the patient excretes milky urine because of the presence of an abnormal connection between the urinary tract and the lymphatic drainage system of the intestine, a so-called chylous fistula. In a similar abnormality, **chylothorax,** there is an abnormal connection between the pleural space and the lymphatic drainage of the small intestine that results in the accumulation of milky pleural fluid. Feeding triacylglycerols in which the fatty acids are of medium chain length (less than 12 carbons) in place of dietary fat results in a disappearance of chyluria. In chylothorax, the use of triacylglycerol with short-chain fatty acids results in the appearance of clear pleural fluid.

Absorption of Amino Acids & Protein

Under normal circumstances, the dietary proteins are almost completely digested to their constituent amino acids, and these end products of protein digestion are then rapidly absorbed from the intestine into the portal blood. It is possible that some hydrolysis, eg, of dipeptides, is completed in the intestinal wall. Animals may be successfully maintained with respect to protein nutrition when a complete amino acid mixture is fed to them. This indicates that intact protein is not necessary.

There is a difference in the rate of absorption from the intestine of the 2 isomers of an amino acid. The natural (L) isomer is actively transported across the intestine from the mucosa to the serosa; vitamin B_6 (pyridoxal phosphate) may be involved in this transfer. The D-isomers, on the other hand, are transported only by free diffusion. This active transport of the L-amino acids is energy-dependent, as evidenced by the fact that, in studies of small pieces of segmented intestine, 2,4-dinitrophenol, the uncoupler of oxidative phosphorylation (see p 139), inhibits the concentration of L-amino acids. Amino acids are transported through the brush border by a multiplicity of carriers, many having Na^+-dependent mechanisms similar to the glucose carrier system (Fig 44–6). Of the Na^+-dependent carriers, there is a neutral amino acid carrier, a phenylalanine and methionine carrier, and a carrier specific for imino acids such as proline and hydroxyproline. Na^+-independent carriers specializing in the transport of neutral and lipophilic amino acids (eg, phenylalanine and leucine) or of cationic amino acids (eg, lysine) have been characterized.

A valuable tool for the study of amino acid transport is the synthetic amino acid α-aminoisobutyric acid. This compound is transported across cell membranes as are the natural amino acids; but once within the cells it cannot be metabolized, so that it remains for

Table 44–3. Site of absorption of nutrients.

Site	Nutrient
Jejunum	Glucose and other monosaccharides; some disaccharides
	Monoacylglycerols, fatty acids, glycerol, cholesterol
	Amino acids, peptides
	Vitamins, folate
	Electrolytes, iron, calcium, water
Ileum	Bile acids
	Vitamin B_{12}
	Electrolytes
	Water

identification and analysis. Another amino acid model is 1-aminocyclopentane-1-carboxylic acid.

When groups of amino acids are fed, there is some evidence that one amino acid fed in excess can retard the absorption of another. These observations are similar to those made with respect to reabsorption of amino acids by the renal tubules.

A puzzling feature of protein absorption is that in some individuals sensitivity to protein (in the immunologic sense) results when they eat certain proteins. It is known that a protein is antigenic, ie, able to stimulate an immunologic response, only if it is in the form of a relatively large molecule; the digestion of a protein even to the polypeptide stage destroys its antigenicity. Those individuals in whom an immunologic response to ingested protein occurs must therefore be able to absorb some unhydrolyzed protein. This is not entirely undocumented, since the antibodies of the colostrum are known to be available to the infant.

There is increasing support for the hypothesis that the basic defect in **nontropical sprue** is located within the mucosal cells of the intestine and permits the polypeptides resulting from the peptic and tryptic digestion of gluten, the principal protein of wheat, not only to exert a local harmful effect within the intestine but also to be absorbed into the circulation and thus to elicit the production of antibodies. It has been definitely established that circulating antibodies to wheat gluten or its fractions are frequently present in patients with nontropical sprue. The harmful entity is a

Table 44–4. Summary of disturbances due to malabsorption.

Sign or Symptom	Substance Malabsorbed
Anemia	Iron, vitamin B_{12}, folate
Edema	Products of protein digestion
Tetany	Calcium, magnesium, vitamin D
Osteoporosis	Calcium, products of protein digestion, vitamin D
Milk intolerance	Lactose
Bleeding, bruising	Vitamin K
Steatorrhea (fatty stools)	Lipids and fat-soluble vitamins
Hartnup disease (defect in intestinal neutral amino acid carrier)	Neutral amino acids

polypeptide composed of 6 or 7 amino acids of which glutamine and proline must be present to ensure the harmful properties of the peptide.

These observations on a disease entity that is undoubtedly the adult analog of celiac disease in children advance the possibility that protein fragments of larger molecular size than amino acids are absorbed from the intestine under certain conditions.

Tables 44–3 and 44–4 summarize the sites of intestinal absorption of some common nutrients and some disorders resulting from malabsorption, respectively.

INTESTINAL PUTREFACTION & FERMENTATION

Most ingested food is absorbed from the small intestine. The residue passes into the large intestine. Here considerable absorption of water takes place, and the semiliquid intestinal contents gradually become more solid. During this period, considerable bacterial activity occurs. By fermentation and putrefaction, the bacteria produce various gases, such as CO_2, methane, hydrogen, nitrogen, and hydrogen sulfide, as well as acetic, lactic, and butyric acids. The bacterial decomposition of lecithin may produce choline and related toxic amines such as neurine.

$$H_3C-\overset{\overset{\displaystyle CH_3}{|}}{\underset{\underset{\displaystyle CH_3}{|}}{N^{(+)}}}-CH_2-CH_2OH \qquad H_3C-\overset{\overset{\displaystyle CH_3}{|}}{\underset{\underset{\displaystyle CH_3}{|}}{N^{(+)}}}-CH=CH_2$$

Choline   Neurine

Fate of Amino Acids

Many amino acids undergo decarboxylation as a result of the action of intestinal bacteria to produce toxic amines (ptomaines).

$$R-\overset{\overset{\displaystyle [COO]H}{|}}{\underset{\underset{\displaystyle H}{|}}{C}}-NH_2 \xrightarrow[\underset{\displaystyle CO_2}{\searrow}]{\boxed{\text{BACTERIAL DECARBOXYLASE}}} RCH_2NH_2$$

A ptomaine

Such decarboxylation reactions produce cadaverine from lysine; agmatine from arginine; tyramine from tyrosine; putrescine from ornithine; and histamine from histidine. Many of these amines are powerful vasopressor substances.

The amino acid tryptophan undergoes a series of reactions to form indole and methylindole (skatole), the substances particularly responsible for the odor of feces.

Indole   Skatole

The sulfur-containing amino acid cysteine undergoes a series of transformations to form mercaptans such as ethyl and methyl mercaptan as well as H_2S.

$$\overset{\overset{\displaystyle CH_3}{|}}{CH_2SH} \qquad\qquad CH_3SH$$

Ethyl mercaptan   Methyl mercaptan

$$CH_3SH \xrightarrow{[2H]} CH_4 + H_2S$$

Methyl mercaptan   Methane and hydrogen sulfide

The large intestine is a source of considerable quantities of ammonia, presumably as a product of the putrefactive activity on nitrogenous substrates by the intestinal bacteria. This ammonia is absorbed into the portal circulation, but under normal conditions it is rapidly removed from the blood by the liver. In liver disease, this function of the liver may be impaired, in which case the concentration of ammonia in the peripheral blood will rise to toxic levels. It is believed that ammonia intoxication may play a role in the genesis of hepatic coma in some patients. In dogs on whom an Eck fistula has been performed (complete diversion of the portal blood to the vena cava), the feeding of large quantities of raw meat will induce symptoms of ammonia intoxication (meat intoxication) accompanied by elevated levels of ammonia in the blood. The oral administration of neomycin has been shown to reduce the quantity of ammonia delivered from the intestine to the blood, owing undoubtedly to the antibacterial action of the drug. The feeding of high-protein diets to patients suffering from advanced liver disease, or the occurrence of gastrointestinal hemorrhage in such patients, may contribute to the development of ammonia intoxication. Neomycin is also beneficial under these circumstances.

Intestinal Bacteria

The intestinal flora may comprise as much as 25% of the dry weight of the feces. In herbivora, whose diet consists largely of cellulose, the intestinal or ruminal bacteria are essential to digestion, since they decompose the polysaccharide and make it available for absorption. In addition, these symbiotic bacteria accomplish the synthesis of essential amino acids and vitamins. In humans, although the intestinal flora is not as important as in the herbivora, nevertheless some nutritional benefit is derived from bacterial activity in the synthesis of certain vitamins, particularly vitamins K and B_{12}, and possibly other members of the B complex, which are made available to the body. Information gained from experiments with animals raised under strictly aseptic conditions should help to define further the precise role of the intestinal bacteria.

●   ●   ●

References

Digestion & Absorption

Borgström B: Importance of phospholipids, pancreatic phospholipase A$_2$, and fatty acid for the digestion of dietary fat. *Gastroenterology* 1980;**78**:954.

Boyer PD (editor): *The Enzymes,* 3rd ed. Vol 16: *Lipid Enzymology.* Academic Press, 1983.

Carey MC, Small DM, Bliss CM: Lipid digestion and absorption. *Annu Rev Physiol* 1983;**45**:651.

Foltmann B: Gastric proteinases. *Essays Biochem* 1981; **17**:52.

Gray GM: Carbohydrate digestion and absorption: Role of the small intestine. *N Engl J Med* 1975;**292**:1225.

Masoro EJ: Lipids and lipid metabolism. *Annu Rev Physiol* 1977;**39**:301.

Scow RO, Stein Y, Stein O: Incorporation of dietary lecithin and lysolecithin into lymph chylomicrons in rat. *J Biol Chem* 1967;**242**:4919.

Semenza G: Intestinal oligo- and disaccharidases. Page 425 in: *Carbohydrate Metabolism and Its Disorders.* Vol 3. Randle PJ, Steiner DF, Whelan WJ (editors). Academic Press, 1981.

Senior JR: Intestinal absorption of fats. *J Lipid Res* 1964; **5**:495.

Shreeve WW: *Physiological Chemistry of Carbohydrates in Mammals.* Saunders, 1974.

Smyth DH (editor): *Intestinal Absorption.* Plenum Press, 1974.

Steven BR, Kaunitz JD, Wright EM: Intestinal transport of amino acids and sugars. *Annu Rev Physiol* 1984;**46**:417.

Bile

Danielsson H, Sjövall J: Bile acid metabolism. *Annu Rev Biochem* 1975;**44**:233.

Dietschy JM (editor): Symposium on bile acids. *Arch Intern Med* 1972;**130**:473.

Forker EL: Mechanisms of hepatic bile formation. *Annu Rev Physiol* 1977;**39**:323.

Ginter E: Marginal vitamin C deficiency, lipid metabolism, and atherosclerosis. *Adv Lipid Res* 1978;**16**:167.

Halloran LG et al: Evidence for high-density lipoprotein-free cholesterol as the primary precursor for bile-acid synthesis in man. *Surgery* 1978;**84**:1.

Nair PP, Kritchevsky D (editors): *The Bile Acids.* 2 vols. Plenum Press, 1971–1973.

Salen G, Shefer S: Bile acid synthesis. *Annu Rev Physiol* 1983;**45**:679.

Blood Plasma & Clotting | 45

David W. Martin, Jr., MD

BLOOD PLASMA

Blood is a tissue that circulates in what is virtually a closed system of blood vessels. It consists of solid elements—the red and white blood cells and the platelets—suspended in a liquid medium, the **plasma.**

Once the blood has clotted (coagulated), as discussed below, the remaining liquid phase is called **serum.** Serum lacks the clotting factors (including fibrinogen) that are normally present in plasma but have been consumed during the process of coagulation. Serum does contain some degradation products of clotting factors—products that have been generated during the coagulation process and thus are *not* normally present in plasma.

The Functions of the Blood

The functions of blood—all except specific cellular ones such as oxygen transport and cell-mediated immunologic defense—are carried out by plasma and its constituents. They are as follows: (1) respiration—transport of oxygen from the lungs to the tissues and of CO_2 from the tissues to the lungs; (2) nutrition—transport of absorbed food materials; (3) excretion—transport of metabolic wastes to the kidneys, lungs, skin, and intestines for removal; (4) maintenance of normal acid-base balance in the body; (5) regulation of water balance through the effects of blood on the exchange of water between the circulating fluid and the tissue fluid; (6) regulation of body temperature by the distribution of body heat; (7) defense against infection by the white cells and the circulating antibodies; (8) transport of hormones and regulation of metabolism; and (9) transport of metabolites.

Plasma consists of water, electrolytes, metabolites, nutrients, proteins, and hormones. Some of the plasma components are listed in Table 45–1. The water and electrolyte composition of plasma is practically the same as that of all extracellular fluids (see Chapter 46).

THE PLASMA PROTEINS

The total protein of the plasma is about 7–7.5 g/dL. Thus, the plasma proteins comprise the major part of the solids of the plasma. The proteins of the plasma are actually a very complex mixture that includes not only simple proteins but also mixed or conjugated proteins such as glycoproteins and various types of lipoproteins.

The separation of individual proteins from a complex mixture is frequently accomplished by the use of various solvents or electrolytes (or both) to remove different protein fractions in accordance with their solubility characteristics. This is the basis of the so-called salting-out methods commonly utilized in the determination of protein fractions in the clinical laboratory. Thus, it is customary to separate the proteins of

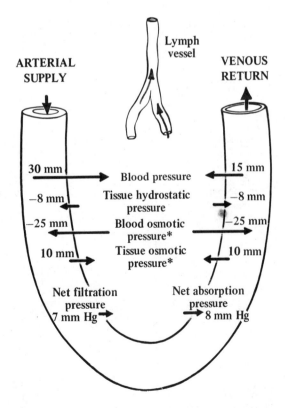

Figure 45–1. Capillary filtration and reabsorption ("Starling hypothesis"). The starred osmotic pressures are actually due only to the protein content of the respective fluids. They do not represent the total osmotic pressure.

Table 45—1. Blood, plasma, or serum values.

Determination	Material Analyzed	Normal Values (Values vary with procedure used)	SI Units
Acetone bodies	Plasma	0.3—2 mg/dL	3—20 mg/L
Aldosterone	Plasma	0.003—0.01 μg/dL	0.03—0.1 μg/L
Amino acid nitrogen	Plasma	3—5.5 mg/dL	2.1—3.9 mmol/L
Ammonia	Blood	40—70 μg/dL	22.16—38.78 μmol/L
Amylase	Serum	80—180 Somogyi units/dL; 0.8—3.2 IU/L	2.48—5.58 μkat/L
Ascorbic acid	Plasma	0.4—1.5 mg/dL (fasting)	23—85 μmol/L
	White cells (blood)	25-40 mg/dL	1420—2272 μmol/L
Bilirubin	Serum	Direct: 0.1—0.4 mg/dL	1.71—6.84 μmol/L
		Indirect: 0.2—0.7 mg/dL	3.42—11.97 μmol/L
Calcium	Serum	9—10.6 mg/dL; 4.5—5.3 meq/L (varies with protein concentration)	2.25—2.65 mmol/L
Carbon dioxide: Content	Serum or plasma	24—29 meq/L; 55—65 vol %	24—29 mmol/L
Combining power	Serum or plasma	55—75 vol %	
Carotenoids	Serum	50—300 μg/dL	
Vitamin A	Serum	24—60 IU/dL; 24—60 μg/dL	0.84—2.10 μmol/L
Chloride	Serum	100—106 meq/L; 350—375 mg/dL (as chloride)	100—106 mmol/L
Cholesterol	Serum	150—280 mg/dL	3.9—7.3 mmol/L
Cholesteryl esters	Serum	50—65% of total cholesterol	
Copper	Serum	100—200 μg/dL	16—31 μmol/L
Cortisol (free)	Plasma	4—18 μg/dL	110—497 nmol/L
Creatinine	Blood or serum	0.7—1.5 mg/dL	60—130 μmol/L
Glucose (Folin)	Blood	80—120 mg/dL (fasting)	4.4—6.6 mmol/L
Glucose (true)	Blood	60—100 mg/dL	3.3—5.5 mmol/L
Hemoglobin	Blood	Women: 12—16 g/dL	1.86—2.48 mmol/L
		Men: 14—18 g/dL	2.17—2.79 mmol/L
Iodine (BEI)	Serum	3—6.5 μg/dL	0.24—0.51 μmol/L
Iodine, protein-bound	Serum	4—8 μg/dL	0.32—0.63 μmol/L
Iron	Serum	65—175 μg/dL	11.6—31.3 μmol/L
Iron-binding capacity	Serum	250—410 μg/dL	44.8—73.3 μmol/L
Lactic acid	Blood (in iodoacetate)	0.44—1.8 mmol/L; 4—16 mg/dL	0.44—1.28 μmol/L
Lactate dehydrogenase	Serum	90—200 IU/L	1.50—3.34 μkat/L
Lipase	Serum	0.2—1.5 units (mL of 0.1 N NaOH)	0.93—6.96 μkat/L
Lipids, total	Serum	500—600 mg/dL	5—6 g/L
Magnesium	Serum	1.5—2.5 meq/L; 1—3 mg/dL	0.75—1.25 mmol/L
Nonprotein nitrogen	Serum or blood	15—35 mg/dL	10.7—25 mmol/L
Oxygen: Capacity	Blood	16—24 vol % (varies with Hb concentration)	0.16—0.24 of volume
Arterial content	Blood	15—23 vol % (varies with Hb content)	0.15—0.23 of volume
Arterial % sat.		94—100% of capacity	0.94—1.00 of total
Venous content	Blood	10—16 vol %	0.1—0.16 of total
Venous % sat.		60—85% of capacity	0.6—0.85 of total
Phosphatase, acid	Plasma	1—5 units (King-Armstrong); 0.5—2 units (Bodansky); 0.5—2 units (Gutman);	4.48—17.94 μkat/L
		0.1—1 unit (Shinowara); 0.1—0.63 unit (Bessey-Lowry)	0.90—8.97 μkat/L 27.5—175.14 μkat/L
		Women: 0.2—9.5 IU/L	3.34—158.65 nkat/L
		Men: 0.5—11 IU/L	8.35—183.7 nkat/L
Phosphatase, alkaline	Plasma	5—13 units (King-Armstrong);	59—153.4 μkat/L
		2—4.5 units (Bodansky);	17.94—40.37 μkat/L
		3—10 units (Gutman);	
		2.2—8.6 units (Shinowara);	19.73—77.14 μkat/L
		Children: 0.1—0.63 unit (Bessey-Lowry)	27.8—175.14 μkat/L
		Adults: 30—85 IU/L;	501—1419 nkat/L
		0.8—2.3 units (Bessey-Lowry)	222.4—639.4 μkat/L
Phospholipid	Serum	145—200 mg/dL	1.87—2.58 mmol/L
Phosphorus, inorganic	Serum	3—4.5 mg/dL (children, 4—7 mg)	1—1.5 mmol/L
Potassium	Serum	2.5—5 meq/L; 14—20 mg/dL	2.5—5.0 mmol/L

Table 45—1 (cont'd). Blood, plasma, or serum values.

Determination	Material Analyzed	Normal Values (Values vary with procedure used)	SI Units
Protein: Total	Serum	5—8 g/dL	60—80 g/L
Albumin*	Serum	3.5—5.5 g/dL	0.54—0.847 mmol/L
Globulin*	Serum	1.5—3 g/dL	15—30 g/L
Fibrinogen	Plasma	0.2—0.6 g/dL	5.8—6.8 μmol/L
Pyruvic acid	Blood	0.07—0.2 mmol/L; 0.7—2 mg/dL	79.8—228 μmol/L
Sodium	Serum	136—145 meq/L; 310—340 mg/dL	136—145 mmol/L
Sulfate	Plasma or serum	0.5—1.5 meq/L	50—150 μmol/L

Transaminases:
  Glutamic-oxaloacetic
    (SGOT)
	Serum	5—40 units
		6—25 IU/L
			40.1—320.8 nkat/L

Glutamic-pyruvic (SGPT)	Serum	5—35 units 3—26 IU/L	40.1—280.7 nkat/L
Triglycerides	Serum	<165 mg/dL	<18 mmol/L
Urea nitrogen	Serum or blood	8—20 mg/dL	2.86—7.14 mmol/L
Uric acid	Serum	3—7.5 mg/dL	0.18—0.29 mmol/L

*Albumin and globulin values obtained by use of 22% sodium sulfate; not in agreement with electrophoretic data.

the plasma into 3 major groups—fibrinogen, albumin, and globulin—by the use of varying concentrations of sodium or ammonium sulfate.

Blood plasma is by definition an intravascular fluid. On the arterial side of the circulation, the intravascular hydrostatic pressure generated by the heart and large vessels is 20–25 mm Hg greater than the hydrostatic pressure in the tissue spaces (Fig 45–1). In order to prevent too much intravascular fluid from being forced into the extravascular tissue spaces, the hydrostatic pressure is opposed by an **intravascular colloid osmotic pressure** generated by the plasma proteins (Fig 45–1).

Albumin

Of the 3 major plasma protein groups, albumin is present in the highest mass concentration (Table 45–1). Albumin also has the lowest molecular weight of the major protein molecules in plasma (Fig 45–2); thus, **albumin is the largest contributor to the intravascular colloid osmotic pressure.** Albumin is synthesized in the liver and consists of a single chain of 610 amino acids. In addition to contributing to the colloid osmotic pressure, albumin also acts as a **carrier molecule** for bilirubin, fatty acids, trace elements, and many drugs. Some of its ligand binding sites are highly specific and saturable, while others are much less so. The major effect of low serum albumin concentration (hypoalbuminemia), which occurs frequently in liver and kidney disease, is soft tissue edema due to the diminished intravascular colloid osmotic pressure.

Globulins

As described in Chapter 4, globulins are protein molecules that are insoluble in plain water but soluble in salt water. The serum globulins are a heterogeneous, complex mixture of protein molecules that are frequently designated as α-, β-, or γ-globulins, sometimes with number designations as well, all based on their electrophoretic mobility (Fig 45–3). A more ra-

tional classification is based on their structure or function.

The **glycoproteins** contain covalently bound oligosaccharide moieties (see Chapter 33) and are found principally in the α_1- and α_2-globulin fractions. Among the glycoproteins are many specific molecules with specific functions, some understood and others not.

Lipoproteins contain lipids, usually noncovalently bound to the protein molecule (see Chapter 18).

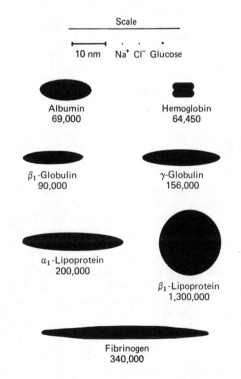

Figure 45–2. Relative dimensions and molecular weights of protein molecules in the blood (Oncley).

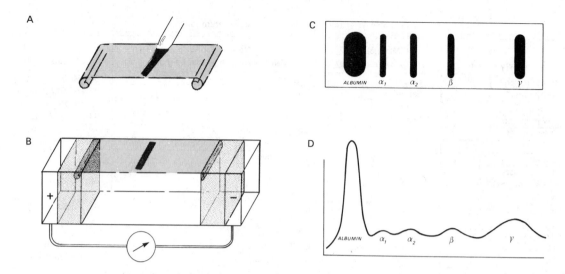

Figure 45–3. Technique of cellulose acetate zone electrophoresis. *A:* Small amount of serum or other fluid is applied to cellulose acetate strip. *B:* Electrophoresis of sample in electrolyte buffer is performed. *C:* Separated protein bands are visualized in characteristic position after being stained. *D:* Densitometer scanning from cellulose acetate strip converts bands to characteristic peaks of albumin, α_1-globulin, α_2-globulin, β-globulin, and γ-globulin. (Reproduced, with permission, from Stites DP et al [editors]: *Basic & Clinical Immunology,* 5th ed. Lange, 1984.)

The lipoproteins migrate with the α-globulins or the β-globulins. The higher the fat content and the lower the protein content of a lipoprotein, the lower its specific gravity. The lipoproteins act as **carrier molecules** for many different types of lipids and lipid-soluble molecules that are not soluble in the plasma water.

Some **metal-binding proteins** such as transferrin have the properties of globulins and act as carriers for trace elements (see Chapter 46).

Plasma normally contains a number of specific **enzyme molecules** such as phosphatases, lipases, lactate dehydrogenase, amylase, and ferroxidase (ceruloplasmin). In addition, as tissues break down or their membranes leak, intracellular enzymes can be released into the intravascular space, and their catalytic activities may serve as qualitative or quantitative indexes of tissue damage. Determinations of serum transaminases, creatine kinases, and acid phosphatases are particularly useful in clinical medicine.

Polypeptide **hormones** circulate in plasma. Hormones such as the hydrophobic steroids and 1,25-dihydroxyvitamin D_3 circulate in plasma bound to specific carrier molecules.

Fibrinogen, the precursor of fibrin that forms blood clots, and **immunoglobulins,** which constitute the effector arm of the humoral immunity system, are important plasma proteins discussed in detail below.

The plasma lipoproteins are described in Chapter 18.

Immunoglobulins

Immunoglobulins, or **antibodies,** are synthesized in B lymphocytes or their derivatives, plasma cells, and with remarkable specificity **bind to antigenic sites** on other molecules.

All immunoglobulin molecules consist of 2 identical light (L) chains (MW 23,000) and 2 identical heavy (H) chains (MW 53,000–75,000) held together as a tetramer (L_2H_2) by disulfide bonds (Fig 45–4). Each chain can be divided conceptually into specific **domains,** or regions, that have structural and functional significance. The half of the **light (L) chain** toward the carboxyl terminus is referred to as the **constant region (C_L),** while the amino-terminal half is the **variable region** of the light chain (V_L). Approximately one-quarter of the **heavy (H) chain** at the amino terminus is referred to as its variable region (V_H), and the other three-quarters of the heavy chain are referred to as the constant regions (C_H1, C_H2, C_H3) of that H chain. The portion of the immunoglobulin molecule that **binds the specific antigen** is formed by the amino-terminal portions (variable regions) of both the H and L chains—ie, the V_H and V_L **domains.** The domains of the protein chains do not simply exist as linear sequences of amino acids but form globular regions with secondary and tertiary structure in order to effect binding of specific antigens.

As depicted in Fig 45–4, digestion of an immunoglobulin by the enzyme papain produces 2 antigen-binding fragments (**Fab**) and one crystallizable fragment (**Fc**). The area in which papain cleaves the immunoglobulin molecule—ie, the region between the C_H1 and C_H2 domains—is referred to as the **hinge region.**

There are 2 general types of light chains, kappa (κ) and lambda (λ), which can be distinguished on the

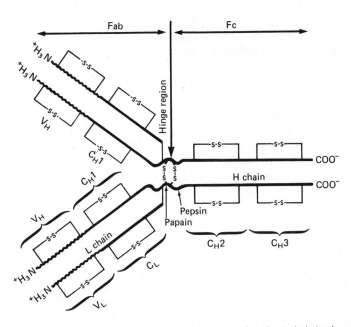

Figure 45–4. A simplified model for an IgG human antibody molecule showing the 4-chain basic structure and domains. V indicates variable region; C, the constant region; and the vertical arrow, the hinge region. Thick lines represent H and L chains; thin lines represent disulfide bonds. (Modified and reproduced, with permission, from Stites DP et al [editors]: *Basic & Clinical Immunology*, 5th ed. Lange, 1984.)

basis of structural differences in their C_L regions (Table 45–2). A given immunoglobulin molecule always contains two κ or two λ light chains, **never a mixture of κ and λ**. In humans, the κ chains are more frequent than λ chains in immunoglobulin molecules.

Five classes of H chains have been found in humans, and these classes can be distinguished by differences in their C_H regions (Table 45–2). The 5 classes of H chains are designated γ, α, μ, δ, and ϵ and vary in molecular weight from 50,000 to 70,000 (Table 45–2). The μ and ϵ chains each have four C_H domains rather than the usual 3. The type of H chain determines the class of immunoglobulin and thus its effector func-

tion. There are 5 immunoglobulin classes: **IgG, IgA, IgM, IgD,** and **IgE.** As shown in Table 45–2, many of the H chain classes can be further divided into subclasses on the basis of subtle structural differences in the C_H regions.

The variable regions of immunoglobulin molecules consist of the V_L and V_H domains and are quite heterogeneous. In fact, no 2 variable regions from different humans have been found to have identical amino acid sequences. However, there are discernible patterns between the regions from different individuals, and these shared patterns have been divided into 3 main groups based on the degree of amino

Table 45–2. Properties of human immunoglobulin chains.*

Designation	H Chains					L Chains		Secretory Component	J Chain
	γ	α	μ	δ	ϵ	κ	λ	SC	J
Classes in which chains occur	IgG	IgA	IgM	IgD	IgE	All classes	All classes	IgA	IgA, IgM
Subclasses or subtypes	1,2,3,4	1,2	1,2	. . .	. . .	. . .	1,2,3,4	. . .	. . .
Allotypic variants	Gm(1)–(25)	A2m(1), (2)	. . .	. . .	. . .	Km(1)–(3)†	. . .	. . .	. . .
Molecular weight (approximate)	50,000‡	55,000	70,000	62,000	70,000	23,000	23,000	70,000	15,000
V region subgroups	V_HI–V_HIV					V_κI–V_κIV	V_λI–V_λVI		
Carbohydrate (average percentage)	4	10	15	18	18	0	0	16	8
Number of oligosaccharides	1	2 or 3	5	?	5	0	0	?	1

*Reproduced, with permission, from Stites DP et al (editors): *Basic & Clinical Immunology*, 5th ed. Lange, 1984.

†Formerly Inv(1)–(3).

‡60,000 for γ3.

acid sequence homology. There is a V_κ group for kappa L chains, a V_λ group for lambda L chains, and a V_H group for the H chains. At higher resolution, there are even subgroups within each of these 3 groups.

Thus, within the variable regions there are some positions that are relatively invariable to account for the groups and subgroups. Upon comparing variable regions from different light chains of the same group or subgroup or different heavy chains from the same group or subgroup, it is apparent that there are **hypervariable regions** interspersed between the relatively invariable (subgroup-determining) positions (Fig 45–5). L chains have 3 hypervariable regions (in V_L), and H chains have 4 (in V_H).

The constant regions of the immunoglobulin molecules, particularly the C_H2 and C_H3 (and C_H4 of IgM and IgE), which constitute the Fc fragment, are responsible for the class-specific effector functions of the different immunoglobulin molecules (Table 45–3). Some immunoglobulins such as immune IgG exist only in the basic tetrameric structure, while others such as IgA and IgM can exist as higher-order polymers of 2, 3 (IgA) or 5 (IgM) tetrameric units (Fig 45–6).

The L chains and H chains are synthesized as separate molecules and are subsequently assembled within the B cell or plasma cell into the mature immunoglobulin molecule, all of which are **glycoproteins** (Table 45–2).

Each immunoglobulin light chain is the product of at least 3 separate structural genes: a variable region (V_L) gene, a joining region (J) gene (bearing no relationship to the J chain of IgA or IgM), and a constant region (C_L) gene. Each heavy chain is the product of at least 4 different genes: a variable region (V_H) gene, a diversity region (D) gene, a joining region (J) gene, and a constant region (C_H) gene. Thus, the "one gene,

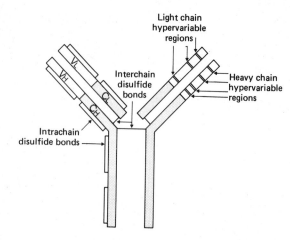

Figure 45–5. Schematic model of an IgG molecule showing approximate positions of the hypervariable regions in heavy and light chains. (Modified and reproduced, with permission, from Stites DP et al [editors]: *Basic & Clinical Immunology,* 5th ed. Lange, 1984.)

one protein" concept is invalid. The molecular mechanisms responsible for the generation of the single immunoglobulin chains from multiple structural genes are discussed in Chapters 28 and 31.

Each person is capable of generating antibodies directed against perhaps 1 million different antigens. The generation of such immense **antibody diversity** appears to depend upon the **combinations of the various structural genes** contributing to the formation of each immunoglobulin chain and upon a high frequency of **somatic mutational events** in the rearranged V_H and V_L genes.

In most humoral immune responses, antibodies

Table 45–3. Properties of human immunoglobulins.*

	IgG	IgA	IgM	IgD	IgE
H chain class	γ	α	μ	δ	ϵ
H chain subclass	$\gamma1, \gamma2, \gamma3, \gamma4$	$\alpha1, \alpha2$	$\mu1, \mu2$		
L chain type	κ and λ	κ and λ	κ and λ	κ and λ	κ and λ
Molecular formula	γ_2L_2	α_2L_2† or $(\alpha_2L_2)_2SC\S J$‡	$(\alpha_2L_2)_5J$‡	δ_2L_2	ϵ_2L_2
Sedimentation coefficient (S)	6–7	7	19	7–8	8
Molecular weight (approximate)	150,000	160,000† 400,000**	900,000	180,000	190,000
Electrophoretic mobility (average)	γ	Fast γ to β	Fast γ to β	Fast γ	Fast γ
Complement fixation (classic)	+	0	++++	0	0
Serum concentration (approximate; mg/dL)	1000	200	120	3	0.05
Placental transfer	+	0	0	0	0
Reaginic activity	?	0	0	0	++++
Antibacterial lysis	+	+	+++	?	?
Antiviral activity	+	+++	+	?	?

*Reproduced, with permission, from Stites DP et al (editors): *Basic & Clinical Immunology,* 5th ed. Lange, 1984.
†For monomeric serum IgA.
‡J chain.
§Secretory component.
**For secretory IgA.

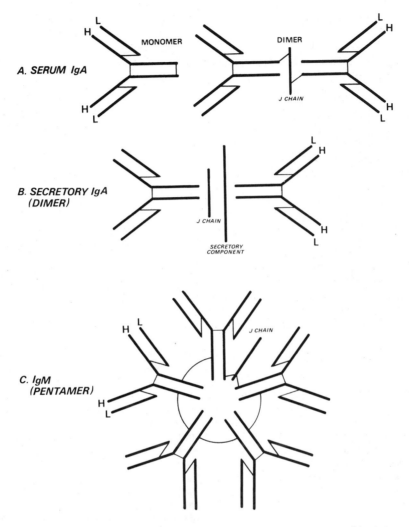

Figure 45–6. Highly schematic illustration of polymeric human immunoglobulins. Polypeptide chains are represented by thick lines; disulfide bonds linking different polypeptide chains are represented by thin lines. (Reproduced, with permission, from Stites DP et al [editors]: *Basic & Clinical Immunology,* 5th ed. Lange, 1984.)

with identical specificity but of different classes are generated in a specific chronologic order in response to the immunogen (immunizing antigen). A single type of immunoglobulin light chain can combine with an antigen-specific μ chain to generate a specific IgM molecule. Subsequently, the same antigen-specific light chain combines with a γ chain with an identical V_H region to generate an IgG molecule with antigen specificity identical to that of the original IgM molecule. Subsequently, the same light chain can combine with an α heavy chain, again containing the identical V_H region, to form an IgA molecule with identical antigen specificity. These 3 classes (IgM, IgG, and IgA) of immunoglobulin molecules against the same antigen have identical variable domains of both their light (V_L) chains and heavy (V_H) chains and are said to share an **idiotype.** The different class **isotypes** are determined by the C_H regions combined with the same antigen-specific V_H region. One aspect

of the genetic regulatory mechanisms responsible for the switching of the C_H region gene is discussed in Chapter 31.

Disorders of immunoglobulins include increased production of specific classes of immunoglobulins or even specific immunoglobulin molecules, the latter by clonal tumors of plasma cells called **myelomas. Hypogammaglobulinemia** may be restricted to a single class of immunoglobulin molecules (eg, IgA or IgG) or may involve underproduction of all classes of immunoglobulins (IgA, IgD, IgE, IgG, and IgM). The disorders of immunoglobulin levels are almost without exception due to disordered rates of immunoglobulin production or secretion, for which there can be many causes.

BLOOD CLOTTING

Hemostasis is the cessation of bleeding that follows traumatic interruption of vascular integrity. There are 4 phases to hemostasis. The **first phase** is **constriction** of the injured vessel to diminish blood flow distal to the injury. The **second phase** consists of formation of a loose **platelet plug,** or white thrombus, at the site of injury. **Collagen** exposed at the site of injury acts as a binding site for platelets, which, in response to binding collagen, undergo disruption of their internal structure and release thromboxane and **ADP.** These induce other platelets to adhere to those bound to collagen, forming the loose and temporary platelet plug. This phase of hemostasis is measured by determining the **bleeding time.** The **third phase** is the formation of the red thrombus (blood clot). The **fourth phase** is the partial or complete **dissolution** of the clot.

There are 3 types of thrombi, or clots. The white thrombus is composed of platelets and fibrin and is relatively poor in erythrocytes. It forms at the site of an injury or abnormal vessel wall, particularly in areas of rapid blood flow (arteries). A second type of thrombus is a disseminated fibrin deposit in very small vessels (capillaries).

The **red thrombus** is the third type of clot and consists of red cells and fibrin. The red thrombus morphologically resembles the clot formed in a test tube. It can form in vivo in areas of **retarded blood flow** without any abnormal vascular wall, or it may form at the site of the **injury** or **abnormal vessel wall** in conjunction with the initiating platelet plug. Initiation of the clot formation in response to tissue injury is carried out by the **extrinsic pathway** of clotting. The initiation of the pure red thrombus in an area of restricted blood flow or in response to an abnormal vessel wall without tissue injury is carried out by the **intrinsic pathway.** The intrinsic and extrinsic pathways converge in a **final common pathway**—the activation of prothrombin to thrombin and the thrombin-catalyzed conversion of fibrinogen to the fibrin clot.

Table 45–4. Numerical system for nomenclature of blood clotting factors. The numbers have no relationship to the order in which the factors act.

Factor	Name
I	Fibrinogen
II	Prothrombin
IV	Calcium
V	Labile factor, proaccelerin, accelerator (Ac-) globulin
VII	Proconvertin, serum prothrombin conversion accelerator (SPCA), cothromboplastin, autoprothrombin I
VIII	Antihemophilic factor, antihemophilic globulin (AHG)
IX	Plasma thromboplastin component (PTC) (Christmas factor)
X	Stuart-Prower factor
XI	Plasma thromboplastin antecedent (PTA)
XII	Hageman factor
XIII	Laki-Lorand factor (LLF)

The Conversion of Fibrinogen to Fibrin by Thrombin

Fibrinogen* (factor I; see Fig 45–2 and Table 45–4) is a soluble plasma glycoprotein, 46 nm in length, with a molecular weight of 340,000, which consists of 6 polypeptide chains synthesized in liver. The 6 chains are two $A\alpha$ chains, two $B\beta$ chains, and two γ chains, making the structure $A\alpha_2 B\beta_2 \gamma_2$. The $B\beta$ and γ chains contain Asn-linked complex oligosaccharides. All 3 genes ($A\alpha$, $B\beta$, and γ) are genetically linked and coordinately regulated in humans. The ends of the fiber-shaped fibrinogen molecule are **highly negatively charged,** the negative charges being contributed by a large number of aspartate and glutamate residues in the A portion of the $A\alpha$ chains and the B portion of the $B\beta$ chains (Fig 45–7). In addition, the B portion of the $B\beta$ chains contains the unusual negatively charged tyrosine O-sulfate residue. These negatively charged termini of the fibrinogen molecules not only contribute to its water solubility but

*Except for fibrinogen and prothrombin (and their activated products) and Ca^{2+}, all clotting factors will be referred to by their designated roman numerals (Table 45–4).

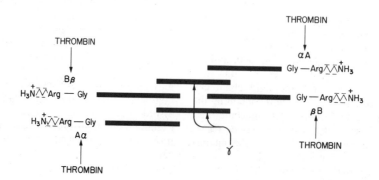

Figure 45–7. Diagrammatic representation of fibrinogen, its ($A\alpha\, B\beta\, \gamma$)₂ structure, charged termini, and the sites of thrombin cleavage (arrows) of four Arg-Gly peptide bonds.

also repulse the termini of other fibrinogen molecules, thereby preventing aggregation.

Thrombin is a 34,000-MW serine **protease** that consists of 2 polypeptide chains and hydrolyzes four Arg-Gly peptide bonds in fibrinogen (Fig 45–7). These 4 peptide bonds are the 2 between the A and α portions of the 2 Aα chains and the 2 between the B and β portions of the Bβ chains. Removal of the A and B portions of the fibrinogen molecule releases these negatively charged **fibrinopeptides** and generates the **fibrin monomer,** which has the subunit structure (α β γ)$_2$. These long insoluble fibrin monomers spontaneously associate in a regularly staggered array to form the insoluble **fibrin polymer clot.** The A and B fibrinopeptides consist of only 18 amino acid residues; thus, the fibrin monomer retains 97% of the amino acid residues of fibrinogen. It is the formation of this fibrin polymer that traps red cells, platelets, and other components to form the red thrombus or the white thrombus (platelet plug). The initial fibrin clot is a rather weak one, held together only by the noncovalent staggered array of insoluble fibrin monomers.

Thrombin, in addition to converting fibrinogen to fibrin, also converts factor XIII to active factor XIII (XIII$_a$). Factor XIII$_a$ is a **transglutaminase.** The transglutaminase covalently **cross-links** fibrin monomers by forming a specific isopeptide bond between the γ-carboxyl group of glutamine and the ϵ-amino group of Lys (Fig 45–8). This strengthening of the initial fibrin clot contributes to retraction of the clot that can be observed in the test tube. Individuals with an inherited deficiency of factor XIII have a bleeding tendency, because they cannot form a stable fibrin clot.

The activity of thrombin must be carefully controlled in order to avoid the formation of uncalled for, potentially catastrophic blood clots. This control is exerted by 2 mechanisms. One is the existence of a thrombin antagonist called antithrombin III (see below). The second mechanism involves the synthesis and circulation of a catalytically **inactive thrombin zymogen, prothrombin.** Prothrombin, or factor II, is synthesized in the liver and contains the vitamin K-dependent Gla residues (see Chapter 11). Prothrombin is a 72,000-MW single-chain glycoprotein; its primary and secondary structure is represented in Fig 45–9. The amino-terminal region of prothrombin, indicated by 1 in Fig 45–9, contains up to fourteen Gla residues. The dotted line represents a disulfide bridge between

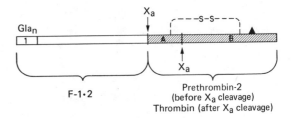

F-1·2

Prethrombin-2
(before X$_a$ cleavage)
Thrombin (after X$_a$ cleavage)

Figure 45–9. Diagrammatic representation of prothrombin. The amino terminus is to the left; region 1 contains all the Gla residues. The sites of cleavage by factor X$_a$ are shown and the products named. The site of the catalytically active serine residue is indicated by ▲. The A and B chains of active thrombin (shaded) are held together by the disulfide bridge.

region A and region B of prothrombin. The serine-dependent active protease site is indicated by the arrowhead.

The **activation of prothrombin occurs on the platelet** and requires platelet anionic phospholipid, Ca^{2+}, factor V$_a$, and factor X$_a$. The phospholipids on the internal side of the platelet plasma membrane must be exposed as a result of the collagen-induced platelet disruption and degranulation. These phospholipids bind Ca^{2+} and prothrombin, the latter at the Gla-containing N-terminal region. The platelets also contain factor V, which, when activated as factor V$_a$, binds to specific receptors in the platelet membrane (Fig 45–10). Factor V$_a$ acts as a receptor for factor X$_a$, which in turn binds prothrombin in the F-1·2 region (Fig 45–9). Factor X$_a$ is a serine protease also and cleaves the catalytically inactive prothrombin at the sites indicated in Fig 45–9, and the amino portion of prothrombin is released. The disulfide bridge holds together the thrombin A and B polypeptides that have been generated by the X$_a$ cleavages.

The bridging of the phospholipid via Ca^{2+} to the Gla residues of prothrombin accelerates the activation of prothrombin 50- to 100-fold, apparently as a result of providing a high local concentration of the prothrombin and factor X$_a$ (Fig 45–10). Factor V$_a$ adds about a 350-fold acceleration, also as the result of locally concentrating factor X$_a$.

Factor V$_a$, which is generated by thrombin, is also subsequently **inactivated by thrombin,** thereby providing a means of limiting the activation of prothrombin to thrombin.

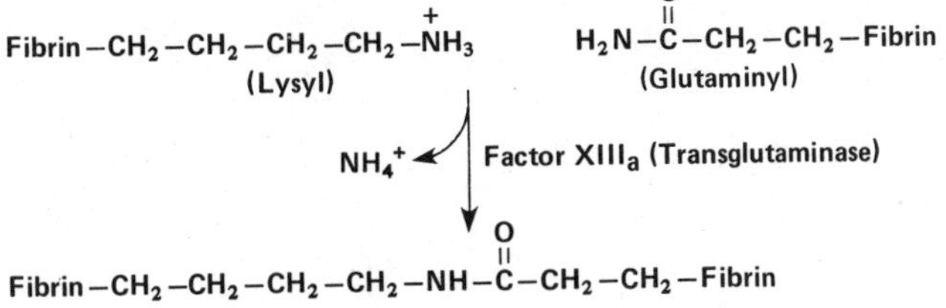

Fibrin—CH_2—CH_2—CH_2—CH_2—$\overset{+}{N}H_3$ H_2N—$\overset{\overset{\displaystyle O}{\|}}{C}$—$CH_2$—$CH_2$—Fibrin
(Lysyl)   (Glutaminyl)

NH_4^+ ← Factor XIII$_a$ (Transglutaminase)

Fibrin—CH_2—CH_2—CH_2—CH_2—NH—$\overset{\overset{\displaystyle O}{\|}}{C}$—$CH_2$—$CH_2$—Fibrin

Figure 45–8. Cross-linking of fibrin monomers by activated factor XIII.

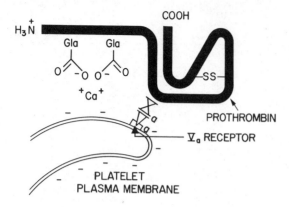

Figure 45–10. Diagrammatic representation of the binding of factors V_a, X_a, Ca^{2+}, and prothrombin to the platelet plasma membrane.

Prothrombin can also be activated by staphylocoagulase as a result of a simple conformational alteration not involving cleavage of the molecule.

Activation of Factor X_a

Activation of factor X_a occurs at the conceptual site where the intrinsic and extrinsic pathways join to form **the final common pathway** (Fig 45–11). Factor X is a zymogen (MW 55,000) of a serine protease and contains Gla residues. As in prothrombin, the Gla residues of factor X are responsible for the calcium-mediated binding of factor X to the acidic phospholipids of platelet membranes. In order to convert factor X to factor X_a, an Arg-Ile bond must be cleaved by still another serine protease. There are 2 serine proteases capable of cleaving the specific Arg-Ile bond of factor X.

The Extrinsic Pathway for Generating Factor X_a

Factor VII_a operates exclusively in the extrin- sic pathway in conjunction with tissue factor to cleave this Arg-Ile bond and generate X_a. This extrinsic pathway is very **rapid in response to tissue injury.** The precursor of factor VII_a is factor VII, another Gla-containing glycoprotein synthesized in the liver. Factor VII can be cleaved by thrombin or factor X_a. Factor VII is a zymogen but has rather high endogenous activity. The **tissue factor** necessary to accelerate the attack of factor VII or VII_a on factor X is abundant in **placenta, lung,** and **brain.**

While there is approximately 3 mg of fibrinogen in 1 mL of plasma, there is only 0.01 mg of factor X per milliliter of plasma. This requires that the clotting system provide the amplification. Conversion of factor X to X_a is an autocatalytic process and therefore an **amplification system.** In this group of reactions, it is difficult to know which came first, the chicken or the egg—II_a (thrombin) or X_a (Fig 45–11).

The Intrinsic Pathway for Generating Factor X_a

The intrinsic pathway for the generation of X_a commences with the exposure of **prekallikrein,** high-molecular-weight **kininogen, factor XII,** and **factor XI** to an activating surface, perhaps collagen in vivo (Fig 45–12). Glass or kaolin will provide an activating surface for in vitro tests of the intrinsic pathway. Exposure to the activating surface makes factor XII more labile to proteolysis by kallikrein. Factor XII_a is generated by kallikrein and attacks prekallikrein to generate more kallikrein, setting up a reciprocal activation. Factor XII_a releases bradykinin from high-molecular-weight kininogen and activates factor XI to XI_a. Factor IX, a Gla-containing zymogen, is activated in a 2-step reaction by factor XI_a. Factor IX_a, in the presence of calcium and acid phospholipids, slowly **activates factor X by cleaving the same Arg-Ile bond** that factor VII_a of the extrinsic system hydrolyzes. The factor IX_a–catalyzed activation of factor X is accelerated about 500-fold by the presence of **factor VIII** or VIII_a. Factor VIII probably

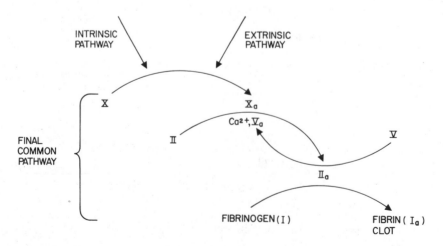

Figure 45–11. Relationship between the intrinsic, extrinsic, and final common pathways of blood clotting.

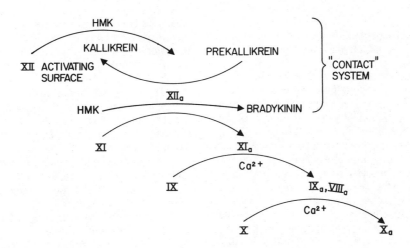

Figure 45–12. The intrinsic pathway for activating factor X to X_a. HMK is high-molecular-weight kininogen.

requires activation by minute quantities of thrombin to form factor VIII_a. **Factor VIII is not a protease** but probably serves as a receptor for factor IX_a as it cleaves the Arg-Ile bond of factor X. The **intrinsic pathway is slow,** because it involves many factors operating in a **cascade mechanism** to generate factor X_a (Fig 45–12).

Table 45–5 lists many of the inherited deficiencies of the clotting system in humans. The most common deficiency is that of factor VIII, which produces a disease known as **hemophilia A.** The X chromosome-linked deficiency of factor VIII has played a major role in the history of the royal families of Europe.

Individuals with **von Willebrand's disease** have an autosomal dominant defect in **platelet adherence** and a deficiency of factor VIII clotting activity (and antigenic material). Individuals with hemophilia A lack only factor VIII clotting activity and have normal platelet adherence. The platelet adherence factor (von Willebrand factor) is a large glycoprotein (MW > 200,000) synthesized in vascular endothelial cells and megakaryocytes (platelet precursor cells). It exists in plasma and platelets tightly associated with the factor VIII molecule. Platelet surfaces seem to possess a glycoprotein receptor for the factor VIII/von Willebrand factor complex. Functionally, the von Willebrand factor also probably stabilizes factor VIII procoagulant activity. Von Willebrand disease may be an inherited defect in a specific oligosaccharide moiety on the von Willebrand glycoprotein factor. The abnormal oligosaccharide may prevent normal platelet adherence and destabilize factor VIII. Hemophilia A is a factor VIII protein defect that interrupts its clotting function but does not adversely affect the platelet adherence function of the von Willebrand factor. Factor VIII is a 2300-amino-acid glycoprotein that has homology with ceruloplasmin and factor V. It is made in the liver, spleen, and kidney.

Table 45–5. Hemorrhagic disorders and their abnormalities.

Factor	Disorder	Bleeding Time	Clotting Time	Activated Partial Thromboplastin Time	Prothrombin Time
I	Afibrinogenemia	Variable	Infinite	Infinite	Infinite
II	Hypoprothrombinemia	Normal	Normal to long	Variable	Long
V	Parahemophilia	Normal	Long	Long	Long
VII	Factor VII deficiency	Normal	Normal	Normal	Long
VIII	Hemophilia A	Normal	Normal to long	Long	Normal
VIII	Von Willebrand's disease	Long	Variable	Variable	Normal
IX	Christmas disease, hemophilia B	Normal	Normal to long	Long	Normal
X	Stuart factor deficiency	Normal	Normal to long	Long	Long
XI	PTA deficiency	Variable	Normal to long	Long	Normal
XII	Hageman trait	Normal	Long	Long	Normal
XIII	Fibrin-stabilizing factor deficiency	Normal	Normal	Normal	Normal
Prekallikrein	Fletcher trait	Normal	Long	Long	Normal
High-molecular-weight kininogen	Fitzgerald trait	Normal	Long	Long	Normal

Clotting Tests

The **bleeding time** determination mentioned above reflects the effectiveness of the initial platelet plug formation at the site of vascular injury. The **Rumpel-Leede** tourniquet test determines capillary fragility and initial platelet plug formation.

All in vitro clotting tests depend upon the formation of a **visible fibrin clot as the end point.** In order to form a visible fibrin clot, only about 10% of the fibrinogen normally present in plasma must be converted to fibrin; thus, all of the clotting tests are insensitive to all but the most severe reductions in fibrinogen concentration. In the cascade system of blood coagulation, the clotting factors function as both enzymes and substrates for other enzymes, and in the latter role the factor concentrations may be relatively high or relatively low. Variations in the concentrations of a given factor therefore may or may not have major effects on the overall rate of fibrin clot formation. The effect will depend upon whether the factor is functioning as an enzyme or as a substrate and—if a substrate—upon whether its concentration is high or low relative to the K_m of the enzyme acting upon it. The design and use of the various clotting tests depend upon whether one wishes to determine the concentration of a factor or factors that participate in the intrinsic system, the extrinsic system, or the final common pathway of fibrin clot formation.

The **one-stage prothrombin time** is a test of the **extrinsic pathway** and the **final common pathway** of clotting. It is performed by adding a tissue factor to the unknown plasma and determining the time necessary for formation of the visible fibrin clot, ie, coagulation. The tissue factor, along with factor VII, activates factor X to X_a in the presence of factor V_a, Ca^{2+}, and platelet phospholipids. This complex on the platelet membrane converts prothrombin to thrombin, which in turn catalyzes the formation of fibrin from fibrinogen. Thus, a deficiency of factor II, V, VII, or X or a severe deficiency of fibrinogen will prolong the prothrombin time. Normal **serum** contains factors VII and X; therefore, if normal serum corrects the prothrombin time, the defect must be due to a deficiency of one of those 2 factors.

The **clotting time** is determined by introducing freshly drawn whole blood into small glass test tubes. Care must be taken not to introduce any tissue factor from the site of venipuncture. In effect, the blood is gently agitated at regular intervals to determine the time required for coagulation. In this test, the **intrinsic pathway** is activated by exposure of whole blood to the glass surface of the tube. It therefore assays the **intrinsic pathway** and the **final common pathway.**

Thus, the clotting time is dependent upon all clotting factors except factors VII and XIII. Although the clotting time is widely used in clinical medicine, it is not sensitive to mild deficiencies of factors VIII, IX, or XI.

The **activated partial thromboplastin time** involves the addition of acid phospholipids and kaolin (an activating surface) to plasma to make certain that platelets are not rate-limiting and that factors XI and XII are fully activated. Therefore, the normal response time of 35–45 seconds requires a nearly normal concentration of **all of the factors in the intrinsic pathway.** Accordingly, it is more useful than the bedside clotting time determination.

The **thromboplastin generation test** activates the intrinsic system to form a prothrombinase, or "plasma thromboplastin." The generated prothrombinase is then assayed on normal plasma, which contains prothrombin. The generated prothrombinase itself will not, of course, clot the fibrinogen; it is only capable of activating prothrombin to thrombin, which in turn will catalyze the formation of the fibrin clot from fibrinogen. Factor VII does not participate in this test, nor does the patient's prothrombin. The test involves mixing the patient's plasma after adsorption (containing factors I, V, VIII, XI, XII) with the patient's serum (containing factors VII, IX, X, XI, XII) and normal platelets (or a platelet substitute) and Ca^{2+}. Thus, everything except prothrombin should have been provided, and the prothrombinase generated is assayed on normal plasma containing prothrombin. If no clot forms and the addition of normal serum or normal plasma corrects the defect, one can narrow down the missing factor or factors (Table 45–6). If only normal serum corrects the defect, factor IX or X must be defective in the patient's serum. If only normal plasma corrects the defect, factor V or VIII must be defective in the patient's plasma. If plasma alone and serum alone both correct the defect, factor XI or XII must be missing from both the patient's serum and plasma. Further studies using plasma or serum from individuals known to be defective in specific single factors will allow one to determine which specific factor is defective. Antisera specific to the various factors are also available for determining which specific component of the clotting system is missing or defective. Table 45–5 lists the inherited deficiencies of different clotting factors and the response of blood from those patients to the various in vivo and in vitro tests.

Anticoagulants

Three naturally occurring antithrombin activities exist in normal plasma. Alpha$_1$-antitrypsin contributes

Table 45–6. Blood clotting factors normally present in plasma, adsorbed plasma, and serum.

Fluid	I	II	V	VII	VIII	IX	X	XI	XII
Plasma	+	+	+		+			+	+
Adsorbed plasma	+		+		+			+	+
Serum				+		+	+	+	+

only a minor antithrombin activity, but a specific α_2-globulin is responsible for about 25% of the antithrombin activity present in plasma. The α_2-globulin forms an irreversible complex with thrombin and other proteases and thereby prevents their binding to their natural (proteinaceous) substrates. The α_2-globulin is referred to as alpha$_2$ plasmin inhibitor, because it also inactivates plasmin, a serine protease with fibrinolytic activity discussed below.

The major antithrombin activity is contributed by antithrombin III. **Antithrombin III** has some endogenous activity but is greatly **activated** by the presence of **heparin,** a strongly anionic proteoglycan (see Chapter 33). Heparin probably binds to a specific cationic site of antithrombin III, inducing a conformational change that promotes the binding of antithrombin III to **all serine proteases,** including trypsin, chymotrypsin, and plasmin. In the clotting system, antithrombin III will **inhibit the activity of thrombin, IX$_a$, X$_a$, XI$_a$, and XII$_a$.** Individuals with inherited deficiencies of antithrombin III are prone to develop frequent and severe widespread clots, providing evidence that antithrombin III has physiologic functions and that the **clotting system in humans is normally very dynamic.**

Heparin is frequently used in clinical medicine to inhibit clotting. Its major anticoagulant action depends upon its activation of antithrombin III, which in turn inhibits the serine proteases described above. Heparin therapy can be monitored by the whole blood clotting time and by the activated partial thromboplastin time, both of which are dependent upon the intrinsic and final common pathways for clot formation. The prothrombin time may also be prolonged by high-dose intermittent heparin therapy but usually is not prolonged by continuous intravenous administration of heparin. In addition, heparin in low doses appears to coat the endothelial lining of vessels and perhaps thereby reduces the activation of the intrinsic pathway. The anticoagulant effects of heparin can be antagonized by the use of strongly cationic polypeptides such as protamine to compete with the antithrombin III cationic region for the binding of the polyanionic heparin.

The **coumarin** drugs, as described in Chapter 11, inhibit the vitamin K–dependent carboxylation of Glu to Gla residues at the amino-terminal regions of factors II, VII, IX, and X. These factors, all of which are synthesized in the liver, are dependent upon the Gla residues for maturation and thus normal function in the intrinsic, extrinsic, and final common pathways. Thus, coumarin therapy can be monitored by the one-stage prothrombin time. The coumarin drugs seem to inhibit reduction of the quinone derivatives of vitamin K to the active hydroquinone forms. Thus, the administration of vitamin K will bypass the coumarin-induced block and allow maturation of the Gla-dependent clotting factors in the liver to occur. Reversal of coumarin effects by vitamin K takes place over 12–24 hours, whereas reversal of the anticoagulant effects of heparin by protamine is practically instantaneous, because of the nature of the antagonistic mechanisms.

Fibrinolysis

As described above, there is ample evidence that the blood clotting system is normally in a dynamic steady state in which fibrin clots are constantly being laid down and subsequently dissolved. **Plasmin** is a serine protease capable of digesting both fibrinogen and fibrin as well as factors V and VIII, complement, and various polypeptide hormones. Plasmin exists normally in plasma in a proenzyme or inactive form, **plasminogen.** Plasminogen activators of various types are found in most body tissues. Tissue plasminogen activator is a serine protease that is catalytically inactive until exposed to fibrin. Upon exposure to fibrin, plasminogen activator cleaves plasminogen to generate plasmin. When plasmin digests fibrin, the plasminogen activator is no longer active and proteolysis ceases, providing a well-regulated fibrinolytic process. The urine contains the proteolytic enzyme **urokinase,** which is also a serine protease and can cleave plasminogen at 2 sites, activating the protease activity of plasmin.

Plasminogen normally coprecipitates with fibrin and thus is **incorporated into fibrin deposits.** When activated, the plasmin in clots digests the fibrin to soluble fragments, dissolving the clot. Cross-linked fibrin clots are less sensitive to dissolution by plasmin.

There are a number of disorders, including cancers and shock, in which the concentrations of plasminogen activators increase. In addition, the antiplasmin activities contributed by alpha$_1$-antitrypsin and alpha$_2$ plasmin inhibitor may be impaired in diseases such as cirrhosis of the liver. Some bacterial products, such as **streptokinase,** are capable of activating plasminogen without cleavage and may be responsible for the diffuse hemorrhage sometimes observed in patients with disseminated bacterial infections.

●　　●　　●

References

Deykin D: Thrombogenesis. *N Engl J Med* 1967;**276:**622.

Genton E et al: Platelet-inhibiting drugs in the prevention of clinical thrombotic disease. (2 parts.) *N Engl J Med* 1975; **293:**1236, 1296.

George JN, Nurden AT, Phillips DR: Molecular defects in interactions of platelets with the vessel wall. *N Engl J Med* 1984;**311:**1084.

Gitschier J et al: Characterization of the human factor VIII gene. *Nature* 1984;**312:**326.

Heimark RL et al: Surface activation of blood coagulation, fibrinolysis and kinin formation. *Nature* 1980;**286:**456.

Jackson CM, Nemerson Y: Blood coagulation. *Annu Rev Biochem* 1980;**49:**767.

Kane WH et al: Factor V_a–dependent binding of factor X_a to human platelets. *J Biol Chem* 1980;**255:**1170.

McKee PA: Hemostasis and disorders of blood coagulation. In: *The Metabolic Basis of Inherited Disease,* 5th ed. Stanbury JB et al (editors). McGraw-Hill, 1983.

Stenflo J, Suttie JW: Vitamin K-dependent formation of gamma-carboxyglutamic acid. *Annu Rev Biochem* 1977;**46:**157.

Stites DP et al (editors): *Basic & Clinical Immunology,* 5th ed. Lange, 1984.

Weiss HJ: Platelet physiology and abnormalities of platelet function. (2 parts.) *N Engl J Med* 1975;**293:**531, 580.

Water & Minerals | 46

David W. Martin, Jr., MD

WATER

The mass of the human body consists mostly of water. Water forms an essential part of all body cells and fluids; it enters into biochemical reactions, acts as a solvent for many ions and molecules, provides a medium of transport for intra- and extracellular processes, and serves as a lubricant. It also regulates body temperature by means of evaporation from lungs and skin.

The total amount of body water ranges from just over 50% to nearly 90% of body weight in direct proportion to body surface area. The proportion of weight as water declines with age and with increased body fat content; it is higher in athletes than in nonathletes.

BODY WATER

Body water is distributed between 2 main compartments: **intracellular** and **extracellular.** Intracellular water comprises 50–60% of the total body water of normal healthy adults. Extracellular water includes that present in plasma, lymph, interstitial fluid, connective tissue, cartilage, skin, bone, and secretory fluids. Because most cells of the body are freely permeable to water, the distinction between intracellular and extracellular water is somewhat arbitrary.

The electrolyte composition of blood plasma and intracellular fluid is shown in Fig 46–1. Blood plasma differs only slightly from interstitial fluid. Because plasma proteins are largely retained within blood vessels, the interstitial fluid utilizes as anion Cl^- rather than plasma proteins. Thus, the composition of plasma can be taken to represent that of extracellular fluid in general. Fig 46–1 reveals 3 major differences in composition between intracellular and extracellular fluids: (1) **Potassium is the principal cation within cells,** whereas sodium predominates in extracellular fluid. (2) Because of the many phosphorylated organic compounds present within cells, **phosphate is the primary intracellular anion;** chloride replaces it in extracellular fluids. (3) Finally, the intracellular protein concentration is higher than that of blood plasma.

WATER BALANCE

In a normal healthy person, total body water volume remains remarkably constant, fluctuating less than 1% of body weight per day, and this constancy is maintained in spite of large variations in water intake.

Typical water balance data for normal human adults are presented in Table 46–1. The average daily intake and output of water in this study was 2750 mL. There is wide individual variation in total intake and output and in day-to-day water balance.

WATER LOSSES

Water is required to replace fluid lost through the skin, lungs, and gastrointestinal tract and to accompany renal excretion of urea, salts, and other osmotically active solutes. The amounts of these **obligatory losses** vary significantly with climate, activity level, state of health, and diet. Hot temperatures, dry climates, vigorous physical activity, and fever all increase water losses from the skin and lungs. These factors can also increase sweat losses to as much as 2.5 L/h. Water secreted into the gastrointestinal tract is usually reabsorbed, but diarrhea and other intestinal disease can result in very large water losses.

Total urine volume generally depends on water intake, but a minimum amount of water—an obligatory volume—is required to accompany the excretion of osmotically active solutes, especially urea and

Table 46–1. Average daily intake and output of water in a normal adult human.*

Water Intake (mL)			Water Output (mL)		
Source	Obligatory	Facultative	Source	Obligatory	Facultative
Drink	650	1000	Urine	700	1000
Preformed	750	....	Skin	500	....
Oxidative	350	....	Lungs	400	....
			Feces	150	....
Subtotals	1750	1000	Subtotals	1750	1000
Total	2750	....	Total	2750	....

*Slightly modified and reproduced, with permission, from Wolf AV: *Thirst.* Thomas, 1958.

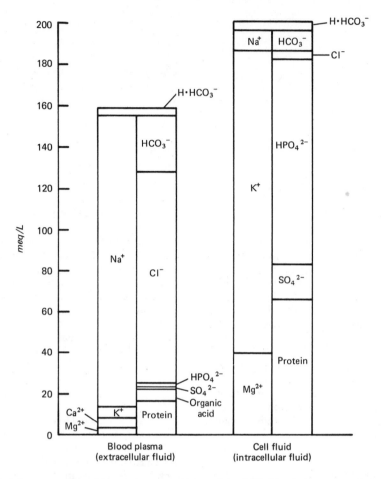

Figure 46–1. Electrolyte composition of blood plasma and intracellular fluid. Blood plasma is typical of extracellular fluid except that its protein content is higher than that of interstitial fluid. (Modified from Gamble.)

sodium chloride. The amount of these substances excreted depends in turn on dietary intake of protein and salt.

The effect of diet on obligatory urine production can be estimated by assuming that each gram of dietary protein contributes 5 milliosmoles (mosm), and each gram of salt yields 34 mosm (1 mosm = mmol solute × n, where n = the number of particles produced by dissociation). These numbers are derived from the following calculations: Protein is approximately 16% nitrogen; thus, 1 g of protein yields 0.16 g of nitrogen. This nitrogen is excreted as urea (MW = 60); N comprises 28/60 of urea. Thus, each gram of protein yields 0.3 g (300 mg) of urea, and 300/60, or 5 mosm. One gram of NaCl yields 34 mosm, because 1 g/58.5 MW = 17 mmol × 2 particles (Na^+ and Cl^-). A typical diet may contain 100 g of protein and 10 g of salt per day; it produces (100 × 5) + (10 × 34) = 840 mosm. As the adult kidney can concentrate urine to about 1400 mosm/L, an obligatory volume of 700 mL (840/1400) of water is required to excrete these solutes.

WATER INTAKE

To maintain fluid balance, all water losses must be replaced. Most water intake derives from drinking water or other beverages or from the preformed water content of food (see Table 46–4). Water is also formed as a product of molecular oxidation reactions. The oxidation of 1 g each of starch, protein, and fat yields 0.6, 0.41, and 1.07 g of water, respectively, but the total amount of metabolic water is quite small relative to that ingested in food or drink.

Because variable factors such as climate and activity are important in determination of water intake, no minimum daily water requirement has been established. For persons in moderate climates, 1 mL/kcal for adults and 1.5 mL/kcal for infants seem adequate, but these amounts must be adjusted to account for the increased fluid needs of exceptionally active people and those in hot climates; of patients with fever, vomiting, diarrhea, or excessive urine losses; and of persons taking diuretics or high-protein diets.

Because variations in water balance of only 1–2% lead to illness or even death, water intake must precisely balance water losses. This balance is achieved by a regulatory system located in the hypothalamus (see Chapter 37).

MINERALS

Of the large number of chemical elements found in the human body, only a few have demonstrable biochemical or physiologic functions. These elements can be considered in 5 groups. The first includes carbon, hydrogen, oxygen, nitrogen, and sulfur, the **major components of body molecules.** These elements are obtained through intake of water and food fats, carbohydrates, and proteins. The second group includes the nutritionally important **minerals**—calcium, phosphorus, magnesium, sodium, potassium, and chloride—that are required in the diet in amounts greater than 100 mg/d. The **trace elements**—chromium, cobalt, copper, iodine, iron, manganese, molybdenum, selenium, and zinc—are required in the human diet in much smaller amounts. Fluorine, which is essential for certain animal species but is not known to be required in the human diet, is usually considered to be part of this group, because fluorides have a well-defined role in the prevention of tooth decay. A fourth group contains additional elements required for animal nutrition but having no known essential functions in humans: arsenic, cadmium, nickel, silicon, tin, and vanadium. The final group contains elements such as lead and mercury that are clearly toxic.

The nutritionally important minerals and trace elements are discussed in this chapter. Most of these elements share many common metabolic characteristics.

Absorption of Minerals

Most minerals (sodium and potassium are notable exceptions) form salts and other compounds that are relatively insoluble; they are not readily absorbed, and most ingested minerals are excreted in feces. Mineral absorption often requires specific carrier proteins; the synthesis of these proteins serves as an important

Table 46–3. Normal routes of trace element excretion.

	Bile	Urine	Pancreatic Juice	Sweat	Mucosal Cell Sloughing
Co		++			
Cr	+	++			
Cu	++				
Fe					+
Mn	++				
Mo		+			
Se	(Not known)				
Zn	+	+	++	++	+

mechanism for control of mineral levels in the body. **Transport** and storage also require specific binding to carrier proteins. The transport molecules for trace metals in blood are shown in Table 46–2. **Excretion** of most minerals is accomplished by the kidneys, but many minerals are also secreted into the digestive juices and bile and lost in feces. The routes of excretion of the trace elements are summarized in Table 46–3.

Disorders Due to Mineral Excess or Deficiency

Deficient intake of all of the essential minerals eventually leads to defined clinical syndromes. Because body mineral concentrations are regulated at the level of absorption or excretion, circulating levels do not necessarily reflect intake. Instead, they represent an equilibrium between the amounts absorbed, utilized, stored, and excreted. Laboratory tests of serum or urine mineral levels are not always accurate indicators of intake. Mineral deficiency syndromes are rare among persons whose diet includes a sufficient variety of foods. When deficiency does occur, it is usually secondary to malabsorption, excess bleeding (iron), renal disease (calcium), or other clinical problems.

Excess intake of almost all of the minerals produces toxic symptoms. For minerals regulated by absorption, toxicity occurs more commonly when control of absorption fails in some way.

Sources & Daily Requirements of Minerals

The essential minerals and trace elements are found in most foods, especially whole-grain cereals, fruits and vegetables, dairy foods, and meats and fish, but they generally occur in these foods only in trace amounts. Thus, it is necessary to consume a sufficient quantity and variety of foods to meet nutritional requirements. The nutritional aspects of mineral metabolism are summarized in Chapter 47.

CALCIUM

Functions

The human body contains more calcium than any of the other essential minerals—as much as 1200 g in a 70-kg adult. At least 99% of the total is in bones and

Table 46–2. Transport of trace elements in blood.

	Transferrin	Albumin	Amino Acids	Transcobalamin II	Globulins
Co				++	
Cr	+				
Cu		+	+		
Fe	++			(+)*	
Mn	+				++
Mo	(Not known)				
Se	(Not known)				
Zn	+	+			

*(+) = Small amount.

teeth. Most skeletal calcium is deposited as a form of hydroxyapatite, $Ca_{10}(PO_4)_6(OH)_2$, but bone also contains considerable amounts of noncrystalline calcium phosphates and carbonates as well as small amounts of other salts. These minerals comprise about 50% of the total skeletal mass; the remaining mass consists of an organic matrix of proteins, glycoproteins, and proteoglycans on which the calcium salts are deposited. Because **bone is constantly being remodeled,** its mineral levels reflect the equilibrium between daily deposits and withdrawals. As much as 700 mg of calcium may enter and leave the bones each day.

The immediate source of new bone calcium is that present in body fluids and cells. Although this amount is extremely small ($<$ 10 g) relative to that in the skeleton, it is critically important to the regulation of a surprisingly large number of vital cellular activities: nerve and muscle function, hormonal actions, blood clotting, cellular motility, and many others. Because calcium is involved in the control of so many processes, it has been described as a "second messenger" that mediates cellular responses to a wide range of stimuli in a manner analogous to the regulatory actions of cyclic nucleotides. The action of calcium appears to be mediated by an intracellular receptor protein, **calmodulin,** that binds calcium ions when their concentration increases in response to a stimulus. Calmodulin has been found to be present in every nucleated cell type examined. When Ca^{2+} is bound to calmodulin, it modulates the activities of a great variety of enzymes, including those involved in cyclic nucleotide metabolism, protein phosphorylation, secretory function, muscle contraction, microtubule assembly, glycogen metabolism, and calcium flux. The widely used phenothiazine drugs, smooth muscle relaxants, and several peptides found in insect venoms are potent inhibitors of calmodulin action.

The importance of Ca^{2+} in these activities is reflected in the precision with which plasma Ca^{2+} levels are regulated. Normal plasma contains the equivalent of 9–11 mg of calcium per deciliter; the daily variation is rarely more than $\pm$ 3%. These narrow limits are maintained by the complex regulatory actions of vitamin D, parathyroid hormone, calcitonin, and other hormones (see Chapters 11, 38, and 39).

Metabolism

Calcium is absorbed in the duodenum and proximal jejunum by means of a calcium-binding protein synthesized in response to the action of 1,25-dihydroxycholecalciferol (1,25-dihydroxyvitamin D_3). Absorption is inhibited by compounds that form insoluble calcium salts (oxalates, phytates, phosphates) and by undigested fat through formation of insoluble calcium soaps. A large part of ingested calcium is not absorbed and is excreted in feces.

Once absorbed, calcium is excreted through several routes. The kidney excretes calcium when the blood calcium level exceeds 7 mg/dL. A large amount of calcium is secreted into the intestinal lumen and mostly lost in feces; small amounts of calcium are also excreted in sweat. For any one individual, urine calcium remains relatively constant while fecal calcium varies widely in response to diet, suggesting that **calcium levels are well controlled at the level of absorption.** High-protein diets have been reported to cause significant increases in calcium excretion.

Deficiency

The symptoms of calcium deficiency include tetany and related muscle and neurologic disorders. These symptoms occur most commonly as a result of vitamin D deficiency, hypoparathyroidism, or renal insufficiency, but calcium deprivation is also a cause. When plasma levels fall below normal, bone calcium is mobilized, thus increasing circulating Ca^{2+}, and new bone formation is hindered. The net negative Ca^{2+} balance leads to **rickets** in children or **osteomalacia** in adults.

An additional factor that bears on bone mineral loss is the ratio of calcium to phosphorus (Ca:P) in the diet. In animals, a Ca:P ratio of 2:1 leads to maximal calcium absorption and minimal bone mineral losses, whereas high phosphate intakes enhance bone loss. In humans, high phosphorus intake leads to large fecal calcium losses. The ideal Ca:P ratio in humans is not known, but recent trends in food consumption patterns in the USA include significant increases in phosphorus consumption as a result of the increased use of phosphate food additives in processed foods and soft drinks. The Ca:P ratio in the current United States diet approaches 1:1.2 to 1:1.5. Whether this ratio is responsible for excess bone loss found in postmenopausal osteoporotic women is not yet clear.

Toxicity

Hypercalcemia does not seem to occur in normal persons as a result of high dietary intake, because excess calcium is simply not absorbed. Excessive intakes, however, may contribute to the high serum Ca^{2+} levels that accompany clinical disorders such as hyperparathyroidism, vitamin D intoxication, sarcoidosis, and cancer.

PHOSPHORUS

Phosphorus as **phosphate** plays a major role in the structure and function of all living cells. Hence, phosphorus depletion from simple dietary deficiency does not occur. Phosphate exists in cells as a free ion at a concentration of a few milliequivalents per liter and is also an integral component of nucleic acids, nucleotides, phospholipids, and some proteins. In the extracellular space, phosphate circulates as free ion and is present as hydroxyapatite, a major component of bone. All cells possess enzymes that can attach phosphates in **ester or acid anhydride linkages** to other molecules. Enzymes also exist both inside and outside of the cells for the removal of phosphates from phosphate-containing molecules. Included in the latter group of enzymes are several phosphatases that have important roles in the intestinal digestion of foodstuffs.

Free phosphate is absorbed in the mid jejunum and enters the bloodstream by way of the portal circulation. The regulation of phosphate absorption is mediated by $1\alpha,25$-dihydroxycholecalciferol (1,25-dihydroxyvitamin D_3), discussed in Chapter 11. Phosphate participates in a regulatory loop with this active derivative of vitamin D_3. When the serum phosphate level is abnormally low, the formation of 1,25-dihydroxyvitamin D_3 in the renal tubule is stimulated, causing enhanced phosphate absorption from the intestine (see Fig 11–8).

The deposition of phosphate as hydroxyapatite in bone is regulated by parathyroid hormone levels. The 1,25-dihydroxyvitamin D_3 plays a permissive role in the parathyroid hormone-mediated mobilization of calcium and phosphate from bone.

Excretion of phosphate occurs primarily in the kidney and is under complex regulation. Eighty-five to 90% of plasma phosphate is filtered at the renal glomeruli, and the amount of phosphate excreted in urine represents the difference between the quantity filtered and that reabsorbed by the proximal and distal tubules of the kidney. 1,25-Dihydroxyvitamin D_3 stimulates reabsorption of phosphate along with calcium in the proximal tubule. However, parathyroid hormone diminishes the renal tubular reabsorption of phosphate and thereby overrides the effect of 1,25-dihydroxyvitamin D_3 on phosphate excretion. In the absence of a strong effect of parathyroid hormone, the kidney is able to respond to 1,25-dihydroxyvitamin D_3 by complete conservation of filtered phosphate.

The depletion of phosphate occurs as a result of diminished absorption from the intestine or excessive wasting through the kidney. The hypophosphatemic state affects most cell types. The effects on the skeleton and the hematologic systems have been most thoroughly studied. **Rickets** in children and **osteomalacia** in adults are the result of abnormal calcium and phosphate metabolism. In addition, there are abnormalities in the erythrocytes, leukocytes, and platelets and in the liver.

Phosphate toxicity is rare except when acute or chronic kidney failure prevents normal phosphate excretion. The presence of hyperphosphatemia is associated with renal disease, and the serum calcium level is usually depressed as a consequence of the regulatory effect phosphate has on the production of 1,25-dihydroxyvitamin D_3. **The absorption of dietary phosphates can be prevented by the use of antacids to bind phosphates in the intestinal lumen.** This will eventually result in return of the concentrations of serum phosphates toward normal and concomitant **increase in 1,25-dihydroxyvitamin D_3**. The latter will then promote calcium absorption from the intestine as discussed above.

MAGNESIUM

Magnesium ions are present in all cells. In essentially all reactions for which ATP is a substrate, the true substrate is Mg^{2+}-ATP. As such, Mg^{2+} is chelated between the beta and gamma phosphates and diminishes the dense anionic character of ATP, so that it can approach and bind reversibly to specific protein sites. Thus, the synthesis of all proteins, nucleic acids, nucleotides, lipids, and carbohydrates and the activation of muscle contraction require magnesium.

Although magnesium is widely available in natural foodstuffs, much Mg^{2+} and Ca^{2+} are lost during refining and processing of food. The absorption of Mg^{2+} occurs throughout the small intestine and apparently depends upon the load presented rather than any single factor, such as vitamin D. On a low-magnesium diet, more than three-fourths of dietary Mg^{2+} can be absorbed, whereas absorption may decrease to one-fourth on a high-magnesium diet. The absorption of Mg^{2+} is not an active process, and there is no common mechanism of transport of calcium and magnesium across the intestinal wall. In the plasma, most of the Mg^{2+} exists in a form that can be filtered by the kidney glomerulus. However, the kidney has an extraordinary ability to conserve Mg^{2+}, so that the daily loss on a low-magnesium diet is only about 1 meq/d. On an average diet, the amount excreted in the urine is 35–45% of the daily intake. Magnesium deficiency is not uncommon. High levels of calcium, protein, and phosphate in the diet will diminish Mg^{2+} absorption from the intestine. Malabsorption in chronic diarrhea from any cause, protein-calorie malnutrition, and adult starvation in the form of alcoholism can all result in magnesium deficiency. The sudden termination of starvation by feeding protein and carbohydrate without cofactors such as thiamin and Mg^{2+} can lead to serious metabolic and neurologic disturbances. In the presence of chronic renal failure, magnesium requirements decline, but in renal tubular acidosis or diabetes mellitus, magnesium wasting by the kidneys increases the dietary requirement of Mg^{2+}. A number of drugs, including the diuretics, promote magnesium wastage. During lactation, magnesium requirements are increased.

Magnesium toxicity is rare in the presence of normal renal function. In patients in renal failure, hypermagnesemia can be an important medical problem. The depressant effects of magnesium on the nervous system usually dominate the toxicity of hypermagnesemia.

SODIUM

Sodium is the major cation (Na^+) of the **extracellular fluid** and is largely associated with chloride and bicarbonate in the regulation of acid-base equilibrium. Na^+ is also important in the maintenance of osmotic pressure of body fluids and thus in protection against excessive fluid loss. Although Na^+ is widely distributed in foodstuffs, the main dietary source is table salt (NaCl) used in cooking and seasoning. In general, meats contain more Na^+ than do vegetable foodstuffs, but some processed foods contain added NaCl.

The dietary consumption of NaCl depends greatly upon cultural and individual eating habits. In the USA, 5–15 g of NaCl may be consumed daily by adults, but 90–95% of this intake is excreted in the urine. Na^+ is readily absorbed in the ileum, and little is present in feces. By mechanisms described in Chapter 40, the kidney is capable of conserving Na^+ at the expense of K^+ or H^+. Accordingly, the daily adult requirement for sodium is only a few milliequivalents. Most of this requirement is due to the nonurinary loss of sodium. The average daily intake of sodium is quite high in relation to the minimal requirement. In **susceptible individuals,** there is a clear relationship between Na^+ intake and diastolic **blood pressure.** Thus, the excessive and wasteful intake of sodium as NaCl may lead to or aggravate preexisting hypertension.

However, whenever a water intake of more than 4 L/d is required to replace sweat loss, extra NaCl should be provided. With prolonged exposure to high temperatures and excessive sweating, the Na^+ loss in sweat will be minimized by an adaptive process involving aldosterone.

Although extravascular Na^+ is in equilibrium with intravascular (plasma) Na^+, the concentration of the latter may not reflect total body stores of sodium. Accordingly, a patient with low serum Na^+ (hyponatremia) may not be depleted of body Na^+ but may have instead an excess of intravascular (and perhaps extravascular) water. Similarly, increased serum Na^+ (hypernatremia) can occur in the face of low or normal body Na^+ content if water depletion (dehydration) is present. In renal disease, the ability to conserve Na^+ is frequently lost, and severe disorders of sodium, chloride, potassium, and water balance can result.

POTASSIUM

Potassium is the principal cation (K^+) of the intracellular fluid. Accordingly, the major sources of dietary K^+ are the cellular materials we consume as foodstuffs; a dietary deficiency is extraordinarily rare except in severe protein-calorie malnutrition. Table 46–4 provides values for the K^+ contents of some common foodstuffs.

K^+ is readily absorbed in the small intestine in proportion to the presented load and circulates in the plasma. Potassium in extracellular fluid invades all tissues in the body and can have profound effects on the function of some organs, particularly depolarization and contraction of the heart.

The kidney cannot conserve K^+ nearly so effectively as it can Na^+. As mentioned above, the conservation of sodium is at the expense of potassium, an effect mediated by aldosterone. Thus, there is an obligatory potassium loss in normal renal function, and this obligatory loss amounts to approximately 40 meq (equivalent to 160 mg) per day. When K^+ intake falls below this minimal requirement, the serum K^+ concentration drops, the intracellular K^+ begins to fall, and both the renal tubules and other cells of the body

Table 46–4. Values for K^+ contents of some common foodstuffs.

	meq K^+		meq K^+
Almonds, 9–10	1.8	Egg (chicken)	1.8
Apple (½), raw, with skin	1.7	Fish, albacore, 3½ oz	7.5
		Frankfurter	3
Asparagus, raw, 5–6 spears	7	Ginger ale, 1 cup	0.03
Avocado (½)	15	Grapes, Thompson seedless, ½ cup	2.8
Banana (½), raw	9.6	Lamb, shoulder blade chop, 3½ oz	11
Beans, lima, 4 tsp	17		
Beef patty, ¼ lb	10	Milk, whole, 1 cup	9
Beer, 1 cup	1	Orange, 1 small	5.1
Bread, whole wheat, 1 slice	1.6	Orange juice, 1 cup	13
		Parsley, raw, 3½ oz	19
Butter, salted, 1 tsp	0.08	Peanut butter, 1 tsp	4.2
Cabbage, raw, 1 cup shredded	6	Pork, loin chop, 3½ oz	15
		Postum, instant, 2 tsp	3
Celery, raw, 1 large stalk	4	Potato, sweet, 1 small	6.2
Cheese, cheddar, ¾-inch cube	0.4	Potatoes, white raw, 2½-inch diameter	10
Chicken, broiler, 3½ oz	8	Prune juice, 1 cup	14
		Tomato juice, 1 cup	14
Cider, sweet, 1 cup	6	Turkey, roasted, 1 slice (3 × 2½ × ¼ inch)	4
Dates, raw, 10 medium	17		

begin to utilize protons (H^+) in place of K^+. Thus, the intracellular H^+ concentration increases, producing an intracellular acidosis. The obligatory K^+ loss incurred by the renal tubules becomes an obligatory H^+ loss, as the renal tubules conserve Na^+ at the expense of H^+ rather than at the expense of K^+. This leads to an **extracellular alkalosis** and **intracellular acidosis.**

In renal failure, the obligatory K^+ loss may be much greater than normal. Similarly, the use of diuretic drugs increases the renal wasting of Na^+ and K^+. The deficiency of K^+ occurs frequently in the setting of inappropriate K^+ replacement during administration of intravenous fluids to replace gastrointestinal fluid losses.

Toxicity of K^+ (hyperkalemia) occurs frequently in renal failure, when the kidney is not capable of excreting excessive K^+. Hyperkalemia produces characteristic electrocardiographic changes reflecting the **profound and life-threatening effect of excess K^+ on the heart.**

The electrical effects of hyperkalemia can be antagonized by increased serum calcium concentration. As described in Chapter 32, the sodium-potassium pump in membranes is sensitive to inhibition by the digitalis preparation ouabain. In the presence of hypokalemia, the heart is sensitized to ouabain, and ouabain toxicity may occur. The toxicity of ouabain can be antagonized by increasing serum potassium concentration.

TRACE ELEMENTS

1. COBALT

The only known function of cobalt in animals is its role as a component of cobalamin, vitamin B_{12} (see Chapter 10). Cobalt must be provided to mammals in the form of vitamin B_{12}, although theoretically elemental cobalt in the diet could be converted to cobalamin by the intestinal bacteria.

Elemental cobalt is well absorbed in the intestine and seems to share a transport mechanism with iron as discussed below. Cobalt absorption, like that of iron, is significantly increased in patients with liver disease, iron overload, and idiopathic hemochromatosis. Cobalt is excreted primarily in the urine and has a low order of toxicity in all species studied.

2. COPPER

The adult human body contains approximately 100 mg of copper; the highest concentrations are in liver, brain, kidney, and heart. The average diet in North America provides 2–4 mg of copper per day in the form of meat, shellfish, nuts, raisins, legumes, and cereals.

The absorption of copper in the gastrointestinal tract requires a specific mechanism, because of the highly insoluble nature of cupric ions (Cu^{2+}). An unidentified low-molecular-weight substance from human saliva and gastric juice complexes with Cu^{2+} to keep it soluble at the pH of intestinal fluid. In the intestinal mucosal cell, copper is probably associated with a low-molecular-weight metal-binding protein called **metallothionein.** Copper enters the plasma, where it is bound to amino acids, particularly histidine, and to serum albumin at a single strong binding site. In less than an hour, the recently absorbed copper is removed from the circulation by the liver.

The liver processes copper through 2 routes. Copper is excreted in bile into the gastrointestinal tract, from which it is not reabsorbed. In fact, **copper homeostasis is maintained almost exclusively by biliary excretion;** the higher the dose of copper, the more is excreted in feces. Normally, human urine contains only traces of copper.

The second route of copper metabolism in the liver is its incorporation as an integral part of **ceruloplasmin,** a glycoprotein synthesized exclusively in the liver. Ceruloplasmin is a copper-dependent **ferroxidase.** It accounts for 95% of the total copper in human plasma. **Ceruloplasmin is not a Cu^{2+} transport protein,** since ceruloplasmin copper is not exchanged with copper ion or copper bound to other molecules. Ceruloplasmin contains 6–8 atoms of copper, half as cuprous (Cu^+) and half as cupric (Cu^{2+}) ions.

As a dispensable component of the gastrointestinal iron absorption mechanism, ceruloplasmin oxidizes Fe^{2+} to Fe^{3+}. Other copper metalloproteins include cytochrome oxidase, tyrosinase, monoamine oxidase, superoxide dismutase, and lysyl oxidase.

Manifestations of copper toxicity include blue-green diarrheal stools and saliva, acute hemolysis, and abnormalities of kidney function.

Menkes' disease (kinky or steely hair syndrome) is an X-linked disorder of intestinal copper absorption. The first phase of copper absorption, its uptake into the mucosal cell, and the second phase, its intracellular transport within the mucosal cell, are both normal in patients with Menkes' disease. The third phase, transport across the serosal aspect of the mucosal cell membrane, is defective. Intravenously administered copper is handled normally by these children, but unless therapy is commenced promptly at birth, many of the severe signs of this disease (mental retardation, temperature instability, abnormal bone formation, and susceptibility to infection) are not prevented.

Wilson's disease is an autosomal, recessively inherited defect in the incorporation of copper into newly synthesized apoceruloplasmin to form ceruloplasmin. It is not clear whether the genetic defect is in the structural gene for ceruloplasmin or in the process of incorporating the Cu^{2+} into ceruloplasmin. In addition, patients with Wilson's disease have an **impaired ability of the liver to excrete copper into the bile.** The total body retention of copper is increased, particularly in the liver, brain, kidney, and cornea. Dementia and liver failure occur. Because the ceruloplasmin in the patient's plasma contains no Cu^{2+}, the **serum copper level is low.** Urinary excretion of copper is markedly increased in these patients. They do not exhibit any abnormality of iron absorption, in spite of the fact that the ceruloplasmin without copper cannot function as a ferroxidase. Chelation of the excess copper can reverse some of the organ damage.

3. IRON

Iron is one of the most abundant elements in the earth's crust, but the body of a normal adult weighing 70 kg contains only 3–4 g of iron. Table 46–5 sets forth the distribution and functions of iron compounds in humans. As described in Chapter 5, the major use of iron is for **oxygen transport** by hemoglobin. Both ferrous (Fe^{2+}) and ferric (Fe^{3+}) iron are highly insoluble at neutral pH, and special systems are therefore required to transport iron and to insert these ions into their functional sites.

Organ meats, legumes, molasses, shellfish, and parsley are rich sources of iron. Food iron is predominantly in the ferric state, tightly bound to organic molecules. In the stomach, where the pH is less than 4, Fe^{3+} can dissociate and react with low-molecular-weight compounds such as fructose, ascorbic acid, citric acid, and amino acids to form complexes that will allow Fe^{3+} to remain soluble at the neutral pH of intestinal fluid. Iron is not lost from heme in the stomach but is delivered as such to the intestine.

Table 46—5. Distribution and functions of the iron compounds in normal humans.*

	Compound	Nature of Compound	Function	Molecular Weight	Amount (Grams)	Amount of Iron (Grams)
5% ⎫ 1%	Transferrin	Nonheme	Iron transport	76,000	14.0	0.007
10%	Cytochrome c	Heme enzyme	Oxidation	13,200	0.8	0.004
9%	Cytochromes a, a₃, b	Heme enzyme	Oxidation		?	?
10%	Peroxidase	Heme enzyme	Oxidation	44,100	?	?
	Catalase	Heme enzyme	H₂O₂ decomposition	225,000	5.0	0.004
	Iron-sulfur	Nonheme enzymes	Flavoproteins, oxidases, hydroxylases		?	?
65%	Unknown					0.20
	Myoglobin	Heme	O₂ storage	17,000	120	0.40
	Hemosiderin	Nonheme	Iron storage	Variable	1.2	0.36
	Ferritin	Nonheme apoferritin	Iron storage	444,000	2.0	0.40
	Hemoglobin	Heme	O₂ transport	66,700	750	2.60
	Total iron (70-kg man)					4 grams

Percent of normal body iron (left margin label)

*Slightly modified and reproduced, with permission, from Stanbury JB, Wyngaarden JB, Fredrickson DS: *The Metabolic Basis of Inherited Disease,* 4th ed. McGraw-Hill, 1978.

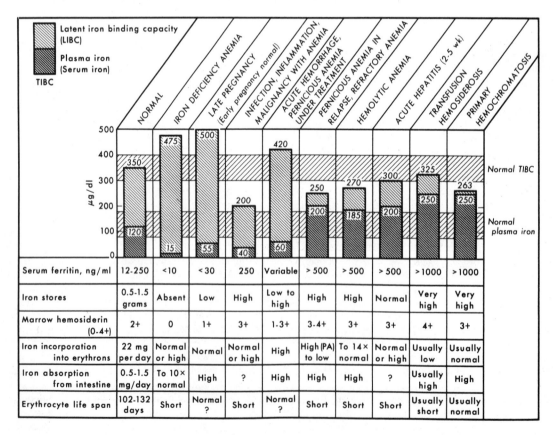

Figure 46–2. Iron metabolism in human beings under various conditions. (Reproduced, with permission, from Stanbury JB, Wyngaarden JB, Fredrickson DS: *The Metabolic Basis of Inherited Disease,* 4th ed. McGraw-Hill, 1978.)

Normally, the loss of iron from the body of a man is limited to 1 mg/d as a result of the sloughing of intestinal and other iron-containing cells. Menstruating women lose iron with menstrual blood. Accordingly, the **only mechanism by which total body stores of iron can be regulated is at the level of iron absorption,** a unique and precarious arrangement. In the ordinary diet, 10–20 mg of iron are taken in each day, but less than 10% of this is absorbed. Thus, under normal conditions, very little dietary iron is absorbed, the amounts excreted in urine are minimal, and a high proportion of total body iron is continuously redistributed throughout the body in several metabolic circuits. The greatest need for iron occurs in **infancy and adolescence;** children in these stages of development absorb a higher percentage of iron from foods than do adults. Iron deficiency in infants, adolescents, and menstruating women can be attributed to dietary inadequacy. Iron deficiency in adult men can usually be attributed to substantial bleeding.

Absorption

Heme iron is absorbed by the intestinal mucosal cell intact, and the heme is subsequently broken down and iron released within the cell. Nonheme iron is **absorbed in the ferrous state.** The Fe^{2+} is absorbed into the mucosal cell of the duodenum and proximal jejunum and promptly oxidized to Fe^{3+}. Ferric ion is bound by an **intracellular carrier molecule.** Within the cell, the carrier molecule delivers Fe^{3+} to mitochondria and then, depending upon the state of iron metabolism of the individual, distributes the Fe^{3+} in specific proportions to apoferritin or to apotransferrin.

Apoferritin is a molecule of approximately 500,000 MW, composed of 24 identical 18,000-MW subunits. Apoferritin assimilates up to **4300 iron atoms** into a single molecule to form **ferritin,** the primary and most available **iron storage protein.**

Apotransferrin is a 90,000-MW protein that can bind **2 atoms of iron** to form transferrin. **Transferrin is the true carrier of iron** that exists in plasma as a β-globulin. The iron-binding capacity of transferrin is normally **20–33% saturated** with iron (Fig 46–2).

Under **normal conditions** in the adult, when approximately **1 mg of iron is absorbed daily,** the intracellular iron carrier of the mucosal cell is nearly saturated (Fig 46–3). It transfers significant quantities of iron to apoferritin to form ferritin and transfers the usual quantity of iron to mitochondria. The remainder is transported across the serosal surface to apotransferrin.

In the **iron-deficient state,** the capacity of the intracellular iron carrier is expanded, and more iron will be absorbed if available in the diet (Fig 46–3). Although the mitochondria receive their usual supply of iron, ferritin is not formed in the cell, and the majority of iron is transferred to the expanded apotransferrin compartment in the plasma.

In the case of **iron overload,** the intracellular iron carrier is simply diminished in capacity and saturated (Fig 46–4). A significant quantity of ferritin is formed

within the mucosal cell, and less iron is transferred to the already nearly saturated apotransferrin. The iron trapped in the mucosal cell ferritin can be lost by exfoliation of those cells. The intracellular mucosal transfer of iron can be regulated to some extent. The hormone erythropoietin, by a mechanism not understood, promotes the rapid transfer of mucosal iron to the transferrin compartment in plasma.

The transfer of iron from the storage ferritin (as Fe^{3+}) form to plasma involves the **reduction to Fe^{2+} in order for it to be released from ferritin.** The Fe^{2+} is subsequently again oxidized to Fe^{3+} so that it can be bound to transferrin.

Transport

Iron is transported to storage sites in the bone marrow and to some extent to the liver **in the Fe^{3+} state, bound to plasma transferrin.** At those storage sites, Fe^{3+} is again transferred to apoferritin as a stable but exchangeable storage form. **Ferritin in the reticuloendothelial system provides an available storage form for iron.** However, ferritin can become denatured, losing apoferritin subunits and subsequently aggregating into micelles of hemosiderin. **Hemosiderin** contains a larger fraction of its mass as iron than does ferritin and exists as **microscopically visible iron-staining particles.** Hemosiderin is usually seen in states of iron overload, when the synthesis of apoferritin and its uptake of iron are maximal. The **iron in hemosiderin is available** for the formation of hemoglobin, but the mobilization of iron is much slower from hemosiderin than from ferritin. The plasma transferrin iron pool is in equilibrium with the iron in storage forms in the gastrointestinal tract and reticuloendothelial system (Fig 46–4).

Although ferritin is not found in plasma, apoferritin is and seems to reflect the size of the pools of stored iron in the reticuloendothelial system. The formation of ferritin from apoferritin involves first the binding of Fe^{2+} to the inner surface of the apoferritin shell. Apoferritin then acts as a ferroxidase and oxidizes Fe^{2+} to Fe^{3+}, which is then tightly bound to ferritin. In order to be released from ferritin, iron must be reduced from Fe^{3+} to Fe^{2+}.

An inherited defect in regulation of mucosal absorption of iron leads to the iron overload syndrome known as **hemochromatosis.** In this multisystem disease, 2 or 3 mg rather than the normal 1 mg of iron is absorbed daily from the gastrointestinal tract. Over a period of 20–30 years in males, this will lead to an accumulation of perhaps 20–30 g of total body iron rather than the normal 3–4 g. The accumulated iron is stored in **hemosiderin deposits in liver, pancreas, skin, and joints,** leading to the disease.

When total body iron stores are increased and hemosiderin deposits are widespread, **hemosiderosis** is said to exist. This might result from increased dietary intake of iron or from increased lysis of red cells and the increased iron absorption that accompanies erythropoiesis, in this case a compensatory mechanism. When the hemosiderin deposits begin to **disrupt**

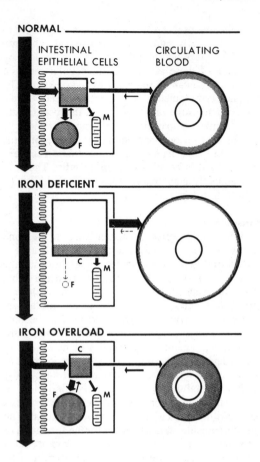

Figure 46–3. Model of distribution and transfer of iron in the intestinal epithelial cell. The rate of iron transfer is proportionate to the square of the width of the arrow. The amounts of intracellular iron carrier (square C) and intracellular ferritin (circle F) and the concentration of transferrin in circulating blood (annulus) are proportionate to the corresponding areas. The fractional saturation of the iron-binding compounds (intracellular carrier and transferrin) is indicated by the fraction of the compartmental area that is crosshatched. M designates mitochondria. In this cybernetic model, the amount of intracellular iron carrier is inversely proportionate to the amount of plasma iron entering and conditioning the cell during development. Normal saturation of intracellular carrier is associated with iron absorption of 1 mg/d of the 3 mg/d incorporated into the mucosal cells from the 15 mg/d entering the lumen. Ferritin deposition and mitochondrial uptake for synthesis of iron enzymes are shown, corresponding to 1.7 mg/d and 0.3 mg/d, respectively. (Reproduced, with permission, from Stanbury JB, Wyngaarden JB, Fredrickson DS: *The Metabolic Basis of Inherited Disease,* 4th ed. McGraw-Hill, 1978.)

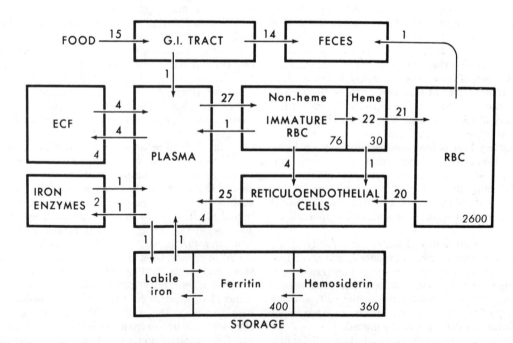

Figure 46–4. Normal iron kinetics: pools and transfer rates. (Reproduced, with permission, from Stanbury JB, Wyngaarden JB, Fredrickson DS: *The Metabolic Basis of Inherited Disease,* 4th ed. McGraw-Hill, 1978.)

normal cellular and organ function, the disorder is called **hemochromatosis.**

4. MOLYBDENUM

Although the human requirements for molybdenum are unknown, this metal is clearly required for the function of the metalloenzymes **xanthine oxidase, aldehyde oxidase,** and **sulfite oxidase.** Molybdenum deficiency has not been observed in humans or any other species under natural conditions. Essentially nothing is known about its metabolism except that the hexavalent water-soluble forms are absorbed well across the intestine. The urine is the major route of molybdenum excretion. The food content of molybdenum is highly dependent upon the soil type in which the foodstuffs are grown.

There is some evidence that molybdenum can interfere with copper metabolism by diminishing the efficiency of copper utilization and perhaps even copper mobilization from tissues.

5. SELENIUM

Selenium is an integral component of **glutathione peroxidase,** an enzyme with an intracellular **antioxidant** role closely similar to the related function of vitamin E or α-tocopherol. The vitamin E-sparing effects of selenium (and the converse) are discussed in Chapter 11. Selenium intake is highly dependent upon the soil in which the foodstuffs are grown. Selenium deficiency occurs in persons living in rural areas of a selenium-deficient zone in China. The deficiency causes a dilatation of the heart and the resulting congestive heart failure. Selenium toxicity does occur in humans and other animals, although its mechanism is not understood. An early hallmark of selenium toxicity is a garlicky breath caused by exhalation of dimethyl selenide. The most likely cause of selenium toxicity is occupational exposure in the electronics, glass, and paint industries.

6. MANGANESE

Manganese is widely distributed in nuts, wholegrain cereals, and vegetables but is present in low concentrations in meat, fish, and dairy products. Tea is exceptionally rich in Mn^{2+}. Manganese is present in high concentrations in mitochondria and functions as a necessary factor for activation of glycosyltransferases responsible for the synthesis of oligosaccharides, glycoproteins, and proteoglycans (see Chapter 33). It is required for superoxide dismutase activity. Manganese is well absorbed throughout the small intestine by a mechanism similar to that described above for iron, involving transfer across the mucosal cells into the portal blood. In fact, Mn^{2+} absorption is increased in iron deficiency and can be inhibited by iron. The presence of ethanol in the intestine can significantly increase Mn^{2+} absorption. The Mn^{2+} ions are delivered to the liver from the portal circulation and there rapidly equilibrate with liver mitochondrial Mn^{2+}. Deficiency of Mn^{2+} seems to profoundly reduce oligosaccharide synthesis and formation of glycoproteins and proteoglycans. In addition, several Mn^{2+} metalloenzymes such as hydrolases, kinases, decarboxylases, and transferases are affected.

Manganese toxicity is extremely rare, but it does occur among miners following occupational exposure to Mn^{2+} ores.

7. ZINC

There are perhaps 2 dozen known zinc metalloenzymes, including carbonic anhydrase, lactate dehydrogenase, glutamate dehydrogenase, alkaline phosphatase, and thymidine kinase. Thus, it is not surprising that a deficiency of zinc is accompanied by multisystem dysfunction. The major zinc protein in saliva, gustin, plays a major role in taste. Animal protein is an important source; processed foods, citrus fruits, and nonleafy vegetables are poor in zinc.

In the intestinal lumen there exists a zinc-binding factor that seems to be secreted by the pancreas and promotes zinc absorption. Zinc, like iron, can be sequestered in the mucosal cell by zinc-binding proteins. It is subsequently transferred to the **albumin** molecule on the serosal side of the mucosal cell membrane. Copper can interfere with zinc absorption by competing for the binding sites on the albumin molecule in the intravascular space. High phosphate and calcium both aggravate zinc deficiency. Zinc is secreted in **pancreatic juice** and to a small extent in bile, and thus feces is the major route of excretion. However, significant quantities of zinc can be lost in **sweat,** particularly in the tropics. Zinc, like copper, can be bound by liver metallothionein when zinc intake increases.

Zinc deficiency can occur as a primary disorder of zinc absorption in **acrodermatitis enteropathica,** a rare autosomal recessive disease characterized by dermatologic, ophthalmologic, gastrointestinal, and neuropsychiatric signs, along with growth retardation and hypogonadism. Secondary Zn deficiency can occur from malabsorption due to any cause or from increased excretion in urine. The latter appears to account for the relatively frequent finding of Zn deficiency in patients with sickle cell disease. Dietary Zn may be bound in the intestinal lumen by phytates (inositol hexaphosphate), which are abundant in unleavened bread. The phytate-zinc complex is not absorbed and can result in an isolated zinc deficiency as a syndrome of growth retardation, hypogonadism, alopecia, and poor appetite. Acute ingestion of alcohol appears to increase urinary zinc excretion.

In patients with zinc deficiencies, serum ribonuclease activity appears to be high, whereas erythrocyte carbonic anhydrase activity is low. Individuals with zinc deficiency exhibit poor wound healing.

8. CHROMIUM

Chromium is thought to play some functional role in the regulation of glucose metabolism, probably as a potentiator of insulin action. The trivalent form of chromium (Cr^{3+}) can improve the glucose tolerance of individuals suffering from protein-calorie malnutrition. Brewer's yeast is rich in chromium, and most grain and cereal products contain significant quantities. There have been suggestions that chromium is important in the metabolism of plasma lipoproteins (see Chapter 18). Chromium is absorbed in the small intestine by a pathway it appears to share with zinc. It is transported to tissues bound to transferrin and appears in liver mitochondria, microsomes, and the cytosol. Chromium is excreted chiefly in the urine.

Hexavalent chromium is much more toxic than the trivalent chromium. Chronic occupational exposure to chromate dust seems to carry an increased risk of lung cancer. Significant chromium is contributed to the diet by cooking in stainless steel cookware.

● ● ●

References

Aisen P, Listowsky I: Iron transport and storage proteins. *Annu Rev Biochem* 1980;**49:**357.

Finch CA, Huebers H: Perspectives in iron metabolism. *N Engl J Med* 1982;**306:**1520.

Fitzgerald F: Trace elements. *West J Med* 1978;**128:**223.

Flink EB: Nutritional aspects of magnesium metabolism. *West J Med* 1980;**133:**304.

Keshan Disease Research Group of the Chinese Academy of Medical Sciences: Observations on effect of sodium selenite in prevention of Keshan disease. *Chin Med J [Engl]* 1979;**92:**471.

Klee CB, Crouch TH, Richman PG: Calmodulin. *Annu Rev Biochem* 1980;**49:**489.

Mertz W: The essential trace elements. *Science* 1981;**213:**1332.

Paterson CR: Calcium requirements in man: A critical review. *Postgrad Med J* 1978;**54:**244.

Prasad AS: *Trace Elements and Iron in Human Metabolism.* Plenum Press, 1978.

Smith LH Jr: Hemochromatosis. *West J Med* 1978;**128:**133.

Underwood EJ: *Trace Elements in Human and Animal Nutrition,* 4th ed. Academic Press, 1977.

Weitzman RE, Kleeman CR: The clinical physiology of water metabolism. *West J Med* 1979;**131:**373.

Nutrition | 47

Marion Nestle, PhD

Humans have evolved to depend on a continuous supply of exogenous substances for growth, development, and maintenance of life. These heterogeneous substances include sources of energy and of carbon, nitrogen, and other inorganic elements, as well as more than 20 complex organic molecules—fatty acids, amino acids, and vitamins—whose biosynthetic pathways have been lost during evolution. All of these nutrients are required in the diet, and all are normally obtained from food.

The goals of nutritional science are to define for each individual the complete set of nutrients required in the diet, the optimal amount of each nutrient, and the combination of foods that best meets these requirements; to determine how these requirements vary throughout the normal life cycle; and to understand how nutritional factors affect and are affected by injury, illness, and treatment. These goals have not yet been entirely achieved. Information currently available on human nutritional requirements is reviewed in this chapter.

NUTRITIONAL REQUIREMENTS IN HUMANS

A nutrient is considered essential if its deficiency results in recognizable clinical symptoms that are relieved by adding it to the diet. Because research studies of human nutritional requirements are notoriously difficult to conduct and to interpret, it has often proved difficult to demonstrate specific biochemical or physiologic lesions produced by a deficiency of any one nutrient. The results of animal studies can only be applied to humans with extreme caution. Consequently, much information on human nutritional requirements remains incomplete.

A summary of the substances required in the human diet is given in Table 47–1. In addition to sources of energy, more than 40 organic compounds or inorganic elements are considered to be essential to human nutrition. For most of them, dietary deficiency results in symptoms of illness in children or adults. Other nutrients are more difficult to classify but are

Table 47–1. Human nutritional requirements.

	Essential for Human Nutrition; Requirement Established	Essential for Certain Animal Species; Human Requirement Not Established
Amino acids	Isoleucine, leucine, lysine, methionine, phenylalanine, threonine, tryptophan, valine, histidine[1]	Arginine
Fatty acids	Linoleic acid	Linolenic acid
Vitamins		
Water-soluble	Ascorbic acid, biotin,[2] cobalamin (B_{12}), folic acid, niacin, pantothenic acid, pyridoxine (B_6), riboflavin, thiamin (B_1)	Choline, myo-inositol
Fat-soluble	Vitamin A, vitamin D, vitamin E,[3] vitamin K[2]	
Minerals		
Minerals ($>$ 100 mg/d)	Calcium, chlorine, magnesium, phosphorus, potassium, sodium	
Trace elements ($<$ 100 mg/d)	Chromium, cobalt (as vitamin B_{12}), copper, iodine, iron, manganese, molybdenum, selenium, zinc	Arsenic, fluoride,[4] nickel, silicon, tin, vanadium
Fiber[4]		
Water[5]		
Energy[6]	Carbohydrate, fat, protein	

[1] Essential for infant nutrition; adult requirement uncertain.
[2] Synthesized by intestinal microorganisms; dietary requirement uncertain.
[3] Human deficiency syndrome undefined; efficacious in treating certain hemolytic disorders of infants and adults.
[4] Functions in human physiology, but no requirement has been determined.
[5] Nutritional aspects of water consumption and utilization are discussed in Chapter 46.
[6] Specific energy sources are not required except as necessary to provide essential amino acids (protein) or fatty acids (fat) or to prevent ketosis (carbohydrate).

Table 47–2. Recommended daily dietary allowances.[1] (Revised 1980.) Designed for the maintenance of good nutrition of practically all healthy people in the USA.

	Age (years)	Weight (kg)	Weight (lb)	Height (cm)	Height (in)	Protein (g)	Fat-Soluble Vitamins			Water-Soluble Vitamins							Minerals					
							Vitamin A (μg RE)[2]	Vitamin D (μg)[3]	Vitamin E (mg α-TE)[4]	Vitamin C (mg)	Thiamin (mg)	Riboflavin (mg)	Niacin (mg NE)[5]	Vitamin B$_6$ (mg)	Folacin[6] (μg)	Vitamin B$_{12}$[6] (μg)	Calcium (mg)	Phosphorus (mg)	Magnesium (mg)	Iron (mg)	Zinc (mg)	Iodine (μg)
Infants	0.0–0.5	6	13	60	24	kg × 2.2	420	10	3	35	0.3	0.4	6	0.3	30	0.5[7]	360	240	50	10	3	40
	0.5–1.0	9	20	71	28	kg × 2.0	400	10	4	35	0.5	0.6	8	0.6	45	1.5	540	360	70	15	5	50
Children	1–3	13	29	90	35	23	400	10	5	45	0.7	0.8	9	0.9	100	2.0	800	800	150	15	10	70
	4–6	20	44	112	44	30	500	10	6	45	0.9	1.0	11	1.3	200	2.5	800	800	200	10	10	90
	7–10	28	62	132	52	34	700	10	7	45	1.2	1.4	16	1.6	300	3.0	800	800	250	10	10	120
Males	11–14	45	99	157	62	45	1000	10	8	50	1.4	1.6	18	1.8	400	3.0	1200	1200	350	18	15	150
	15–18	66	145	176	69	56	1000	10	10	60	1.4	1.7	18	2.0	400	3.0	1200	1200	400	18	15	150
	19–22	70	154	177	70	56	1000	7.5	10	60	1.5	1.7	19	2.2	400	3.0	800	800	350	10	15	150
	23–50	70	154	178	70	56	1000	5	10	60	1.4	1.6	18	2.2	400	3.0	800	800	350	10	15	150
	51+	70	154	178	70	56	1000	5	10	60	1.2	1.4	16	2.2	400	3.0	800	800	350	10	15	150
Females	11–14	46	101	157	62	46	800	10	8	50	1.1	1.3	15	1.8	400	3.0	1200	1200	300	18	15	150
	15–18	55	120	163	64	46	800	10	8	60	1.1	1.3	14	2.0	400	3.0	1200	1200	300	18	15	150
	19–22	55	120	163	64	44	800	7.5	8	60	1.1	1.3	14	2.0	400	3.0	800	800	300	18	15	150
	23–50	55	120	163	64	44	800	5	8	60	1.0	1.2	13	2.0	400	3.0	800	800	300	18	15	150
	51+	55	120	163	64	44	800	5	8	60	1.0	1.2	13	2.0	400	3.0	800	800	300	10	15	150
Pregnant						+30	+200	+5	+2	+20	+0.4	+0.3	+2	+0.6	+400	+1.0	+400	+400	+150	[8]	+5	+25
Lactating						+20	+400	+5	+3	+40	+0.5	+0.5	+5	+0.5	+100	+1.0	+400	+400	+150	[8]	+10	+50

Reference: *Recommended Dietary Allowances*, 9th ed. Food and Nutrition Board, National Research Council–National Academy of Sciences, 1980.

[1] The allowances are intended to provide for individual variations among most normal persons as they live in the United States under usual environmental stresses. Diets should be based on a variety of common foods in order to provide other nutrients for which human requirements have been less well defined.

[2] Retinol equivalents. 1 retinol equivalent = 1 μg retinol or 6 μg β-carotene.

[3] As cholecalciferol. 10 μg cholecalciferol = 400 IU of vitamin D.

[4] α-Tocopherol equivalents. 1 mg α-tocopherol = 1 α-TE.

[5] 1 NE (niacin equivalent) is equal to 1 mg of niacin or 60 mg of dietary tryptophan.

[6] The folacin allowances refer to dietary sources as determined by *Lactobacillus casei* assay after treatment with enzymes (conjugases) to make polyglutamyl forms of the vitamin available to the test organism.

[7] The recommended dietary allowance for vitamin B$_{12}$ in infants is based on average concentration of the vitamin in human milk. The allowances after weaning are based on energy intake (as recommended by the American Academy of Pediatrics) and consideration of other factors, such as intestinal absorption.

[8] The increased requirement during pregnancy cannot be met by the iron content of habitual North American diets or by the existing iron stores of many women; therefore, the use of 30–60 mg of supplemental iron is recommended. Iron needs during lactation are not substantially different from those of nonpregnant women, but continued supplementation of the mother for 2–3 months after parturition is advisable in order to replenish stores depleted by pregnancy.

assumed to be essential because of the observed effects of deficiency on animals (eg, vitamin E) or because clinical symptoms have been produced by specific antagonists (eg, biotin, vitamin K).

The role in human nutrition of a number of nutrients known to be required by certain animal species—fluoride, vanadium, and linolenic acid, for example—is poorly understood. Only one case of human linolenic acid deficiency has been reported. Fluoride contributes to the hardness of bones and to the resistance of teeth to caries, but its role in human growth has not been established. The status of fiber is also undefined; it has beneficial effects on gastrointestinal function but does not seem to be required for normal growth and development. An important goal of recent research has been to clarify the nutritional role of these substances.

Quantitative Aspects of Nutrient Requirements

The minimum quantity of each nutrient necessary to maintain normal function and health has long been the subject of active investigation. An ideal research study would determine the average requirement for each nutrient among a large, statistically significant group of healthy people of varying ages and would assess the statistical variability of requirements within each age group. It would then calculate the amount by which the average requirements should be increased to meet the needs of nearly all healthy individuals within the various age groups. In practice, few studies of nutrient requirements meet these criteria; human nutrition research becomes too difficult and costly when it involves more than just a few adult subjects. Because of the limited data available for many nutrients, it has not been possible to define a precise set of minimum requirements for any one individual. Established nutrient requirements are generous overestimations that attempt to include the needs of most individuals within a given population.

Recommended Dietary Allowances

The most thorough review of data on daily needs for essential nutrients is published by the Food and Nutrition Board of the National Academy of Sciences–National Research Council as *Recommended Dietary Allowances* (RDA) (Table 47–2). In establishing its recommendations, the Board considered a variety of factors that affect the specific requirements of individuals—height, weight, sex, developmental stage, physical activity level, and climate. Some of these factors appear in the table. In general, the allowances increase gradually from infancy to early adulthood. The lower recommendations for adults reflect cessation of growth. Significant increases in nutrient intake are recommended for pregnant or lactating women. For most nutrients, recommendations are higher for males, who generally have a larger lean body mass, than for females. Iron is a notable exception; premenopausal adult women must replace iron losses incurred during menstruation.

Recommended Dietary Allowances includes spe-

cific recommendations for protein, 10 vitamins, and 6 minerals. For the remaining essential nutrients, too little information is available to establish a meaningful allowance. Instead, the Board has established ranges of intake of these nutrients that appear to be safe and adequate. These estimates are presented in Table 47–3 according to age group.

Because *Recommended Dietary Allowances* is used to establish standards for individual dietary intake, food labeling, and food supplementation programs, it is important to recognize its limitations. An individual whose dietary intake falls below the allowance for a specific nutrient may have an *average* requirement for that nutrient and, therefore, an entirely adequate intake. Conversely, a person with a very high nutrient requirement may fail to achieve an adequate intake by simply following the recommendations in Table 47–2.

Even more important, the Food and Nutrition Board bases its recommendations on the needs of healthy people; little information is available on the requirements of people who are ill or stressed. Studies of patients with bone fractures, infected surgical wounds, or severe burns reveal that nitrogen losses and energy expenditures are greatly increased by such conditions. Requirements for energy and protein as well as for other nutrients increase during injury and illness, but not nearly enough is known at present to establish specific allowances that compensate for pathologic disorders.

Finally, *Recommended Dietary Allowances* does not address directly the question of nutrient toxicity. Excessive intake of fat-soluble vitamins (vitamins A, D, E, and K) and many—if not all—of the minerals produces toxic symptoms. Excessive consumption of carbohydrate, fat, or protein may also be harmful. Overweight results from an excess intake of energy over expenditure, whereas high-protein diets can produce symptoms of uric acid excess (from the accompanying nucleic acids) and calcium losses in susceptible individuals. For most nutrients, intakes below minimum requirements result in deficiency disorders, but toxic symptoms develop when safe levels are surpassed. Maximal health benefits seem to accrue from a moderate range of intake of essential nutrients.

COMPOSITION OF FOODS

The selection of foods that must be consumed to ensure an adequate intake of required nutrients depends on cultural and economic factors as well as on biologic necessity, and societies have developed many different ways to meet their nutritional needs.

Foods contain a great many nutrient and nonnutrient substances, but most analyses of their composition are incomplete. Standard food tables provide data for only a limited number of essential nutrients.

Typical food composition data are presented in Table 47–4. The values presented are derived from small samples of each food and represent average

Table 47–3. Estimated safe and adequate daily dietary intakes of selected vitamins and minerals.*

	Age (years)	Vitamins			Trace Elements						Electrolytes		
		Vitamin K (µg)	Biotin (µg)	Pantothenic Acid (mg)	Copper (mg)	Manganese (mg)	Fluoride (mg)	Chromium (mg)	Selenium (mg)	Molybdenum (mg)	Sodium (mg)	Potassium (mg)	Chloride (mg)
Infants	0–0.5	12	35	2	0.5–0.7	0.5–0.7	0.1–0.5	0.01–0.04	0.01–0.04	0.03–0.06	115–350	350–925	275–700
	0.5–1	10–20	50	3	0.7–1.0	0.7–1.0	0.2–1.0	0.02–0.06	0.02–0.06	0.04–0.08	250–750	425–1275	400–1200
Children	1–3	15–30	65	3	1.0–1.5	1.0–1.5	0.5–1.5	0.02–0.08	0.02–0.08	0.05–0.1	325–975	550–1650	500–1500
and ado-	4–6	20–40	85	3–4	1.5–2.0	1.5–2.0	1.0–2.5	0.03–0.12	0.03–0.12	0.06–0.15	450–1350	775–2325	700–2100
lescents	7–10	30–60	120	4–5	2.0–2.5	2.0–3.0	1.5–2.5	0.05–0.2	0.05–0.2	0.10–0.3	600–1800	1000–3000	925–2775
	11+	50–100	100–200	4–7	2.0–3.0	2.5–5.0	1.5–2.5	0.05–0.2	0.05–0.2	0.15–0.5	900–2700	1525–4575	1400–4200
Adults		70–140	100–200	4–7	2.0–3.0	2.5–5.0	1.5–4.0	0.05–0.2	0.05–0.2	0.15–0.5	1100–3300	1875–5625	1700–5100

*From: Recommended Dietary Allowances, 9th ed. Food and Nutrition Board, National Research Council–National Academy of Sciences, 1980.

Table 47—4. Composition of foods: 100 g, edible portion.*

	Water (%)	Food Energy (kcal)	Protein (g)	Fat				Carbohydrate		Minerals						Vitamins				
				Total Fat (g)	Saturated Fatty Acids (g)	Linoleic Acid (g)	Cholesterol (g)	Total (g)	Crude Fiber (g)	Calcium (mg)	Phosphorus (mg)	Iron (mg)	Sodium (mg)	Potassium (mg)	Magnesium (mg)	Vitamin A (IU†)	Thiamin (mg)	Riboflavin (mg)	Niacin (mg)	Ascorbic Acid (mg)
Beverages																				
Beer (4.5% by volume)	92.1	42	0.3	...	...	...	...	3.8	...	5	30	Trace	7	25	...	...	Trace	0.03	0.6	...
Gin, rum, vodka, whiskey (80 proof)	66.6	231	...	...	...	...	...	Trace	...	...	...	...	1	2	...	...	...	...	...	...
Wine (12.2% by volume)	85.6	85	0.1	...	...	...	...	4.2	...	9	10	0.4	5	92	...	...	Trace	0.01	0.1	...
Club soda	100	...	...	...	...	...	...	...	...	...	...	...	...	...	...	...	...	...	...	...
Cola	90	39	...	...	...	...	...	10	...	...	...	...	...	...	...	...	...	...	...	...
Milk: Whole	87.4	65	3.5	3.5	2	Trace	11	4.9	...	118	93	Trace	50	144	13	140	0.03	0.17	0.1	1
Skim	90.5	36	3.6	0.1	1	Trace	3	5.1	...	121	95	Trace	52	145	14	Trace	0.04	0.18	0.1	1
Bread: Whole wheat	36.4	243	10.5	3.0	...	...	...	47.7	1.6	99	238	2.3	527	273	78	Trace	0.26	0.12	2.8	Trace
White, enriched‡	35.8	269	8.7	3.2	...	...	...	50.4	0.2	70	87	2.4‡	507	85	22	Trace	0.25‡	0.17‡	2.3‡	Trace
Broccoli: Raw	89.1	32	3.6	0.3	...	...	...	5.9	1.5	103	78	1.1	15	382	24	2500	0.1	0.23	0.9	113
Cooked, boiled, drained	91.3	26	3.1	0.3	...	...	...	4.5	1.5	88	62	0.8	10	267	...	2500	0.09	0.2	0.8	90
Frozen	90.6	29	3.2	0.3	...	...	...	5.2	1.1	58	59	0.7	17	241	21	2600	0.07	0.13	0.6	70
Frozen, cooked, drained	91.6	26	2.9	0.3	...	...	...	4.6	1.1	54	56	0.7	15	212	...	2600	0.06	0.12	0.5	57
Carrots, raw	88.2	42	1.1	0.2	...	...	...	9.7	1.0	37	36	0.7	47	341	23	11000	0.06	0.05	0.6	8
Chicken, cooked	75.4	120	19.9	3.9	2	1	60	...	...	11	211	1.3	...	...	23	130	0.05	0.16	6.7	...
Eggs, hard cooked	73.7	163	12.9	11.5	4	1	550	0.9	...	54	205	2.3	122	129	...	1180	0.09	0.28	0.1	...
Hamburger, lean, cooked	60	219	27.4	11.3	5	4	70	...	...	12	230	3.5	48	558	25	20	0.09	0.23	6	...
Oil, cooking	...	884	...	100	23	7	...	...	...	...	...	...	...	...	...	...	...	...	...	...
Oranges, peeled	86	49	1	0.2	...	...	...	12.2	0.5	41	20	0.4	1	200	11	200	0.1	0.04	0.4	50
Sugar: Brown	2.1	373	...	...	...	...	...	96.4	...	85	19	3.4	30	344	...	...	0.01	0.03	0.2	...
White	0.5	385	...	...	...	...	...	99.5	...	...	...	0.1	1	3	...	...	...	...	...	...

*Data from Watt BK, Merrill AL: *Composition of Food: Raw, Processed, Prepared.* Agriculture Handbook No. 8, US Department of Agriculture, 1963. If no figure is given, either none of the nutrient is present or it was not measured.

†One IU (international unit) of vitamin A is approximately equivalent to 0.2 µg retinol equivalents.

‡These nutrients are added to enrich white flour to the levels found in whole wheat.

determinations for each nutrient reported. The actual nutrient content of a food depends on several variables: genetic strain, growing location, soil nutrient content, handling and storage, and cooking and processing. Even without this information, Table 47–4 reveals that individual foods vary greatly in their nutrient composition. No single food contains adequate amounts of all essential nutrients. Each plant and animal food contributes a unique complement of nutrients. Thus, the human diet must include sufficient quantities of a wide variety of foods in order to provide the full range of nutritional requirements.

In assessing the nutritional value of any food, it is important to consider its content of essential nutrients relative to its energy value. When 2 foods with equivalent energy values are compared, the one with the higher nutrient content has the higher **nutrient concentration,** or **nutrient density.** Equivalent energy portions of eggs and oranges, for example, differ in nutrient concentration depending on which nutrient is being considered; eggs have more protein and vitamin A but oranges more ascorbic acid and fiber. In practice, these terms do not make such fine distinctions but are used to classify foods into 2 general groups—those of relatively high and those of relatively low nutrient concentration. The first group includes foods that contain significant amounts of essential nutrients or fiber along with their energy. Foods of low nutrient concentration, however, always contain relatively large amounts of fat, which is high in energy, or sugar and alcohol, which have few nutrients. Food processing and storage, illustrated by the data for broccoli in Table 47–4, generally reduce nutrient concentration by destroying or inactivating vitamins.

FOOD ENERGY

Food energy is contained in molecules of carbohydrate, fat, protein, and alcohol. The metabolic oxidation of these molecules releases energy in the form of ATP and other high-energy compounds that are used to maintain concentration gradients of ions, to carry out biosynthetic reactions, to transport and secrete molecules across cell membranes, and to provide power for cell movement and muscle activity. The transduction of food energy to mechanical work occurs at a maximal efficiency of about 25%. The remainder is lost as heat, some of which functions to maintain body temperature.

In the USA, energy intake and expenditure are measured in kilocalories (kcal), or calories (Cal); 1 kcal or Cal is the amount of heat needed to raise the temperature of 1 L of water from 14.5 °C to 15.5 °C. The international unit of energy measurement is the kilojoule (kJ), defined as the energy required to lift 1 kilogram up 1 meter. One megajoule (MJ) = 1000 kJ. The conversion factor for the 2 systems of units is 1 kcal = 4.2 kJ.

The amount of energy available in food is measured by taking advantage of the fact that biologic

Table 47–5. Heats of combustion and energy available from the major food sources.[*]

	Energy kcal/g (kJ/g)		
	Heat of Combustion (Bomb Calorimeter)	**Human Oxidation**	**Standard Conversion Factors[†]**
Protein	5.4 (22.6)	4.1 (17.2)[‡]	4 (17)
Fat	9.3 (38.9)	9.3 (38.9)	9 (38)
Carbohydrate	4.1 (17.2)	4.1 (17.2)	4 (17)
Ethanol	7.1 (29.7)	7.1 (29.7)	7 (29)

[*]Adapted from Davidson S et al: *Human Nutrition and Dietetics,* 7th ed. Churchill Livingstone, 1979.
[†]Conversion factors are obtained by rounding off heats of combustion and correcting for estimates of absorption efficiency.
[‡]Protein oxidation corrected for loss of amino groups excreted in urine.

oxidation reactions are thermodynamically equivalent to chemical oxidation reactions outside the body. When food molecules are heated to high temperature in the presence of oxygen in a closed chamber (a bomb calorimeter), they undergo complete oxidation. In the body, fat and carbohydrate are oxidized completely to carbon dioxide and water, and the heat they release in the calorimeter is equivalent to their available biochemical energy.

The biologic oxidation of protein, however, is not complete; its amino groups are converted to urea or creatinine, compounds that are eventually excreted in urine.

Calorimeter heats of combustion for the major food molecules are presented in Table 47–5. In order to determine the usable amount of energy that can be obtained from food, calorimeter values must be corrected to account for the loss of protein amino groups and for incomplete absorption of food molecules. Finally, the figures are rounded off to standard conversion factors for each of the major energy sources. These factors are used routinely to estimate the energy content of foods with known weights of carbohydrate, fat, and protein. Note that the energy content per unit mass for fat is twice that for either carbohydrate or protein and that alcohol also has a relatively high energy content.

Energy Expenditure

Food must supply enough energy to maintain body functions, muscle activity, and growth. The amount of energy required for these processes has been calculated by both direct and indirect methods. Human energy expenditure was determined directly in classic turn-of-the-century studies of young men who rested or worked in a sealed, insulated chamber while the energy value of their food, excretory products, and heat loss was measured. These experiments were difficult, time-consuming, and expensive, but they produced 2 important results. They confirmed that the total energy of this system was conserved and that the amount of energy expended—heat, work, and excreted products—was equivalent to the energy value of the food consumed. With the subject at rest, nearly all ingested energy could be accounted for by heat loss.

The studies also demonstrated that energy expenditure was almost directly proportionate to the consumption of oxygen. For every liter of oxygen consumed, 4.83 kcal (20 kJ) was expended. This useful result made it possible to calculate the energy expenditure indirectly by measuring the amount of oxygen consumed by individuals engaged in a great variety of activities. Such measurements have demonstrated that for any individual, energy output depends on 3 factors: the basal metabolic rate, the thermogenic effects of food, and the level of physical activity.

The **basal metabolic rate** (BMR) is the approximate energy cost of maintaining basic physiologic activities—heartbeat, respiration, kidney function, osmotic balance, brain activity, and body temperature. It compares measured oxygen consumption with predicted standard values and is expressed as a percentage of the prediction, with the normal variation considered to be ± 10–15%. The BMR is measured under a defined set of standard conditions; the subject must be in a warm room, awake, at rest, and not have eaten for at least 12 hours. Thus, it closely approximates energy expenditure during sleep. Among patients in the hospital, however, it is often difficult to maintain these standard conditions during oxygen uptake measurements. Under these circumstances, energy requirements are expressed as the **resting metabolic expenditure** (RME). Because the BMR and RME differ by no more than about 3%, they may be considered to be equivalent for practical purposes.

Measurements of resting metabolic expenditures are shown in Table 47–6. The RME is proportionate to body surface area and to the percentage of lean body mass. It is somewhat higher than these values in men and in young children, in cold climates, and in various disease states; it is generally depressed during starvation.

The RME must be measured 12 hours after eating, because of the immediate postabsorptive **thermogenic effect** ("specific dynamic action") of food. Within a few minutes after eating, the RME may rise as much as 30% over resting values. The cause of this effect is uncertain; it has been attributed to gastric secretion,

Table 47–6. Normal values for the resting metabolic expenditure of adults.*

Percent Body Fat	Weight (kg)			
	50	60	70	80
	kcal/min (kJ/min)			
5	0.98 (4.1)	1.12 (4.7)	1.27 (5.3)	1.39 (5.8)
10	0.93 (3.9)	1.08 (4.5)	1.22 (5.1)	1.34 (5.6)
15	0.88 (3.7)	1.03 (4.3)	1.17 (4.9)	1.29 (5.4)
20	0.83 (3.5)	0.98 (4.1)	1.12 (4.7)	1.24 (5.2)
25	0.79 (3.3)	0.93 (3.9)	1.08 (4.5)	1.20 (5.0)
30	. . .	0.88 (3.7)	1.03 (4.3)	1.15 (4.8)

*Data from Davidson S et al: *Human Nutrition and Dietetics,* 7th ed. Churchill Livingstone, 1979.

Table 47–7. Energy expended in physical activity.*

	kcal/min (kJ/min)	
Very light work Card playing, eating, ironing, lying down, knitting, writing, typing	< 2.5	(< 10.5)
Light work Carpentry, cleaning house, cooking, dancing (ballroom), food shopping, table tennis, walking	2.5–4.9	(10.5–20.5)
Moderate work Cycling (9½ mph), gardening, golf, scrubbing floors, shoveling, tennis	5–7.4	(20.9–31)
Heavy work Basketball, field hockey, football, swimming (slow crawl)	7.5–9.9	(31.4–41.4)
Very heavy work Cycling (racing), chopping trees, judo, marathon running, skiing uphill, snowshoeing, squash	> 10	(> 41.8)

*Data from Katch FI, McArdle WD: *Nutrition, Weight Control, and Exercise.* Houghton Mifflin, 1977.

protein synthesis, and protein turnover. It appears that over a 24-hour period, the thermogenic effect amounts to no more than 5–10% of metabolic expenditure and that its effect on overall energy balance is minimal.

Muscle activity, however, is a highly significant factor affecting oxygen consumption. The energy costs of many activities have been measured and are summarized in Table 47–7. These figures indicate that the amount of energy expended is proportionate to the rate of sustained muscle contraction. For an individual, energy expenditure at any intensity level depends on body weight, as shown in Table 47–8.

Energy Requirement

Body weight is determined by the balance between energy consumed and energy expended; if more energy is consumed than expended, body weight increases. One pound (0.45 kg) of body fat contains a potential energy of approximately 3500 kcal or 14.7 MJ. This figure is based on the assumption that adipose tissue is 85% fat: 454 g/lb × 9 kcal/g × 0.85 = 3500 kcal/lb, and it implies that a 1-lb per week weight loss requires a daily energy deficit of 500 kcal (2.1 MJ).

Reference weight ranges for men and women of various heights are given in Table 47–9. These figures represent body weights associated with the lowest mortality rates among healthy people —mostly white, male, and middle- or upper-class —who hold life insurance policies. The reference weight ranges have been criticized for inaccuracy (subjects wore shoes and clothing), inadequate definitions of frame size, and failure to account for weight changes with age. Nevertheless, they are widely used to establish standards of obesity and undernutrition.

Table 47—8. Energy expenditure in kcal (kJ) while running depends on body weight and speed.*

Speed Per Mile	Body Weight, lb (kg)				
	110 (50)	130 (59)	150 (68)	170 (77)	190 (86)
11½ min	6.8 (28.5)	8 (33.5)	9.2 (38.5)	10.5 (43.9)	11.7 (49)
9 min	9.7 (40.6)	11.4 (47.7)	13.1 (54.8)	14.9 (62.3)	16.6 (69.5)
8 min	10.8 (45.2)	12.5 (52.3)	14.2 (59.4)	16 (66.9)	17.7 (74.1)
7 min	12.2 (51)	13.9 (58.2)	15.6 (65.3)	17.4 (72.8)	19.1 (79.8)
6 min	13.9 (58.2)	15.6 (65.3)	17.3 (72.4)	19.1 (79.9)	20.8 (87)
5½ min	14.5 (60.7)	17.1 (71.5)	19.7 (82.4)	22.3 (93.2)	24.9 (104.2)

*Data from tables in Katch FI, McArdle WD: *Nutrition, Weight Control, and Exercise.* Houghton Mifflin, 1977.

Recommended energy intake ranges are summarized in Table 47–10. At least 5 variables affect energy intake: activity levels, body size and composition, age, climate, and state of health. The values given in Table 47–10 assume light activity levels, and they must be increased for additional work and exercise, for larger or leaner (see Table 47–6) bodies, and to meet the requirements of body growth in infancy, childhood, and adolescence. Pregnancy and lactation increase requirements by an additional 300–500 kcal per day.

Studies of hospitalized patients reveal that injury and illness have a major effect on energy requirements and nitrogen balance; the resting energy expenditure can increase by more than 100% during severe catabolic stress. Nutritional support greatly in excess of amounts normally needed to maintain body weight and nitrogen balance must be provided to compensate for the increased requirements of very sick patients.

SOURCES OF ENERGY

The 3 major sources of food energy are carbohydrates, fats, and proteins; alcohol also contributes variable amounts of energy.

Based on US Department of Agriculture statistics, the present diet in the USA contains 46% of total energy intake as carbohydrate, 42% as fat, and 12% as protein. The proportions of energy from fat and carbohydrate have changed significantly during this century. Fig 47–1 displays these changes. Since 1909–1913, the proportion of calories from fat has increased while that from carbohydrate has decreased. The overall increase in fat calories derives mainly from a large increase in the use of vegetable oils, shortenings, and margarine. Fat intake from meat consumption has increased only slightly, and the use of butter has declined. The overall decrease in calories derived from carbohydrate is due to a large reduction in intake of

Table 47—9. Reference height and body weight ranges for adult males and females.*†

Height, Men and Women		Weight, lb (kg)					
		Men			Women		
in	cm	Small Frame	Medium Frame	Large Frame	Small Frame	Medium Frame	Large Frame
58	147	. . .	. . .	. . .	102–111 (46–50)	109–121 (49–55)	118–131 (54–59)
59	150	. . .	. . .	. . .	103–113 (47–51)	111–123 (50–56)	120–134 (54–61)
60	152	. . .	. . .	. . .	104–115 (47–52)	113–126 (51–57)	122–137 (55–62)
61	155	. . .	. . .	. . .	106–118 (48–54)	115–129 (52–59)	125–140 (57–64)
62	158	128–134 (58–61)	131–141 (59–64)	138–150 (63–68)	108–121 (49–55)	118–132 (54–60)	128–143 (58–65)
63	160	130–136 (59–62)	133–143 (60–65)	140–153 (64–69)	111–124 (50–56)	121–135 (55–61)	131–147 (59–67)
64	163	132–138 (60–63)	135–145 (61–66)	142–156 (64–71)	114–127 (52–58)	124–138 (56–63)	134–151 (61–68)
65	165	134–140 (61–64)	137–148 (62–67)	144–160 (65–73)	117–130 (53–59)	127–141 (58–64)	137–155 (62–70)
66	168	136–142 (62–65)	139–151 (63–68)	146–164 (66–74)	120–133 (54–60)	130–144 (59–65)	140–159 (64–72)
67	170	138–145 (63–66)	142–154 (64–69)	149–168 (68–76)	123–136 (56–62)	133–147 (60–67)	143–163 (65–74)
68	173	140–148 (64–67)	145–157 (66–71)	152–172 (69–78)	126–139 (57–63)	136–150 (62–68)	146–167 (66–76)
69	175	142–151 (64–68)	148–160 (67–73)	155–176 (70–80)	129–142 (59–64)	139–153 (63–69)	149–170 (68–77)
70	178	144–154 (65–69)	151–163 (68–74)	158–180 (72–82)	132–145 (60–66)	142–156 (64–71)	152–173 (69–78)
71	181	146–157 (66–71)	154–166 (70–75)	161–184 (73–83)	135–148 (61–67)	145–159 (66–72)	155–176 (70–80)
72	183	149–160 (68–73)	157–170 (71–77)	164–188 (74–85)	138–151 (63–68)	148–162 (67–73)	158–179 (71–81)
73	185	152–164 (69–74)	160–174 (73–79)	168–192 (76–87)	. . .	. . .	. . .
74	188	155–168 (70–76)	164–178 (74–81)	172–197 (78–89)	. . .	. . .	. . .
75	190	158–172 (72–78)	167–182 (76–83)	176–202 (80–92)	. . .	. . .	. . .
76	193	162–176 (73–80)	171–187 (78–85)	181–207 (82–94)	. . .	. . .	. . .

*From: Metropolitan Life Foundation: 1983 Metropolitan height and weight tables. *Stat Bull Metropol Life Insur Co* 1983;64:2.
†Ages 25 through 59, for 5 lb of indoor clothing for men and 3 lb of indoor clothing for women, and 1-in heels for both.

Table 47—10. Mean heights and weights and recommended energy intake.*

Category	Age (years)	Weight (kg)	Weight (lb)	Height (cm)	Height (in)	Energy Needs (With Range) (kcal)		(MJ)
Infants	0.0—0.5	6	13	60	24	kg × 115	(95—145)	kg × 0.48
	0.5—1.0	9	20	71	28	kg × 105	(80—135)	kg × 0.44
Children	1—3	13	29	90	35	1300	(900—1800)	5.5
	4—6	20	44	112	44	1700	(1300—2300)	7.1
	7—10	28	62	132	52	2400	(1650—3300)	10.1
Males	11—14	45	99	157	62	2700	(2000—3700)	11.3
	15—18	66	145	176	69	2800	(2100—3900)	11.8
	19—22	70	154	177	70	2900	(2500—3300)	12.2
	23—50	70	154	178	70	2700	(2300—3100)	11.3
	51—75	70	154	178	70	2400	(2000—2800)	10.1
	76+	70	154	178	70	2050	(1650—2450)	8.6
Females	11—14	46	101	157	62	2200	(1500—3000)	9.2
	15—18	55	120	163	64	2100	(1200—3000)	8.8
	19—22	55	120	163	64	2100	(1700—2500)	8.8
	23—50	55	120	163	64	2000	(1600—2400)	8.4
	51—75	55	120	163	64	1800	(1400—2200)	7.6
	76+	55	120	163	64	1600	(1200—2000)	6.7
Pregnancy						+300		
Lactation						+500		

*From: *Recommended Dietary Allowances,* 9th ed. Food and Nutrition Board, National Research Council—National Academy of Sciences, 1980.

complex carbohydrate (starches), especially flour and cereals; in contrast, sugar intake has increased considerably. Consumption of food energy and of dietary protein has remained relatively constant throughout this period.

These trends also include significant increases in consumption of frozen and processed foods, food additives, alcohol, and foods prepared and eaten outside the home. Taken together, they point toward a general decrease in the proportion of essential nutrients to energy among foods consumed in the USA, and they raise disturbing questions about the adequacy of the average North American diet.

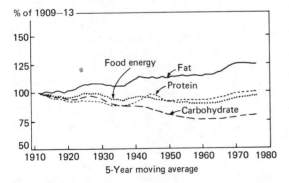

Figure 47—1. Trends in food energy, protein, fat, and carbohydrate consumption per capita in the USA. (Adapted from Friend B: *Changes in Nutrients in the US Diet Caused by Alterations in Food Intake Patterns.* Agricultural Research Service. US Department of Agriculture.)

Carbohydrate

Food carbohydrates include starches (complex carbohydrate), sugars, and fiber. Because some amino acids and the glycerol portion of triglyceride can be converted into glucose, dietary carbohydrate would not seem to be essential. In the absence of carbohydrate, however, ketosis occurs, along with excessive breakdown of muscle protein and significant salt and water losses. To prevent these effects, the Food and Nutrition Board recommends a minimum daily carbohydrate intake of 50–100 g.

Although only a small amount of carbohydrate prevents ketosis, recent dietary recommendations suggest that more than half the total energy intake be derived from **complex carbohydrates** such as wheat, rice, legumes, and potatoes. These foods provide large amounts of vitamins and minerals and are relatively low in energy content.

Unfortunately, many of the nutrients in complex carbohydrate foods may be removed or destroyed during food processing. When whole wheat is converted to white flour, for example, the outer bran layers and embryo (wheat germ) are removed. This process leaves about 70% of the original seed but far less of the essential nutrients. The percentage of several nutrients that remains in white flour is illustrated in Table 47—11. In the USA, 3 vitamins—niacin, riboflavin, thiamin—and iron are restored to their original levels through enrichment of white flour, but the concentration of the remaining nutrients remains greatly reduced.

Food carbohydrates also include the **sugars** such as glucose and fructose that are found in fruits and honey, lactose from milk, and maltose from beer. By

Table 47–11. Percentage of nutrients in whole wheat flour remaining in white flour (72% extraction) per 100 g.*

Energy	100	Riboflavin	33†
Protein	85	Niacin	20†
Linoleic acid	50	Pyridoxine	17
Fiber	13	Folic acid	25
Calcium	50	Vitamin E	2
Copper	20	Vitamin K	24
Potassium	22	Iron	20
Thiamin	18†	Zinc	20

*Data from Davis DR: Wheat and nutrition. Part 1. *Nutrition Today* (July/Aug) 1981;19.

†Fortified to original levels in the USA.

far the most important sugar, however, is sucrose, or common table sugar, which is extracted from beets and cane. The increased consumption of sucrose and other caloric sweeteners during this century is of concern, because foods that contain large amounts of sugars generally lack essential nutrients and contribute "empty calories" to the diet. While sucrose is certainly one of the major etiologic factors in dental caries, its role in diabetes, heart disease, or obesity is less certain. Populations with a high incidence of these disorders tend to consume large amounts of sucrose, but other dietary and environmental factors may be far more important in disease causation.

The third important component of food carbohydrate is **dietary fiber,** a collective term that includes all indigestible plant cell wall components: celluloses, hemicelluloses, lignins, gums, pectins, and pentosans. Dietary fiber must be distinguished from the **crude fiber** listed in food composition data such as that presented in Table 47–4. Crude fiber includes only those components that remain after chemical extraction with solvents, hot acid, and hot alkali, and it comprises only a small fraction (10–50%) of dietary fiber. The indigestible dietary fiber carbohydrates add bulk to the diet. They absorb water in the intestinal lumen and produce larger, softer feces that are easier to eliminate. Epidemiologic studies have associated high-fiber diets with low incidences of diverticulosis, colon cancer, cardiovascular disease, and diabetes. Dietary fiber is reported to reduce serum levels of cholesterol (by preventing enterohepatic circulation) and of glucose (perhaps by delaying intestinal absorption) and to control blood glucose and insulin levels in patients with diabetes. Thus, the Food and Nutrition Board recommends eating fruits, vegetables, and whole-grain cereals to increase fiber consumption.

Fat

Fats increase the palatability of foods by absorbing and retaining flavors. As they tend to be digested slowly, they produce a feeling of satiety. With more than twice the energy value of either protein or carbohydrate, fats provide a concentrated source of food energy. Most cells of the body (erythrocytes and the central nervous system are notable exceptions) can utilize fatty acids directly as sources of energy. During

starvation, the brain adapts and uses ketones derived from fatty acid breakdown as fuel.

In addition, dietary fat has 2 functions that are essential to human nutrition: It acts as a solvent for the absorption of fat-soluble vitamins, and it provides the essential fatty acid **linoleic acid** ($\omega 6$, C18:2). Humans lack the capacity to introduce an additional unsaturated bond between the ω carbon and the existing double bond ($\omega 9$) of oleic acid and thus cannot synthesize linoleic acid (see Chapter 17). Linoleic acid is required for the synthesis of arachidonic acid ($\omega 6$, C20:4), which is the major precursor for the biosynthesis of prostaglandins (Figs 17–12 to 17–15).

Linoleic acid deficiency is exceedingly rare in humans, although it has been reported in infants restricted to a skim milk diet and in children and adults fed a lipid-free diet intravenously. The major symptoms are a scaly dermatitis, hair loss, and poor wound healing. Laboratory studies reveal depressed serum levels of polyunsaturated fatty acids and unusual elevations of serum 5,8,11-eicosatrienoic ($\omega 9$, C20:3) acid. When linoleic acid (and, therefore, arachidonic acid) is deficient in serum, the body attempts to compensate by increased synthesis of oleic acid ($\omega 9$, C18:1) and its products (Fig 47–2). One of these products, 5,8,11-eicosatrienoic acid (triene), is usually present in serum in very small amounts; its elevation relative to arachidonic acid (tetraene) is diagnostic of essential fatty acid deficiency, and the triene:tetraene ratio has been used experimentally to monitor the effectiveness of linoleic acid in patients with this deficiency.

Linoleic acid is widely distributed in the lipid portion of both plant and animal foods; vegetable seed oils are especially rich sources (see Table 18–2). (In premature infants, linoleic acid can be effectively administered by applying vegetable seed oil to the skin.) No recommended allowance has been established for essential fatty acids, but 1–2% of the total dietary energy consumed as linoleic acid prevents clinical signs of deficiency. For a diet containing 2000–3000 kcal/d (8.4–12.6 MJ/d), 5 g of linoleic acid meets the requirements; this amount is well below the quantity (23 g/d) estimated to be available in the food supply in the USA. The wide availability of linoleic acid in the food supply is consistent with the absence of essential fatty acid deficiency in the general population.

Linolenic acid ($\omega 3$, C18:3) may also be an essential fatty acid. Long-chain derivatives of linolenic acid (especially $\omega 3$, C22:6) accumulate in the human cerebral cortex, retina, and testes. Another intermediate ($\omega 3$, C20:5) is a precursor of certain prostaglandins that inhibit platelet aggregation. The low incidence of coronary heart disease among Greenland Eskimos has been attributed to the presence of $\omega 3$ fatty acids in salmon and mackerel fats. The one reported case of linolenic acid deficiency (a child maintained by prolonged total parenteral nutrition who exhibited symptoms of numbness, weakness, inability to walk, and blurred vision that were corrected by the addition of linolenic acid to the feeding solution) did not exclude other nutrient deficiencies as a source of these symptoms.

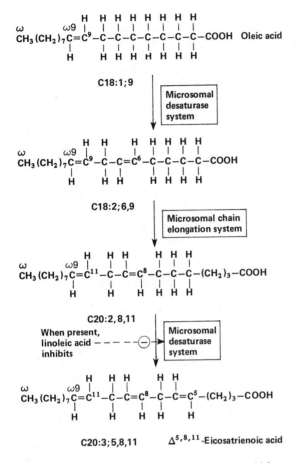

Figure 47–2. Synthesis of $\Delta^{5,8,11}$-eicosatrienoic acid from oleic acid. Eicosatrienoate accumulates in plasma in linoleate deficiency.

Fats of animal origin differ from vegetable fats in 2 significant ways: Animal foods generally contain a higher proportion of saturated fatty acids than do vegetable foods, and cholesterol is found only in foods of animal origin (Table 47–4).

These differences may have important implications for health. In societies where fat forms a major proportion of total energy intake, the population tends to develop a high incidence of obesity, cancers of the bowel and breast, and coronary heart disease. The high energy value of fat accounts for its relationship to obesity. The association between fat intake and certain cancers is still unexplained.

A large number of studies, however, point toward a relationship between dietary fat and coronary heart disease. Along with smoking and hypertension, the level of cholesterol in serum is a major risk factor for the development of atherosclerosis. It is now well established that blood cholesterol levels can be reduced significantly by changing the diet to one that contains less saturated fat and cholesterol. The effect of these changes on the clinical course of heart disease is currently under investigation. While aspects of these relationships remain controversial, it seems prudent to advise at least a moderate reduction in fat intake from levels typical of the average diet consumed in the USA. Thus, most current dietary recommendations suggest a reduction in cholesterol, saturated fat, and overall fat intake and an increase in the ratio of polyunsaturated to saturated fatty acids within the remaining fat allowance. As discussed in Chapter 17, the effects of consuming large amounts of partially hydrogenated vegetable oils and margarine containing *trans*-unsaturated fatty acids are as yet unknown. Because they may be hazardous, *Recommended Dietary Allowances* advises an upper limit of 10% of dietary energy as polyunsaturated fatty acids. This recommendation is consistent with the dietary goals set forth in Table 47–17.

Protein

Protein is required in the diet as a source of essential amino acids and of the **nitrogen** needed for de novo synthesis of nonessential amino acids and other nitrogen-containing compounds. Nitrogen in plant food proteins (and, therefore, in animal proteins) derives from the reduction (or ''fixation'') of the inert N_2 of air. Certain bacterial species that inhabit the root nodules of legumes (peas and beans) and a few blue-green algae are responsible for all biologic **nitrogen fixation.** Nitrogen fixation is also accomplished by lightning and by industrial methods (eg, nitrogenous fertilizer production). All methods for fixing nitrogen gas require large amounts of energy, making nitrogen fixation a rate-limiting and expensive process. Thus, the **availability of fixed nitrogen** is almost always the limiting factor in the production of plant food crops.

The synthesis of protein can occur only when all 20 amino acids are readily available for polypeptide formation. The immediate source of amino acids for protein synthesis is the body pool formed from amino acids released by the normal breakdown of body proteins (protein turnover), those provided by digestion of food proteins, and those newly synthesized by the biochemical pathways described in Chapter 20.

At least 8 (possibly 9) amino acids must be supplied by the diet. These are listed in Table 47–12 along with estimations of the amounts of each required by infants, children, and adults. Histidine has been shown to be essential in the diet of infants, but an adult requirement has not been established. Arginine is no longer considered to be required for growth of the normal human infant, although its synthesis may be inadequate under certain conditions.

The protein content of the diet must be sufficient to replace the essential amino acids and nitrogen lost through normal protein turnover, excreted in feces, sweat, and saliva, or lost through sloughed skin, hair, and nails. Normal protein turnover amounts to 1–2% of total body protein per day. On a protein-free diet, daily nitrogen losses from all sources have been estimated to be 54 mg/kg body weight, or 3.8 g/d for a 70-kg person. Assuming that protein contains approximately 16% nitrogen, this figure is equivalent to about

Table 47–12. Estimated protein and amino acid requirements and intakes.*

	Requirement (mg/kg Body Weight/d)			Intake (g/d)	
	Infant (4–6 months)	Child (10–12 years)	Adult	Adult (70 kg) Allowance*	Estimated US Adult Intake†
Protein	2000	1400	800	56	101
Animal	...	...	...	...	71
Vegetable	...	...	...	...	30
Essential amino acids					
Histidine	33	?	?	?	?
Isoleucine	83	28	12	0.84	5.3
Leucine	135	42	16	1.12	8.2
Lysine	99	44	12	0.84	6.7
Methionine (and cysteine)	49	22	10	0.70	2.1
Phenylalanine (and tyrosine)	141	22	16	1.12	4.7
Threonine	68	28	8	0.56	4.1
Tryptophan	21	4	3	0.21	1.2
Valine	92	25	14	0.98	5.7

*Data from *Recommended Dietary Allowances,* 9th ed. Food and Nutrition Board, National Research Council–National Academy of Sciences, 1980.

†Data from Munro HN, Crim M: The proteins and amino acids. In: Goodhart RS, Shils ME: *Modern Nutrition in Health and Disease,* 6th ed. Lea & Febiger, 1980.

24 g of protein (3.8 ÷ 0.16). Increasing this amount by 2 standard deviations to include the requirements of most healthy individuals brings the 70-kg adult requirement to the 56 g of protein per day listed in Table 47–12.

For most individuals, this amount of protein is sufficient to maintain **nitrogen balance**—the equilibrium between nitrogen incorporated into protein and other nitrogen-containing compounds and the amount excreted in urine or lost in skin and sweat. Regardless of their source, amino acids that are not immediately incorporated into new protein are rapidly degraded. Their carbon skeletons are either converted to fatty acids or glucose or oxidized as an energy source; their amino groups are excreted as urea and other nitrogenous compounds.

The utilization of dietary protein, as reflected in nitrogen balance, depends not only upon the quantity of protein available but also upon 2 additional factors: protein quality and the ratio of energy to nitrogen in the diet. **Protein quality** refers to the proportion of essential amino acids in a food relative to the human requirement for them (as estimated in Table 47–12). In general, animal food proteins are closer in amino acid composition to human proteins than are those from vegetable foods. (From a strictly biochemical aspect, the best source of food protein for humans would be healthy humans.)

Because egg and milk proteins are utilized efficiently in balance studies performed on growing laboratory animals, they are used as standards for comparison of protein quality. The major vegetable food crops serve less well in such studies, because they are especially deficient in one or another essential amino acid.

The most deficient amino acid in a protein relative to the composition of standard egg or milk proteins is said to be the **limiting amino acid.** Fortunately, the limiting amino acids of the major food crops differ; corn is limiting in tryptophan and lysine, wheat in lysine, and certain beans in methionine. The consumption of 2 low-quality proteins can be synergistic and can yield an entirely adequate amino acid intake if the proteins are complementary in amino acid composition. Complementary vegetable proteins form the basis of vegetarian diets and many traditional vegetable food combinations such as succotash (lima beans and corn), tortillas and beans, and bread and peanut butter.

The second factor affecting protein utilization is the **ratio of energy to protein in the diet.** Nitrogen balance requires an adequate intake of both protein and energy. Dietary deficiency of either one results in negative nitrogen balance in which more nitrogen is excreted than is retained. The higher the energy intake, the less protein is required to achieve nitrogen balance, because there is less need to break down amino acids to produce energy. The relationship between energy and protein is a continuous one in which nitrogen balance has been found to change by about 0.2–0.3 g of nitrogen (equivalent to 1–2 g of protein) for every increase or decrease of 100 kcal (420 kJ) in the diet. In severe illnesses such as those resulting from trauma or infection, energy intakes of 150 kcal per gram of nitrogen or even higher may be necessary to compensate for protein catabolism and to restore nitrogen balance.

Even for healthy individuals, an energy intake equivalent to 1½ times the basal metabolic expenditure seems to be necessary to maintain nitrogen balance. At least some of this energy should be supplied as carbohydrate in order to spare protein from use in gluconeogenesis. Finally, physical activity has been shown to increase nitrogen retention and is important in determining nitrogen equilibrium.

Protein allowances must be increased to meet the biosynthetic demands of growth, pregnancy, and lactation; to compensate for higher physical activity levels at work or during exercise; to maintain nitrogen balance in the elderly; and to replace excessive nitrogen losses during injury-induced protein catabolism. As summarized in Table 47–12, the average protein intake in the USA is well above the amounts listed in *Recommended Dietary Allowances;* it usually accounts for 12–20% of the total daily energy. This average amount should be more than sufficient to maintain nitrogen balance for most individuals. High-protein diets appear to confer no special advantage; they may, in fact, be disadvantageous. Diets with excessive amounts of protein have produced toxic effects in premature infants, have been associated with calcium losses in adults, and may damage kidney function. A diet that contains 12–15% of energy as protein appears to be both adequate and safe.

Various human societies routinely subsist on diets that range from less than 50 g to more than 200 g of protein per day. At the lowest end of this range are vast numbers of people in developing countries in Asia, Africa, and South America whose consumption of energy and essential amino acids is inadequate to sustain optimal biosynthetic activity. Lack of food, in the presence of chronic infectious diseases, leads to the clinical symptoms of starvation known collectively as **protein-energy malnutrition,** a condition that is especially severe in growing children and that constitutes the single most important worldwide nutrition problem.

When edema is present in children who consume **adequate energy but limited protein,** the condition is known as **kwashiorkor.** The generalized loss of body tissue that occurs with **deficient intake of both energy and protein** is called **marasmus.** Both forms of starvation lead to enormous waste of human life; they result from poverty and ignorance and require social and economic intervention to increase the quantity and quality of the food supply.

Typical protein-energy malnutrition also occurs in developed countries among adults as a consequence of malabsorption, gastrointestinal surgery, or severe illness. Surveys of medical and surgical wards in major urban hospitals suggest that as many as 30–50% of patients hospitalized for more than 2 weeks meet World Health Organization standards for protein-energy malnutrition. Many of these patients require nutritional support to aid their recovery.

VITAMINS

Vitamins are organic molecules in food that are required for normal metabolism but cannot be synthesized in adequate amounts by the human body. A dietary or physiologic deficiency of any one of them leads to a specific set of disease symptoms that can be corrected by administration of that vitamin alone.

Vitamins were given alphabetic designations in the order of their discovery. They were named when they were isolated individually and their chemical structures identified. Nine compounds or groups of closely related compounds are considered to be vitamins for human nutrition. Although they are exceedingly heterogeneous in chemical structure and biochemical function, they can be grouped conveniently into 2 classes that share common characteristics: water-soluble vitamins and fat-soluble vitamins. The chemistry, metabolism, and physiologic functions of the vitamins are discussed in detail in Chapters 10 and 11. Their most important characteristics are summarized in Tables 47–13 and 47–14.

The **water-soluble vitamins** include the B complex group and ascorbic acid (vitamin C). Because they are soluble in water, they are generally associated with the fluid compartment of the body. They are excreted in urine when their serum levels exceed tissue saturation (which, in turn, reflects the binding of vitamin cofactors to enzymes and transport proteins). Thus, the water-soluble vitamins must be supplied continually in the diet even though tissue saturation levels may not be depleted for months (ascorbic acid) or even years (vitamin B_{12}). Because water-soluble vitamins taken in excess are usually excreted, they are generally nontoxic, although symptoms have been reported in some individuals ingesting megadose quantities of niacin, ascorbic acid, or pyridoxine.

Water-soluble vitamins are found together in the same foods. Whole-grain cereals, legumes, leafy green vegetables, meat, and dairy products are good sources of all of them except ascorbic acid and vitamin B_{12}. Ascorbic acid is found in fresh fruits and vegetables, especially citrus fruits. Vitamin B_{12} is synthesized by microorganisms; it is incorporated into animal tissues and is present only in meat and dairy foods. Thus, strict vegetarians may be at risk for vitamin B_{12} deficiency.

As described in Chapter 10, most of the vitamins present in food must be metabolized to active coenzyme forms. Inborn errors in these pathways that cause coenzyme binding defects or that inactivate coenzymes may lead to symptoms of vitamin deficiency even when the diet is adequate. In some cases, deficiency symptoms can be corrected by administration of large amounts of the missing vitamin. Examples of these **vitamin-responsive syndromes** are listed in Table 47–14.

The biochemical roles of water-soluble vitamin cofactors are reasonably well defined (Chapter 10); among this group, only ascorbic acid lacks a known coenzyme function. The roles of these vitamins are closely interrelated, and several of them may function in the same pathway or even in the same enzyme complex. For example, both biotin and vitamin B_{12} are required for the metabolism of propionyl-CoA to succinyl-CoA (Fig 15–16); the pyruvate dehydrogenase complex includes cofactors of 4 vitamins: thiamin,

Table 47—13. Essential water-soluble vitamins: Summary of major characteristics.*

Vitamin	Coenzymes	Biochemical or Physiologic Function[1]	Deficiency Syndrome or Symptoms[2] (and Associated Diet)	Sources[3]	Stability[4]
Niacin (nicotinic acid, nicotinamide)	Nicotinamide adenine dinucleotide (NAD); nicotinamide adenine dinucleotide phosphate (NADP).	Electron (hydrogen) transfer reactions carried out by dehydrogenase enzymes, eg, pyruvate dehydrogenase, glyceraldehyde-3-phosphate dehydrogenase.	Pellagra (milled corn).	Protein foods containing tryptophan, in addition to niacin sources in note[3].	Stable.
Thiamin (vitamin B$_1$)	Thiamin pyrophosphate (TPP).	Oxidative decarboxylation of α-ketoacids (pyruvate and α-ketoglutarate dehydrogenases) and 2-ketosugars (transketolases).	Beriberi (milled rice); Wernicke-Korsakoff syndrome (alcohol). Antagonized by thiaminase in raw fish.		Stable in acid solution.
Riboflavin (vitamin B$_2$)	Flavin adenine dinucleotide (FAD); flavin mononucleotide (FMN).	Electron (hydrogen) transfer reactions (eg, pyruvate dehydrogenase, acyl-CoA dehydrogenase).	Cheilosis.		Stable in acid solution. Light-sensitive.
Pantothenic acid	CoA.	Acyl transfer reactions (citrate synthase, choline acetylase, etc).			Stable in neutral solution.
Vitamin B$_6$, pyridoxine, pyridoxal, pyridoxamine	Pyridoxal phosphate (PLP).	Transamination and decarboxylation via Schiff's base (many aminotransferase and decarboxylase enzymes).	Low serum levels are associated with pregnancy and oral contraceptive agents. Antagonized by isoniazid, penicillamine, and other drugs.		Stable in acid solution. Light-sensitive.
Biotin	N-Carboxybiotinyl lysine.	CO_2 transfer reactions of carboxylase coenzymes (pyruvate carboxylase, acetyl-CoA carboxylase).	Induced by avidin, a protein in raw egg whites, or by antibiotic therapy.	Synthesized by intestinal microorganisms.	
Vitamin B$_{12}$ (cobalamin)	Methylcobalamin; 5'-deoxyadenosyl cobalamin.	Methylation of homocysteine to methionine; conversion of methylmalonyl-CoA to succinyl-CoA.	Megaloblastic anemia, methylmalonic aciduria, peripheral neuropathy (strict vegetarian diet). Pernicious anemia induced by lack of intrinsic factor.	Animal foods (meat, dairy) only.	Stable in neutral solutions.
Folic acid (folacin)	Derivatives of tetrahydrofolic acid.	One-carbon transfer reactions, eg, purine nucleotide and thymidylate synthesis.	Megaloblastic anemia.		
Ascorbic acid (vitamin C)	Unknown.	Antioxidant; collagen biosynthesis; tyrosine catabolism (?).	Scurvy (lack of fresh fruits and vegetables).	Fresh fruits (especially citrus) and vegetables.	Especially unstable to heat. Easily oxidized in the presence of copper or iron.

*Consult Chapter 10 for detailed information.

[1] The metabolism of most water-soluble vitamins is similar. They are absorbed in the intestine, stored bound to enzymes and transport proteins, and excreted in urine when plasma levels exceed kidney thresholds. The one notable exception is vitamin B$_{12}$, which requires intrinsic factor (synthesized by gastric parietal cells) for absorption in the distal ileum, is stored in milligram amounts in the liver, and is excreted in bile (and reabsorbed via the enterohepatic circulation) as well as in urine.

[2] Excess intake of water-soluble vitamins is not usually toxic. Exceptions: Excess nicotinic acid—but not nicotinamide—causes vascular dilatation of skin ("flushing"); megadose intake of ascorbic acid has been reported to produce diarrhea, oxalate kidney stones, and a variety of other toxic symptoms; high-dose pyridoxine (5 g/d) has caused sensory ataxia, sensory nerve dysfunction, and axonal degeneration in a few cases. Deficiency of these vitamins affects actively metabolizing tissues; symptoms usually include disorders of the digestive and nervous systems, skin, and blood cells.

[3] Unless otherwise stated, a varied intake of adequate amounts of foods from the following groups will meet nutritional requirements for water-soluble vitamins: whole-grain cereals, legumes, leafy green vegetables, meat, and dairy products.

[4] Stability refers to survival of vitamin activity during normal food preparation, cooking, and storage. Unless noted to the contrary, water-soluble vitamins are unstable to heat, strong acid or alkali solutions, and prolonged storage. These vitamins all dissolve in cooking water.

Table 47–14. Vitamin-responsive syndromes. Examples of specific defects in vitamin cofactor metabolism that can be corrected by vitamin therapy, usually requiring very large doses.*

Vitamin	Disease	Biochemical Defect
Biotin	Propionic acidemia	Propionyl-CoA carboxylase
Vitamin B$_{12}$	Methylmalonic aciduria	Formation of cobamide coenzyme
Folic acid	Folate malabsorption	Folic acid transport
Niacin	Hartnup disease	Tryptophan transport
Pyridoxine (vitamin B$_6$)	Infantile convulsions	Glutamic acid decarboxylase (?)
	Cystathioninuria	Cystathioninase
	Homocystinuria	Cystathionine synthase
Thiamin	Hyperalaninemia	Pyruvate decarboxylase
	Thiamin-responsive lactic acidosis	Hepatic pyruvate carboxylase

*From: Herman RH, Stifel FB, Greene HL: Vitamin-deficient states and other related diseases. In: *Disorders of the Gastrointestinal Tract; Disorders of the Liver; Nutritional Disorders.* Dietschy JM (editor). Grune & Stratton, 1976.

pantothenic acid, riboflavin, and niacin (Fig 15–6). Thus, a dietary deficiency of any one vitamin may adversely affect the utilization or metabolism of another.

Because water-soluble vitamins occur in the same foods and in interrelated biochemical pathways, deficiency diseases caused by the lack of a single vitamin are rare; their symptoms reflect the lack of the most limiting vitamin in the diet. Only 5 of the water-soluble vitamins are associated with major syndromes, and each of these disorders can be attributed to consumption of a diet highly restricted in food choices. This information is summarized in Table 47–13. In general, the lack of water-soluble vitamins affects tissues that are growing or metabolizing rapidly: skin, blood, the digestive tract, and the nervous system. Correspondingly, deficiency symptoms nearly always consist of dermatitis, anemia, digestive difficulties, and neurologic disorders.

As a group, water-soluble vitamins are somewhat unstable to heat, light, and strong acid or alkali solutions; they dissolve in cooking water, which should therefore be kept to a minimum to prevent vitamin losses. The effect of food preparation on vitamin content is illustrated for broccoli in Table 47–4. Ascorbic acid is especially labile to heat, and large losses occur during cooking of vegetables. Because of nutrient removal during cereal refinement, 3 of the B vitamins (riboflavin, niacin, and thiamin) are used in the USA to enrich white flour and corn meal to the original level of these nutrients (Table 47–11).

The **fat-soluble vitamins** (vitamins A, D, E, and K) differ from the water-soluble group in significant ways. They are present in food fats: fatty meats, liver, dairy fats, egg yolks, vegetable seed oils, and leafy green vegetables. Fortification of milk with vitamin D and margarine with vitamin A makes these foods the major dietary sources of vitamins A and D in the USA.

The most important characteristics of the fat-soluble vitamins are discussed in Chapter 11 and summarized in Table 47–15. In general these vitamins are metabolized along with fat in the body. They are digested with fat, require fat for absorption, are transported with fat in chylomicrons and lipoproteins, and are stored in the liver or in adipose tissue. They are not excreted in urine and can therefore accumulate in storage tissues to toxic levels. Well-defined toxicity syndromes have been described for vitamins A and D. Megadose intakes of vitamin E have been reported to produce symptoms of toxicity, and cases of vitamin K toxicity have occurred among patients undergoing therapy with water-dispersible preparations of this vitamin. Fat-soluble hypervitaminoses occasionally result from acute poisoning, but they can also occur with chronic administration of amounts 25–100 times higher than the recommended dietary allowance for long periods. Except as indicated therapeutically, megadose administration of fat-soluble vitamins is potentially dangerous and should be avoided.

Deficiencies of fat-soluble vitamins occur primarily in young children who lack adequate body stores. Deficiencies are rare in adults; when they do occur, they are almost always secondary to malabsorption, biliary obstruction, or other conditions that affect fat metabolism.

MINERALS

Body composition studies demonstrate that nearly all of the known chemical elements can be found in the human body. Elements known to have defined physiologic functions (essential nutrients) are listed in Table 47–1. Elements for which requirements are greater than 100 mg/d are referred to as **minerals.** The so-called **trace elements** are needed in much smaller amounts. Present knowledge of the function of many of these elements is limited; additional minerals are known to be required for certain animal species, and others are found in the body but have no known function. Some of these elements eventually may prove to be required for human nutrition.

Minerals are described in Chapter 46; this information is summarized in Table 47–16. The metabolism of most minerals is incompletely understood. Certain generalizations, however, apply to nearly all of them. **Absorption** of minerals in the intestine is usually inefficient, and greater quantities of them are excreted in the feces than are absorbed. Specific proteins are required for their absorption, and the synthesis of these specific proteins is a necessary part of mineral metabolism. Absorption of minerals can be affected by chelating agents (phytates, oxalates), protein, fat, other minerals, and fiber in the diet, but the results of studies of such interactions do not lead to any consistent pattern. Iron, for example, is absorbed better from meat than from vegetable foods, but high-

Table 47–15. Essential fat-soluble vitamins: Summary of major characteristics.*

Vitamin/Provitamin[1]	Metabolism[2]	Active Metabolite: Physiologic Function	Deficiency Syndrome or Symptoms	Toxicity Syndrome or Symptoms	Sources[3]
Vitamin A Provitamin: β-caro-tene Vitamin: retinol	Transported in lymph as retinyl esters in blood bound to reti-nol-binding protein and prealbumin.	11-*Cis* retinal: constit-uent of rhodopsin and other light-receptor pigments. Unknown metabolites (retinoic acid?): required for growth and differen-tiation of epithelial, nervous, and bone tis-sues.	Children: poor dark adaptation, xerosis, keratomalacia, growth failure, death. Adults: night blind-ness, xeroderma.	Hypervitaminosis A: headache, dizziness, nausea, skin slough-ing, bone pain.	Highly pig-mented vege-tables (con-taining caro-tenes), forti-fied margarine.
Vitamin D Provitamins: ergos-terol (plants, yeast) and 7-de-hydrocholesterol (skin) Vitamins D_2 (ergo-calciferol) and D_3 (cholecalcif-erol)	Provitamins converted to vitamins by ultra-violet irradiation. Vi-tamins hydroxylated in liver to 25-hydroxy-vitamin D and in kid-ney to 1,25-dihy-droxy-vitamin D and other metabolites.	1,25-Dihydroxy-vita-min D_3 is major hor-monal regulator of bone mineral (calcium and phosphorus) me-tabolism.	Children: rickets. Adults: osteomalacia.	Hypervitaminosis D: hypercalcemia, hy-percalciuria, nephro-calcinosis.	Fortified milk; sunlight on skin.
Vitamin E tocopherols, tocotrienols	Generally unknown.	Active metabolite un-known. Functions as an antioxidant.	Children: anemia in premature infants. Adults: no known syndrome.	Undefined. Mega-dose intake reported to induce blurred vision, headaches.	Vegetable seed oils are major source.
Vitamin K K_1 (phylloquinone), K_2 (menaquinone), others	Generally undefined.	Active metabolite un-known but probably hydroquinone deriva-tive. Activates blood clotting factors II, VII, IX, and X by γ-car-boxylating glutamic acid residues; also car-boxylates bone and kidney proteins.	Infants: hemorrhagic disease of newborn. Adults: defective blood clotting. Defi-ciency symptoms can be produced by cou-marin anticoagulants and by antibiotic ther-apy.	Can be induced by water-dispersible analogs: hemolytic anemia, liver damage.	Synthesized by intestinal bac-teria.

*For more detailed information, consult Chapter 11.

[1] The fat-soluble vitamins are insoluble in water but dissolve in fats and oils. They are relatively stable to normal cooking tempera-tures but are slowly inactivated by ultraviolet light and by oxidation.

[2] Absorption of fat-soluble vitamins requires dietary fat and bile; malabsorption or biliary obstruction leads to deficiency. Transport is via lipoproteins or specific transport proteins. Storage is mainly in liver, some in adipose tissue. These vitamins are excreted in bile and either reabsorbed via the enterohepatic circulation or excreted in feces. Some metabolites may be excreted in urine.

[3] Food sources of all fat-soluble vitamins include leafy green vegetables, vegetable seed oils, and fat-containing meat and dairy prod-ucts, in addition to the specific sources listed here.

protein diets increase zinc and calcium requirements. Vitamin C improves the absorption of iron but de-creases copper absorption. Diets high in fiber inhibit the absorption of calcium and magnesium but not of phosphorus. These interactions clearly need further study before dietary changes to alter mineral intake can be recommended.

Once absorbed, minerals are transported in blood by albumin or specific carrier proteins. They may be stored in liver and other tissues in association with special proteins. Nearly all essential minerals can ac-cumulate to toxic concentrations. Because mineral in-take is usually controlled at the level of absorption, toxicity generally occurs secondary to some malfunc-tion in the regulation of absorption.

The mineral nutrients are widely distributed in whole-grain cereals, fruits and vegetables, dairy prod-ucts, meats, and seafood, but they are usually present in these foods in very small quantities. A sufficient quantity and variety of food must be consumed to meet daily requirements. Food processing removes signifi-cant amounts of minerals (Table 47–11). In the USA, iron is the only mineral replaced by fortification. People whose energy intake is low as a result of diet-ing, aging, or sedentary life-style or whose diet con-tains a large proportion of foods with a low nutrient content may not consume sufficient minerals. Defi-cient mineral intake results in the syndromes outlined in Table 47–16. In addition, marginal mineral de-ficiencies have been associated with a wide variety of diseases of multifactorial causation. Coronary heart disease, for example, has been attributed to trace element deficiencies, but this association is only one of many factors that might be responsible. Until more is known about trace mineral metabolism, such associations must be considered suggestive but unproved. In the absence of contrary evidence, optimal mineral nutrition depends on the consumption of a wide variety of foods of relatively high nutrient concentration.

WATER

Enough water must be consumed to meet physiologic requirements (covered in detail in Chapter 46). A significant fraction of these requirements can be met by the water present in food. The first column of Table 47–4 gives the range of water content of some typical foods. Hydrophobic energy sources such as cooking oil or concentrated ones such as sugar contain almost no water, whereas fruits and vegetables contain most of their weight as water.

NUTRITIONAL SUPPLEMENTS

The diet that best meets human nutritional requirements is one that contains many different foods of high nutrient concentration. Persons whose overall energy intake is low, those whose diet consists largely of processed foods of low nutritional content, and those who have increased nutritional needs as a result of pregnancy, drug therapy, or illness may not be able to meet their nutrient requirements from food. For such people, pharmacies and health food stores make available a great variety of nutritional supplements. These products include dietary supplements (liquid protein formulas), whole food extracts (alfalfa, bone meal, kelp, etc), nutrients that function in the body but are not known to be essential in the human diet (choline, *p*-aminobenzoic acid, bioflavonoids), and essential nutrients (vitamins, minerals, amino acids). Many people, however, take diet supplements in the belief that they will prevent or cure specific illnesses. For most nutritional supplements, insufficient evidence exists to determine whether these products are either safe or effective.

As an approach to dealing with these questions, it is useful to keep in mind that neither the exact number of required nutrients nor the amounts required are completely defined. As many as 40–50 nutrients are essential in the diet, and the absence of any one of them leads to disease. Because the biochemical functions of nutrients are interrelated, supplying one in the absence of the others can never meet nutritional requirements.

The safety of most nutritional products has not been tested. Among the products that have been studied, however, are several whose safety is at least questionable. The incidence of deaths among users of the liquid protein diet and the discovery of the mutagenic potential of pangamic acid are 2 recent examples. Ingestion of supplemental minerals and fat-soluble vitamins greatly in excess of the amounts required produces well-defined toxic syndromes. While megadose intakes of water-soluble vitamins appear to be generally nontoxic, there are 3 exceptions: Large doses of niacin induce vasodilatation and have been reported to cause abnormal liver function; ingestion of gram quantities of ascorbic acid induces diarrhea (and other symptoms reported but controversial); and excessive pyridoxine is reported to induce a sensory neuropathy.

The effects of nutritional supplements in prevention and treatment of diseases other than those known to be caused by nutrient deficiency have been shown, in most cases, to be indistinguishable from the effects of placebo.

FOOD TOXINS & ADDITIVES

Foods contain a large number of potentially harmful compounds. Some occur naturally; they include harmful substances such as the neurotoxins from shellfish or mushrooms, goitrogens from plants of the cabbage family, bean compounds that interfere with collagen formation, and the carcinogenic aflatoxin from peanut mold. Pesticides and packaging materials may be added to food through inadvertent contamination. About 2500 compounds are added to foods in order to preserve them or to add color, flavor, or texture. Although most food additives appear harmless, the safety of some of them (eg, nitrates, saccharin, sulfites) is questionable. Others have been inadequately tested. Since most foods have not been analyzed for their content of natural or added toxins, prudent advice would be to avoid substances known to be toxic, to eat moderate amounts of a wide variety of foods, and to emphasize consumption of fresh, unprocessed foods in order to minimize intake of natural toxins and additives whose biologic effects are as yet unknown.

NUTRITION & HEALTH

Nutritional deficiency syndromes are rare among people whose income is adequate. They are found chiefly among the poor, the elderly, individuals with unusually high nutrient requirements (growing children, pregnant and lactating women), those who are seriously ill, and alcoholics or other people whose diets are restricted out of choice or necessity to one food as the primary energy source.

In contrast, diseases or disorders associated with nutrient excess—obesity, for example—are common in developed societies. Of the 10 leading causes of death in the USA, 6 have been associated with excess intake of certain foods: coronary heart disease, cancers of the bowel and breast, cerebrovascular disease, diabetes, arteriosclerosis, and cirrhosis of the liver. The evidence that relates diet to these conditions

Table 47—16. Essential minerals and trace elements: Summary of major characteristics.[*]

Elements	Functions	Metabolism[1]	Deficiency Disease or Symptoms	Toxicity Disease or Symptoms[2]	Sources[3]
Minerals: required intake > 100 mg/d					
Calcium	Constituent of bones, teeth; regulation of nerve, muscle function.	Absorption requires calcium-binding protein. Regulated by vitamin D, parathyroid hormone, calcitonin, etc.	Children: rickets. Adults: osteomalacia. May contribute to osteoporosis.	Occurs with excess absorption due to hypervitaminosis D or hypercalcemia due to hyperparathyroidism, or idiopathic hypercalcemia.	Dairy products, beans, leafy vegetables.
Phosphorus	Constituent of bones, teeth, ATP, phosphorylated metabolic intermediates. Nucleic acids.	Control of absorption unknown (vitamin D?). Serum levels regulated by kidney reabsorption.	Children: rickets. Adults: osteomalacia.	Low serum Ca^{2+}/P_i ratio stimulates secondary hyperthyroidism; may lead to bone loss.	Phosphate food additives.
Sodium	Principal cation in extracellular fluid. Regulates plasma volume, acid-base balance, nerve and muscle function, Na^+, K^+-ATPase.	Regulated by aldosterone.	Unknown on normal diet; secondary to injury or illness.	Hypertension (in susceptible individuals).	Table salt; salt added to prepared food.
Potassium	Principal cation in intracellular fluid; nerve and muscle function, Na^+, K^+-ATPase.	Also regulated by aldosterone.	Occurs secondary to illness, injury, or diuretic therapy; muscular weakness, paralysis, mental confusion. Low Na^+/K^+ ratio may predispose to hypertension.	Cardiac arrest, small bowel ulcers.	
Chloride	Fluid and electrolyte balance; gastric fluid.		Infants fed salt-free formula. Secondary to vomiting, diuretic therapy, renal disease.		Table salt.
Magnesium	Constituent of bones, teeth; enzyme cofactor (kinases, etc).		Secondary to malabsorption or diarrhea, alcoholism.	Depressed deep tendon reflexes and respiration.	Leafy green vegetables (containing chlorophyll).
Trace elements: required intake < 100 mg/d					
Chromium	Trivalent chromium, a constituent of "glucose tolerance factor."	Undefined.	Impaired glucose intolerance; secondary to parenteral nutrition.		
Cobalt	Constituent of vitamin B_{12}.	As for vitamin B_{12}.	Vitamin B_{12} deficiency.		Foods of animal origin.
Copper	Oxidase enzymes: cytochrome C oxidase, tyrosinase, ferroxidase, etc.	Transported by albumin; bound to ceruloplasmin.	Anemia (hypochromic, microcytic); secondary to malnutrition, Menke's syndrome.	Rare; secondary to Wilson's disease.	
Iodine	Thyroxine, triiodothyronine.	Stored in thyroid as thyroglobulin.	Children: cretinism. Adults: goiter and hypothyroidism, myxedema.	Thyrotoxicosis, goiter.	Iodized salt, seafood.
Iron	Heme enzymes (hemoglobin, cytochromes, etc).	Transported as transferrin; stored as ferritin or hemosiderin; excreted in sloughed cells and by bleeding.	Anemia (hypochromic, microcytic).	Siderosis; hereditary hemochromatosis.	Iron cookware.
Manganese	Hydrolase, decarboxylase, and transferase enzymes. Glycoprotein and proteoglycan synthesis.		Unknown in humans.	Inhalation poisoning produces psychotic symptoms and parkinsonism.	
Molybdenum	Oxidase enzymes (xanthine oxidase).		Secondary to parenteral nutrition.		
Selenium	Glutathione peroxidase.	Synergistic antioxidant with vitamin E.	Marginal deficiency when soil content is low; secondary to parenteral nutrition, protein-energy malnutrition.	Megadose supplementation induces hair loss, dermatitis, and irritability.	

Table 47–16 (cont'd). Essential minerals and trace elements: Summary of major characteristics.*

Elements	Functions	Metabolism[1]	Deficiency Disease or Symptoms	Toxicity Disease or Symptoms[2]	Sources[3]
Trace elements: required intake < 100 mg/d (cont'd)					
Zinc	Cofactor of many enzymes: lactic dehydrogenase, alkaline phosphatase, carbonic anhydrase, etc.		Hypogonadism, growth failure, impaired wound healing, decreased taste and smell acuity; secondary to acrodermatitis enteropathica, parenteral nutrition.	Gastrointestinal irritation, vomiting.	
Fluoride[4]	Increases hardness of bones and teeth.		Dental caries; osteoporosis(?).	Dental fluorosis.	Drinking water.

*For detailed information, see Chapter 46.

[1] In general, minerals require carrier proteins for absorption. Absorption is rarely complete; it is affected by other nutrients and compounds in the diet (eg, oxalates and phytates that chelate divalent cations). Transport and storage also require special proteins. Excretion occurs in feces (unabsorbed minerals) and in urine, sweat, and bile.

[2] Excess mineral intake produces toxic symptoms. Unless otherwise specified, symptoms include nonspecific nausea, diarrhea, and irritability.

[3] Mineral requirements are met by a varied intake of adequate amounts of whole-grain cereals, legumes, leafy green vegetables, meat, and dairy products.

[4] Fluoride is essential for rat growth. While not proved to be strictly essential for human nutrition, fluorides have a well-defined role in prevention and treatment of dental caries.

is often controversial. For example, some studies have demonstrated that populations with a high salt intake exhibit a greater frequency of hypertension than occurs among groups whose salt intake is low. Populations of pigs or rats who had salt added to their food have higher blood pressures than animals raised on salt-free diets. Do these results imply that dietary salt causes hypertension in humans? Clinical trials that might answer this question—and similar questions regarding nutrition as a factor in the etiology of heart disease, cancer, or diabetes—are exceedingly difficult to design and carry out. The studies are expensive and must often be conducted on samples too small to be statistically significant; they are subject to investigator and subject bias (placebo effects); they reveal considerable genetic variation among individuals; and they depend on the presence of well-designed control populations. These difficulties lead to great variation in the results of human nutritional research and make the results difficult to interpret. Dietary advice must take these problems into consideration.

DIETARY RECOMMENDATIONS

A similar approach to diet and health has been recommended in at least 2 major US Government publications. In the more specific of these reports, *Dietary Goals for the United States*, the US Senate Select Committee on Nutrition and Human Needs reviewed the proportion of energy derived from protein, fat, and carbohydrate in the current US diet and developed specific recommendations for changing these proportions to achieve a healthier food intake. Table 47–17 summarizes these recommendations. To

achieve these goals, the Committee suggested specific changes in food selection and preparation: increased consumption of fruits, vegetables, and whole-grain cereals; decreased consumption of foods containing large amounts of sugars, fats (especially saturated fat and cholesterol), and salt; partial replacement of saturated fats with unsaturated fats; and substitution of low-fat for high-fat dairy products (except in young children). The net result of following these recommendations is to increase the proportion of nutrients in the diet relative to energy intake.

The dietary goals were designed to improve the food intake of healthy people, but they are very similar to the recommendations proposed for several years by

Table 47–17. Dietary goals for the USA. Current and recommended intakes of carbohydrate, fat, and protein as percent of total energy consumption, and of cholesterol and salt.*

	Percentage of Total Energy	
	Current Diet	Dietary Goals
Carbohydrate, total	46	58
Complex carbohydrate and naturally occurring sugars	28	48
Sugars, refined and processed	18	10
Protein, total	12	12
Fat, total	42	30
Saturated	16	10
Monounsaturated	19	10
Polyunsaturated	7	10
Cholesterol, mg/d	600	300
Salt, g/d	6–18	5

*Data from Select Committee on Nutrition and Human Needs, US Senate: *Dietary Goals for the US,* 2nd ed. US Government Printing Office, 1977.

the American Heart Association, whose main nutritional concern has been to reduce the atherogenic potential of the North American diet, and the American Diabetes Association, which since 1979 has suggested that patients with diabetes mellitus eat a diet high in complex carbohydrate and low in fat, in proportions almost identical to those presented in *Dietary Goals*. The recent recommendations of the American Cancer Society for dietary means of preventing cancer are also consistent with the *Dietary Goals*.

Dietary Goals, therefore, represents a working hypothesis for both normal and therapeutic diets. Whether such recommendations are appropriate for everyone or, instead, should be restricted to individuals especially susceptible to diseases of overconsumption cannot be established until more effective methods are developed for identifying susceptible individuals before they become ill. Until then, the goals appear likely to be safe and effective; they are also capable of being assessed, evaluated, and modified as needed, consistent with the results of future nutritional research.

• • •

References

Ahrens EH, Connor WE (Cochairmen): Symposium report of the task force on the evidence relating 6 dietary factors to the nation's health. *Am J Clin Nutr* (Dec) 1979;**32(12 Suppl):** 2627.

American Cancer Society: Nutrition and cancer: Cause and prevention. (Special report.) *CA* 1984;**34:**121.

Bieri JG et al: Medical uses of vitamin E. *N Engl J Med* 1983;**308:**1063.

Bivens BA et al: Linoleic acid versus linolenic acid: What is essential? *JPEN* 1983;**7:**473.

Brewster L, Jacobson MF: The changing American diet. Center for Science in the Public Interest, 1978.

Committee on Dietary Allowances, Food and Nutrition Board, National Research Council: *Recommended Dietary Allowances*, 9th ed. National Academy of Sciences, 1980.

Davidson S et al: *Human Nutrition and Dietetics*, 7th ed. Churchill Livingstone, 1979.

Dubick MA, Rucker RB: Dietary supplements and health aids: A critical evaluation. (3 parts.) *J Nutr Educ* 1983;**15:**47, 88, 123.

Dwyer J: Dietary recommendations and policy implications: The US experience. Page 315 in: *Nutrition Update.* Vol 1. Weininger J, Briggs GM (editors). Wiley, 1983.

Goodhart RS, Shils ME: *Modern Nutrition in Health and Disease,* 6th ed. Lea & Febiger, 1980.

Hathcock JN: *Nutritional Toxicology*. Vol 1. Academic Press, 1982.

Katch FI, McArdle WD: *Nutrition, Weight Control, and Exercise,* 2nd ed. Lea & Febiger, 1983.

Knapp TR: A methodological critique of the "ideal weight" concept. *JAMA* 1983;**250:**506.

Nestle M: *Nutrition in Clinical Practice*. Jones Medical Publications, 1985.

Rennie MJ, Harrison R: Effects of injury, disease, and malnutrition on protein metabolism in man: Unanswered questions. *Lancet* 1984;**1:**323.

Schaumberg H et al: Sensory neuropathy from pyridoxine abuse: A new megavitamin syndrome. *N Engl J Med* 1983;**309:**445.

Schneider HA et al (editors): *Nutritional Support of Medical Practice,* 2nd ed. Lippincott, 1983.

Select Committee on Nutrition and Human Needs, United States Senate: *Dietary Goals for the United States,* 2nd ed. US Government Printing Office, 1977.

Stanbury JB et al (editors): *The Metabolic Basis of Inherited Disease,* 5th ed. McGraw-Hill, 1983.

Steffee WP: Malnutrition in hospitalized patients: A statement by the ASPEN Board of Directors. *JPEN* 1983;**7:**219.

Taylor RJ: *Food Additives.* Wiley, 1980.

Willett WC, MacMahon B: Diet and cancer: An overview. (2 parts.) *N Engl J Med* 1984;**310:**633, 697.

ABBREVIATIONS ENCOUNTERED IN BIOCHEMISTRY

A (Å)	Angstrom unit(s) (10^{-10} m, 0.1 nm)
AA	Amino acid
α-AA	α-Amino acid
ACTH	Adrenocorticotropic hormone, adreno-corticotropin, corticotropin
Acyl-CoA	An acyl derivative of coenzyme A (eg, butyryl-CoA)
ADH	Alcohol dehydrogenase
ADH	Antidiuretic hormone
AHG	Antihemophilic globulin
Ala	Alanine
ALA	Aminolevulinic acid
AmLev	Aminolevulinic acid
AMP	Adenosine monophosphate
Arg	Arginine
Asn	Asparagine
Asp	Aspartic acid
ATP	Adenosine triphosphate
BAL	Dimercaprol (British anti-lewisite)
cAMP	3',5'-Cyclic adenosine monophosphate, cyclic AMP
CBG	Corticosteroid-binding globulin
CBZ	Carbobenzoxy
CCCP	m-Chlorocarbonyl cyanide phenyl-hydrazone
CCK(PZ)	Cholecystokinin (pancreozymin)
CDP	Cytidine diphosphocholine
Cer	Ceramide
cGMP	3',5'-guanosine monophosphate, cyclic GMP
CI	Chain-initiating
CK	Creatine phosphokinase (see also CPK)
CMP	Cytidine monophosphate; 5'-phospho-ribosyl cytosine
CoA·SH	Free (uncombined) coenzyme A. A pan-tothenic acid–containing nucleotide that functions in the metabolism of fatty acids, ketone bodies, acetate, and amino acids

$$\text{CoA·S·}\overset{\overset{\displaystyle O}{\|}}{C}\text{·CH}_3$$

	Acetyl-CoA, "activated acetate." The form in which acetate is "activated" by combination with coenzyme A for participation in various reactions
CPK	Creatine phosphokinase (see also CK)
CRH (CRF)	Corticotropin-releasing hormone
CRP	C-reactive protein
CTP	Cytidine triphosphate
Cys	Cysteine
D-	Dextrorotatory
D$_2$ (vitamin)	Ergocalciferol
D$_3$ (vitamin)	Cholecalciferol
1,25(OH)$_2$-D$_3$	1,25-Dihydroxycholecalciferol
dA	Deoxyadenosine
dC	Deoxycytosine
dG	Deoxyguanosine
DNA	Deoxyribonucleic acid
DNP	Dinitrophenol
Dopa	3,4-Dihydroxyphenylalanine
DPG	Diphosphoglycerate (bisphospho-glycerate)

DPN	Diphosphopyridine nucleotide (now replaced by NAD)
dT	Deoxythymidine
dTMP	Deoxythymidine 5'-monophosphate
dUMP	Deoxyribose uridine 5'-phosphate
E	Enzyme (also Enz)
E.C.	Enzyme code number (IUB system)
EDTA	Ethylenediaminetetraacetic acid. A reagent used to chelate divalent metals
Enz	Enzyme (also E)
Eq	Equivalent
eu	Enzyme unit
FAD	Flavin adenine dinucleotide (oxidized)
FADH$_2$	Flavin adenine dinucleotide (reduced)
FDA	Food & Drug Administration
FFA	Free fatty acids
Figlu	Formiminoglutamic acid
FMN	Flavin mononucleotide
FP	Flavoprotein
FSF	Fibrin stabilizing factor
FSH	Follicle-stimulating hormone
FSHRH (FSHRF)	Follicle-stimulating hormone–releasing hormone
g	Gram(s)
g	Gravity
Gal	Galactose
GalNAc	N-Acetylgalactosamine
GDP	Guanosine diphosphate
GFR	Glomerular filtration rate
GH	Growth hormone
GHRH (GHRF)	Growth hormone–releasing hormone
GHRIH (GHRIF)	Growth hormone release–inhibiting hormone (somatostatin)
GLC	Gas-liquid chromatography
Glc	Glucose
GlcNAc	N-Acetylglucosamine
GlcUA	Glucuronic acid
Gln	Glutamine
Glu	Glutamic acid
Gly	Glycine
GMP	Guanosine monophosphate
GnRH	Gonadotropin-releasing hormone
GTP	Guanosine triphosphate
Hb	Hemoglobin
hCG	Human chorionic gonadotropin
hCS	Human chorionic somatomammotropin
HDL	High-density lipoproteins
H$_2$folate	Dihydrofolate
H$_4$folate	Tetrahydrofolate
His	Histidine
HMG-CoA	β-Hydroxy-β-methylglutaryl-CoA
Hyl	Hydroxylysine
Hyp	4-Hydroxyproline
ICD	Isocitric dehydrogenase
IDL	Intermediate-density lipoproteins
IDP	Inosine diphosphate
IF	Initiation factor (for protein synthesis)
Ile	Isoleucine
IMP	Inosine monophosphate; hypoxanthine ribonucleotide
INH	Isonicotinic acid hydrazide (isoniazid)

ITP	Inosine triphosphate		**PRL**	Prolactin
ITyr	Monoiodotyrosine		**Pro**	Proline
I$_2$Tyr	Diiodotyrosine		**PRPP**	5-Phosphoribosyl 1-pyrophosphate
IU	International unit(s)		**PTA**	Plasma thromboplastin antecedent
IUB	International Union of Biochemistry		**PTC**	Plasma thromboplastin component
α-KA	α-Keto acid		**RBC**	Red blood cell
kcal	Kilocalorie (calorie)		**RDA**	Recommended daily allowance
α-KG	α-Ketoglutarate		**RE**	Retinol equivalents
kJ	Kilojoule		**RNA**	Ribonucleic acid
K$_m$	Substrate concentration producing half-maximal velocity (Michaelis constant)		**RQ**	Respiratory quotient
			rRNA	Ribosomal RNA
L-	Levorotatory		**S (Sf) units**	Svedberg units of flotation
LCAT	Lecithin:cholesterol acyltransferase		**SDA**	Specific dynamic action
LD	Lactate dehydrogenase (see also LDH)		**SDS**	Sodium dodecyl sulfate
LDH	Lactic dehydrogenase		**Ser**	Serine
LDL	Low-density lipoproteins		**SGOT**	Serum glutamic oxaloacetic trans-aminase
Leu	Leucine			
LH	Luteinizing hormone		**SGPT**	Serum glutamic pyruvic transaminase
LHRH	Luteinizing hormone–releasing		**SH**	Sulfhydryl
(LHRF)	hormone		**SLR**	*Streptococcus lactis* R
LLF	Laki-Lorand factor		**SPCA**	Serum prothrombin conversion accelerator
LTH	Luteotropic hormone			
Lys	Lysine		**SRIH (SRIF)**	Somatostatin (growth hormone release–inhibiting hormone)
M	Molar			
MAO	Monoamine oxidase		**sRNA**	Soluble RNA (same as tRNA, which term is preferred)
MCH	Mean corpuscular hemoglobin			
MCHC	Mean corpuscular hemoglobin concen-tration		**STP**	Standard temperature and pressure (273° absolute, 760 mm Hg)
			T$_3$	Triiodothyronine
MCV	Mean corpuscular volume		**T$_4$**	Tetraiodothyronine; thyroxine
Met	Methionine		**TEBG**	Testosterone-estrogen–binding globulin
mol	Mole(s)		**TG**	Triacylglycerols (formerly called triglycerides)
MRF	Melanocyte releasing factor			
MRH	Melanocyte releasing hormone		**Thr**	Threonine
MRIH	Melanocyte release–inhibiting hormone		**TLC**	Thin layer chromatography
mRNA	Messenger RNA		**Tm$_{Ca}$**	Tubular maximum for calcium
MSH	Melanocyte-stimulating hormone		**Tm$_G$**	Tubular maximum for glucose
MW	Molecular weight		**TPN**	Triphosphopyridine nucleotide (now replaced by NADP)
NAD	Nicotinamide adenine dinucleotide (oxidized)			
			TRH (TRF)	Thyrotropin-releasing hormone
NADH	Nicotinamide adenine dinucleotide (reduced)		**Tris**	Tris(hydroxymethyl)aminomethane, a buffer
NADP	Nicotinamide adenine dinucleotide phosphate (oxidized)		**tRNA**	Transfer RNA (see also sRNA)
			Trp	Tryptophan
NADPH	Nicotinamide adenine dinucleotide phosphate (reduced)		**TSH**	Thyroid-stimulating hormone; thyro-tropin
Nana	N-acetylneuraminic acid		**Tyr**	Tyrosine
NDP	Any nucleoside diphosphate		**UDP**	Uridine diphosphate
NTP	Any nucleoside triphosphate		**UDPG**	Uridine diphosphoglucose
OA	Oxaloacetic acid		**UDPGal**	Uridine diphosphogalactose
OD	Optical density		**UDPGlcUA**	Uridine diphosphoglucuronic acid
P	Phosphate (radical)		**UDPGluc**	Uridine diphosphoglucuronic acid
P$_i$	Inorganic phosphate (orthophosphate)		**UMP**	Uridine monophosphate; uridine-5′-phosphate; uridylic acid
PCV	Packed cell volume			
Phe	Phenylalanine		**UTP**	Uridine triphosphate
PIH (PIF)	Prolactin release–inhibiting hormone		**V$_{max}$**	Maximal velocity
PL	Pyridoxal		**Val**	Valine
PLP	Pyridoxal phosphate		**VLDL**	Very low density lipoproteins
PP$_i$	Inorganic pyrophosphate		**VMA**	Vanilmandelic acid
PRH (PRF)	Prolactin releasing hormone		**vol%**	Volumes percent
PRIH (PRIF)	Prolactin release–inhibiting hormone			

Index